ADVENTURES IN
Earth History

FRONT ENDPAPER NOTES

1. Where names of worldwide applicability are not agreed upon, those names in general use in North America are used for subdivisions of the Phanerozoic Eon, and those of the editor's preference are used for the Cryptozoic Eon (pre-Paleozoic).

2. Series and epoch names below the Cenozoic Erathem and Era are not agreed upon. *Lower, Middle,* and *Upper* are in general use for time-rock (series) terms, as are *Early, Middle,* and *Late* for time (epoch) terms; but practice is not uniform, and local series and epoch names are common. Major time-rock and time divisions and provincial series recognized by the U.S. Geological Survey are given in *Stratigraphic Nomenclature in Reports of the U.S. Geologic Survey.* This publication, which includes a reprinting of the American *Code of Stratigraphic Nomenclature,* is available from the Survey. Rock units *per se* are always local and include *member, formation, group,* and *supergroup* in hierarchical ascent. The greatest irregularity is found in the use of *supergroup* (mainly in North America) and *series* (which, outside of North America, is a rock term equivalent to *supergroup*).

3. The curves for plutonism, volcanism, and atmospheric evolution are gross approximations based on fragmentary data, and are subject to drastic revision as more data become available.

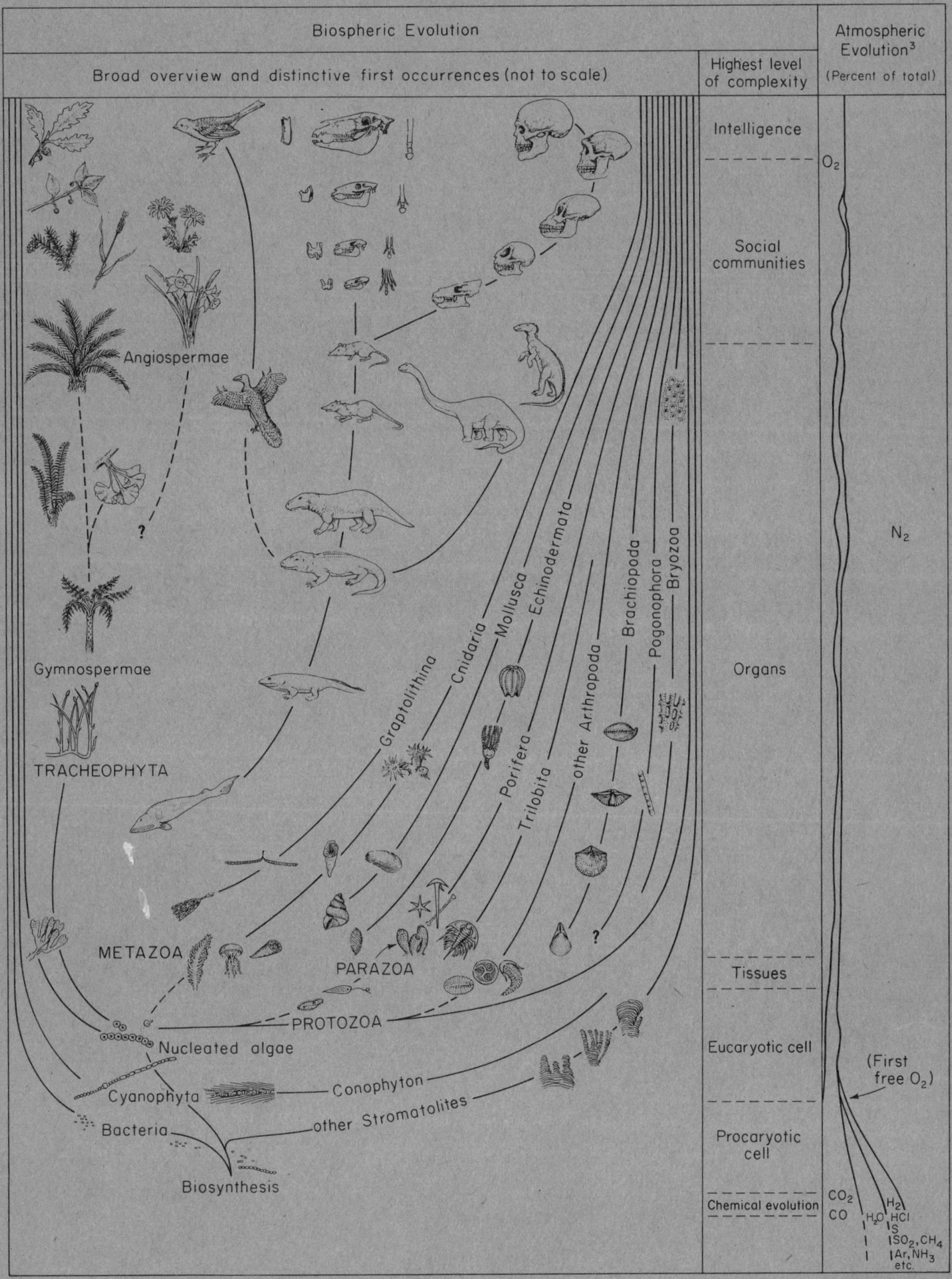
Biospheric Evolution
Broad overview and distinctive first occurrences (not to scale)
Highest level of complexity
Atmospheric Evolution³
(Percent of total)
Intelligence
Social communities
Organs
Tissues
Eucaryotic cell
Procaryotic cell
Chemical evolution
O2
N2
(First free O2)
CO2
CO
H2O
H2
HCl
S
SO2, CH4
Ar, NH3
etc.
Angiospermae
?
Gymnospermae
TRACHEOPHYTA
METAZOA
PARAZOA
PROTOZOA
Nucleated algae
Cyanophyta
Conophyton
other Stromatolites
Bacteria
Biosynthesis
Graptolithina
Cnidaria
Mollusca
Echinodermata
Porifera
Trilobita
other Arthropoda
Brachiopoda
Pogonophora
Bryozoa
?

Coll. Gonv. et Caius

EXPLANATION OF FRONTISPIECE

Early afternoon view of the Imbrian region of the moon, illustrating criteria for a sequence of lunar events. (*Photographed by and reproduced with the permission of the Lick Observatory, University of California*).

Interpretation of lunar photographs based on the law of superposition permits geologists to array lunar materials and events into three main sequences: those older than the maria, those represented by and contemporaneous with the maria, and those younger than the maria. Astrogeologists of the U.S. Geological Survey call the mare rocks the Imbrian System, from the exposures here displayed. Pre-Imbrian and post-Imbrian deposits and time can also be divided into a number of systems and periods. Although neither ages nor rock types were known with precision for any part of the moon as these words were written (19 July 1969), data from the Apollo 11 landing site at the southwest corner of Mare Tranquillitatis should apply to the Imbrian System in general.

The basis for the interpretations above is as follows: The well-defined rays of the crater Copernicus overlap Eratosthenes and Mare Imbrium. Mare Imbrium (like the other maria, including Oceanus Procellarum) cuts across the lighter colored Lunar Highlands as well as the feeble rays of the crater Eratosthenes, and mare material has flooded the floor of Archimedes, apparently from beneath. Archimedes, however, is superposed on, and its feeble rays overlap, the lunar highlands.

From this, we can array the features shown from older to younger, in the following order:

1. Lunar Highlands
2. Archimedes and Eratosthenes
3. Mare Imbrium
4. Copernicus

Younger craters can also be observed to interrupt the rays of Copernicus. The youngest major feature on the lunar surface is the impact crater Tycho, near the lunar south pole, whose rays extend over most of the lunar southern hemisphere and beyond. This can be observed with field glasses when Tycho is visible at the full moon.

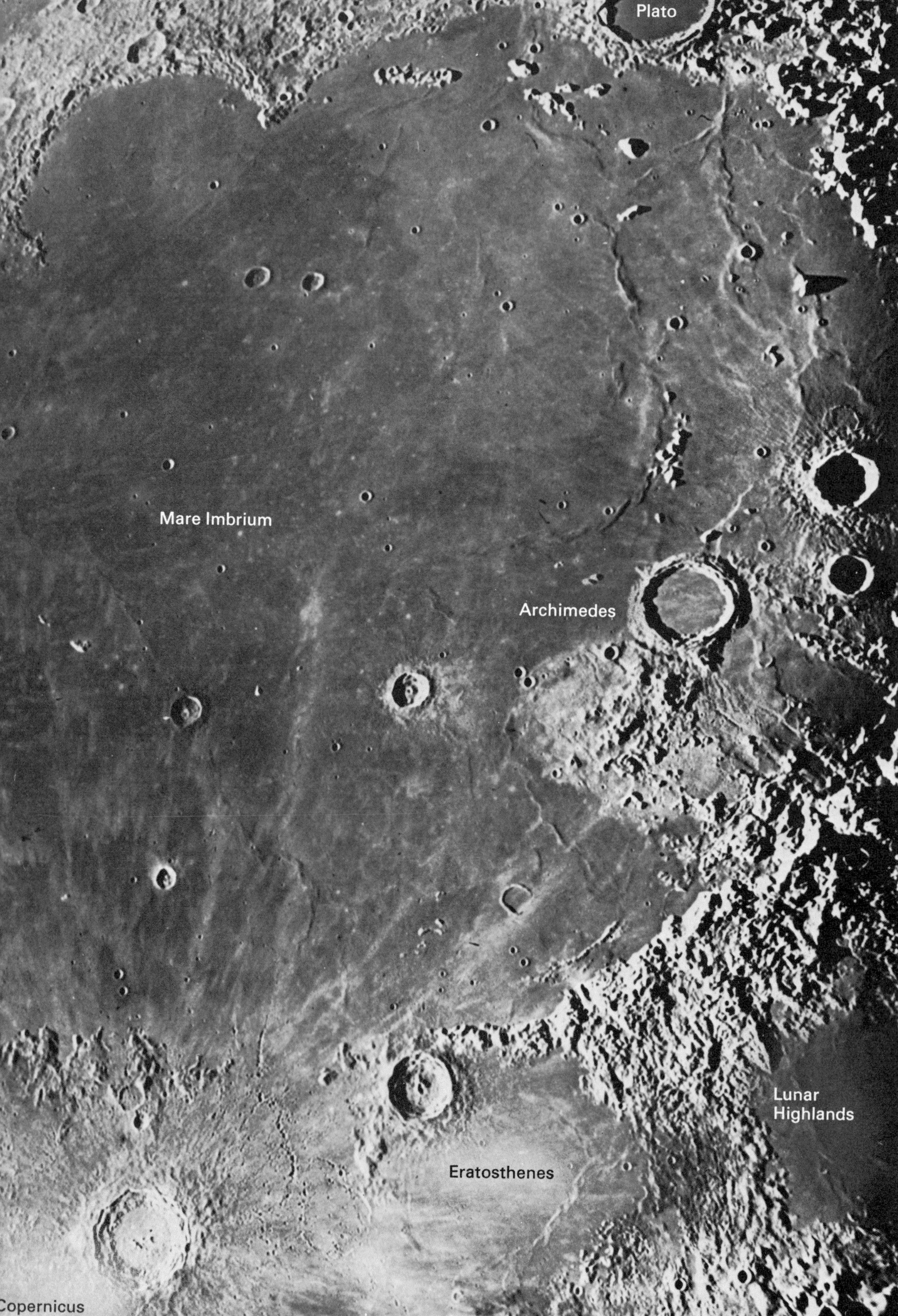

Plato
Mare Imbrium
Archimedes
Lunar Highlands
Eratosthenes
Copernicus

ADVENTURES IN Earth History

Being a Volume of Significant Writings
from Original Sources,
on Cosmology, Geology, Climatology, Oceanography,
Organic Evolution, and Related Topics
of Interest to Students of Earth History,
from the Time of Nicolaus Steno to the Present.

Selected, Edited, and with Introductions by

Preston Cloud
University of California, Santa Barbara

W. H. FREEMAN AND COMPANY
San Francisco

Printed in the United States of America
Library of Congress Catalog Card Number: 79–94871
International Standard Book Number:
0–7167–0426–0 (cloth); 0–7167–0252–5 (paper)

1 2 3 4 5 6 7 8 9

CONTENTS

Part Two THE GEOLOGIC RECORD

CONTENTS BY AUTHOR

PREFACE

Earth history is a subject intrinsically so fascinating that it readily grips and holds the interest of anyone having the good fortune to receive a favorable introduction to it. The best introduction is one in which the student is given a sense of contact with real problems and real people in the field; that kind of introduction is not provided by the usual textbook. Indeed, if a choice were available and had to be made between a textbook and a suitable collection of original papers and essays, I would prefer the latter. The difficulty has been the lack of such an anthology of papers, the existence of which would allow a number of students to read the same sources concurrently.

This book aims to overcome that difficulty. By having available a broad selection of informative and provocative readings from original sources, the student can simultaneously grasp the varied scope of the field and get the flavor of direct dialog with some of those who make it what it is—a lively intellectual adventure.

The papers here included are intended to serve two purposes (1) to be a source of selected supplemental reading (skipping difficult items) for the introductory course in historical geology, and (2) to provide the core reading for an advanced course or seminar on problems in earth history at an upper-division undergraduate or beginning graduate level. Indeed I find myself increasingly dissatisfied with the idea of teaching historical geology as the second course in the college program, immediately following introductory physical geology. Many students nowadays get a fair exposure to traditional introductory physical and historical geology in high school. The first course in introductory college geology can move at a higher level. In addition to a reasonably rigorous treatment of earth processes and structure, it should include a broad introduction to the principles of historical geology and geochronology, including the main features of the fossil record. After field geology and a sequence of related sciences the senior or beginning graduate student will then be better prepared to grasp the full and central aspect for the earth sciences of the historical ordering principles and the succession of events they reveal.

Although a prior introduction to geology would be helpful, I would not *require* a geological background for the advanced undergraduate or beginning graduate course I have in mind. Experience with the use of such readings in an upper division honors seminar reveals that bright students without previous geology can do well with most of them. Advanced undergraduate and graduate students provide a fruitful mixture in such a course—uninhibited undergraduates, especially if they are *not* geology majors, ask the hard questions that tend to be barred as naive, ignorant, or unanswerable by those who have passed the introductory stages and begun to specialize. Thus, ideally, a course using this book might serve at once as a summation of the historical aspects of the undergraduate program in geology and related sciences and an introduction to geology for advanced students in other fields. The need, moreover, for a relatively advanced introductory course in earth history for undergraduates and beginning graduates increases with the growing emphasis on the need for geologists to have a strong foundation in other sciences and the growing tendency, therefore, of geology to become primarily a graduate program and to draw its majors from among those who have followed other undergraduate curricula.

It was an agonizing dilemma to choose, from the large body of possible selections, what to include in the book I had envisaged. Papers included, obviously, had to be comprehensible at an only moderately sophisticated level, and to deal with relevant and challenging problems or issues. Selections made had to sample the field and be arranged in a reasonably logical sequence. Balance was essential. And volume had to be controlled. I regretfully decided to limit selections to the English language and to concentrate on North America. Some otherwise excellent papers were also eliminated simply because they were too long or involved copyright impasses. Others were condensed by deleting matter not essential for present purposes. Where condensation could be achieved by cutting whole phrases, sentences, or larger sections without deflecting the line of thought, that was done. Acknowledgments and abstracts, customary in scientific publication, were deleted (or the abstracts were placed at the end, as summaries). Clearly typographical errors have been corrected, and other minor adjustments have been made to adapt the papers selected to present purposes. Illustrative matter has been renumbered, and in some instances relabeled, for systematic reference, and some has been deleted. References to papers cited are included with the articles. But the language of the original papers has not been altered, and the original method of reference citation and original units of measurement have been preserved as intrinsic to the style of the author and the format of the source.

In some instances papers partially duplicate one another. This is intentional—to show parallelism, conflict, or evolution of views, and to generate discussion. A few papers are "old" by modern standards. The origins of modern views and the relevance—and often the charm—of earlier studies are thus brought out.

The book is arranged in two parts and ten sections. The first five sections deal with origins and basic concepts. Sections six through ten deal with different aspects of the history of the evolving earth. Some sections include enough papers that selections can be made, or different papers assigned to different groups of students. The relative difficulty of the papers varies from section to section and within sections, depending on the level at which problems dealt with are to be considered. The pattern I strove for as an ideal begins with a theme-setting general discussion or a paper of unusual historical interest, moves through a sequence of related papers of greater difficulty, and concludes, where practicable, with an easily comprehended summary paper. Even though the ideal may have been missed, and even if the student finds that he does not understand perfectly all aspects of all of these papers, they can nevertheless all be read with profit.

Selected general factual data that will be referred to recurrently are included on the endpapers, and a Glossary is provided for terms not sufficiently explained where they appear and not likely to be found or sufficiently explained in an ordinary abridged dictionary. Additional definitions may be found in the American Geological Institute's *Glossary of Geology and Related Sciences* (J. V. Howell, Chairman, second edition, 1960, published by the National Academy of Sciences; also available as Dolphin Reference Book C360, 1962) or in other technical glossaries. Students needing help with the characterization of the phyla of organisms will find illustrated summaries of such data at the back of a number of textbooks in common use.

It has seemed advisable, in addition, to provide a few introductory remarks for each section, in order to suggest the main content of the readings chosen and to indicate how they interrelate. Lists of suggested (and in part rather advanced) Supplemental Reading follows the introductory remarks for each section; and, of course, other supplemental reading is suggested by the bibliographies of the papers included. The list of Forty Questions at the end of the book suggests the range of problems to which the student should be able to make thoughtful response after having completed a course of study using this book.

Laboratory exercises to go with a course in earth history built around selected readings such as these are easily devised and varied from year to year. Weather permitting, my own preference is for a series of short field trips, interspersed with laboratory sessions where the student investigates and reports on local materials that he or she has personally collected in the field—again using original sources and standard reference guides.

Like all first efforts, this one will have its defects. It will be obvious that my conception of earth history, reaching from the origin of the universe to the future of man, is so broad as to extend far beyond my own direct experience, with consequent opportunity for misjudgment. I think it is worth that risk to try for the scope. Critical comments on the selections made and suggestions for addition or deletion are invited.

There remains the pedagogical question—isn't the breadth too great to be treated in a one-quarter or one-semester undergraduate course? The answer to this question depends on whether one believes that a geologist should never have to revisit an outcrop, or whether one supposes that he might risk a provisional examination on the chance that the answer might be more clearly revealed on the other side of the hill. People who think about the environmental sciences must apprehend the stochastic, indeterminate nature of the evidence. They must become accustomed to having problems remain unsolved for long periods of time and to having the "answers" change. If they can learn to live with uncertainty they may share in the pleasure that comes periodically as the evidence from often seemingly unrelated individual researches converges on some stirring prospect or new liberating concept such as recent developments in the early record of life, the sedimentary implications of turbidity currents, or the new plate tectonics. Geology majors will be introduced or redirected to central problems in their science. Others, hopefully, will emerge with the realization that historical geology is something more than a secular model of Genesis—and that it includes some fascinating pre-Paleozoic events. It will remain a matter of choice, based on level, quality, and size of class, what is practicable to include and how it should be supplemented. Selections may have to be made; but then the reading can be varied from year to year, or different reading can be assigned to different students. My experience has been that students at all levels react well to the challenge of dealing with comprehensible original material and creative conflict.

Finally, it is a pleasant duty to express my gratitude to those who have made this book possible, in particular to the authors and publishers of articles here reprinted. I am also indebted to A. O. Woodford and James Gilluly for their constructive suggestions on the plan of the book, its contents, and my commentary; to Mrs. Joan Licari for help in selecting terms for the glossary; and to Miss Shirley Bruce Henderson for putting the pieces together. Whatever value this work may have, however, must be attributed in large part to the perceptive and critical former and present students who have helped in narrowing down the choices. Among those whose critical reactions were most useful are George Seddon, Gerald Licari, Wm. C. Cornell, W. Bruce Knapp, and Mrs. Linda Engel.

Preston Cloud

SANTA BARBARA, MARCH 1969

PART ONE

PRINCIPLES, PROCESSES, ORIGINS

SECTION I

ORDERING PRINCIPLES IN EARTH HISTORY

Science seeks to reduce the connections discovered to the smallest possible number of independent elements.

Albert Einstein

THE BASIC PRINCIPLES

Science aims to formulate simplifying descriptions and explanations for complex configurations, events, and histories. It seeks order within apparent disorder. Its record of success in finding such order is grounds for a high level of confidence that nature is fundamentally lawful. To understand any science, therefore, we must first grasp its basic ordering principles and its history. In Section I, we shall come to the principles by an essentially historical route, but without belaboring the history. First, however, we must decide what we mean by ordering principles, and then identify those principles that are important to historical geology.

All science starts with the principles of induction and simplicity. The observed common characteristics of a number of similar things (or events, or processes) are, by induction, inferred to be significant. If the significance of the induced common factors continues to be reinforced by repeated observations and tests, a generalization may be formulated from which it may be deduced, by analogy, that other similar phenomena are likely to have similar primary characteristics. Relations are expressed either in precise language or in mathematical symbolism, and tests for consistency are devised. If a relation proves to be invariable in all circumstances observed, and if it is believed to be fundamental, it may be called a law. Because scientific laws are written by men, they can only describe how nature seems to behave in observed circumstances. Depending on the exactness, frequency and representativeness of the observations, statements of scientific law may closely approximate how nature actually behaves in *all* circumstances, but we cannot be absolutely sure that they tell us that for all of time and space. Our confidence in specific laws is a function of the number of opportunities for disproof that they have survived. Like human laws, natural laws tend to be rewritten from time to time, as new observational and experimental data need to be incorporated. If, in fact, nature is not orderly, laws cannot make it so. Scientific laws in the most general sense are characteristic of the primary sciences—of physics and chemistry. Through the application of physics and chemistry to other sciences, however, these laws become the property of all science. Each separate science also tends to develop its own set of more specific laws and principles that represent particular applications of the general laws, or which may contribute to the formulation of new general laws or the refinement of existing ones.

Geology is a derived science. It attempts to integrate other sciences to produce a synthesis of the structure and history of the earth. In order for geology to function as a science, therefore, it is necessary to postulate as a first axiom that the scientific laws that now describe the properties and behavior of matter have applied and operated essentially unchanged throughout the earth's history—or that if changes have affected any of the universal constants (e.g., the force of gravity), such changes themselves have taken place in a lawful and verifiable way. It follows, then, that structures and events of the past can be interpreted in terms of observable processes and relations, and that any appeals to the supernatural (or to other *ad hoc* explanations) are excluded. These are the elements of the so-called principle of *uniformitarianism* or "uniformity," often and correctly cited as the cornerstone of geology. As we shall see, *uniformitarianism* is no longer a very important word as long as we grant that its premises are basic to a science of geology (as nearly everyone does).

That the foregoing is a valid basis for the study of the earth is supported not only by the rationality and internal consistency of the results that have been obtained but also by some specific signals from the past. Notably, the pleochroic halos or radiohalos that form about grains of radioactive minerals in ancient biotites retain sharp images, instead of being blurred as they would be if there had been change in the rate of nuclear energy release. Moveover, had the force of gravity decreased perceptibly with time in the range of planetary history, the sun would have burned hotter when gravity was stronger, and the earth and its hydrosphere would have been too hot to support the life whose traces are found in the oldest known sedimentary rocks.

In geology, as in other sciences, then, *induction* is the prevailing operational method, and its keystone is the universal principle of *simplicity:* an explanation should be no more complex than is necessary to reconcile available observations within a single hypothesis.

How do we create earth history? The essentials of earth history, of course, are sequence and action. We must infer, by accurate analogical appeal to natural causes, what probably happened at particular places, and we must array all these different inferred events in a chronological sequence. The elaboration of a time scale and the development of methods for correlating the signals from the past that tell of geological events are essential: correlation and geochronometry interact with the records of geological action to give us earth history. The means by which order is introduced into this complex of interactions are the *ordering principles of historical geology.*

Consider the time scale, the *geochronometry,* without which there is only a static of signals and no history. To begin with, there are two general classes of geochronometry, or two systems of *geochronology.* One is *sequence* (relative) *geochronology;* the other is *metric* (numerical) *geochronology.* Sequence geochronology includes the principles and methods by which rocks and events inferred from them are arrayed in chronological order. Metric geochronology provides means of introducing numbers of years or other units of measurement to known sequences, and of arraying rocks and events of unknown sequence in a numerical and, presumably, a sequential order. As sequence geochronology is the earliest, most basic, and most widely used method, however, we shall examine it here, reserving a more detailed discussion of metric geochronology for Section III.

The fundamental rule in sequence geochronology, and the nearest thing we have to a general scientific law in geology, is *the law of superposition.* First enunciated by Steno in 1669, in a statement that we shall read, it is comparable in simplicity and sweep to Newton's law of gravity—indeed, these two great syntheses were nearly contemporaneous, and have important elements in common. The law of superposition says, simply, that the rocks in a given succession of strata decrease in age from bottom to top, and that evidence seemingly to the contrary always indicates post-depositional disturbance of the original order. The classical illustration of superposition is the layer-cake stratigraphy of the Phanerozoic rocks in the Grand Canyon (see Figure 47.1). The principle becomes more difficult to apply when (as in the folded mountain ranges of the world and in the older rocks of the Grand Canyon) the rocks are tilted, stood on end, overturned, and torn apart; and when older, sedimentary rocks are intruded by younger, igneous rocks that enter from below and may even squeeze in between successive layers of the older rock.

The application of the law of superposition to such sequences, or to photogeology or lunar geology (see Frontispiece), calls upon a number of lesser ordering principles. The first of these is *the principle of original horizontality,* formulated by Steno in 1669. It refers to the fact that the upper surfaces of sedimentary deposits initially come to rest essentially parallel to the surface of deposition, which is usually parallel to the horizon or inclined to it at relatively low angles (although initial dips in subaerial sediments are occasionally as great as 34°). Steeply inclined strata, therefore, are likely to have been disturbed, and the geologist is warned to look for an inversion of sequence.

The principle of original lateral extension, also formulated by Steno in 1669, reminds us that a given stratum of rock resulting from the dumping of sediment into a basin must eventually thin out in all directions, unless it abuts a steep margin of preexisting matter. Where a deposit neither thins out nor abuts, it must once have continued beyond the point of observation, as a distinctive rock unit in one wall of the Grand Canyon can be matched to the opposite canyon wall and across the pinnacles between (see Figure 47.1). Where erosion has dissected older rocks, therefore, younger sedimentary or volcanic rocks may come to rest far beneath the exposed surfaces of the older sediments in positions that look like, but are not, exceptions to the law of superposition.

The principle of cross-cutting relationships is exemplified where younger rocks are intruded into older rocks (as in igneous intrusions or clastic dikes), or where sediments are deposited unconformably on the eroded or upturned edges of preexisting rocks. The cross-cutting rock is always the younger. *Intrusive contacts* cut across preexisting structures, and the younger intrusive rock is essentially surrounded by the rock into which it has intruded. *Unconformable contacts* truncate the upper surfaces or terminal edges of the rocks below them, and separate the underlying from the younger overlying rocks along a simple (though often highly irregular) surface. Both intrusive and unconformable contacts call for great caution in interpreting the details of the rock sequence in which they occur.

There are many other, more specific, principles of sedimentation that will not be elaborated here, except to mention that sedimentary processes that give rise to cross-bedding, graded bedding, and other features that serve to distinguish top from bottom of a stratum, are employed in determining which side is up in vertical or overturned sequences of rocks. As long as the orientation can be worked out, the superpositional sequence can be kept in order, even for rocks which may not individually include the orienting criteria. To understand these criteria it is usually helpful to look at samples in the field or laboratory, or to reproduce the textures and structures in flumes or settling tanks.

The most reliable systems of geochronology are those that deal with *universal, unidirectional, non-recurrent processes.* These include *biologic evolution* in sequence geochronology and *nuclear decay* in a metric geochronology. The evolutionary criterion is expressed in the *law of biologic succession,* enunciated on empirical grounds by William Smith sixty years before Darwin's *Origin of Species.* Smith recognized that succeeding beds contained distinctive and changing associations of fossils, but the subtleties of this principle are still being developed. Suffice it to say that the changing evolutionary sequence of plant and animal fossils in rock is the most discriminating and most widely applicable tool for deciphering historical sequences and correlations in Phanerozoic rocks too old to be dated by carbon-14 decay.

Some special techniques of sequence geochronology that are also metric include the matching of varves (or pairs of annual laminae) in glacial or other sedimentary deposits, and the use of the annual growth rings of trees to determine climatologic evolution.

Metric geochronology, on the other hand, rests firmly on the various systems of nuclear decay that are discussed in Section III. Metric methods that have given unreliable results, and which are of historical interest only, are those that utilize rates of sedimentation and the hypothesis of changing salinity of the oceans. Other systems of great interest (to be discussed later) include geochronology based on the rate of retreat of the moon from the earth and on the changing length of day, and cosmochronology based on the doppler shifts of starlight toward the red ends of the stellar spectra.

The subdivision of pre-Paleozoic time, in particular, is most generally done by nuclear or radiometric methods. Fossils of that age appear to be missing from many stratigraphic sequences, and studies of their evolutionary development have as yet revealed only very broad geochronological divisions (Reading Selection 45). If we take as our base lines for historical geology the present instant and the time of origin of the solar system, we can say, by analogy with a geodetic survey, that nuclear methods provide the first order triangulation and the system of bench marks to which all else is now referred. In practice, other methods may be more useful or have higher resolving power for Phanerozoic time. For the nearly seven-eights of earth history preceding Phanerozoic time, nuclear methods remain paramount, but the possibility of eventually achieving a refined pre-Paleozoic biostratigraphy is now being intensively investigated.

Correlation is the important counterpart of geochronometry that, together with geochronology, results in the elaboration of the sequences of action that we call earth history. Correlation, which amounts to a statement of equivalency, is based on two main sorts of criteria. The first consists of *unique or recurrent events or processes* that leave distinctive records in the rocks. These might include records of lithogenetic, diastrophic, climatic, or biologic episodes, such as an ash fall, a change of sea level, a glacial deposit, or the appearance or disappearance of a particular biota. The other consists of observable *trends* of various sorts—such as organic evolution, nuclear decay, climatologic change, lithogenetic cycles, paleomagnetism, or secular changes in the earth's orbit and precession or in solar radiation and sunspot cycles.

It is important in correlation to discriminate between *what is correlated* (rocks, fossils, surfaces, time), *what is demonstrated* (physical continuity, similarity, difference), and *what is inferred* (kinds of similarity or difference). Correlation may demonstrate the physical continuity of a stratum or surface from one place to another, the similarity or change of aspect (facies) of a rock in different locations, or the similarity of different sequences of rocks or fossils. We may then infer either *synchronism* or *time transgression* for the rocks observed and the events deduced at different localities. Without geochronologic criteria to back up a time correlation, we demonstrate only a similarity or dissimilarity in the genetic processes involved at the places where the signals were recorded, not necessarily a simultaneity of occurrence.

Let us tabulate some of the methods of correlation, without discussing them in detail, simply to have them in mind as we read on into the history of the earth and how it is compiled.

I. Continuous tracing
    A. Walking out beds or surfaces
    B. Photogeology

II. Correlating separated sequences (isolated sections, boreholes)
    A. Records of unique, dominant, or distinctive recurrent events of limited duration
        1. Lithogenetic or chemogenetic episodes or cycles
            a. Volcanism (ash falls, mineralogically or chemically distinctive volcanic suites)
            b. Plutonism (important in the pre-Paleozoic)
            c. Sedimentary events and cycles (banded iron formation, evaporites, red beds, coal, glauconite, phosphorite, oölite, chalk, cyclothems, etc.)

2. Climatic episodes (usually reflected in results of feedback to lithogenetic episodes)
    a. Glacial deposits and surfaces
    b. Coal, red beds, desert sands, etc.
    c. Cyclothems (repeated complex sequences of distinctive rock types)
3. Biologic episodes
    a. New appearances and extinctions
    b. Recurrent facies biotas
    c. Biotal sequences
4. Diastrophism
    a. Unconformities
    b. Feedback to sedimentary cycles

B. "Fingerprinting" methods
1. Matching complex sequences, mineral assemblages, or geophysical records

C. Trends
1. Evolution
2. Nuclear decay and radioactivity
3. Climatologic cycles
4. Lithogenetic cycles
5. Paleomagnetism
6. Records of secular changes in planetary or solar phenomena

The diagram on the following page recapitulates these ideas in the form of a simplified "flow sheet." Earth history, of course, requires both that there be a record of past events that took place within and among the atmosphere, hydrosphere, biosphere, and lithosphere of the earth; and that we be able to decipher the succession in which those events occurred. In punctuating the flow of events (naming rock units and time units) we look for conspicuous changes in the rate or nature of historical processes as reflected in the geologic record (that is, we employ geochronology and correlation). What we should read out of this flow sheet is a recurrent theme of this collection of papers—that is, that the fundamental objective of historical geology is nothing less than the completest possible reconstruction of the interactions in and among the biosphere, lithosphere, atmosphere, and hydrosphere from the origin of the earth until now. The student should keep this in mind and keep asking how it may best be achieved.

One other thing ought to be borne in mind from the beginning: most of the questions and many of the answers in the study of earth history come not from the laboratory, but from an imaginative combination of field work and laboratory research. We cannot recreate in the laboratory, in all their complexity, the conditions that characterize and determine a mountain system, an ocean, the trade winds, or the evolution of the horse through 60 million years of geologic time. Even if all the rest of geology were merely physics, chemistry, mathematics, and biology as applied to the study of the history and structure of the earth, there would remain as uniquely geological the sequence and history of experiments performed by nature herself—on such a scale and over so many millenia that it stretches our imagination and our ingenuity to devise simplified models that will condense our findings into comprehensible form.

ILLUSTRATIVE ESSAYS

The reader's understanding of the principles outlined above will grow with study of their applications. As a beginning, Section I offers seven brief selected essays toward the growth of that understanding.

The first of these, by the philosopher Alfred North Whitehead (Reading Selection 1), considers the origins of science itself. Why, he asks, did science develop in still barbaric Western Europe, at a time when high civilization had already been achieved in the Orient? He explains that this was as a consequence of the different religious philosophies: the religions of Asia were pluralistic, and their gods were irrational despots; whereas the Judeo-Christian movement, with roots in Greek and Essenian philosophy, believed in a single supreme being, no less despotic, but one who decreed a specific order to nature. Because, to the western mind, there was no conflict between the schemes of various gods, nature could be seen as orderly—as something to be understood, not simply accepted as unknowable and chaotic. And science was heretical—even anti-intellectual, in the sense that it recoiled from the inflexible rationality of medieval clerical thought. The founders of science sought irreducible and stubborn facts, and set

Flow Sheet for Earth History

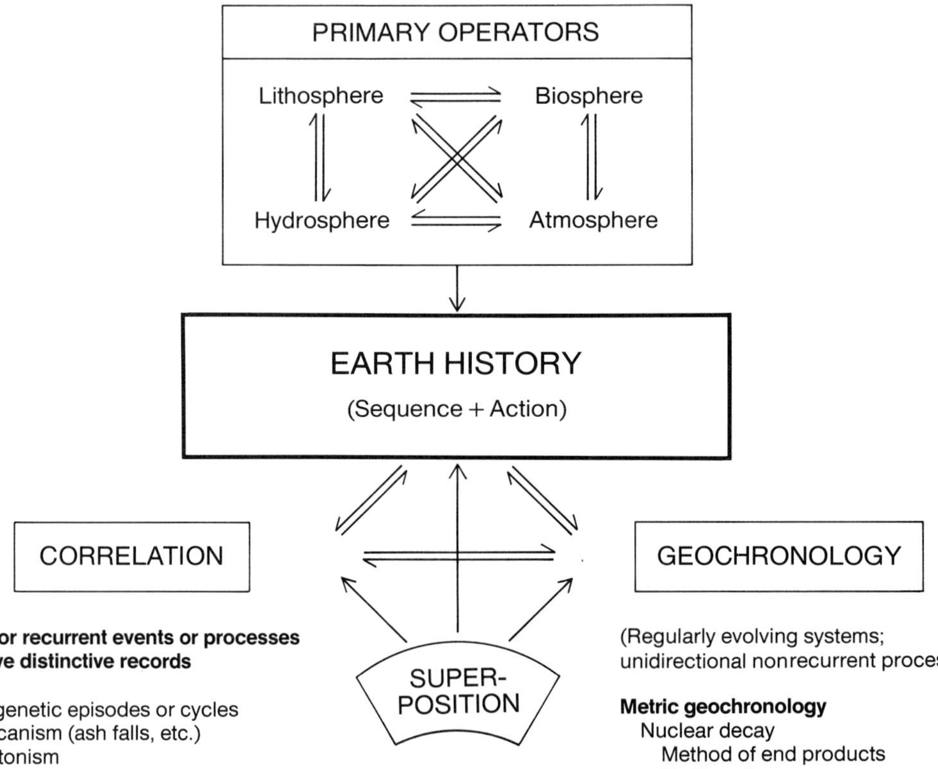

Unique or recurrent events or processes that leave distinctive records

- Lithogenetic episodes or cycles
  - Volcanism (ash falls, etc.)
  - Plutonism
  - Sedimentary events and cycles (heavy minerals, cyclothems)
- Climatic episodes or cycles
  - Glaciation, coal, redbeds, cyclothems, etc. (through feedback to sedimentation)
- Biologic episodes
  - New appearances and extinctions
- Diastrophism
  - Unconformities
  - Feedback to sedimentary cycles

Trends

- Evolution
- Radioactivity
- Climatologic cycles (pollen spectra, etc.)
- Lithogenetic cycles
- Paleomagnetism
- Secular changes in earth's orbit and precession
- Secular changes in solar radiation and sun-spot cycles

(Regularly evolving systems; unidirectional nonrecurrent processes)

Metric geochronology

- Nuclear decay
  - Method of end products
  - Radiocarbon
- Retreat of moon and changing length of day (Feedback to sequence geochronology)

Sequence geochronology

- Continuous
  - Biologic evolution
- Local
  - Varves
  - Growth rings
  - Climatologic evolution

out to determine whether what was rational was also true. They asked forbidden questions. They challenged authority. Science became the "union of a passionate interest in the detailed facts with equal devotion to abstract generalization." It developed a distinctive mode of operation that is based on the constant re-examination of first principles, and that insists upon the inadmissibility of authority *per se* as intellectual evidence.

Despite earlier philosophical stirrings, the date of geology's emergence as a distinctive science with principles of its own can be neatly set at the year 1669. It was then that the Danish priest Niels Steensen published his *Prodromus*, written in Latin under his Latinized name, Nicolaus Steno. Reading Selection 2, an excerpt from Steno's generally rambling treatise, states, with a clarity and directness then unusual, three fundamental concepts of historical geology: the law of superposition, the principle of original horizontality, and the principle of original lateral extension.

The next big step—the elaboration of uniformitarianism as a central principle—began with the work of James Hutton in the late eighteenth century. With the publication of Sir Charles Lyell's *Principles of Geology* in 1830–32, uniformitarianism became a widely influential principle. The story of this development, with allusion to the works of William Smith and others, is told in Reading Selection 5 by M. K. Hubbert. As Reading Selection 3, however, it seems especially fitting to include Playfair's stirring account of Hutton's visit, with Playfair and Sir James Hall (not the equally famous geologist, James Hall of New York, who lived about a half century later) to the spectacular unconformity at Siccar Point, east of Edinburgh, Scotland. This angular unconformity, between nearly vertical early Paleozoic (Silurian) graywackes and shales and the nearly horizontal Devonian Old Red Sandstone above them, profoundly illuminated the force of the uniformitarian principle and the magnitude of geologic time (see Figure 3.1).

Next we turn to the problem of achieving freedom from subjective judgments in geologic analysis, to which G. K. Gilbert, a great pioneer in American geology, addresses himself in Reading Selection 4. To rely upon a ruling theory, or a single working hypothesis, is to risk emotional attachment and a failure to consider all the alternatives in sufficient detail. That multiple hypotheses provide the best antidote for subjectivity was a principle long recognized but not regularly put into practice. It was first explicitly applied to geology in 1886 in the paper by Gilbert, and four years later T. C. Chamberlin named it "the method of multiple working hypotheses" and amplified its applications (see Supplemental Reading). Gilbert illustrates the method with his provisional analysis of three hypotheses for the systematic deformation of the former shore line of ancient Lake Bonneville (whose present remnant is the Great Salt Lake). Gilbert's paper amply illustrates his precept that "the great investigator is primarily and pre-eminently the man who is rich in hypotheses." The problem with the method is to avoid using it simply to set up straw men to enhance the appeal of preconceived views.

That the geologic record can be interpreted scientifically only by reference to naturalistic principles seems obvious today. It is difficult to believe that the idea was considered revolutionary when first enunciated by Hutton, Playfair, and Lyell. It was not they, however, but Lyell's opponent William Whewell (1837) who first applied the term "uniformitarianism" (derisively) to this concept (often also called "actualism" or "uniformity"). Reading Selection 5, entitled "Critique of the Principle of Uniformity," is by geophysicist M. King Hubbert of the U.S. Geological Survey, a former president of the Geological Society of America. Hubbert's engrossing examination of this concept and its history leads him to the conclusion that, although much progress has resulted from the rejection of the miraculous and the search for naturalistic explanations, the usual formulations of the "principle of uniformitarianism" are vague or redundant, and are no longer useful to modern geologists.

Next is a brief essay by paleontologist Stephen Jay Gould of Harvard University (Reading Selection 6). Gould holds that (methodological) uniformitarianism is simply a composite term for the principles of induction and simplicity, widely applicable in other fields of science. He asks: Why not stress the relationships between geology and the rest of the scientific enterprise instead of erecting terminological barriers?

In fact, the connections between geology and the primary sciences are, and always have been, at the heart of the most significant advances in geology. When we lose touch with those connections, we risk losing touch with reality—but we can also lose touch with reality by supposing either that we can solve all of our problems in the laboratory, or that any data that are practicable to collect can provide meaningful answers to "problems" that are not meaningful or not meaningfully stated. Geochemist Konrad B. Krauskopf of Stanford University expresses these reservations in "A Tale of Ten Plutons" (Reading Selection 7), his retiring presidential address to the Geological Society of America in 1968. Krauskopf speaks of randomness and order in nature, illustrating the discussion with problems of the classification, composition, and origin of a cluster of deep-seated intrusive rock bodies known as plutons. How many plutons make up the Inyo batholith of eastern California? What was their sequence of intrusion? What genetic relation do they bear to one another? Informed intuition rather than quantitative analysis plays the main part in deciding how far it is sensible to pursue such questions and what the most probable solutions are. The hazard of bogging down in trivial detail where the random element is not recognized increases as the complexities of a question unfold—for, as Krauskopf asserts, "randomness, or anarchy, is in some measure the law of nature, and . . . some of the order we think we see is a dream in our own minds." That warning, of course, is difficult to heed when the introduction of order is our central goal, and when we should like eventually to answer all questions in detail. To ignore it, however, is to court frustration. Uncertainty is an aspect of science that we must learn to live with. Even problems whose solutions appear simple after the fact may be obdurate at a particular stage of knowledge, methodology, or instrumentation. The same problems may find different apparent "solutions" at different stages in the evolution of knowledge. Our models of nature, for all their usefulness, never correspond in detail with absolute reality, and we would have no way of verifying it if they did. Indeed, the utility of models is precisely that they portray nature in a manner so simplified that the mind can cope with it. Far from detracting from the joy of creative research, uncertainty breeds humility, and humility prepares us for the failures that temper all success. Krauskopf is not telling us that we should avoid important problems merely because they seem to be insoluble when considered at a particular stage of knowledge, instrumentation, or methodology. One may be wise to budget the time one allots to such research, but it is always possible that a rephrasing of the question, an advancement of knowledge, or an improvement of instrumentation or methodology, will permit its solution.

Among the Supplemental Reading, books and papers of special value for more extended discussions of the ordering principles of geology are those by Woodford (1965, especially Chapters 1–3); Gilluly, Waters, and Woodford (1968, especially Chapter 3); Eicher (1968); and the essays in the two volumes edited by Albritton (1963, 1967). The paper by White (1967) points out that Judeo-Christian tradition not only made possible a scientific understanding of nature, but also, and with appalling and worsening consequences, led to the establishment of anthropomorphic goals for the conquest and exploitation of nature. The papers by Conant (1967) and Siever (1968) consider the question of the wide misconception that all science operates according to some simple and inexorable system called the scientific method. They emphasize instead the plurality and diversity of science under the broad general themes of economy and simplicity.

If there had been room for another paper in Section I, it would have been the chapter entitled "The Latest Revolution" from the book *Modern Science and the Nature of Life* by W. S. Beck (1961, pp. 155–175). Beck takes up the discussion of the nature of science where Whitehead left off. The main concern of science, as he sees it, is the relation between the real world and our knowledge of it. Even in defining our own locus in space, we may be faced with a choice of conflicting "realities": if there are a number of possible geometries, does one more closely coincide with the real world, or do different geometries best describe different, but equally real, relations in space? The nature of truth is intimately bound up with semantics. Man, a symbol-using animal, gets tied up in the complexities of language and numbers. Science, which once seemed a triumph of common sense, becomes less tidy with advancing knowledge of the very small and the very large. Ultimately, scientific notions can rest only on operational analyses (like determining the specific gravity or symmetry of a substance, or the succession of biotas or strata).

A proposition, then, is meaningful only if it can be determined, by repeated operational analysis, to be more or less probable. This is fundamental, and should be borne in mind constantly as we read and evaluate the papers that follow. We must ask again and again: What are the testable corollaries? What are the logical extrapolations (the predictions or "postdictions") that can be verified or shown to be mistaken? A proposition, of course, can never be established as true except within a framework of postulates taken as true. Our confidence in it will be enhanced each time it survives an opportunity for disproof, or each time it proves consistent with new evidence: it must be discarded or modified when it fails to meet either test.

Supplemental Reading

Adams, F. D., 1938, The birth and development of the geological sciences: Baltimore, Williams and Wilkins, 506 p. (Reprinted by Dover Publications, 1954.)

Albritton, C. C., Jr., ed., 1963, The fabric of geology: San Francisco, Freeman, Cooper, 372 p. (Essays by Simpson, Bradley, Gilluly, and others.)

———, ed., 1967, Uniformity and simplicity: Geol. Soc. America Spec. Paper 89, 99 p.

Beck, W. S., 1961, Modern science and the nature of life: New York, Doubleday, Anchor Books, 334 p.

Chamberlin, T. C., 1965, The method of multiple working hypotheses: Science, v. 148, p. 754–759. (Reprint of 1890 paper.)

Conant, J. B., 1967, Scientific principles and moral conduct: Am. Scientist, v. 55, p. 311–328.

Dunbar, C. O., and John Rodgers, 1957, Principles of stratigraphy: New York, John Wiley and Sons, 356 p.

Eicher, D. L., 1968, Geologic time: New York, Prentice Hall, 149 p.

Geikie, Archibald, 1897, The founders of geology: London, Macmillan, 297 p.

Gould, S. J., 1965, Is uniformitarianism necessary?: Am. Jour. Sci., v. 263, p. 223–228.

Gilluly, James, A. C. Waters, and A. O. Woodford, 1968, Principles of geology (3d ed.): San Francisco, W. H. Freeman and Company, 687 p.

Grabau, A. W., 1913, Principles of stratigraphy: New York, A. G. Seiler, 1183 p. (Reprinted by Dover Publications, 1963.)

Hempel, C. G., 1965, Aspects of scientific explanation: New York, Macmillan, Free Press, 502 p. (See especially p. 331–496.)

Mayr, Ernst, 1968, The role of systematics in biology: Science, v. 159, p. 595–599.

Platt, J. R., 1964, Strong inference: Science, v. 146, p. 347–352.

Siever, Raymond, 1968, Science—observational, experimental, historical: Am. Scientist, v. 56, p. 70–77.

Simpson, G. G., 1963, Biology and the nature of science: Science, v. 139, p. 81–88.

Watson, R. A., 1966, Discussion: Is geology different?: Philos. Sci., v. 33, p. 172–185.

Whewell, William, 1837, History of the inductive sciences: London, John W. Parker. (See especially p. 615–617 in v. 3.)

White, Lynn, Jr., 1967, The historical roots of our ecologic crisis: Science, v. 155, p. 1203–1207.

Wiener, Norbert, 1960, Some moral and technical consequences of automation: Science, v. 131, p. 1355–1358.

Woodford, A. O., 1965, Historical geology: San Francisco, W. H. Freeman and Company, 512 p.

1

The Origins of Modern Science

ALFRED NORTH WHITEHEAD

1925

The Progress of Civilisation is not wholly a uniform drift towards better things. It may perhaps wear this aspect if we map it on a scale which is large enough. But such broad views obscure the details on which rests our whole understanding of the process. New epochs emerge with comparative suddenness, if we have regard to the scores of thousands of years throughout which the complete history extends. Secluded races suddenly take their places in the main stream of events: technological discoveries transform the mechanism of human life: a primitive art quickly flowers into full satisfaction of some aesthetic craving: great religions in their crusading youth spread through the nations the peace of Heaven and the sword of the Lord.

The sixteenth century of our era saw the disruption of Western Christianity and the rise of modern science. It was an age of ferment. Nothing was settled, though much was opened —new worlds and new ideas. In science, Copernicus and Vesalius may be chosen as representative figures: they typify the new cosmology and the scientific emphasis on direct observation. . . . The Reformation, for all its importance, may be considered as a domestic affair of the European races. Even the Christianity of the East viewed it with profound disengagement. Furthermore, such disruptions are no new phenomena in the history of Christianity or of other religions. When we project this great revolution upon the whole history of the Christian Church, we cannot look upon it as introducing a new principle into human life. For good or for evil, it was a great transformation of religion; but it was not the coming of religion. It did not itself claim to be so. Reformers maintained that they were only restoring what had been forgotten.

It is quite otherwise with the rise of modern science. In every way it contrasts with the contemporary religious movement. The Reformation was a popular uprising, and for a century and a half drenched Europe in blood. The beginnings of the scientific movement were confined to a minority among the intellectual élite. In a generation which saw the Thirty Years' War and remembered Alva in the Netherlands, the worst that happened to men of science was that Galileo suffered an honourable detention and a mild reproof, before dying peacefully in his bed. The way in which the persecution of Galileo has been remembered is a tribute to the quiet commencement of the most intimate change in outlook which the human race had yet encountered. . . .

The thesis which these lectures will illustrate is that this quiet growth of science has practically recoloured our mentality so that modes of thought which in former times were exceptional are now broadly spread through the educated world. This new colouring of ways of thought had been proceeding slowly for many ages in the European peoples. At last it issued in the rapid development of science; and has thereby strengthened itself by its most obvious application. The new mentality is more important even than the new science and the new technology. It has altered the metaphysical presuppositions and the imaginative contents of our minds; so that now the old stimuli provoke a new response. . . .

This new tinge to modern minds is a vehement and passionate interest in the relation of general principles to irreducible and stubborn facts. All the world over and at all times there have been practical men, absorbed in 'irreducible and stubborn facts': all the world over and at all times there have been men of philosophic temperament who have been absorbed in the weaving of general principles. It is this union of passionate interest in the detailed facts with equal devotion to abstract generalisation which forms the novelty in our present society. Previously it had appeared sporadically and as if by chance. This balance of mind has now become part of the tradition which infects cultivated thought. It is the salt which keeps life sweet. The main business of universities is to transmit this tradition as a widespread inheritance from generation to generation.

Another contrast which singles out science from among the European movements of the sixteenth and seventeenth centuries is its universality. Modern science was born in Europe, but its home is the whole world. In the last two centuries there has been a long and confused impact of western modes upon the civilisation of Asia. The wise men of the East have been puzzling, and are puzzling, as to what may be the regulative secret of life which can be passed from West to East without the wanton destruction of their own inheritance which they so rightly prize. More and more it is becoming evident that what the West can most readily give to the East is its science and its scientific outlook. This is transferable from country to country, and from race to race, wherever there is a rational society.

I shall not discuss the details of scientific discovery. My theme is the energising of a state of mind in the modern world, its broad generalisation, and its impact upon other spiritual forces. There are two ways of reading history, forwards and backwards. In the history of thought, we require both methods. A climate of opinion—to use the happy phrase of a seventeenth century writer—requires for its understanding the consideration of its antecedents and its issues. Accordingly I shall consider some of the antecedents of our modern approach to the investigation of nature.

In the first place, there can be no living science unless there is a widespread instinctive conviction in the existence of an *Order of Things*, and, in particular, of an *Order of Nature*. I have used the word *instinctive* advisedly. It does not matter what men say in words, so long as their activities are controlled by settled instincts. . . .

Of course we all share in this faith, and we therefore believe that the reason for the faith is our apprehension of its truth. But the formation of a general idea—such as the idea of the Order of Nature—and the grasp of its importance, and the observation of its exemplification in a variety of occasions are by no means the necessary consequences of the truth of the idea in question. Familiar things happen, and mankind does not bother about them. It requires a very unusual mind to undertake the analysis of the obvious. Accordingly I wish to consider the stages in which this analysis became explicit, and finally became unalterably impressed upon the educated minds of Western Europe.

Obviously, the main recurrences of life are too insistent to escape the notice of the least rational of humans; and even before the dawn of rationality, they have impressed themselves upon the instincts of animals. It is unnecessary to labour the point, that in broad outline certain general states of nature recur, and that our very natures have adapted themselves to such repetitions.

But there is a complementary fact which is equally true and equally obvious:—nothing ever really recurs in exact detail. No two days are identical, no two winters. What has gone, has gone forever. Accordingly the practical philosophy of mankind has been to expect the broad recurrences, and to accept the details as emanating from the inscrutable womb of things beyond the ken of rationality. Men expected the sun to rise, but the wind bloweth where it listeth.

Certainly from the classical Greek civilisation onwards there have been men, and indeed groups of men, who have placed themselves beyond this acceptance of an ultimate irrationality. Such men have endeavoured to explain all phenomena as the outcome of an order of things which extends to every detail. Geniuses such as Aristotle, or Archimedes, or Roger Bacon, must have been endowed with the full scientific mentality, which instinctively holds that all things great and small are conceivable as exemplifications of general principles which reign throughout the natural order.

But until the close of the Middle Ages the general educated public did not feel that intimate conviction, and that detailed interest, in such an idea, so as to lead to an unceasing supply of men, with ability and opportunity adequate to maintain a coördinated search for the discovery of these hypothetical principles. Either people were doubtful about the existence of such principles, or were doubtful about any success in finding them, or took no interest in thinking about them, or were oblivious to their practical importance when found. For whatever reason, search was languid, if we have regard to the opportunities of a high civilisation and the length of time concerned. Why did the pace suddenly quicken in the sixteenth and seventeenth centuries? At the close of the Middle Ages a new mentality discloses itself. Invention stimulated thought, thought quickened physical speculation, Greek manuscripts disclosed what the ancients had discovered. Finally although in the year 1500 Europe knew less than Archimedes who died in the year 212 B.C., yet in the year 1700, Newton's *Principia* had been written and the world was well started on the modern epoch.

There have been great civilisations in which the peculiar balance of mind required for science has only fitfully appeared and has produced the feeblest result. For example, the more we know of Chinese art, of Chinese literature, and of the Chinese philosophy of life, the more we admire the heights to which that civilisation attained. For thousands of years, there have been in China acute and learned men patiently devoting their lives to study. Having regard to the span of time, and to the population concerned, China forms the largest volume of civilisation which the world has seen. There is no reason to doubt the intrinsic capacity of individual Chinamen for the pursuit of science. And yet Chinese science is practically negligible. There is no reason to believe that China if left to itself would have ever produced any progress in science. The same may be said of India. Furthermore, if the Persians had enslaved the Greeks, there is no definite ground for belief that science would have flourished in Europe. The Romans showed no particular originality in that line. Even as it was, the Greeks, though they founded the movement, did not sustain it with the concentrated interest which modern Europe has shown. I am not alluding to the last few generations of the European peoples on both sides of the ocean; I mean the smaller Europe of the Reformation period, distracted as it was with wars and religious disputes. Consider the world of the eastern Mediterranean, from Sicily to western Asia, during the period of about 1400 years from the death of Archimedes [in 212 B.C.] to the irruption of the Tartars. There were wars and revolutions and large changes of religion: but nothing much worse than the wars of the sixteenth and seventeenth centuries throughout Europe. There was a great and wealthy civilisation, Pagan, Christian, Mahometan. In that period a great deal was added to science. But on the whole the progress was slow and wavering; and, except in mathematics, the men of the Renaissance practically started from the position which Archimedes had reached. There had been some progress in medicine and some progress in astronomy. But the total advance was very little compared to the marvellous success of the seventeenth century. For example, compare the progress of scientific knowledge from the year 1560, just before the births of Galileo and of Kepler, up to the year 1700, when Newton was in the height of his fame, with the progress in the ancient period, already mentioned, exactly ten times as long.

Nevertheless, Greece was the mother of Europe; and it is to Greece that we must look in order to find the origin of our modern ideas. We all know that on the eastern shores of the Mediterranean there was a very flourishing school of Ionian philosophers, deeply interested in theories concerning nature. Their ideas have been transmitted to us, enriched by the genius of Plato and Aristotle. But, with the exception of Aristotle, and it is a large exception, this school of thought had not attained to the complete scientific mentality. In some ways, it was better. The Greek genius was philosophical, lucid and logical. The men of this group were primarily asking philosophical questions. What is the substratum of nature? Is it fire, or earth, or water, or some combination of any two, or of all three? Or is it a mere flux, not reducible to some static material? Mathematics interested them mightily. They invented its generality, analysed its premises, and made notable discoveries of theorems by a rigid adherence to deductive reasoning. Their minds were infected with an eager generality. They demanded clear, bold ideas, and strict reasoning from them. All this was excellent; it was genius; it was ideal preparatory work. But it was not science as we understand it. The patience of minute observation was not nearly so prominent. Their genius was not so apt for the state of imaginative muddled suspense which precedes successful inductive generalisation. They were lucid thinkers and bold reasoners.

Of course there were exceptions, and at the very top: for example, Aristotle and Archimedes. Also for patient observation, there were the astronomers. There was a mathematical lucidity about the stars, and a fascination about the small numerable band of run-a-way planets.

Every philosophy is tinged with the colouring of some secret imaginative background, which never emerges explicitly into its trains of reasoning. The Greek view of nature, at least that cosmology transmitted from them to later ages, was essentially dramatic. It is not necessarily wrong for this reason: but it was overwhelmingly dramatic. It thus conceived nature as articulated in the way of a work of dramatic art, for the exemplification of general ideas converging to an end. Nature was differentiated so as to provide its proper end for each thing. There was the centre of the universe as the end of motion for those things which are heavy, and the celestial spheres as the end of motion for those things whose natures lead them upwards. The celestial spheres were for things which are impassible and ingenerable, the lower regions for things passible and generable. Nature was a drama in which each thing played its part.

I do not say that this is a view to which Aristotle would have subscribed without severe reservations, in fact without the sort of reservations which we ourselves would make. But it was the view which subsequent Greek thought extracted from Aristotle and passed on to the Middle Ages. The effect of such an imaginative setting for nature was to damp down the historical spirit. For it was the end which seemed illuminating, so why bother about the beginning? The Reformation and the scientific movement were two aspects of the revolt which was the dominant intellectual movement of the later Renaissance. The appeal to the origins of Christianity, and Francis Bacon's appeal to efficient causes as against final causes, were two sides of one movement of thought. Also for this reason Galileo and his adversaries were at hopeless cross purposes, as can be seen from his *Dialogues on the Two Systems of the World.*

Galileo keeps harping on how things happen, whereas his adversaries had a complete theory as to why things happen. Unfortunately the two theories did not bring out the same results. Galileo insists upon 'irreducible and stubborn facts,' and Simplicius, his opponent, brings forward reasons, completely satisfactory, at least to himself. It is a great mistake to conceive this historical revolt as an appeal to reason. On the contrary, it was through and through an anti-intellectualist movement. It was the return to the contemplation of brute fact; and it was based on a recoil from the inflexible rationality of medieval thought. In making this statement I am merely summarising what at the time the adherents of the old régime themselves asserted. For example, in the fourth book of Father Paul Sarpi's *History of the Council of Trent*, you will find that in the year 1551 the Papal Legates who presided over the Council ordered: 'That the Divines ought to confirm their opinions with the holy Scripture, Traditions of the Apostles, sacred and approved Councils, and by the Constitutions and Authorities of the holy Fathers; that they ought to use brevity, and avoid superfluous and unprofitable questions, and perverse contentions. . . .'

Forty-three years after the Italian divines had written this memorial, Richard Hooker in his famous *Laws of Ecclesiastical Polity* makes exactly the same complaint of his Puritan adversaries. Hooker's balanced thought—from which the appellation 'The Judicious Hooker' is derived—and his diffuse style, which is the vehicle of such thought, make his writings singularly unfit for the process of summarising by a short, pointed quotation. But, in the section referred to, he reproaches his opponents with *Their Disparagement of Reason;* and in support of his own position definitely refers to 'The greatest amongst the school-divines' by which designation I presume that he refers to St. Thomas Aquinas.

Hooker's *Ecclesiastical Polity* was published just before Sarpi's *Council of Trent*. Accordingly there was complete independence between the two works. But both the Italian divines of 1551, and Hooker at the end of that century testify to the anti-rationalist trend of thought at that epoch, and in this respect contrast their own age with the epoch of scholasticism.

This reaction was undoubtedly a very necessary corrective to the unguarded rationalism of the Middle Ages. But reactions run to extremes. Accordingly, although one outcome of this reaction was the birth of modern science, yet we must remember that science thereby inherited the bias of thought to which it owes its origin.

The effect of Greek dramatic literature was manysided so far as concerns the various ways in which it indirectly affected medieval thought. The pilgrim fathers of the scientific imagination as it exists today are the great tragedians of ancient Athens, Aeschylus, Sophocles, Euripides. Their vision of fate, remorseless and indifferent, urging a tragic incident to its inevitable issue, is the vision possessed by science. Fate in Greek Tragedy becomes the order of nature in modern thought. The absorbing interest in the particular heroic incidents, as an example and a verification of the workings of fate, reappears in our epoch as concentration of interest on the crucial experiments. It was my good fortune to be present at the meeting of the Royal Society in London when the Astronomer Royal for England announced that the photographic plates of the famous eclipse, as measured by his colleagues in Greenwich Observatory, had verified the prediction of Einstein that rays of light are bent as they pass in the neighbourhood of the sun. The whole atmosphere of tense interest was exactly that of the Greek drama: we were the chorus commenting on the decree of destiny as disclosed in the development of a supreme incident. There was dramatic quality in the very staging:—the traditional ceremonial, and in the background the picture of Newton to remind us that the greatest of scientific generalisations was now, after more than two centuries, to receive its first modification. Nor was the personal interest wanting: a great adventure in thought had at length come safe to shore.

Let me here remind you that the essence of dramatic tragedy is not unhappiness. It resides in the solemnity of the remorseless working of things. This inevitableness of destiny can only be illustrated in terms of human life by incidents which in fact involve unhappiness. For it is only by them that the futility of escape can be made evident in the drama. This remorseless inevitableness is what pervades scientific thought. The laws of physics are the decrees of fate.

The conception of the moral order in the Greek plays was certainly not a discovery of the dramatists. It must have passed into the literary tradition from the general serious opinion of the times. But in finding this magnificent expression, it thereby deepened the stream of thought from which it arose. The spectacle of a moral order was impressed upon the imagination of a classical civilisation.

The time came when that great society decayed, and Europe passed into the Middle Ages. The direct influence of Greek literature vanished. But the concept of the moral order and of the order of nature had enshrined itself in the Stoic philosophy. For example, Lecky in his *History of European Morals* tells us 'Seneca maintains that the Divinity has determined all things by an inexorable law of destiny, which He has decreed, but which He Himself obeys.' But the most effective way in which the Stoics influenced the mentality of the Middle Ages was by the diffused sense of order which arose from Roman law. Again to quote Lecky: 'The Roman legislation was in a twofold manner the child of philosophy. It was in the first place formed upon the philosophical model, for, instead of being a mere empirical system adjusted to the existing requirements of society, it laid down abstract principles of right to which it endeavoured to conform; and, in the next place, these principles were borrowed directly from Stoicism.' . . .

But for science something more is wanted than a general sense of the order in things. It needs but a sentence to point out how the habit of definite exact thought was implanted in the European mind by the long dominance of scholastic logic and scholastic divinity. The habit remained after the philosophy had been repudiated, the priceless habit of looking for an exact point and of sticking to it when found. Galileo owes more to Aristotle than appears on the surface of his *Dialogues*: he owes to him his clear head and his analytic mind.

I do not think, however, that I have even yet brought out the greatest contribution of medievalism to the formation of the scientific movement. I mean the inexpugnable belief that every detailed occurrence can be correlated with its antecedents in a perfectly definite manner, exemplifying general principles. Without this belief the incredible labours of scientists would be without hope. It is this instinctive conviction, vividly poised before the imagination, which is the motive power of research:—that there is a secret, a secret which can be unveiled. How has this conviction been so vividly implanted on the European mind?

When we compare this tone of thought in Europe with the attitude of other civilisations when left to themselves, there seems but one source for its origin. It must come from the medieval insistence on the rationality of God, conceived as with the personal energy of Jehovah and with the rationality of a Greek philosopher. Every detail was supervised and ordered: the search into nature could only result in the vindication of the faith in rationality. Remember that I am not talking of the explicit beliefs of a few individuals. What I mean is the impress on the European mind arising from the unquestioned faith of centuries. By this I mean the instinctive tone of thought and not a mere creed of words.

In Asia, the conceptions of God were of a being who was either too arbitrary or too impersonal for such ideas to have much effect on instinctive habits of mind. Any definite occurrence might be due to the fiat of an irrational despot, or might issue from some impersonal, inscrutable origin of things. There was not the same confidence as in the intelligible rationality of a personal being. I am not arguing that the European trust in the scrutability of nature was logically justified even by its own theology. My only point is to understand how it arose. My explanation is that the faith in the possibility of science, generated antecedently to the development of modern scientific theory, is an unconscious derivative from medieval theology.

But science is not merely the outcome of instinctive faith. It also requires an active interest in the simple occurrences of life for their own sake. . . .

In order to understand the contrast between these early Middle Ages and the atmosphere required by the scientific mentality, we should compare the sixth century in Italy with the sixteenth century. In both centuries the Italian genius was laying the foundations of a new epoch. The history of the three centuries preceding the earlier period, despite the promise for the future introduced by the rise of Christianity, is overwhelmingly infected by the sense of the decline of civilisation. In each generation something has been lost. As we read the records, we are haunted by the shadow of the coming barbarism. There are great men, with fine achievements in action or in thought. But their total effect is merely for some short time to arrest the general decline. In the sixth century we are, so far as Italy is concerned, at the lowest point of the curve. But in that century every action is laying the foundation for the tremendous rise of the new European civilisation. In the background the Byzantine Empire, under Justinian, in three ways determined the character of the early Middle Ages in Western Europe. In the first place, its armies, under Belisarius and Narses, cleared Italy from the Gothic domination. In this way, the stage was freed for the exercise of the old Italian genius for creating organisations which shall be protective of ideals of cultural activity. It is impossible not to sympathise with the Goths: yet there can be no doubt but that a thousand years of the Papacy were infinitely more valuable for Europe than any effects derivable from a well-established Gothic kingdom of Italy.

In the second place, the codification of the Roman law established the ideal of legality which dominated the sociological thought of Europe in the succeeding centuries. Law is both an engine for government and a condition restraining government. The canon law of the Church, and the civil law of the State, owe to Justinian's lawyers their influence on the development of Europe. They established in the Western mind the ideal that an authority should be at once lawful, and law-enforcing, and should in itself exhibit a rationally adjusted system of organisation. The sixth century in Italy gave the initial exhibition of the way in which the impress of these ideas was fostered by contact with the Byzantine Empire.

Thirdly, in the non-political spheres of art and learning Constantinople exhibited a standard of realised achievement which, partly by the impulse to direct imitation, and partly by the indirect inspiration arising from the mere knowledge that such things existed, acted as a perpetual spur to Western culture. The wisdom of the Byzantines, as it stood in the imagination of the first phase of medieval mentality, and the wisdom of the Egyptians as it stood in the imagination of the early Greeks, played analogous rôles. Probably the actual knowledge of these respective wisdoms was, in either case, about as much as was good for the recipients. They knew enough to know the sort of standards which are attainable, and not enough to be fettered by static and traditional ways of thought. Accordingly, in both cases men went ahead on their own and did better. No account of the rise of the European scientific mentality can omit some notice of this influence of the Byzantine civilisation in the background. In the sixth century there is a crisis in the history of the relations between the Byzantines and the West; and this crisis is to be contrasted with the influence of Greek literature on European thought in the fifteenth and sixteenth centuries. The two outstanding men, who in the Italy of the sixth century laid the foundations of the future, were St. Benedict and Gregory the Great. By reference to them, we can at once see how absolutely in ruins was the approach to the scientific mentality which had been attained by the Greeks. We are at the zero point of scientific temperature. But the life-work of Gregory and of Benedict contributed elements to the reconstruction of Europe which secured that this reconstruction, when it arrived, should include a more effective scientific mentality than that of the ancient world. The Greeks were over-theoretical. For them science was an offshoot of philosophy. Gregory and Benedict were practical men, with an eye for the importance of ordinary things; and they combined this practical temperament with their religious and cultural activities. In particular, we owe it to St. Benedict that the monasteries were the homes of practical agriculturalists, as well as of saints and of artists and men of learning. The alliance of science with technology, by which learning is kept in contact with irreducible and stubborn facts, owes much to the practical bent of the early Benedictines. Modern science derives from Rome as well as from Greece, and this Roman strain explains its gain in an energy of thought kept closely in contact with the world of facts.

But the influence of this contact between the monasteries and the facts of nature showed itself first in art. The rise of Naturalism in the later Middle Ages was the entry into the European mind of the final ingredient necessary for the rise of science. It was the rise of interest in natural objects and in natural occurrences, for their own sakes. The natural foliage of a district was sculptured in out-of-the-way spots of the later buildings, merely as exhibiting delight in those familiar objects. The whole atmosphere of every art exhibited a direct joy in the apprehension of the things which lie around us. The craftsmen who executed the late medieval decorative sculpture, Giotto, Chaucer, Wordsworth, Walt Whitman, and the New England poet Robert Frost, are all akin to each other in this respect. The simple immediate facts are the topics of interest, and these reappear in the thought of science as the 'irreducible stubborn facts.'

The mind of Europe was now prepared for its new venture of thought. It is unnecessary to tell in detail the various incidents which marked the rise of science: the growth of wealth and leisure; the expansion of universities; the invention of printing; the taking of Constantinople; Copernicus; Vasco da Gama; Columbus; the telescope. The soil, the climate, the seeds, were there, and the forest grew. Science has never shaken off the impress of its origin in the historical revolt of the later Renaissance. It has remained predominantly an anti-rationalistic movement, based upon a naïve faith. What reasoning it has wanted, has been borrowed from mathematics which is a surviving relic of Greek rationalism, following the deductive method. . . .

Of course the historical revolt was fully justified. It was wanted. It was more than wanted: it was an absolute necessity for healthy progress. The world required centuries of contemplation of irreducible and stubborn facts. It is difficult for men to do more than one thing at a time, and that was the sort of thing they had to do after the rationalistic orgy of the Middle Ages. It was a very sensible reaction; but it was not a protest on behalf of reason.

There is, however, a Nemesis which waits upon those who deliberately avoid avenues of knowledge. Oliver Cromwell's cry echoes down the ages, 'My brethren, by the bowels of Christ I beseech you, bethink you that you may be mistaken.'

The progress of science has now reached a turning point. The stable foundations of physics have broken up: also for the first time physiology is asserting itself as an effective body of knowledge, as distinct from a scrap-heap. The old foundations of scientific thought are becoming unintelligible. Time, space, matter, material, ether, electricity, mechanism, organism, configuration, structure, pattern, function, all require reinterpretation. What is the sense of talking about a mechanical explanation when you do not know what you mean by mechanics?

The truth is that science started its modern career by taking over ideas derived from the weakest side of the philosophies of Aristotle's successors. In some respects it was a happy choice. It enabled the knowledge of the seventeenth century to be formularised so far as physics and chemistry were concerned, with a completeness which has lasted to the present time. But the progress of biology and psychology has probably been checked by the uncritical assumption of half-truths. If science is not to degenerate into a medley of *ad hoc* hypotheses, it must become philosophical and must enter upon a thorough criticism of its own foundations.

2

An Early Statement of Ordering Principles in Earth History

NICOLAUS STENO
1669

From *The Prodromus of Nicolaus Steno's Dissertation concerning a Solid Body enclosed by Process of Nature within a Solid* (University of Michigan, Humanistic Studies, vol. XI, part 2, 1916), translated from the Latin by J. G. Winter, pp. 229–230. The Macmillan Company, 1916; Hafner Publishing Company, Inc., 1968. Reprinted with permission of the publisher.

Concerning the position of strata, the following can be considered as certain:

1. At the time when a given stratum was being formed, there was beneath it another substance which prevented the further descent of the comminuted matter; and so at the time when the lowest stratum was being formed either another solid substance was beneath it, or if some fluid existed there, then it was not only of a different character from the upper fluid, but also heavier than the solid sediment of the upper fluid.
2. At the time when one of the upper strata was being formed, the lower stratum had already gained the consistency of a solid.
3. At the time when any given stratum was being formed it was either encompassed on its sides by another solid substance, or it covered the entire spherical surface of the earth. Hence it follows that in whatever place the bared sides of the strata are seen, either a continuation of the same strata must be sought, or another solid substance must be found which kept the matter of the strata from dispersion.
4. At the time when any given stratum was being formed, all the matter resting upon it was fluid, and, therefore, at the time when the lowest stratum was being formed, none of the upper strata existed.

As regards form, it is certain that at the time when any given stratum was being produced its lower surface, as also its lateral surfaces, corresponded to the surfaces of the lower substance and lateral substances, but that the upper surface was parallel to the horizon, so far as possible; and that all strata, therefore, except the lowest, were bounded by two planes parallel to the horizon. Hence it follows that strata either perpendicular to the horizon or inclined toward it, were at one time parallel to the horizon.

3

James Hutton Observes the Great Unconformity at Siccar Point

JOHN PLAYFAIR
1822

From *The Works of John Playfair,* vol. 4, pp. 78–81. Archibald Constable & Co., 1822.

In 1788 he [James Hutton] made some other valuable observations . . . The ridge of the Lammermuir Hills, in the south of Scotland, consists of primary micaceous schistus, and extends from St Abb's Head westward, till it join the metalliferous mountains about the sources of the Clyde. The sea coast affords a transverse section of this alpine tract at its eastern extermity, and exhibits the change from the primary to the secondary strata, both on the south and on the north. Dr Hutton wished particularly to examine the latter of these, and on this occasion Sir James Hall and I had the pleasure to accompany him. We sailed in a boat from Dunglass, on a day when the fineness of the weather permitted us to keep close to the foot of the rocks which line the shore in that quarter, directing our course southwards, in search of the termination of the secondary strata. We made for a high rocky point or head-land, the Siccar, near which, from our observations on shore, we knew that the object we were in search of was likely to be discovered. On landing at this point, we found that we actually trode on the primeval rock, which forms alternately the base and the summit of the present land. It is here a micaceous schistus, in beds nearly vertical, highly indurated, and stretching from S.E. to N.W. The surface of this rock runs with a moderate ascent from the level of low-water, at which we landed, nearly to that of high-water, where the schistus has a thin covering of red horizontal sandstone laid over it; and this sandstone, at the distance of a few yards farther back, rises into a very high perpendicular cliff. Here, therefore, the immediate contact of the two rocks is not only visible, but is curiously dissected and laid open by the action of the waves. The rugged tops of the schistus are seen penetrating into the horizontal beds of sandstone, and the lowest of these last form a breccia containing fragments of schistus, some round and others angular, united by an arenaceous cement [see Figure 3.1].

Dr Hutton was highly pleased with appearances that set in so clear a light the different

FIGURE 3.1
The great unconformity at Siccar Point. 12.5 km west of St. Abb's Head, southeastern Scotland. Shows gently dipping Devonian sandstone overlying vertical Silurian strata. (Crown Copyright Geological Survey Photograph by R. Lunn. Reproduced by permission of the Controller, H.M. Stationery Office.)

formations of the parts which compose the exterior crust of the earth, and where all the circumstances were combined that could render the observation satisfactory and precise. On us who saw these phenomena for the first time, the impression made will not easily be forgotten. The palpable evidence presented to us, of one of the most extraordinary and important facts in the natural history of the earth, gave a reality and substance to those theoretical speculations which, however probable, had never till now been directly authenticated by the testimony of the senses. We often said to ourselves, What clearer evidence could we have had of the different formation of these rocks, and of the long interval which separated their formation, had we actually seen them emerging from the bosom of the deep? We felt ourselves necessarily carried back to the time when the schistus on which we stood was yet at the bottom of the sea, and when the sandstone before us was only beginning to be deposited, in the shape of sand or mud, from the waters of a superincumbent ocean. An epocha still more remote presented itself, when even the most ancient of these rocks, instead of standing upright in vertical beds lay in horizontal planes at the bottom of the sea and was not yet disturbed by that immeasurable force which has burst asunder the solid pavement of the globe. Revolutions still more remote appeared in the distance of this extraordinary perspective. The mind seemed to grow giddy by looking so far into the abyss of time; and while we listened with earnestness and admiration to the philosopher who was now unfolding to us the order and series of these wonderful events, we became sensible how much farther reason may sometimes go than imagination can venture to follow.

4

The Inculcation of Scientific Method by Example

with an Illustration Drawn from the Quaternary Geology of Utah

G. K. GILBERT

1886

Presidential address read before the American Society of Naturalists at Boston, December 27, 1885. From *American Journal of Science*, ser. 3, vol. 31, pp. 284–299, 1886. Reprinted with permission of the *American Journal of Science*.

The teacher's work is susceptible of a logical division into two parts. He stores minds, and he trains them. The modern educator believes the second function to be the higher, because the trained mind can store itself. Nevertheless the two go hand in hand and are in great part inseparable. The effort of the intelligent teacher is to employ such methods in storing the minds of his pupils with knowledge that they shall acquire at the same time the best training.

In that particular department of teaching which is called scientific, there is the same logical duality, and to a great extent there is a practical unity; but in this case there is a pre-determined classification of those who fall under the teacher's instruction, which has the effect of practically dividing his methods. A portion of his pupils are preparing to engage in the work of research, and look to a scientific career. Another portion are to be occupied with business or in other pursuits not implying research, at least in the ordinary sense, and desire to obtain, as a part of a liberal education, an acquaintance with the materials and results of science. The first demand a training in methods, the second consciously ask only for a store of knowledge. Nevertheless, the general student can best accomplish his purpose with the aid of a certain amount of training in method, while to him who proposes a career of investigation, there is an equal necessity for a large amount of positive knowledge.

Before proceeding to amplify these propositions it seems best to give consideration to the essential nature of scientific research—to restate, for the sake of a common understanding, the process by which science advances.

Scientific research consists of the observation of phenomena and the discovery of their relations. Scientific observation is not sharply distinguished from other observation. It may even be doubted whether there is such a thing as unscientific observation. If there is a valid distinction, it probably rests on the two following characters. Scientific observation, or the observation of the investigator, endeavors to discriminate the phenomena observed from the observer's inference in regard to them, and to record the phenomena pure and simple. I say "endeavors," for in my judgment he does not ordinarily succeed. His failure is primarily due to subjective conditions; perception and inference are so intimately associated that a body of inferences has become incorporated in the constitution of the mind. And the record of an untainted fact is obstructed not only directly by the constitution of the mind, but indirectly through the constitution of language, the creature and imitator of the mind. But while the investigator does not succeed in his effort to obtain pure facts, his effort creates a tendency, and that tendency gives scientific observation and its record a distinctive character.

Scientific observation is moreover selective and concentrated. It does not gather facts indiscriminately, but, recognizing their classification, it seeks new facts that will augment established groups. The investigator, by restricting his observation to a limited number of groups of phenomena, is enabled to concentrate his attention, and thus sharpens his vision for the detection of matters that are unnoticed by the ordinary observer.

The superficial relations of phenomena are discovered by induction—by the grouping of facts in accordance with their conspicuous common characters—or, in other words, by empiric classification. Such empiric classification is a preliminary work in all sciences. It is a convenient and temporary sorting of our knowledge, and with the increase of knowledge it is perpetually remodeled. But it is more than a mere convenience; it is a stepping-stone to a logical, or rational, or, more strictly, relational classification; for it leads to the understanding of those deeper relations which constitute the order of nature.

Phenomena are arranged in chains of necessary sequence. In such a chain each link is the necessary consequent of that which precedes, and the necessary antecedent of that which follows. The rising of the sun is consequent on the rotation of the earth. It is the logical antecedent of morning light. Morning light is in turn the consequent of sunrise and the antecedent of numerous other phenomena. If we examine any link of the chain, we find that it has more than one antecedent and more than one consequent. The rising of the sun depends on the position of the earth's axis as well as on its rotation, and it causes morning heat as well as morning light. Antecedent and consequent relations are therefore not merely linear, but constitute a plexus; and this plexus pervades nature. . . .

It is the province of research to discover the antecedents of phenomena. This is done by the aid of hypothesis. A phenomenon having been observed, or a group of phenomena having been established by empiric classification, the investigator invents an hypothesis in explanation. He then devises and applies a test of the validity of the hypothesis. If it does not stand the test he discards it and invents a new one. If it survives the test, he proceeds at once to devise a second test. And he thus continues until he finds an hypothesis that remains unscathed after all the tests his imagination can suggest.

This, however, is not his universal course, for he is not restricted to the employment of one hypothesis at a time. There is indeed an advantage in entertaining several at once, for then it is possible to discover their mutual antagonisms and inconsistencies, and to devise crucial tests,—tests which will necessarily debar some of the hypotheses from further consideration. The process of testing is then a process of elimination, at least until all but one of the hypotheses have been disproved. . . .

Evidently, if the investigator is to succeed in the discovery of veritable explanations of phenomena, he must be fertile in the invention of hypotheses and ingenious in the application of tests. The practical questions for the teacher are, whether it is possible by training to improve the guessing faculty, and if so, how it is to be done. To answer these, we must give attention to the nature of the scientific guess considered as a mental process. Like other mental processes, the framing of hypotheses is usually unconscious, but by attention it can be brought into consciousness and analyzed.

Given a phenomenon, A, whose antecedent we seek. First we ransack the memory for some different phenomenon, B, which has one or more features in common with A, and whose antecedent we know. Then we pass by analogy from the antecedent of B, to the hypothetical antecedent of A, solving the analogic proportion—as B is to A, so is the antecedent of B to the antecedent of A.

Having thus obtained an hypothesis, we proceed to test it. If the hypothetical antecedent is a familiar phenomenon, we compare its known or deduced consequents with A, and observe whether they agree or differ. If it is unfamiliar, we ascertain its consequents by experiment or some other form of observation; and in the selection of the particular experiments or observations to serve as tests, we are guided once more by analogy, inverting the previous formula.

The question, whether or not the function of the mind in devising hypotheses and the tests of them is creative, is foreign to the present purpose. It suffices that we recognize the process as analogic, requiring for its success a preliminary knowledge of numerous instances of consequential relations. The consequential relations of nature are infinite in variety, and he who is acquainted with the largest number has the broadest base for the analogic suggestion of hypotheses. It is true that a store of scientific knowledge cannot take the place of mental strength and training, i.e. of functional ability inherited and acquired, but it is nevertheless a pre-requisite of fertility in hypothesis.

The great investigator is primarily and preëminently the man who is rich in hypotheses. In the plenitude of his wealth he can spare the weaklings without regret; and having many from which to select, his mind maintains a judicial attitude. . . .

Returning now to the subject of education, take first the case in which the student is to become an investigator. He is to observe phenomena, he is to frame and test hypotheses. As a matter of course, in order to learn to do these things he must do them. Sooner or later he must be sent directly to nature, out of doors or in the laboratory, and must in her presence train his faculties by practice. But before he undertakes this, the teacher can aid him by imparting methods. It is probably not best to offer them in the abstract until he has become well acquainted with them in the concrete. Typical investigations should be described in detail, illustrating the varied phases of the method of hypothesis, and not omitting to show how its successes are achieved through series of failures. The history of at least one science should be developed, with the rise and fall of its successive theories. These educational factors are directed to the training of his mind, but his mind needs also to be stored with scientific knowledge, which shall serve as a foundation for analogies. If he would explain some feature of nature, he must depend on the explanations others have reached for other features; and he needs large resources of knowledge of the relations of phenomena.

The course of training for the apprentice of science should give him, in the study room and in the class room, a varied acquaintance with the laws of nature that have been discovered by research. It should not needlessly burden his memory with empiric classifications, for these belong to the humbler walks of science, and it is unwise to impress on the novice the high importance of that which the master regards as provisional. It should teach observation by actual practice,—practice rigorously restricted to selected groups of phenomena. It should illustrate with varied reiteration—by books, by lectures, by demonstrations in the laboratory—the method of discovery by the aid of hypotheses. It should assign him actual investigation and subject his methods to criticism.

Students whose projected careers are not scientific, but who are unwilling to ignore so important a subject, naturally wish to cover a wide field in a short time. Their teacher, imbued with the vastness of science, is tempted to give them a maximum number of facts, with such order and classification as best favor their rapid statement. If he yields to the temptation, there is reason to fear that a permanent misapprehension is established, and the essence of science is not communicated. In my judgment he will do better to contract the phenomenal, and enlarge the logical scope of his subject, so as to dwell on the philosophy of the science rather than its material. . . .

The investigator becomes an educator when in giving his work to the world he describes the route by which his end was reached. It is not denied that the publication of sound conclusions is in itself educational, but it is maintained that the publication of the concrete illustration of a good method is educational in a higher sense. It is not insisted that all skillful investigations should be published *in extenso;* it is only affirmed that the number of such publications is far too small. We need for educational purposes more narratives of good work in all departments of research. Let the discoverer of a new principle recite evey hypothesis that occurred to him in the course of his search, telling, if he can, how it was suggested. Let him lay bare the considerations which rendered it plausible, the tests that were conceived, and those which were applied. Let him show in what way the failure of one hypothesis aided in the invention of another. Let him set forth not only the tests which verify his final hypothesis, but the considerations which leave a residuum of doubt as to its validity. And finally let him indicate, if he can, the line or lines of research that promise to throw more light.

By so doing he will accomplish many things. He will guard himself against an overestimate of the strength of his uneliminated hypothesis, and he will thus diminish his self-conceit. By conscious attention to his methods he will improve them. He will therefore educate himself. . . . Not all are willing to be educated, not all need be; the majority of those who examine an essay seek only to learn its conclusions and have time for nothing more. For their use there should be appended or prefaced a concise summary of results. . . .

It was intimated a moment ago that precept unsupported by example could not be depended on to infuse method—and the dictum applies even to the burden of this discourse. I am persuaded that my meaning will be better apprehended if I supplement my disquisition by an outline of an investigation of my own. The seeming egotism must be condoned, for it is manifestly impossible for me to trace out the actual course of observation and reasoning in the case of another's work.

To guard against possible misapprehension it is necessary to emphasize the fact that the following discussion contains an outline merely of its subject. Its subject is a certain geologic uplift that has been observed in Utah. To render it intelligible to those who are unacquainted with the literature of the geology of Utah, it will be introduced by a short account of Lake Bonneville.

The basin of Great Salt Lake lies in a region of mountains; to picture its character to your mind, conceive a plain the surface of which is embossed by parallel ridges of moderate length, from fifteen to twenty-five miles apart, and from 2,000 to 6,000 or 7,000 feet high. Conceive further that portions of this plain are uplifted, together with their mountain ridges, so as to enclose a basin 150 miles in either dimension, and you have the general structure of the district in question. The debris washed down from the mountains has for ages accumulated in this depression, so that the central-lying mountain ridges are nearly buried; indeed there is reason to suspect that some of them are quite buried, a plain of fine silt being spread smoothly over them. Great Salt Lake itself lies on the east side of the basin; the western half, which is only a few feet higher, is a saline desert.

In the last geologic epoch—the Glacial Epoch—the lake expanded so as to fill the basin to overflowing. The water surface was then very much larger, and as its area included the basins of several lakes now independent, it has been given a separate name. Lake Bonneville was very irregular in form; the mountain ranges of the basin ran long peninsulas from its north and south shores, and projected from its surface in numerous islands. The Quaternary winds, playing on its surface, dashed waves against its shores, and the spits and beaches and cliffs wrought by these waves remain in a high state of preservation to testify to the position of the ancient water margin. Through the greater part of its extent this shore-line forms a conspicuous feature in the topography of the country, and is readily traceable. It has been actually traced out, surveyed, and mapped with much care, and our knowledge of the old lake is in many other respects definite and full.

Its width from a few miles east of Great Salt Lake to the west side of the Great Salt Lake desert was 125 miles. From the mountains on the north of the desert to those on the south its expanse was about the same, but it did not terminate with the southerly mountains. It extended through them in several straits and formed beyond a second and much smaller body of water. The main body was 1,000 feet deep, the minor body about 500 feet.

Manifestly, when this old shore-line was made, all parts of it lay in the same horizontal plane, with no other curvature than that which belongs to the figure of the earth; that is, all parts of it were level. If it is not now level—if some parts are higher than others, it seems equally manifest that there have been local elevations or subsidences of the land. It is to such differences of level in the shore-line as it stands, and to their interpretation, that I desire to call your attention.

As far as the eye can judge, the shore is still level, and so long as no measurements were made its horizontality remained unquestioned. The two geologists who were probably the first to measure its height recorded their results in language implying no suspicion that more than one determination was necessary.

It happened that in the year of my first exploration of the Bonneville area I saw the shore-line not only in the Salt Lake basin but in the more southerly basin, and that I passed from one basin to the other by a route that did not reveal their connection. In doubt whether two lakes were under observation or only one, I sought to answer the question by determining the height of the shore-line in each, my instrument for the purpose being the barometer. The verdict of the barometer was that the southerly shore-line was somewhat higher than the northerly, but the computations necessary to deduce it were not made until the mutual continuity of the two shore-lines had been ascertained by direct observation. The barometric measurement was therefore superseded as an answer to the original question, but it answered another which had not been asked, for it indicated that the ancient shore at one point had come to stand higher than at another. The postulate of horizontality was thus overthrown.

An hypothesis immediately took its place. It is one of the great inductions of geology that as the ages roll by the surface of the earth rises and falls in a way that may be called undulatory. I do not now refer to the anticlinal and synclinal flexures of strata, so conspicuous in some mountainous regions, but to broader and far gentler flexures which are inconstant in position from period to period. By such undulations the Tertiary lake basins of the Far West were not only formed but were remodeled and rearranged many times. By such undulations the basin of Great Salt Lake was created. As to their cause, geology is absolutely ignorant, and she is almost absolutely silent. When it was ascertained that the Bonneville shore-line at two distant points had not the same height, the first hypothesis to suggest itself merely referred the difference to this gentle undulatory movement of the crust. As other hypotheses are to be mentioned, it will be convenient to christen this one the hypothesis of unexplained undulation.

A few years later the discovery was made that a fault had occurred along the western base of the Wasatch range of mountains since the Bonneville epoch. This range lies just east of Great Salt Lake, and the Bonneville shore is traced across its western face. The effect of the fault was to lift the mountain higher, with reference to the lake bottom, and to carry that part of the old shore-line upward. The amount of the uplift varied in different parts of the fault from ten to fifty feet.

This discovery was something more than the finding of a post-Bonneville fault; it was the discovery also of a new method of recognizing faults—of a peculiar type of cliff produced by faulting, which, though by no means obscure, had previously been overlooked by geologists. It gave rise to a new tentative explanation for the displacement of shore-line discovered by barometer, namely, that it arose by faulting; and it opened a new line of observation.

Two hypotheses were now under consideration, but they were not strictly alternative. Perhaps it would be better to say that the origination of the second not only gave an alternative but also modified the first. The Wasatch fault must affect the height of the shore-line, and wherever it crossed the shore-line that line must be discontinuous and exhibit two levels. The admission of disturbance by faulting was therefore compulsory, but faulting might or might not be sufficient alone. If it was not sufficient, then undulation might complement it. The modified first hypothesis was, undulation and faulting combined, the second, faulting alone—both undulation and faulting being themselves unexplained.

It was not difficult to devise tests. An instrumental level line might be carried along the old beach so as to ascertain whether it rose or fell in regions where no faults occur; or its height might be carefully measured at two points and the difference of altitude compared with the total throw of the intervening post-

Bonneville faults. The second of these tests was applied, and with success. By means of the surveyor's level the height of the old shore above the water surface at the shore of Great Salt Lake was measured at two points twenty miles apart. One of these points is on the Wasatch range near Salt Lake City; the other is on the next range west, the Oquirrh. The only post-Bonneville fault between them is that at the base of the Wasatch, and its throw is there about fifty feet, the west side having gone down. If then faulting is alone responsible for shore-displacement, the beach on the Oquirrh range should be fifty feet lower than that on the Wasatch. The measurement however showed it to be twenty-eight feet higher, and thus demonstrated a difference of seventy-eight feet to be referred to undulation.

Thus a step was made in advance, but the resulting position was not final, for the inquiring mind could find no satisfaction in the knowledge that crust undulation and crust faulting were conjointly efficient, so long as both these remained without explanation. No new hypotheses were at once invented, but it was determined to continue observation until the solitary phenomena at command were expanded into a group, and to seek new light in the classification of this group. As the basin was traversed in the conduct of the general investigation of the old lake, a search was made for the records of recent faults and at every opportunity the height of the shore was accurately measured. Six such measurements were made in the immediate vicinity of Great Salt Lake, the lake affording a common datum plane. Ten others were made on the lines of railways, where the leveling data of the railway engineers could be utilized. At some points the height was found greater than on the Oquirrh, at others less than on the Wasatch, the range from highest to lowest being 168 feet.

Faults were discovered at the bases of numerous mountain ranges, but none of them are so great as that along the Wasatch, and nearly all are very small. None were found associated with the half-buried mountains of the center of the desert, and yet on these same mountains are the highest shore records to which measurement was carried.

In general it was found that the displacements recorded by the shores have been much larger than the displacements demonstrated by faults, so that faulting can be appealed to in explanation of shore-displacement only to a small extent. It was found that the throw of the faults was in some cases opposed in direction to the total deformation on the shore-line and in other cases coincident. For these reasons faulting was provisionally regarded as a disturbing factor merely, and the deformation demonstrated by the measurements of shore-height was treated as simply flexural or undulatory.

To classify the shore-heights, as a basis for further hypothesis, they were platted on a map, and their grouping was compared with geographic features. It appeared that the highest measured points lay within the area of the main body of Lake Bonneville, that the lowest points lay at the extreme north and at the extreme south, that the eastern shore of Lake Bonneville in the vicinity of Great Salt Lake was intermediate in height, and that the single point determined on the western shore of the old lake agreed in height with the eastern shore. Unfortunately, the distribution of the measurements, which had been largely determined by the distribution of railroad lines, was not equable throughout the basis of the lake, and nearly the whole of its western shore was undetermined in altitude. When lines of equal altitude were drawn among the figures representing measurements, after the manner of the isobars on a Signal Service weather map, it was found that they were not fully controlled by the determined points; but when they had been given the most satisfactory adjustment, they contoured a figure of deformation which may be characterized as a low, broad dome, having its crest over the center of the main body of Lake Bonneville, and extending a subordinate member to the region of the southern body of the lake. One half of this figure was fairly inferred from the data of observation; the remaining half was imaginary and its drawing merely gave graphic expression to the hypothesis suggested by the incomplete contours —the hypothesis that the deformation stands in some necessary or causal relation to the lake and its disappearance.

Now it has been independently determined that the cause of the lake and the cause of its disappearance were climatic; it was not drained by the wearing down of its outlet, nor emptied by the unequal uplift of portions of its rim, but it was dissipated by evaporation. If then the disappearance of the lake and the deformation of the land are connected in a causal way the change in the lake was the cause, and the change in the land was the effect. How can we suppose the drying up of the water to have produced the up-arching of the plain on which the water lay?

In the attempt to answer this question three tentative explanations were suggested, and these will be stated in the order of their origination.

It is well known to geologists that in several instances a great formation thousands of feet in thickness consists wholly or chiefly of shore deposits. To account for them it is necessary to suppose that the sea floor locally sank down as rapidly as the sediments were added. Conversely there is reason to believe that the adjacent continent, which by erosion furnished the sediment, rose up as rapidly as its surface was degraded. It is a favorite theory—at least with that large division of geologists who consider the interior of the earth as mobile—that the sea-bottom sinks in such cases because of the load of sediment that is added and that the land is forced up hydrostatically because it is unloaded by erosion. A similar theory might explain the up-arching of the desiccated bed of Lake Bonneville, for the unloading of 1000 feet of water from an area more than one hundred miles across would give to the supposed liquid interior an irresistible uplifting force. This was the first explanation to suggest itself.

The second suggestion did not spring from any geological theory consciously retained in memory, but I have since suspected that the germ of the idea may have been caught from a passage in Croll's 'Climate and Time.' It is this: The geoid of which the ocean's surface is a visible portion is not an ellipsoid of revolution, but differs from that symmetric surface by undulations which depend on local inequalities in the density and in the superficial configuration of the earth. The water level is everywhere normal to the plumb-line, but the plumb-line, as geodesy has shown, is subject to local deflection. Now the ocean itself is one of the attracting factors, and if the ocean were to be removed, the geoid would thereby be modified. The surface of Lake Bonneville was part of a geoid at a higher plane than that of the ocean surface, and the removal of the water of the lake unquestionably modified the local form of the geoid. Only at first blush the cause seems too small for the effect observed.

The third suggestion relates to the distribution of temperatures beneath the surface of the earth. It is well established that the inner parts of the earth are extremely hot. The outer surface is relatively cool, and in the intermediate region there is a gradation of temperatures. The isogeotherms, or planes of equal temperature, are not even surfaces, but undulate in response to variations of conductivity and of superficial temperature. At the poles, where the external surface of the crust is exceptionally cold, the isogeotherms lie lower down than in warmer latitudes; and if a portion of the earth's surface undergoes a permanent change in temperature, the influence of this change is propagated slowly downward through the crust, and the isogeotherms are locally raised or lowered. Where they are raised, the crust is locally expanded, and its surface is uplifted; where they are depressed the surface of the crust subsides. If, therefore, it can be shown that the temperature at the bottom of Lake Bonneville was raised in connection with the desiccation of the lake, we have a true cause of upward movement, and if we can show furthermore that the temperature of the surrounding region was not equally raised, we have at least a qualitative explanation of the differential uplift, the phenomenon to be accounted for.

It is now several years since these explanations were first suggested, and subsequent reflection has developed no others. While all of them appear perfectly rational, only a very slight inspection was necessary to raise a doubt as to the quantitative sufficiency of the second and third. It was therefore determined to ascertain as accurately as possible the maximum change which might be ascribed to each of the three suggested causes, and to compare it with the actual change. The actual change is susceptible of various statements. If we consider only the measurements on the margin of the main body of water, and in its center we find a difference of 100 feet; by including observations on outlying bays we get a maximum difference of 168 feet; and a study of the peripheral slopes of the uplift suggests that they extend somewhat beyond the boundaries of the lake. Crude extrapolation gives 200 feet as a maximum estimate of the height of the crustal dome.

Take first the hypothesis that the crust of the earth, floating on a molten nucleus, rose up in the region of the basin when its weight was locally diminished by the removal of the water of the lake. The weight of the load removed is measured by the depth of the water before evaporation, 1000 feet. The theory supposes that as the crust rose there flowed in beneath enough molten rock to replace the weight of the evaporated water. If the rock was very heavy, a layer of moderate depth was necessary; if it was less heavy, more was required; but in any event the thickness of the introduced layer must be equal to the amount of the superficial uplift. It is known that the density of the earth's material increases downward, for the mean density of the earth, expressed in terms of the density of water, is about 5.5, while that of the upper portion of the crust is about 2.7. Nothing is known however of the law under which the density increases, and nothing is known as to the depth of the zone at which matter is sufficiently mobile to be moved beneath the Bonneville basin. We may, however, indicate limits, and I think this is fairly done by assuming that the density of the introduced matter was not less than 3, nor more than 5.5. If it was 5.5, the uplift consequent on the evaporation of 1000 feet of water would be 182 feet. If it was 3, the uplift would be 333 feet. Now it has already been stated that the greatest value observation suggests for the amount of the uplift is 200 feet. The postulate is therefore abundantly competent in a quantitative way.

To evaluate the effect produced under the second hypothesis (the hypothesis, that is, that the geoid represented by the water surface of Lake Bonneville has been deformed by the withdrawal of the attraction exerted by the water itself) it is necessary to employ mathematical analysis of a high order. As my schooling in mathematics did not qualify me to undertake this, I submitted the problem to an eminently competent colleague, who has solved it rigorously and deduced for the deformation of the geoid within the area of Lake Bonneville a maximum amount of two feet. The second explanation is therefore eliminated from consideration, because quantitatively insufficient.

It remains to consider the rise of the isogeotherms, and to evaluate the resulting elevation of the basin. It has been established by numerous observations that in all lakes having a depth as great as 1000 feet, the temperature at the bottom is about 39° F. This depends upon the fact that water at that temperature is heavier than at any other, and having once reached the bottom of a deep lake, it is withdrawn from the circulation to which the upper layers are subject, and remains undisturbed. The meteorological records show that the mean annual temperature of the desiccated basin of Lake Bonneville at the present time is 52°. The change from a humid to an arid condition has therefore raised its temperature 13°. The temperature of the surrounding regions has at the same time undergone a change, of which we have no precise estimate. The epoch of Lake Bonneville was the Glacial Epoch, and the local climate was then in all probability cooler. If it was 13° cooler, the isogeotherms would be no more affected at the center of the basin than at its margins, and there would be no differential elevation. If it was cooler by less than 13° a differential uplift would occur. For the sake of giving this uplift a maximum value, we will assign a very small figure to the general change of temperature, namely 3°, and asume that the differential change with respect to the basin was 10°. A formula devised by Fourier enables us to estimate the rise of the isogeotherms, if only we know the conductivity of the material of the earth, and the time which has elapsed since the Bonneville shore line was carved. Then, if we know additionally the rate of expansion of rock for a degree of temperature, we are able to estimate the upheaval. Sir William Thompson has determined experimentally a coefficient of conductivity. The late Prof. Barlett, of West Point, has determined the coefficient of expansion for several building stones, which may be assumed to represent the crust beneath the Bonneville basin. We do not know how these coefficients are affected by high temperatures and great pressures, such as exist deep in the crust, and an element of uncertainty attaches for that reason. In order to obtain a maximum result despite this uncertainty, I have made an extreme assumption in regard to time. The shore line of Lake Bonneville is in a wonderfully perfect state of preservation. While one stands upon it, it is easy to believe that it is but a few centuries old, and the geologist, accustomed as he is to the contemplation of eons of time, hesitates to estimate its antiquity in greater units than thousands or at most tens of thousands of years. When therefore we postulate its antiquity at one hundred millions of years, we pass so far beyond the range of probability as to protect ourselves against a possible underestimate. With these data the computation has been made, and it has been ascertained that a maximum uplift of 36 feet can thus be accounted for. Since observation shows an uplift of not less than 100 feet, the thermal explanation is shown to be entirely inadequate; and if we were able to substitute for our imperfect data the actual data, we should probably find the computed uplift too small to be taken into consideration.

If therefore we admit that the removal of the water of the lake was the cause of the upheaval of the lake-bottom, there seems no way to avoid the conclusion that the efficient *modus operandi* was an upbending of the solid crust of the earth, caused by hydrostatic pressure communicated through a mobile substratum. But we are far from being forced to that admission. The coincidence in locus of the uplifted dome and the Quaternary lake may have been fortuitous; or there may even have been no coincidence, for the contoured figure of deformation was in part supplied by the imagination; and in either of these cases we can fall back on the agnostic hypothesis of unexplained undulation. In the present state of observation and inference the hypothesis of the hydrostatic restoration of equilibrium by the underflow of heavy earth-matter is the only explanation which explains, and none of the observed facts antagonize it; but the alternative hypothesis is not barred out.

To reach a satisfactory conclusion more observation is necessary, and this discussion of the subject would be premature were it not that the necessary observation is very expensive, and there is no immediate prospect that it will be supplied. It is fitting, however, that the desirable lines of research be pointed out.

The undertaking that promises most is an exhaustive hypsometric survey of the Bonneville shore line, including all bays and islands. If this were executed, it would be possible to deduce a much more satisfactory expression of the shape of the uplift, and to determine either that it is intimately related to the form of the body of water removed, or that it is not so related. If the relation were demonstrated, the observations might so far indicate its nature as to render possible an evaluation of the rigidity of the earth's crust.

Another profitable method of continuing the inquiry would be to make a similar investigation of the shore of another extinct lake, for example, the one to which Clarence King has given the name of Lahontan, and which ranks second to Lake Bonneville among the Quaternary lakes of the Great Basin. If in a second instance the center of the desiccated lake were found to be the locus of upheaval, the hydrostatic theory would be practically established.

5

Critique of the Principle of Uniformity

M. KING HUBBERT
1967

From *Uniformity and Simplicity* (GSA Special Paper 89), edited by C. C. Albritton, Jr., pp. 3–33. The Geological Society of America, 1967. Reprinted with permission of the author and the publisher.

In terms of the profundity of their effects in altering the intellectual outlook of the learned world, two scientific developments since the fifteenth century are outstanding. The first of these is the Copernican-Keplerian-Galilean revolution during which the Ptolemaic geocentric universe was displaced by the heliocentric solar system and the foundations were laid for the appropriate system of mechanics perfected during the succeeding half century by Isaac Newton. Inevitably, the demise of the geocentric system carried with it strong repercussions for the philosophical systems and theological dogmas which formed its principal supports. The theological dogma that the earth, being the abode of God's favorite Creation, Man, could not occupy a lesser place than the seat of honor at the center of the universe, was severely shaken by the establishment of the earth, not as the stationary center of the universe, but as only one of the six known planets encircling the sun.

The second major scientific revolution is that which may be referred to as the Huttonian-Lyellian-Darwinian. During this, an earth with a presumed Biblical history of only some 6000 years, whose plant and animal inhabitants were initiated by Divine Creation, was supplanted by an earth the length of whose decipherable history was estimated to be at least hundreds of millions of years, and whose plant and animal inhabitants had evolved during those years from ever more primitive ancestral forms. Man, instead of being God's highest and most favored Creation, was reduced to being a direct biological descendent, in common with all other members of the animal kingdom, of the long animal evolutionary chain.

Our attention will focus upon this second intellectual revolution, and particularly upon the role and significance of one of its major philosophical tenets, the so-called Principle of Uniformity. In examining current or recent English-language textbooks of geology, one will find statements to the effect that the Principle of Uniformity constitutes the foundation of the whole subject of historical geology. In informal discussions among geologists, the question frequently arises whether it is possible for a science such as geology to develop "laws" comparable to the well-known "laws" of physics and chemistry. In reply to such questions, the Principle of Uniformity is most often proposed as a geologic example of a fundamental law or principle of an importance comparable to the major laws of physics.

If the question be asked, however, just what, precisely, *is* the Principle of Uniformity, a variety of nonequivalent answers such as the following is likely to be received*:

(1) The present is the key to the past.
(2) Former changes of the earth's surface may be explained by reference to causes now in operation.
(3) The history of the earth may be deciphered in terms of present observations, on the assumption that physical and chemical laws are invariant with time.
(4) Not only are physical laws uniform, that is invariant with time, but the events of the geologic past have proceeded at an approximately uniform rate, and have involved the same processes as those which occur at present.

Despite the variety of its definitions, the fact remains that the use of the Principle of Uniformity has been fundamental in the working out of the history of the earth, and in the evolution of geologic science itself. The object of this inquiry is to re-examine this principle in the light of present scientific knowledge, with the view of determining the extent of its validity.

An understanding of this principle can best be achieved in the historical context in which it originated. In 1785, on March 7 and April 4, before two successive meetings of the Royal Society of Edinburgh, James Hutton presented a paper entitled *Theory of the Earth; or an Investigation of the Laws observable in the Composition, Dissolution and Restoration of Land upon the Globe*. In this paper (1788), in outlining the subject to be treated, Hutton stated (p. 209–210):

> When we trace the parts of which this terrestrial system is composed, and when we view the connection of those several parts, the whole presents a machine of a peculiar construction by which it is adapted to a certain end. We perceive a fabric, erected in wisdom, to obtain a purpose worthy of the power that is apparent in the production of it. . . . We shall thus also be led to acknowledge an order, not unworthy of Divine wisdom, in a subject which, in another view, has appeared as the work of chance, or as absolute disorder and confusion.

The purpose of this machine, Hutton continued, is to produce an habitable world for living forms. He then pointed out that the whole system is composed of three different bodies: (1) a solid body of earth, (2) an aqueous body of sea, and (3) an elastic fluid of air. The interaction of these three bodies forms the theory of the machine which he proposed to examine.

He then stated that soil is nothing but the materials collected from the destruction of the solid rock and traced the cycle of weathering to produce soil, the erosion and transportation of soil by running water, and finally its deposition in the sea in stratified deposits. He noted that the fossils in limestones and marble are evidences of the marine deposition of these rocks and estimated that nine tenths of the visible parts of the earth consist of strata originally deposited in the depths of the ocean. From this he concluded that a mechanism must exist to elevate the bottom of the sea above sea level and produce the observed consolidation of the sediments.

Hutton pointed out that this consolidation had to occur outside the domain of observation. This, he postulated, must have occurred at the bottom of the ocean in response to heat, causing actual fusion of the sediments. The same heat caused expansion of the rock and its uplift above sea level.

Observation of angular unconformities and stratigraphic and structural evidence convinced Hutton that the cyclical sequence of erosion of sedimentary and other rocks now above sea

* For a comprehensive review of the different formulations of the Principle of Uniformity *see* Hooykaas, 1959.

level, deposition in the ocean as new sediments, and renewed uplift had been operative since the earliest geologic time for which evidence exists, a conclusion which he masterfully stated (p. 304):

> But if the succession of worlds is established in the system of nature, it is in vain to look for anything higher in the origin of the earth.
>
> The result, therefore, of our present enquiry is, that we find no vestige of a beginning,—no prospect of an end.

Hutton's philosophical premises are set forth in the following two significant passages:

> In examining things present, we have data from which to reason with regard to what has been; and, from what has actually been, we have data for concluding with regard to that which is to happen here after. Therefore, upon the supposition that the operations of nature are equable and steady, we find, in natural appearances, a means of concluding a certain portion of time to have necessarily elapsed, in the production of those events of which we see the effects. (p. 217)

> But how shall we describe a process which nobody has seen performed, and of which no written history gives any account? This is only to be investigated, *first*, in examining the nature of those solid bodies, the history of which we want to know; and, *2ndly*, In examining the natural operations of the globe, in order to see if there now actually exist such operations, as, from the nature of the solid bodies, appear to have been necessary in their formation. (p. 219)

Hutton further stated (p. 285):

> Therefore, there is no occasion for having recourse to any unnatural supposition of evil, to any destructive accident in nature, or to the agency of any preternatural cause, in explaining that which actually appears.

Concerning plants and animals, Hutton speculated that the same species of marine animals as exist now must have existed throughout geologic time (p. 291), "The animals of the former world must have been sustained during indefinite successions of ages"; Man, however, was of recent origin. He also pointed out that fossil wood and coal are evidences of former plant life, and that animal life depends upon plant life.

Concerning the length of geologic time he stated (p. 294), ". . . in nature, we find no deficiency in respect of time, nor any limitation with regard to power." For an idea of the length of time from the deposition of rocks now forming the land, to the present, Hutton pointed out that no perceptible changes in coastlines occur during a lifetime and that comparisons between recent and ancient maps show no significant changes since Greek and Roman times. He then concluded (p. 301):

> To sum up the argument, we are certain, that all the coasts of the present continents are wasted by the sea, and constantly wearing away the whole; but this operation is so extremely slow, that we cannot find a measure of the quantity in order to form an estimate. Therefore, the present continents of the earth, which we consider as in a state of perfection, would, in the natural operations of the globe, require a time indefinite for their destruction.

This classical paper of Hutton has been dwelt upon at some length because it represents one of the earlier formulations of what later became known as the Principle of Uniformity. Hutton's method of investigating the geologic past consisted of studying the evidence contained in the rocks themselves, interpreted in terms of processes such as weathering and erosion, transportation, and deposition of sediments in the ocean, and, finally, renewed uplift. Coupled with this was the explicit rejection of any form of supernaturalism.

Among the most important conclusions reached was that concerning the immensity of geologic time, and the lack of any evidence of a beginning or ending of the sequence.

Hutton's inferences which have proved untenable are the fusion of sediments as a means of consolidation and the cataclysmic rate at which he considered the uplifts to have taken place. Also, although he observed the occurrence of marine fossils in sedimentary rocks, he made no special study of these. Consequently his inference that the same species (except man) have always existed was not based on the evidence available.

Despite Hutton's disavowal of "the agency of any preternatural cause," a strong theological flavor permeates his entire treatise. This is to be noted in his apparent conviction that the working of the "machine," which he described, was evidence of a preordained plan "not unworthy of Divine wisdom" to render the earth a suitable abode for its biological inhabitants, particularly man.

Hutton (1726–1797) was a physician by education (but not by practice), a gentleman farmer, and a member of a brilliant scientific group associated with the University of Edinburgh. He was a contemporary of the French chemist, Lavoisier (1743–1794), and was familiar with the chemistry of his day, including the newly established principle of conservation of matter. The properties of energy were yet unknown since the first and second laws of thermodynamics were not formulated until about 60 and 75 years later.

With regard to the knowledge of geology at the time, there had been three centuries of largely sporadic writing by western European authors in which the principal subject of concern had been the origin of stratified rocks and their contained fossils. On this subject, the expressed views (Geikie, 1905, p. 50–73; Lyell, 1875, Chapt. 3, p. 27–66) ranged from the rational inferences of Leonardo da Vinci (1452–1519), Fracastoro (1483–1553), Nicolaus Steno (1613–1683), Robert Hooke (1625–1703), and others, that stratified rocks with their contained shell-like forms found in inland and even in mountainous localities had originated as sediments deposited in the sea, to the opposing views that the fossils in such rocks were nonorganic in origin and represented "sports of nature" created by some mysterious "plastic force," or else were due to the influence of the stars.

By the eighteenth century there was a convergence toward the view that these rocks and their contained fossils were the result of the Biblical flood on an earth which had been divinely created some 6000 years previously and whose subsequent history had been in accordance with Biblical chronology. The dominance of the latter views in seventeenth- and eighteenth-century British geology is readily understandable when it is considered that most of the British writers on geological subjects during that period were orthodox members of the established churches, and that the preponderance of them bore the title of "Reverend" (Gillispie, 1959).

Space here will permit only the briefest account of the geological developments during the 42 years between the publication of Hutton's *Theory of the Earth* in which the Principle of Uniformity was clearly stated and applied, and the publication of Charles Lyell's *Principles of Geology* for which the Principle of Uniformity was taken as the theoretical foundation. The history of this period, however, has been treated in great detail by various authors (Geikie, 1905; Adams, 1938; Gillispie, 1959), on whose writings the following synopsis is based.

In view of the disparity between Hutton's views and those of most of his contemporaries concerning the nature of geological processes, and, particularly, their bearing on the history of the earth and immensity of geologic time, it was almost inevitable that conflicts should arise. The first of these, which raged until about 1820, was that which came to be known as the Neptunist-Vulcanist controversy.

In 1775, Abraham Gottlob Werner (1749–1817) became Inspector and Teacher of Mining and Mineralogy at the Academy of Mines in Saxony (Adams, 1938, p. 209–249; Geikie, 1905, p. 201–240). Werner was perhaps the leading mineralogist of his time, and, as a teacher, he appears to have exercised an almost hypnotic influence over his students. Within a short time, he attracted students from all over Europe and became recognized as the foremost teacher of geological subjects of his generation. In addition to mineralogy, Werner developed what he called "geognosy" (Adams, 1938, p. 207–227; Geikie, 1905, p. 201–236). Although he had never traveled far from Freiberg, he generalized his observations of the rocks in that vicinity into what he supposed to be a worldwide system. In order of descending age, the rocks of the earth, according to Werner (Adams, 1938, p. 217–227), could be classified into five principal systems —Primary, Transitional, Flötz, Alluvial, and Volcanic.

Initially the earth had been covered by a universal ocean rising above the crests of the highest mountains. Out of this universal ocean the Primary rocks, comprising granite and associated crystalline rocks, had been formed by chemical precipitation. As this ocean began to subside, the rocks of the later sequences, a series comprising diminishing proportions of chemical precipitates and increasing mechanical deposits, were formed.

This fanciful and incredible scheme of supposed geology and geological history was taught by Werner to his students, who in turn went out into the world zealous to establish the master's system in whatever part of the world they happened to be. This geological dogma had the virtue of being in approximate agreement stratigraphically with the rocks in the vicinity of Freiberg; it had the virtue of simplicity and easy comprehensibility; it had an implied time scale which was compatible with Biblical chronology; and, finally, it had the sanction of authority—the professor himself had said that it was so!

Werner's system was seized upon by Hutton's critics as the geological basis for his refutation. Because, according to this scheme, all rocks (including granite and basalt) except recent volcanic lavas, were presumed to be chemical or mechanical deposits in the universal ocean, the followers of Werner became known as Neptunists. The defenders of the Huttonian system were known as Vulcanists.

The attacks began as early as 1793 when the Irish chemist, Richard Kirwan, with no personal knowledge of geology, coupled the Wernerian system to a literal interpretation of the Bible in support of the charge of atheism against Hutton. In response, Hutton expanded his original paper into a two-volume treatise entitled *Theory of the Earth with Proofs and Illustrations,* which was published in Edinburgh in 1795, 2 years before his death.

In 1797 and 1799 (Gillispie, 1959, p. 49–56), Kirwan's renewal of the attack brought Hutton's friend John Playfair, professor of mathematics at the University of Edinburgh, to his defense with the book *Illustrations of the Huttonian Theory of the Earth,* which was published in 1802.

The situation was further complicated when a Scottish student of Werner, Robert Jameson (1774–1854), was appointed professor of natural history at the University of Edinburgh in 1804 (Gillispie, 1959, p. 66–69) and promptly became the master's principal advocate in Great Britain. Jameson organized the Wernerian Natural History Society (with himself as permanent president) whose Memoirs afforded a vehicle for the Neptunist views. He also wrote a *System of Mineralogy,* volume III of which (1808), subtitled *Oryctognosie, Mineralogy, Geognosie, Mineral Geography and Economic Mineralogy,* was an exposition of the Wernerian system.

Throughout its history the Neptunist-Vulcanist controversy was a mixture of geology and theology, and the central issue was the Huttonian versus the Biblical interpretation of geologic history. Gradually, as geologic work progressed, the evidence for great lengths of time became so convincing that even the Neptunists found it necessary to amend the Biblical interpretation whereby Biblical "days" came to mean geologic periods. Then, on the purely geological side, the fundamental issue of whether basalt is an igneous rock or a Wernerian aqueous precipitate, was finally resolved by overwhelming evidence in favor of the Vulcanist view.

No sooner had the Neptunist-Vulcanist controversy begun to wane than a new anti-Uniformitarian storm blew up. In 1812, Georges Cuvier (1769–1832), one of the leading paleontologists of France, published, as a preface to a paleontological treatise, his own comprehensive theory of the earth (Adams, 1938, p. 263–268; Geikie, 1905, p. 363–376; Gillispie, 1959, p. 98–102). This theory, in essence, was that during the long history of the earth, the land had been repeatedly invaded by the sea or by transient floods. These invasions did not come gradually. On the contrary, the majority of the cataclysms that produced them were sudden, as attested by the dislocations, shifting, and overturning of the strata. As a result of each of these cataclysms, the animals and plants of both land and sea were largely destroyed. This, in turn, led to the necessity of a series of successive biological creations in which animals at each successive stage were more advanced than in the one preceding. Furthermore, in stratigraphic successions, the order of fossils is: fish, amphibia, reptilia, mammalia, which also agrees with the order of Creation.

This catastrophic view of geologic history achieved almost universal acceptance among British geologists during the 1820's. By this time it was fairly generally admitted that geological history was much longer than had been assumed by all except the Huttonians. Furthermore, geologic and Biblical evidence were in complete agreement on the one most recent catastrophe, the Mosaic flood. This last became such a firm geological data that geological history was readily divided into the Ante-Diluvial and Post-Diluvial eras; as Gillispie (1959, p. 91) has remarked, "The flood itself was not a speculative matter in 1820."

One of the more solid geological achievements during this period occurred largely without regard to the contemporary geological controversies. This was the work of William Smith (1769–1839) who was a land surveyor engaged in work on canals and drainage projects in various parts of England (Geikie, 1905, p. 381–396). As a by-product of his work, Smith discovered about 1794 that separate strata had distinctive suites of fossils by which they could be recognized. Following up this interest, he traced out and mapped the principal stratigraphic systems of England and, in 1815, published the first geological map of the country.

The period of confusion following the Hutton and Playfair publications was brought to a termination by Charles Lyell's *Principles of Geology* (1830–1833). Lyell (1797–1875), the son of a well-to-do Scottish family, was born in the family mansion, Kinnordy, in Forfarshire, Scotland, in 1797, the year of Hutton's death (Bonney, 1895; Bailey, 1963). From 1816–1819 he attended Oxford University where he prepared for a career in law. During the period 1820–1830 he finished his law studies, was admitted to the bar, and practiced law for 2 years, but apparently without enthusiasm.

As a student at Oxford, Lyell had attended the lectures of William Buckland, the most influential British geologist of that period (Gillispie, 1959, p. 98–120). His interest in geology soon became so overwhelming that he devoted all available time to geological field observations, the study of collections in museums, visits with prominent geologists, and extensive geological excursions in the United Kingdom, and in France, Switzerland, Italy, and Spain.

Until about 1825, Lyell's geological interpretations were largely in accord with the Catastrophic-Diluvial school represented by Buckland and most other contemporary British geologists. As his own field studies were extended into more and more areas, however, he began to be convinced that the postulated catastrophic events could not be supported by field evidence.

By 1827 he had begun to consider writing a book setting forth his new views and countering the prevailing Catastrophic-Diluvial opinion. He began writing about 1828 or 1829 and in 1830 published volume I of the new geological treatise, *Principles of Geology, Being an Attempt to Explain the Former Changes of the Earth's Surface by Reference to Causes Now in Operation*. Volume II appeared in 1832, and volume III in 1833.

The work, an immediate success, went through several printings. In 1832, while volumes II and III were still being published, volume I had already been revised and re-issued.

Except for the brief period 1831–1833, when he was persuaded to accept the newly created Chair of Geology at King's College, London, Lyell devoted his life to his geological studies and to the repeated revisions of the *Principles*. The twelfth and last edition, published in 1875, was being revised when Lyell died.

As its title implies, Lyell's *Principles of Geology* was devoted almost exclusively to the deciphering of the history of the earth on the basis of his own modification of the Huttonian thesis that the former changes of the earth's surface may be explained by reference to causes which are now in operation. Since this involved the assumption of "uniform" operations in geologic processes, the Huttonian-

Lyellian philosophy became known as Uniformitarianism, and its basic premise, the Principle of Uniformity.

Because Lyell's entire treatise is an exposition of the uniformitarian philosophy, statements on different aspects of this philosophy are widely distributed throughout the work. The first four chapters of volume I are devoted to historical review of the development of geologic thought. In Chapter V, *Review of the causes which have retarded the progress of Geology*, he stated (p. 75–76):

> We have seen that, during the progress of geology, there have been great fluctuations of opinion respecting the nature of the causes to which all former changes of the earth's surface are referable. The first observers conceived that the monuments which the geologist endeavours to decipher, relate to a period when the physical constitution of the earth differed entirely from the present, and that, even after the creation of living beings, there have been causes in action distinct in kind or degree from those now forming part of the economy of nature. These views have been gradually modified, and some of them entirely abandoned in proportion as observations have been multiplied, and the signs of former mutations more skilfully interpreted. Many appearances, which for a long time were regarded as indicating mysterious and extraordinary agency, are finally recognized as the necessary result of the laws now governing the material world; and the discovery of this unlooked for conformity has induced some geologists to infer that there has never been any interruption to the same uniform order of physical events. The same assemblage of general causes, they conceive, may have been sufficient to produce, by their various combinations, the endless diversity of effects, of which the shell of the earth has preserved the memorials, and, consistently with these principles, the recurrence of analogous changes is expected by them in time to come.
>
> Whether we coincide or not in this doctrine, we must admit that the gradual progress of opinion concerning the succession of phenomena in remote eras, resembles in a singular manner that which accompanies the growing intelligence of every people, in regard to the economy of nature in modern times. In an early stage of advancement, when a great number of natural appearances are unintelligible, an eclipse, an earthquake, a flood, or the approach of a comet, with many other occurrences afterwards found to belong to the regular course of events, are regarded as prodigies. The same delusion prevails as to moral phenomena, and many of these are ascribed to the intervention of demons, ghosts, witches, and other immaterial and supernatural agents. By degrees, many of the enigmas of the moral and physical world are explained, and, instead of being due to extrinsic and irregular causes, they are found to depend on fixed and invariable laws. The philosopher at last becomes convinced of the undeviating uniformity of secondary causes, and, guided by his faith in this principle, he determines the probability of accounts transmitted to him of former occurrences, and often rejects the fabulous tales of former ages, on the ground of their being irreconciliable with the experience of more enlightened ages.

Thus, after an extensive summary of earlier views which had come to be recognized as untenable, Lyell's own view was embodied in the statement, "The philosopher at last becomes convinced of the undeviating uniformity of secondary causes . . ."

The term "secondary causes" pertains, in the philosophy and theology of that period, to events subsequent to the "First Cause" which ordinarily is synonymous with "Divine Creation." Hence, Lyell's "undeviating uniformity of secondary causes" appears to be equivalent to asserting the permanency of physical laws and a rejection of any form of supernaturalism or interferences by Divine Providence in post-Creational geological phenomena.

Lyell further enlarged on his views by the remarks:

> Our estimate, indeed, of the value of all geological evidence, and the interest derived from the investigation of the earth's history, must depend entirely on the degree of confidence which we feel in regard to the permanency of the laws of nature. Their immutable constancy alone can enable us to reason from analogy, by the strict rules of induction, respecting the events of former ages, or, by a comparison of the state of things at

> two distinct geological epochs, to arrive at the knowledge of general principles in the economy of our terrestrial system. (p. 165)

> Those geologists who are not averse to presume that the course of Nature has been uniform from the earliest ages, and that causes now in action have produced the former changes of the earth's surface, will consult the ancient strata for instruction in regard to the reproductive effects of tides and currents. (p. 311)

Concerning a beginning and an ending in the history of the earth, Lyell essentially accepted the Huttonian view that it is fruitless to talk of either. He dismissed the earlier cosmological discussions as impediments to understanding the history of the earth.

Regarding the rates of geological processes in the past as compared with those of the present, he stated in the second edition of volume I (1832, p. 73):

> There can be no doubt, that periods of disturbance and repose have followed each other in succession in every region of the globe, but it may be equally true, that the energy of the subterranean movements has been always uniform as regards the *whole earth*. The force of earthquakes may for a cycle of years have been invariably confined, as it is now, to large but determinate spaces, and may then have gradually shifted its position, so that another region, which had for ages been at rest, became in its turn the grand theatre of action.

We infer from these quotations, and from the treatise as a whole, that Lyell essentially accepted Hutton's view that the phenomena displayed by the rocks of the earth may be entirely accounted for by geologic processes which are in operation now, on the assumption that the laws of nature throughout geologic history are invariant with time. Like Hutton's, Lyell's view of the history of the earth involves a panorama of events extending indefinitely into a past of essentially unlimited geologic time.

Lyell's greatest difficulty in the application of the Principle of Uniformity arose in connection with the plant and animal life of the earth, evidently a source of some embarrassment. He rejected the Lamarckian theory of gradual development in favor of permanency of species and cited evidence for the recent origin of man. After reviewing this problem for several chapters in volume II (1832), Lyell's principal conclusion regarding species was as follows (p. 65):

> 6thly. From the above considerations, it appears that species have a real existence in nature, and that each was endowed, at the time of its creation, with the attributes and organization by which it is now distinguished.

Concerning the origin of man, Lyell (v. I, 1830, p. 156) commented:

> But another, and a far more difficult question may arise out of the admission that man is comparatively of modern origin. Is not the interference of the human species, it may be asked, such a deviation from the antecedent course of physical events, that the knowledge of such a fact tends to destroy all our confidence in the uniformity of the order of nature, both in regard to time past and future?

After wrestling with the problem for several pages, Lyell finally reached the somewhat lame conclusion (p. 164):

> To this question we may reply, that had he previously presumed to dogmatize respecting the absolute uniformity of the order of nature, he would undoubtedly be checked by witnessing this new and unexpected event, and would form a more just estimate of the limited range of his own knowledge, and the unbounded extent of the scheme of the universe. But he would soon perceive that no one of the fixed and constant laws of the animate and inanimate world was subverted by human agency, and that the modifications produced were on the occurrence of new and extraordinary circumstances, and those not of a *physical*, but a *moral* nature.

It is thus clear that although Lyell had gone far beyond his contemporaries in emancipating himself from such theological tenets as Providential interference with terrestrial events on the inorganic side and had succeeded completely in eliminating Biblical chronology as a basis for geological history, he was still frustrated when confronted with biological phenomena. To account for the origin of organic species, he found it necessary to resort to Divine Creation, in complete contradiction to his exclusion of supernatural considerations in other respects. His rescue from this difficulty came only when Charles Darwin's *On the Origin of Species* was published in 1859.

Charles Darwin (1809–1882) attended the University of Cambridge from 1827–1831 where he studied geology under Adam Sedgwick and botany under John Stephens Henslow (de Beer, 1964). In 1831, upon Henslow's recommendation, he signed on as the Naturalist on the exploration ship H.M.S. BEAGLE, for a round-the-world voyage which lasted from December 27, 1831, until October 2, 1836. Upon Henslow's recommendation that it should be read, but on no account believed, one of the few books which Darwin took with him was the first volume of Lyell's *Principles of Geology* which had been published only the preceding year. As Darwin subsequently related in his *Voyage of the Beagle* (1839), Lyell's book was fairly digested within the first few days of the voyage and formed the foundation for his own geological work throughout the expedition. In Chapter IX of his master work *On the Origin of Species* (1859, p. 282), Darwin stated, "He who can read Sir Charles Lyell's grand work on the PRINCIPLES OF GEOLOGY, which the future historian will recognize as having produced a revolution in natural science, yet does not admit how incomprehensibly vast have been the past periods of time, may at once close this volume."

It is clear, therefore, that Lyell's work profoundly influenced Charles Darwin in his progression toward his major biological synthesis. In effect, what Darwin did was to develop paleontology from the point where Lyell had left it. By the rejection of Lyell's residual supernaturalism where organisms were concerned, and by an extension of Lyell's Principle of Uniformity to the plant and animal kingdoms, the theory of evolution was an almost inevitable consequence.

In 1859, when *On the Origin of Species* was first published, Lyell was 62 years old. There is no greater measure of the man's intellectual integrity than the fact that he was one of the first to accept the Darwinian theory of evolution and to promptly develop it further than Darwin had by applying it explicitly to the origin of man in *The Geological Evidences of the Antiquity of Man with Remarks on Theories of the Origin of Species by Variation* (1863).

In addition, in 1866, 13 years after the publication of the ninth edition, Lyell published the tenth edition of *Principles of Geology* in which the ninth chapter, on the progressive development of organic life, was entirely re-written, to conform to the Darwinian theory.

Up until the 1860's, the opposition to the Huttonian-Lyellian Uniformitarianism had been largely a rearguard action—often a very powerful one—of the defenders, geological as well as clerical, of the prerogatives of Divine Providence to set aside the laws of nature and to interfere with terrestrial activities in any arbitrary manner. At about this time a criticism arose from an entirely different quarter. In 1862 William Thomson published two related papers: (1) *On the Age of the Sun's Heat* (1862a), and (2) *On the Secular Cooling of the Earth* (1862b), in which entirely new relationships were introduced into the consideration of terrestrial and solar phenomena.

William Thomson (later Lord Kelvin, 1824–1907) was Professor of Natural Philosophy at the University of Glasgow and one of the leading British physicists of the nineteenth century. He was a young man when James P. Joule (1818–1889) was performing his epoch-making experiments on the mechanical equivalent of heat during the 1840's and was one of Joule's strongest supporters in the establishment of the principle of conservation of energy, or the first law of thermodynamics. Through the 1850's, Thomson was one of the leading researchers in further thermodynamic investigation and was one of the formulators of the second law of thermodynamics. He was also responsible for the concept of absolute zero of temperature and for the absolute scale of temperature, now known, in his honor, as the Kelvin scale. Thomson was also fascinated with the mathematical theory of heat conduction introduced in 1822 by Joseph Fourier (1768–1830) in his classical treatise, *Théorie Analytique de la Chaleur*.

This was the background from which Thomson wrote the two papers cited. In the second, *On the Secular Cooling of the Earth* (*in* Thomson and Tait, 1890, pt. II, p. 468–469), he presented his basic thesis as follows:

> (*a.*) For eighteen years it has pressed on my mind, that essential principles of Thermo-dynamics have been overlooked by those geologists who uncompromisingly oppose all paroxysmal hypotheses, and maintain not only that we have examples now before us, on the earth, of all the different actions by which its crust has been modified in geological history, but that these actions have never, or have not on the whole, been more violent in past time than they are at present.
>
> (*b.*) It is quite certain the solar system cannot have gone on, even as at present, for a few hundred thousand or a few million years, without the irrevocable loss (by dissipation, not by *annihilation*) of a very considerable proportion of the entire energy initially in store for sun heat, and for Plutonic action. It is quite certain that the whole store of energy in the solar system has been greater in all past time than at present; but it is conceivable that the rate at which it has been drawn upon and dissipated, whether by solar radiation, or by volcanic action in the earth or other dark bodies of the system, may have been nearly equable, or may even have been less rapid, in certain periods of the past. But it is far more probable that the secular rate of dissipation has been in some direct proportion to the total amount of energy in store, at any time after the commencement of the present order of things, and has been therefore very slowly diminishing from age to age.

Because of the geothermal gradient, Thomson's argument continued, the earth is losing heat by conduction. Since there was no known source of this heat except an earth which must have been originally much hotter—presumably molten—than at present, then it followed by means of the Fourier theory, that it should be possible to calculate within broad limits the time that it had taken for the earth to reach its present geothermal gradient since first becoming solidified. The result obtained by Thomson was that this period could not have been less than 20,000,000 nor more than 400,000,000 years. Later, based on a lower melting temperature of 7000°, this larger figure was reduced to 98,000,000 years.

Thomson particularly challenged the Uniformitarian school, whose views, he pointed out, were equivalent to an earth operating as a perpetual-motion mechanism. Specifically, he cited a passage from the 1853 edition of *Principles of Geology* in which Lyell had postulated that the earth's heat could be generated by internal chemical reactions which could then be undone electrolytically by thermo-electric currents. Concerning this supposed mechanism, Thomson commented (p. 471) ". . . thus the chemical action and its heat continued in an endless cycle, violates the principles of natural philosophy in exactly the same manner, and to the same degree, as to believe that a clock constructed with a self-winding movement may fulfil the expectations of its ingenious inventor by going for ever."

Thomson also challenged the Uniformitarian view that the past diastrophic events of the earth were of the same magnitude and occurred at the same rates as those of the present, in view of the fact that throughout geologic history the earth has been an energy-dissipating system. Concerning this, he stated (p. 472):

> It would be very wonderful, but not an absolutely incredible result, that volcanic action has never been more violent on the whole than during the last two or three centuries; but it is as certain that there is now less volcanic energy in the whole earth than there was a thousand years ago, as it is that there is less gunpowder in a 'Monitor' after she has been seen to discharge shot and shell, whether at a nearly equable rate or not, for five hours without receiving fresh supplies, than there was at the beginning of the action. Yet this truth has been ignored or denied by many of the leading geologists of the present day, because they believe that the facts within their province do not demonstrate greater violence in ancient changes

of the earth's surface, or do demonstrate a nearly equable action in all periods.

In the first paper, *On the Age of the Sun's Heat,* Thomson followed a similar line of reasoning. His opening statement was, "The second law of Thermodynamics involves a certain principle of *irreversible action in nature*." He pointed out that the sun is radiating energy at an enormous rate, the most plausible source of which is the infalling of meteorites and gravitational contraction, the theory of which had been developed by Hermann von Helmholtz (1821–1894).

After considering the various magnitudes involved in the sun's activities, Thomson concluded that the sun probably has not illuminated the earth for 100,000,000 years, and almost certainly not for 500,000,000 years. This, however, was qualified by the following concluding statement (*in* Thomson and Tait, 1890, pt. II, p. 494):

> As for the future, we may say, with equal certainty, that inhabitants of the earth cannot continue to enjoy the light and heat essential to their life, for many million years longer, unless sources now unknown to us are prepared in the great storehouse of creation.

This is one of the few cautionary statements by Thomson on record with regard to this subject.

The next 35 years was a period of intermittent strife between Thomson and the British geologists. In geology textbooks of the 1860's, as later cited by Thomson, many of the authors had gone so far as to postulate unlimited time for the history of the earth. Some geologists, impressed by Thomson's estimates of the earth's age since its cooling enough to sustain life, had attempted to compress geological history within 20 to 40 million years; others, including Darwin, considering the slowness of erosion and deposition and the aggregate thickness of strata of different ages, estimated the length of geologic time since the beginning of the Paleozoic era to be of the order of magnitude of hundreds of millions of years.

During this period an almost complete impasse developed because the natural-history estimates of the age of the earth and the physical estimates of Thomson—each within its own premises accurate to about an order of magnitude—differed from one another by a factor of 100–1000.

This situation culminated in 1899, when Lord Kelvin's address on *The Age of the Earth as an Abode Fitted for Life* was published in *Science.* In this address, Kelvin quoted extensively from geological works written from about 1850 to 1870, pertaining to the length of geologic time. These included a statement by Charles Darwin from the first edition (1859) of *On the Origin of Species* that "In all probability a far longer period than 300,000,000 years has elapsed since the latter part of the secondary period."

Statements from other authors were quoted, including the following:

> . . . the student should never lose sight of the element TIME, *an element to which we can set no bounds in the past* . . . (1859, *Advanced Student's Text-Book of Geology*)
>
> The time required for such a slow process to effect such enormous results must, of course, be inconceivably great. (Jukes, 1862, *The Student's Manual of Geology*, p. 290)

In addition, Kelvin cited a conversation with Andrew Ramsay in 1867 during which he had asked whether Ramsay thought geologic time could be as long as 10^9 years, or 10^{10}. To both questions Ramsay had replied, "Certainly I do."

Kelvin then renewed his attack on the "doctrine of eternity and uniformity" of Hutton, Playfair, and Lyell as representing a system of perpetual motion. Finally, he reviewed his own cumulative studies of the preceding half century. These involved the assumption of an originally white-hot molten earth and its subsequent cooling to its present temperature. He mentioned his own earlier estimates of the time since the earth had solidified, and then cited an 1893 paper by Clarence King, in which King, using measurements of the thermal properties of rocks by Carl Barus and the Kelvin premises, had obtained a figure of 24 million years as the maximum age of the earth. Kelvin stated that his own recent calculations were in substantial agreement with this figure.

In outlining the history of the earth from its supposed consolidation, Kelvin noted that it was doubtful if there could have been any free oxygen in the atmosphere initially. Within a century after consolidation, however, the earth would have been suitable for plant life, and only a few thousand years (or possibly hundreds) of plant life would have been required to produce oxygen for animal life.

Concerning the mode of origin of plant and animal life, Kelvin stated (p. 711):

> Mathematics and dynamics fail us when we contemplate the earth, fitted for life but lifeless, and try to imagine the commencement of life upon it. This certainly did not take place by any action of chemistry, or electricity, or crystalline grouping of molecules under the influence of force, or by any possible kind of fortuitous concourse of atoms. We must pause, face to face with the mystery and miracle of the creation of living creatures.

Obviously the physicist Kelvin had not emancipated himself from the replacement of the laws of nature by Divine Providence.

Later, during the same year, *Science* published a reply to the Kelvin address by the American geologist, T. C. Chamberlin (1843–1928). Chamberlin had spent many of his earlier years studying the geology of Wisconsin and the neighboring states where one of his major interests had been the Pleistocene glaciation, which, in accordance with the views expressed by Kelvin and others, would represent a late stage in the earth's cooling before final refrigeration.

However, the Pleistocene glaciation did not exhibit a monotonic cooling, as might have been expected, but alternate periods of cooling and warming, as evidenced by the successively younger tills that resulted from advances and retreats of the glaciers, with lengthy interglacial intervals. The problem was still further complicated by the discoveries of such earlier continental glaciations during both the Paleozoic and Proterozoic eras.

These observations had led Chamberlin to inquire into the sources of the opinion that the earth had once been a molten white-hot body now cooling off in the manner postulated by Kelvin. At the time Chamberlin wrote his reply to Kelvin he had already been engaged in this critical inquiry for some 10 years.

In the reply, Chamberlin expressed the indebtedness and gratitude of the geological profession to Lord Kelvin for reminding the geologists that unlimited geological time was not a tenable hypothesis. He acknowledged that during the first half of the century, when more sober modes of interpreting geological data were struggling to displace the cataclysmic extravagances of more primitive times, it was not strange that there should have arisen, as a material outgrowth of the contest, an ultra-Uniformitarianism which demanded for the evolution of the earth an immeasurable length of time. He mentioned, however, that "there were other camps in Israel even then." There were the ultra-Catastrophists as well as the ultra-Uniformitarians.

It was Chamberlin's opinion that "The great body of serious geologists have moved forward neither by the right flank nor by the left, but on median lines." These lines, he thought, had lain ". . . rather in the field of a qualified uniformitarianism than in the field of catastrophism," and the body of competent geologists of Chamberlin's time were probably more nearly disciples of Hutton, Playfair, and Lyell than of their opponents.

With regard to Kelvin's reasoning, Chamberlin warned that a physical deduction which postulates excessively short geological history may as easily lead to false views as did the reckless license of earlier times, and added (p. 890):

> The fascinating impressiveness of rigorous mathematical analysis, with its atmosphere of precision and elegance, should not blind us to the defects of the premises that condition the whole process. There is, perhaps, no beguilement more insidious and dangerous than an elaborate and elegant mathematical process built upon unfortified premises.

Chamberlin quoted Kelvin's estimate that the time since consolidation of the earth had been more than 20 and less than 40 million years, and probably nearer 20. He then asked (p. 891),

> Can these definite statements, bearing so much the air of irrefutable truth, be allowed

to pass without challenge? What is their real nature and their true degree of certitude when tested respecting their fundamental postulates and their basic assumptions?

Chamberlin quoted Kelvin's statement that his results were based upon the "very sure assumption" that the solid earth was once a white-hot liquid, and added (p. 891):

> I beg leave to challenge the certitude of this assumption of a white-hot liquid earth, current as it is among geologists alike with astronomers and physicists. Though but an understudent of physics, I venture to challenge it on the basis of physical laws and physical antecedents.

In examining Kelvin's premises concerning the initial white-hot molten earth, Chamberlin pointed out that, according to Kelvin, the heat required for this result was supposed to have been generated by a sudden infall and accumulation of meteorites. Chamberlin admitted that had the earth been formed by such a brief event the heat generated would indeed have been sufficient to produce a white-hot molten earth. He questioned, however, both on physical and astronomical grounds, whether such a sudden infall was likely to have occurred. On the other hand, should the earth have been formed by a slow infall of meteorites over a very long period the heat of fall and impact would largely have been dissipated by outward radiation, so that the earth need never to have acquired a temperature anywhere near the melting point of rocks.

Chamberlin next examined Kelvin's premises regarding the energy of the sun and the length of time during which the sun may have been hot enough to give sufficient radiation to support life on earth. He quoted (p. 12) the Kelvin statement:

> If the consolidation of the earth was finished 20 or 25 million years ago the sun was probably ready, though probably not then quite so warm as at present, yet warm enough to support some kind of vegetable and animal life on the earth.

Concerning this statement Chamberlin added:

> Here is an unqualified assumption of the completeness of the Helmholtzian theory of the sun's heat and of the correctness of deductions drawn from it in relation to the past life of the sun. There is the further assumption, by implication, that no other essential factors entered into the problem. Are these assumptions beyond legitimate question? In the first place, without questioning its *correctness*, is it safe to assume that the Helmholtzian hypothesis of the heat of the sun is a *complete* theory? Is present knowledge relative to the behavior of matter under such extraordinary conditions as obtain in the interior of the sun sufficiently exhaustive to warrant the assertion that no unrecognized sources of heat reside there? What the internal constitution of the atoms may be is yet an open question. It is not improbable that they are complex organizations and the seats of enormous energies. Certainly, no careful chemist would affirm either that the atoms are really elementary or that there may not be locked up in them energies of the first order of magnitude. No cautious chemist would probably venture to assert that the component atomecules, to use a convenient phrase, may not have energies of rotation, revolution, position and be otherwise comparable in kind and proportion to those of a planetary system. Nor would he probably feel prepared to affirm or deny that the extraordinary conditions which reside in the center of the sun may not set free a portion of this energy. The Helmholtzian theory takes no cognizance of latent and occluded energies of an atomic or ultra-atomic nature.

In view of its date, 1899, the foregoing stands as one of the more prophetic statements in the annals of science. The phenomenon of radioactivity had been discovered by Henri Becquerel only 3 years before. The isolation of radium (1902), the discovery that radioactivity involves transmutations of chemical elements (1902), the development of the law of radioactive disintegration (1902) and the measurement of the amount of energy released (1903), the hypothesis of the planetary atom (1911), the working out of the mechanism for the fusion of hydrogen to helium as the source of the energy from the sun (1939), and the achievement of controlled fission (1942) and of uncontrolled fusion in the hydrogen bomb a few years later, were all in the future (Andrade, 1964).

As a result of these subsequent developments, however, the half-century of wide discrepancies between physical estimates of the possible age of the earth and the sun, and the much longer geological estimates, has completely been resolved. The work of Rutherford and Soddy (1902; 1903) on the law of radioactive disintegration, and their partial determination of three radioactive disintegration series, provided the theoretical basis for the subsequent development of radioactive age determinations of geological events. The present estimate by these means that the Paleozoic era began about 600 million years ago is in substantial agreement with the estimate by Charles Darwin (cited by Lord Kelvin in his address) that the time elapsed since the later part of this era must have been about 300 million years.

The anomaly of the source of the earth's heat was largely resolved by Rutherford and Soddy in 1903 by their initial determination of the approximate amount of heat generated during radioactive disintegration. They found that the heat released by the disintegration of 1 gram of radium and its daughter products through five stages of alpha-particle generation amounts to 10^8 gram-calories, whereas the energy released in a typical chemical reaction, such as the combination of oxygen and hydrogen to produce water, is only to about 4000 gram-calories per gram.

The appreciation of these authors for the cosmological implications of their new discoveries is clearly indicated in the concluding paragraph of their paper on *Radioactive Change* (1903, p. 590–591):

> All these considerations point to the conclusion that the energy latent in the atom must be enormous compared with that rendered free in ordinary chemical change. Now the radio-elements differ in no way from the other elements in their chemical and physical behaviour. On the one hand they resemble chemically their inactive prototypes in the periodic system very closely, and on the other they possess no common chemical characteristic which could be associated with their radioactivity. Hence there is no reason to assume that this enormous store of energy is possessed by the radio-elements alone. It seems probable that atomic energy in general is of a similar, high order of magnitude, although the absence of change prevents its existence being manifested. . . . It must be taken into account in cosmical physics. The maintenance of solar energy, for example, no longer presents any fundamental difficulty if the internal energy of the component elements is considered to be available, *i.e.* if processes of sub-atomic change are going on.

As has already been noted, these surmises have been confirmed theoretically by Bethe (1939) in his work on the possible hydrogen-to-helium fusion transformation producing the heat of the sun and other stars; they have been confirmed experimentally by the first nuclear pile at Chicago in 1942 (Smyth, 1945) in which controlled fission was achieved, and by the subsequent development of the hydrogen bomb involving the explosive release of energy from the fusion of hydrogen or other light elements.

In looking back at the dissensions between Kelvin and the geologists concerning the age of the earth, what we now principally remember is how enormously wrong Lord Kelvin was. At the same time, with regard to another fundamental aspect of earth history, that is, that the various geological processes, past and present, are all energy-dissipative processes and involve continuous losses of energy by the earth, we tend to forget how right he was.

The energy inputs into the earth's surface environment consists of radiation from outer space—overwhelmingly from sunshine—tidal energy from the kinetic and potential energy of the earth-moon–sun system, and thermal, chemical, and mechanical energy from the earth's interior. In view of the approximate constancy of the earth's surface temperature when averaged over a year or more, and the nearly fixed quantity of stored surface energy, it follows that the outward flux of energy from this sytem must be very nearly equal to the inward flux. Because of the temperature increase with depth, thermal energy from the outside can penetrate only to shallow depths beneath the earths' surface. Hence, the ourward flux must be by means of radiation from the earth into outer space. In this process, solar energy is used principally to produce a continuous circulation of the atmosphere and the oceans which not only degrades the solar energy but also, by erosion, continuously dissipates into heat the potential energy of the earth's topographic configuration.

Thermodynamically, erosion and transportation of sediments are irreversible processes in which the initial mechanical energy is converted by friction into low-temperature heat. This heat is added to the thermal input of the surface environment of the earth which it leaves by long-wave-length radiation. Thus the topography of the earth represents a large reservoir of mechanical energy which the erosional process continuously dissipates. The energy of one orogeny, therefore, can never be used to produce another, since that energy is completely dissipated and discharged from the earth by one cycle of erosion. Hence, after peneplanation of any area of the earth, new mountains can be formed only from a new source of energy from inside the earth. Because there have been repeated orogenies and episodes of vulcanism throughout the earth's history, these can only have occurred at the expense of a continuous diminution of the earth's initial supply of energy.

In addition to the energy lost from the earth by orogenies, there is also the energy transported to the earth's surface from its interior by heat conduction in virtue of the geothermal gradient, and that convected by mass transport resulting from the activities of volcanoes and hot springs.

It is for these reasons, that the Huttonian-Lyellian view of an earth on which the same processes have been and always will be operative, and at about the same rates, is, as Lord Kelvin pointed out, equivalent to a perpetual-motion mechanism and a physical impossibility. Because of its involvement in thermodynamically irreversible processes, the earth history, despite the long timescale, can only be in the long run a unidirectional progression from some initial state characterized by a large store of available energy to a later state in which this energy has been discharged from the earth. In this latter state, if the earth continues in its planetary orbit about the sun, and if the solar energy has not also been exhausted by that time, we may anticipate the continuance of atmospheric and oceanic circulations, but an ultimate cessation of diastrophic and vulcanic activities, with a corresponding permanent peneplanation of the land areas.

The opposite result is obtained when we extrapolate backward in time. Considering that the radioactive isotopes of uranium and thorium have been declining exponentially and producing radiogenic isotopes of lead throughout geologic history, backward extrapolation requires an exponential increase in the amounts of these radioactive materials and of their heat-generation rates. A limit is set to the time to which such extrapolations can be carried by the fact that the disintegration of one atom of uranium-238 produces eventually one atom of the isotope lead-206, and one atom of thorium-232 degrades to one atom of lead-208. Hence the sum of the atoms of lead produced plus the atoms of uranium (or thorium) remaining must represent the number of atoms of uranium (or thorium) present initially.

For any given rock, backward extrapolation cannot be extended beyond the time required for all the radiogenic lead to be restored to its original state as uranium or thorium. This limiting time, in fact, is said to respresent the "age" of the rock considered. Such measurements are commonly made on igneous rocks in which the radiogenic lead produced since crystallization from an igneous melt has been trapped inside the crystal structure of the minerals containing the radioactive element. The limiting time so obtained represents, therefore, the time since the consolidation of the igneous rock.

The oldest age found so far for any terrestrial rock identified by this procedure is 3.6 to 3.7×10^9 years. However, similar measurements made on meteorites give a consistent limiting time of 4.5×10^9 years. Numerous rocks have dates of approximately $3.1–3.2 \times 10^9$ years, and these rocks are associated with ancient marine sediments. (Personal communication from Thomas W. Stern, Isotope Geology Branch, U.S. Geol. Survey.)

We are thus led to the conclusion that backward extrapolation of the decay of the long-life radioactive isotopes cannot be extended indefinitely. On the assumption that the meteorites of the solar system are products of the same cosmic event which produced the earth and other planets, the time of 4.5×10^9 years before the present appears to be the approximate time at which this event occurred. Because the half-life period for U-238, the common isotope of uranium, is 4.5×10^9 years, and that for Th-232 is 13.9×10^9 years, it would appear that the maximum amounts of these two elements which the earth, as a planet, could ever have contained would have been about 2 and 1.3, respectively, times the earth's present content of these radioactive materials. The rate of heat generation from these sources, with allowance for their relative geochemical abundances, would have been about 1.5 times that of the present.

From such considerations based on present knowledge, we may conclude that the earth originated in an as yet indefinite manner from some cosmic event which occurred about 4.5×10^9 years ago and has been undergoing a unidirectional evolution ever since. In the early stages this must also have involved the origin and development of the oceans (Rubey, 1951) and atmosphere. It also appears unlikely that the earth, during its formation and earliest history, could have afforded an environment in which life in any form would have been possible. . . .

Returning now to the Principle of Uniformity as understood by Hutton and Lyell, it is appropriate to ask to what degree we may still regard this principle as valid. In our historical review, we have traced a somewhat tortuous, but essentially unidirectional, progression toward emancipation from the idea that so-called natural laws could be set aside arbitrarily and terrestrial affairs manipulated at will by the dictates of a Divine Providence. . . .

This first postulate of the Principle of Uniformity, namely, that the laws of nature are invariant with time, is not peculiar to that principle or to geology, but is a common denominator of all science. In fact, instead of being an assumption or an *ad hoc* hypothesis, it is simply a succinct summation of the totality of all experimental and observational evidence.

The second part of the Principle of Uniformity, namely that the events of the geologic past involved essentially the same activities as those occurring on the earth at present, and proceeded at essentially the same rates, with no evidence of a beginning or an ending, rests upon much less secure grounds. As Kelvin pointed out, and we agree, this is equivalent to a perpetual-motion mechanism, and hence is physically impossible. The earth throughout its history must have been an evolving system undergoing a continuous loss of energy.

Despite this, however, for the period of geological history in which Hutton and Lyell were most interested—that since the beginning of the Paleozoic era—the rate of heat generation from the radioactivity of uranium and thorium has declined so slightly that the resulting average rate of thermally induced diastrophism and vulcanism need not have declined perceptibly. Therefore, the assumption of Hutton and Lyell that the events of the geologic past, at least during this period, consisted of the same kinds of activities as those of today, and occurred at about the same rate, is probably a valid approximation. For much longer periods of time, the assumption cannot be regarded as generally valid; neither can it be taken too literally even for recent geological eras. Otherwise, we should have to face the necessity of postulating continental glaciation during all geologic history. Or, conversely, were there no glaciation of any kind at present, we should probably still be embarrassed to find a rational explanation for the phenomena now explained by the hypothesis of continental glaciation.

Is it possible, therefore, that the Principle of Uniformity, having played a strategic role in the development of a valid history of the earth, has by now largely lost its usefulness? Perhaps in answer to this we should consider what are the logical essentials in the deciphering of history, not just geological history, but any kind of history. Because it is impossible for us to observe anything except the present, our interpretations of prior events must necessarily consist of inferences based upon present observations. *History, human or geological, represents our hypothesis, couched in terms of past events, devised to explain our present-day observations.*

What are our assumptions in such a procedure? Fundamentally, they are two:

(1) We assume that natural laws are invariant with time.

(2) We exclude hypotheses of the violation of natural laws by Divine Providence, or other forms of supernaturalism.

These are not arbitrary assumptions, nor are they peculiar to geologic science. Rather, they represent the distilled essence of all human experience, and are common to all sciences. Were the first assumption not valid, it could not be assumed that the freezing temperature of water would be the same tomorrow as it is today, nor that oxygen and hydrogen, which today combine under given conditions to form water, might not in the future, under the same conditions, combine to form alcohol or even sulfuric acid.

The second assumption is actually a corollary of the first, but it requires to be explicitly stated in view of the fact that for centuries the failure to accept this assumption has been one of the principal hindrances to the advancement of scientific understanding.

Thus, we conclude that books and other documents, fragments of pottery, cuneiform tablets, flint tools, and temples, pyramids and similar structures, which were in existence prior to our arrival, have all been the work of man, despite the fact that these postulated past activities have been outside the domain of any possible present-day observations. Having excluded supernaturalism, we draw these conclusions because man is the only known agent capable of producing the effects observed. Similarly, in geology, we conclude the ripple-mark-like forms in folded quartzites were in fact formed by wave action on a sandy beach, or, that sea-urchin-like forms found in inland limestones are indeed the skeletons of sea urchins which lived in a now nonexistent sea, because in neither instance are there other known means of producing these results.

At the same time we must be mindful of the fact that deficiencies in present knowledge will also be reflected in our interpretations of past events. This, in fact, was the principal weakness of the interpretations of geological history by Hutton and Lyell, neither of whom was aware of the limitations imposed by the laws of thermodynamics. . . .

Historical chronology, human or geological, depends also upon comparable impersonal principles. If one scribes with a stylus on a plate of wet clay two marks, the second crossing the first, another person on examining these marks can tell unambiguously which was made first and which second, because the latter event irreversibly disturbes its predecessor. In virtue of the fact that most of the rocks of the earth contain imprints of a succession of such irreversible events, an unambiguous working out of the chronological sequence of these events becomes possible.

During the last five hundred years, the tortuous evolution of geological science has been characterized by a progressive emancipation from the constraints and impediments imposed by assumptions of special Creations and interferences by Divine Providence in geological (and human) affairs. A major part of this emancipation has been accomplished by the employment of the Principle of Uniformity, but this rests upon insecure grounds due in large part to its having been formulated in ignorance of the later-developed laws of thermodynamics.

It has been recounted (Bell, 1937, p. 181) that when the French astronomer Pierre Simon Laplace had completed one of the volumes of his great work, *Mécanique Céleste*, a copy was presented to the Emperor Napoleon. Upon leafing through the volume Napoleon took the author to task for an apparent oversight, "You have written this large book on the system of the world without once mentioning the author of the universe." "Sire," Laplace replied, "I had no need for that hypothesis." It may be that the time has now arrived when geologists too may explicitly declare their lack of necessity for that particular hypothesis, as well as for a vaguely formulated Principle of Uniformity.

REFERENCES CITED

Adams, Frank Dawson, 1938, The birth and development of the geological sciences: Baltimore, Md., Williams and Wilkins Co., 506 p. (Reprinted in 1954 by Dover, New York.)

Andrade, E. N. da C., 1964, Rutherford and the nature of the atom: Garden City, N.Y., Anchor Books, Doubleday, 218 p.

Bailey, Edward, 1963, Charles Lyell: Garden City, N.Y., Doubleday, 214 p.

Bell, Eric Temple, 1937, Men of mathematics: New York, Simon and Schuster, 592 p.

Bethe, H. A., 1939, Energy production in stars: Phys. Rev., v. 55, p. 434–456.

Bonney, T. G., 1895, Charles Lyell and modern geology: New York, Macmillan, 224 p.

Chamberlin, T. C., 1899, Lord Kelvin's address on the age of the earth as an abode fitted for life. Part I: Science, new ser., v. 9, p. 889–901; Part II: Science, new ser., v. 10, p. 11–18.

Darwin, Charles, 1839, Journal of researches into the natural history and geology of the countries visited during the voyage round the world of H.M.S. 'Beagle' under the command of Captain Fitz Roy, R. N.: London, Henry Colburn, 615 p.

———, 1859, On the origin of species by means of natural selection; or, the preservation of favoured races in the struggle for life (1st Ed.): London, John Murray, 511 p. (Facsimile reprint, 1964, Cambridge, Mass., Harvard University Press.)

de Beer, Gavin, 1964, Charles Darwin: Garden City, N.Y., Doubleday, 290 p.

Fourier, Joseph, 1822, Théorie analytique de la chaleur; translated by Alexander Freeman, 1878, The analytical theory of heat: Reprinted in 1945 by G. E. Stechert, New York, 466 p.

Geikie, Archibald, 1905, The founders of geology: London, Macmillan. (Reprinted in 1962 by Dover, New York, 486 p.)

Gillispie, Charles Coulston, 1959, Genesis and geology: New York, Harper Torchbooks, Harper and Brothers, 306 p.

Hooykaas, R., 1959, Natural law and divine miracle: Leiden, E. J. Brill, 237 p.

Hutton, James, 1788, Theory of the earth, or an investigation of the laws observable in the composition, dissolution, and restoration of land upon the globe: Royal Soc. Edinburgh Trans., v. 1, p. 209–304.

———, 1795, Theory of the earth with proofs and illustrations: Edinburgh, William Creech; London, Cadell, Jr., and Davies, v. I, 620 p.; v. II, 567 p. (Facsimile reprint, 1959, Weinheim/Bergstr., Germany, H. R. Engelmann [J. Cramer]; Codicote, Herts, Wheldon and Wesley.)

Jameson, Robert, 1808, System of mineralogy comprehending aryctognosie, mineralogy, geognosie, mineral geography and economic mineralogy (1st Ed.): Edinburgh, v. III.

Lord Kelvin (William Thomson), 1899, The age of the earth as an abode fitted for life: Science, new ser., v. 9, p. 665–674, 704–711.

King, Clarence, 1893, The age of the earth: Am. Jour. Sci., 3rd ser., v. 45, p. 1–20.

Lyell, Charles, 1830–33, Principles of geology (1st ed.): London, John Murray, v. I, 1830, 511 p.; v. II, 1832, 330 p.; v. III, 1833, Text 398 p., Appendices and Index 109 p.

———, 1863, The geological evidences of the antiquity of man: Philadelphia, Pa., Geo. W. Childs, 518 p.

———, 1875, Principles of geology (12th ed.): London, John Murray, v. I, 655 p.; v. II, 652 p.

Playfair, John, 1802, Illustrations of the Huttonian theory of the earth: Edinburgh, William Creech; London, Cadell, Jr., and Davies, 528 p. (Facsimile reprint, 1956, University of Illinois Press, with an introduction by George W. White.)

Rubey, William W., 1951, Geologic history of sea water: Geol. Soc. America Bull., v. 62, p. 1111–1148.

Rutherford, E., and F. Soddy, 1902, On the cause and nature of radioactivity. Part I: Philos. Mag., ser. 6, v. 4, p. 370–396

———, 1903, Radioactive change: Philos. Mag., ser. 6, v. 5. p. 576–591.

Smyth, Henry DeWolf, 1954, Atomic energy for military purposes: Princeton, N.J., Princeton University Press, 264 p.

Thomson, William, 1862a, On the age of the sun's heat: Macmillan's Mag., March, p. 388–393 (Reprinted *in* Thomson and Tait, 1890, Treatise on natural philosophy. Part II: Cambridge University Press, p. 485–494.)

———, 1862b, On the secular cooling of the earth: Royal Soc. Edinburgh Trans., v. 23, p. 157–169 (Reprinted *in* Thomson and Tait, 1890, Treatise on natural philosophy. Part II: Cambridge University Press, p. 468–485.)

6

Is Uniformitarianism Useful?

STEPHEN JAY GOULD
1967

Uniformitarianism, the complex notion that provided a focus for the greatest philosophical debate in the history of geology, is again under discussion in the current context of renewed interest in the basic principles of our science. In a recent article (Gould, 1965a) I maintained that uniformitarianism is a dual notion with two strictly separable aspects:

1. A substantive uniformitarianism, dismissed as untrue, which postulates a uniformity of material conditions or of rates of processes.
2. A methodological uniformitarianism comprising a set of two procedural assumptions which are basic to historical inquiry in any empirical science. These assumptions are (a) that natural laws are constant in space and time, and (b) that no hypothetical unknown processes be invoked if observed historical results can be explained by presently observable processes.

The first of these assumptions provides a warrant for inductive inference while the second affirms the procedural notion of simplicity (Gould, 1965a, p. 226–227).

Although these assumptions will always remain basic in geology, I suggest that "uniformitarianism" as a *term* to describe them be dropped since it leads students to the false idea that our science possesses a unique philosophical tool and thus obscures the relationship of geology to other empirical sciences. In titling that article "Is Uniformitarianism Necessary?" I did not suggest, as some critics have stated (Longwell, 1965 and Hay, 1967 in the *Journal of Geological Education*) that the *concept* of methodological uniformitarianism is unnecessary (since it is only the *term* that I wish to abandon), but rather that it is every bit as inevitable as the phenomenon which provided, via the analysis of James Thurber and E. B. White, a source for the title (Thurber and White, 1929). I only ask that the concepts embodied in our unwieldly octo-syllable be given their rightful names—induction and simplicity. For I believe that the cause of good

From *Journal of Geological Education*, vol. 15, pp. 149–150, 1967. Reprinted with permission of the author and the National Association of Geology Teachers.

pedagogy is advanced by clarity of concepts and the search for principles that unify the various fields into which the intellectual world is fragmented.

Hay (1967, p. 11) gives the false impression that I recommend the jettisoning of uniformitarianism because of its ambiguities: "The historical and present state of this ambiguity should in no way demand the abandonment of the doctrine of uniformitarianism or the maxim 'the present is the key to the past,' although such drastic action has recently been advocated by Gould (1965a) and Valentine (1966)." I tried, rather, to resolve the ambiguity and thereby reached the conclusion, as noted above, that the concept of substantive uniformitarianism is false while that of methodologial uniformitarianism is synonymous with procedural assumptions known under different names to philosophers and scientists in other fields for centuries.

Since redundancy of language is not prohibited, the decision on keeping or dropping the term (methodological) "uniformitarianism" should be based on its effectiveness in teaching. Which is better? Shall we demonstrate to students that the geological method of studying present processes in order to interpret the past is based upon the assumptions of induction and simplicity common to all empirical science? Or shall we use a special term to emphasize the prominent role that these assumptions play when attempts are made to infer something about processes which operated in an unobservable past? Hay (1967, p. 11) lists two reasons for preferring the latter alternative:

1. "Geology is not simply one of the empirical sciences." It is indeed because of the special nature of geological inquiry—the study of events in remote and unobservable past time—that the importance of these assumptions intrudes upon our consciousness more often than it does upon that of other scientists. Still, special emphasis does not demand special terminology, for geology cannot count assumptions of induction and simplicity among its unique aspects.
2. "Good pedagogy often demands explanations and elaborations of much which may seem obvious to those having a more sophisticated perspective." I agree entirely, but maintain that proper explanation and elaboration can only lead to the conclusion that the assumptions of methodological uniformitarianism are shared by other sciences under different names. Often, I am afraid, the subject is taught superficially with Geikie's maxim "the present is the key to the past" used as a catechism and the imposing term "uniformitarianism" as a smokescreen to hide confusion both of student and teacher.

The dereliction of some teachers should not be used to impugn others who employ the term and maxim conscientiously. Superficiality can best be avoided, however, by presenting the historical and philosophical analysis required to illustrate the synonymy of methodological uniformotarianism with shared assumptions of other sciences. Such an analysis would require:

a) An elucidation of issues involved in the 19th century debate between catastrophists and the Hutton-Lyell school of uniformitarianism. Most prominent among these is the role of Divine power in the operations of nature.
b) An analysis of the hybrid concept of uniformitarianism into its two component parts and an assessment of the status of each.
c) An identification and examination of the geologist's use of induction and simplicity as a model for an understanding of scientific method in general.

One other point about teaching: Hay (1967) devotes half his article to a defense of using the present to interpret the past, implying that I have urged otherwise: "To show a beginning student a photograph of the cross-bedded Coconino Sandstone and comment only to the extent that gravity and pressure differences have operated lawfully on air masses throughout earth history would be a serious dereliction of pedagogy. The student of geology must search for the complex association of general conditions that can produce the physical reality called 'cross-bedding.' The only place to begin that search is in the present!" (Hay, 1967, p. 11–12). My identification of methodological uniformitarianism with the principles of induction and simplicity does not prescribe a methodology for approaching field problems and I am in complete agreement with Hay's statement. As I replied to a similar misunderstanding (Gould, 1965b, p. 919): "The only observable processes are present processes. Of the operation of processes in past times, we have only fossilized results. Any inference as to the mode of action of past processes can be made only by comparing ancient results with modern ones formed by processes we can directly observe." I would emphasize to students that it is by the principle of induction that we identify the observable cause of modern cross-beds as the producer of similar Coconino structures and by the principle of simplicity that we exclude as causes of Coconino cross-beds the set of logically possible alternatives which depend upon hypothetical unobserved processes.

The disagreement between Hay and myself is thus not as great as a first reading might imply. We agree that uniformitarianism is an ambiguous term with substantive and methodological aspects. We agree that geologists must study present processes to understand the past. We disagree on use of the term (methodological) "uniformitarianism": I would abandon it as redundant; Hay would keep it to emphasize the importance of induction and simplicity in a science which deals with remote and unobservable past time. Is this then just a trivial semantic quibble? I think not because very basic attitudes to the teaching of geology are involved. The subject matter of "uniformitarianism" is given most heavy emphasis in our introductory and general education courses. It is at this level that we should be stressing the relationship of geology to the scientific enterprise in general, not erecting terminological barriers that preclude the recognition of common themes in human knowledge and enhance the isolation of each discipline. Our majors will specialize sufficiently in their subsequent studies. Let us begin discussion of the philosophy of geology with an interdisciplinary perspective. In this way, I believe, we shall produce not only better scholars, but also better geologists.

REFERENCES CITED

Gould, Stephen Jay, 1965a, Is uniformitarianism necessary?: Am. Jour. Sci., v. 263, p. 223–228.

———, 1965b, Reply to criticism of C. R. Longwell: Am. Jour. Sci., v. 263, p. 919–921.

Hay, Edward A., 1967, Uniformitarianism reconsidered: Jour. Geol. Education, v. 15, p. 11–12.

Longwell, Chester R., 1965, Comment on S. J. Gould's paper "Is uniformitarianism necessary?": Am. Jour. Sci., v. 263, p. 917–918.

Thurber, James and E. B. White, 1929, Is sex necessary?: New York, Harper and Brothers, 197 p.

Valentine, James W., 1966, The present is the key to the present: Jour. Geol. Educ., v. 14, p 59–60.

7

A Tale of Ten Plutons

KONRAD B. KRAUSKOPF

1968

From *Geological Society of America Bulletin*, vol. 79, pp. 1–17, 1968. Reprinted with permission of the author and the Geological Society of America.

I begin with a line from Henry Adams: "Anarchy is the law of nature, and order is the dream of man." It would be hard to find a statement that on first reading sounds more anti-scientific. If nature is indeed chaotic, and if our minds impose order upon it, then the whole scientific enterprise is misguided. For in science we proceed on the assumption—perhaps better, on the faith—that order exists in nature, and that our mission as scientists is to discover it. To support our faith we need only reflect on all the proud accomplishments of science over the past four centuries.

In fairness to Adams I should note that he does not defend his pronouncement wholeheartedly. He uses it to summarize his impressions of the writings of the British mathematician Karl Pearson, and then proceeds to play with it as one of several alternative ways of interpreting man's relation to his surroundings. The play is amusing, and I think worth continuing in a direction different from that taken by Adams. Let us cling to our faith that nature is basically orderly, but let us ask to what limits we are willing to carry our faith. Is nature orderly only to a degree, or is it so rigidly ordered that every movement of every atom is predetermined for all time by the laws of physics and chemistry? This is not really a scientific question, for we have no way of judging how far in space and time the laws of physics and chemistry can be extended. All we know about them, all we can ever know, is that they hold within limits fixed by the ability of our senses and our instruments, to give us information about the world. We may extrapolate them to every movement of every atom if we wish, in order to make the world seem deterministic; but this is an act of faith, unsupported by scientific reasoning or evidence. Most of us, I think, would not go this far, because the notion of a completely predetermined universe is somehow repellent. But if we conclude that somewhere a boundary exists to the orderliness of nature, we must then inquire where the boundary may be drawn.

Of all the sciences, the one that goes furthest in the search for ultimate order is physics. And it is from physics that we get our clearest refutation of the proposition that deterministic order will be discovered on whatever scale we choose to examine the natural world. The information we can obtain about a single particle of matter, according to the indeterminacy principle, is insufficient for accurate predictions about its future behavior. The limitation is not the fault of present-day theory or instruments, but is inherent in the nature of the particle and its interaction with the radiation we use to detect it. In everyday experiments with large objects, of course, the limitation is not apparent. We express the behavior of aggregates as statistical probabilities, and the number of particles involved is so enormous that such statements have the force of statements of absolute law. Randomness exists in nature, but it is evident only in the behavior of individual particles.

If there is an ultimate randomness in nature, would it ever affect geologic conclusions? Offhand we would say no. The objects of concern in geology are so large that no deviation from the statistical rules of particle aggregates would ever be expected, which is a roundabout way of saying that we can use the ordinary laws of physics and chemistry in geologic reasoning with complete confidence. At least this is true for geologic processes taking place today. A question might be raised as to whether the indeterminacy of particle behavior is additive over time, thus making geologic conclusions about the distant past to some extent unsure. So far as I know this possibility has never been explored. That is not the question that interests me here, however, because I don't think we need look this far into the structure of matter to find evidence for a necessary uncertainty in geology.

The disturbing thing about the indeterminacy principle is its emphasis on our inability to obtain information. We ask, what are the position and speed of a particle at a given time? We find that we cannot get this information, because any instrument we try to use interacts with the particle. Not only no present instrument, but no conceivable instrument, could answer our question. In different words, we say that the information we want does not exist. Our question sounds plausible because we think of measuring the position and speed of larger objects, which is a simple operation; but on a very small scale the nature of reality changes, and our question becomes meaningless. Might we find analogous situations in a natural science like geology? Perhaps some of the information we seek about geologic processes does not exist, and some of our questions sound plausible only because we try to extend concepts from one environment to another where they have no significance.

Not everyone would agree with this suggestion. The confirmed determinist maintains that science has infinite capabilities, that any question is answerable, at least in principle. Look at the progesss science has already made; with new and better instruments just around the corner, surely questions that baffle us today will be easily solved tomorrow. The argument is hard to refute. Its one flaw is the fact that it does not rest on scientific evidence, but only on faith in the ultimate orderliness of nature. Questions of faith cannot be argued; I cannot prove our determinist wrong, but he is equally powerless to prove himself right. All we can say is that indications of a necessary randomness in nature are sufficiently strong so that the burden of proof rests on his shoulders.

How do we recognize geologic questions that may be meaningless? I see no way of approaching a general answer, but study of specific situations should provide examples. I would guess that a number of the longstanding and plausible-sounding geologic questions that so often elicit the remark about more research being needed are actually unanswerable because they assume the possibility of obtaining information that does not exist.

In this long preamble I have said nothing very profound, but I am trying to go a little beyond the familiar cliché that lack of evidence makes impossible a complete reconstruction of past events. Over and above lack of evidence, there may well be a degree of anarchy in nature that will forever defeat our attempts to see the past in fine detail. If we ask questions about the fine detail, we may be only projecting a dream of order from our minds onto nature.

To find examples of questions that sound plausible but may be meaningless, I turn now to the problems of unraveling sequences of intrusive igneous rocks. The particular rocks I have in mind belong to the Inyo batholith, a satellite of the much larger Sierra Nevada batholith, which straddles the California-Nevada border straight east of San Francisco (Figure 7.1). The part of the batholith with which I am most familiar lies in the Mt. Barcroft quadrangle, a 15′ quadrangle covering much of the east slope of the White Mountains (Figure 7.2). Total relief from White Mountain Peak to Fish Lake Valley is nearly 3000 meters; the extreme relief and dry climate give good three-dimensional exposures, which are indispensable for detailed study of granitic rocks.

Let me first mention some other geologists who have worked in and near this area recently and to whom I am greatly indebted. Donald Emerson (1966), in an excellent petrologic study of the granites, has proved that an earlier interpretation of some of the rocks as a product of granitization in place cannot be correct. Dwight Crowder is mapping the adjacent quadrangle to the west, and Paul Bateman (1963, 1965, 1967) has spent years in detailed study of similar rocks in nearby parts of the Sierra Nevada. All three have been most generous in giving me the benefit of their experience, and have helped to clarify my thoughts by arguing at length about the problems of batholiths. Three documents contributed much to the mapping: Nelson's map (1966)

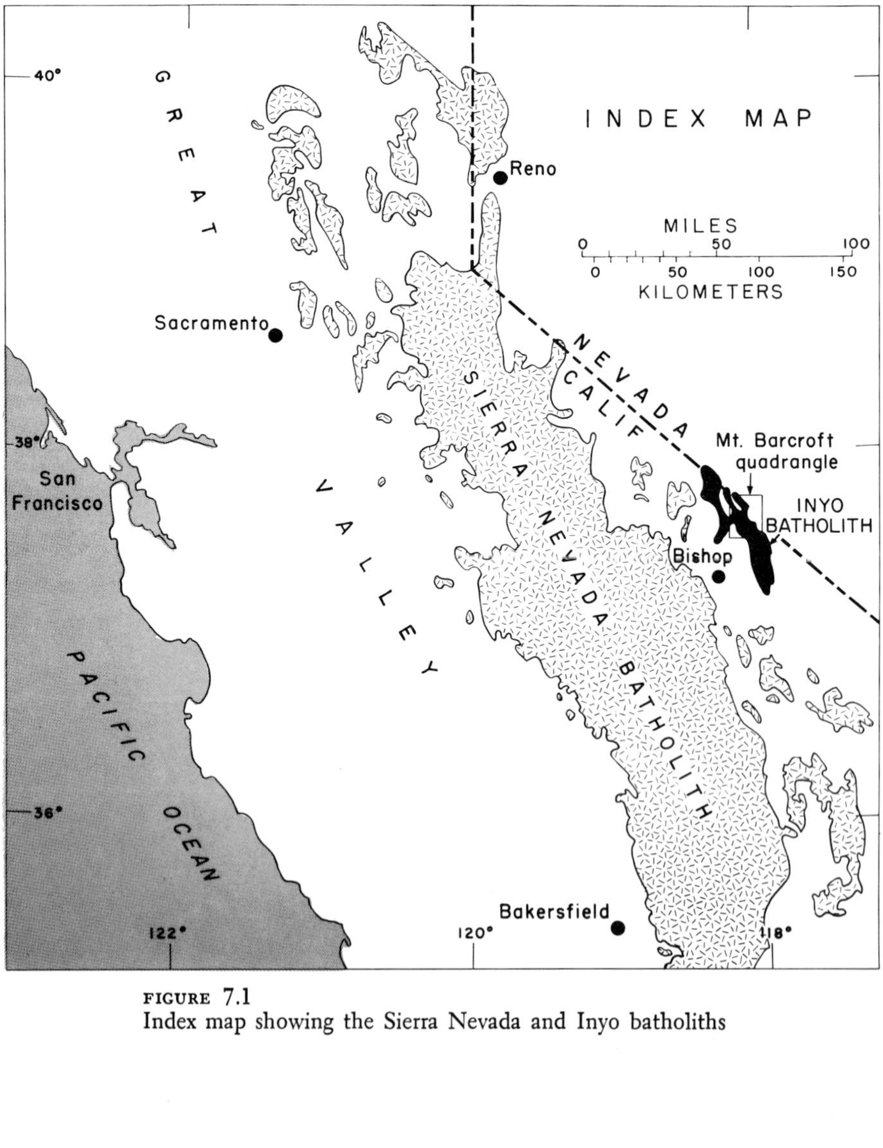

FIGURE 7.1
Index map showing the Sierra Nevada and Inyo batholiths

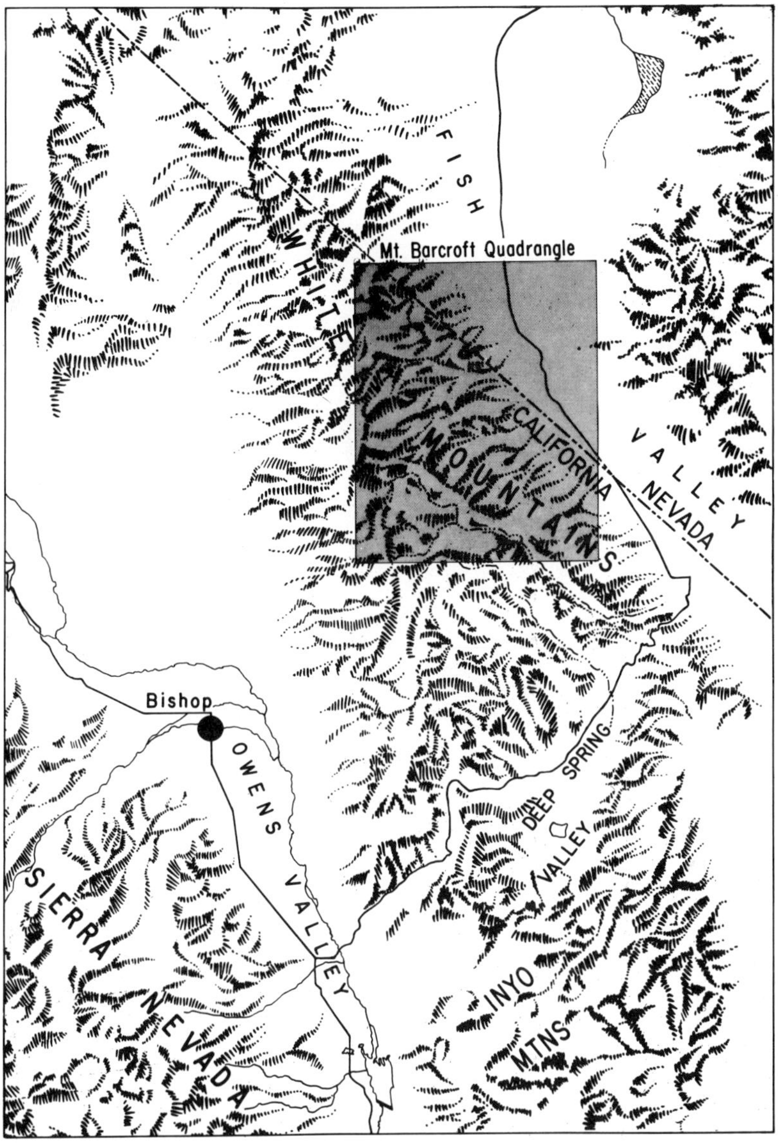

FIGURE 7.2
Map showing location of the White Mountains and the Mt. Barcroft quadrangle

of the next quadrangle south, a preliminary map by Albers and Stewart (1965) of adjacent parts of Nevada, and a master's thesis by M. N. Hall (1964) covering the southwest corner of the quadrangle. The writings of many others who have worked in the Sierra Nevada, particularly Frank Calkins, Robert Compton, Warren Hamilton, James Moore, Dean Rinehart, and Donald Ross, have given me valuable background. If I have gone astray in trying to interpret a complex batholith, it is not for lack of expert guidance.

The rocks of the Inyo batholith resemble other granites of the large Mesozoic bodies that are so abundant near the margins of the Pacific basin. They are granites of Buddington's mesozone (1959): not so gneissic or so intimately mixed with metamorphic rocks as those formed at deeper levels, and not so closely associated with volcanic rocks as those that have intruded levels near the earth's surface. Their homogeneity over broad areas and sharp contacts with adjacent rocks mean that they cannot have formed in any large measure by granitization in place, but must have moved as fluid masses from an origin elsewhere. The rocks occur in distinct units which I shall call plutons, and the batholith consists of a mosaic of these units. This usage of the term pluton is not everywhere accepted, but it has become common in recent literature on the batholiths of western North America.

I should emphasize that these are very ordinary igneous rocks. The range from mafic granodiorite to granite covers their compositions. Textures are represented from micrograniticto coarsely porphyritic. Some plutons are full of inclusions and dikes of several kinds; others are remarkably free from such variations. Varietal minerals are the usual biotite and hornblende, and the list of accessory minerals contains no surprises. Contacts are sharp and for

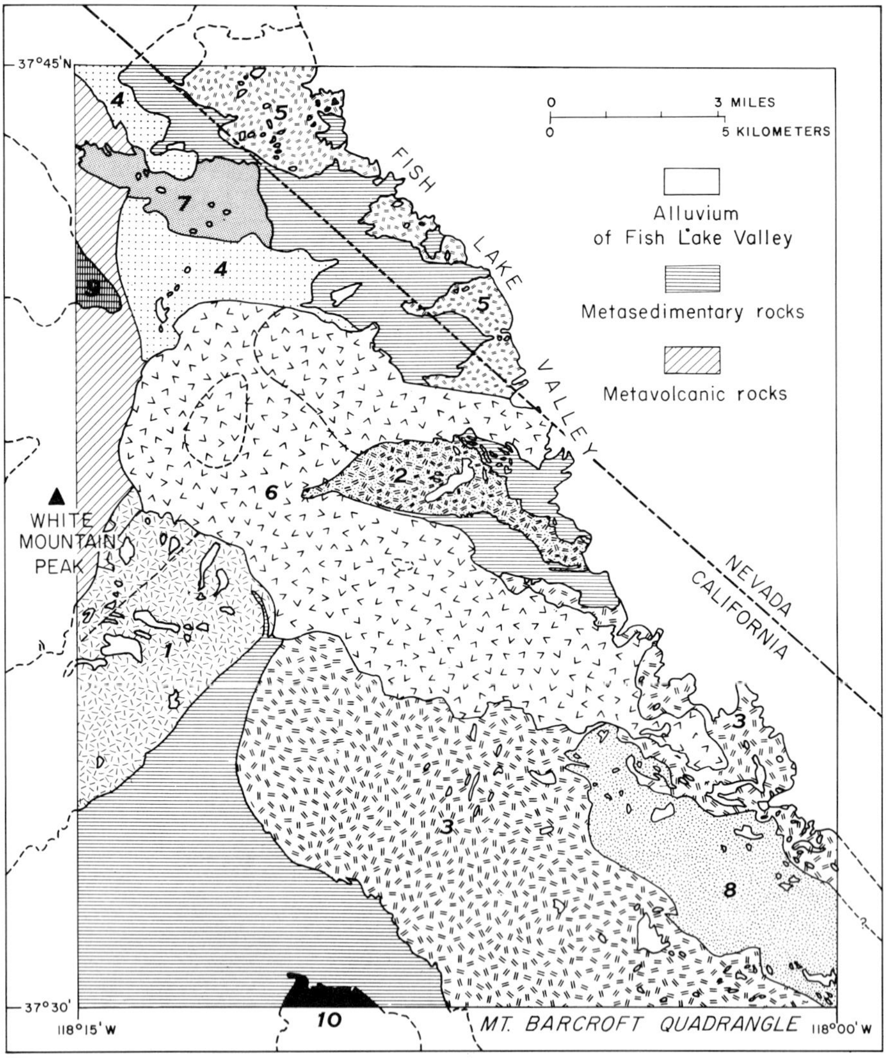

FIGURE 7.3
Sketch map of ten plutons in the Mt. Barcroft quadrangle

the most part steeply dipping. In all these respects the granites duplicate characteristics of plutons in adjacent parts of the Sierra Nevada batholith. The rocks are so ordinary, so similar to those of many other Mesozoic batholiths in the western states, that generalizations won from them should be widely applicable elsewhere.

Figure 7.3 displays ten plutons that can be distinguished in this representative part of the Inyo batholith. I shall refer to them by number rather than name, because here we are not concerned with details of local geology. The ten plutons are merely examples to illustrate a general inquiry into the kinds of geologic questions that are worthwhile asking and the kinds of answers that can be expected. For the same reason I do not identify the metamorphic rocks which the granites intrude. All we need know about them is that the metasedimentary rocks are equivalents of Precambrian and early Paleozoic limestones, dolomites, and fine-grained clastics, and that the metavolcanic rocks have compositions covering a range from basalt to rhyolite and dacite.

A generalized map like this makes the geology look neat and simple. How simple is it in actual fact? How much of the apparent order exists in nature, and how much is imposed by the more or less unconscious functioning of my order-loving mind? Geology of this sort, it seems to me, is admirably suited for a test of how far we are willing and able to go in seeking to find order among the raw observations we make of a natural setting.

Out of the many questions that might be asked, we limit ourselves to two simple ones: How many plutons are there, and how did they get to the positions where we find them? These are but variants of the standard queries in geology—how are things to be classified, and how did they form? It is a commonplace that the two are not always independent, for a hypothesis of formation often rests in part on the kind of classification assumed. So I will not discuss the questions separately, but rather will spin a tale about my ten plutons in the course of which various aspects of both questions can be illuminated.

What we set out to do is to build up, in effect, a "stratigraphy" of granite bodies. The plutons were intruded, if I may borrow Bateman's (1967) reasoning about similar bodies west of Owens Valley, at depths between 4 and 10 kilometers. Contact relations make possible a partial ordering of plutons according to their time of intrusion. So our problem is to work out a sequence of geologic units that were formed at an intermediate level in the earth's crust, just as a stratigrapher seeks to establish sequences of layered rocks deposited at the surface.

We set the stage by reconstructing the geology before any of the plutons appeared, much as a surface geologist might describe the geologic framework for a sedimentary sequence. A possible reconstruction is shown in Figure 7.4, with the metasedimentary rocks divided into their principal rock types. However wrong details of the picture may be, it shows the general features of the rocks and structures into which the first pluton made its way: sedimentary strata deformed only by open folds and a few faults, overlain unconformably by a sequence of lavas and pyroclastic beds. A preliminary comparison of Figures 7.3 and 7.4, even before our tale is well under way, shows that some of the common textbook generalities about batholiths are questionable. This batholith, at least, is not intruded into complexly deformed eugeosynclinal strata, and it seems to show a magnificent disregard for pre-existing structural trends.

Now we bring the first intrusives onto the scene (plutons 1 and 2, Figure 7.5). The problem of classification arises at once: do the two bodies of similar rock, separated at their closest approach by two kilometers of a younger intrusive, represent one pluton or two? Petrographically the rocks are so very close (dark-gray color, low quartz, high mafic content, presence of pyroxene as well as biotite and hornblende in some thin sections), that an original connection between the two bodies seems assured. A skeptic could point out that the western mass has more variety, notably a portion conspicuously coarse-grained and many large bodies of aplite, but these seem minor differences compared with the petrographic resemblance. A suggestion of Bateman's (1965) is appropriate here: the rock may be given a "formational" name, say the "Barcroft Granodiorite," while the two bodies are designated as separate plutons because of the distance between them.

Why are plutons 1 and 2 selected as the earliest ones? The choice is not entirely certain. These bodies are clearly older than the one pluton with which they make visible intrusive contact, but their relations to all other plutons are speculative. On the general grounds that these are by far the most mafic of all the plutons, and that felsic granites postdate more mafic ones at all exposed intrusive contacts in the area, an early date for this granodiorite seems reasonable.

How were plutons 1 and 2 formed? By intrusion of silicate magma from below, according to the evidence of steep, sharp contacts. As befits a mass of mafic composition, high temperatures at the contacts are indicated by wide zones of metamorphic rocks and small patches of migmatite locally. Possibly earlier more extensive migmatization at lower levels in the crust is suggested by areas of "ghost" xenoliths in the granodiorite, xenoliths with hazy

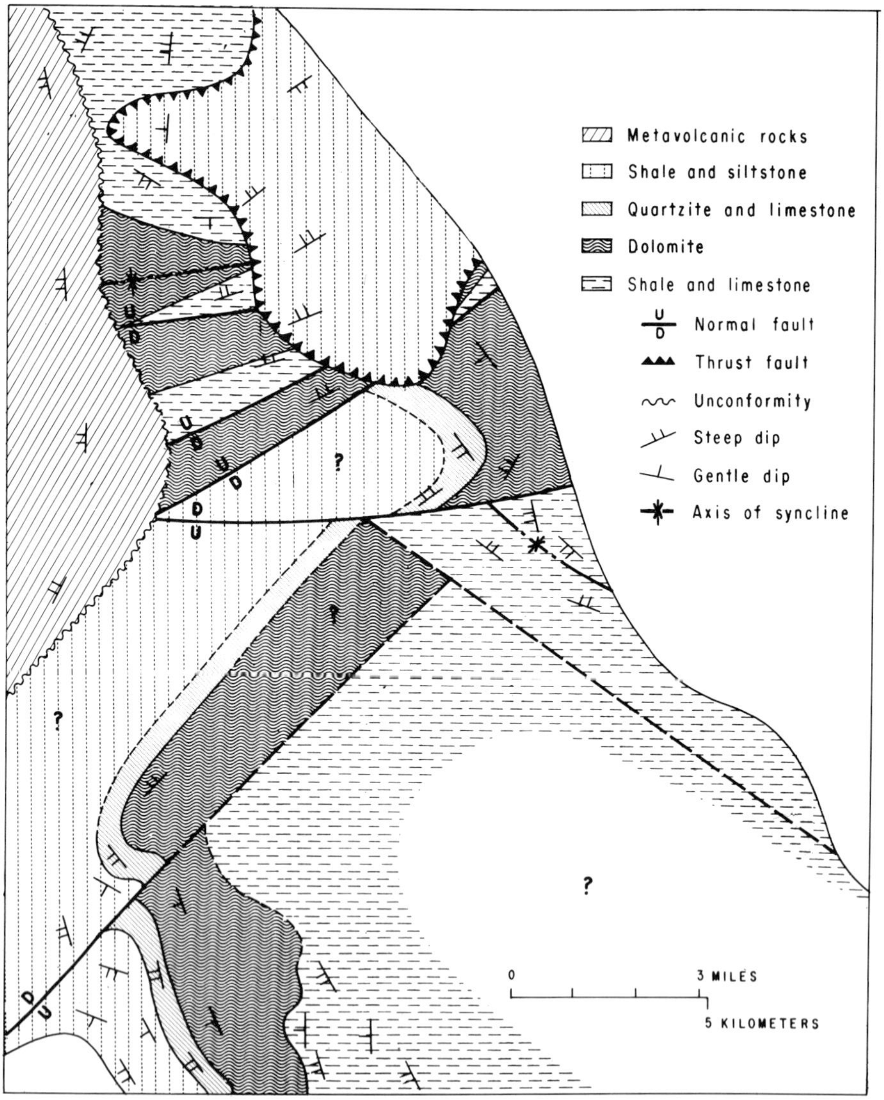

FIGURE 7.4
Sketch map showing inferred pre-pluton geology

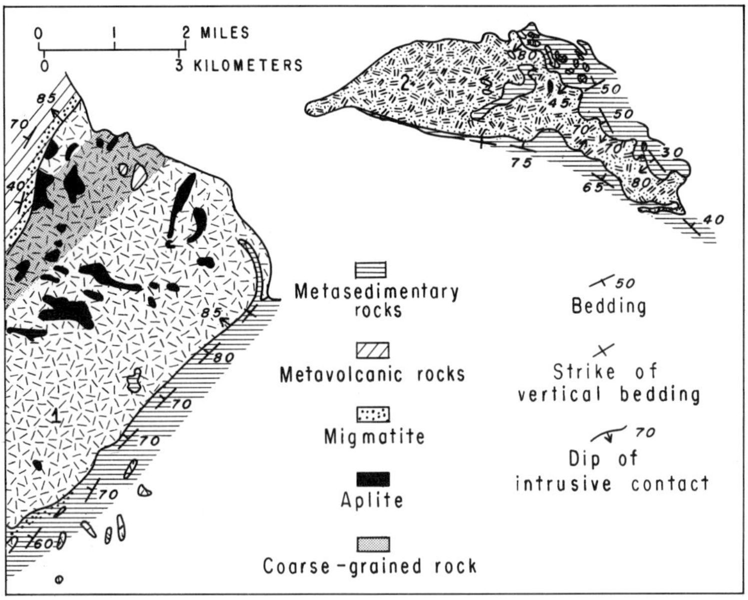

FIGURE 7.5
Map of geologic features in and near plutons 1 and 2. (Unofficial names: Barcroft West and Barcroft East plutons.) This and the following maps are enlargements of individual plutons shown on Figure 7.3. They do not show the geology in detail, but highlight the general field relations of the plutons and their immediate surroundings.

boundaries looking as if caught in the last stage of being made over into igneous material. But actual contacts of the mass as a whole are perfectly sharp, providing no hint of granitization at the level in the crust represented by present outcrops.

How did a mass of granodiorite magma make its way upward into the pre-existing structures shown in Figure 7.4? This is a question that is always asked about large intrusive bodies, and these two plutons illustrate beautifully the contradictory evidence often obtained. Looking at the southeast border of pluton 1, where metasedimentary beds are turned up on end, made strongly schistose, and attenuated to less than a quarter of their normal thickness, one can readily visualize a blob of magma pushing its way muscularly upward and creating space by deforming the rocks at its side. At the northwest border of this same pluton one sees an apparently more passive process at work, the intrusive heating its border rock and exuding dikes and silica-rich solutions that gradually make the rock assimilable into the melt. In the central part of pluton 2, big xenoliths of quartzite and marble suggest a third process, the stoping or quarrying out of blocks of wall rock by the advancing magma. The southeastern end of pluton 2, on the other hand, is a tongue implanted along the axis of an open syncline, where adjacent rocks show no sign of deformation or assimilation or stoping. Faced with such seeming ambiguity, one can adopt a pose of broad tolerance and grant the efficacy of all the traditional methods of granite emplacement. Or perhaps better, one can fall back on an old suggestion made by Mayo (1941) that granite magmas are not active agents but simply enter older rocks "permissively," following lines of structural weakness being created simultaneously by large-scale orogenic movement.

So far there is nothing new or particularly troublesome. One brings a degree of satisfying order to the field facts about plutons 1 and 2 by supposing that they are part of the same intrusive, and by going through the familiar exercise of weighing evidence for various possible methods of emplacement. This is all standard procedure, applied over and over again in many studies of granites. Difficulties arise only as we continue our tale by bringing in additional plutons.

Next in line is a large body in the southern part of the area (Figure 7.6), a pluton that Nelson (1966) and McKee and Nelson (1967) have followed southward and eastward for many kilometers into adjacent quadrangles. The rock is conspicuously different from the monotonous somber gray of plutons 1 and 2: it is light-colored, uniformly porphyritic with big phenocrysts of potassium feldspar, everywhere speckled with small mafic xenoliths. Unlike all other granites in the quadrangle, it contains as much or more hornblende than biotite. In its extreme local abundance of large aplite bodies, it differs from all other plutons except pluton 1. Something in its composition or structure causes large areas to weather into a hummocky topography that sets it apart, even without closer examination, from the other plutons.

Already this language introduces a degree of ordering. Pluton 3 is described as "one" body, although it is divided by a younger intrusive into an eastern and western part, just as are plutons 1 and 2. The eastern section is subdivided further, by alluvial cover and by the young intrusive, into many small distinct masses. Why, then, do we not regard this body as consisting of two plutons, or a dozen plutons? It is true that the major parts are separated by only a few hundred meters rather than two kilometers, and the smaller masses by still shorter distances. Is this really a sufficient basis for treating pluton 3 differently from plutons 1 and 2? There is no answer in strict logic; we can say only that describing it as a single body seems intuitively reasonable.

What evidence does this pluton give about its mode of emplacement? On both northeast and southwest contacts it cuts sharply across older structures. Only locally do adjacent beds show apparent disturbance by the intrusive. The prong of metamorphosed strata between plutons 1 and 3 is a temptation for those who prefer violent explanations, for it looks like a septum squeezed between two forcefully intruded bodies; but there is little evidence along the contact of pluton 3 to support such a

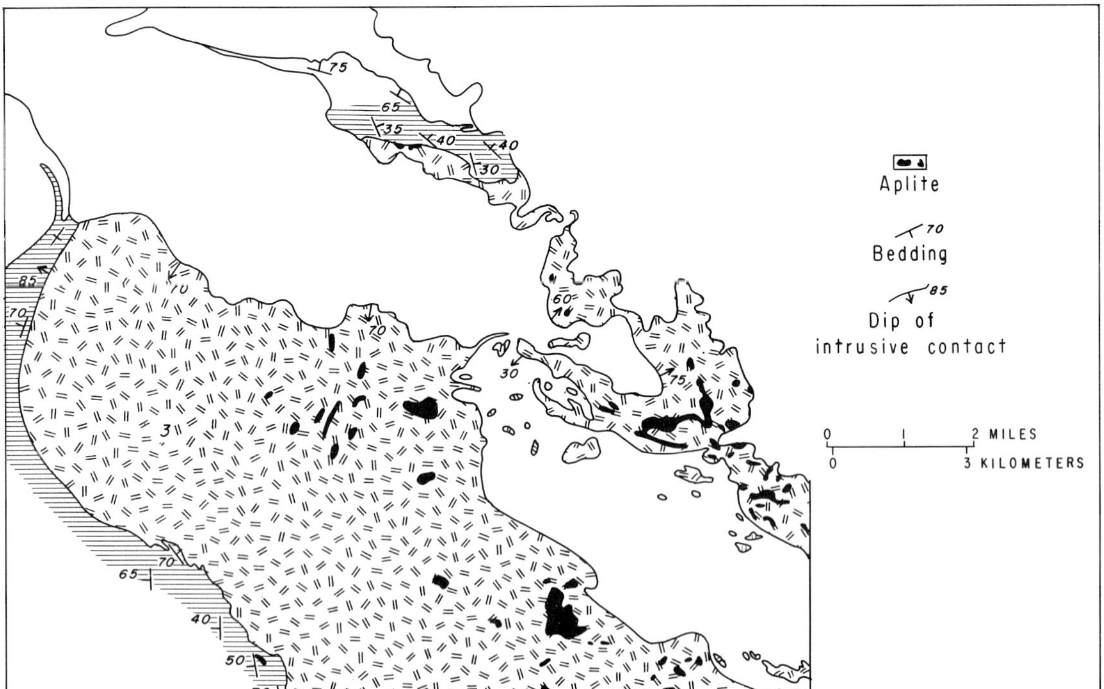

FIGURE 7.6
Map of geologic features in and near pluton 3. (Unofficial name: Cottonwood pluton.)

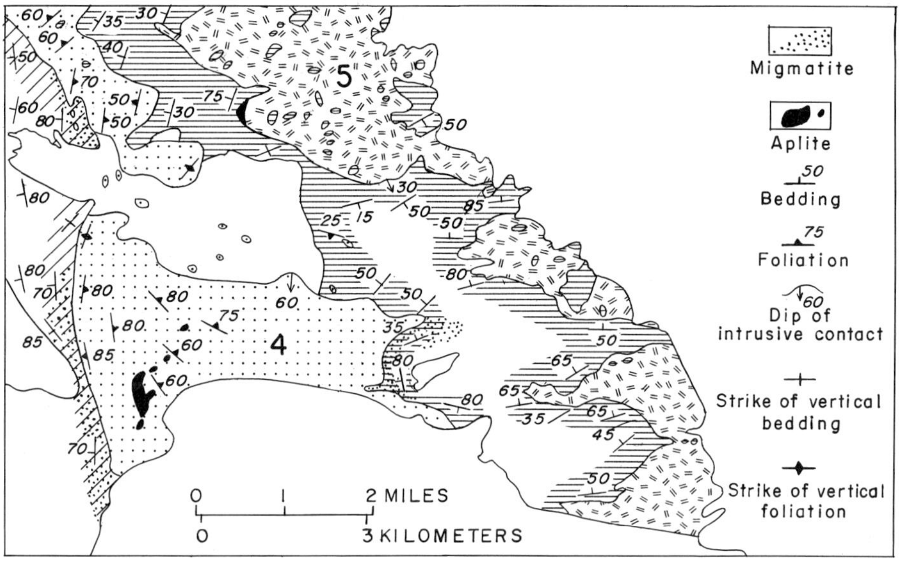

FIGURE 7.7
Map of geologic features in and near plutons 4 and 5. (Unofficial names: Cabin and Marble Creek plutons.)

guess. Heat from the pluton coarsened the grain of dolomite and biotite schist near its contacts, and fluids converted carbonate rocks to skarn very locally. Migmatite is conspicuously absent, and there is no evidence for assimilation or granitization at presently exposed levels. The two or three large xenoliths near the contact give scant comfort to advocates of stoping as a major mechanism of emplacement. A passive rise of magma accompanying tectonic disturbance with little relation to local structures is again a plausible postulate.

We turn next to the north, where two other plutons of porphyritic rock appear on either side of a deeply embayed strip of metasediments (Figure 7.7). These are separated from pluton 3 by minimum distances of four and eight kilometers, distances large enough so that we can map them unhesitatingly as distinct plutons. This does not answer the question, however, as to whether the rocks have enough petrographic resemblance so that they may be reasonably considered as belonging, at least originally, to a single intrusive body.

A similar question was answered readily in the affirmative for plutons 1 and 2, but here the situation is less clear. As a broad generalization one can say that the three plutons resemble each other in that they all have large areas of conspicuously porphyritic rock, and in that their content of mafic minerals is fairly high and includes hornblende as well as biotite. To go beyond this statement is difficult because of petrographic variations within plutons 4 and 5. Selected specimens of the two plutons look similar to specimens from pluton 3, but other parts of these bodies are quite different. The variability of pluton 5 is especially marked: textures run the gamut from coarsely porphyritic to aplitic, and compositions from alaskite to mafic granodiorite. Pluton 4 also has porphyritic and nonporphyritic varieties; over-all it is fairly mafic in composition, but grades into felsic rocks locally; it differs from all other plutons of the area in the presence of conspicuous planar foliation in its western part. Are these petrographic details sufficient to set plutons 4 and 5 apart from pluton 3, or does their general compositional resemblance and the widespread occurrence of porphyritic rock in all of them establish consanguinity?

Added to this question should be a query about the relations between plutons 4 and 5, exclusive of pluton 3. These two approach each other within a few hundred meters, and some varieties show a close resemblance.

Should they therefore be mapped as single body? Or we could ask the opposite question: since they are so variable internally, should the different varieties of each be mapped as separate plutons? This question is especially pertinent because the rock varieties are irregularly distributed, showing no pattern of zoning and no discernible relation to contacts. If there were some order in their distribution we might imagine them to be differentiates from a single magma, but the arrangement is so haphazard that some of the varieties may well be separate intrusive bodies. Mapping them on this scale would not be easy, but a persistent subdivider might find it possible.

Could other characteristics of the plutons aid in resolving the difficulty? Dikes of pink aplite, for example, are more numerous in pluton 5 than in pluton 4. Xenoliths also are more common, both the usual small mafic bodies of uncertain origin and large masses that can clearly be related to adjacent metasedimentary rocks; a number of these latter are big enough to show on the map, giving the pluton a pockmarked appearance. Contact metamorphism is a dubious criterion because it varies from place to place around each pluton; in general biotite schists are coarser adjacent to pluton 4 and areas of migmatite are more conspicuous; but on the other hand the borders of this pluton lack the andalusite metacrysts that appear locally in biotite schist near pluton 5. Generalizations like these are no more conclusive then the petrographic details but perhaps weight the evidence in favor of separating the two plutons.

The plain fact is that we have no single criterion and no set of criteria by which to pin down the relation of one granite body to another. Proximity, petrographic character, structure, abundance and kind of dikes and inclusions, contact-metamorphic effects—we juggle these intuitively, but their relative importance in characterizing what we would like to map as a granitic "unit" is a matter of subjective judgment. We can be happy with our judgment, we can think that we have perceived some new facet of the orderliness of nature, as long as we deal with plutons of uniform composition separated by decent intervals of other rocks. But when plutons like numbers 4 and 5 show more variation within themselves than we expect between different bodies, and when use of many criteria leads to conflicting interpretations, the order of nature seems far less satisfying.

Pragmatically, plutons 4 and 5 are separable, in that they can be mapped as units. They may well be, in some sense, parts of a single larger unit, and they may also be closely related (whatever this may mean) to pluton 3. The three bodies are nowhere in visible contact, so that relative ages are not determinable in the field. Because they have intermediate compositions between the mafic rocks of plutons 1 and 2 and the felsic compositions of plutons that intrude them, we may reasonably guess that their ages are not far apart, and that together they constitute the second chapter in the story of the building of the batholith.

Regarding the method by which plutons 4 and 5 moved into their present positions, the evidence is no better than for their predecessors. A new detail is the foliation in pluton 4, but it gives little help. Along much of the western border the foliation runs approximately parallel to the steep contact surface, suggesting laminar flow in a nearly solid mass; but in the northwest corner of the map the foliation turns abruptly to a position almost at right angles to the western contact. Bedding and foliation in adjacent metamorphic rocks show the usual puzzling combination of local conformity and sharp disconformity to granite borders. Pluton 4 shows more response to preexisting structure than most of the plutons, in that it follows an unconformable contact between metavolcanic and metasedimentary rocks. One can see evidence, as usual, for local stoping and pushing aside and assimilation, but it takes real imagination to picture any one of these as a principal mode of intrusion.

Among the younger, more felsic plutons, we look first at the largest one, a mass which seemingly plowed its way into the middle of the cluster of older plutons and which is responsible for most of the gaps between their outcrops (Figure 7.8). Pluton 6 is a singularly monotonous biotite quartz monzonite, a coarse-grained, light-colored, quartz-rich rock that accounts for the conspicuous whiteness of many ridges at intermediate elevations. It seems a real cause for wonder that any granite body can be as featureless as this one—almost

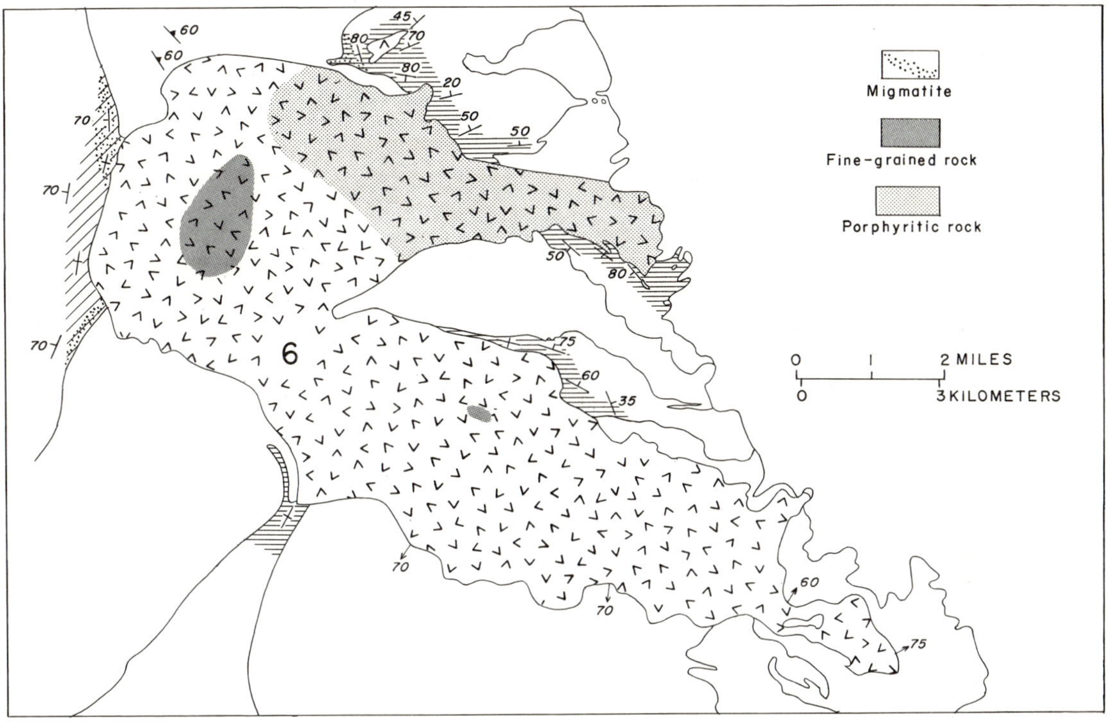

FIGURE 7.8
Map of geologic features in and near pluton 6. (Unofficial name: McAfee pluton.)

no dikes, no inclusions, no directional structures; a classically simple, easily recognized rock that persists without detectable change for many kilometers across country.

The uniformity has limits, of course, as the map shows. Toward the east the rock becomes porphyritic, not flamboyantly porphyritic like plutons 3 and 5 but modestly peppered with small, square, white potassium-feldspar phenocrysts, spaced so widely that a square meter seldom shows more than a dozen. Two patches in the interior of the pluton have a markedly smaller grain-size than most of the rock, and even less biotite than the small amount normally present. Both porphyritic and microgranitic variants grade imperceptibly into the normal quartz monzonite. We could ask our usual question about the propriety of mapping this body as a single pluton rather than three; but the gradational contacts, the persistently felsic composition, and the fact that similar variations have been described from many plutons in the Sierra Nevada are perhaps sufficient justification for including the three variants in a single body.

If we try to imagine pluton 6 ascending from below into the mosaic of older plutons that we have reconstructed, its behavior seems odd indeed. Plutons 1 and 2 formed a continuous east-west barrier; pluton 3 abutted the barrier on the south and pluton 4 on the north, and pluton 5 came close to the barrier's eastern end. The metamorphic rocks must have occupied about the same space they do today. From the point of view of ascending magma, there would be many lines of structural weakness to exploit: contacts of the plutons with each other and with their wall rocks, and planes of bedding, foliation, and faulting in the metamorphic rocks. The magma ignored all such inviting pathways, making its way rather into the middle of pluton 3, cutting through the barrier of plutons 1 and 2, and apparently lopping off the southern end of pluton 4. All this was accomplished without leaving a sign of violent disturbance. Contacts of the pluton are beautifully sharp, only the faintest of structures are preserved at its borders, and adjacent rocks give no hint of alteration except for a possible slight coarsening of dolomite and schist. The essential mystery of granite emplacement is epitomized by this body. There was obviously no room for it, yet somehow it found a place without being guided by pre-existing structures and without noticeably disturbing them. Some process of passive response to contemporary deformation again seems likely.

Much the same story is suggested by field relations of a small body (Figure 7.9) that lies athwart pluton 4. Pluton 7 is another light-colored, very felsic quartz monzonite, with razor-sharp contacts and little evidence of metamorphic effects on adjacent rocks. Unlike pluton 6, it shows faint foliation locally and considerable variation in composition. Its western end in particular is finer-grained and more mafic than the typical rock. The usual questions arise to plague us: Is this pluton related to pluton 6, despite a separation of two kilometers between their closest outcrops, or are the differences enough to characterize them as distinct bodies? Is pluton 7 really a single pluton, or is it made up of two or more small ones?

Difficulties of this sort become extreme in the southeast corner of the quadrangle, where pluton 8 invades pluton 3 (Figure 7.10). Petrographically this pluton strongly resembles number 6: it also is a felsic biotite quartz monzonite, lacking foliation and uniform in composition over broad areas. The conspicuous difference is its smaller grain-size. Much of the rock, from hand-specimen examination, would be labeled aplite, and it is practically indistinguishable from rock in the small aplite bodies that are so numerous in adjacent parts of pluton 3. On the detailed map of pluton 3 (Figure 7.6) a great number of the aplites are shown, the name carrying the usual assumption that these small bodies represent residual fluid formed during a late stage in the cooling of the pluton that contains them. In Figure 7.10 only a few of the larger aplitic bodies are depicted, on the assumption now that they are outliers of pluton 8. Clearly there is a basic unanswered question here. Are the aplites of pluton 3 really different from pluton 8 and its outliers, so that a sufficiently clever petrographer could map them as one or the other? Or are all the aplites in pluton 3 dikes and stringers of material exuded by the central mass of pluton 8? Or could all the bodies of aplite, including the whole of pluton 8 as the largest body, be simply late residual material squeezed out during the crystallization of pluton 3?

As if these questions were not troublesome enough, the rock of pluton 8 also is practically identical with the fine-grained parts of pluton 6. In fact the general similarity in composition and kind of outcrops between plutons 6 and 8 led Emerson (1966) to call them two "facies" of a single pluton; this is as reasonable a way as any to describe their relation, although the

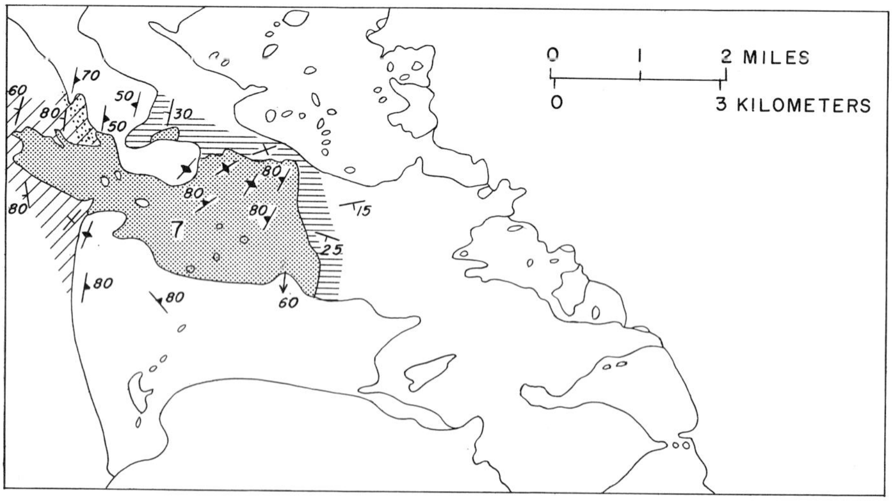

FIGURE 7.9
Map of geologic features in and near pluton 7. (Unofficial name: Leidy pluton.)

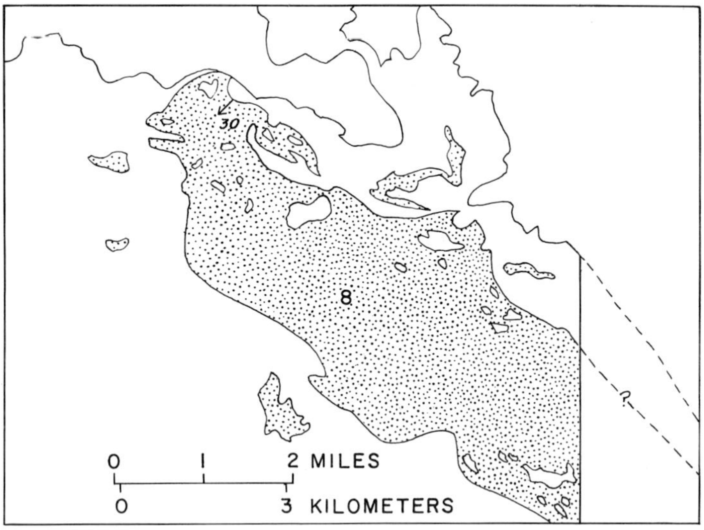

FIGURE 7.10
Map of geologic features in and near pluton 8. (Unofficial name: Indian Garden pluton.)

meaning of "facies" in this context is not entirely clear. Unfortunately the actual contact between the plutons is not exposed. In the few places where the two bodies approach each other without an intervening screen of pluton 3, they show no sign of gradational textures. For this reason, and also because pluton 8 is distinctive in its abundance of big xenoliths, the two are here mapped separately.

With pluton 8 the problems of recognizing different intrusives and working out their spatial and temporal relations become major conundrums. Problems like these should be the elementary ones, the ones that must be solved before we can go on to more sophisticated queries. How, for example, can we frame a sensible question about the mode of intrusion of pluton 8 when we cannot decide whether it is part of one of its big neighbors or intrusive into both of them?

The remaining two plutons, numbers 9 and 10 (Figure 7.3), can be dismissed with a few words. It is not that they are uninteresting, but simply that their story belongs more properly to other parts of the batholith. Pluton 9 is an enormous mass extending many kilometers into adjacent quadrangles to the west and northwest; the small nose that appears in the Mt. Barcroft area is unusual in that the rock has the composition of a true granite, with potassium feldspar far in excess of plagioclase. It is also notable for an indistinct contact with metavolcanic rocks, the intrusive and its border rocks forming a broad strip of sheared migmatite. Pluton 10, finally, is a roughly circular mass of felsic quartz monzonite about 3 kilometers in diameter, with sharp contacts and with a few quartz veins near its borders from which, according to rumor, some rich pockets of gold were mined in the last century.

This completes our tale of the ten plutons that make up this central part of the Inyo batholith. The number, I need hardly repeat, is quite arbitrary. The ten bodies are mappable units, and they form a neat pattern; but they could just as well be lumped into five plutons, or subdivided into twenty, and the units would be equally mappable. What is their real number? If we are to find order in the structure of a batholith, this is the first question that needs answering. When the number is established, we could go on to the next question: how did the plutons reach their present positions? Regarding both questions the field evidence is plentiful but contradictory.

Contradictory evidence is nothing new in geology. How do we handle it? Usually, by remarking that further research is needed. In the Mt. Barcroft area, for example, I could think comfortably that I had accomplished a reconnaissance mission, that I could now pass the torch to eager youngsters of the next generation who will be more nimble at climbing steep hills, and that their more detailed research will bring the questions I have posed nearer to solution. More research, more money, more refined techniques: it may take centuries, so the argument goes, but ultimately our questions will yield to this attack. Order exists anywhere in nature, and with enough hard work we can discover it.

The other possibility, a radically different possibility, is that our questions are the wrong ones, that they are essentially meaningless. Could we perhaps be seeking an order that does not exist?

How many plutons are there? The question has meaning only if criteria can be set up for distinguishing one pluton from another. Look at the criteria we have tried to use: two bodies of granite belong to the same pluton if their outcrops are sufficiently close together, if they have gradational contacts, if they are petrographically alike, if they have similar numbers and kinds of inclusions and dikes, if they have similar relations to the structures of their wall rocks, and if they exert similar metamorphic effects on their surroundings. Which one or ones of these are most important? Can they be made quantitative? How can we be sure that they distinguish different plutons rather than parts of the same pluton? With our present knowledge of granites such questions are largely unanswerable, as this exploration of the Mt. Barcroft quadrangle has shown.

Will they *ever* be answerable? Suppose, for example, that we had radiometric dates for all the granites, as we surely will have in a very few years; would this information solve the problem? It would help, certainly, but at best it would be only one more criterion. How far apart in age, we would have to ask, must two granite bodies be before we can assign them indisputably to different plutons? What difference in age between parts of one body can be tolerated before we subdivide it? Or suppose we had analyses of the trace-element content of each pluton. This would be useful information, surely, but past studies of trace elements in all manner of geologic materials give little hope that they alone would provide an unambiguous answer. Suppose that experimental petrologists succeed in learning so much about granites that we can interpret porphyritic textures, dikes, inclusions, and so on in terms of specific composition-temperature-pressure conditions; would this make the problem easier? Again we would be grateful for the data, but the nagging question would remain as to what ranges of these variables might permit us to lump or subdivide granite masses into plutons.

I hope it is clear that I am not trying to disparage in any way the value of more precise experimental data. I doubt only that *for this particular problem* any conceivable instrumental data could provide a final solution. Distinguishing plutons in a batholith is a field problem, and its solvability or lack of solvability must rest in the end on field criteria. When field relations lead to the sort of contradictions displayed by the Inyo batholith, there is a good chance that we have posed an unsolvable problem. Perhaps as granite magma is formed at lower levels in the crust of upper mantle, masses of it ascend and subdivide and differentiate and intermingle in a fairly random fashion, so that attempts to distribute outcrops of a batholith among a finite number of discrete plutons are foredoomed to failure. Some tongues of granite, to be sure, will form reasonably homogeneous bodies that can be usefully mapped, but in other parts of a batholith the distinctions may be entirely arbitrary. In other words, to establish a complete "stratigraphy" of intrusive units is impossible. It seems like a reasonable undertaking only because our minds are so eager to find order that we draw unreal analogies between very different geologic environments.

The second question we have raised, the vexing problem of granite emplacement, may have a similar unreal aspect. Again this is a field problem, and again the field evidence is hopelessly contradictory. Does the problem have meaning? Is there reason to expect that the position of a pluton will have some definite relation to surrounding rocks and structures? If we assume that a relation exists, is there any conceivable way by which it might be discovered? Suppose, for example, that one of my successors in the White Mountains makes a detailed petrofabric analysis of the plutons and adjacent metamorphic rocks. He might learn a great deal about broad relations of structural patterns, and about details of late movements in the plutons before they froze. Would he know more, however, about why the plutons so largely ignore previous structural trends, why contacts are in part conformable and in part disconformable to adjacent metamorphic structures, why a late granite invades an early granite rather than following lines of structural weakness? Or imagine that a new episode of granite formation occurs, causing a tongue of magma to invade this area; would his data be of any use at all in predicting where the new pluton would emplace itself?

Again I hope it is clear that I am not questioning the importance of petrofabric analysis. I wonder only if it can help much in answering a specific query as to why a pluton emplaces itself in one location rather than another. Is it not possible that here again we are dealing with an essentially random process? On a broad scale the plutons of the Inyo batholith were finding their place at a time when granite magma was being generated over a huge area, probably centering under the present Sierra Nevada, and when it was rising intermittently into the crust in response to density differences and large-scale orogenic disturbance. Perhaps the tongues of magma rose passively and at random, much like bubbles in boiling water, paying little heed to pre-existing rocks and only locally exerting any influence on adjacent structures. A possible indication of random motion is just the fact that granite exists in the White and Inyo mountains; this is far from the center of magma formation under the Sierra Nevada, and the rocks invaded are much less deformed and of quite different composition from those usually associated with large intrusive bodies. These plutons can be pictured as forming on the periphery of a granite-generating area and making their way essentially by accident into relatively undeformed rocks. On this supposition the emplacement of the plutons is a random, passive process, and we only delude ourselves if we seek order in their relations to surrounding rocks.

By speculating in this fashion I put myself in a most uncomfortable position. To appeal to a random element in nature is, in a sense, to admit defeat. This is the easy way out: my problem becomes difficult, and I respond simply by avoiding it. One can always maintain that more work, more accumulation of data, more applications of sophisticated techniques will enable us ultimately to sort out plutons and find reasons for their locations. To this argument I have no reply, except to say that on the basis of present knowledge it sounds more like an expression of faith than a sober scientific conclusion.

Let me rephrase the philosophical position. I am suggesting the thesis that some questions about the makeup and formation of batholiths are essentially unanswerable. I don't mean unanswerable because present methods of study are inadequate, but unanswerable in the nature of things, unanswerable no matter how refined our methods become. We try to see relations that do not exist, to find order in processes that are largely random. Further study can give us more data, more correlations, more understanding of details, but the central questions will forever elude us—because the questions themselves are meaningless. In much the same way that physicist find questions about the exact location and speed of a particular electron meaningless, perhaps we are asking the wrong questions about the separation and movements of the units that make up a batholith.

As these and other problems of geology are examined with modern techniques in ever greater detail, I am often astonished at the vistas of formidable complexities that open before us. Somewhere in our pursuit of these complexities we must encounter the results of random events, or the limits to our capacity for obtaining information; otherwise we go back to a rigid determinism, for which there is no warrant in the physical laws on which our science rests. We can wallow indefinitely in such complexities if the random element is not recognized. Perhaps the problems of plutons that we have considered here are examples of points where randomness may lead us astray. I am not at all sure that these are good examples, but here or elsewhere in our reconstructions of past events we must inevitably find limits to the possibilities of precise logical explanation.

Perhaps part of the mission of a natural science like ours should be to define the role of randomness in historical processes. For it is true that randomness, or anarchy, is in some measure the law of nature, and that some of the order we think we see is a dream in our own minds. As geologists we are in a better position than most to set limits to the anarchy, and also limits to the dream.

REFERENCES CITED

Albers, John P., and John H. Stewart, 1965, Preliminary geologic map of Esmeralda County, Nevada: U.S. Geol. Survey, Mineral Inv., Field Studies Map MF-298.

Bateman, Paul C., Lorin D. Clark, M. King Hubbert, James G. Moore, and C. Dean Rinehart, 1963, The Sierra Nevada batholith, a synthesis of recent work across the central part: U.S. Geol. Survey Prof. Paper 414-D, 46 p.

Bateman, Paul C., 1965, Geology and tungsten mineralization of the Bishop district, California: U.S. Geol. Survey Prof. Paper 470, 208 p.

Bateman, Paul C., and James G. Moore, 1965, Geologic map of the Mount Goddard quadrangle, Fresno and Inyo counties, California: U.S. Geol. Survey Geol. Quad. Map GQ-429.

Bateman, Paul C., and Jerry P. Eaton, 1967, The Sierra Nevada batholith: Science, v. 158, p. 1407–1417.

Buddington, A. F., 1959, Granite emplacement with special reference to North America: Geol. Soc. America Bull., v. 70, p. 671–748.

Emerson, D. O., 1966, Granitic rocks of the Mt. Barcroft quadrangle, Inyo batholith, California-Nevada: Geol. Soc. America Bull., v. 77, p. 127–152.

Hall, M. L., 1964, Intrusive truncation of the Precambrian-Cambrian succession in the White Mountains, California: M. A. Thesis, Univ. California at Berkeley, 90 p.

Mayo, E. B., 1941, Deformation in the interval Mount Lyell–Mount Whitney, California: Geol. Soc. America Bull., v. 52, p. 1001–1084.

McKee, E. H., and C. A. Nelson, 1967, Geologic map of the Soldier Pass quadrangle, California-Nevada: U.S. Geol. Survey Geol. Quad. Map GQ-654.

Nelson, C. A., 1966, Geologic map of the Blanco Mountain quadrangle, California: U.S. Geol. Survey Geol. Quad. Map GQ-529.

SECTION II

ORIGIN OF THE UNIVERSE SOLAR SYSTEM, AND PLANETS

Ah, but a man's reach should exceed his grasp,
Or what's a heaven for?

Robert Browning, ANDREA DEL SARTO

Discussion of the origin of the universe, solar system, and planets is introduced in a sprightly essay by Harlow Shapley, dean of American astronomers (Reading Selection 8). He sketches the high points of the then most prevalent concepts of the origin of the universe —the steady state hypothesis which, in effect, dismissed the question by considering both time and space to be infinite and new matter to be constantly created in interstellar space; and the hypothesis of an evolving universe. The salient features of the universe, for which all theories of its origin must account, are its staggering dimensions and its apparent expansion at speeds that increase with distance from the observer. Estimates of those distances and speeds have risen considerably since Shapley wrote, but the measurements that imply an expanding universe have found no explanation more compelling. The universe has evolved, however, regardless of how it originated. Hydrogen has "burned" to form heavier elements at temperatures above 10 million degrees Kelvin, and the heaviest elements at temperatures of billions of degrees Kelvin, in novae and supernovae; matter has clustered into stars and nebulae, which also evolve; and star formation has led, perhaps commonly, to the birth of planets. Man cannot refrain from asking how many other planets there are like the earth, and how many of these might support life.

Scientific discussion of the origin of the universe really began with Einstein's general theory of relativity in 1916. There was, however, one flaw in Einstein's model: it did not take account of the later discovered fact that the red shift of stars beyond our own galaxy implies that the parts of the universe are moving away from each other at speeds that increase with distance. Until about 1924, the galaxy we call the Milky Way was believed by most astronomers to represent the entire universe. By that time, study of the stars of regularly pulsating luminosity called Cepheid variables enabled Edwin Hubble of the Mt. Wilson Observatory, extending work begun by Shapley, to state unequivocally that there were other galaxies beyond our own. He then turned his attention to evidence for the expansion of the universe—namely, that given by the red shift, a Doppler effect, whereby the wave length of light from receding objects is attenuated toward the red end of the spectrum. Calculation of the velocities of receding objects by measuring their red shifts began with Sir William Huggins in 1868. The velocity is a simple function of the change in wave length, divided by the original wave length, times the speed of light; that is, $v = (\lambda\Delta/\lambda)c$. The problem remained, however, of how to translate this into distance. Distances determined by trigonometry using the earth's orbital diameter as a base are limited to about 300 light years. However, a regular relation between luminosity (brightness on a scale of magnitude) and intensity of absorption spectra allows the distances to the nearer Cepheid variables (approximately 800 light years) to be estimated. Knowing the red shift of star groups containing Cepheid variables, such as M81 (Tammann and Sandage, 1968, see Supplemental Reading), enables us to correlate red shift with distance for more remote star groups. Intrinsic luminosities of more distant star clusters can be approximated by extrapolation, and, from these too, red shifts can be correlated with distance. Distances throughout the observable universe can then be approximated, given the assumptions that the red shift is not due to changes in the energy of light or the rate of flow of time, and that the ratio between the observed shift and distance remains regular.

A simply written summary of the basic work on the measurement of distance in the universe is the essay "The Expansion of the Universe," by physicist James A. Coleman (Reading Selection 9). It must be kept in mind, however, that both interpretation and measurement are still in a state of flux. A value for the Hubble constant, whereby velocity from red shift is converted to distance, is not yet known with assurance, although it is believed to be close to 14 miles per second per million light years. The red shifts of some remote galaxies suggest speeds of nearly 49 percent of the speed of light; and those for some quasars, speeds perhaps as great as 80 percent of the speed of light, approaching the limits of the visible universe. Coleman discusses alternatives to the idea of an expanding universe, including Milne's concept of different scales for clock time and atomic time; but he concludes that only an expanding universe can keep our earth from overheating, and that the evidence of the red shift must be interpreted literally according to the present laws of physics. New measurements and new interpretations, of course, will eventually modify or eliminate all models of the universe now extant, but the development by successive refinements of our present concepts of stellar distances will remain an exciting example of the methods of investigation in historical cosmology.

How the introduction of new evidence may result in dramatic changes in outlook is well illustrated in cosmogony (the special study of cosmic origins) by the dramatic collapse of the steady state hypothesis. The now seemingly fatal objections to this hypothesis—four lines of evidence all pointing to a universe of a denser state in the past—are detailed in an extraordinary paper (Reading Selection 10) by one of its former leading champions. Fred Hoyle, renowned University of Cambridge mathematician, astrophysicist, and humanist, explains why he found it necessary, in 1965, to abandon the hypothesis he had so long defended in favor of either a finite oscillating universe, or an infinite universe with oscillating regions. Hoyle thus fulfilled his own precept as quoted in Newsweek (May 25, 1964, p. 64): "You must push to the limit to see where it leads . . . when a theory is finally proven wrong it means in fact that you have discovered a new truth."

Those wishing to pursue questions raised by the first three papers in this section are referred to Chapters 22 to 24 in *The Physical Universe* by Krauskopf and Beiser (1960) and to the papers by Sandage, Hoyle, and Gamow in the Supplemental Reading. Cosmogony is an engrossing and rapidly changing field. The rapid growth of the science requires continual critical examination of existing hypotheses and prompts repeated efforts to formulate better ones. Here is a place where multiple working hypotheses are very much in order. If they are to be fruitful, however, they must not only be consistent with a large body of evidence, they must also have testable corollaries.

The history of the solar system is a part of cosmogony. It is discussed in Reading Selection 11 by Fred Whipple of the Smithsonian Astrophysical Observatory at Cambridge,

Massachusetts. He discusses first the observable characteristics of the solar system, then the hypotheses that have been advanced to explain its origin. He argues that the observable characteristics of the solar system are most consistent with the hypothesis that it originated by condensation from a discoidal solar nebula having a diameter extending beyond what is now the orbit of Pluto. The major difficulties inherent in this hypothesis are: how to explain the present distribution of mass between the terrestrial and the outer planets; and how to explain the fact that the sun, with nearly 99.9 percent of the total mass of the solar system, accounts for less than 0.5 percent of the angular momentum of the system. If an initial solar disc or nebula of large diameter had simply contracted, leaving the planets behind, then the rate of rotation should have increased, and the sun should now be rotating much faster than it is. To get around those difficulties, Whipple postulates the existence of magnetohydrodynamic processes in hot ionized gases moving along magnetic fields in space. In such a situation, charged particles will move easily along field lines but will cross them only with difficulty. A strong magnetic field related to an expanded rotating sun could facilitate the outward transfer of both matter and angular momentum; and differences in temperature, condensation processes, and time of condensation could account for the differences in density and composition between the terrestrial and outer planets.

Harold Urey of the University of California, a Nobel laureate in chemistry, expresses his views concerning the evolution of our planet and its satellite in "The Origin of the Earth" (Reading Selection 12). After reviewing and rejecting older hypotheses, Urey proposes a model somewhat different from that of Whipple but akin to one developed by Kuiper in 1951 (see Supplemental Reading). This calls for condensation of the planets and their satellites from particles dispersed in gas eddies of irregular size around the protosun. This is similar to the model suggested by the German physicist von Weizsäcker in 1944 (see Figure 11.5), except that von Weizsäcker proposed gas eddies of uniform size. Difficulties persist with transfer of angular momentum in the Urey model, and with how to account for the temperatures that would have been required to produce metallic iron meteorites in parent bodies smaller than the moon. Gas is also necessary to dissipate collisional energies of the planetesimals so that they can aggregate instead of breaking up, but terrestrial depletion of the noble gases tells us there cannot be much gas in the final stages of accretion. More extensive and more recent discussions of the model are found in Urey's 1954, 1958, and 1963 papers listed under Supplemental Reading. We shall see repeatedly that, although the models are rational and help us to visualize what *might* have happened, none is free from inconsistency, and that the issues they treat are far from settled.

Whatever its origin, however, we should like to know *when* the solar system originated. Reading Selection 13, by geophysicist John Reynolds of the University of California, concludes this section with an examination of several lines of evidence bearing on when, and over what span of time, the solar system and the earth came into being. In addition to the usual methods, Reynolds, pursuing an idea originally suggested by geochemist Harrison Brown of the California Institute of Technology, sought for—and found—meteorites that show slight excesses of xenon-129, a decay product of short-lived iodine-129. Since iodine-129 is formed only at nuclear temperatures, it originates in our solar system only in nuclear explosions or in the solar disc. Computations from measurements of xenon-129 concentrations in the meteorites imply that condensation of the relatively cold planets from the hot solar nebula probably took place rather rapidly, over a span of time lasting no more than about 120 to 290 million years and that it was completed about 4.6 aeons ago (4.6×10^9 years). It is interesting and rewarding to follow through the various interwoven lines of evidence that led to this conclusion. The student should examine them thoroughly and critically to see if other interpretations are permissible.

A consideration of planetary and terrestrial characteristics is incomplete without more discussion of the planetary satellites—particularly of the earth's moon—than has been included here. Some of that discussion is provided in Reading Selections 18 and 42; but among the best sources are those listed under Supplemental Reading below. They include papers on lunar origin by MacDonald (1965), Singer (1967), and Öpik (1969), as well as a fascinating note on "Lunar Rivers" by Lingenfelter and others (1968) and a perceptive article by Eugene Shoemaker (1964) describing how the major features of the "geology" of the moon (selenology) can be worked out from a distance, applying ordering principles evolved from terrestrial geology (see Frontispiece). It would be a good laboratory exercise to extend the principles outlined by Shoemaker to the interpretation of similar or other lunar features not discussed by him.

Other papers of interest under Supplemental Reading include a concise modern summary of distances and ages in the universe by Sandage (1968) and a paper by Firsoff (1965) that takes issue with the conventional interpretation of the red shift as evidence for an expanding universe.

Supplemental Reading

The Scientific American Offprints listed below and in the other lists of Supplemental Readings in this book are available from your bookstore; or they may be ordered directly from W. H. Freeman and Company, 660 Market Street, San Francisco, California 94104, or from W. H. Freeman and Company Ltd., 58 Kings Road, Reading, England. Please order by the Offprint number.

Bowen, I. S., 1964, Explorations with the Hale telescope: Science, v. 145, p. 1391–1398.

Burbidge, Margaret, and Geoffrey Burbidge, 1958, Formation of elements in the stars: Science, v. 128, p. 287–399.

Firsoff, V. A., 1965, Is the universe expanding?: Discovery, April 1965, p. 18–21.

Fowler, W. A., 1956, The origin of the elements. Scientific American Offprint 210, 11 p.

Gamow, George, 1956, The evolutionary universe: Scientific American Offprint 211, 9 p.

———, 1967, History of the universe: Science, v. 158, p. 766–769.

Gibson, R. E., 1964, Our heritage from Galileo Galilei: Science, v. 145, p. 1271–1276.

Gilbert, G. K., 1893, The moon's face—a study of the origin of its features: Philos. Soc. Washington Bull., v. 12, p. 241–292.

Greenstein, J. L., 1963, Stellar evolution and the origin of the chemical elements, *in* W. A. Brose, ed., Science in progress (ser. 13): New Haven, Conn., Yale University Press, p. 173–208.

Hack, Margherita, 1966, The Hertzsprung-Russell diagram today, I–II: Sky and Telescope, v. 31, no. 5, p. 260–263; no. 6, p. 333–336.

Hoyle, Fred, 1950, The nature of the universe: New York, Harper & Row, 124 p. (Reprinted by New American Library, Signet Books, 1955.)

———, 1956, The steady-state universe: Scientific American Offprint 218, 6 p.

Hubble, Edwin, 1936, The realm of the nebulae: New Haven, Conn., Yale University Press, 207 p. (Reprinted by Dover Publications, 1958.)

Krauskopf, Konrad, and Arthur Beiser, 1960, The physical universe: New York, McGraw-Hill, 536 p.

Kuiper, G. P., 1951, On the origin of the solar system, *in* J. A. Hynek, ed., Astrophysics: Chicago, University of Chicago Press, p. 357–424.

Lingenfelter, R. E., S. J. Peale, and G. Shubert, 1968, Lunar rivers: Science, v. 161, p. 266–269.

MacDonald, G. J. F., 1965, Origin of the moon—dynamical considerations: New York Acad. Sci. Annals, v. 118, art. 20, p. 739–782.

McCrea, W. H., 1968, Cosmology after half a century: Science, v. 160, p. 1295–1299.

Öpik, E. J., 1969, The moon's surface: Ann. Rev. Astronomy and Geophysics, v. 7, p. 473–526.

Ringwood, A. E., 1966, Chemical evolution of the terrestrial planets: Geochim. et Cosmochim. Acta, v. 30, p. 41–104.

Sandage, A. R., 1956, The red-shift: Scientific American Offprint 240, 9 p.

———, 1968, The age of creation, *in* Science Year 1968: Chicago, Field Enterprises, p. 57–69.

Shoemaker, Eugene, 1964, The geology of the moon: Scientific American, Dec. 1964, p. 38–46.

Singer, S. F., 1967, Where did the moon come from? A new capture theory: Scientific Research (McGraw-Hill), Nov. 1967, p. 69–72.

Tammann, G. A., and Allan Sandage, 1968, The stellar content and distance of the Galaxy NGC #2403 in the M81 Group: Astrophys. Jour., v. 151, p. 825–860.

Urey, H. C., 1954, The origin of the earth, *in* Henry Faul, ed., Nuclear geology: New York, John Wiley and Sons, p. 355–371.

———, 1958, The early history of the solar system as indicated by meteorites: Chem. Soc. [London] Proc., March 1958, p. 67–78.

———, 1963, The origin and evolution of the solar system, *in* D. P. Le Galley, ed., Space science: New York, John Wiley and Sons, p. 123–168.

Wheeler, J. A., 1968, Our universe—the known and the unknown: Am. Scientist, v. 56, p. 1–20.

8

On the Evolution of Atoms, Stars and Galaxies

HARLOW SHAPLEY

1963

THE CREATION

Concerning the origin of the universe, two incomplete and not very satisfactory hypotheses have been seriously proposed and explored. In their present development one theory can be identified by associating it with the names of Georges Lemaître and George Gamow, and the other, with Hermann Bondi, Thomas Gold, and Fred Hoyle.

In dealing with such ancient, complicated, and mysterious matters as the origin of the universe, we are hardly concerning ourselves with science *in sensu strictu*. The subject is stained with metaphysics, religion, and mental aberrations.

To put it briefly, Canon Lemaître and his followers (there are not many of them) postulate an all-inclusive Primeval Atom, the radioactive bursting of which, some ten billion years ago, was the beginning of all material things. It is suggested that time and space also first appeared when the burst of the Primeval Atom inaugurated the expanding material universe. Immediately after the burst (Creation!) the now well-known natural laws took complete charge, and what is now observed in the macrocosmos and the microcosmos has been the *natural* development of the universe. The natural operations include (1) the observed scattering of the galaxies as a consequence of cosmic repulsion overriding gravitation, and (2) the creation of all the chemical atoms out of quanta of energy and out of the proton-electron-neutron-meson basic corpuscles.

The explosive creation hypothesis, without considerable refinement and protection by subhypotheses, gets into trouble with certain observations and with some theory. For example, many stars are much too young to have been born in the original outburst, though we can, of course, propose subsequent secondary bursts.

As to the alternate hypothesis, the proposers and their followers (and again we note that they are not numerous) solve the problem of the original creation by saying that there never

Chapter 4 of *The View From a Distant Star* by Harlow Shapley, © 1963 by Basic Books, Inc., Publishers, New York. Reprinted with permission of the author and publisher.

was an original creation. The universe we know, according to this hypothesis, had no beginning and presumably will have no end; it is in a "steady state," and although there are numerous small-scale and localized regressions and progressions (evolution), the universe as a whole does not continuously progress or regress.

This second interpretation also is not wholly satisfactory, and it, too, may perish under the onslaught of observational data. So far it has survived, but in a few years it may be of historical interest only. Currently one of its difficulties is with the preliminary evidence that the universe is now expanding less rapidly than a billion years ago. This evidence from Palomar's Hale telescope suggests a "pulsating" universe—one that alternately expands and contracts. If the indication of a slowing down of expansion stands up under further observation and calculation, the steady-state hypothesis may be withdrawn by its proposers, or drastically modified.

We appear, therefore, to be rather helpless with regard to explaining the origin of the universe. But once it is set going, we can do a little better at interpretation. Accepting the strong evidence of an expansion from a denser conglomeration of matter, we can say that the speed of scattering is a linear or nearly linear function of the distance from the observer, and the size of the Metagalaxy is a function of time. The rate is still under investigation. The temporarily accepted expansion speed at a million light-years distance is only some 20 miles a second, but at a hundred million light-years' distance it is 2,000 miles a second, and at a billion light-years, 20,000.

Is space infinite? Can the recession of galaxies exceed 186,000 miles a second—the velocity of light? Those questions call for extrapolations too large to make our guesses dependable. But advances in theory and observation should in a few years make the guessing less wild. Already the various theoretical cosmogonists give confident answers to cosmogonical questions; the answers, however, are rarely in agreement.

With bold advances in cosmogony we may in the future hear less of a Creator and more of such things as "anti-matter," "mirror worlds," and "closed space-time." Finality, however, may always elude us. That the whole universe evolves can be our reasonable deduction, but just why it evolves, or from where, or where to—the answers to those questions may be among the Unknowables.

THE HIGHER ALCHEMY IN STARS

The many kinds of atoms that constitute living and inanimate matter show no evidence at this time of growing in mass, no evidence of changing now from one atomic species to another, with the exception, of course, of the natural radioactivity of a few kinds of heavy atoms, such as uranium, thorium, and radium. But the natural radioactive change of radium into lead and helium, for example, is in itself a suggestion that under proper physical conditions other kinds of atoms might be transmuted. The medieval alchemists tried to change mercury into gold, but failed. They did not have at hand enough heat, or high enough atomic speeds. Our later cyclotrons have achieved such transmutation—established the higher alchemy.

The evidence that the masses of atoms of the heavy elements are integral multiples of the masses of lighter elements (when allowance is made for the isotope mixtures) naturally hints at the evolution of atoms—from simple to complex, from light to heavy. We agree that somewhere and at some time the organization of matter has evolved. If the evolution has not occurred on earth or in it, where has it occurred? And if not now, when?

There are those who believe, or at least suggest, that the birth of all the elements from simple hydrogen beginnings occurred at the time of the hypothetical burst of the hypothetical primeval atom. There would have been energy enough at that time and place. Such a theory of the evolution of matter would indicate that the elements may be all essentially of the same age.

In the beginning was the Word, it has been piously recorded, and I might venture that modern astrophysics suggests that the Word was hydrogen gas. In the very beginning, we say, were hydrogen atoms; of course there must have been something antecedent, but we are not wise enough to know what. Whence came these atoms of hydrogen, these atoms, 20,000,000,000,000 (and 66 additional zeros) in number—atoms that we now believe have been forged into the material make-up of the universe? What preceded their appearance, if anything? That is perhaps a question for metaphysics. The origin of origins is beyond astronomy. It is perhaps beyond philosophy, in the realm of the to us Unknowable.

Ordinary physics and astronomy suggest that *if* several billions of our years ago we had all that hydrogen and the natural physical laws, what we now see would have followed without the intervention of miracles, and without supernatural intercession. Gravitation, radiation, and eventually photosynthesis, genetics, and so forth—with operators such as these and the widely dispersed hydrogen atoms, the universe of galaxies, stars, planets, life, and man would have emerged—nothing supernatural required.

A most amazing scheme of evolution of the chemical elements, of which all matter is made, has recently emerged, thanks to erudite studies in astrophysics and nuclear physics. The evolution of the whole series of elements is concerned, from hydrogen and helium (the lightest atoms) through carbon, oxygen, iron, and three score other middle-weight atoms, to lead, radium, and the devil atom, uranium.

The interiors of the stars provide the locale of the atom building. High temperatures are required. Here on earth, and in the earth, there are no atomic mutations—except the natural radioactive breakdown of radium and some others into lead, helium, calcium, and argon. Not even the most elemental mutation, $4H = 1He + radiation$, occurs naturally on the earth, for it maintains no natural temperature high enough for that operation. The same holds for the other planets. Nor is it hot enough on the surface of the sun for the hydrogen burning, nor on the surface of other stars, nor in the diffuse nebulosities from which stars apparently are born.

To start the fusion involving hydrogen, helium and the heavier elements, we need temperatures in excess of ten millions degrees absolute. In the middle of the sun, such temperatures prevail—hot enough for the hydrogen-into-helium reaction, but not hot enough for the "cooking" of the heavier elements—not hot enough for the further steps in the evolution of complex inanimate matter. How were these heavier elements born? They appear to be built out of hydrogen "blocks"; the common carbon atom is exactly twelve times the hydrogen atom in weight; iron, 56 times; uranium, 238 times.

Our question to the cosmographer is: How are these heavier atomic structures evolved from simple hydrogen and helium?

Calculations show that at about ten or twelve million degrees the hydrogen fuel in average stars (like our sun) is gradually transformed into helium ashes. At densities above a thousand grams per cubic centimeter, and temperatures of one or two hundred million degrees in the nuclei of giant stars, the helium is transformed (burned) into the main isotopes of carbon, oxygen, and neon. And at temperatures from two to five billion degrees the nuclei of atoms like iron and nickel would be made. In quiet, quasi-stable, giant stars, however, such temperatures are not normally reached, even at the tremendously compressed centers.

But when a star blows up (nova and supernova) there is heat enough. Suppose the sun blew up and became a nova. Every year there are a score or so of such disasters in our star-populated galaxy. Something goes wrong with the control of the energy output. A star in such trouble suddenly increases its size and brightness. It blows off its outer atmospheric shells.

If the sun erupted into a nova, its brightness would increase, probably in a single day, to five or ten thousand times normal. The internal temperature would rise toward 100 million degrees, and some of the helium atoms, which had been born more calmly out of hydrogen, would be violently transformed into heavier elements. The explosion would scatter these new elements into space, as well as the helium and unburned hydrogen. From this scattered material eventually new stars would be formed, as a result of gravitational contraction and radiation pressure. The new-born stars would radiate with a higher central temperature, because the heavier elements would be involved. Such stars could then start again their risky lives where thermostatic controls may fail to function and novation again ensue.

Ordinary novae are not competent to do the synthesis of the heaviest elements. Their central temperatures are not hot enough. But here another violent operation enters—the supernova.

In the year 1054 A.D., a dazzling new light appeared in the sky—a star-like radiator which apparently outshone all others. The oriental astrologers made a record of it. It was visible in the daytime for a week or more and visible at night for a couple of years, but then it faded away from the sky and from the memory of man. Centuries later, in the same position among the constellations, a faint, small nebulosity was noticed. It was named the Crab Nebula because of its fancy shape. This nebula was not much unlike other well-known nebulosities, such as the famed one in the Sword of Orion. But closer examination with the photographic and spectropic tools of the astronomer showed that it was expanding, and at such a steady rate that, counting backward, we can accurately date its origin. The nebula is indeed the product of the explosion recorded in 1054—an explosion that actually occurred some 4,000 years before the supernova was first seen. It took about 40 centuries for the light from the explosion to reach the earth. This explosion was not a simple blowing off of the star's upper atmosphere but essentially its complete annihilation. The temperatures involved in the explosion are what astrophysicists would look for—a temperature source hot enough to cook the heavier elements.

The exploding supernova serves not only as a billion-degree oven for forming heavy atoms but also as an explosive agent for returning atomic material to interstellar space for subsequent star building. Also, much material is returned to space through the leaking of matter at the turbulent surfaces of supergiant reddish stars whose surface gravity is so weak (because of size) that rapidly moving atoms cannot be retained.

In summary, the evolution of matter appears to be a synthesis inside the stars of the heavy atoms out of hydrogen, which is accepted as the primordial, abundant, and simple No. 1 chemical element. The synthesizing agency is high temperature and the consequent intense radiation. The atoms that mutate from hydrogen into heavier species as a result of rising temperature reach iron as a goal of stability. In 10^x years hydrogen may approach exhaustion throughout the universe and iron rise to top abundance. (The exponent x is not small!)

Although the evolution of atoms is essentially a one-way building-up process, except for natural radioactivity, which breaks atoms down, a cyclic phenomenon is involved in stellar evolution. It consists of the continual gravitational forming of stars out of gas and dust, and the explosive transformation of unstable stars by supernovation back into dust and gas again.

The earliest stars must have been made almost wholly of hydrogen, with helium and perhaps a little of the oxygen group of elements appearing when the central temperatures were increased above 10 million degrees through the agency of gravitational compression. After a supernovation spreads some of the evolved star stuff into space again, "second generation" stars may form from this dust, which then contains some of the heavier elements as well as hydrogen. In time, some of these second-generation stars, it is surmised, go through the supernova operation and still heavier elements are synthesized by the higher temperatures, and again dispersed in space. Another generation of stars then arises and so on. Our sun may be a third-generation star, for it contains all kinds of heavy atoms.

Perhaps the details of the foregoing mixture of brave speculation, intricate calculation, and sound interpretation are prematurely proposed. Nevertheless, the evolution of matter in stellar interiors appears to be a proper deduction from current theory and observation.

GALACTIC EVOLUTION

The evidence for inorganic evolution at the galaxy level is clear. We know that there are many kinds of galaxies. A gross classification would mention the ellipsoidal systems, the spirals, and irregular galaxies like the Clouds of Magellan. A finer classification divides the spheroidals into eight subclasses, the spirals also into eight subclasses, and the irregulars into several ill-defined categories. But all galaxies have one thing in common: they are composed of stars. There is much local clustering of giant stars in the open-armed spirals and in the irregular galaxies, and in them is also much interstellar gas and dust.

Finer classifications of galaxies, involving their spectra, the amount of included smog, characteristics of the spiral arms, etc., can be set up; actually one might propose a separate class for nearly every galaxy, because exact duplicates seem to be very rare. It is possible to arrange the galaxies in a continuous series, according either to form or to spectrum, and the existence of such a series immediately suggests evolution.

Three other indicators of the progressive evolution of galaxies can be cited.

The first is that, since galaxies are star-composed, and, as already noted, starshine itself is necessarily an indication of stellar evolution, so galaxy shine must mean galactic evolution.

The second is that, so far as we have been able to measure them, the galaxies are found to be rotating around their central axes or nuclei, and the rotational speeds vary with distance from the axis. The consequent shearing action smooths out the clustering and tends to dissolve the spiral arms (in our galaxy as well as others). Therefore, the direction of evolutionary progress, I believe, is from the irregular galaxies and open-armed spirals toward the close-armed spirals and spheroidals. This, of course, means an evolution of form on the galactic level, and we do not see it as reversible.

The third indicator of galactic evolution is that supergiant stars are numerous in the open-armed spirals, and practically absent from the spheroidals. Such supergiants radiate away their mass so rapidly that in a few million years they will disappear, not to return. That again means evolution in the structure of galaxies, as well as in their light and mass—an evolution from spiral toward spheroidal. There is, however, a possibility that the dying supergiants are replaced by other supergiant stars, newly born from the generally present gas and dust.

Although no one questions the assertion that galaxies, the great cosmic units of the universe, evolve, to visualize the nature of their evolution we need much fuller knowledge of the changes in form, light, and internal motion, as a function of time.

The Metagalaxy as a whole is expanding, but we know of thousands of clusters of galaxies where cosmic repulsion has not yet dissolved the local gravitational organization. As mentioned earlier, our own galaxy is in such a group, along with the Magellanic Clouds, the Andromeda triplet, and a few others, all of which are not more than two or three million light-years distant. These groups of galaxies undoubtedly evolve, perhaps by slow dispersion, but at what rate we cannot say.

STELLAR EVOLUTION

Finally, a few words on the evidence of stellar evolution. Here also we are able to put practically all stars into various continuous series. For example, a *surface-temperature* series runs from about 3,000°C. to more than 30,000°C. —from cool reddish stars through yellow and greenish to hot bluish stars like the bright ones in Orion. In *size* a series runs from stars less than a tenth the volume of the sun to stars with a million times the sun's volume or more. In the *mean-density* series the variation is from the collapsed and degenerate white dwarfs, more than a thousand times the density of water, to the supergiant red stars, which are essentially vacua with mean densities only a millionth that of water. There is no question but that evolution, sometimes in strange ways, prevails along these three series.

It is our current belief, subject of course to modifications as the amount and strength of the evidence increases, that the white dwarfs, such as the companion of the bright star Sirius, are at the end of their careers—or rather, that they represent a major approach toward the extinction they may never quite reach.

The beginning of stars—that is, their birth out of radiation, dust, and gases—appears to be well represented by the lightless "globules" of matter in interstellar space. They can be detected only when they have bright diffuse nebulosity as a background. A few score of these photostars have been noted by Bart J.

Bok and others. In diameter the globules are very large, dwarfing the greatest supergiant red stars. But gravitational contraction is inevitable, and eventually their dimensions will shrink, their interiors heat up, energy of radiation will flow to the surface, and a faint reddish glow will herald the arrival of a new light in the firmament.

The stars, especially those in crowded regions and those deep in nebulosity, are subject to various vicissitudes. Some blow off their outer atmospheres and become novae; some blow up completely (supernovae). Some lose matter disastrously through centrifugal spilling out; the giant red stars slowly leak material into space. Rapidly rotating stars may fission into doubles or triples. Some apparently are born into loose gravitation-controlled groups like the Pleiades, and others into the spectacular tight globular clusters. Everywhere the stars and their systems are evolving, some growing heavier by meteorite capture, all losing mass through their radiation.

One of the vicissitudes of star life, which we have mentioned as inevitable and very common, is the birth of planets.

9

The Expansion of the Universe

JAMES A. COLEMAN
1963

THE DOPPLER EFFECT

The Einstein model and the other relativistic models of the universe were important in their time, but they are now mostly of historical interest because of a development which occurred in 1929. But the story of this development really goes back to 1842, when an Austrian physicist, Christian Doppler, discovered what is now known as the Doppler effect. This refers to the phenomenon that occurs when the source of a sound wave and an observer who hears it are either approaching or separating from each other.

The listener hears the pitch of the sound decrease—that is, the frequency of the note emitted is apparently lowered—when he and the source are separating. This explains the mournful wail of the old-fashioned steam locomotive as it passed and disappeared in the distance. Conversely, the listener hears the tone rise in pitch—that is, the frequency apparently increases—when the sound source and the listener have relative motion toward each other. By appropriate use of the mathematical formulas which apply, the velocities of the moving source and/or listener may be determined.

Doppler realized that the same phenomenon would also apply to alter the color of the light coming from moving objects. The physicist Fizeau showed, in 1848, that the wave lengths of spectral lines for moving sources are similarly altered. Since the frequency of a sound or light wave decreases when the source and the observer are separating the corresponding wave length increases, because the frequency and wave length are inversely proportional. Conversely, the wave length decreases when the source and the observer are approaching each other. The change in wave length is very small, however, except for relatively high velocities of separation and of approach.

It was the English astronomer Sir William Huggins (1824–1910) who realized that the Doppler effect could be used to determine the relative velocities of approach and separation of celestial bodies from us. Huggins announced, in 1868, that the star Sirius was receding from us at 29 miles a second. This marked the first application of the Doppler effect to obtaining velocities in astronomy. It was also a very difficult piece of research because there were no photographic techniques available at that time and Huggins had to depend on his visual acuity and excellent research ability.

It wasn't until the late 1800's that photography was adapted to astronomical problems and the spectra of celestial objects could be photographed and analyzed. Starting in 1912, V. M. Slipher of the Lowell Observatory determined the velocities of various nebulae. One of his first results showed that the Andromeda Nebula, the one nearest our own, was approaching us with a velocity of 125 miles a second. By 1917 he had determined the velocities of fifteen of the nearest nebulae, all of which were found to be receding with velocities up to 400 miles a second. In 1918 the 100-inch telescope at the Mt. Wilson Observatory was put into operation, and with it even higher velocities were measured. By 1922 Slipher had determined velocities of forty-two nebulae, with the highest being about 1,100 miles a second.

With the exception of two of these, of which the Andromeda Nebula was one, all of the velocities obtained were velocities of recession; that is, the various nebulae whose velocities were measured were running away from our solar system. This was surprising in itself because it was believed that the nebulae were distributed in a random manner throughout the universe, which, taken as a whole, was considered to be static. Consequently, all nebula velocities should be random velocities, and with a sufficiently high number of measurements, we should find just as many with components of velocity toward as away from us.

It was as if the universe were like a gas in a containing vessel. The container as a whole does not move—the analogy of the static universe—but the gas molecules inside have random velocities in all directions. If one were able to travel along with one of the gas molecules as the reference point "at rest," the relative velocities of the others would be randomly distributed, with half of them having velocity components toward the observer and half with components away.

Slipher's results were incomplete and gave no hint of the momentous discovery to come because he did not know the distances of the various nebulae whose velocities he had measured. In fact, it was not even known whether they were within our Milky Way Galaxy or beyond it. This question was taken up by the American astronomer Edwin P. Hubble (1889–1953) at the Mt. Wilson Observatory, beginning in 1923. The method he used for determining the distances was the one which had been developed by Harlow Shapley in 1917. The method employs the characteristics of what are called *Cepheid variables* (after the star Delta Cephei, one of the earliest discovered). These are stars which vary in brightness with periods up to forty-five days. They also possess the property that the longer the period the higher the luminosity of the star. The relationship can be expressed mathematically, and then by measuring the period the luminosity of the star can be determined. The difference between this and the brightness actually observed is due to the star's distance; and since the brightness of a star falls off inversely as the square of the distance, the distance can thus be determined.

One of the most important discoveries, announced in 1926, was that the apparent velocity of approach of 150 miles a second of the Andromeda Nebula is due to the fact that our galaxy is rotating such that the linear velocity of the sun about the galactic center is about 150 miles a second. When the apparent high velocity of approach of the Andromeda Nebula was corrected for this factor, its velocity of approach was only about 30 miles a second.

THE RED SHIFT AND HUBBLE'S LAW

The distances which Hubble obtained for the various nebulae whose velocities had been measured by Slipher and others up to 1929 were truly phenomenal for that time. The largest distance was 6.5 million light years. Furthermore, he proved conclusively that the various nebulae were separate galaxies of stars far removed from our own galaxy. (These nebulae are now more frequently called galaxies.) The Andromeda Galaxy was found to be about 700,000 light years distant. (Today this distance is believed to be about 1,500,000 light years as a result of subsequent changes in the astronomical distance scale.) The belief, held by many astronomers, that the universe is made up of islands of stars was now firmly established.

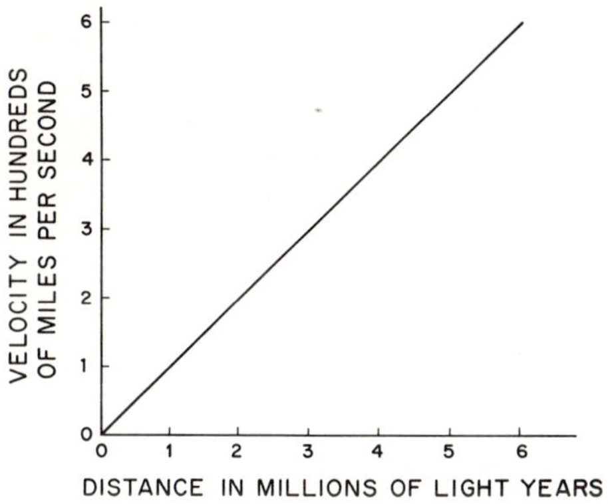

FIGURE 9.1
Hubble's law

Hubble's really great contribution to astronomy and cosmology was his discovery, which he announced in 1929, that the distant galaxies were receding from us with velocities proportional to their distance. The farther away a galaxy was, the higher was its velocity. The velocity of a galaxy, or group of galaxies, at any distance was twice that of a galaxy at half the distance. Now known as *Hubble's law*, the relation is illustrated in Figure 9.1. Hubble's law stated as an equation is

$$v = Hr$$

where v is the velocity of the galaxy, r its distance, and H the proportionality constant known as *Hubble's constant*. The equation is that of a straight line with H the slope of the line shown in Figure 9.1. H specifies the rate at which the velocity increases with distance. Hubble originally found this to be about 100 miles a second per million light years. Thus, for every million light years distant from us (a total distance of about 6 billion billion miles) the velocity of recession increases by 100 miles a second.

In obtaining this result a model had to be assumed for the universe. The most logical one to assume is that the universe is, on the whole, homogeneous. Not only is this in keeping with the reasoning behind the cosmological principle, but for obvious reasons such an assumption is almost necessary in treating the universe mathematically. For a universe which is not assumed to be homogeneous, Hubble's constant would be different.

The actual method used in obtaining the velocities of recession is to photograph the spectrum of the galaxy of interest. Now, the spectrum of a distant star or galaxy usually contains lines by means of which the predominant elements which compose the spectrum can be identified. Each of these lines has a definite wave length which is known to a high degree of precision. In the light from a receding galaxy the wave lengths of the lines, when measured, are found to be increased toward the red end of the spectrum, corresponding to an increase in wave length of the emitted light. The amount of the *red shift* is thus a measure of the velocity of recession of the source. The formula governing the phenomenon is given approximately by

$$v = \frac{\Delta\lambda}{\lambda} c$$

where $\Delta\lambda$ is the change in wave length, λ the original wave length, and c the velocity of light.

The physical interpretation of the recession of the galaxies is much broader than the mere recognition of separation of the galaxies. It is the entire universe which is expanding, and the effect is referred to as the universal expansion. It is as though the space between the galaxies and clusters of galaxies is itself expanding, with the galaxies being carried along with it like clouds in a windy sky. Space is no longer considered as a vast nothingness devoid of all being but now assumes a dynamic role as the main "stuff" of the universe with an occasional intrusion by material matter. The galaxies themselves do not expand—that is, the stars within the galaxies do not recede from each other; in fact, many clusters of galaxies behave as a single entity and move as a unit. Galaxies in these clusters do not recede from each other, either. It is as if the gravitational attraction between the various galaxies in the cluster were stronger than the universal expansion.

Recognizing the desirability of extensive verification of Hubble's law for distances considerably beyond the limited region of space which Slipher and Hubble had explored, an extensive program for measuring velocities and distances to the extreme limit of the 100-inch telescope at Mt. Wilson Observatory was carried out by Milton Humason starting in 1928. By 1935 he had added 150 new velocities covering distances out to about 240 million light years with a maximum velocity of about 26,000 miles a second, or about one-seventh the velocity of light.

With the beginning of operation of the 200-inch telescope at the Mt. Palomar Observatory in 1949 a considerably extended region of the observable universe was available for exploration. The velocities and distances measured have been increased correspondingly. But other changes, too, have occurred. The scale by which the distances of the various galaxies have been measured has been found to be in error. In particular, Hubble's distance scale was several times too short, that is, the actual distances have been found to be several times greater than originally believed. The net result is that the distance rate of expansion, Hubble's constant, is now believed to be about 14 miles a second per million light years.

With the help of the 200-inch telescope the largest velocity determined by Humason was that of two galaxies in the Hydra cluster—about 38,000 miles a second, or about one-fifth the velocity of light. In 1956 Baum obtained a velocity of about 75,000 miles a second, or two-fifths the velocity of light. And in 1960 R. Minkowski obtained a velocity of about 86,000 miles a second, or about .46 of the velocity of light, for what may be two galaxies in collision. The distance corresponding to this highest velocity yet obtained can be determined from Hubble's law using the present accepted value for H; the result is 6 billion light years. These galaxies collided (if it was a collision of two galaxies) 6 billion years ago, and it is only now that the light waves from this event are reaching us. These galaxies may not even be in existence now!

So far we have discussed the red shift as detected in optical telescopes, wherein the wave lengths of the light exhibiting the phenomenon lie in the range from about .3 to .6 of a millionth of a centimeter. It had long been recognized that a convincing proof of the red shift as due to the Doppler effect would be to show that radiation of markedly different wave lengths, either shorter or longer, also evinced the effect. An excellent opportunity presented itself with the development of radio astronomy. Here, the ideal wave length for astronomical investigations is 21 centimeters, or about 8 inches.

In 1956 A. E. Lilley and E. F. McLain, at the U.S. Naval Research Laboratory in Washington, investigated the red shift for Cygnus A, a source of radiation which may also be the result of the collision of two galaxies. The red shift in the optical part of the spectrum indicated a velocity of recession of 16,800 kilometers a second. When Lilley and McLain measured the wave length of the spectrum line normally located at 21.1 cm. they found it was lengthened to 22.3 cm., a shift of over 1.2 centimeters. The corresponding velocity of recession was about 16,700 kilometers a second. This lends considerable support to the red shift as a Doppler effect and the reality of the universal expansion.

Further verification of the red shift in the radio region and its agreement with the photographic results of the optical region has also been made since 1956 by other investigators in radio astronomy. The ability of radio telescopes to "see" beyond the range of the 200-inch optical telescope has in recent years raised the exciting possibility that the universal expansion can be investigated right on out to the very limits of the observable universe.

OTHER INTERPRETATIONS OF THE RED SHIFT

So far we have assumed that the spectral red shifts of distant galaxies and clusters of galaxies actually do represent velocities as a manifestation of the Doppler effect. Is this necessarily true? That is, could any other interpretation be placed on the red shifts? The only other suggestion which has received serious consideration is that the light loses its energy by some mechanism during its passage through through the vast reaches of space on its way to us. And since the wave length of the light photons is inversely proportional to their energy the wave length would increase as the energy decreases. Thus, the wave length would shift to the red end of the spectrum to produce the red shift. This theory of "tired light" is rejected by most astronomers because it would necessitate an entirely new principle of physics which has no other support. Moreover, one cannot ignore the interpretation of the Doppler shift as a manifestation of a velocity effect since the same phenomenon is used, among other things, to determine the rotational period of Jupiter and to study the motions of double star systems, with the results being confirmed by other supporting evidence. It is generally agreed among astronomers that the red shifts of the spectra of distant galaxies and clusters of galaxies do indeed indicate velocities of recession.

But what causes the universal expansion? The subtleties of the answer are inextricably intertwined with the two main contemporary theories of the universe which we will consider in later chapters. However, a complete discussion of the possibilities must include two general possibilities, either or both of which could produce the observed expansion. The first, and most obvious, is that at the very beginning (if we assume that the universe began at a definite starting time in the past) an infinite explosive force was unleashed which started all of the physical matter of the universe flying apart. It would be as if the universe as a whole were like a huge cosmic bomb detonated at time $t = 0$, the start of all physical being and reality, with the explosion having continued ever since. The universal expansion observed today would then be the remnants of this explosion of the universe. But this possibility represents the epitome of the evolutionary theory, which we will discuss in detail later.

The other possible general explanation for the universal expansion ascribes it to some present "built-in" property of the universe. Just as gravitational attraction is a universal property of matter itself, so, too, some form of "cosmic repulsion" may also be an intrinsic property of matter. This idea was an integral part of many of the earlier cosmological theories. As we have seen, Einstein's model of the universe as being finite and unbounded was based on the universe being static, since the fact that the universe is expanding was not known at that time. A static universe would tend to collapse because of the mutual gravitational attraction of its contents. The cosmic repulsion was hypothesized as an artifact to "hold back the wall" of gravitational collapse. The amount of the cosmic repulsion was just sufficient to counteract the gravitational attraction. Without the cosmic repulsion Einstein's mathematics, which conformed to a static universe, would not have applied to the real universe as it appeared to be at that time.

One theory which has a certain degree of plausibility is that the gravitational attraction weakens at great distances at a much faster rate than inversely as the square of the distance. While the ordinary law of gravitation as discovered by Newton and later slightly modified by Einstein does fit the solar system perfectly, the distances involved here are of the order of millions to hundreds of millions of miles. It may very well be that for distances between the galaxies—distances over a million times those of the diameter of the solar system—the gravitational attraction, if it exists at all, would obey a law completely different from Newton's law of gravitation as we now know it. It is entirely possible that at these large distances the force between galaxies is repulsive. This would provide a natural physical law for a smooth and continuous process of expansion without the need for an original super-explosion. Such a continuous process with neither a beginning nor an end is the essence of the steady-state theory, also to be discussed in detail later.

This possibility, though appearing highly speculative on the surface, does have an analogue in our smaller everyday world. At the opposite end of the macroscopic scale of the universe lies the microscopic and submicroscopic scale of the atomic world. The forces between the particles of atomic nuclei are very peculiar in comparison with those of the everyday world. In the latter the forces between electrostatic charges and magnetic poles vary inversely as the square of the distance, just as the force in Newton's law of gravitation does. But between the constituents of nuclei of atoms the forces are attractive out to certain distances and then become repulsive. Other peculiar properties of these forces are even more odd—so odd, in fact, that they defy description in terms of ordinary algebraic equations. To suggest that gravitational forces weaken faster than inversely as the square of the distance for very large distances or that they even become repulsive at greater distances is not to defy credulity but rather to partake of real possibilities that might exist as evinced by the transition from the everyday world to the atomic domain.

Unfortunately, not only does astronomy not give any really convincing reason for a weakening of the gravitational force with distance, but the ways in which it could conceivably change are many; and it would be difficult to choose the one most likely to be correct from the myriads of possibilities. Then, too, an acceptance of a variation in the law of gravitation as an explanation for the universal expansion would preclude serious consideration of other theories, such as the evolutionary theory. So, from a purely philosophical point of view, not to mention the many subtle scientific points involved which cannot be discussed here, the possibility of a cosmic repulsion as a serious explanation for the universal expansion is, on the whole, currently considered to be pure speculation. This view may, of course, change in time in the light of new discoveries.

A novel possibility to account for the universal expansion was the suggestion in 1959 by the English mathematicians Raymond A. Lyttleton of Cambridge University and Hermann Bondi of the University of London that the charge of the proton was not exactly equal in magnitude (though still opposite in sign) to that of the electron but was slightly greater. If this is true, the universal expansion would be due to the many, many protons in the universe exerting their excess charge to repel each other. Due to the large number of protons in the universe, the excess charge would only have to be very slight (about one part in a billion billion) to cause the observed expansion.

The charge of the proton and that of the electron have always been assumed to be equal numerically, but this had never been proven experimentally to the degree called for by Lyttleton's and Bondi's suggestion. The experiment was carried out in 1960 by J. C. Zorn, G. E. Chamberlain, and V. W. Hughes, physicist at Yale University, and they found that no difference in charge between the proton and electron exists to within even one-fifth of that required by the theory.

THE MILNE THEORY

A refreshingly original theory which, as one of its results, interpreted the red shifts not as a velocity effect but rather as due to a change in the rate of flow of time was that of the British astronomer E. A. Milne (1896–1950). Starting in 1932, he developed a completely new system of cosmology which was not based primarily on relativity, although some of the results of relativity were an integral part of it. In fact, Milne showed that the various expanding world models of relativistic cosmology had analogues using only the classical physics of Newton. Milne based his work on certain general hypotheses and called the resultant theory *kinematic relativity* to distinguish it from Einstein's theory of relativity. Milne's ideas are important in the history of cosmology not only because of the added insight into the universe which they supplied but because they may eventually prove to be correct.

Since by 1932 it had become firmly established that the universe was not static but was expanding, Milne concerned himself only with an expanding universe. He assumed space to be Euclidean throughout, since he did not consider it necessary to introduce the mathematical concepts of non-Euclidean space into a physical model of the universe. He did retain the assumptions of previous investigators regarding the homogeneity and isotropy of the universe but lumped them together into one basic assumption called the *cosmological principle*. This says that for all observers *everywhere* the universe appears the same now as in its past history.

Milne treated the universe as similar to a group of a great many particles originally distributed at random in a very small region of space. They are all moving with uniform velocities but in different directions. Individual particles which fly away from the group are pulled back by gravitational attraction. For a sufficiently high average particle velocity the group as a whole expands, the mutual gravitational attraction diminishes, and the group ultimately acts as a system of separate particles expanding outward radially, the separation distance between any two particles being proportional to the time of the expansion.

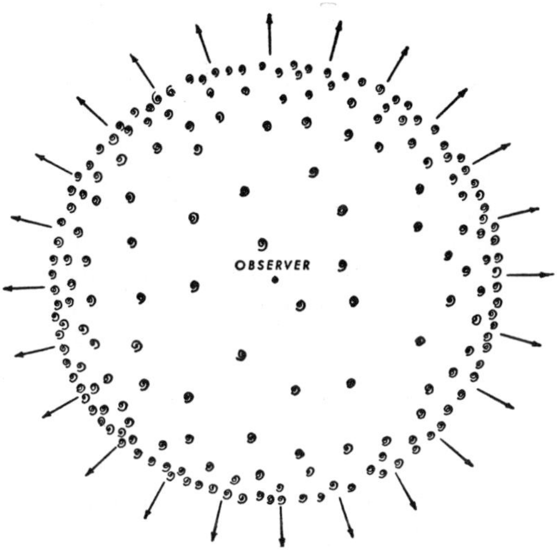

FIGURE 9.2
Milne's picture of the universe in atomic time

In our own universe the galaxies correspond to the particles, and, according to Milne, the view of an observer *anywhere* in the universe would correspond to Figure 9.2. The universe is contained in an expanding sphere of Euclidean space whose outermost shell moves outward radially at the highest velocity because it is at the farthest distance from the observer (at the center) and has been moving the longest time. The highest velocity at the edge is equal to that of light because the Special Theory of relativity predicts this to be the highest measurable velocity for a material object. The expanding radius of this universe is then equal to the velocity of light times the total time of the expansion. Since the galaxies, like the particles, keep increasing their velocity but cannot go beyond that of light, they will be bunched together at the spherical surface of the universe. The drawing shows what an observer would see *if* he could actually see the galaxies at the edge.

The main contribution of Milne to cosmology was his later suggestion that the rate of flow of time may have changed through the years. Einstein had married time to space, but he, like everyone else, had always assumed that the processes whereby we measure time, and hence time itself, did not change. Milne emphasized that there are two kinds of time in the universe. One of these is given by the rate of rotation of the earth on its axis, a swinging pendulum, the revolution of the moon about the earth, the revolution of the earth about the sun, etc. This time of the macroscopic world which we use every day he called *clock time*. The other governs the phenomena of the atomic world and is related to the frequencies of spectral lines from "vibrating atoms," radioactive decay rates of nuclei, etc. This latter he called *atomic time*. We ordinarily use both these times interchangeably and assume that their rates were the same in the past. But are they really? Could they not have been slowing down or speeding up relative to each other since the universe began?

Milne found a convincing reason to show that the two types of time have not been uniform in the past. He was able to construct a model of the universe which was *static* but which also agreed with the observational data that indicated the universe was expanding *provided* that clock time is slowing down relative to atomic time. In the past the "clock year" has been shorter than the "atomic year," and in the future it will be longer. (They are defined to be equal at the present time.) Or, since the decision as to which of the two times we should call the "correct" one is completely arbitrary, we can say that the atomic year has been longer than the clock year in the past but will be shorter in the future.

The relation between the two times is a very precise one and is contained in an equation deduced by Milne. If we use atomic time as the correct time and if the clock year in the past was shorter than it is now, then a period of time stretching into the past will contain many more clock years than atomic years. In particular, if we take a stretch of atomic time equal to the present accepted age of the universe (about 10 to 13 billion years), we obtain an infinite number for the age of the universe on the clock time scale. Thus, according to clock time and the theory, the universe has been here an infinite length of time.

Another important result of the theory and

the deduced disparity between atomic time and clock time is that the universe is not expanding at all but is static. When we look far out into space we see galaxies whose light left them many years ago. Consider a particular galaxy, at a distance of, say, a million light years. The light from this galaxy by which we see it left it about a million years ago. (This is one reason why we use light years as a measure for the distances of galaxies.) What we see, then, is not what the galaxy looks like today (in fact, it may not even be there today) but what it looked like a million years ago. The light from such a galaxy, then, would have been generated a million years ago.

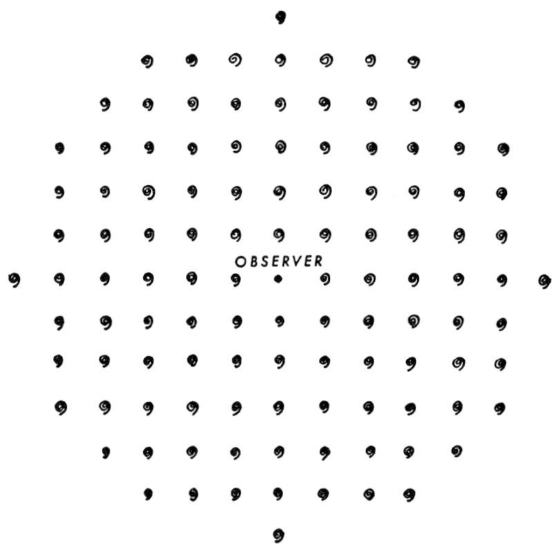

FIGURE 9.3
Milne's picture of the universe in clock time

Now, according to the Milne theory atomic time has been slower than clock time in the past. But since atomic time refers to the vibrations of atoms, this means that these were slower in the past and the frequencies of the light emitted by these atoms was therefore lower. The corresponding wave lengths of the emitted light would be longer, since the wave lengths of low-frequency vibrations or waves are longer than those of high frequency. We would thus expect that the light from the older, more distant galaxies would be shifted toward the red, or longer, wave-length end of the spectrum. And the more distant the galaxy the greater the expected red shift, in direct proportion to the distance. This is precisely what is observed as Hubble's law. Milne's theory, then, explains Hubble's law, ordinarily quoted as proof of an *expanding* universe, in terms of a *static* universe.

A representation of the universe in the clock time of the Milne theory is shown in Figure 9.3. The universe is now static, with the galaxies evenly distributed. We cannot really see an edge now because of the excessively long wave lengths, or extreme red shift, of the emitted light. Physically, the region near the edge would correspond to galaxies many, many years old, when atomic time was moving so slowly in comparison with clock time that the atoms in these galaxies did not vibrate fast enough to generate sufficient energy in the form of light waves to reach us. And at the edge itself time would stand still, which means that nothing would be there, since no material object can exist without time. The edge, then, is really a gradual fading away to a nothingness of nonexistence. Furthermore, we must also remember that the view as seen by us in our galaxy would be the same as that seen by an observer *anywhere* in this infinite, unbounded universe.

The real test of Milne's theory is whether or not clock time is *really* slowing down relative to atomic time or, conversely, whether atomic time is speeding up relative to clock time. This would be manifested by a standard spectral line in the laboratory having its frequency increase by one part in about 13 billion per year. Such precision measurement should be possible in the not too distant future using the precise time-comparison techniques being made possible with masers but a thorough discussion of this exciting possibility is beyond the scope of this book.

THE LIMIT OF THE OBSERVABLE UNIVERSE

Assuming strict linearity of Hubble's law, what can we expect to "see" as we build better optical and radio telescopes and keep extending their ranges out into the vast reaches of space? Hubble's law appears to say that as we increase our range of exploration the velocities of the outermost galaxies will be higher and that we will ultimately observe velocities for these outermost galaxies equal to or greater than that of light. Is this true?

No, it isn't. Not only because Hubble's law is not valid for velocities close to that of light (because of the universe model assumed) but because of another effect connected with a moving source of light. Consider two galaxies which are both of the same intrinsic brightness and which are also at the same distance from the earth originally except that one is moving away from the earth while the other is at rest relative to the earth. If we on earth measured the intensity of the light from each, we would find that from the receding galaxy to be weaker. The higher the velocity of recession of the receding galaxy the weaker the light received here on earth would be. And, in fact, theory predicts that as the velocity of the moving galaxy approaches that of light the intensity of the light reaching the earth would approach zero!

In other words, we would not receive any light at all from a galaxy receding with the velocity of light (assuming this were possible), and it would disappear completely. (The Special Theory of relativity also predicts the disappearance of an object as its velocity approaches that of light but the contraction is in the direction of motion. Here, however, the galaxy is being observed by its dimension perpendicular to the direction of motion, which does not change.) For us, such a galaxy wouldn't even exist! The distance at which the galaxies would be expected to attain the velocity of light thus represents the limit of our observable universe.

We can use Hubble's law to obtain a rough estimate of the limit of the observable universe by solving the equation for the distance when the velocity of light, 186,000 miles a second, is inserted. The result is called the *Hubble radius* of the universe and is about 13 billion light years, or about 76,000,000,000,000,000,000,000 miles. This represents the distance beyond which it is absolutely impossible for us now or ever to see or penetrate physically in any way (unless the laws of physics change). At this distance an inky blackness of nothingness surrounds us and limits our universe.

The edge is not a sharp one like an opaque wall around a yard; the observable universe gradually fades in intensity throughout the entire distance from the earth to the radius at which no light reaches us from any celestial objects which may be at or near the limit. It can be compared with a brightly lit yard at nighttime without a boundary. The surrounding land is gradually less and less illuminated with increasing distance from the lights until a point is reached where the illumination is not detectable, but it would be difficult to define the distance precisely.

The expansion of the universe answers a question originally asked by a German astronomer, Heinrich Olbers, in 1826. Now known as *Olbers' paradox*, the question deals with the total radiation we would expect to receive on earth, or at any other place in the universe, from all of the stars in the universe.

The radiation we receive from any one star depends not only on the energy radiated by the star but also on its distance from us. The greater the distance the less is the radiation received—or, stating the relation mathematically, the radiation received varies inversely as the square of the distance. Even though a star may be very, very far away we always receive some radiation from it, however slight.

Now, if the universe extends a very great distance out into space it will contain many, many stars, and each one of these will have some of its radiation intercepted by the earth, providing intervening stars and other celestial material do not mask the radiation completely. While the average density of matter in the universe is quite small, corresponding to an average distance of about 10 light years between stars, one would ultimately intercept a star in every possible direction in traveling radially outward away from the earth.

The situation is roughly comparable to that which exists in a thick forest. In looking up from the ground toward the tops of the trees one's view of the sky above at any point or in any direction is blocked by one or more leaves. Similarly, one's view in any direction outward away from the earth is ultimately blocked by a star.

In the forest the leaf cover prevents light from entering and in the extreme case would make the area under the trees completely dark. For the earth the "star cover" acts in the opposite manner and prevents the stellar radiation from escaping beyond. The net result is that the total radiation received at the earth is expected to be very large. If this reasoning is correct, the night sky would never be dark but would always be lit up by the accumulated radiation in the form of light from the stars. But even more important is the fact that the stellar radiation represents energy which would act to heat up the earth, with the result that, after a sufficient length of time, the earth would be almost as hot as a star.

Why, then, is the sky dark at night and not luminous, and why, especially, has the earth not been heated to incandescence long before this? This is the statement of Olbers' paradox.

The answer is not that interstellar dust and other material intersects the incoming stellar radiation and absorbs it. While this would help for a time, all intersecting matter would itself be heated to incandescence ultimately and would reradiate the energy originally absorbed. There is no way by which the earth could be protected indefinitely from the impinging radiation. The situation is similar to what happens to an object completely surrounded by fire. Although it could be insulated against the surrounding radiation for a time, it would ultimately attain a temperature close to that of the surrounding flame.

Olbers did not know the answer to the paradox, and his question was forgotten. Today we know the answer. It is because of the weakening of the stellar radiation received here due to the expansion of the universe. As explained above, the higher the velocity of a distant galaxy, the weaker is the radiation received from it; and since the distant galaxies move with successively higher velocities, the farther they are from the earth the less is the fraction of their radiated light which we receive here. And from galaxies at the edge of the universe whose velocities are presumably equal to that of light we would not receive any radiation at all.

Thus, the total radiation received here on earth from all stars within the observable universe is finite, and we are not completely enclosed within an infinitely large radiation shell. And since the earth can reradiate all impinging radiation back into space, the radiation does not accumulate to raise the earth's temperature beyond an intolerable degree.

The point raised by Olbers provides additional confirmation for the expansion of the universe. One can safely conclude that if the universe were not expanding, there would be no life on earth or anywhere else in the universe, because the universe would be at a very high temperature throughout. No planet anywhere in the universe would be cool enough to permit biological life of any kind. An expanding universe, then, is the only one possible for the existence of man and life in general.

Since these rather elementary considerations show that a universal expansion is necessary for the existence of man, the universal expansion should have been predicted long before it was observed. If it were, our knowledge of the universe would undoubtedly be considerably greater than it is today.

10

Recent Developments in Cosmology

FRED HOYLE
1965

I shall start from the observed shift of the spectrum lines of galaxies interpreted in terms of the expansion of the universe. The red shift implies that distances between galaxies, measured with an imaginary ruler for example, increase with time. An immediate question is whether the universe was denser in the past than it is to-day. If so, how much denser was the universe?

A definitive answer to this critical problem could be obtained in principle by observing the state of the universe in the past. This is possible because of the finite speed of light. We do not observe a galaxy as it is now but as it was at the moment the light started on its journey. In the case of very distant galaxies the light started several billion years ago, so we have direct evidence of the state of affairs several billion years ago. All that need be done, again in principle, is to observe the density of galaxies as it was a few billion years ago and to compare it with the density in our immediate neighbourhood. This would be a direct way of settling the density problem. This indeed was the way in which Hubble tried to settle it more than thirty years ago. He failed to do so because of the extreme difficulty of making a fair count of distant galaxies. The tendency is to count the brighter galaxies but to miss the fainter ones. Since Hubble's attempt nobody has had the hardihood to make a direct assault on the problem by attempting to count galaxies.

Ryle and his associated have counted radio sources instead of galaxies, and here the result has turned out to be much more clear-cut, at any rate so far as the counting process itself is concerned. The difficulty with radio sources is that we are still far from sure exactly what it is that is being counted. Developments in the past two years, the discovery of the quasi-stellar sources in particular, have shown the situation to be more complex than it was at first thought to be. The indication of the radio counts is that the universe was more dense in the past than it is to-day. However, further knowledge is needed concerning the nature of

From *Nature*, vol. 208, pp. 111–114, 1965. Reprinted with permission of the author and Macmillan (Journals) Ltd.

the radio sources before this conclusion can be regarded as definitive.

If the quasi-stellar objects are truly cosmological a great deal becomes pretty well settled. Imagine an object of fixed intrinsic brightness to be moved to increasingly great distances. Two things will happen. The apparent luminosity of the object will decrease and the red-shift of the spectrum lines will increase. A theoretical relation between these quantities can be determined for any specified cosmological theory. The relation is different in different theories, so that in principle it would be possible to distinguish between one cosmological theory and another if we could experiment in this way with a standard object of fixed brightness. Unfortunately it is impossible to move a single object to increasing distances; so the astronomer must rely on similar objects just happening to lie at different distances. The question then arises of how sure we can be that the objects are really similar to each other. Massive galaxies do seem to be quite remarkably similar, but the theoretical differences we are looking for are rather slight in the case of galaxies. This is because galaxies, even the brightest galaxies, cannot be observed far enough away for the theoretical differences to be more than slight. At greater distances the theoretical differences become much more appreciable, however. The technical problem is that of photographing spectrum lines when the light intensity is very small. What is needed is more light. It is here that the quasi-stellar sources are of critical importance. Accepting for the moment that the red-shift of the spectrum lines in these sources is cosmological in character, the quasi-stellar sources are brighter than the most massive galaxies by about four magnitudes, a factor of about forty.

At present, red-shift measurements are available for about fifteen quasi-stellar objects. The shifts are dimensionless numbers given by dividing the wave-length shift of any spectrum line by the laboratory wave-length of the same line. The result is the same for all lines. The measured values range from quite small values, for example 0.16 for 3C 273, up to the enormous value of 2 for the source 3C 9. The theoretical differences become quite large for red-shifts as great as this, so that a distinction between different cosmological theories should be straightforward once a sample of the order of a hundred quasi-stellar objects has been obtained. The present indication based on the small sample of fifteen is that the universe has expanded from a state of higher density, although the statistical scatter in the sample is large enough to be comparable to the effects that are being looked for.

For spectral shifts as large as two, the Lyman-α line is displaced from the unobservable ultra-violet into the blue, at about 3700 A. It is possible to look for a continuum on the blue-ward side of Lyman-α. This continuum is subject to asborption by neutral hydrogen atoms in intergalactic space. A very small density of neutral atoms would be sufficient to absorb out the light completely. Schmidt's observation of 3C 9 shows the continuum to be present but to be weakened, that is, to be lower than the continuum on the redward side of Lyman-α. The implication is that intergalactic gas, if it exists, must be hot, perhaps above 10^6 °K. The weakening of the continuum is rather strange, for in a sensitive situation like this one would expect either the continuum to be essentially unweakened or to be absent. The intermediate case seems *a priori* unlikely, since it depends on a closely defined value of the hydrogen density. It is rather in the nature of a coincidence that the density has this critical value.

These remarks are all subject to a cosmological interpretation of the red-shift of the spectrum lines of the quasi-stellar objects. If much smaller, fainter objects were fired out of our own galaxy, or out of some neighbouring galaxy, with speeds close to light the same red-shifts would be observed. Can we be sure that such a 'local' interpretation is wrong?

Even though on a 'local' hypothesis the quasi-stellars are much less spectacular objects, the total mass involved in all such objects must be as high as $10^6 M_\odot$, or perhaps even more. For such a quantity of matter ejected at speeds close to light, the kinetic energy must be comparable with the rest mass energy, 10^{60} ergs. This is of a similar order of magnitude to the energy involved in the outburst of a major radio galaxy. The energy in the latter case is also in the form of particle motions. The difference is that the particles in the radio galaxies have been thought of in the past as occupying large volumes, not as being condensed into compact objects. However, we now have to ask whether a radio galaxy may not eject compact pieces as well as diffuse clouds of high-speed particles.

Radio galaxies do not eject their material with an initial isotropy. The typical pattern is of two centres of radio emission on opposite sides of a galaxy, with the two centres and the nucleus of the galaxy more or less colinear. To me personally, this has always suggested that an object in the nucleus of the galaxy separates violently into two pieces with a large relative motion. The colinear property then follows from conservation of momentum. Exactly the same phenomenon is observed in the quasi-stellar source *MH* 14–121, two regions of radio emission on opposite sides of, and colinear with, a centre of optical emission. The possibility must be considered that a cascade process is involved. An initial object in the centre of a galaxy breaks violently into two pieces. Later, each of these pieces breaks into two further pieces; and so on. As the cascade develops, and as the objects spread out from the parent galaxy, an approximation to an isotropic situation would then gradually develop.

From independent evidence it has been suggested that an explosion occurred in the nucleus of our own galaxy about ten million years ago. If the quasi-stellar objects emerged in this explosion, as Terrell has suggested, the brightest of the objects, 3C 273, would now be distant about 0.5 million parsecs, about one-thousandth of the cosmological distance. The optical emission, instead of the enormous cosmological value of 10^{46} ergs sec^{-1}, would be 10^{40} ergs sec^{-1}. The burning of some 300 solar masses of hydrogen gives sufficient energy to supply such an output for as long as ten million years. Since the mass of 3C 273 could be set as $10^4 M_{\odot}$ there would seem to be no difficulty in explaining the optical output. The kinetic energy of 3C 273 would then be $\sim 10^{56}$ ergs, about one order of magnitude less than the total energy of the galactic explosion, as estimated by Burbidge and Hoyle. The masses of other quasi-stellar objects can be set lower than 3C 273, because 3C 273 is intrinsically considerably brighter than the others, at any rate for the sources so far observed. Setting $10^3 M_{\odot}$ as the mass per object, and taking the mean speed as half the velocity of light, the kinetic energy per object is comparable with that of 3C 273. The total energy estimated by Burbidge and Hoyle, 10^{57} ergs, would provide only for ~ 10 objects. It would seem therefore that either Burbidge and Hoyle underestimated the violence of the galactic explosion, or an energy difficulty arises.

The same difficulty does not arise in the case of the galaxy *NGC* 5128. This is a nearby massive elliptical, distant about four million parsec. At least one major outburst is known to have occurred in the nucleus of this galaxy within the past ten million years. The probability must also be considered that both *NGC* 5128 and our galaxy are involved, with our galaxy contributing the comparatively low-speed objects and *NGC* 5128 contributing the high-speed objects.

These questions can undoubtedly be resolved by observation. Observations leading to size estimates for the quasi-stellar objects are coming along with rapidly mounting impetus. The light from 3C 273 has been known to be variable in a characteristic time of about ten years. This sets the maximum radius of the optical object at ten light years. In addition, rapid flashes in the light over only a few weeks have been suggested. Largely because the maximum radius would have to be reduced to a tenth of a light-year, or even less, there has been a disposition not to believe this evidence in the case of 3C 273. On the cosmological hypothesis, how can one have an optical emission a hundred times brighter than the most luminous galaxies pouring out of an object only a tenth of a light-year in diameter? The issue appears to have been resolved by a recent observation of a doubling of the light of a quasi-stellar source in less than a month.

On the radio side, fluctuations from 3C 273 have been found, first by Dent and more recently by Moffet and Maltby. The radio data set stronger constraints than the optical data, particularly for the cosmological theory. The present state of the argument is that the cosmological theory just survives the existing data. Whether it will continue to do so remains to be seen. My judgment of the situation is that survival for the cosmological theory depends on there being a sharp saturation in the accumulation of fluctuation data, that not much more in the way of fluctuations can be tolerated. If we are already near the end of the road, the theory will survive and will then probably turn out the correct theory. But if we are still near the beginning of the road, the prospects for the theory will be slight. I would say we have to do with a fifty-fifty situation.

I would like to turn now to quite different issues; but still bearing on the question I asked at the beginning: Has the universe emerged from a more dense state? The kinds of observation I have discussed so far all relate to great distances. Observations can be made in our own neighbourhood which also bear on the problem. I am now going to describe three such observations, together with the related arguments. The three are utterly different in character, illustrating how wide are the issues in cosmology, and how very many phenomena have to be made to fit into a consistent picture.

Recently, Penzias and Wilson have observed a radio background at a wave-length of about 7 cm, which they do not believe to be due to their equipment or to the nearby terrestrial environment. The intensity is between 10 and 100 times greater than can be attributed to radio sources. The suggestion is that the universe has a thermodynamic radiation background corresponding to about 3.5° K. Observations at two other wave-lengths at least are needed to confirm this suggestion. One such observation is now being planned by Dicke at Princeton.

There seems no way in which such a background can be explained in terms of current astrophysical processes. Hence, if we accept the suggestion of Penzias and Wilson, the immediate implication is that the universe must have been different in the past from what it is to-day. Particularly, a higher density is needed to generate the background.

A similar result follows from the entirely different consideration of the helium-to-hydrogen ratio in stars and gaseous nebulae within our galaxy. Determinations of this ratio range from 0.08 to 0.18; and the ratio seems to be just as high in old stars as in most young stars. The ratio to be expected from current stellar activity is only 0.01. So either activity in the galaxy was much greater in the past, or the helium cannot be explained in terms of production from hydrogen through thermonuclear processes within the galaxy. Failure to observe any stars or any object with a low helium content points to the second of these possibilities.

It is possible to show by detailed calculation that, if matter in the universe has emerged from a state in which the temperature was above 10^{10} °K, the helium-to-hydrogen ratio must be about 0.14, a value which falls in the centre of the observed range. However, no values less than a truly universal value should be found. Two independent determinations for the Sun, one from structure calculations, one from observations of solar cosmic rays, give concordant results close to 0.09. This seems significantly below the expected universal value; but further work is needed to establish whether the discrepancy is real or not.

All the lines of investigation which I have mentioned so far point to an affirmative answer to the initial question: they point to the universal density in the past being higher than it is at present. Yet in every case the argument has been fraught with uncertainty. The probability seems against a negative answer, yet the possibility cannot be excluded. Speaking personally, I believe the case for a negative answer would still be arguable if it were not for the third of my three lines of attack. This again is entirely different in character from the helium/hydrogen ratio and from the microwave observation of Penzias and Wilson. I refer to the problem of the origin of elliptical galaxies. In my view, a consideration of this problem points decisively toward the universe having been very much denser in the past than it is at present.

Galaxies have been broadly classified into two types—ellipticals and spirals. There is an incontrovertible argument to show that spirals must have condensed from a more diffuse form. The spirals are rotating. Their angular momenta prevent them from being compressed into more compact forms. The flattened ellipticals have always been supposed to be similarly in rotation, but this has never been properly checked by observation. Because the ellipticals were thought to be in rotation it was similarly supposed that they were formed by a condensation process. This, I am now convinced, is wrong. I believe ellipticals to have formed through expansion from a higher density state.

Elliptical galaxies are remarkably amorphous. The star distribution is everywhere smooth. If one measures the surface brightness it is found to behave very nearly as an inverse square law, rising with great steepness toward the centre. The centres possess extremely bright central pips. How sharp these centres really are, how star-like, is impossible to say at the moment, for atmospheric seeing effects smear the central pip into an apparent disk.

Suppose the universe expanded from a much denser state, say 10^{-12} g cm^{-3}, and suppose the gas at the beginning of the expansion was not entirely smooth, suppose there were condensation knots already within it. It appears that such condensation knots can restrain the expanding gas to a degree which can be subject to precise calculation. A knot of mass $10^9 M_\odot$ can restrain a total mass of $10^{12} M_\odot$ within a region of galactic dimensions. A knot of $10^7 M_\odot$ can restrain a mass of about $5 \cdot 10^{10} M_\odot$. The critical point now emerges, that the surface brightness of the resulting aggregation can be calculated (assuming the material forms into stars) and the calculations yield quite unambiguously a law close to the inverse square, in fact just what is observed.

The point I wish to make is that whereas the steep rise towards the centre is expected, and is predicted, by the expansion picture, this characteristic feature of elliptical galaxies cannot, I believe, be understood at all within the condensation picture.

The clinching factor, it seems to me, is that a condensation knot—a memory of the initial dense state—is to be expected at the centre of every major elliptical galaxy. It is these condensation knots that give rise to the phenomenon of the radio galaxy. These are the massive objects which Fowler and I postulated some three years ago. Questions were asked of us at the time as to how our objects ever managed to form. Difficulties of angular momentum were raised. The answer which can now be given is that the objects never formed, in the sense in which the questions were asked. They are relics of a much higher density phase of the universe. They have been there since the galaxies themselves were formed, and in the sense of the radio astronomer they have been smouldering throughout the lifetimes of the galaxies. They are systems which remain at the very edge of stability. Whenever instabilities occur, violent outbursts serve to restabilize them.

Why is my initial question so important? Why make such a fuss about whether the universe has been in a more dense state? Because the present physical theory suggests that there is no limit to how great the density must have been in the past. I use the word 'suggests' because the physical divergence of the density was first demonstrated for a homogeneous and isotropic universe. Divergence also occurs when the isotropic restriction is removed. Does it also occur when homogeneity is removed? I have always believed the answer to this question was also affirmative, but my belief was based more on the failure of those who maintained the opposite to demonstrate their case than on any positive demonstration on the affirmative side. However, progress on the affirmative side has been made very recently, and opinion has generally moved toward the view that the equations of physics contain a universal singularity.

I have always had a rooted objection to this conclusion. It seems as objectionable to me as if phenomena should be discovered in the laboratory which not only defied present physical laws but which also defied all possible physical laws. On the other hand, I see no objection to supposing that present laws are incomplete, for they are almost surely incomplete. The issue therefore presents itself as to how the physical laws must be modified in order to prevent a universal singularity, in other words how to prevent a collapse of physics.

It was with this background to the problem that several of us suggested, some twenty years ago, that matter might be created continuously. The idea was to keep the universe in a steady-state with creation of matter compensating the effects of expansion. In such a theory the density in the universe would not be higher in the past than it is at present. From the data I have presented here it seems likely that the idea will now have to be discarded, at any rate in the form it has become widely known—the steady-state universe. But let me proceed with the theoretical ideas which have grown out of the notions of twenty years ago, for they may turn out to have a value going beyond the first suggestions.

During the past ten years the struggle has been to invent a form of mathematics operating in the manner customary in physics, namely, starting from an action principle. It was found possible to represent the creation of matter through the introduction of a new field. The manner in which the field was treated was quite normal. What was different from ordinary physics was the motive underlying the investigation, the avoidance of a universal singularity, rather than an experiment in the laboratory. Physicists will introduce a new field at the drop of a hat, if experiments in the laboratory should direct them so; but the physicist is unhappy to do so for any other reason.

Having obtained the mathematical structure of the new field it was found that singularities never occur, quite regardless of whether matter is being created or not. So long as the new field exists there will be no singularity either of the universe or of a local imploding body. In other words, the models available for investigation, the models without singularities, were very much wider than the old steady-state theory. During the past few years it is these other models which have been under investigation. What has turned out?

The simplest case is that in which the new field exists but in which there is no creation of matter. It is then possible to obtain a finite, oscillating universe of the kind that has been sought for so long in the usual theory. The universe alternately expands and contracts. Gravitation causes the reversal from expansion to contraction, while the new field causes the rebound from contraction to expansion.

So far as I am aware, such an oscillating model is in satisfactory agreement with all available data. The model is less dull than it seems at first sight, for it contains the possibility of some carry-through from one cycle to the next. Suppose the universe as we observe it eventually stops expanding. Suppose it falls back to a state of comparatively high density, a state in which stars are evaporated, a state in which even the nuclei of heavy elements are disrupted, a state from which matter emerges with the helium-to-hydrogen ratio I described before, about 0.14. In the state of high density things will not be quite uniform. Because of the existence of galaxies, and of clusters of galaxies, there will inevitably be some departures from uniformity. These departures will form the condensation knots round which a new generation of galaxies will form. Thus the condensation knots of which I spoke at an earlier stage are not merely random perturbations. One generation of galaxies acts as the seeds for the next generation. Magnetic fields will also persist from cycle to cycle.

There are two objections to this model. The new field is without sources. It is introduced *ad hoc*, along with the matter. There is never any coupling between the matter and the field. Then there is the subtle, but I believe the correct, objection that a series of oscillations must eventually damp out. Unless dissipative processes are precisely zero, which seems unlikely, the amplitude of the oscillation will gradually die away and the universe will come to rest in an intermediate static state.

For these reasons it is of interest to examine the models with creation of matter, noticing there is no specification from theory as to what the density must be in the steady-state situation. In the past the density was set empirically, by requiring it to be equal to the present-day density. Perhaps this step was wrong. Perhaps the true steady-state density should be very much higher.

During the past year, Dr. Narlikar and I managed to investigate a possibility which had previously proved too difficult to handle, the case in which there are departures from homogeneity, the case in which there are fluctuations from one region of space to another. To our surprise we found that under certain conditions the creation of matter could fall away in a localized region, and that if it did so the region would break into a series of oscillations of a kind that were closely analogous to the oscillations I have just been describing. In the former case we had oscillations of the whole universe, but of a universe of finite volume and finite mass. In this new case we have oscillations of a finite region of an infinite universe. From the point of view of an observer living in such a region it would be difficult to tell the difference. The oscillations would eventually damp away, but in this second case there would simply be a return to the steady-state condition. In this second case there will be many localized oscillating regions, not merely one. The regions will not in general be in justaposition with each other; they will usually be separated like islands in an ocean: and, like islands, they will be of different sizes and the amplitudes of their oscillations will be different.

I have already mentioned the philosophy of the physicist, that the whole of physics is discoverable in the laboratory. What has been discovered is a remarkable mixture of elegance—invariance properties for example—and of ugliness, the fine structure constant being 137 . . . for example. The properties of matter depend critically on the dimensionless numbers of physics, as well as on the structure of the laws. One can take three views on the dimensionless numbers:

(1) They just happen to have the values we find for them and no explanation of these values will ever be found.
(2) The observed values are necessary to the logical consistency of physics.
(3) The observed values are of non-local origin.

I imagine few will be satisfied with the first of these possibilities. I also imagine most physicists prefer (2). But what if (3) should be correct? Could the curious values we observe for the dimensionless numbers be connected with the particular oscillating and finite region in which we happen to live? If this were so, the universe would be far richer in its possibilities and content than we normally imagine. In other regions the numbers would be different and the gross properties of matter, the science of chemistry for example, would be entirely changed.

11

The History of the Solar System

FRED L. WHIPPLE
1964

From *Proceedings of the National Academy of Sciences*, vol. 52, pp. 565–594, 1964. Reprinted with permission of the author and the National Academy of Sciences.

What has happened in the past appears to be almost as vague and uncertain as what will happen in the future: the story depends upon the teller. Contrast the histories of a war as written by the winner and the loser, or the stories of a courtship as related by the bride, by the groom, or by friends. Note that observers of automobile accidents almost invariably disagree as to the actual sequence of events. And so it is, even in science. We can reconstruct the history of the solar system with little more confidence than we can predict its future. Actually, we possess only a fragmentary knowledge of the system today and have inadequate theoretical tools to deal with many of the physical processes that have taken place.

Since there are many contradictory arguments regarding the history of the solar system, this will also be a biased account stressing a few of the areas where there is a strong consensus, and presenting only part of the counterevidence where great uncertainties or unusually strong differences of opinion exist.

We must make one general assumption to avoid wallowing in the quicksands of sheer speculation (or metaphysics?), viz., that the laws of nature have remained unchanged for some five aeons (an aeon is defined as 10^9 years). To my knowledge only one measurable quantity has certainly remained constant over some three aeons, i.e., the range of alpha particles from specific radioactive atoms in mica, as evidenced in pleochroic halos [1] (Figure 11.1). . . . There is no similar evidence to substantiate the assumption that such fundamental quantities as the velocity of light, the constant of gravitation, or other physical constants have remained unchanged during the past five aeons. (Note that P. Pochado and M. Schwarzschild [*Astrophys. Jour.*, v. 139, p. 587 (1964)] find for the Sun that g cannot have varied more rapidly than by $(\text{time})^{-0.2}$.)

HISTORY OF THE EARTH

Assuming, however, that all is well with the physical laws, we can determine an age of the Earth, that is to say, the time interval since the

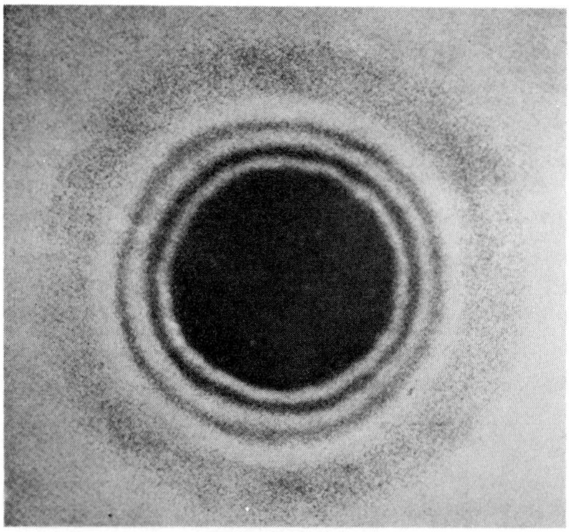

FIGURE 11.1
A pleochroic halo

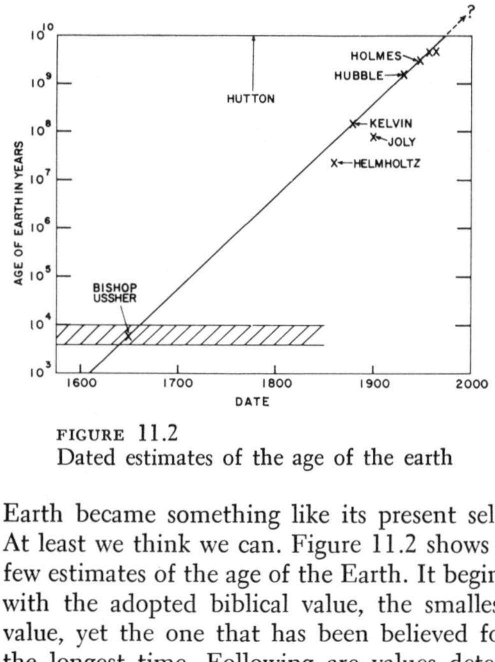

FIGURE 11.2
Dated estimates of the age of the earth

Earth became something like its present self. At least we think we can. Figure 11.2 shows a few estimates of the age of the Earth. It begins with the adopted biblical value, the smallest value, yet the one that has been believed for the longest time. Following are values determined by Helmholtz from the rate of the contraction of the Sun, by Kelvin from heat conductivity, by Joly from the transport of salt to the oceans, by Holmes from radioactivity measures, and by recent investigators who employed a number of techniques involving radioactivity. On the average, the "age" of the Earth has been doubling every 15 years for the past three centuries; the rate, perhaps, has been somewhat faster during the past century.

TABLE 11.1
Radioactive atoms

Atom	Decay products	Half-life, aeons
U^{238}	$Pb^{206} + 8\ He^{4}$	4.51
U^{235}	$Pb^{207} + 7\ He^{4}$	0.71
Th^{232}	$Pb^{208} + 6\ He^{4}$	13.9
Rb^{87}	Sr^{87}	46
K^{40} (11%)	Ar^{40}	1.25

TABLE 11.2
Ages (in aeons, 10^9 years)

Method	Earth	Meteorites
U, Th-He	~3 Max	4.0 (peak)
K-Ar	~3 Max	4.3 (peak)
Rb-Sr	~3 Max	4.4
Lead-Lead	4.55	4.6 ± 0.2

There are some notable exceptions to these more classical estimates. Some Eastern philosophies postulate much greater ages. In the West, James Hutton, a geologist of the late 18th century, could see no evidence of a beginning or an end to geological processes. Perhaps these estimates best illustrate my first point that the past is highly variable. Actually, there is some real basis for thinking that the numbers are now converging. I list in Table 11.1 some of the major processes of radioactivity that are useful in determining the age of the Earth and of meteorites; included are certain end products and the half-lives, or the intervals of time in which half of the atoms spontaneously decay. By measuring the parent atom and its daughter decay products *in a sample for which both are preserved,* we can now determine the length of time these atoms have been contained in the sample. . . . The gases helium and argon, of course, can leak out of some kinds of rocks or meteorites, and oftentimes ages calculated for them are less than the time since the material became solid.

Table 11.2 lists ages determined for the Earth and meteorites. Meteorites, of course, are stones and irons that have fallen from the sky. We have ample evidence that they belong to the solar system. No Earth rocks yet found have remained cool and solid for more than three aeons. The lead-lead method, however, measures the age since the Earth was assembled, regardless of thermal processes, mixing, and loss of gases. Claire Patterson [2] finds an age of 4.55 aeons by this method. Many of the meteorites solidified 4.0–4.4 aeons ago [3], but the age since their major consolidation, as measured by the lead-lead method, is in excellent agreement with that of the Earth. Thus, a mean value of the age of the Earth and meteorites appears to be within a few hundred million years of 4.6 aeons. William A. Fowler [4], fortunately, synthesizes the elements in time for the Earth to appear. There is, however, a real possibility not to be ignored that the lead-lead method may err appreciably; thus, the consolidation of the Earth and the parent bodies of the meteorites may have occurred earlier than we now believe (see Figure 11.2).

NEWTONIAN FACTS

Until about the beginning of this century, our knowledge of the solar system consisted almost entirely of what I shall call *Newtonian facts*, or those deductions that could be drawn from geometrical observations interpreted according to Newton's laws of motion and gravitation. A central star, the Sun, containing more than 99 per cent of the total mass, controls gravitationally the motion of nine planets, all of which move in nearly circular orbits close to a common plane and in a common direction. Their distances from the Sun follow a simple empirical relationship, the Titius-Bode law, as shown in Table 11.3. This so-called law requires a hiatus between Mars and Jupiter to account for a huge number of minor planets and asteroids where the fourth planet should move. These asteroids, together comprising perhaps a thousandth of the Earth's mass, move in the direct motion common to the planets, but with somewhat greater orbital eccentricities and inclinations to the common plane. They are almost certainly the source of the meteorites. Note that the "law" fails for Neptune.

Beyond the reaches of the planetary system, more than 50 AU from the Sun (i.e., 50 times the Earth's distance), we have reason to believe a cloud of comets, nearly in random motion, extends out to distances greater than 100,000 AU, still gravitationally a part of the solar system. Jan Oort [5] estimates that there is a total of some 10^{11} comets containing possibly one Earth's mass. A few are randomly disturbed by the passing stars and successively by Jupiter to become visible for a few revolutions through the inner reaches of the solar system. Most astronomers seem to agree with my theory [6] that the nuclei of comets are fundamentally frozen ices and dirt, that is, the expected cosmic material that can freeze at less than 100°K. We have learned from photographic meteor studies that ordinary meteors, or shooting stars, arise from cometary debris [7]. The incoming bodies are fragile in structure, not solid like most meteorites [8].

TABLE 11.3
The Titius-Bode law

Planet	Basis	Sum/10	Distance, AU
Mercury	4 + 0	0.4	0.39
Venus	4 + 3	0.7	0.72
Earth	4 + 6	1.0	1.00
Mars	4 + 12	1.6	1.52
Asteroids	4 + 24	2.8	—
Jupiter	4 + 48	5.2	5.20
Saturn	4 + 96	10.0	9.54
Uranus	4 + 192	19.6	19.18
Neptune	—	—	30.06
Pluto	4 + 384	38.8	39.52

The common motion of the planets is repeated in their rotations and in the motions of a considerable number of natural satellites, particularly around the great planets, Jupiter and Saturn. But there are exceptions. Uranus and its satellites are tilted a little more than 90° to the common plane, while a few of the satellites have retrograde motions, viz., the outer four of Jupiter's twelve, the outer-most of Saturn's nine, and the inner and larger of Neptune's pair. Radar measurements [9] suggest that Venus, almost the counterpart of the Earth, may also rotate (slowly) in a retrograde sense. Mercury keeps the same face toward the Sun as does the Moon toward the Earth, presumably an effect of tidal friction.

The giant planets rotate very rapidly on their axes with periods of the order of 10 hr,

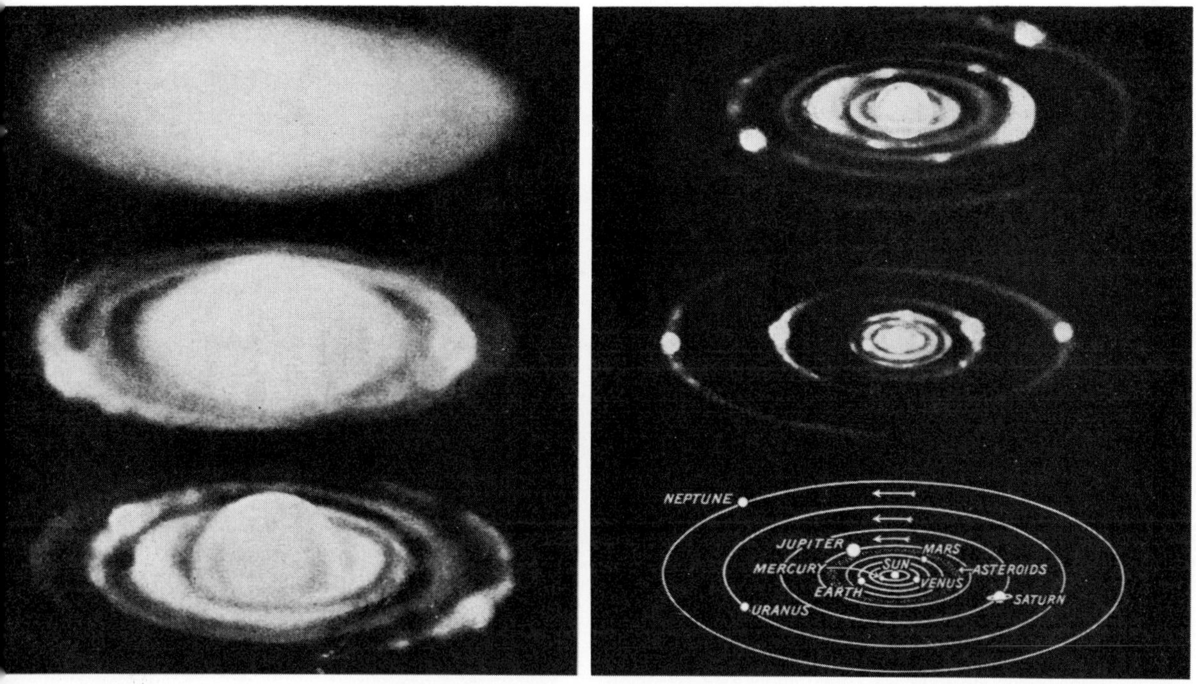

FIGURE 11.3
Drawings of Laplace's nebular hypothesis

while Mars rotates at about the Earth's rate and Pluto, which possibly may not be a planet at all, in about six days. The Sun rotates directly, but its equator is tilted 7° to the plane of the planets, as is the plane of Mercury's orbit.

TABLE 11.4
Mass and angular momentum

Material	Mass, per cent	Angular momentum, per cent
Sun	99.865	0.5
Terrestrial planets	0.0006	0.2
Giant planets	0.134	99.3

The extremely slow rotation of the Sun in 25 days presents an anomaly of enormous significance to our historic interpretation. Within a single system, Newtonian mechanics conserves an important quantity besides energy, viz., angular momentum. For a body in circular motion around the center of gravity, angular momentum is the product of velocity, mass, and distance. The sum of this quantity over all the masses in the system cannot be changed by an internal forces, but only by external transfer to material outside the system. The Sun, amazingly enough, carries less than half a per cent of the angular momentum of the solar system, although it contains more than 99 per cent of the mass (Table 11.4). This peculiar distribution of angular momentum in the solar system proved a stumbling block to all early theories of evolution.

No *likely* method of accumulating planetary masses about the Sun, or of condensing the Sun and the planetary masses from a larger aggregate, can result in a slowly rotating central mass, if we base our theory on classical dynamics and hydrodynamics. Hence, the well-known early theories [10] formulated by Immanuel Kant and Pierre Simon Laplace in the late 18th century, even when modernized, cannot account for the Sun's slow rotation. Figure 11.3 shows an artist's concept of Laplace's nebular hypothesis, in which the rotating and collapsing Sun leaves off successive rings of material at the distance of the present planets. Even granting with Laplace that such a condensing Sun can, indeed, leave behind rings or discoids of material in rotation, we cannot escape by any process of hydrodynamics from the conclusion that the finally condensed Sun, comprising most of the mass, will be rotating very rapidly with a period of 10 hr or less.

Yet all old stars like the Sun are rotating slowly, even though new stars often show extremely rapid rates of rotation. Some force not included in classical dynamics and hydrodynamics is clearly at work. To explain the anomaly, a number of investigators following Buffon in 1745 have postulated that the Sun was struck by an external body (Buffon called it a comet) tearing out and spinning the mass necessary to produce the planets. Such theories, including passing or colliding stars and even a destroyed solar companion, have all failed when subjected to the detailed application of dynamical theory. Sir James Jeans' tidal theory is illustrated in Figure 11.4. As a step beyond Newtonian facts, Lyman Spitzer [11] has shown that stellar (solar) gas at a temperature of a million or more degrees within the Sun or companion star and under high gravitational pressure would, upon violent release, explode far too rapidly for condensation into planetary masses or for accumulation into a disk about the Sun.

C. von Weizsäcker [12] applied modern turbulence theory to transfer angular momentum from the Sun to a Laplacian nebular disk (Figure 11.5), but the process stops when the velocity at the equator becomes comparable with the circular orbital velocity. The Sun is left rotating with a period of only a few hours. Hence, turbulence offers no solution.

MAGNETOHYDRODYNAMICS

Today the problem of angular momentum appears to have a likely solution only when we postulate the action of *magnetohydrodynamic* processes. Their study is as difficult and important as the name is complicated. Magnetohydrodynamics deals with processes in hot, ionized gases where electrical currents and magnetic fields have energies comparable to those of normal gas motions, pressure, heat, and thermodynamic interactions. Where there is a magnetic field in space, charged particles can move easily *along* the field lines but can move *across* them only with difficulty. Thus, the magnetic lines of the Earth's field hold the extremely energetic charged particles of the Van Allen belts, as satellite astronomy has recently demonstrated. When such fields are produced within the gas itself by a flow of the charged gas particles, all of the theoretical complexities of hydrodynamics are multiplied by the additional comparable complexities of electromagnetic effects.

In 1912 K. Birkeland [13] first suggested that a strong solar magnetic field might play a major role in planetary formation. H. P. Berlage [14] in subsequent decades investigated various electromagnetic processes, as did H. Alfvén [15] in 1942. Their theories, however, all required sets of physical processes too specialized to be acceptable. In 1948 D. ter Haar [16] suggested a method whereby a strong magnetic field in the early, rapidly rotating Sun might transfer angular momentum to the interstellar medium of gas. In 1957 Donald H. Menzel [17], and in 1960 Fred Hoyle [18], suggested that ionized gas may have been thrown from the collapsing Sun by magnetohydrodynamic forces to slow its rotation and remove gases from the system. In Menzel's theory the electromagnetic forces of an electric current produced a Saturn-like protrusion of the solar equator. These same forces restrained the gases of the expanding ring from evaporating into space. In Hoyle's theory the Sun contracted rapidly to about the dimensions of Mercury's present orbit; at that time its rotation and increasing temperature produced strong magnetic fields near the surface. These fields produced "wiry" rigidity in the ionized gas, which caused the rotating Sun to drag behind it the outermost gases and wind up the magnetic lines of force in discoids about the Sun (Figures 11.6 and 11.7). The angular momentum of the Sun was then transferred to this gaseous discoid, slowly carrying the gases outward from the Sun in the plane of rotation.

Hoyle has calculated that about 1 per cent of the solar mass would be adequate for this process and that as the material cooled, the outgoing gas would carry with it the solid planetesimals which were below about 10 meters' radius. The solids and some of the gases

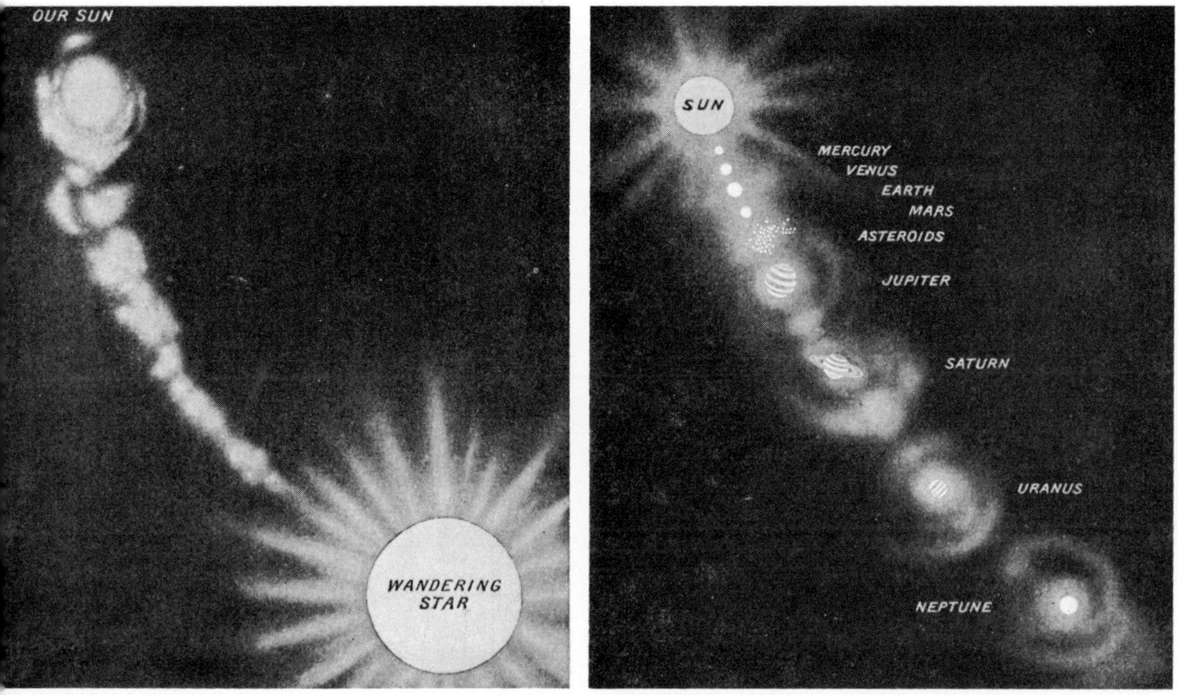

FIGURE 11.4
Sir James Jeans' tidal theory

would collect into the various planets. Today, whether or not we accept these detailed processes, we must of necessity call on some magnetohydrodynamic process for transferring angular momentum from the early rotating Sun.

CHEMISTRY AND PHYSICS

The factual basis for our history has been richly increased this past century by the developments in chemistry and physics, coupled with the concomitant advances in engineering and observational techniques. Spectroscopy enables us to determine much about the composition and character of stellar and planetary atmospheres [19]. Thus, ammonia, methane, and hydrogen appear in the spectra of Jupiter and Saturn, while a considerable percentage of helium can be demonstrated by indirect means. Methane appears in the spectra of Uranus and Neptune but ammonia is apparently frozen out. Correspondingly, carbon dioxide occurs in the atmospheres of Mars and Venus . . . Most of the known stable elements are observed in the Sun's atmosphere and their relative abundances have been determined.

Progress in the theory of stellar interiors and energy generation provides excellent knowledge of the distribution of temperature and pressure within the Sun. Correspondingly, high-pressure and solid-state physics have provided considerable information concerning the internal structure of the giant planets. R. Wildt [20], W. H. Ramsey [21], and W. C. DeMarcus [22] have shown that Jupiter must consist primarily of hydrogen and is almost the maximum size for a cold planet. Were it much more massive (Figure 11.8), its central material would become physically *degenerate* (i.e., very much denser) and it would be smaller; if less massive, it would also be smaller. Saturn, with a much lower mean density—0.7 versus 1.3 that of water—actually contains a larger fraction of the heavier elements.

Seismic data and theoretical studies of the Earth's interior show that it, on the other hand, may contain an iron ore, possibly liquid. This supposition is strongly supported by the

FIGURE 11.5
C. von Weizsäcker's concept of turbulent eddies in the solar nebula

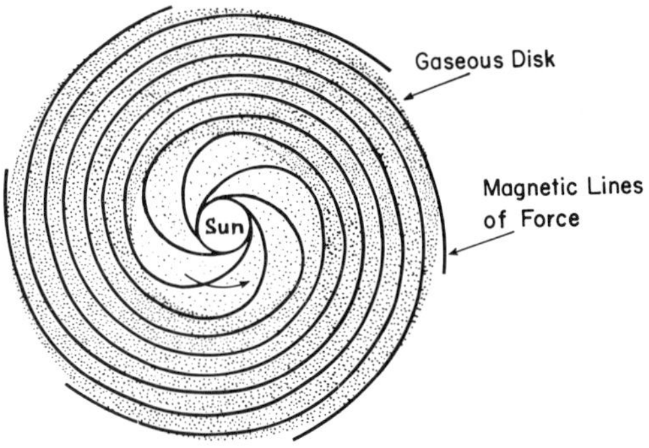

FIGURE 11.6
Magnetic lines in the solar nebula according to F. Hoyle

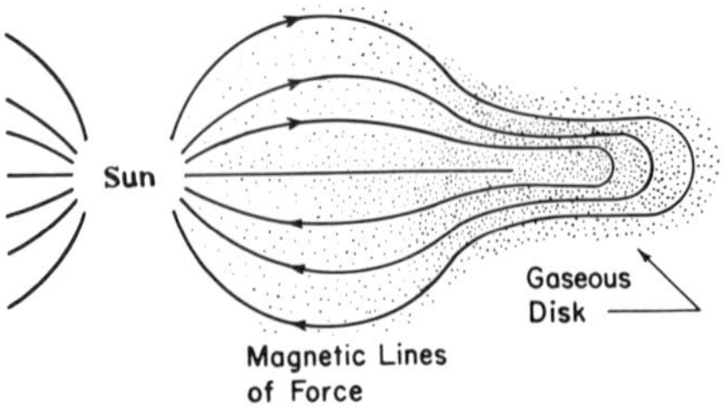

FIGURE 11.7
Edge view of Hoyle's magnetic lines

occurrence of many iron-nickel meteorites, which suggests a sequence of events: (*a*) the growth of two or more sizeable asteroids whose interiors were or became heated; (*b*) the gravitational separation of the denser melted iron toward the centers, leaving the lighter silicates in the mantles; (*c*) the breakup of the asteroids presumably by collisions after a huge interval of cooling; (*d*) the final encounters of a few fragments with the earth. This evidence once strengthened the intuitive feeling that the Earth must have been born as a hot gaseous body and cooled over the aeons. We shall see that the chemical evidence, adduced particularly by Harold C. Urey [23], disproves this hypothesis.

Among the terrestrial planets we have an interesting decrease in mean density from the Sun outward, as shown in Table 11.5. The correction to the uncompressed state follows Urey's calculations. Mercury must certainly represent a much higher concentration of iron than the Earth and Mars.

Urey [24] has repeatedly pointed out that the Moon presents a puzzle of major significance; it is less dense than the stony meteorites and comparable in density to the rocks of the Earth's upper mantle. How could it have been formed from the same materials as the Earth and at the same time and place? Furthermore, he stresses that its irregularities and surface features indicate that it has never been thoroughly melted. With regard to its density, note too that the satellites, where data are available, become less dense as we go outward through the solar system, and also as we go outward in Jupiter's system (Table 11.6).

Measures of atomic abundances in the Sun show that hydrogen is an overwhelming constituent, perhaps 60 per cent or more; helium perhaps half as abundant by weight; lithium, beryllium, and boron practically absent; while carbon, nitrogen, and oxygen constitute about 1–2 per cent. All the heavier elements comprise less than 1 per cent of the total mass. Beginning with carbon, nitrogen, and oxygen, the heavier elements in meteorites and in the Earth show much the same abundances as in the Sun, with a few notable exceptions, particularly the noble gases, which are essentially absent from the Earth and most meteorites. Among the comets we have no detailed information concerning composition except that fragmentary compounds of carbon, nitrogen, oxygen, and hydrogen are detected in the spectra while the meteoric spectra show largely earthy elements such as iron, silicon, magnesium, sodium, calcium, etc.

Harrison Brown [25] pointed out that the elements could be divided into three natural groups in terms of abundance and physical characteristics. The most abundant elements, hydrogen and helium, remain gaseous at extremely low temperatures and constitute what I shall call the *gaseous group*. The compounds of carbon, nitrogen, and oxygen with hydrogen, such as ammonia (NH_3), methane (CH_4), and water (H_2O), vaporize at room temperature but freeze at moderately low temperatures, the *icy group*. The remaining heavier elements excluding the noble gases constitute the *earthy group*. The three most abundant, silicon, magnesium, and iron, either as compounds or as elements, remain solid to rather high temperatures, generally melting around 2000°K. Table 11.7 illustrates the relative abundances of the three groups of elements and their melting points. The data are based upon determinations by Goldberg, Müller, and Aller [26] for the Sun, and a compilation by H. E. Suess [27].

We can estimate the relative abundances of the earthy, icy, and gaseous materials in the planets and in the comets, as shown in Table 11.8. The earthy elements constitute essentially all of the mass of the terrestrial planets but rather small fractions of the giant planets and comets. I assume that comets consist entirely of the icy plus the earthy groups. Actually, it appears that Jupiter and Saturn contain a few Earth masses of earthy materials and Uranus and Neptune perhaps one or two each. The icy materials become increasingly significant as we go outward from the Sun. Uranus and Neptune could be made almost entirely of comets. Jupiter and Saturn probably contain somewhat more icy material in absolute amounts than Uranus and Neptune, even though the relative abundances are lower.

We may reasonably assume that the original source of building material was essentially the same for the Sun as for the planets, whether the planets were derived from solar material or whether they were all condensed from the same gaseous clouds. The abundance of the elements strengthens this natural assumption even though there are some striking discrepancies. On this basis, the terrestrial planets, which contain only the earthy fraction, must have been derived from about 500 times their present mass. We see from Table 11.9 that the original source material for the terrestrial planets was somewhat comparable to that for the giant planets. For the comets I assume 10 Earth masses of original earthy and icy material. This allows for a 90 per cent loss during

TABLE 11.5
Densities of the terrestrial planets

Planet	Actual (water = 1)	Uncompressed (water = 1)
Mercury	5.5	5.0
Venus	5.1	4.4(?)
Earth	5.52	4.4
Mars	4.0	3.7
Moon	3.34	3.31

TABLE 11.6
The large satellites

Satellite	Diameter	Density (water = 1)
Moon (E)	1.00	3.3
Io (J)	0.99	3.1
Europa (J)	0.86	3.0
Ganymede (J)	1.28	1.7
Callisto (J)	1.10	1.4
Titan (S)	1.38	2.3
Triton (N)	1.06	?

TABLE 11.7
Classes of material

Material	Elements	Mass available	Melting point
Earthy	Si, Mg, Fe, etc., plus 0	1	~2000°K
Icy	C, N, O, plus H (Ne?)	4–7	≤ 273°K
Gaseous	H, He	300–600	≤ 14°K

orbital changes by perturbations of the major planets to produce the huge cometary cloud, extending to 100,000 AU from the Sun. Thus we see that if the condensation process were highly efficient, we require about 3 per cent of the present solar mass to provide the original material from which the planets and comets were derived. The efficiency of the collection processes surely must have been low so that the original source of material must have been at least one tenth of the solar mass, an order of magnitude more than Hoyle assumes.

On this basis then, the original material from which the Earth was formed constituted at least Jupiter's present mass of primordial material which, if it had been collected together, would surely have condensed into a planet much like Jupiter and remained as a giant planet. The same is even more certain for Uranus and Neptune. The difficulty of removing so much gas from large "protoplanets," as postulated by Gerald P. Kuiper [28], has invalidated his detailed theory of planetary formation. His contributions to the subject, however, are highly significant. We must find some process whereby the gaseous and icy materials were separated from the terrestrial planets or by which the earthy materials condensed, leaving behind the volatile materials at temperatures much like those that obtain on the Earth today, or higher. At the present time a small body made of the icy materials will vaporize in the vacuum of space out beyond the distance of the asteroids.

In 1924 F. W. Aston [29] noted the scarcity of the noble gases in the Earth's atmosphere possibly due to their being gaseous and inert. Urey, by an extensive chemical study, has shown that the Earth and the meteorites show significant losses of relatively *volatile* materials, compounds and elements more volatile than the element mercury. The icy elements were probably lost in the form of water, ammonia, and methane but some of the water, nitrogen, and carbon were preserved in compounds with the earthy elements. From this truly beautiful line of chemical evidence, which is too involved for our discussion, he visualizes that objects of several hundreds of kilometers in dimension accumulated at temperatures below 0°C early in the history of the solar system. These primary objects were then heated variously, possibly by internal radioactivity, to temperatures sometimes reaching 2000°C. They were then broken up by collisions and reaccumulated into the present asteroids, Moon, and terrestrial planets. "During the process of breakup and reaccumulation, fractionization of the silicate and metal phases occurred, with a preferential loss of silicate phases in various degrees. This variable loss accounts for the variation in densities of the planets." Thus, we now have a sound chemical basis for a planetesimal concept of planetary accretion, much more advanced and detailed but supporting some of the ideas in the well-known theory presented by Chamberlin and Moulton early this century.

For the Earth, it is difficult to see how even the secondary planetesimals could have aggregated into such a large body with the volatiles

TABLE 11.8
Composition of the planets

Planet	Material: Earthy	Icy	Gaseous
Terrestrial planets	1.00	<0.01	0
Jupiter	<0.01	0.1	0.9
Saturn	0.01	0.3	0.7
Uranus	0.1	0.8	0.1
Neptune	0.2	0.7	0.1
Comets	0.15	0.85	0

TABLE 11.9
Original planetary mass

Planet	Present mass (Earth = 1)	Factor	Original material (Sun = 1)
Terrestrial planets	1.9	500	0.0028
Jupiter	317	10	0.0095
Saturn	95	30	0.0086
Uranus and Neptune	32	75	0.0072
Comets	1	900	0.0027
Minimum original mass			0.0308

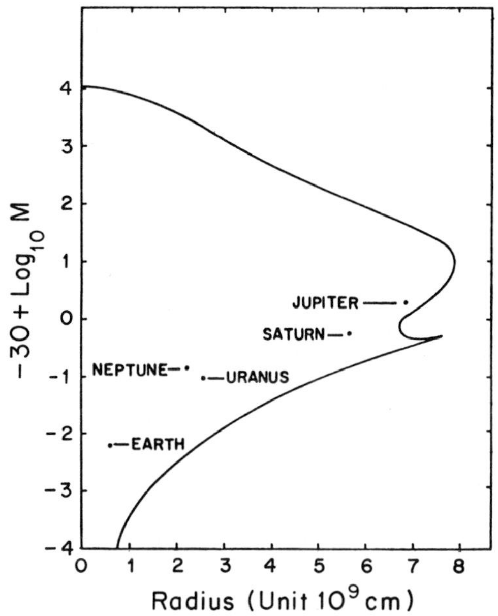

FIGURE 11.8
The radii of the planets as compared to hydrogen spheres of the same mass. (After W. C. DeMarcus.)

so *completely* removed, particularly the heavy noble gases such as xenon and krypton. (Note that some meteorites contain appreciable quantities of these gases.) It seems very likely that the Earth was in some fashion stripped of its atmosphere after formation and that the present atmosphere and oceans are all of secondary origin, probably derived from chemical compounds released by heating from within the Earth, as the work of William Rubey [30] supports. The thin atmosphere of Mars and the absence of an appreciable one on Mercury present no problems. Because of their low surface gravities, atmospheres are easily lost. We still await more information about the atmosphere of Venus.

For the meteorites and the asteroids the historical problems are extremely difficult, as suggested by the complicated sequence of events required by Urey. It was long believed that two planets or more, possibly comparable to the Earth in size, were formed in the asteroid belt to develop iron cores and finally, after collisions, form the present asteroids and the iron and stony meteorites. Conceivably, evidence for two major parent asteroids can be derived from the discovery by Urey and Craig [31] that the chondritic (stony) meteorites divide into two classes with differing iron content and correlated abundance differences among the less abundant elements. This remarkable and complex separation of the meteorites into two classes still remains unexplained by any chemical or physical theory.

In recent decades the presumed dimensions of the parent asteroidal bodies have continuously decreased from planetary to lunar size and recently, through the arguments of Goles, Fish, and Anders [32], to relatively small asteroids of only a very few hundred kilometers in diameter. This theoretical shrinking arises from the difficulty of cooling large bodies within the time scale allotted, the order of a few hundred million years. Note from Table 11.2 that some of the meteorites have remained fairly cool and undifferentiated for more than 4.0 of our total of 4.6 aeons. The problem of maximum asteroid size is not yet settled. Almost no one nowadays maintains that the original asteroids were more than lunar size, but various investigators advocate original dimensions from 300 to 3000 kilometers in diameter.

There is a wide difference of opinion as to the pressures required to produce the famous Widmannstätten figures in iron meteorites, somewhere in the range between values in the Moon and in asteroids. Slow cooling is definitely required below a few hundred degrees centigrade, but almost all theories allow for this. The diamonds occasionally found in certain meteorites point to a high-pressure, steady state in the original asteroid, although a minority of investigators believe that they can be produced by intense shock. When a complete theoretical understanding of the production of diamonds and the Widmannstätten figures is reached, the problem of the maximum size of asteroids will be solved.

The Moon enters the discussion because of its extremely low density and its irregularity in shape (more than 1 km), which suggests that the Moon was never completely molten. If the Moon has not been thoroughly melted by radioactivity, how could 300-km diameter asteroids have been so melted? Their larger area per unit mass would surely accelerate radiative cooling and reduce the efficiency of heating processes.

We are not certain enough of the total radioactive content of the Earth and meteorites to state definitely whether the known sources of radioactivity, particularly potassium^{40}, uranium, and thorium, could indeed melt the Moon in 4.6 aeons. For smaller bodies this source of heat supply is too small unless they were originally hot, very near the melting point. An alternative would be to push back the date of formation so that the amount of K^{40} (with a half-life of 1.25 aeons) would have been more abundant, thus providing more heat. Remember that we are allowed only 4.6 minus 4.0 aeons, or 600 million years (or less), for the asteroids to heat and cool. Perhaps we should extrapolate our time-scale diagram (Figure 11.2) for another few years, gaining perhaps an aeon.

Analysis of meteorites [33] is today adding a wealth of information regarding the asteroids and the planetesimals that formed them. Of vital importance are the *chondrules,* small silicate droplets of dimension the order of 1 mm, present and sometimes highly abundant in almost all stony meteorites (Figure 11.9). Many are glassy, indicating extremely quick cooling in a matter of minutes. In them the relative abundances of nonvolatile substances fall closer to the observed solar abundances than in any other type of substance. Furthermore, they tend to contain metallic iron rather than oxidized iron, suggesting that they were formed in a reducing atmosphere, presumably hydrogen, as one would postulate in the original solar cloud. Their ages are great, indicating their formation during the early stages of planetary formation.

Hans E. Suess [34] and John A. Wood, Jr. [35], have suggested that chondrules condensed directly in the primitive nebula, a theory that Urey doubts. It is rather difficult, moreover, seriously to postulate conditions of sufficiently high pressure to make such direct condensation possible. As an alternative to this, Wood suggests that after having aggregated as small collections of dust, they may have been quickly melted and cooled by the passage of intense shock waves through the primitive nebula. Whatever the origin of the chondrules, no theory of the formation of the

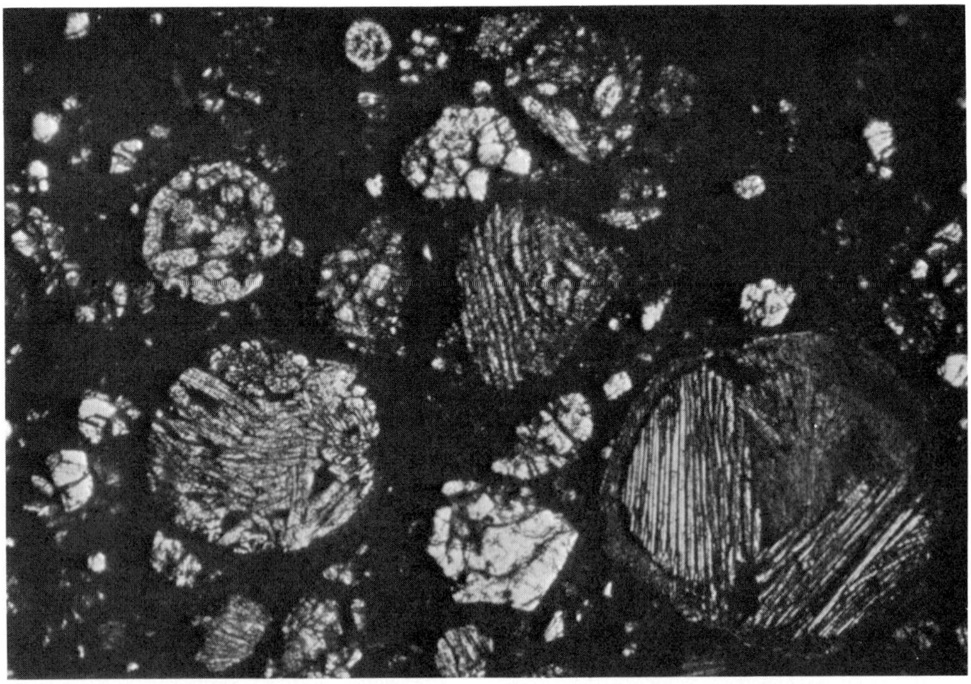

FIGURE 11.9
Section of the Tieschitz stony meteorite showing chondrules. (Diameters approximately 1 mm.)

terrestrial planets can be complete without describing in detail the formation of so numerous a class of objects.

NUCLEAR PHYSICS AND RADIOCHEMISTRY

In 1947 Harrison Brown [25] suggested that the time interval from nucleosynthesis of the elements to the formation of the asteroids might be determined if the daughter product of an extinct nuclear isotope could be detected in meteorites. A possibility for early planet heating is iodine^{129}, having a half-life of 17 million years. The daughter product is xenon^{129}, retained in a large planet or in a cool stone or iron. After considerable search, Reynolds [36] found this isotope with an excessive abundance in the Richardton chondrite and subsequent studies have shown that its abundance in other meteorites is highly variable with respect to the other isotopes of xenon, sometimes being more than three times as abundant relatively as on the Earth. This result suggested that a period of only 20–40 million years elapsed from the formation of the elements in stars or a supernova to the formation of the asteroids! Such a limitation on the time scale is exceedingly worrisome because it leaves no adequate time for cooling of the asteroids even if the contraction and planetary-forming processes could occur so surprisingly fast. . . .

FORMATION OF THE GIANT PLANETS AND THEIR SATELLITES

With these facts in mind I shall first attempt to reconstruct a possible historical sequence for the aggregation of the giant planets and their satellites. My picture leans heavily on the conceptual developments by A. G. W. Cameron [37], who in turn leaned heavily on theories by other investigators including G. P. Kuiper [28], F. Hoyle [18], L. Mestel and L. Spitzer [38], and E. Schatzman [39].

Our starting point can begin no later than with a protosun of 1.2 or more solar masses extending over a volume with diameter perhaps 100,000 AU. It is gravitationally unstable and about to collapse. It will be a cool ($\sim$ 50°K) and relatively dense interstellar cloud containing perhaps 1000 hydrogen atoms per cc and considerable dust. It may be associated with or a part of a much larger cloud (see Figure 11.10). There is some turbulence in the cloud and a mean rotation much like the rate of rotation of the galaxy with a period the order of 10^8 years. It has become gravitationally unstable possibly because of increased pressure applied externally, e.g., by the pressure of nearby supernova explosions, by large turbulent eddies in the Milky Way or in the associated larger cloud, or possibly by instabilities in the larger cloud.

Our protosolar system carries a weak magnetic field of perhaps 5×10^{-6} gauss (10^{-5} of the Earth's field). There is probably some central condensation prior to the major collapse, the central temperature and density being appreciably higher than the mean. As the cloud collapses, the core probably picks up more rotation and the magnetic lines of force are twisted through the cloud. Dust in the cloud helps radiate away some of the energy of contraction.

Collapse in such a cloud requires some specific disposal mechanism for removing the potential energy of gravitation. Radiation to space may be slow or difficult for various reasons, including the possibility that hotter regions may exist in space nearby. Heating of the gas by compression provides a sink for some heat, but not much. We turn to the dissociation of hydrogen molecules as a major sink, which can be followed by the ionization of hydrogen and double ionization of helium, plus the smaller energy sinks involved in heating, dissociating, and ionizing the heavier atoms. Thus the collapse takes place at a far, far greater pace than would be required by Helmholtz' contraction concept, which depended mostly on radiation to remove gravitational energy. The time of collapse can be surprisingly short, perhaps only a few million years, not much longer than free fall to the center.

During collapse, Cameron finds that the cloud can transfer very little angular momentum to the nearby gas field, although the magnetic fields can be maintained. Cosmic rays and radioactive substances continuously produce the ions and electrons needed. In the early stages, the magnetic field lines soon become badly twisted. The total angular momentum of the cloud finally becomes a serious factor in collapse when the equatorial diameter has contracted to an uncertain value in the broad range between 1000 and 50 AU. The energy sink provided by the ionization of hydrogen and helium is so great that continued rapid collapse would occur except for rotation. The protostar must shed rapidly rotating material at its equator, leaving a huge disk tens to hundreds of AU across. This is precisely the nebular disk as visualized by Laplace. The central temperatures of the protostar will be fairly high, but the disk temperatures may be well below 2000°K at the moment the material is shed from the equator. The temperature will drop extremely fast because of radiation. The fall to room temperature at the present distance of Uranus may take place in the order of a year and to 10°K in perhaps a million years.

Thus, contraction will certainly vaporize all of the icy material but may not vaporize all of the earthy material out to the present distance of Jupiter or Saturn. Here the total disk material, if compacted to the plane, would correspond in mass to about 10 m of water. The disk, however, consisting mostly of hydrogen, would initially extend across the equatorial plane more than an AU at a temperature of 1000° and contract toward the disk's plane proportionally to the temperature. Perhaps one tenth of a solar mass is spread out over this very large discoid beyond Jupiter's present orbit. Within less than a century the radiation cools this material to about 1000°K.

If not all the dust grains of earthy materials initially present in the gas cloud have been vaporized, the earthy and then the icy materials will quickly condense on any earthy nuclei left to produce what I shall call "cometesimals." This occurs at all distances beyond the neighborhood of Saturn until the nebular cloud becomes too thin.

Now we have the task of making the giant planets and getting rid of the large excess of hydrogen and helium in our nebular disk. Most of the gas, dust, and cometesimals rotate regularly in fairly circular orbits about the protosun, which is not yet hot enough to radiate appreciable energy. Some irregular gas globs or sheets are still falling in to disturb the uniformity.

We expect to eliminate the excess gas by tying the magnetic lines of force from the Sun to the gas via the partial ionization produced by radioactive material, cosmic rays, and giant flares from the Sun. The latter may play a major role in the momentum transfer. The Sun at this time can be considered to have a real surface perhaps in the neighborhood of Mercury's present orbit, perhaps much farther out.

Jupiter and Saturn, because of their high gas content, must have accumulated much of their mass from the original nebular cloud. Urey [40] suggests that the temperature dropped so low (~ 4°K) in the region of Jupiter and Saturn *that hydrogen froze!* Thus the cometesimals there and at greater solar distances should have contained solid hydrogen. We do not know enough about the chemistry of comets to confirm this assumption. On the other hand, a temperature of 4°K is extremely low for an active, violent region of space near a contracting star. Not only would one expect material to be falling in sporadically, but the general volume at great distances may contain early-type new stars and other contracting clouds. At an assumed low temperature of only 10°K, the vapor pressure of solid hydrogen has gone up by more than a million times and the possibility of freezing hydrogen has vanished (by a factor of 10^3).

It seems more likely that Jupiter and Saturn must have accumulated primarily from the gaseous cloud, perhaps by the process discussed by Kuiper. Chance concentrations brought the mean density above the critical limit calculated by Roche (in 1850). The Roche limit is the minimum density at which a mass of gas could be gravitationally stable against the attraction of a central mass, here the protosun. At lower densities the tidal circulation would prevent the gas from collecting gravitationally, while at

FIGURE 11.10
The Rosette Nebula in Monoceros showing dark clouds. (Harvard College Observatory photograph.)

higher densities a stable gravitational unit would accumulate. It is probable that the continued existence of magnetic field lines spiraling in the disk tends to retard the accumulation of large gaseous masses. Our postulated nebular cloud is near the critical surface density. No theory can predict such details *a priori* but it can provide circumstances which might reasonably lead to such results.

At greater distances from the protosun than the region of Saturn the cometesimals became the building blocks and rapidly collect into the planets Uranus and Neptune, besides contributing a comparable but relatively small fractional mass each to Jupiter and Saturn.

The direct rotation of Jupiter and Saturn should reflect the rotation of the cloud from which they condensed. A planet formed by the aggregation of small solid bodies should also rotate in the forward sense. It will overtake bodies in smaller orbits at aphelion, where they move slower than the planet, and will also tend to collect them on the sunward side to produce forward rotation. Encounters with bodies in larger orbits will occur near perihelion and more frequently on the night side, to produce a similar result. Uranus must have swallowed a rather large cometesimal or protoplanet that tilted its plane of rotation.

The giant planets move in planes that never deviate much more than 1° from their common plane. This proves that they were formed by a process that involved average motions of the accreting matter rather precisely in the plane. The high inclination of Pluto's orbit (17°) may be accounted for by perturbations, since Pluto's perihelion falls within Neptune's orbit. Is Pluto really a large comet? Or is it a lost satellite of Neptune? Perhaps we will never know until we land a space probe on it.

I suspect that the Titius-Bode law, which does not hold well for the outer planets, states only that protoplanets collect material over larger areas at greater distances from the central gravitational mass. Possibly, mutual perturbation of the planets tends eventually to smooth out the gross irregularities in the original orbital distribution.

Because of their satellite systems, it is clear that during formation the giant planets all possessed great thin rings not dissimilar to the Laplacian disk about the Sun (Figure 11.11). Probably magnetohydrodynamics played little part in their development. The giant planets are still rotating quite rapidly.

We find that the innermost satellites of Jupiter are nearly of the density corresponding to earthy material. This suggests two possibilities: (1) that Jupiter in its formation was first gaseous but collected about it a large discoid, something like Saturn's rings, first of earthy material and later, as the discoid grew, of captured cometesimals; or (2) that the temperatures in the massive disk close to Jupiter were high enough to have vaporized the ices for a relatively long period of time so that the inner moonlets were composed of earthy material. At greater distances from the planet the cooling permitted the ices to collect into sizeable satellites. Probably the original discoids about Jupiter and Saturn were even larger than the extent of their present satellite systems.

For Saturn, we find that the satellite Titan is intermediate in density between icy and earthy materials, suggesting that Saturn developed an inner and earlier earthy ring that was subsequently increased by lower-density icy material to form Titan. Unfortunately, we have no information concerning the densities of other satellites at the present time. The retrograde motion of the inner and massive Triton about Neptune, and the presence of only one other small satellite in a much larger direct orbit, point strongly to one conclusion: Triton was captured, and in the process destroyed most of the satellite discoid or the actual satellites. Lyttleton [41] suggests that Pluto was then ejected from the system.

THE ORIGIN OF THE COMETS

This reconstruction of the origin of the giant planets provides us with a multitude of comets found near the common plane of motion. Those that formed well beyond Neptune are presumably still there, as Cameron observes, forming a thin disk or belt in the deep freeze of outer space. They cannot contribute appreciably to the supply of comets that we now observe. They will be the subject of further discussion.

The great comet cloud extending out to perhaps 100,000 AU from the Sun provides

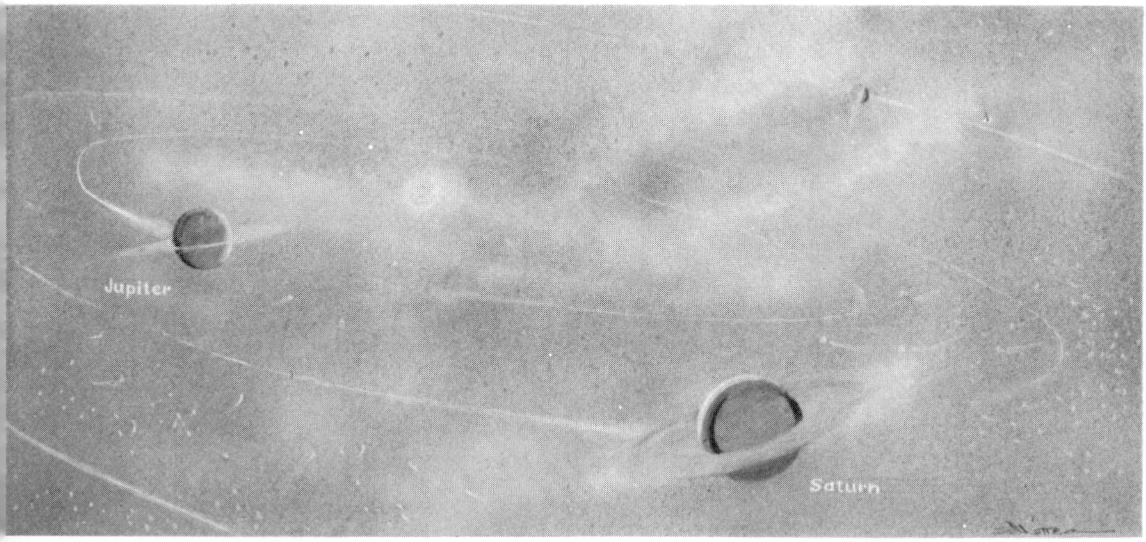

FIGURE 11.11
Drawing of planets during later stages of formation when comets were abundant

our present comets via the perturbations of passing stars. The comets of this cloud may well have originated near the plane of the disk in the region between Saturn and Neptune, having been perturbed into their present orbits by the gravitational actions of the planets. There are no stable orbits for small bodies in this region of space. Most of the cometesimals were probably captured by the planets to constitute the major fraction of Uranus and Neptune and a comparable mass each in Jupiter and Saturn. Some were perturbed into the Sun and others thrown out to interstellar space. Still others decayed in the inner regions of the system as they do today, while rapid collisions eliminated many. The remainder were thrown into extremely elongated orbits to provide our comet supply. . . .

THE FORMATION OF THE TERRESTRIAL PLANETS

Let us return now to the possible sequence of events within Jupiter's orbit. I see no reason to assume that the collapsing protosun should have ceased to leave a Laplacian discoid within Jupiter's present orbit. The density of the discoid per unit area of the plane should have increased fairly uniformly with decreasing solar distance until the protosun reached some temporary equilibrium, perhaps near the dimension of Mercury's present orbit. Any other assumption has a purely *ad hoc* character although many other possibilities cannot be disproved.

All evidence points to an accumulation of earthy planetesimals within Jupiter's orbit.

A combination of three factors, however, could have prevented a large planet from forming within Jupiter's distance. These are: (1) the higher densities and the greater heat of collapse of the discoid within Jupiter's orbit may have kept the ices from freezing while the gases were eliminated from the inner part of the system; (2) the magnetic lines of force were strengthened and the solar activity continuously increased in the later stages of collapse, preventing larger gaseous aggregates from collecting within Jupiter's orbit; (3) Jupiter's mass perturbed the motions of the solid aggregating planetesimals, increasing their orbital inclinations and eccentricities, thus increasing the violence of collisions and decreasing the rate of accumulation.

Before trying to reconstruct the early stages, let us work backwards from the present, at least with regard to the asteroid belt. All our evidence indicates that the asteroid belt is now a dissipative system; that is, collisions are etching away the asteroids, not building them. The velocity of escape even from the largest, Ceres, is only about 0.3 km/sec, while collisional velocities are typically 2 km/sec or more. Hence, practically all collisions among all asteroids, large or small, cause both participating bodies to lose more mass than they gain. We may conclude without question that all asteroids are now losing mass.

The present rate of dissipation of the asteroid belt, however, is not well established either theoretically or observationally. The etching rate for meteorites in space is too great to permit them to spiral toward the Sun by the momentum exchange with solar radiation, i.e., by the Poynting-Robertson effect. We observe the major collisional debris only in the form of fine dust in the Earth's neighborhood. The dust particles, if sufficiently small, can spiral in fast enough to avoid collisional destruction. From present rate estimates extrapolated backward in time, we can calculate that the asteroid belt may have lost as little as 1 per cent of its mass over the last four aeons.

Thus, as Sir Harold Jeffreys [42] has stressed, isolated small planetesimals without a gaseous discoid could never have collected into the present asteroids, once Jupiter began perturbing their orbits! No reasonable, though large, increase in the number and total mass of the early planetesimals will improve this situation.

We must conclude, therefore, that the asteroids were formed by one or more of the following classes of processes, which are not mutually exclusive: (*a*) from cometesimals or dirty snow, the ices and their vapors being lost after solar radiation became appreciable; (*b*) from planetesimals at a time when there was sufficient gas both to keep the orbits nearly circular near the fundamental plane and to form quasi-permanent atmospheres about the growing asteroids to cushion the collisions; (*c*) from sizable planetoids that, as in (*a*) or (*b*), accumulated rapidly in the early stages and later broke up into relatively small pieces.

The meteorites, whether or not they are typical of the asteroids, provide our only detailed information about these bodies. We cannot yet measure even the mass or density of any asteroid. The variety of mineralogical structures among the meteorites is evident from the fact that the 1,700 examples are individuals; almost all are readily distinguishable from the others. They were both formed and metamorphosed under a wide variety of physical circumstances. No simple single process or single sequence of processes can account for them all.

The prevalent chondrules possibly represent rather primitive matter, droplets that were formed and cooled quickly, possibly in the early stages of the collapsing nebular disk. It is quite probable that the earthy material was all or mostly vaporized just prior to the major condensation process near the plane of the planets within Jupiter's orbit. The pressures, however, could not have been great enough to have condensed out liquid droplets even at Mercury's orbit. Rather we expect the material, whether earthy or icy, to have condensed initially into rather fluffy, smoke-type particles which then accumulated into larger aggregates. The early ones could have been melted into droplets by heat in the nebula near the Sun, very likely by violent shock waves as Wood suggests, or conceivably by falling through the primitive atmospheres of asteroidal bodies. None of these concepts has yet any real theoretical support. The last requires velocities of several kilometers per second, which one might prefer to provide by gravitational attraction; this would then suggest rather massive parent bodies for the meteorites, i.e., the size of the Moon or greater. We have seen that slow cooling rates in solid bodies tend to preclude this explanation. Conceivably, chondrules may have formed in droplets within pools of molten silicates on the surface of asteroids that still retained their primitive hydrogen atmospheres. . . .

The capture of chondrules on sizable asteroidal bodies could be accomplished with little damage by the cushioning effect of extremely tenuous atmospheres with densities the order of 10^{-9}gm/cc, or less. These atmospheres need not be permanent but could be quasi-permanent, continuously replaced in relatively short intervals of time.

That we find so much meteoritic material with chondritic structure follows immediately from the nature of the collection and dissipation processes for such bodies. Having collected an appreciable amount of the incoming material in the form of chondrules, the asteroid grows, the pressure increases, and the deeper material tends to outgas with the increasing pressure. For asteroids of sufficient size, the eventual radioactive heating produces a molten center in which the iron is segregated gravitationally; but unless the asteroid is quite large there is a considerable volume near the center where the gravitational field is small. There we might expect to find a mixture of iron and stone, the pallasites. Somewhat farther out radially, the melting has become rather complete to produce the achondritic material in which the chrondrules have completely lost their identity. At higher levels the pressures and temperatures are modified by the outgassing process and surface cooling to produce the complex structures of chondrites. Near the surface the pressures and temperatures are low so that none of the inflowing material under the relatively low surface gravities melts; it sinters somewhat into material of low structural strength which is easily destroyed by collisions. The same situation applies to very small asteroids, perhaps the order of 30 km in diameter. All such asteroids now in existence would therefore be fragments of larger ones.

For the probably most abundant small asteroids without an iron core, the above sequence leads to a final state in which very little gas is retained, even in the upper layers. Most of the asteroid is a chondrite. The nature of the trace of gas depends heavily upon the time at which the asteroid grows and probably also upon its position with respect to the Sun. Early formation will occur in a reducing atmosphere. Late formation in larger bodies could result in considerable accumulation of the heavier gases, including water. Also, it is possible that some contributions have been made by cometesimals, particularly in the outer regions of the asteroidal belt near Jupiter.

Among asteroids in which the heavier gases are appreciable, the outer cold structure could form an ice trap near the surface, below which water and other volatile materials may have collected—a suggestion by DuFresne and Anders [43]. The cargonaceous chondrites could have developed in this manner.

On collisional breakage of the asteroid, the fragile outer material is quickly lost. If the breakup occurs early, while some of the solar nebula is still present, part of the material may be reaccumulated. Later on it will be ground to fine dust or gas and lost completely to small asteroids. The nickel-iron of the core will persist in space far better than the achondritic and chondritic material. We may today overestimate the original nickel-iron fraction by a large factor (10 or 100 times?). Probably most of the mechanically stronger material was chondritic from the smaller asteroids, the iron cores constituting a very minor fraction of the total asteroidal mass.

In discussing the complex processes of asteroidal formation and disintegration, it is vital to remember that these processes are continuous as stressed in the theory of O. J. Schmidt and B. Lévine [44]. At all stages collisions can produce a type of structure that Urey would class as a *secondary type* of meteorite, distinguished from the *primary* type that was quickly and immediately formed from the solar condensation. Note that his primary type was a gas sphere comparable to the Earth in mass with an earthy core of about a lunar mass. Consider two asteroids that collide at low velocities such that the breakage is not dissipative, that is, such that the final mass of the two after encounter is greater than the mass of either one originally. In such encounters an enormous amount of crushing and cracking will occur. This permits a certain redistribution of material between superficial and deeper layers. Immediately after the collision the broken mass will be rounded in form by gravity and the interior sealed.

If such collisions occur in the early stage of the nebula, they will produce bodies that continue through the cycle of radioactive heating so that their centers may be indistinguishable from those that were formed, particle by particle, without large disruptive collisional effects. Collisions of this type at successively later periods will produce meteorites of increasing complexity and variety. The nondissipative and moderately dissipative collisions can lead to anomalous juxtaposition of minerals with strikingly different histories, both with regard to temperature and composition, and subjected to further conditioning. Thus, it becomes apparent that Urey's concept of primary and secondary bodies can be modified to avoid the difficulty of two distinct accumulation periods or types of processes among the planetesimals. We need not wonder at the enormous variation among meteorites.

Nondissipative collisions would be limited to successively larger bodies as gas from the nebula is eliminated. In the very early stages the relative velocities among the smoke particles and the early accumulations would be small, allowing a rapid accumulation process. Perhaps magnetic attraction is important, as Wood suggests. After Jupiter perturbations have increased the relative velocities of the planetesimals, collisions among the smaller ones with negligible gravitational fields would become increasingly dissipative. Collisional dissipation of lunar-sized planetesimals would appear to be a rare phenomenon at any stage because of the high velocities required to overcome the internal potential energy. Consequently it seems unlikely that any asteroids larger than the Moon ever developed and dissipated by collision. A very few of lunar size or greater may have been enveloped by the terrestrial planets, and conceivably the Moon may have been captured by the Earth after it reached approximately its present size.

The detailed mechanism for eliminating the gases from the discoid is not yet clear, except that it must involve magnetohydrodynamics and violent solar activity, visualized as giant solar flares. A marked divergence from Hoyle's picture of planetary evolution, however, is evident. He calculates that the condensation process of the protosun continued without the formation of an appreciable discoid initially beyond a diameter roughly that of Mercury's present orbit. The magnetic lines of force in the Sun then strengthened to approximately a field of one gauss near the surface. The angular momentum transfer to reduce the Sun's rotation was effected through the loss of matter which was given higher and higher angular momentum in spiraling and twisted lines of force (Figure 11.6). He calculates that the outgoing gas carried with it cometesimals up to dimensions the order of 10 m and that these, plus the outgoing gases, condensed to form the various planets as we observe them.

Unfortunately, I cannot accept part of Hoyle's argument. His evidence that outflowing gas under these circumstances should carry along solid particles appears to be wrong. In the situation he presents, the magnetic lines exert a pressure on each other and tend to separate. In his diagram the major effect on the gas is an outward pressure from the Sun and a smaller component directed in the forward sense of rotation due to the lines of force. The outward pressure, as Hoyle indicates, will not remove the gas from the system, the removal being accomplished by the much smaller component of force forward along the direction of motion, which causes the gas to spiral outward and escape. The larger outward pressure, however, partially counteracts the solar attraction, thus effectively causing the gas to move in a smaller gravitational field than that of the solar mass alone. Consequently, at a given distance from the Sun the gas will be moving at a lower velocity than the solid particles. The solids effectively meet a resisting medium of gas; this tends to reduce their angular momentum and cause them to spiral slowly toward the Sun. Hoyle's process, I believe, fails to eject solid or icy aggregates at distances beyond the initial discoid. Consequently, I must agree with Cameron that some process of momentum transfer by magnetohydrodynamics begins, not within the orbit of Mercury, but at very much greater solar distances.

A major problem concerns the increasing iron content of the planets toward the Sun. It seems impossible that the pressure could have been high enough near the plane of the discoid to produce droplets of iron while silicates remained vapor. A remaining process suggested by Urey depends upon the relative strength of iron versus silicate particles to withstand collision. Whether the smaller particles tend to spiral inward or outward from the Sun does not greatly affect the situation. Rapid spiraling in either direction reduces the rate of capture by the planets. Slow spiraling increases the capture rate. The stony material will more easily be pulverized to extremely fine particles forced out by light pressure or to gas carried out by the solar wind or by solar flares. It is difficult to evaluate the likelihood of this collisional separation process, but one serious objection is outstanding; viz., the process does not operate for the newly condensed smoke but only after the particles are largely differentiated and the gas is dispersed. It hardly seems possible that enough iron could have been added to the planets in the later stages to have produced such a large density variation (refer to Table 11.5).

The iron abundance in the meteorites and planets is possibly high compared to that in the Sun. Note that the orbit of Mercury is much more inclined to the mean plane (4°.5–9°.8) than those of the outer terrestrial planets, much like the Sun's equator (7°.2). Could it be that Mercury was formed later than the other planets, from a final nebular wisp rotating at an appreciable angle to the original nebula and containing a greater abundance of iron? Such speculation is probably futile but does indicate the wide range of unprovable possibilities.

With resect to the abundances of the elements, the brilliant theory by Fowler, Greenstein, and Hoyle has some observational support. The theory requires heavy particulate irradiation by solar flares of planetesimals to produce: (1) the observed isotopic anomalies [45] among the light elements, (2) the $xenon^{129}$ anomaly, and (3) the production of short-lived radioactive isotopes like Al^{26}, to heat the asteroids quickly. Since FGH require that only 0.1 to 10 per cent of the Earth's mass and of the asteroids need be irradiated, the major accumulation could have occurred before the nebula had been largely cleared away. H. Mitler has also shown that enough water could have been supplied in hydrates so that icy cometesimals are not required. Thus, we need not postulate such extremely low temperatures near the Earth nor meet with the difficulty of removing a large fraction of water from the Earth's initial mass. If these ideas are correct, we should perhaps find somewhat higher abundances of the light elements in some of the meteorites than we find on the Earth. The absolute values of these abundances are not yet well enough determined to establish or disprove this concept. The cometesimals formed early at great solar distances could contain appreciable quantities of methane and carbon compounds to contribute to the carbonaceous chondrites. Thus, their composition may more closely represent the primitive nebula, as is suspected. Until we actually explore individual asteroids by space probes, we may never be able to determine the distance from the Sun at which any given meteorite originated.

The high- and the low-iron content groups of chondrites as found by Urey and Craig might conceivably arise from condensation near the Sun for the high-iron group and at greater distances for the low-iron group. No adequate explanation has yet been presented.

Thus, still speaking qualitatively, the asteroids and the terrestrial planets appear to have accumulated from planetesimals. It would appear, too, that most of the satellites developed much in the same fashion about their primaries. The Moon may be an exception.

The data and theory are not yet adequate to permit a choice between the FGH irradiation theory of isotopic distribution and other possible theories depending upon the genesis of the isotopes in stellar interiors, supernovae explosions, and the like. The large number of measurable isotopes should eventually make possible a clear-cut solution of the contribution made to the isotopic abundances by each of a large number of specific processes. The histories of the isotopes should then clarify the history of the terrestrial planets and asteroids.

REFERENCES AND NOTES

1. G. H. Henderson and S. Bateson, *Royal Soc. [London] Proc.*, v. A 145, p. 563–591 (1934).
2. C. C. Patterson, *Nuclear Processes in Geological Settings, II*, Pennsylvania State University, NAS–NRC Pub. 400 (1955), p. 157; C. C. Patterson, *Geochim. et Cosmochim. Acta*, v. 10, p. 230 (1956).
3. E. Anders, in *The Moon, Meteorites and Comets*, ed. G. P. Kuiper and B. M. Middlehurst (Chicago: University of Chicago Press, 1963), p. 402.
4. W. A. Fowler, *[U.S.] Natl. Acad. Sci. Proc.*, v. 52, p. 524 (1964).
5. J. H. Oort, *Astron. Inst. Netherlands Bull.*, v. 11, p. 91 (1950).
6. F. L. Whipple, *Astrophys. Jour.*, v. 111, p. 375 (1950); *Astrophys. Jour.*, v. 113, p. 464 (1951); "The physics of comets," *Soc. Royale sci. Liege Mem.*, v. 13, p. 321 (1953).
7. F. L. Whipple and L. G. Jacchia, *Smithsonian Contrib. Astrophys.*, v. 4, p. 97 (1961).
8. R. E. McCrosky, *Astron. Jour.*, v. 60, p. 170, Abstract (1955).
9. R. M. Goldstein and R. L. Carpenter, *Science*, v. 139, p. 910 (1963).
10. D. ter Haar and A. G. W. Cameron, in *Origin of the Solar System*, ed. R. Jastrow and A. G. W. Cameron (New York: Academic Press, 1963), p. 4.
11. L. Spitzer, Jr., *Astrophys. Jour.*, v. 90, p. 675 (1939).
12. C. F. von Weizsäcker, *Zeitschr. Astrophys.*, v. 22, p. 319 (1944).
13. K. Birkeland, *Acad. sci. [Paris] Comptes rendus*, v. 155, p. 892 (1912).

14. H. P. Berlage, Jr., *Koninkl. Nederlandse Akad. Wetensch. Proc.*, ser. B, v. 33, p. 614 (1930); v. 33, p. 719 (1930); v. 35, p. 553 (1932); v. 37, p. 221 (1934); v. 38, p. 857 (1935); v. 43, p. 532 (1940); v. 43, p. 557 (1940); v. 51, p. 796 (1948); v. 51, p. 965 (1948).
15. H. Alfvén, *Stockholms Obs. Ann.*, v. 14, no. 2 (1942); no. 5 (1943).
16. D. ter Haar, *Kgl. Danske Vidensk. Selsk. Mat-Fys. Medd.*, v. 25, no. 3 (1948).
17. D. H. Menzel, *The Universe in Action* (The Rushton Lectures Foundation, Birmingham: Birmingham Printing Company, 1957); also private communication.
18. F. Hoyle, *Royal Astron. Soc. Quart. Jour.*, v. 1, p. 28 (1960).
19. G. P. Kuiper and B. M. Middlehurst, eds., *Planets and Satellites* (Chicago: University of Chicago Press, 1961).
20. R. Wildt, *Royal Astron. Soc. Monthly Notices*, v. 107, p. 84 (1947).
21. W. H. Ramsey, *Roy. Astron. Soc. Monthly Notices*, v. 111, p. 427 (1951); v. 125, p. 469 (1963).
22. W. C. DeMarcus, *Astron. Jour.*, v. 63, p. 2 (1958); W. C. DeMarcus, in *Handbuch der Physik*, ed. S. Flugge (Berlin: Springer-Verlag, 1959), v. 52, p. 419.
23. H. C. Urey, *The Planets, Their Origin and Development* (New Haven: Yale University Press, 1952).
24. H. C. Urey, in *Physics and Astronomy of the Moon*, ed. Z. Kopal (New York: Academic Press, 1962), chap. 13.
25. H. Brown, *Astrophys. Jour.*, v. 111, p. 641 (1950); H. Brown and M. G. Ingraham, *Phys. Rev.*, v. 72, p. 347 (1947).
26. L. Goldberg, E. A. Muller, and L. H. Aller, *Astrophys. Jour. Supp.*, v. 5, no. 45, p. 1 (1960).
27. H. E. Suess, in *Summer Course on Nuclear Geology, Varenna*, 1960 (Comitato Nazionale per l'Energia Nucleare, Laboratorio de Geologia Nucleare, Pisa, Italy, 1960), p. 28.
28. G. P. Kuiper, in *Astrophysics*, ed. J. A. Hynek (New York: McGraw-Hill Book Co., 1951), chap. 8.
29. F. W. Aston, *Nature*, v. 114, p. 786 (1924).
30. W. W. Rubey, *Geol. Soc. America Bull.*, v. 62, p. 1111 (1951).
31. H. C. Urey and H. Craig, *Geochim. et Cosmochim. Acta*, v. 4, p. 36 (1953).
32. G. G. Goles, R. A. Fish, and E. Anders, *Geochim. et Cosmochim. Acta*, v. 19, p. 177 (1960).
33. H. H. Nininger, *Out of the Sky, an Introduction to Meteoritics* (New York: Dover Publications, 1952); E. L. Krinov, *Principles of Meteoritics* (New York: Pergamon Press, 1960); B. Mason, *Meteorites* (New York: John Wiley and Sons, 1962).
34. H. E. Suess, *Zeitschr. Elektrochemie*, v. 53, p. 237 (1949).
35. J. A. Wood, Jr., *Geochim. et Cosmochim. Acta*, v. 26, p. 739 (1962); J. A. Wood, Jr., *Icarus*, v. 2, p. 152 (1963); J. A. Wood, Jr., in *The Moon, Meteorites and Comets*, ed. G. P. Kuiper and B. M. Middlehurst (Chicago: University of Chicago Press, 1963), v. 4, chap. 12.
36. J. H. Reynolds, *Phys. Rev. Letters*, v. 4, p. 8 (1960).
37. A. G. W. Cameron, *Icarus*, v. 1, p. 13 (1962).
38. L. Mestel and L. Spitzer, *Royal Astron. Soc. Monthly Notices*, v. 116, p. 503 (1956).
39. E. Schatzman, *Mt. Wilson and Palomar Obs. Spec. Tech. Rept.* 3 (1960).
40. H. C. Urey, *Chem. Soc. Proc.*, v. 67 (1958).
41. R. A. Lyttleton, *Royal Astron. Soc. Monthly Notices*, v. 97, p. 108 (1936).
42. Sir Harold Jeffreys, *The Earth* (Cambridge: University Press, 1959), 4th ed.
43. R. R. DuFresne and E. Anders, *Geochim. et Cosmochim. Acta*, v. 26, p. 1085 (1962).
44. B. Levine, *L'Origine de la Terre et des Planetes* (Moscow: Editions en Langues Etrangeres 1958).
45. These observational data are now in question.

The Origin of the Earth

HAROLD C. UREY
1952

It is probable that as soon as man acquired a large brain and the mind that goes with it he began to speculate on how far the earth extended, on what held it up, on the nature of the sun and moon and stars, and on the origin of all these things. He embodied his speculations in religious writings, of which the first chapter of *Genesis* is a poetic and beautiful example. For centuries these writings have been part of our culture, so that many of us do not realize that some of the ancient peoples had very definite ideas about the earth and the solar system which are quite acceptable today.

Aristarchus of the Aegean island of Samos first suggested that the earth and the other planets moved about the sun—an idea that was rejected by astronomers until Copernicus proposed it again 2,000 years later. The Greeks knew the shape and the approximate size of the earth, and the cause of eclipses of the sun. After Copernicus the Danish astronomer Tycho Brahe watched the motions of the planet Mars from his observatory on the Baltic island of Hveen; as a result Johannes Kepler was able to show that Mars and the earth and the other planets move in ellipses about the sun. Then the great Isaac Newton proposed his universal law of gravitation and laws of motion, and from these it was possible to derive an exact description of the entire solar system. This occupied the minds of some of the greatest scientists and mathematicians in the centuries that followed.

Unfortunately it is a far more difficult problem to describe the origin of the solar system than the motion of its parts. The materials that we find in the earth and the sun must originally have been in a rather different condition. An understanding of the process by which these materials were assembled requires the knowledge of many new concepts of science such as the molecular theory of gases, thermodynamics, radioactivity and quantum theory. It is not surprising that little progress was made along these lines until the 20th century.

From *Scientific American,* vol. 187, no. 4, pp. 53–60 (*Scientific American* Offprint 833).

THE EARLIER THEORIES

It is widely assumed by well-informed people that the moon came out of the earth, presumably from what is now the Pacific Ocean. This was proposed about 60 years ago by Sir George Darwin. The notion was considered in detail by F. R. Moulton, who concluded that it was not possible. In 1917 it was again considered by Harold Jeffreys, who thought that his analysis indicated the possibility that the moon had been removed from a completely molten earth by tides. In 1931, however, Jeffreys reviewed the subject and concluded that this could not have happened; since then most astronomers have agreed with him.

But although Moulton and Jeffreys showed the improbability of the origin of the moon from the earth, they proposed theories for the origin of the solar system involving the removal of the earth and the other planets from the sun. Together with James Jeans and T. C. Chamberlin they proposed that another star passed near or collided with the sun, and that the loose material resulting from this cosmic encounter later coagulated into planets. This idea of the origin of the solar system has been widely held right up to the present.

The evidence gathered by our great telescopes now tells us that most of the stars in the heavens are pairs or triplets or quadruplets. We have determined the masses of multiple stars by means of Newton's laws of motion and his universal law of gravitation; we have also studied the velocities of these stars by significant changes in their spectra and by actually measuring the motions of nearby examples. We find that the two stars of a pair seldom have exactly the same mass, and that the ratio of the mass of one star to that of the other varies considerably. Gerard P. Kuiper of the University of Chicago concludes that the number of pairs of stars is entirely independent of the ratios of their masses; that is, there is very little probability that one ratio of masses would occur more often than another. . . .

Of course it would be very difficult to see a double star in which the secondary was only a thousandth as large as the primary, particularly if the second emitted no light. The sun and Jupiter, the largest of the planets, might be viewed as such a double star: Jupiter weighs about a thousandth as much as the sun, and it shines only by reflected sunlight. Even from the nearest star Jupiter would be invisible. There is much evidence, however, that a double star such as the sun and Jupiter should occur as a regular event in our galaxy, and the same considerations would seem to indicate that there may be as many as a hundred million solar systems within it. Solar systems are almost certainly commonplace, and not the special things that one might expect from the collision of two stars.

THE DUST CLOUD HYPOTHESIS

Many years ago E. E. Barnard of the Yerkes Observatory observed certain black spots in front of the great diffuse nebulae that occur throughout our galaxy. Bart J. Bok of Harvard University has investigated these opaque globules of dust and gas; they have about the mass of the sun and about the dimensions of the space between the sun and the nearest star. Lyman Spitzer, Jr., of Princeton University has shown that if large masses of dust and gas exist in space, they should be pushed together by the light of neighboring stars. Eventually, when the dust particles are sufficiently compressed, gravity should collapse the whole mass, and the pressure and temperature in its interior should be enough to start the thermonuclear reaction of a star.

It would seem reasonable to believe that if a star such as the sun resulted from a process of this kind, there might be enough material left over to make a solar system. And if the process was more complex we might even end up with two stars instead of one. Or again we might have triple stars or quadruple stars. Theories along this line are more plausible to us today than the hypothesis that the planets were in some way removed from the sun after its formation had been completed. In my opinion the older hypotheses were unsatisfactory because they attempted to account for the origin of the planets without accounting for the origin of the sun. When we try to specify how the sun was formed, we immediately find ways in which the material that now comprises the planets may have remained outside of it.

One piece of evidence that must be included in any theory about the origin of the solar system consists in our observation of the angular momentum that resides in the spinning sun and the planets that travel around it. The angular momentum of a planet is equal to its mass times its velocity times its distance from the sun. Jupiter possesses the largest fraction of the angular momentum in the solar system; only about two per cent resides in the sun. Another fact that must be encompassed by any theory is the so-called Titius-Bode law, which points out in a simple mathematical way how the distances of the planets from the sun vary: the inner planets are closer together and the outer ones are farther apart. This is only an approximate law which does not hold very well, and perhaps more emphasis has been put upon it than it deserves. In my own study of the problem I have looked for other evidence regarding the origin of the solar system.

In 1933, Henry Norris Russell of Princeton and Donald H. Menzel of Harvard pointed out that there was a very curious relationship between the proportions of the elements in the atmosphere of the earth and the atmospheres of the stars, including the sun. It is particularly noteworthy that neon, the gas that we use in electric signs, is very rare in the atmosphere of the earth but is comparatively abundant in the stars. Russell and Menzel concluded that neon, which forms no chemical compounds, escaped from the earth during a hot early period in its history, together with all of the water and other volatile materials that constituted its atmosphere at that time. The present atmosphere and oceans, they proposed, have been produced by the escape of nitrogen, carbon and water from the interior of the earth. The German physicist C. F. von Weizsäcker similarly suggested that the argon of the air has resulted mostly from the decay of radioactive potassium during geologic time, and has escaped from the interior of the earth. F. W. Aston of Cambridge University also pointed out that the other inert gases, krypton and xenon, were virtually missing from the earth.

THE CHEMICAL APPROACH

My own studies in the origin of the earth started with such thoughts about the loss of volatile chemical elements from the earth's surface. Exactly how did these elements escape from the earth, and when? I came to the conclusion that it was impossible that they were evaporated from a completely formed earth; the evaporation must have occurred at some earlier time in the earth's history. Once the earth was formed its gravitational field was much too strong for volatile gases to escape into space. But if these gases escaped from the earth at an earlier stage, what is the origin of those that we find on the earth today? Water, for example, would have tended to escape with neon, yet now it forms oceans. The answer seems to be that the chemical properties of water are such that it does not enter into volatile combinations at low temperatures. Thus if the earth had been even cooler than it is today, it might have retained some water in its interior that could have emerged later. But meteorites contain graphite and iron carbide, which require high temperatures for their formation. If the earth and the other planets were cool, how did these chemical combinations come about?

Indeed, what was the process by which the earth and other planets were formed? None of us was there at the time, and any suggestions that I may make can hardly be considered as certainly true. The most that can be done is to outline a possible course of events which does not contradict physical laws and observed facts. For the present we cannot deduce by rigorous mathematical methods the exact history that began with a globule of dust. And if we cannot do this, we cannot rigorously include or exclude the various steps that have been proposed to account for the evolution of the planets. However, we may be able to show which steps are probable and which improbable.

Kuiper believes that the original mass of dust and gas became differentiated into one portion that formed the sun and others that eventually became the planets. The precursors of the so-called terrestrial planets—Mercury, Venus, the earth and Mars—lost their gases. The giant planets Jupiter and Saturn retained the gases, even most of their exceedingly volatile hydrogen and helium. Uranus and Neptune lost much of their hydrogen, helium, methane and neon, but retained water and ammonia and less volatile materials. All this checks with the present densities of the planets.

It seems reasonably certain that water and ammonia and hydrocarbons such as methane condensed in solid or liquid form in parts of these protoplanets. The dust must have coagulated in vast snowstorms that extended over regions as great as those between the planets of today. After a time substantial objects consisting of water, ammonia, hydrocarbons and iron or iron oxide were formed. Some of these planetesimals must have been as big as the moon; indeed, the moon may have originated in this way. The accumulation of a body as large as the moon would have generated enough heat to evaporate its volatile substances, but a smaller body would have held them. Most of the smaller bodies doubtless fell into the larger; Deimos and Phobos, the two tiny moons of Mars, may be the survivors of such small bodies.

Massive chunks of iron must also have been formed. On the moon there is a huge plain called Mare Imbrium; it is encircled by mountains gashed by several long grooves. It would seem that the whole formation was created by the fall of a body perhaps 60 miles in diameter; this has been suggested by Robert S. Dietz of the U.S. Naval Electronics Laboratory, and by Ralph B. Baldwin, the author of a book entitled *The Face of the Moon*. The grooves must have been cut by fragments of some very strong material, presumably an alloy of iron and nickel, that were imbedded in this body. Of course large objects of iron still float through interplanetary space; occasionally one of them crashes into the earth as a meteorite.

How were such metallic objects made from the fine material of the primordial dust cloud? In addition to dust the planetesimals contained large amounts of gas, mostly hydrogen. I suggest that the compression of the gases in a contracting planetesimal generated high temperatures that melted silicates, the compounds that today form much of the earth's rocky crust. The same high temperatures, in the presence of hydrogen, reduced iron oxide to iron. The molten iron sank through the silicates and accumulated in large pools.

It now seems that the meteorites were once part of a minor planet that traveled around the sun between the orbits of Mars and Jupiter. The pools of iron that formed in this body may have been a few yards thick. In the case of the object that was responsible for Mare Imbrium and its surrounding grooves, the depth of the pools must have been several miles. If the temperature of such a planetesimal had been high enough, its silicates would have evaporated, leaving it rich in metallic iron. The object must eventually have cooled off, for otherwise its nickel-iron fragments could scarcely have been hard enough to plow 50-mile grooves on the surface of the moon.

It was at this stage that the planetesimals lost their gases; Kuiper believes that they were probably driven off by the pressure of light from the sun. This left the iron-rich bodies that are today the earth and the other planets. The whole process bequeathed a few meaningful fossils to the modern solar system: the meteorites and the surface of the moon, and perhaps the moons of Mars.

THE MOMENT OF INERTIA

Recently we have redetermined the density of the various planets and the moon. The densities of some, calculated at low pressures, are as follows: Mercury, 5; Venus, 4.4; the earth, 4.4; Mars, 3.96, and the moon, 3.31. The variation is most plausibly explained by a difference in the iron content of these bodies. And this in turn is most plausibly explained by a difference in the amount of silicate that had evaporated from them. Obviously a planet that had lost much of its silicate would have proportionately more iron than one that had lost less.

It is assumed by practically everyone that the earth was completely molten when it was formed, and that the iron sank to the center of the earth at that time. This idea, like the conception of an earth torn out of the sun, and a moon torn out of the earth, almost has the validity of folklore. Was the earth really liquid in the beginning? N. L. Bowen and other geologists at the Rancho Santa Fe Conference of the National Academy of Sciences in January, 1950, did not think so. They argued that if the earth had been liquid we should expect to find less iron and more silica in its outer parts.

There is other evidence. Mars, which should resemble the earth in some respects, contains about 30 per cent of iron and nickel by weight, and yet we have learned by astronomical means that the chemical composition of Mars is nearly uniform throughout. If this is the

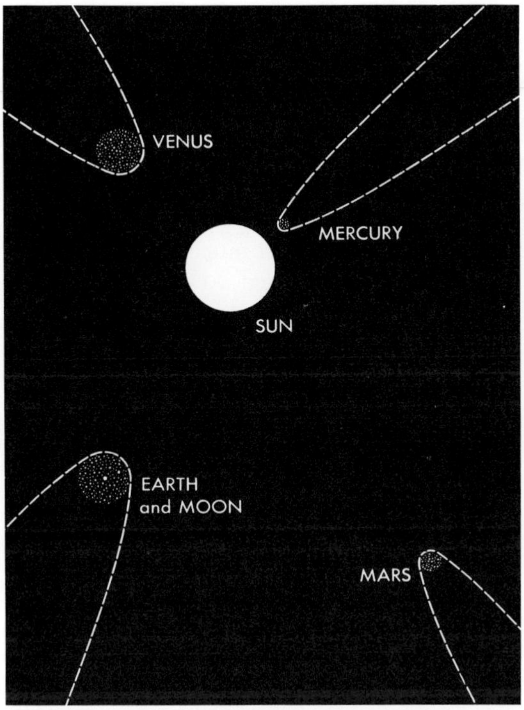

A

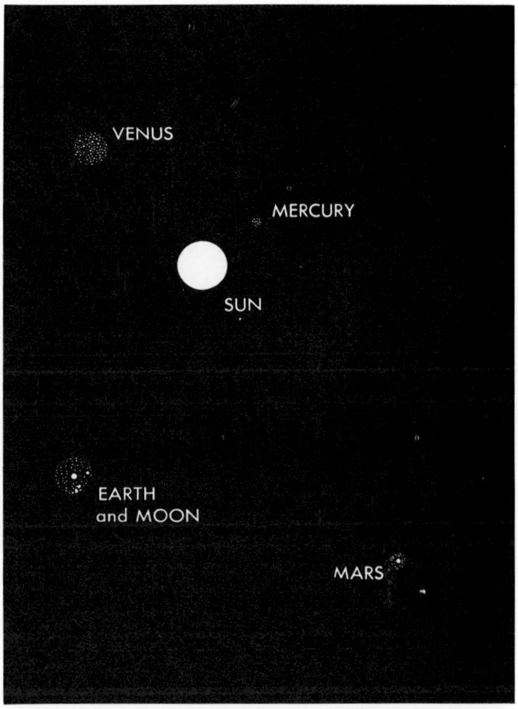

B

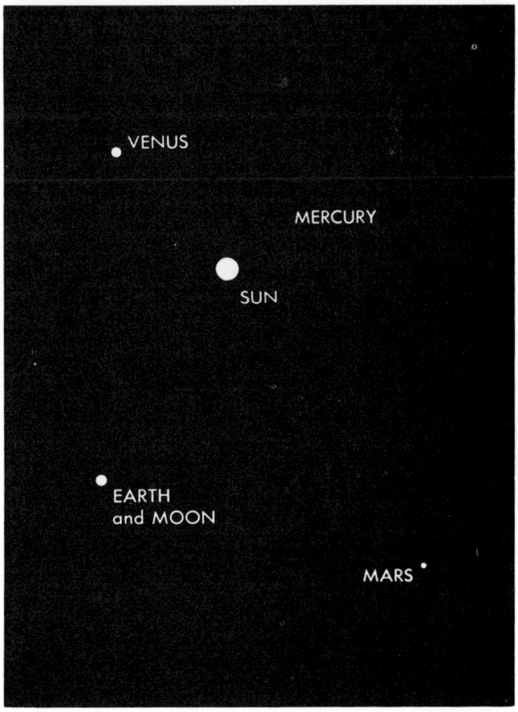

C

FIGURE 12.1
Evolution of the earth. The planets Mercury, Venus, Earth, and Mars are depicted in this series of schematic drawings. In *A* the primordial dust cloud has coagulated into protoplanets composed of planetesimals. The gases that have coagulated with the planetesimals are driven away (*dashed lines*) by the pressure of the light from the sun. In *B* the gas has been completely removed from the protoplanets. In *C* the planetesimals have formed the planets. The relative sizes of the sun and planets and the distances between them have been distorted for purposes of diagramatic clarity.

case, Mars could never have been molten. The scars on the face of the moon indicate that at the terminal stages of its formation metallic nickel-iron was falling on its surface. The same nickel-iron must have fallen on the earth, but there it would have been vaporized by the energy of its fall into a much larger body. Even so, if the earth had not been molten at the time, some of the nickel-iron might still be found in its outer mantle.

If there is iron in the mantle of the earth, it may be sifting toward the center of the earth; and if it is moving toward the center of the earth, it will change the moment of inertia of the earth. The moment of inertia may be defined as the sum of the mass at each point in the earth multiplied by the square of the distance to the axis of rotation, and added up for the whole earth. If iron were flowing toward the interior of the earth, this quantity should decrease. It is a requirement of mechanics that if the moment of inertia of a rotating body decreases, its speed of rotation must increase. Finally if the speed of the earth's rotation is increasing, our days should slowly be getting shorter.

Now we know that our unit of time is changing; but it is getting longer, not shorter. That is, the earth is not speeding up but is slowing down. Very precise astronomical measurements, some of them dating back to the observation of eclipses 2,500 years ago, indicate that the day is increasing in length by about one- or two-thousandths of a second per day per century. It has been thought that the lengthening of the day was due to the friction of the tides caused by the sun and the moon. But if we attempt to predict changes in the apparent position of the moon on the basis of this effect alone, we find that our calculations do not agree with the observations at all. If on the other hand we assume that iron is sinking to the core of the earth, the changing moment of inertia would also influence the length of the day. Indeed, calculations made on the basis of both the tides and the changing moment of inertia do agree with the observations.

In order to make the calculations agree we must postulate a flow of 50,000 tons of iron from the mantle to the core of the earth every second. Staggering though this flow may seem, it would take 500 million years to form the metallic core of the earth. . . .

THE LAST STAGES

Let us briefly retell what the course of events may have been. A vast cloud of dust and gas in an empty region of our galaxy was compressed by starlight. Later gravitational forces accelerated the accumulation process. In some way which is not yet clear the sun was formed, and produced light and heat much as it does today. Around the sun wheeled a cloud of dust and gas which broke up into turbulent eddies and formed protoplanets, one for each of the planets and probably one for each of the larger asteroids between Mars and Jupiter (see Figure 12.1). At this stage in the process the accumulation of large planetesimals took place through the condensation of water and ammonia. Among these was a rather large planetesimal which made up the main body of the moon; there was also a larger one that eventually formed the earth. The temperature of the planetesimals at first was low, but later rose high enough to melt iron. In the low-temperature stage water accumulated in these objects, and at the high-temperature stage carbon was captured as graphite and iron carbide. Now the gases escaped, and the planetesimals combined by collision.

So, perhaps, the earth was formed!

But what has happened since then? Many things, of course, among them the evolution of the earth's atmosphere. At the time of its completion as a solid body, the earth very likely had an atmosphere of water vapor, nitrogen, methane, some hydrogen and small amounts of other gases. J. H. J. Poole of the University of Dublin has made the fundamental suggestion that the escape of hydrogen from the earth led to its oxidizing atmosphere. The hydrogen of methane (CH_4) and ammonia (NH_3) might slowly have escaped, leaving nitrogen, carbon dioxide, water and free oxygen. I believe this took place, but many other molecules containing hydrogen, carbon, nitrogen and oxygen must have appeared before free oxygen. Finally life evolved, and photosynthesis, that basic process by which plants convert carbon dioxide and water into foodstuffs and oxygen. Then began the development of the oxidizing atmosphere as we know it today. And the physical and chemical evolution of the earth and its atmosphere is continuing even now.

The Age of the Elements in the Solar System

JOHN H. REYNOLDS

1960

From *Scientific American,* vol. 203, no. 5, pp. 171–182 (*Scientific American* Offprint 253).

How old is the solar system? The question is a big one, and it suggests research tools of commensurate size—large telescopes on mountaintops and rockets roaring into space. On the contrary, the answer is coming from the analysis of minute bits of matter by quite modest instruments mounted on the laboratory bench. It is true that the bits of matter come from meteorites: those samples of interplanetary rubble that are swept up by the earth's gravitational field. But the passage of cosmic time is measured by counting the few atoms of the "noble" gases—helium, argon, neon, krypton and xenon—that are trapped in the crystal lattices of meteoritic stone and iron.

Certain isotopes (atoms of the same element that have slightly different masses) of the noble gases represent clocks that have stopped. They are dead ends to which nuclear transformations have carried other atoms higher up in the table of elements. The transformation of some atoms proceeds spontaneously by radioactive decay. Since the rate of decay is immutable and is known, time can be measured by comparing the relative abundance of the parent elements and their noble-gas daughters present in a sample of matter. Some nuclear transformations in nature are induced by the impact of the highly energetic particles called cosmic rays. The rate at which these latter transformations occur can be estimated within reasonable ranges of error to yield another sort of time-scale.

As investigators have mastered these ways to tell time, they have found in the noble gases an independent check on the ticking of the classic uranium clock in the rocks of the earth. As a result it now appears that the cold planetary bodies of the solar system all crystallized at about the same time: some 4.5 or 4.6 billion years ago. The noble gas technique also dates the more recent breakup of some of these massive bodies into meteorites and provides clues to the life histories of the fragments. And one noble-gas clock that ran down and stopped at the very dawn of time has made it possible to reach into the twilight of cosmology and measure the full age of the solar system, from the epoch in which the elements that compose it were formed.

The uranium clock was one of the first fruits of the discovery of radioactivity. As early as 1907 workers in the Cavendish Laboratory of the University of Cambridge recognized that the decay of uranium to helium offered a way to measure the age of rocks. Natural uranium consists of two different isotopes that decay to helium at different rates. The helium-to-uranium ratio in a rock yields, therefore, a measurement of time, although the ratio must be qualified by the realization that the helium tends to leak away. Fortunately the decay of each uranium isotope also yields a different isotope of lead. These lead-to-uranium and lead-to-lead ratios lie behind most of the readings of the uranium clock.

The interest of investigators in helium was renewed about a decade ago, when measurement of the helium-to-uranium ratio in meteorites produced a startling result. In studying the ages of a number of iron meteorites, F. A. Paneth of the University of Durham arrived at values ranging from about one million years to 7.6 billion years. The upper figure raised a paradox; it was more than twice the then estimated age of the solar system. Since there was too much helium in the meteorites with respect to the uranium, it was suggested that some of the helium might have evolved from the breakdown of iron atoms under cosmic ray bombardment as the meteorite traveled on its orbit around the sun. If this were the case, the excess helium would turn out to be partly helium 3 rather than only the helium 4 which terminates the decay of uranium.

However, measuring the relative abundance of isotopes of the elements calls for procedures quite different from those that distinguish one element from another. Since isotopes differ primarily in mass, they must be discriminated by the tools of physics rather than of chemistry. With the help of the mass spectrometer, an instrument that sorts out atoms according to their masses, investigators soon established that helium 3 accounted for the paradoxical "age" of the meteorites. This work also had the larger consequence of stimulating studies of the other noble gases that occur in meteorites.

The radioactive isotopes that are produced by cosmic ray bombardment—for example, the carbon 14 in the earth's atmosphere—are easily detected. They proclaim their presence to sensitive radiation counters of various kinds. But when such isotopes are stable, it is normally all but impossible to detect a change in their relative abundance. The change is so small that even over geologic time it lies within the range of error of the best mass spectrometers. Happily the stable isotopes of helium and the other noble gases in meteorites represent an exception. They are so scarce to begin with that any change in their abundance ratios looms quite large. What is more, the chemical inertness that gives them their patent of nobility makes it possible to isolate the tiny quantities that occur in meteorites, without significant contamination by noble gases of terrestrial origin.

The chemical segregation of chemically active elements by conventional procedures necessarily involves great contamination. Suppose that an element of atomic weight 40 is to be isolated from a sample weighing one gram. The first step is to dissolve the sample in some way, for example by using hydrofluoric acid. The next step will involve distillation, precipitation or passing the sample through an ion-exchange column. In any case the sample will be mixed with as much as 100 grams of liquid, including a number of extraneous atoms of atomic weight 40. Assuming that a purity (with respect to that atomic weight) of a few parts in a billion can be achieved, the procedure will still introduce about two billionths of 100 grams, or .0000002 gram, of contaminating material. This corresponds to about three million billion (3×10^{15}) atoms of an element of atomic weight 40.

In noble gas "chemistry" the procedure is quite different. To start with, the sample of meteorite is melted in a vacuum. Exposure of the released gas to hot copper oxide, to a trap cooled with liquid air and to a few milligrams of hot calcium or titanium accomplishes the required purification. All but the noble-gas elements either freeze out in the liquid-air trap or combine with the calcium or titanium, leaving a phase of almost pure noble gas ready for study in the mass spectrometer. Under typical conditions the background pressure in the pur-

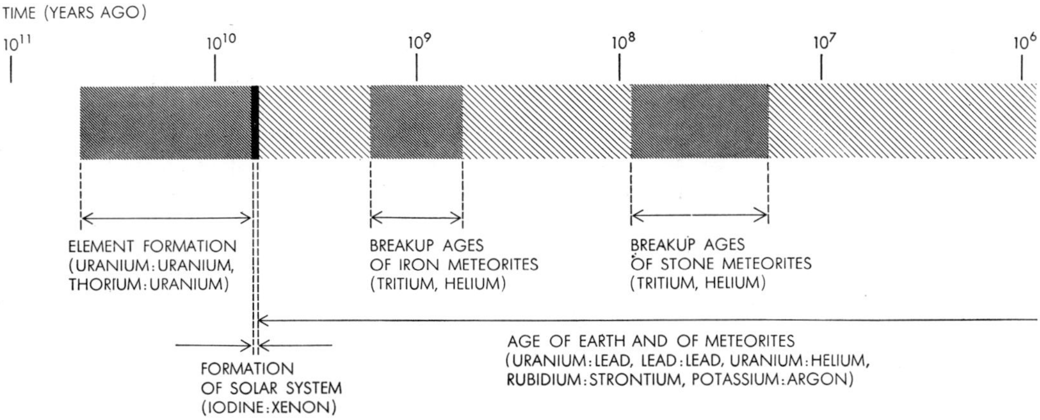

FIGURE 13.1
History of the solar system. Calculation from the element ratios shown in parentheses is plotted logarithmically. On the theory that the formation of the heavier elements took 10 billion years, the interval (*formation of solar system*) from the end of element formation to the crystallization of the earth's crust is 120 million years. On the theory that the elements were created at about the same time some five billion years ago, the interval is 290 million years. The age of earth and of meteorites is 4.6 billion years. The breakup ages of meteorites represent the time since the parent bodies of which they are fragments last broke up. The lowest value shown for iron meteorites (600 million years) is the average breakup age; the highest age is 1.7 billion years. Corresponding values for stone meteorites are 20 million and 90 million years. The ages are computed from the content of helium 3 in a meteorite and its rate of production (calculated from the tritium decay-rate).

ification system is about one billionth of an atmosphere. The volume of the system is typically one liter; at this pressure there is about one millionth of a cubic centimeter of extraneous gas. Assuming that the gas has the composition of air, 1 per cent of it will be argon, mostly argon 40. The contamination level at atomic weight 40 is then one hundred-millionth of a standard cubic centimeter, or 300 billion (3×10^{11}) atoms; that is, one ten-thousandth of the contamination in conventional chemistry. For the less abundant noble gases the number of contaminating atoms is correspondingly less. For neon, krypton and xenon the approximate levels of contamination are respectively 500 million, 30 million and two million atoms. Helium is rather a special case because it diffuses so readily in hot solids; special precautions must be taken if helium contamination from the atmosphere is to be kept at a minimum. The last step, measuring the isotopic abundances in the tiny noble gas samples, is accomplished with mass spectrometers especially designed for this task.

Dramatic proof of cosmic-ray production of helium 3 in meteorites came in 1952, when K. I. Mayne of the University of Oxford and Paneth and P. Reasbeck at Durham announced that they had found a helium-3 to helium-4 ratio of about one to three in a number of meteorites. In the earth's atmosphere, by contrast, the ratio is one to a million. Two years later Mayne and Reasbeck found that the ratios among the neon isotopes in meteorites also differ markedly from those in the atmosphere. The neon isotopes of mass 20, 21 and 22 appear in the atmosphere in the ratios of 350 to 1 to 34. In meteorites these three isotopes occur in roughly equal abundance. At about the same time W. Gentner and Josef Zähringer in Germany discovered similar variations in meteoritic argon.

These findings not only brought the ages of meteorites into line with the age of the earth's crust as measured by the uranium clock; they also opened up the history of the meteorites to study. It became possible to determine with considerable accuracy how long a meteorite had been exposed to cosmic radiation before it reached the earth [see Figure 13.1]. This involves measuring the amount of helium 3 in a meteoritic sample and dividing this figure by a calculated cosmic-ray production rate. The exposure ages of meteorites vary considerably. In most common stone meteorites it is a few tens of millions of years, with individual ages ranging all the way from four million to 90 million years. The average exposure age of iron meteorites is considerably longer—about 600 million years, with individual ages ranging up to 1.7 billion years.

Though these extreme variations present some difficulties, it is generally agreed that the exposure ages represent breakup ages, that is, the time since a given fragment was last detached from a larger parent body. In a planet or planetoid, the main mass of the material is shielded from cosmic radiation. When such a body breaks up in collisions with other sizable objects, its various fragments are exposed to cosmic rays and, with each successive breakup, still smaller fragments become exposed to bombardment. The systematic difference in the breakup ages of stone and iron meteorites is explained by the deduction that the latter do not break up as easily.

These studies have also told something about the individual life histories of meteorites. By analyzing the distribution of helium 3 in thin cross-sectional slabs of metal cut from two iron meteorites—the Grant meteorite and the Carbo meteorite—investigators were able to determine the distribution of helium 3 in the body of a meteorite. "Contour maps" prepared by J. H. Hoffman and Alfred O. C. Nier at the University of Minnesota show that the helium-3 content falls off toward the center of the bodies, as would be expected. The contours also show that the Grant meteorite reached the earth in something like its original shape, though it lost about half of its original mass to erosion by friction in the earth's atmosphere. In the case of Carbo the helium-3 contours indicate that most of one half was eroded away. Edward L. Fireman of Harvard University has measured the helium-3 content in Carbo with essentially the same results.

Helium 3 thus yields clues to the age and biography of the meteorite as a fragment of some larger parent body. But it does not reflect the age of the stone or iron that constitutes the meteorite. This is a more general and significant question because it bears upon the age of the solar system as a whole. If all the cold bodies in the solar system cooled down and crystallized at about the same time, as other considerations suggest, then a meteorite is as good a sample for this determination as a terrestrial rock which dates its crystallization from the most primitive era of our planet. Many meteorites have accordingly been subjected to the standard uranium-clock measurements. But stone meteorites also contain argon, which provides an independent check on the uranium clock.

Argon is the daughter of potassium 40, the relatively rare radioactive isotope of this common mineral element. The half-life of potassium 40 is 1.3 billion years, that is, half of the atoms of the isotope present in the rock disintegrate spontaneously in that period. The reaction yields two daughter elements: 89 per cent of the potassium 40 turns into calcium 40; the other 11 per cent turns into argon 40. As a consequence any mineral containing potassium gradually accumulates argon 40 in its lattice. So long as the system is undisturbed, the rate of argon accumulation is definite and immutable, governed only by the potassium content and by the rate of decay. By measuring both the potassium-40 and the argon-40 content in such an undisturbed sample it is possible to compute how long the system has been accumulating argon or, in other words, to calculate the date at which the sample crystallized.

This method was first applied to meteorites in 1951 by E. K. Gerling and his coworkers in the U.S.S.R. Since then investigators at various laboratories have dated many stone meteorites. A consistent pattern has emerged from the results: the potassium-argon ages of the most common stone meteorites tend to clump in the range of 4 to 4.5 billion years. Some of the ages fall below this clump, but none are higher. These findings are consistent with the age of 4.6 billion years indicated by the lead-to-uranium ratios and the parallel decay of rubidium to strontium. That the potassium-argon age is somewhat "younger" is taken to reflect the fact that the parent body of the meteorites was hot early in its history; some of the argon would thus have been lost before the body cooled to a temperature at which it began to retain argon. The still younger ages found for some meteorites indicate either that the potassium occurred in minerals unfavorable for argon retention or that some argon may have boiled out of the meteorite on an unusually close passage around the sun.

An age of 4.6 billion years is now generally accepted for both meteorites and the crust of the earth. All evidence indicates that the stable, cold objects in the solar system took their present form at about that time.

Before the advent of the noble-gas technique for measuring time, it was quite difficult to go back further into the past with anything like certainty. The success of the technique in recent years encouraged investigators to apply it to the task of dating the origin of the elements themselves. With that ultimate starting point established, it might be possible to learn more about events in the period during which the solar system took shape from primordial matter. Inquiry into the age of the elements, however, takes one almost immediately into the thick of the controversy that divides cosmologists into two camps: the proponents of the "evolutionary" cosmology, who hold that the heavier elements were formed (along with hydrogen) all at once; and the "steady state" theorists, who contend that the formation of elements (including hydrogen) has been going on all along.

The simpler choice is to assume that the heavier elements were all created at once, or in a very brief period. One can then ask: When were they formed? Or, speaking of meteorites specifically, what was the time interval between the formation of the elements they contain and the time at which they crystallized?

One of the most important keys to the answer is the abundance ratio of the two long-lived radioactive isotopes of uranium—uranium 235 and uranium 238. Of the two, uranium 235 is much shorter lived, having a half-life of 700 million years, compared to 4.5 billion years for uranium 238. The relative abundance of these two isotopes is about 1 to 137. Going back in time, it is apparent that the ratio has doubled about every 850 million years. If the original ratio was unity, as seems reasonable to assume, then these isotopes were formed no more than approximately 6.6 billion years ago. The very existence now of uranium 235, with its shorter half-life, places an upper limit on the age of the elements in the solar system.

The difficulty is that the original abundance ratio is not known. For each uncertainty of two, that is, with each doubling of the ratio, there is a corresponding uncertainty of about 850 million years in the time interval between element formation and the crystallization of the planetary bodies. The problem may be illustrated by a simple analogy. Suppose a clock is provided with a counter to indicate the number of times it has struck 12. The reading on the counter then tells how long the clock has run. But the reading has an inherent 12-hour error, because one does not know the hour at which the clock was set when it was wound. Under such circumstances another clock, wound at the same time but running, say, 40 times faster, would be highly useful. If the counter of the first clock were to read 1, the counter of the second would show something like 40. The original setting of the first clock could ten be calculated with an error of only 18 minutes (one 40th of 12 hours).

Harrison Brown, now at the California Institute of Technology, suggested in 1947 that one of the shorter-lived radioactive elements might be used in just this way—as a faster-running clock to calibrate the original setting of the uranium clock. The original element would now be extinct, having disappeared from the solar system long ago by virtue of its relatively rapid decay; the clock would have by now completely run down. But it might still have been running at the time the meteorites were formed. In this case some atoms of the element would have been incorporated in the meteorites, and, under favorable conditions, they would have left a detectable "fossil" there. This fossil would be the daughter isotope to which all the radioactive material would have eventually decayed.

Following Brown's suggestion, the table of elements was searched for possible parent-daughter pairs. Since the parent isotope was necessarily extinct, it had to be found among the "artificially" radioactive products of the nuclear reactor or the high-energy accelerator. The most likely pair proved to be iodine 129

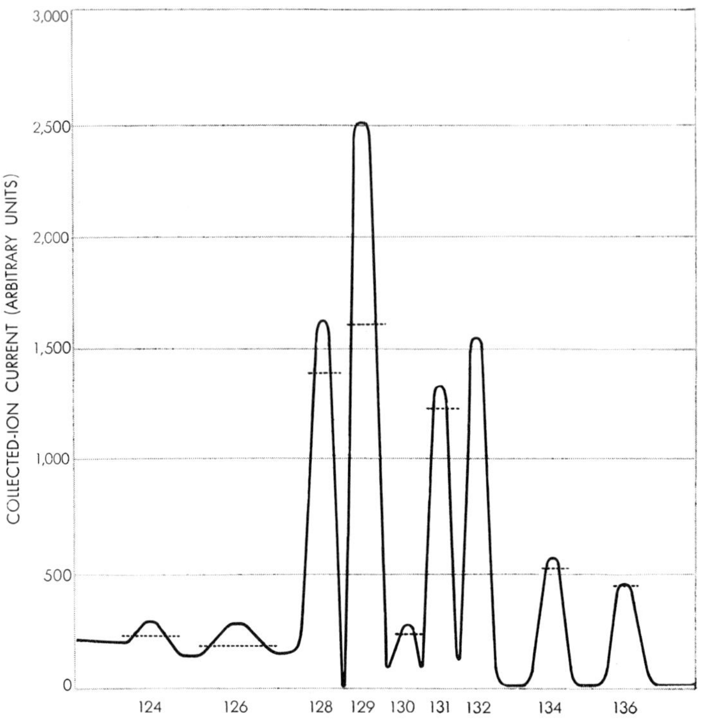

FIGURE 13.2
Excess xenon 129 in the Richardton meteorite.. Here the scale of the mass spectrum is linear. Xenon 124, 126, and 128 (*numbers at bottom*) are recorded at a sensitivity 10 times that for others. The standard was xenon 132. In a normal sample the peaks would be at the dotted lines.

and its daughter xenon 129. A fairly common fission-product, iodine 129 was almost certainly formed in nature along with ordinary stable iodine 127, and in approximately equal abundance. Because it has a half-life of only 17 million years, it has completely disappeared. This half-life seemed to be in just the right range—long enough so that some of the isotope might have been incorporated in meteorites, but short enough to provide a clock that runs down about 40 times faster than the uranium clock. The daughter, xenon 129, also seemed ideal for the purpose. It is a noble gas, and that portion of it which arose from the decay of iodine 129 would show up in meteorites as an excess over the average ratio of xenon 129 to xenon 132. But when the first attempts in 1955 and 1956 failed to reveal such excess xenon 129, the prospects for finding extinct radioactivity seemed poor indeed.

Then in November of 1959 a small piece of very crumbly stone that fell in Richardton, N.D., in 1918 yielded the looked-for excess in our laboratory at the University of California. The mass spectrometer showed clearly that several of the isotopes, when compared to the reference isotope xenon 132, were in anomalous abundance in the Richardton meteorite, but the most striking excess was that of xenon 129 [see Figure 13.2.] This effect has since been confirmed in samples of Richardton studied at the University of Minnesota and at Heidelberg University, and in other meteorites studied at the University of California. In the black stone Indarch, which fell in 1891 in Transcaucasia, the xenon-129 peak is 3.4 times higher than the xenon-132 peak, a reading that is five times as striking as that in Richardton.

Quantitative studies of Richardton samples have already yielded preliminary figures. The amount of excess xenon 129 and the amount of stable iodine 127—which serves as an indication of the amount of iodine 129 originally formed—have been measured. The ratio of these two quantities is .000010. Calculating from the 17-million-year half-life, the time required for the iodine-129 to iodine-127 ratio to fall from 1, or thereabouts, to .000010 proves to be 290 million years.

This interval is not greatly affected when it is recalculated on the assumption (which accords with steady-state cosmology) that the heavier elements were built up over billions of years. William A. Fowler and Fred Hoyle at the California Institute of Technology and A. G. W. Cameron of the Chalk River Laboratory in Canada think it likely that a long succession of exploding stars have gradually built up the present inventory of these elements. Their estimates of this buildup period, based on theoretical production rates of the two uranium isotopes and of thorium, run close to 10 billion years. In this case the ratio of iodine 129 to iodine 127 at the conclusion of element formation in the vicinity of the solar system would not be 1 but .0025. Steady decay of iodine 129 over the long buildup period accounts for the large decline in the ratio. The time required thereafter to bring the ratio down from .0025 to .000010—that is, the time from the formation of the elements to the incorporation of the elements in the solid bodies of the solar system—would be 137 million years. If iodine production was not uniform over the 10 billion years of element formation, but declined throughout this interval as some astrophysicists believe, another small correction must be applied—giving 120 million years instead of 137.

In terms of cosmological time the difference between 120 million years and 290 million years is not great. In either case it can be stated that there has been element-building which contributed to the solar system within the last 4.9 billion years.

The iodine-xenon clock is not yet fully calibrated. Past experience with other important radioactive clocks has shown that the clock becomes more reliable as experimental techniques improve. The iodine-xenon clock should ultimately provide a reliable time-scale for events which took place at about the time the solar system was formed. It is clear, however, that the time interval between element formation and the formation of the minerals in the meteorites is relatively short. Otherwise the iodine clock would have completely run down before the minerals were formed. The possibility that billions of years intervened between the formation of the elements of the solar system and the time its planetary bodies were formed is now conclusively ruled out.

BIBLIOGRAPHY

Fowler, William A., and F. Hoyle, 1960, Nuclear cosmochronology: Ann. Phys., v. 10, no. 2, p. 280–302.

Hurley, Patrick M., 1959, How old is the earth?: New York, Anchor Books, Doubleday.

Reynolds, J. H., 1960a, Determination of the age of the elements: Phys. Rev. Letters, v. 4, no. 1, p. 8–10.

———, 1960b, Isotopic composition of primordial xenon: Phys. Rev. Letters, v. 4, no. 7, p. 351–354.

SECTION **III**

THE ANTIQUITY OF THE EARTH AND THE RECORDS OF GEOLOGIC TIME

The poor world is almost six thousand years old.

William Shakespeare, AS YOU LIKE IT

Charles Darwin, as much a geologist as he was a biologist, worried about whether enough time had passed for life to have achieved its great diversity by means of natural selection, and about the absence of intermediate forms in the geologic record as he knew it. He discussed these and many other problems in Chapter 10 of *The Origin of Species* under the title "On the Imperfection of the Geological Record" (Reading Selection 14). Darwin, of course, did not invent the idea of evolution, as he made abundantly clear in the preface to his great work. He did what is always more important and more difficult than merely formulating an idea: he marshalled the evidence that made the idea compelling, and then proposed a plausible mechanism to explain it. Eventually, many of the gaps that troubled him were to be filled. The geologic record came to provide the strongest documentation for evolution, time was ultimately seen to have been adequate for organic evolution, and the evolving sequences of life forms provided grounds for sequential subdivision and correlation of the conspicuously fossiliferous rocks. Although he insisted that much time had been required for evolutionary history to unfold, Darwin recognized the inapplicability of some of the "criteria" that were then accepted for great age in rocks—metamorphism for example. He also reached other essentially modern geological conclusions—for instance, that exposure of crystalline rocks at the surface means deep erosion, and that the absence of older sediments on oceanic islands implies something significant about oceanic history. In this essay, in effect, Darwin posed some of the most basic problems of geochronology before the means to solve them had been visualized. He also expressed some conjectures which time has not validated. The value of his essay here is retrospective: In reading Darwin's views, and then in seeing how, with the passage of time, they have been substantiated, modified, or negated, we can imagine how the best natural science of our time may look a century from now.

The discovery of radioactivity by Becquerel in 1885 pointed the way to the resolution of Darwin's geochronological dilemma. It was followed in 1907 by the first radiometric age determinations, based on lead-uranium ratios determined by B. B. Boltwood of Yale University. Over the next half century a brilliant array of new discoveries, techniques, and measurements pushed the age of the earth and the limits of resolution to a magnitude and refinement undreamed of by Darwin and his contemporaries. The story of geochronology by nuclear decay series owes its elaboration to a number of meticulous and determined investigators whose work is summarized by A. O. Woodford in Reading Selection 15. Woodford is not a nuclear geochemist himself, but an outstanding geologist and teacher who understands the methods and their limitations and is able to explain them clearly.

Reading Selection 16 is a classic and tightly reasoned paper by geochemist Clair Patterson of the California Institute of Technology titled "Age of Meteorites and the Earth." Assuming that meteorites (1) were all formed at about the same time, (2) have since existed as isolated and essentially closed systems, (3) originally contained lead of identical isotopic composition, and (4) contain uranium of the same isotopic composition as the earth, the age of an array of meteoritic lead isotope and lead-uranium ratios can be found. Patterson found that such an array closely fixes the time of a common homogenization event affecting all meteorites at about 4.55 aeons ago, give or take 70 million years. Does this also imply a common age for the origin of meteorites and the origin of the earth? Of interest, in this regard, is the low uranium content of the lead isolated from the ferrous sulfide mineral troilite in the Canyon Diablo meteorite. The amount of uranium in the troilite is so small that no observable change in the isotopic composition of the associated lead can have resulted from its decay. That isotopic composition, therefore, is taken as the primeval isotopic composition of lead, and from this an equation is derived that shows terrestrial galenas and oceanic lead to fall on the same isochron as that defined by meteoritic lead, indicating a common age of roughly 4.55 aeons for both. Although Tilton and Steiger (1965, see Supplemental Reading) question the exact number and suggest an age of perhaps as much as 4.8 aeons, it seems that we are narrowing in on a highly probable age for the earth, (or at least for the primary materials from which it was formed) of around 4.6 to 4.8 aeons.

The older rocks are now rapidly yielding a more refined geochronology to the nuclear decay series, enhancing the prospect that the very long record of earth history that preceded the time of differentiated multicellular animal life (the Phanerozoic) may yet be written in comparable detail. Other exciting discoveries are being made about the Pleistocene—that time in the history of the earth that encompasses the circumstances of man's origin, diversification, and dispersal. Here, improved resolution has been introduced by the radiocarbon method, described by Nobel laureate W. F. Libby of the University of California in Reading Selection 17. The paper has been adapted from Libby's Nobel address on the development of radiocarbon dating. The difficulties, the diversity of interaction, and the triumphs of scientific investigation are nowhere better illustrated than in this lucid paper. There are, of course, limitations to the radiocarbon method, and these are here examined along with its applications.

But radiometric determination is not the only method for accurately measuring the ages of very ancient rocks. One of the more remarkable recent developments in geochronology, planetology, and paleontology occurred in 1963, when John Wells of Cornell University recognized that the calcareous exoskeletons of certain fossil corals preserve a record of incremental growth that strongly suggests both daily and yearly cycles. So interpreted, those growth lines show that there was a regular increase in the number of days per year and therefore a decrease in length of day in the geologic past. This has opened up a new field of research that promises: (1) a new basis for assigning numerical ages to Phanerozoic rocks, (2) more reliable measurements of the frictional retardation of the earth's rotation through geologic time and the transfer of angular momentum from earth to moon, and (3) new information about the nature of circadian rhythms. The important studies by Wells and by C. T. Scrutton (who discovered a monthly cycle) and some of their implications, particularly with regard to the frictional retardation of the earth's motion, are described by S. K. Runcorn in Reading Selection 18. Although the significance of that work for geochronology is not stressed in this paper, as it is in those papers by Wells (1963), Scrutton (1965), and Runcorn (1966) listed under Supplemental Reading, it is obvious that if a few reliable points define a curve showing a regular relation between the geologic age and the number of days in the year, then any fossil showing daily growth increments, when located at the appropriate place on this curve, will give the approximate probable age of the source rocks in years. This, of course, is a self-checking system, as the same fossil will likely also reveal its approximate age by the evolutionary stage it represents.

Thus we come to paleontology, which, as expressed in William Smith's principle of biologic succession, provided the first subdivision of geologic time—although this subdivision was purely sequential and incomplete. Master stratigrapher W. J. Arkell explains briefly how sequential subdivision is accomplished in an introductory chapter titled "Classification and Correlation" (Reading Selection 19) from his great book *Jurassic Geology of the World*. Arkell describes the nature and uses of formation, zone, and stage, and emphasizes the wide utility of stages in subdivision and correlation of Phanerozoic time. These concepts are much more extensively discussed by W. B. N. Berry (1968, see Supplemental Reading) in his review of the growth of sequence geochronology.

Indeed, those who may be stimulated to seek additional reading will find an embarrassment of riches in the Supplemental Reading. One of the truly remarkable papers listed is that of Barrell (1917) who, with a handful of crude lead-uranium numbers and some shrewd geological inference, came up with a geochronologic framework that has been modified surprisingly little by subsequent refinements. The papers by Knopf (1957) and Holmes (1959) are written with much verve and provide good historical background. Milne's book (1952) poses some tantalizing problems in the geochronologic interpretation of nuclear-decay ages. Smiley's compendium (1955) discusses a full array of geochronologic methods other than nuclear decay. Glaessner's paper (1966) emphasizes the increasing refinement in stratigraphic subdivision and correlation that has resulted from increasingly detailed studies of the evolutionary sequences of fossils and their lithologic associations. Kitt's essay (1966) is a provocative critique of geologic concepts of time, correlation, and time-stratigraphic nomenclature. The origin of the formal names of eras, periods, and epochs is described with great care by M. Grace Wilmarth (1925), and the rules for selecting or creating valid stratigraphic names are formulated in the "Code of Stratigraphic Nomenclature" by the American Commission on Stratigraphic Nomenclature (1961); such matters should be apprehended by all students of historical geology.

Supplemental Reading

Aldrich, L. T., and G. W. Wetherill, 1958, Geochronology by radioactive decay: Ann. Rev. Nuclear Sci., v. 8, p. 257–298.

American Commission on Stratigraphic Nomenclature, 1961, Code of stratigraphic nomenclature: Am. Assoc. Petroleum Geologists Bull., v. 45, p. 645–665.

Barrell, Joseph, 1917, Rhythms and the measurements of geologic time: Geol. Soc. America Bull., v. 28, p. 745–904.

Berry, W. B. N., 1968, Growth of a prehistoric time scale: San Francisco, W. H. Freeman and Company, 158 p.

Bradley, W. H., 1929, The varves and climate of the Green River epoch: U.S. Geol. Survey Prof. Paper 158-E, p. 87–110.

Brown, Harrison, 1957, The age of the solar system: Scientific American Offprint 102, 11 p.

Eicher, D. L., 1968, Geologic time: New York, Prentice-Hall, 149 p.

Faul, Henry, ed., 1954, Nuclear geology: New York, John Wiley and Sons, 414 p.

———, 1966, Ages of rocks, planets, and stars: New York, McGraw-Hill, 109 p.

Glaessner, M. F., 1966, Problems of paleontology: Geol. Soc. India Jour., v. 7, p. 14–27.

Goldich, S. S., and others, 1961, The Precambrian geology and geochronology of Minnesota: Minnesota Geol. Survey Bull. 41, p. 8–35.

Harland, W. B., A. G. Smith, and B. Wilcock, 1964, The Phanerozoic time-scale: Geol. Soc. London Quart. Jour., v. 120S, 458 p.

Holmes, Arthur, 1965, Principles of physical geology (2d ed.): New York, Ronald Press, 1288 p. (p. 346–385, Dating the pages of earth history).

Hurley, P. M., 1949, Radioactivity and time: Scientific American Offprint 220, 6 p.

Kitts, D. B., 1966, Geologic time: Jour. Geology, v. 74, p. 127–146.

Knopf, Adolph, 1957, Measuring geologic time: Scientific Monthly, v. 85, no. 5, p. 225–236.

Kulp, J. L., 1961, Geologic time scale: Science, v. 133, p. 1105–1114.

Milne, E. A., 1952, Modern cosmology and the Christian idea of God: London, Oxford University Press, 160 p.

Rosholt, J. N., C. Emiliani, J. Geiss, F. F. Koczy, and P. J. Wangersky, 1961, Absolute dating of deep-sea cores by the Pa^{231}/Th^{230} method: Jour. Geology, v. 69, p. 162–185.

Runcorn, S. K., 1966, Corals as paleontological clocks: Scientific American Offprint 871, 9 p.

Scrutton, C. T., 1965, Periodicity in Devonian coral growth: Palaeontology, v. 7, pt. 4, p. 552–558.

Smiley, T. L., and others, 1955, Geochronology: Univ. Arizona Phys. Sci. Bull. no. 2, 200 p.

Tilton, G. R., and S. R. Hart, 1963, Geochronology: Science, v. 140, p. 357–366.

Tilton, G. R., and R. H. Steiger, 1965, Lead isotopes and the age of the earth: Science, v. 150, p. 1805–1808.

Wells, J. W., 1963, Coral growth and geochronometry: Nature, v. 197, p. 948–950.

Wilmarth, M. Grace, 1925, The geologic time classification of the United States Geological Survey compared with other classifications: U.S. Geol. Survey Bull. 769, 138 p.

Woodford, A. O., 1963, Correlation by fossils, *in* C. C. Albritton, Jr., ed., The fabric of geology: San Francisco, Freeman, Cooper, p. 75–111.

14

On the Imperfection of the Geological Record

CHARLES DARWIN

1859

Revised 1883

From *On the Origin of Species* (6th edition) by Charles Darwin, pp. 264–289. D. Appleton & Co., 1883.

In the sixth chapter I enumerated the chief objections which might be justly urged against the views maintained in this volume. Most of them have now been discussed. One, namely the distinctness of specific forms, and their not being blended together by innumerable transitional links, is a very obvious difficulty. I assigned reasons why such links do not commonly occur at the present day under the circumstances apparently most favourable for their presence, namely on an extensive and continuous area with graduated physical conditions. I endeavoured to show, that the life of each species depends in a more important manner on the presence of other already defined organic forms, than on climate; and, therefore, that the really governing conditions of life do not graduate away quite insensibly like heat or moisture. I endeavoured, also, to show that intermediate varieties, from existing in lesser numbers than the forms which they connect, will generally be beaten out and exterminated during the course of further modification and improvement. The main cause, however, of innumerable intermediate links not now occurring everywhere throughout nature, depends on the very process of natural selection, through which new varieties continually take the places of and supplant their parent-forms. But just in proportion as this process of extermination has acted on an enormous scale, so must the number of intermediate varieties, which have formerly existed, be truly enormous. Why then is not every geological formation and every stratum full of such intermediate links? Geology assuredly does not reveal any such finely-graduated organic chain; and this, perhaps, is the most obvious and serious objection which can be urged against the theory. The explanation lies, as I believe, in the extreme imperfection of the geological record.

In the first place, it should always be borne in mind what sort of intermediate forms must, on the theory, have formerly existed. I have found it difficult, when looking at any two species, to avoid picturing to myself forms *directly* intermediate between them. But this is a wholly false view; we should always look for forms intermediate between each species and a common but unknown progenitor; and the progenitor will generally have differed in some respects from all its modified descendants. To give a simple illustration: the fantail and pouter pigeons are both descended from the rock-pigeon; if we possessed all the intermediate varieties which have ever existed, we should have an extremely close series between both and the rock-pigeon; but we should have no varieties directly intermediate between the fantail and pouter; none, for instance, combining a tail somewhat expanded with a crop somewhat enlarged, the characteristic features of these two breeds. These two breeds, moreover, have become so much modified, that, if we had no historical or indirect evidence regarding their origin, it would not have been possible to have determined, from a mere comparison of their structure with that of the rock-pigeon, C. livia, whether they had descended from this species or from some other allied form, such as C. oenas.

So with natural species, if we look to forms very distinct, for instance to the horse and tapir, we have no reason to suppose that links directly intermediate between them ever existed, but between each and an unknown common parent. The common parent will have had in its whole organisation much general resemblance to the tapir and to the horse; but in some points of structure may have differed considerably from both, even perhaps more than they differ from each other. Hence, in all such cases, we should be unable to recognise the parent-form of any two or more species, even if we closely compared the structure of the parent with that of its modified descendants, unless at the same time we had a nearly perfect chain of the intermediate links.

It is just possible by the theory, that one of two living forms might have descended from the other; for instance, a horse from a tapir; and in this case *direct* intermediate links will have existed between them. But such a case would imply that one form had remained for a very long period unaltered, whilst its descendants had undergone a vast amount of change; and the principle of competition between organism and organism, between child and parent, will render this a very rare event; for in all cases the new and improved forms of life tend to supplant the old and unimproved forms.

By the theory of natural selection all living species have been connected with the parent-species of each genus, by differences not greater than we see between the natural and domestic varieties of the same species at the present day; and these parent-species, now generally extinct, have in their turn been similarly connected with more ancient forms; and so on backwards, always converging to the common ancestor of each great class. So that the number of intermediate and transitional links, between all living and extinct species, must have been inconceivably great. But assuredly, if this theory be true, such have lived upon the earth.

ON THE LAPSE OF TIME, AS INFERRED FROM THE RATE OF DEPOSITION AND EXTENT OF DENUDATION

Independently of our not finding fossil remains of such infinitely numerous connecting links, it may be objected that time cannot have sufficed for so great an amount of organic change, all changes having been effected slowly. It is hardly possible for me to recall to the reader who is not a practical geologist, the facts leading the mind feebly to comprehend the lapse of time. He who can read Sir Charles Lyell's grand work on the Principles of Geology, which the future historian will recognise as having produced a revolution in natural science, and yet does not admit how vast have been the past periods of time, may at once close this volume. Not that it suffices to study the Principles of Geology, or to read special treatises by different observers on separate formations, and to mark how each author attempts to give an inadequate idea of the duration of each formation, or even of each stratum. We can best gain some idea of past time by knowing the agencies at work, and learning how deeply the surface of the land has been denuded, and how much sediment has been deposited. As Lyell has well remarked, the extent and thickness of our sedimentary formations are the result and the measure of the denudation which the earth's crust has elsewhere undergone. Therefore a man should examine for himself the great piles of superimposed strata, and watch the rivulets bringing down mud, and the waves wearing away the sea-cliffs, in order to comprehend something about the duration of past time, the monuments of which we see all around us.

It is good to wander along the coast, when formed of moderately hard rocks, and mark the process of degradation. The tides in most cases reach the cliffs only for a short time twice a day, and the waves eat into them only when they are charged with sand or pebbles; for there is good evidence that pure water effects nothing in wearing away rock. At last the base of the cliff is undermined, huge fragments fall down, and these, remaining fixed, have to be worn away atom by atom, until after being reduced in size they can be rolled about by the waves, and then they are more quickly ground into pebbles, sand, or mud. But how often do we see along the bases of retreating cliffs rounded boulders, all thickly clothed by marine productions, showing how little they are abraded and how seldom they are rolled about! Moreover, if we follow for a few miles any line of rocky cliff, which is undergoing degradation, we find that it is only here and there, along a short length or round a promontory, that the cliffs are at the present time suffering. The appearance of the surface and the vegetation show that elsewhere years have elapsed since the waters washed their base.

We have, however, recently learnt from the observations of Ramsay, in the van of many excellent observers—of Jukes, Geikie, Croll, and others, that subaerial degradation is a much more important agency than coast-action, or the power of the waves. The whole surface of the land is exposed to the chemical action of the air and of the rain-water with its dissolved carbonic acid, and in colder countries to frost; the disintegrated matter is carried down even gentle slopes during heavy rain, and to a greater extent than might be supposed, especially in arid districts, by the wind; it is then transported by the streams and rivers, which when rapid deepen their channels, and triturate the fragments. On a rainy day, even in a gently undulating country, we see the effects of subaerial degradation in the muddy rills which flow down every slope. Messrs. Ramsay and Whitaker have shown, and the observation is a most striking one, that the great lines of escarpment in the Wealden district and those ranging across England, which formerly were looked at as ancient sea-coasts, cannot have been thus formed, for each line is composed of one and the same formation, whilst our sea-cliffs are everywhere formed by the intersection of various formations. This being the case, we are compelled to admit that the escarpments owe their origin in chief part to the rocks of which they are composed having resisted subaerial denudation better than the surrounding surface; this surface consequently has been gradually lowered, with the lines of harder rocks left projecting. Nothing impresses the mind with the vast duration of time, according to our ideas of time, more forcibly than the conviction thus gained that subaerial agencies which apparently have so little power, and which seem to work so slowly, have produced great results.

When thus impressed with the slow rate at which the land is worn away through subaerial and littoral action, it is good, in order to appreciate the past duration of time, to consider, on the one hand, the masses of rock which have been removed over many extensive areas, and on the other hand the thickness of our sedimentary formations. I remember having been much struck when viewing volcanic islands, which have been worn by the waves and pared all round into perpendicular cliffs of one or two thousand feet in height; for the gentle slope of the lava-streams, due to their formerly liquid state, showed at a glance how far the hard, rocky beds had once extended into the open ocean. The same story is told still more plainly by faults,—those great cracks along which the strata have been upheaved on one side, or thrown down on the other, to the height or depth of thousands of feet; for since the crust cracked, and it makes no great difference whether the upheaval was sudden, or, as most geologists now believe, was slow and effected by many starts, the surface of the land has been so completely planed down that no trace of these vast dislocations is externally visible. The Craven fault, for instance, extends for upwards of 30 miles, and along this line the vertical displacement of the strata varies from 600 to 3000 feet. Professor Ramsay has published an account of a downthrow in

Anglesea of 2300 feet; and he informs me that he fully believes that there is one in Merionethshire of 12,000 feet; yet in these cases there is nothing on the surface of the land to show such prodigious movements; the pile of rocks on either side of the crack having been smoothly swept away.

On the other hand, in all parts of the world the piles of sedimentary strata are of wonderful thickness. In the Cordillera I estimated one mass of conglomerate at ten thousand feet; and although conglomerates have probably been accumulated at a quicker rate than finer sediments, yet from being formed of worn and rounded pebbles, each of which bears the stamp of time, they are good to show how slowly the mass must have been heaped together. Professor Ramsay has given me the maximum thickness, from actual measurement in most cases, of the successive formations in *different* parts of Great Britain; and this is the result:—

	Feet
Palæozoic strata (not including igneous beds)	57,154
Secondary strata	13,190
Tertiary strata	2,240

—making altogether 72,584 feet; that is, very nearly thirteen and three-quarters British miles. Some of the formations, which are represented in England by thin beds, are thousands of feet in thickness on the Continent. Moreover, between each successive formation, we have, in the opinion of most geologists, blank periods of enormous length. So that the lofty pile of sedimentary rocks in Britain gives but an inadequate idea of the time which has elapsed during their accumulation. The consideration of these various facts impresses the mind almost in the same manner as does the vain endeavour to grapple with the idea of eternity.

Nevertheless this impression is partly false. Mr. Croll, in an interesting paper, remarks that we do not err "in forming too great a conception of the length of geological periods," but in estimating them by years. When geologists look at large and complicated phenomena, and then at the figures representing several million years, the two produce a totally different effect on the mind, and the figures are at once pronounced too small. In regard to subaerial denudation, Mr. Croll shows, by calculating the known amount of sediment annually brought down by certain rivers, relatively to their areas of drainage, that 1000 feet of solid rock, as it became gradually disintegrated, would thus be removed from the mean level of the whole area in the course of six million years. This seems an astonishing result, and some considerations lead to the suspicion that it may be too large, but even if halved or quartered it is still very surprising. Few of us, however, know what a million really means: Mr. Croll gives the following illustration: take a narrow strip of paper, 83 feet 4 inches in length, and stretch it along the wall of a large hall; then mark off at one end the tenth of an inch. This tenth of an inch will represent one hundred years, and the entire strip a million years. But let it be borne in mind, in relation to the subject of this work, what a hundred years implies, represented as it is by a measure utterly insignificant in a hall of the above dimensions. Several eminent breeders, during a single lifetime, have so largely modified some of the higher animals, which propagate their kind much more slowly than most of the lower animals, that they have formed what well deserves to be called a new sub-breed. Few men have attended with due care to any one strain for more than half a century, so that a hundred years represents the work of two breeders in succession. It is not to be supposed that species in a state of nature ever change so quickly as domestic animals under the guidance of methodical selection. The comparison would be in every way fairer with the effects which follow from unconscious selection, that is the preservation of the most useful or beautiful animals, with no intention of modifying the breed; but by this process of unconscious selection, various breeds have been sensibly changed in the course of two or three centuries.

Species, however, probably change much more slowly, and within the same country only a few change at the same time. This slowness follows from all the inhabitants of the same country being already so well adapted to each other, that new places in the polity of nature do not occur until after long intervals, due to the occurrence of physical changes of some kind, or through the immigration of new forms. Moreover variations or individual differences of the right nature, by which some of the inhabitants might be better fitted to their new places under the altered circumstances, would not always occur at once. Unfortunately we have no means of determining, according to the standard of years, how long a period it takes to modify a species; but to the subject of time we must return.

ON THE POORNESS OF OUR PALÆONTOLOGICAL COLLECTIONS

Now let us turn to our richest geological museums, and what a paltry display we behold! That our collections are imperfect is admitted by every one. The remark of that admirable palæontologist, Edward Forbes, should never be forgotten, namely, that very many fossil species are known and named from single and often broken specimens, or from a few specimens collected on some one spot. Only a small portion of the surface of the earth has been geologically explored, and no part with sufficient care, as the important discoveries made every year in Europe prove. No organism wholly soft can be preserved. Shells and bones decay and disappear when left on the bottom of the sea, where sediment is not accumulating. We probably take a quite erroneous view, when we assume that sediment is being deposited over nearly the whole bed of the sea, at a rate sufficiently quick to embed and preserve fossil remains. Throughout an enormously large proportion of the ocean, the bright blue tint of the water bespeaks its purity. The many cases on record of a formation conformably covered, after an immense interval of time, by another and later formation, without the underlying bed having suffered in the interval any wear and tear, seem explicable only on the view of the bottom of the sea not rarely lying for ages in an unaltered condition. The remains which do become embedded, if in sand or gravel, will, when the beds are upraised, generally be dissolved by the percolation of rain-water charged with carbonic acid. Some of the many kinds of animals which live on the beach between high and low water mark seem to be rarely preserved. For instance, the several species of the Chthamalinæ (a sub-family of sessile cirripedes) coat the rocks all over the world in infinite numbers: they are all strictly littoral, with the exception of a single Mediterranean species, which inhabits deep water, and this has been found fossil in Sicily, whereas not one other species has hitherto been found in any tertiary formation: yet it is known that the genus Chthamalus existed during the Chalk period. Lastly, many great deposits requiring a vast length of time for their accumulation, are entirely destitute of organic remains, without our being able to assign any reason: one of the most striking instances is that of the Flysch formation, which consists of shale and sandstone, several thousand, occasionally even six thousand feet, in thickness, and extending for at least 300 miles from Vienna to Switzerland; and although this great mass has been most carefully searched, no fossils, except a few vegetable remains, have been found.

With respect to the terrestrial productions which lived during the Secondary and Palæozoic periods, it is superfluous to state that our evidence is fragmentary in an extreme degree. For instance, until recently not a land shell was known belonging to either of these vast periods, with the exception of one species discovered by Sir C. Lyell and Dr. Dawson in the carboniferous strata of North America; but now land-shells have been found in the lias. In regard to mammiferous remains, a glance at the historical table published in Lyell's Manual will bring home the truth, how accidental and rare is their preservation, far better than pages of detail. Nor is their rarity surprising, when we remember how large a proportion of the bones of tertiary mammals have been discovered either in caves or in lacustrine deposits; and that not a cave or true lacustrine bed is known belonging to the age of our secondary or palæozoic formations.

But the imperfection in the geological record largely results from another and more important cause than any of the foregoing; namely, from the several formations being separated from each other by wide intervals of time. This doctrine has been emphatically admitted by many geologists and palæontologists, who, like E. Forbes, entirely disbelieve in the change of species. When we see the formations tabulated in written works, or when we follow them in nature, it is difficult to avoid believing that they are closely consecutive. But we know, for instance, from Sir R. Murchison's great work on Russia, what wide gaps there are in that country between the superimposed formations; so it is in North America, and in many other parts of the world. The most skilful geologist, if his attention had been confined exclusively to these large territories, would never have suspected that, during the periods which were blank and barren in his own country, great piles of sediment, charged with new and peculiar forms of life, had elsewhere been accumulated. And if, in each separate territory, hardly any idea can be formed of the length of time which has elapsed between the consecutive formations, we may infer that this could nowhere be ascertained. The frequent and great changes in the mineralogical composition of consecutive formations, generally implying great changes in the geography of the surrounding lands, whence the sediment was derived, accord with the belief of vast intervals of time having elapsed between each formation.

We can, I think, see why the geological formations of each region are almost invariably intermittent; that is, have not followed each other in close sequence. Scarcely any fact struck me more when examining many hundred miles of the South American coasts, which have been upraised several hundred feet within the recent period, than the absence of any recent deposits sufficiently extensive to last for even a short geological period. Along the whole west coast, which is inhabited by a peculiar marine fauna, tertiary beds are so poorly developed, that no record of several successive and peculiar marine faunas will probably be preserved to a distant age. A little reflection will explain why, along the rising coast of the western side of South America, no extensive formations with recent or tertiary remains can anywhere be found, though the supply of sediment must for ages have been great, from the enormous degradation of the coast-rocks and from muddy streams entering the sea. The explanation, no doubt, is, that the littoral and sub-littoral deposits are continually worn away, as soon as they are brought up by the slow and gradual rising of the land within the grinding action of the coast-waves.

We may, I think, conclude that sediment must be accumulated in extremely thick, solid, or extensive masses, in order to withstand the incessant action of the waves, when first upraised and during successive oscillations of level, as well as the subsequent subaerial degradation. Such thick and extensive accumulations of sediment may be formed in two ways; either in profound depths of the sea, in which case the bottom will not be inhabited by so many and such varied forms of life, as the more shallow seas; and the mass when upraised will give an imperfect record of the organisms which existed in the neighbourhood during the period of its accumulation. Or, sediment may be deposited to any thickness and extent over a shallow bottom, if it continue slowly to subside. In this latter case, as long as the rate of subsidence and the supply of sediment nearly balance each other, the sea will remain shallow and favourable for many and varied forms, and thus a rich fossiliferous formation, thick enough, when upraised, to resist a large amount of denudation, may be formed.

I am convinced that nearly all our ancient formations, which are throughout the greater part of their thickness *rich in fossils*, have thus been formed during subsidence. Since publishing my views on this subject in 1845, I have watched the progress of Geology, and have been surprised to note how author after author, in treating of this or that great formation, has come to the conclusion that it was accumulated during subsidence. I may add, that the only ancient tertiary formation on the west coast of South America, which has been bulky enough to resist such degradation as it has as yet suffered, but which will hardly last to a distant geological age, was deposited during a downward oscillation of level, and thus gained considerable thickness.

All geological facts tell us plainly that each area has undergone numerous slow oscillations of level, and apparently these oscillations have affected wide spaces. Consequently, formations rich in fossils and sufficiently thick and extensive to resist subsequent degradation, will have been formed over wide spaces during periods of subsidence, but only where the supply of sediment was sufficient to keep the sea shallow and to embed and preserve the remains before they had time to decay. On the other hand, as long as the bed of the sea remains stationary, *thick* deposits cannot have been accumulated in the shallow parts, which are the most favourable to life. Still less can this have happened during the alternate periods of elevation; or, to speak more accurately, the beds which were then accumulated will generally have been destroyed by being upraised and brought within the limits of the coast-action.

These remarks apply chiefly to littoral and sublittoral deposits. In the case of an extensive and shallow sea, such as that within a large part of the Malay Archipelago, where the depth varies from 30 or 40 to 60 fanthoms, a widely extended formation might be formed during a period of elevation, and yet not suffer excessively from denudation during its slow upheaval; but the thickness of the formation could not be great, for owing to the elevatory movement it would be less than the depth in which it was formed; nor would the deposit be much consolidated, nor be capped by overlying formations, so that it would run a good chance of being worn away by atmospheric degradation and by the action of the sea during subsequent oscillations of level. It has, however, been suggested by Mr. Hopkins, that if one part of the area, after rising and before being denuded, subsided, the deposit formed during the rising movement, though not thick, might afterwards become protected by fresh accumulations, and thus be preserved for a long period.

Mr. Hopkins also expresses his belief that sedimentary beds of considerable horizontal extent have rarely been completely destroyed. But all geologists, excepting the few who believe that our present metamorphic schists and plutonic rocks once formed the primordial nucleus of the globe, will admit that these latter rocks have been stript of their covering to an enormous extent. For it is scarcely possible that such rocks could have been solidified and crystallized whilst uncovered; but if the metamorphic action occurred at profound depths of the ocean, the former protecting mantle of rock may not have been very thick. Admitting then that gneiss, micaschist, granite, diorite, &c., were once necessarily covered up, how can we account for the naked and extensive areas of such rocks in many parts of the world, except on the belief that they have subsequently been completely denuded of all overlying strata? That such extensive areas do exist cannot be doubted: the granitic region of Parime is described by Humboldt as being at least nineteen times as large as Switzerland. South of the Amazon, Boué colours an area composed of rocks of this nature as equal to that of Spain, France, Italy, part of Germany, and the British Islands, all conjoined. This region has not been carefully explored, but from the concurrent testimony of travellers, the granitic area is very large: thus, Von Eschwege gives a detailed section of these rocks, stretching from Rio de Janeiro for 260 geographical miles inland in a straight line; and I travelled for 150 miles in another direction, and saw nothing but granitic rocks. Numerous specimens, collected along the whole coast from near Rio de Janeiro to the mouth of the Plata, a distance of 1100 geographical miles, were examined by me, and they all belonged to this class. Inland, along the whole northern bank of the Plata I saw, besides modern tertiary beds, only one small patch of slightly metamorphosed rock, which alone could have formed a part of the original capping of the granitic series. Turning to a well-known region, namely, to the United States and Canada, as shown in Professor H. D. Rogers's beautiful map, I have estimated the areas by cutting out and weighing the paper, and I find that the metamorphic (excluding "the semi-metamorphic") and granitic rocks exceed, in the proportion of 19 to 12.5, the whole of the newer Palæozoic formations. In many regions the metamorphic and granitic rocks would be found much more widely extended than they appear to be, if all the sedimentary beds were removed which rest unconformably on them, and which could not have formed part of the original mantle under which they were crystallized. Hence it is probable that in some parts of the world whole formations have been completely denuded, with not a wreck left behind.

One remark is here worth a passing notice. During periods of elevation the area of the land and of the adjoining shoal parts of the sea will be increased, and new stations will often be formed;—all circumstances favourable, as previously explained, for the formation of new varieties and species; but during such periods there will generally be a blank in the geological record. On the other hand, during subsidence, the inhabited area and number of inhabitants will decrease (excepting on the shores of a continent when first broken up into an archipelago), and consequently during subsidence, though there will be much extinction, few new varieties or species will be formed; and it is during these very periods of subsidence, that the deposits which are richest in fossils have been accumulated.

ON THE ABSENCE OF NUMEROUS INTERMEDIATE VARIETIES IN ANY SINGLE FORMATION

From these several considerations, it cannot be doubted that the geological record, viewed as a whole, is extremely imperfect; but if we confine our attention to any one formation, it becomes much more difficult to understand why we do not therein find closely graduated varieties between the allied species which lived at its commencement and at its close. Several cases are on record of the same species presenting varieties in the upper and lower parts of the same formation: thus, Trautschold gives a number of instances with Ammonites; and Hilgendorf has described a most curious case of ten graduated forms of Planorbis multiformis in the successive beds of a fresh-water formation in Switzerland. Although each formation has indisputably required a vast number of years for its deposition, several reasons can be given why each should not commonly include a graduated series of links between the species which lived at its commencement and close; but I cannot assign due proportional weight to the following considerations.

Although each formation may mark a very long lapse of years, each probably is short compared with the period requisite to change one species into another. I am aware that two palæontologists, whose opinions are worthy of much deference, namely Bronn and Woodward, have concluded that the average duration of each formation is twice or thrice as long as the average duration of specific forms. But insuperable difficulties, as it seems to me, prevent us from coming to any just conclusion on this head. When we see a species first appearing in the middle of any formation, it would be rash in the extreme to infer that it had not elsewhere previously existed. So again when we find a species disappearing before the last layers have been deposited, it would be equally rash to suppose that it then became extinct. We forget how small the area of Europe is compared with the rest of the world; nor have the several stages of the same formation throughout Europe been correlated with perfect accuracy.

We may safely infer that with marine animals of all kinds there has been a large amount of migration due to climatal and other changes; and when we see a species first appearing in any formation, the probability is that it only then first immigrated into that area. It is well known, for instance, that several species appeared somewhat earlier in the palæozoic beds of North America than in those of Europe; time having apparently been required for their migration from the American to the European seas. In examining the latest deposits in various quarters of the world, it has everywhere been noted, that some few still existing species are common in the deposit, but have become extinct in the immediately surrounding sea; or, conversely, that some are now abundant in the neighbouring sea, but are rare or absent in this particular deposit. It is an excellent lesson to reflect on the ascertained amount of migration of the inhabitants of Europe during the glacial epoch, which forms only a part of one whole geological period; and likewise to reflect on the changes of level, on the extreme change of climate, and on the great lapse of time, all included within this same glacial period. Yet it may be doubted whether, in any quarter of the world, sedimentary deposits, *including fossil remains,* have gone on accumulating within the same area during the whole of this period. It is not, for instance, probable that sediment was deposited during the whole of the glacial period near the mouth of the Mississippi, within that limit of depth at which marine animals can best flourish: for we know that great geographical changes occurred in other parts of America during this space of time. When such beds as were deposited in shallow water near the mouth of the Mississippi during some part of the glacial period shall have been upraised, organic remains will probably first appear and disappear at different levels, owing to the migrations of species and to geographical changes. And in the distant future, a geologist, examining these beds, would be tempted to conclude that the average duration of life of the embedded fossils had been less than that of the glacial period, instead of having been really far greater, that is, extending from before the glacial epoch to the present day.

In order to get a perfect gradation between two forms in the upper and lower parts of the same formation, the deposit must have gone on continuously accumulating during a long period, sufficient for the slow process of modification; hence the deposit must be a very thick one; and the species undergoing change must have lived in the same district throughout the whole time. But we have seen that a thick formation, fossiliferous throughout its entire thickness, can accumulate only during a period of subsidence; and to keep the depth approximately the same, which is necessary that the same marine species may live on the same space, the supply of sediment must nearly counterbalance the amount of subsidence. But this same movement of subsidence will tend to submerge the area whence the sediment is derived, and thus diminish the supply, whilst the downward movement continues. In fact, this nearly exact balancing between the supply of sediment and the amount of subsidence is probably a rare contingency; for it has been observed by more than one palæontologist, that very thick deposits are usually barren of organic remains, except near their upper or lower limits.

It would seem that each separate formation, like the whole pile of formations in any country, has generally been intermittent in its accumulation. When we see, as is so often the case, a formation composed of beds of widely different mineralogical composition, we may reasonably suspect that the process of deposition has been more or less interrupted. Nor will the closest inspection of a formation give us any idea of the length of time which its deposition may have consumed. Many instances could be given of beds only a few feet in thickness, representing formations, which are elsewhere thousands of feet in thickness, and which must have required an enormous period for their accumulation; yet no one ignorant of this fact would have even suspected the vast lapse of time represented by the thinner formation. Many cases could be given of the lower beds of a formation having been upraised, denuded, submerged, and then re-covered by the upper beds of the same formation,—facts, showing what wide, yet easily overlooked, intervals have occurred in its accumulation. In other cases we have the plainest evidence in great fossilised trees, still standing upright as they grew, of many long intervals of time and changes of level during the process of deposition, which would not have been suspected, had not the trees been preserved: thus Sir C. Lyell and Dr. Dawson found carboniferous beds 1400 feet thick in Nova Scotia, with ancient root-bearing strata, one above the other at no less than sixty-eight different levels. Hence, when the same species occurs at the bottom, middle, and top of a formation, the probability is that it has not lived on the same spot during the whole period of deposition, but has disappeared and reappeared, perhaps many times, during the same geological period. Consequently if it were to undergo a considerable amount of modification during the deposition of any one geological formation, a section would not include all the fine intermediate gradations which must on our theory have existed, but abrupt, though perhaps slight, changes of form.

It is all-important to remember that naturalists have no golden rule by which to distinguish species and varieties; they grant some little variability to each species, but when they meet with a somewhat greater amount of difference between any two forms, they rank both as species, unless they are enabled to connect them together by the closest intermediate gradations; and this, from the reasons just assigned, we can seldom hope to effect in any one geological section. Supposing B and C to be two species, and a third, A, to be found in an older and underlying bed; even if A were strictly intermediate between B and C, it would simply be ranked as a third and distinct species, unless at the same time it could be closely connected by intermediate varieties with either one or both forms. Nor should it be forgotten, as before explained, that A might be the actual progenitor of B and C, and yet would not necessarily be strictly intermediate between them in all respects. So that we might obtain the parent-species and its several modified descendants from the lower and upper beds of the same formation, and unless we obtained numerous transitional gradations, we should not recognise their blood-relationship, and should consequently rank them as distinct species.

It is notorious on what excessively slight differences many palæontologists have founded their species; and they do this the more readily if the specimens come from different sub-stages of the same formation. Some experienced conchologists are now sinking many of the very fine species of D'Orbigny and others into the rank of varieties; and on this view we do find the kind of evidence of change which on the theory we ought to find. Look again at the later tertiary deposits, which include many shells believed by the majority of naturalists to be identical with existing species; but some excellent naturalists, as Agassiz and Pictet, maintain that all these tertiary species are specifically distinct, though the distinction is admitted to be very slight; so that here, unless we believe that these eminent naturalists have been misled by their imaginations, and that these late tertiary species really present no difference whatever from their living representatives, or unless we admit, in opposition to the judgment of most naturalists, that these tertiary species are all truly distinct from the recent, we have evidence of the frequent occurrence of slight modifications of the kind required. If we look to rather wider intervals of time, namely, to distinct but consecutive stages of the same great formation, we find that the embedded fossils, though universally ranked as specifically different, yet are far more closely related to each other than are the species found in more widely separated formations; so that here again we have undoubted evidence of change in the direction required by the theory.

With animals and plants that propagate rapidly and do not wander much, there is reason to suspect, as we have formerly seen, that their varieties are generally at first local; and that such local varieties do not spread widely and supplant their parent-forms until they have been modified and perfected in some considerable degree. According to this view, the chance of discovering in a formation in any one country all the early stages of transition between any two forms, is small, for the successive changes are supposed to have been local or confined to some one spot. Most marine animals have a wide range; and we have seen that with plants it is those which had the widest range, that oftenest present varieties; so that, with shells and other marine animals, it is probable that those which had the widest range, far exceeding the limits of the known geological formations of Europe, have oftenest given rise, first to local varieties and ultimately to new species; and this again would greatly lessen the chance of our being able to trace the stages of transition in any one geological formation.

It is a more important consideration, leading to the same result, as lately insisted on by Dr. Falconer, namely, that the period during which each species underwent modification, though long as measured by years, was probably short in comparison with that during which it remained without undergoing any change.

It should not be forgotten, that at the present day, with perfect specimens for examination, two forms can seldom be connected by intermediate varieties, and thus proved to be the same species, until many specimens are collected from many places; and with fossil species this can rarely be done. We shall, perhaps, best perceive the improbability of our being enabled to connect species by numerous, fine, intermediate, fossil links, by asking ourselves whether, for instance, geologists at some future period will be able to prove that our different breeds of cattle, sheep, horses, and dogs are descended from a single stock or from several aboriginal stocks; or, again, whether certain sea-shells inhabiting the shores of North America, which are ranked by some conchologists as distinct species from their European representatives, and by other conchologists as only varieties, are really varieties, or are, as it is called, specifically distinct. This could be effected by the future geologist only by his discovering in a fossil state numerous intermediate gradations; and such success is improbable in the highest degree.

It has been asserted over and over again, by writers who believe in the immutability of species, that geology yields no linking forms. This assertion is certainly erroneous. As Sir J. Lubbock has remarked, "Every species is a link between other allied forms." If we take a genus having a score of species, recent and extinct, and destroy four-fifths of them, no one doubts that the remainder will stand much more distinct from each other. If the extreme forms in the genus happen to have been thus destroyed, the genus itself will stand more distinct from other allied genera. What geological research has not revealed, is the former existence of infinitely numerous gradations, as fine as existing varieties, connecting together nearly all existing and extinct species. But this ought not to be expected; yet this has been repeatedly advanced as a most serious objection against my views.

It may be worth while to sum up the foregoing remarks on the causes of the imperfection of the geological record under an imaginary illustration. The Malay Archipelago is about the size of Europe from the North Cape to the Mediterranean, and from Britain to Russia; and therefore equals all the geological formations which have been examined with any accuracy, excepting those of the United States of America. I fully agree with Mr. Godwin-Austen, that the present condition of the Malay Archipelago, with its numerous large islands separated by wide and shallow seas, probably represents the former state of Europe, whilst most of our formations were accumulating. The Malay Archipelago is one of the richest regions in organic beings; yet if all the species were to be collected which have ever lived there, how imperfectly would they represent the natural history of the world!

But we have every reason to believe that the terrestrial productions of the archipelago would be preserved in an extremely imperfect manner in the formations which we suppose to be there accumulating. Not many of the strictly littoral animals, or of those which lived on naked submarine rocks, would be embedded; and those embedded in gravel or sand would not endure to a distant epoch. Wherever sediment did not accumulate on the bed of the sea, or where it did not accumulate at a sufficient rate to protect organic bodies from decay, no remains could be preserved.

Formations rich in fossils of many kinds, and of thickness sufficient to last to an age as distant in futurity as the secondary formations lie in the past, would generally be formed in the archipelago only during periods of subsidence. These periods of subsidence would be separated from each other by immense intervals of time, during which the area would be either stationary or rising; whilst rising, the fossiliferous formations on the steeper shores would be destroyed, almost as soon as accumulated, by the incessant coast-action, as we now see on the shores of South America. Even throughout the extensive and shallow seas within the archipelago, sedimentary beds could hardly be accumulated of great thickness during the periods of elevation, or become capped and protected by subsequent deposits, so as to have a good chance of enduring to a very distant future. During the periods of subsidence, there would probably be much extinction of life; during the periods of elevation, there would be much variation, but the geological record would then be less perfect.

It may be doubted whether the duration of any one great period of subsidence over the whole or part of the archipelago, together with a contemporaneous accumulation of sediment, would *exceed* the average duration of the same specific forms; and these contingencies are indispensable for the preservation of all the transitional gradations between any two or more species. If such gradations were not all fully preserved, transitional varieties would merely appear as so many new, though closely allied species. It is also probable that each great period of subsidence would be interrupted by oscillations of level, and that slight climatal changes would intervene during such lengthy periods; and in these cases the inhabitants of the archipelago would migrate, and no closely consecutive record of their modifications could be preserved in any one formation.

Very many of the marine inhabitants of the archipelago now range thousands of miles beyond its confines; and analogy plainly leads to the belief that it would be chiefly these far-ranging species, though only some of them, which would oftenest produce new varieties; and the varieties would at first be local or confined to one place, but if possessed of any decided advantage, or when further modified and improved, they would slowly spread and supplant their parent-forms. When such varieties returned to their ancient homes, as they would differ from their former state in a nearly uniform, though perhaps extremely slight degree, and as they would be found embedded in slightly different sub-stages of the same formation, they would, according to the principles followed by many palæontologists, be ranked as new and distinct species.

If then there be some degree of truth in these remarks, we have no right to expect to find, in our geological formations, an infinite number of those fine transitional forms which, on our theory, have connected all the past and present species of the same group into one long and branching chain of life. We ought only to look for a few links, and such assuredly we do find—some more distantly, some more closely, related to each other; and these links, let them be ever so close, if found in different stages of the same formation, would, by many palæontologists, be ranked as distinct species. But I do not pretend that I should ever have suspected how poor was the record in the best preserved geological sections, had not the absence of innumerable transitional links between the species which lived at the commencement and close of each formation, pressed so hardly on my theory.

ON THE SUDDEN APPEARANCE OF WHOLE GROUPS OF ALLIED SPECIES

The abrupt manner in which whole groups of species suddenly appear in certain formations, has been urged by several palæontologists—for instance, by Agassiz, Pictet, and Sedgwick—as a fatal objection to the belief in the transmutation of species. If numerous species, belonging to the same genera or families, have really started into life at once, the fact would be fatal to the theory of evolution through natural selection. For the development by this means of a group of forms, all of which are descended from some one progenitor, must have been an extremely slow process; and the progenitors must have lived long before their modified descendants. But we continually overrate the perfection of the geological record, and falsely infer, because certain genera or families have not been found beneath a certain stage, that they did not exist before that stage. In all cases positive palæontological evidence may be implicitly trusted; negative evidence is worthless, as experience has so often shown. We continually forget how large the world is, compared with the area over which our geological formations have been carefully examined; we forget that groups of species may elsewhere have long existed, and have slowly multiplied, before they invaded the ancient archipelagoes of Europe and the United States. We do not make due allowance for the intervals of time which have elapsed between our consecutive formations, —longer perhaps in many cases than the time required for the accumulation of each formation. These intervals will have given time for the multiplication of species from some one parent-form; and in the succeeding formation, such groups or species will appear as if suddenly created. . . .

I will now give a few examples to illustrate the foregoing remarks, and to show how liable we are to error in supposing that whole groups of species have suddenly been produced. Even in so short an interval as that between the first and second editions of Pictet's great work on Palæontology, the conclusions on the first appearance and disappearance of several groups of animals have been considerably modified; and a third edition would require still further changes. I may recall the well-known fact that in geological treatises, published not many years ago, mammals were always spoken of as having abruptly come in at the commencement of the tertiary series. And now one of the richest known accumulations of fossil mammals belongs to the middle of the secondary series. . . . Cuvier used to urge that no monkey occurred in any tertiary stratum; but now extinct species have been discovered in India, South America, and in Europe, as far back as the miocene stage. . . . Not long ago, palæontologists maintained that the whole class of birds came suddenly into existence during the eocene period; but now we know, on the authority of Professor Owen, that a bird certainly lived during the deposition of the upper greensand; and still more recently, that strange bird, the Archeopteryx, with a long lizard-like tail, bearing a pair of feathers on each joint, and with its wings furnished with two free claws, has been discovered in the oolitic slates of Solenhofen. Hardly any recent discovery shows more forcibly than this, how little we as yet know of the former inhabitants of the world.

I may give another instance, which, from having passed under my own eyes, has much struck me. In a memoir on Fossil Sessile Cirripedes, I stated that, from the large number of existing and extinct tertiary species; from the extraordinary abundance of the individuals of many species all over the world, from the Arctic regions to the equator, inhabiting various zones of depths from the upper tidal limits to 50 fathoms; from the perfect manner in which specimens are preserved in the oldest tertiary beds; from the case with which even a fragment of a valve can be recognised; from all these circumstances, I inferred that, had sessile cirripedes existed during the secondary periods, they would certainly have been preserved and discovered; and as not one species had then been discovered in beds of this age, I concluded that this great group had been suddenly developed at the commencement of the tertiary series. This was a sore trouble to me, adding as I then thought one more instance of the abrupt appearance of a great group of species. But my work had hardly been published, when a skilful palæontologist, M. Bosquet, sent me a drawing of a perfect specimen of an unmistakeable sessile cirripede, which he had himself extracted from the chalk of Belgium. And, as if to make the case as striking as possible, this cirripede was a Chthamalus, a very common, large, and ubiquitous genus, of which not one species has as yet been found even in any tertiary stratum. Still more recently, a Pyrgoma, a member of a distinct sub-family of sessile cirripedes, has been discovered by Mr. Woodward in the upper chalk; so that we now have abundant evidence of the existence of this group of animals during the secondary period.

The case most frequently insisted on by palæontologists of the apparently sudden appearance of a whole group of species, is that of the teleostean fishes, low down, according to Agassiz, in the Chalk period. This group includes the large majority of existing species. But certain Jurassic and Triassic forms are now commonly admitted to be teleostean; and even some palæozoic forms have thus been classed by one high authority. If the teleosteans had really appeared suddenly in the northern hemisphere at the commencement of the chalk formation, the fact would have been highly remarkable; but it would not have formed an insuperable difficulty, unless it could likewise have been shown that at the same period the species were suddenly and simultaneously developed in other quarters of the world. It is almost superfluous to remark that hardly any fossil-fish are known from south of the equator; and by running through Pictet's Palæontology it will be seen that very few species are known from several formations in Europe. Some few families of fish now have a confined range; the teleostean fishes might formerly have had a similarly confined range, and after having been largely developed in some one sea, have spread widely. Nor have we any right to suppose that the seas of the world have always been so freely open from south to north as they are at present. Even at this day, if the Malay Archipelago were converted into land, the tropical parts of the Indian Ocean would form a large and perfectly enclosed basin, in which any great group of marine animals might be multiplied; and here they would remain confined, until some of the species became adapted to a cooler climate, and were enabled to double the Southern capes of Africa or Australia, and thus reach other and distant seas.

From these considerations, from our ignorance of the geology of other countries beyond the confines of Europe and the United States, and from the revolution in our palæontological knowledge effected by the discoveries of the last dozen years, it seems to me to be about as rash to dogmatize on the succession of organic forms throughout the world, as it would be for a naturalist to land for five minutes on a barren point in Australia, and then to discuss the number and range of its productions.

ON THE SUDDEN APPEARANCE OF GROUPS OF ALLIED SPECIES IN THE LOWEST KNOWN FOSSILIFEROUS STRATA

There is another and allied difficulty, which is much more serious. I allude to the manner in which species belonging to several of the main divisions of the animal kingdom suddenly appear in the lowest known fossiliferous rocks.

Most of the arguments which have convinced me that all the existing species of the same group are descended from a single progenitor, apply with equal force to the earliest known species. For instance, it cannot be doubted that all the Cambrian and Silurian trilobites are descended from some one crustacean, which must have lived long before the Cambrian age, and which probably differed greatly from any known animal. Some of the most ancient animals, as the Nautilus, Lingula, &c., do not differ much from living species; and it cannot on our theory be supposed, that these old species were the progenitors of all the species belonging to the same groups which have subsequently appeared, for they are not in any degree intermediate in character.

Consequently, if the theory be true, it is indisputable that before the lowest Cambrian stratum was deposited, long periods elapsed, as long as, or probably far longer than, the whole interval from the Cambrian age to the present day; and that during these vast periods the world swarmed with living creatures. Here we encounter a formidable objection; for it seems doubtful whether the earth, in a fit state for the habitation of living creatures, has lasted long enough. Sir W. Thompson concludes that the consolidation of the crust can hardly have occurred less than 20 or more than 400 million years ago, but probably not less than 98 or more than 200 million years. These very wide limits show how doubtful the data are; and other elements may have hereafter to be introduced into the problem. Mr. Croll estimates that about 60 million years have elapsed since the Cambrian period, but this, judging from the small amount of organic change since the commencement of the Glacial epoch, appears a very short time for the many and great mutations of life, which have certainly occurred since the Cambrian formation; and the previous 140 million years can hardly be considered as sufficient for the development of the varied forms of life which already existed during the Cambrian period. It is, however, probable, as Sir William Thompson insists, that the world at a very early period was subjected to more rapid and violent changes in its physical conditions than those now occurring; and such changes would have tended to induce changes at a corresponding rate in the organisms which then existed.

To the question why we do not find rich fossiliferous deposits belonging to these assumed earliest periods prior to the Cambrian system, I can give no satisfactory answer. Several eminent geologists, with Sir R. Murchison at their head, were until recently convinced that we beheld in the organic remains of the lowest Silurian stratum the first dawn of life. Other highly competent judges, as Lyell and E. Forbes, have disputed this conclusion. We should not forget that only a small portion of the world is known with accuracy. Not very long ago M. Barrande added another and lower stage, abounding with new and peculiar species, beneath the then known Silurian system; and now, still lower down in the Lower Cambrian formation, Mr. Hicks has found in South Wales beds rich in trilobites, and containing various molluscs and annelids. The presence of phosphatic nodules and bituminous matter, even in some of the lowest azoic rocks, probably indicates life at these periods; and the existence of the Eozoon in the Laurentian formation of Canada is generally admitted. There are three great series of strata beneath the Silurian system in Canada, in the lowest of which the Eozoon is found. Sir W. Logan states that their ". . . united thickness may possibly far surpass that of all the succeeding rocks, from the base of the palæozoic series to the present time. We are thus carried back to a period so remote, that the appearance of the so-called Primordial fauna (of Barrande) may by some be considered as a comparatively modern event.". . . Thus the words, which I wrote in 1859, about the existence of living beings long before the Cambrian period, and which are almost the same with those since used by Sir W. Logan, have proved true. Nevertheless, the difficulty of assigning any good reason for the absence of vast piles of strata rich in fossils beneath the Cambrian system is very great. It does not seem probable that the most ancient beds have been quite worn away by denudation, or that their fossils have been wholly obliterated by metamorphic action, for if this had been the case we should have found only small remnants of the formations next succeeding them in age, and these would always have existed in a partially metamorphosed condition. But the descriptions which we possess of the Silurian deposits over immense territories in Russia and in North America, do not support the view, that the older a formation is, the more invariably it has suffered extreme denudation and metamorphism.

The case at present must remain inexplicable; and may be truly urged as a valid argument against the views here entertained. To show that it may hereafter receive some explanation, I will give the following hypothesis. From the nature of the organic remains which do not appear to have inhabited profound depths, in the several formations of Europe and of the United States; and from the amount of sediment, miles in thickness, of which the formations are composed, we may infer that from first to last large islands or tracts of land, whence the sediment was derived, occurred in the neighbourhood of the now existing continents of Europe and North America. This same view has since been maintained by Agassiz and others. But we do not know what was the state of things in the intervals between the several successive formations; whether Europe and the United States during these intervals existed as dry land, or as a submarine surface near land, on which sediment was not deposited, or as the bed of an open and unfathomable sea.

Looking to the existing oceans, which are thrice as extensive as the land, we see them studded with many islands; but hardly one truly oceanic island (with the exception of New Zealand, if this can be called a truly oceanic island) is as yet known to afford even a remnant of any palæozoic or secondary formation. Hence we may perhaps infer, that during the palæozoic and secondary periods, neither continents nor continental islands existed where our oceans now extend; for had they existed, palæozoic and secondary formations would in all probability have been accumulated from sediment derived from their wear and tear; and these would have been at least partially upheaved by the oscillations of level, which must have intervened during these enormously long periods. If then we may infer anything from these facts, we may infer that, where our oceans now extend, oceans have extended from the remotest period of which we have any record; and on the other hand, that where continents now exist, large tracts of land have existed, subjected no doubt to great oscillations of level, since the Cambrian period. The coloured map appended to my volume on Coral Reefs, led me to conclude that the great oceans are still mainly areas of subsidence, the great archipelagoes still areas of oscillations of level, and the continents areas of elevation. But we have no reason to assume that things have thus remained from the beginning of the world. Our continents seem to have been formed by a preponderance, during many oscillations of level, of the force of elevation; but may not the areas of preponderant movement have changed in the lapse of ages? At a period long antecedent to the Cambrian epoch, continents may have existed where oceans are now spread out; and clear and open oceans may have existed where our continents now stand. Nor should we be justified in assuming that if, for instance, the bed of the Pacific Ocean were now converted into a continent we should there find sedimentary formations in a recognisable condition older than the Cambrian strata, supposing such to have been formerly deposited; for it might well happen that strata which had subsided some miles nearer to the centre of the earth, and which had been pressed on by an enormous weight of superincumbent water, might have undergone far more metamorphic action than strata which have always remained nearer to the surface. The immense areas in some parts of the world, for instance in South America, of naked metamorphic rocks, which must have been heated under great pressure, have always seemed to me to require some special explanation; and we may perhaps believe that we see in these large areas, the many formations long anterior to the Cambrian epoch in a completely metamorphosed and denuded condition.

The several difficulties here discussed, namely—that, though we find in our geological formations many links between the species which now exist and which formerly existed, we do not find infinitely numerous fine transitional forms closely joining them all together;

—the sudden manner in which several groups of species first appear in our European formations;—the almost entire absence, as at present known, of formations rich in fossils beneath the Cambrian strata,—are all undoubtedly of the most serious nature. We see this in the fact that the most eminent palæontologists, namely Cuvier, Agassiz, Barrande, Pictet, Falconer, E. Forbes, &c., and all our greatest geologists, as Lyell, Murchison, Sedgwick, &c., have unanimously, often vehemently, maintained the immutability of species. But Sir Charles Lyell now gives the support of his high authority to the opposite side; and most geologists and palæontologists are much shaken in their former belief. Those who believe that the geological record is in any degree perfect, will undoubtedly at once reject the theory. For my part, following out Lyell's metaphor, I look at the geological record as a history of the world imperfectly kept, and written in a changing dialect; of this history we possess the last volume alone, relating only to two or three countries. Of this volume, only here and there a short chapter has been preserved; and of each page, only here and there a few lines. Each word of the slowly-changing language, more or less different in the successive chapters, may represent the forms of life, which are entombed in our consecutive formations, and which falsely appear to us to have been abruptly introduced. On this view, the difficulties above discussed are greatly diminished, or even disappear.

15

Radiometric Ages

A. O. WOODFORD

1965

From *Historical Geology* by A. O. Woodford, pp. 191–220. W. H. Freeman and Company, 1965.

ELEMENTS AND ISOTOPES

Determination of the absolute ages of rocks is based on the steady, spontaneous decomposition of atoms, the chemical building blocks once considered indestructible. Before discussing this kind of decomposition we must review briefly some aspects of the structure of matter. Atoms are small units; a hundred million of them, side by side, would make a row about an inch long. Each atom consists of a **nucleus** and one or more **electrons.** The nucleus is very small indeed, with a diameter about 1/10,000 that of the atom itself. The mass (or weight) of the tiny nucleus is small, but that of the electron is very much smaller, 1/1,836 that of the lightest nucleus. The electron or electrons of an atom seem to move about rapidly, for they effectively fill the space that is called the volume of the atom, preventing other atoms from intruding. The smallest and lightest nucleus is a single **proton.** It carries one unit of positive charge; with an electron, which carries one unit of negative charge, it forms a neutral atom of the chemical element hydrogen. . . .

Most hydrogen atoms are made up of one proton and one electron, but in elemental hydrogen or in compounds such as water about one part in 5,000 is made up of hydrogen atoms that are approximately twice as heavy. Each heavy hydrogen atom has a nucleus composed of two parts, a positively charged proton and a neutral **neutron.** A neutron has about the same mass as a proton. The two kinds of hydrogen atoms are called **isotopes.** . . . Most of the hundred or so chemical elements are composed of two or more isotopes. The isotopes of an element are atoms whose nuclei contain the same number of protons but different numbers of neutrons. The **atomic number** of an element is the number of protons in the nucleus of an atom of the element. The **mass number** of an isotope is the number of protons plus the number of neutrons in its nucleus. The hypothetical structures of some

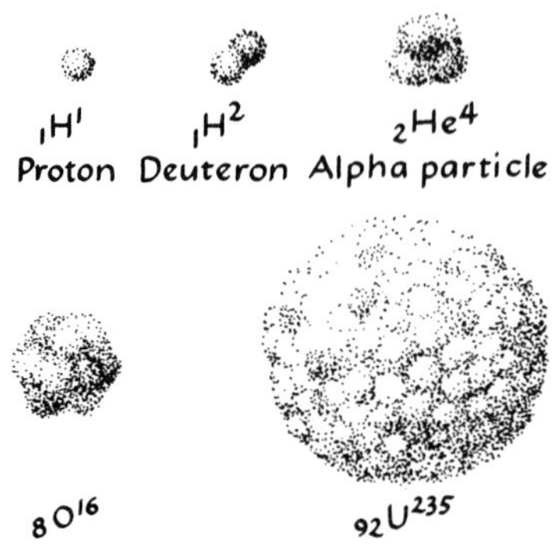

FIGURE 15.1
Range of complexity in atomic nuclei. Proton and deuteron of hydrogen; alpha particle (helium nucleus); nuclei of oxygen and uranium. (From Linus Pauling, *General Chemistry*, W. H. Freeman and Company, 1953.)

atomic nuclei are shown in Figure 15.1. Ordinary hydrogen, made up of atoms containing one proton and one electron, is called hydrogen 1, and heavy hydrogen, made up of atoms containing one proton, one neutron, and one electron, is called hydrogen 2 (deuterium). The element with two protons, and hence with atomic number 2, is helium. The heaviest element known in nature is uranium, with atomic number 92. Uranium 235 (the uranium isotope with mass number 235) has a nucleus containing 92 protons and 143 neutrons; it also contains 92 electrons.

Some atoms of an element are short one or more electrons or carry one or more extra electrons that are easily detached. If an atom is short one electron, it has a positive electrical charge of 1; if it has an extra electron, it has a negative charge of 1. An atom with a charge is called an **ion.**

Each element has a symbol, H for hydrogen, O for oxygen, C for carbon, Ca for calcium, U for uranium, Pb for lead, etc. [see back endpapers]. These symbols are used in the chemical formulas of compounds. Water's formula, H_2O, shows that water is made up of two hydrogen atoms to each oxygen atom. Note that the subscript follows the H, to which it refers. A subscript position having been used up in this way, a superscript position is commonly used for the mass number of an isotope, such as H^1 or H^2 (Figure 15.1). In this discussion, however, isotope mass numbers are used so often that they are written, for convenience, as full-size numerals in normal alignment: H1

TABLE 15.1
Some chemical elements and isotopes

Element	Symbol	Atomic Number	Mass (weight) numbers of some isotopes				State at usual temperature and pressure
Argon	Ar	18		36	38	40	Gas
Calcium	Ca	20			40		Solid
Carbon	C	6			12	14	Solid
Helium	He	2			4		Gas
Hydrogen	H	1			1		Gas*
Lead	Pb	82	204	206	207	208	Solid
Nitrogen	N	7			14		Gas*
Oxygen	O	8			16		Gas*
Potassium	K	19		39	40	41	Solid
Radium	Ra	88	223	224	226	228	Solid
Rubidium	Rb	37			85	87	Solid
Strontium	Sr	38		86	87	88	Solid
Thorium	Th	90		230	232		Solid
Uranium	U	92		235	238		Solid
Zirconium	Zr	40	90	91	92	94	Solid

* Occurs commonly in compounds that are liquid or solid.

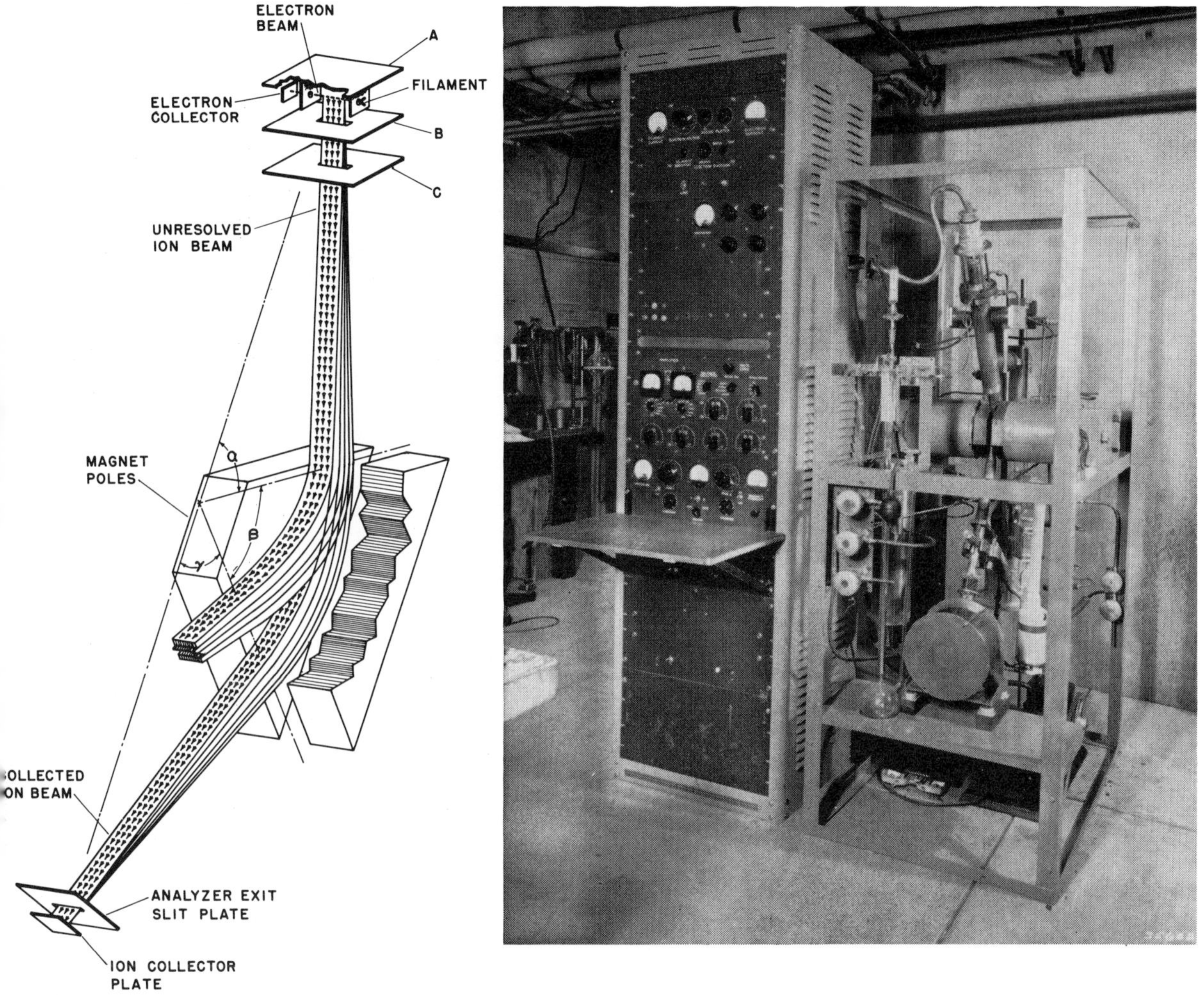

FIGURE 15.2
Nier's 60° mass spectrometer. (Courtesy of A. O. C. Nier.)

for hydrogen 1, H2 for hydrogen 2, C12 for carbon 12, U238 for uranium 238, etc. The names, atomic numbers, and symbols, and selected isotope mass numbers, of the elements considered in this chapter are given in Table 15.1.*

The larger the mass number of an isotope, the heavier are its atoms and ions. As a result, the isotopic composition of a sample of gaseous ions of an element can be determined in a low-pressure chamber called a mass spectrometer (Figure 15.2), where the attraction of a powerful electromagnet deflects moving ions in inverse proportion to their masses.

* [Note: standard notation of atomic and mass numbers has now been shifted to the left side, to leave right superscripts available for valence and right subscripts for combining numbers.—P.C.]

SPONTANEOUS TRANSMUTATION OF ELEMENTS

Spontaneous change, called decay, of one element into others was demonstrated by Pierre and Marie Curie in the eighteen-nineties. They and those who followed showed that uranium changes into a series of other substances, including radium (which the Curies discovered).

All the newly formed substances are called **radiogenic.** One of the radiogenic substances, early called the *alpha particle,* is now known to be a helium nucleus, an ion with two positive charges from its two protons (Figure 15.1). An atom of uranium 238 loses eight successive alpha particles, finally reaching a stable state as lead 206 (Figure 15.3). After a few hundred thousand years the transmutations are in a steady state, with an almost unchanging amount of each intermediate substance, all these amounts being small compared with that of uranium. The amount of the parent isotope, uranium 238, decreases continually, and the amount of the stable daughter isotope, lead 206, increases continually, both at approximately the same low rate. Laboratory studies of the uranium-lead and other radioactive series have shown that changes of temperature, pressure, and chemical environment have practically no effect on the **decay rate,** or rate of transmutation. A logical extrapolation, basic for our purposes, is the conclusion that the radioactive transmutations must have gone on at the present rates under all the conditions that have existed on earth in the geologic past.

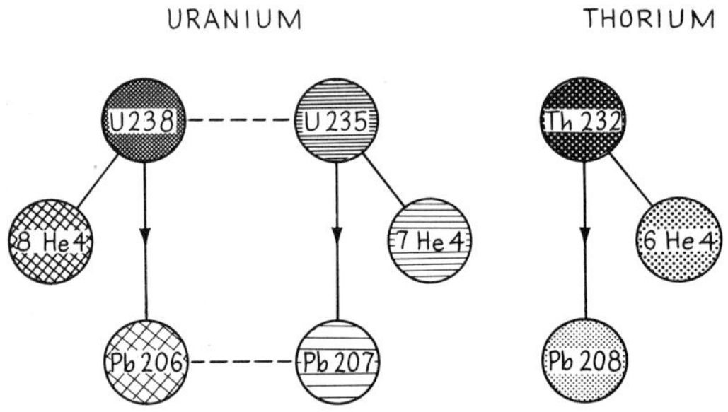

FIGURE 15.3
Decay of uranium and thorium. (Adapted from J. N. Rosholt, U.S. Geological Survey, 1959.)

The decay of uranium 238 to lead 206 would produce, after 4.5 billion years, new lead atoms equal in number to the uranium atoms remaining (Table 15.2); that period is therefore said to be the **half-life** of uranium 238. The other decay rates that we shall consider here are similarly low. One geologically important transmutation, the change of carbon 14 into nitrogen 14, is much more rapid. . . . [Late Pleistocene ages are] of the same order of magnitude as carbon 14's half-life.

AGE FROM RADIOACTIVITY

If the exact quantities of parent and daughter isotopes in a mineral are known, the ratio of these quantities—for example, Pb206/U238—can be used in an appropriate formula to give the **radiometric age** of the mineral—the number of years since it crystallized.

SOME TRANSMUTATIONS USEFUL IN DATING ROCKS

Existing uranium is 99.3 percent U238. The remaining 0.7 percent is practically all U235, which, decaying somewhat faster than U238, yields seven alpha particles and a final stable lead 207 (Figure 15.3 and Table 15.2). Thorium 232, associated with uranium in some minerals, yields six alpha particles and a final stable lead 208. The age of a uranium-thorium mineral may be calculated from any one of the three ratios: Pb206/U238, Pb207/U235, and Pb208/Th232. Each of these ratios involves an original parent isotope and a final daughter isotope; each such pair may be called a **decay pair.**

The ages of the potassium-bearing micas—muscovite, biotite, and lepidolite—and of some other potassium minerals, such as potassium feldspars, can be calculated from transmutations less disruptive than those involving the discharge of alpha particles. Potassium 40 changes to argon 40 (and calcium 40), and rubidium 87 changes to strontium 87, as results of minor internal rearrangements. Potassium 40 is a subordinate but ever-present potassium isotope that changes to argon 40 if an electron is captured by the nucleus. Rubidium is a nearly constant minor associate of potassium. Rubidium 87 is usually somewhat less rare in a potassium mineral than potassium 40, though both are usually measured in parts per million. Rubidium 87 changes to strontium 87 by emission of a beta particle (a nuclear electron).

Before we use a decay pair in dating rocks,

TABLE 15.2
Transmutations of chemical elements useful in determinations of age

From	To	Decay constant (per year)	Parent's Half-life	Method first used
Carbon 14	Nitrogen 14	—	5,730 years	1947
Potassium 40	Argon 40 and calcium 40	To Ar40, 5.85×10^{-11}; to Ca40, 4.72×10^{-10}	—	1948
Rubidium 87	Strontium 87	1.39×10^{-11}, geologically determined, used here; 1.47×10^{-11}, experimentally determined	47,000 m.y.	1946
Thorium 232	6 α-particles + lead 208	4.99×10^{-11}	13,900 m.y.	1938
Uranium 235	7 α-particles + lead 207	9.72×10^{-10}	713 m.y.	1938
Uranium 238	8 α-particles + lead 206	1.54×10^{-10}	4,510 m.y.	1938
Uranium	Lead (ordinary weighing on chemical balance)	—	—	1907

Note: m.y. = million years.

we need to know the assumptions involved, so that we can make the necessary qualifications. The present-day procedures and computations are moderately complicated. We shall consider first the simpler calculations made a half century ago, when the relative quantities of the elements lead and uranium, rather than those of specific isotopes, were used, and the formula was crude.

A SIMPLE TREATMENT

The first radiometric ages were calculated by Professor B. B. Boltwood of Yale University. In 1905 he reached the conclusion that the lead in uranium minerals must be the end product of uranium decay, and in 1907 he used the simple lead/uranium ratios to obtain the approximate ages of ten mineral occurrences. Estimating that one ten-billionth of the uranium changes to lead each year, he multiplied each lead/uranium ratio by 10 billion to get the age of the mineral in years. Boltwood's youngest specimen was a uraninite (uranium oxide) from Glastonbury, Connecticut, with a Pb/U ratio of 0.041 (average of five analyses) and hence an estimated age of 410 million years. This age is surprisingly close to the latest estimates, 250–275 million years, and would have been much closer had the uranium-lead decay rates been accurately known. The material Boltwood thought oldest was a thorianite (thorium and uranium oxide) from Ceylon with a lead/uranium ratio of 0.22 and a supposed age of 2,200 million years. This age was far too high because Boltwood considered thorium a stable element that did not yield radiogenic lead.

PROPER CALCULATIONS

Boltwood did not use properly the rate of uranium decay. He treated the change from uranium to lead as though the material were sand passing through an hourglass (Figure 15.4, A). In his hourglass the parent material would lose one ten-billionth of its original amouht every year. In 10 billion years it would all be gone (straight-line relation, Figure 15.4, B). Actually, an unchanging fraction of the *remaining* uranium is lost each year (Figure 15.4, C). Let us consider an individual isotope, even though here a distinction between isotopes is not necessarily involved. The decay constant for uranium 238 is 1.54 ten-billionths per year (Table 15.2); that is, this fraction of the remaining uranium, if at least a few trillion atoms are involved, will decay each year. The loss the second year would not be appreciably different from that for the first year, and even after a billion years the amount lost per year would be five-sixths of the first year's loss. But after 4.5 billion years the U238 would be half gone, and the quantity decaying each year would be only half of what decayed each year at the beginning. As worked out mathematically by H. Bateman of England in 1910, the decay curve is logarithmic (Figure 15.4, C); the original uranium would never be completely exhausted, though after 50 or 100 billion years the amount remaining might not be detectable. The time of decay of a particular atom is not predictable; Bateman's equations apply only to large numbers of atoms.

GENERAL ASSUMPTIONS AND QUALIFICATIONS

Even though the hourglass analogy is not applicable to decay rates, it is useful in other ways. The material in the upper part of the glass (Figure 15.4, A) is the parent isotope, that at the bottom is the daughter isotope, and the band of dots between represents intermediate substances such as radium. In determining age, we assume not only that the decay rate is logarithmic and constant but also that all the parent isotope entered the hourglass (the mineral grain or grains) at the time it started operating (the time of mineral crystallization) and that at this time none of the daughter isotope was present. If these assumptions are not correct, we must find means of measuring departures from them. We also either assume that the enclosing rock has provided impermeable walls for the hourglass, so that no measurable amount of either isotope can be added or removed, or attempt to compensate for any such changes. Any compensation must be rigorously justified.

AGES FROM RATIOS INVOLVING LEAD

In calculations of isotopic ages from lead/uranium and lead/thorium ratios, some of the assumptions mentioned above can be checked. In particular, non-radiogenic lead can be recognized and allowed for, because, fortunately, one isotope, lead 204, has no known radioactive source (Figure 15.5). The non-radiogenic lead indicated by the presence of Pb204, including appropriate amounts of Pb206 and Pb207, is therefore subtracted. The proportions of the lead isotopes in non-radiogenic lead vary somewhat from place to place, but are always of the order shown in Figure 15.5.

The minerals whose ages have been determined by Pb/U and Pb/Th ratios fall into two groups, one made up of a few minerals with high percentages of uranium or thorium,

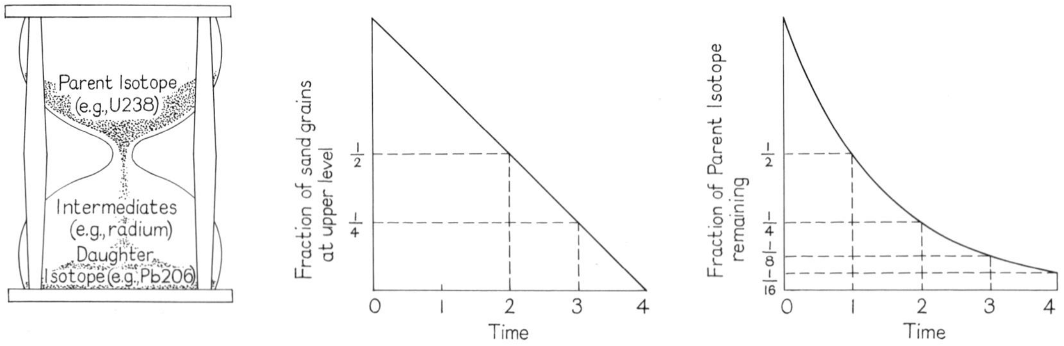

FIGURE 15.4
Hourglass diagram and decay curves for radioactivity. A, section through hourglass; B, hypothetical graph of the hourglass type of decay; C, graph of actual radioactive decay.

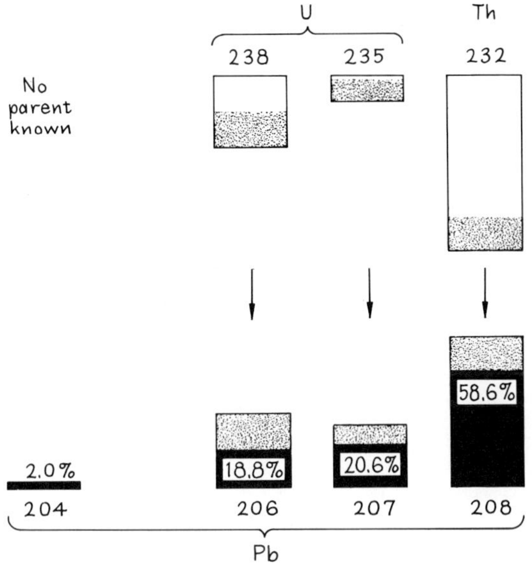

FIGURE 15.5
Relations between uranium, thorium, and lead isotopes. *Black*, primeval lead (proportion in Canyon Diablo meteorite); *gray*, uranium and thorium decayed to radiogenic lead during 4.55 billion years of earth history; *white*, remaining uranium and thorium. (Redrawn from R. S. Cannon, Jr., and others, *Economic Geology*, 1961.)

the other made up of zirconium and rare-earth minerals that are hospitable to the substitution of uranium or thorium in a particular structural position. In the second group, of which the most important minerals are monazite (a rare-earth phosphate) and zircon (zirconium silicate), the radioactive elements have partially replaced elements of similar atomic volume and similar chemical bonding characteristics. Only a few of the zirconium (or rare-earth element) positions in the crystal structure, perhaps one in ten thousand, are occupied by uranium atoms; in monazite, however, thorium is much more abundant.

Minerals of high uranium content commonly weather rather easily. Zircon, however, is extremely resistant to weathering and monazite moderately so. The few uranium atoms in zircon and monazite appear to be well protected, for they persist through many environmental changes, including those involved in weathering, transportation, and deposition in a sedimentary bed. The products of radioactivity are somewhat more likely to get away; the lead atom, for example, is too large for the zirconium position, and its chemical bonding is inadequate.

Two products of uranium and thorium decay are gasses under ordinary conditions. One, helium, has been shown to leak slowly away. As the leakage cannot be estimated satisfactorily, ages involving helium are not now being used. A second gas, radon, isotopes of which are produced in both the U238–Pb208 and the U235–Pb207 series, is short-lived, the Rn222 of the U238 series having a half-life of 3.83 days, the Rn219 of the U235 series one of 3.92 seconds. The isotopes of radon probably do not, therefore, under natural conditions, escape from a crystal of zircon or other slightly radioactive mineral in significant amounts. If any radon does escape, it is probably in the U238 rather than in the U235 series. Therefore, if the Pb207/U235 age is the greater, loss of radon may be suspected; if the Pb207/U235 and Pb206/U238 ages are about the same, loss of radon has probably been unimportant. Even in minerals rich in uranium, loss of radon may be less serious than loss of radium if we may judge from analyses of Colorado Plateau uranium ores.

Since the half-life of U235 is much shorter than that of U238 (Table 8–2), the amount of Pb207 produced in a mineral per year drops off much more rapidly than the amount of Pb206 produced per year. As a result, the ratio Pb207/Pb206 is itself a radioactivity clock, one that becomes easier to read with increasing age, especially above 500 million years. This clock is independent of recent partial loss of lead, as the two leads behave similarly in all chemical reactions. It is also practically independent of recent loss of uranium and does not require the determination of the amount of uranium in the mineral. The ratio Pb207/Pb206 is one of the most important measures of age.

The Pb207/U235 and Pb206/U238 ratios of a mineral, taken together, provide exceptionally important evidence of age. If the ages derived from the two ratios are about the same, they are called **concordant.** Few pairs of ages are exactly concordant, but many pairs —perhaps one-third of all that have been determined—are within about 10 percent of each other. Such approximately concordant ages corroborate one another. If the age discrepancy is greater than 10 percent of the larger, the ages are called **discordant.** Even discordant pairs, under some circumstances, give useful indications of the age of a rock and also of its post-consolidation thermal history.

The Pb207/U235 and Pb206/U238 ratios and ages obtained in a region may be plotted against each other in a regional diagram. Figure 15.6 is such a diagram, representing analyses of three Rhodesian monazites. The Pb207/U235 ratios and the corresponding ages are scaled along the *y*-axis, the Pb206/U238 ratios and the corresponding ages along the *x*-axis. In the rare case where a pair of ages are exactly concordant, the point representing the pair is plotted on the curve labeled Concordia. If the Pb206/U238 ages are the smaller, as they are for all three analyses plotted, the pairs, which here vary from slightly to greatly discordant, plot to the left of the Concordia curve, on its concave side.

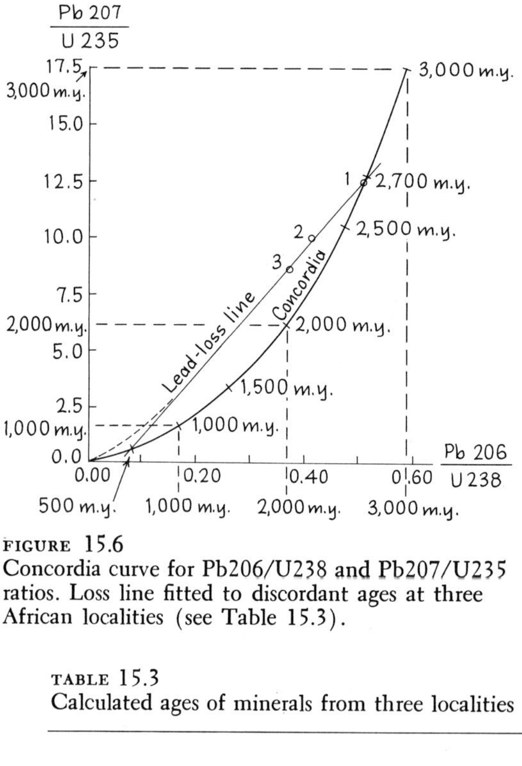

FIGURE 15.6
Concordia curve for Pb206/U238 and Pb207/U235 ratios. Loss line fitted to discordant ages at three African localities (see Table 15.3).

The ages calculated for the three Rhodesian monazites (perhaps all from pegmatites) are given in Table 15.3. The Bikita ages are almost concordant. The other two localities give discordant ages. The plots (1, 2, and 3 in the diagram) determine a straight line that, if extended, cuts Concordia at about 2,700 and 500 m.y. When one notes also that the Jack Claim and Irumi Hills Pb207/Pb206 ages are within 2.3 percent of Bikita's 2,680 m.y., one is tempted to consider the low Pb206/U238 and Pb207/U235 ages the effects of leakage of lead at the two northern localities (compare Figure 15.7 for geographic positions), the two leads being equally affected, just as chemical considerations would lead one to expect. The oblique straight line in Figure 15.6 can then be considered a **loss line.** Its slope is determined by the Pb207/Pb206 ratios, for the ratio between U238 and U235 is everywhere the same at any one time, including the present, and therefore does not affect the slope. All the data may be explained as the result of two events: (1) the crystallization of the monazites, no doubt from a quartz-plutonite magma, 2,700 m.y. ago; (2) the partial recrystallization or other alteration of two monazites 500 m.y. ago. Since the second event was relatively recent, the lead dissolved at that time had attained a Pb207/Pb206 ratio that has not changed much since. The loss line gives nearly as good evidence for a single definite age of

TABLE 15.3
Calculated ages of minerals from three localities in southern Africa

Locality	Mineral	Ages in millions of years: Pb206/U238	Pb207/U235	Pb207/Pb206	Pb208/Th232	Ar40/K40	Sr87/Rb87
1. Bikita, Southern Rhodesia	Monazite	2,675	2,680	2,680	2,645		
	Mica					2,310	2,500*
2. Jack Claim, near Salisbury, Southern Rhodesia	Monazite	2,260	2,470	2,650			
3. Irumi Hills, Northern Rhodesia (Zambia)	Monazite	2,040	2,330	2,620			

* (2,400–2,600)

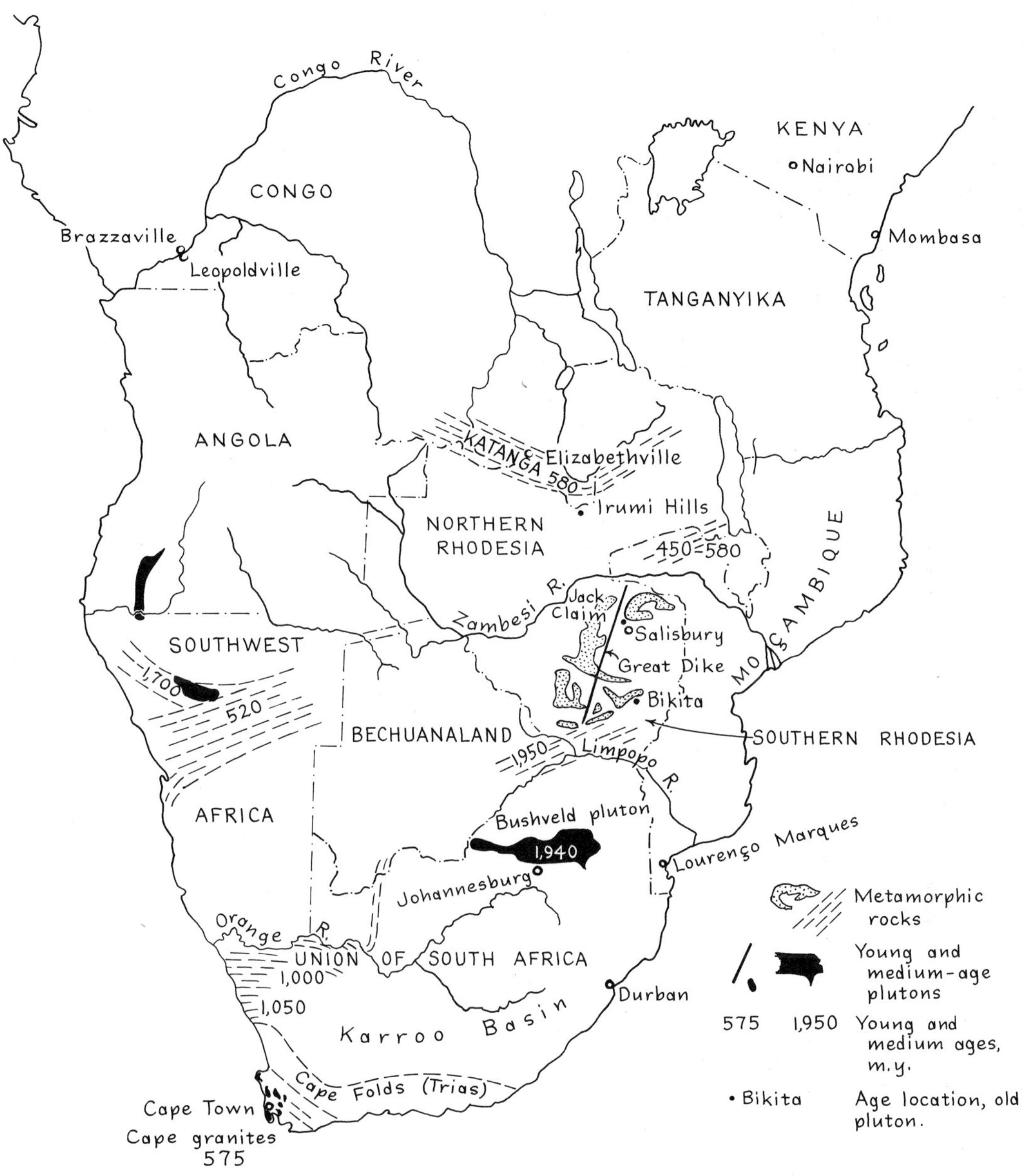

FIGURE 15.7
Map showing structures and some ages in central and southern Africa. (Structural lines adapted from L. O. Nicolaysen, *in* A. E. J. Engel, H. L. James, and B. F. Leonard, eds., *Petrologic Studies–A Volume in Honor of A. F. Buddington*, Geol. Soc. Am., 1962.)

original crystallization (here 2,700 m.y.) as concordant Pb206/U238 and Pb207/U235 ages would.

The field geological evidence is consistent with these conclusions. All three Rhodesian monazites might be expected to have about the same age, for all probably came from the same sea of quartz-plutonite rocks, in which roughly parallel belts of metasediments and metavolcanic rocks lie (Figure 15.7). (There is some uncertainty about the Irumi Hills material, which was collected, not from bedrock, but from a natural alluvial concentrate.) In northeastern and northwestern Rhodesia, and in an adjacent part of Katanga Province of the Congo, pegmatites and veins yield minerals with ages of 485–640 m.y. (marked on Figure 15.7). All the geological and geochemical evidence is consistent with the previously stated idea that the old intrusions of 2,700 m.y. ago were followed 600–500 m.y. ago by new localized northern intrusions. The latter may have reheated the whole northern part of the ancient mass of Rhodesian crystalline rocks. (One wonders a little why the belt of metamorphism southwest of Bikita, which is 1,950 m.y. old, did not affect that locality.) Finally, erosion of the Irumi Hills made possible the formation of heavy-mineral alluvial concentrates that seem to have lost lead and other substances, during weathering, without changing the Pb207/Pb206 ratio.

A short extension of the loss line to an intersection with Concordia is more reliable than a long extrapolation. In Figure 15.6 the age of the original crystallization of the monazites, obtained by a short extension of the loss line, is therefore much better established than the supposed age of reheating and leakage, obtained by a long extrapolation. The latter would not be taken seriously were it not for the independent evidence of central African plutonism about 500 m.y. ago. Even so, another possible interpretation of the data, as the result of continuous solid diffusion, gives a curve that coincides for most of its length with the straight loss line previously discussed but curves away finally to the origin as shown by the dashed line of Figure 15.6.

The Pb208/Th232 age of a mineral or rock is often different from and usually less than the Pb206/U238 and Pb207/U235 ages, even if the latter are concordant. Under such circumstances the lead/thorium age is commonly ignored. Some Russian workers, however, consider a low lead/thorium age a warning (Vinogradoff and others, 1960). Stating that "experiments have shown that uranium is more easily leached out of different radioactive minerals than thorium," they interpret concordant lead/uranium ages greater than lead/thorium ages as the result of the leaching of both lead and uranium. The best ages are those for which the lead/ uranium and the lead/thorium ages are all concordant, but most workers are willing to accept concordant lead/uranium, argon/potassium, and strontium/rubidium ages even if the lead/thorium age is much lower.

AGES FROM ARGON/POTASSIUM RATIOS

Potassium 40 decays to argon 40 and calcium 40. Calcium 40 is not very useful for age determinations, for radiogenic Ca40 cannot be distinguished from Ca40 of other origin and is only a small part of the total Ca40 in most rocks. The argon 40 found in the analysis of a potassium mineral or rock is also only partly radiogenic; the remainder comes from the atmosphere. A correction, however, can be made for atmospheric argon 40 after the amount of a non-radiogenic argon isotope has been determined. This correction is similar to that made for common lead. Argon, which is a gas under ordinary conditions, is quickly expelled from minerals at high temperatures. Nevertheless, the minute quantities of argon evolved from potassium seem to be retained for at least 100 million years in feldspar and for much longer periods in micas if the rocks containing these minerals have been neither reheated nor intensely deformed.

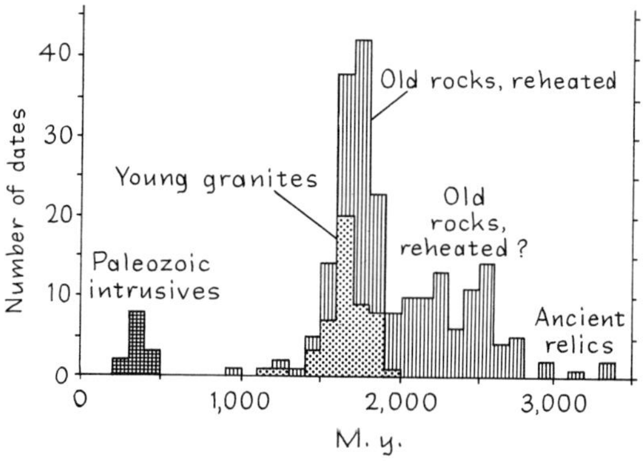

FIGURE 15.8
Diagram showing distribution of 226 Ar/K ages, northwestern Russia, by 100 m.y. intervals. (Ages recalculated with the American decay constants of Table 15.2 from data of E. K. Gerling and A. A. Polkanov, 1958.)

The behavior of argon in some rocks that were reheated during metamorphism, in large part near younger granite masses, is revealed by a set of argon/potassium ages for micas in the Russian part of the Baltic Shield. These ages are plotted in Figure 15.8. The 226 ages, fortunately, have fairly wide geographical distribution and represent several parts of the Baltic geologic column. In Figure 15.8 the ages are shown in 100 m.y. groups. The ages between 200 and 500 m.y. are for granites . . . known from independent evidence to be Paleozoic. The largest group of ages is made up of the eighty between 1,600 and 1,800 m.y.; it includes twenty-nine ages for two sets of relatively young Precambrian granites . . . which no doubt crystallized 1,800–1,600 m.y. ago.

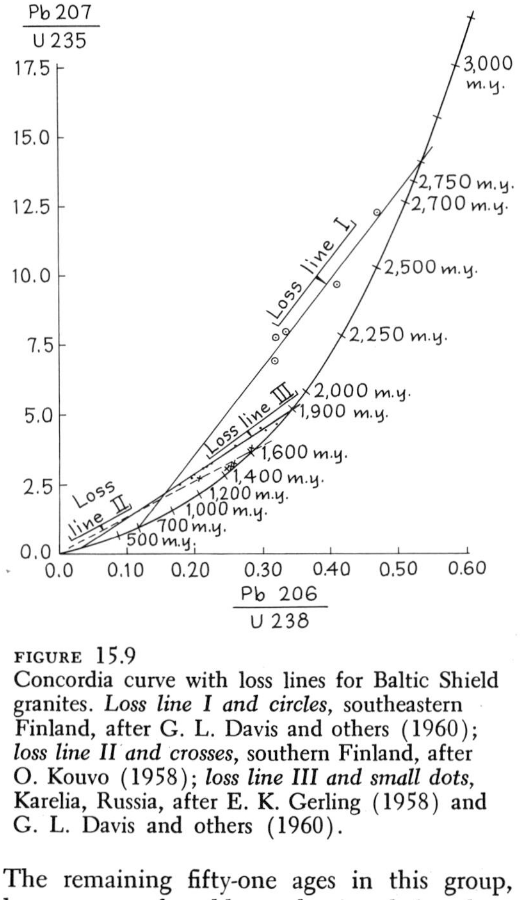

FIGURE 15.9
Concordia curve with loss lines for Baltic Shield granites. *Loss line I and circles*, southeastern Finland, after G. L. Davis and others (1960); *loss line II and crosses*, southern Finland, after O. Kouvo (1958); *loss line III and small dots*, Karelia, Russia, after E. K. Gerling (1958) and G. L. Davis and others (1960).

The remaining fifty-one ages in this group, however, are for older rocks, invaded and reheated by the granites. The long sequence of greater ages, extending to 3,400 m.y., with minor maxima at 2,200–2,300 and 2,500–2,600 m.y., may be interpreted as representing relics of ancient rocks that kept some early radiogenic argon through all vicissitudes.

Three lead/uranium loss lines (Figure 15.9) for three sets of granite rocks in the Baltic Shield area of Finland and northwestern Russia, give ages consistent with those of Figure 15.8. They indicate that two groups of young Precambrian granites originated 1,650 and 1,900 m.y. ago and a group of older granite gneisses 2,775 m.y. ago. One of the groups of young granites is in Belomoria, west of the White Sea, and the other is in southern Finland; the granitic gneisses are also in southern Finland, near Joensuu. In view of the evidence of four areas of young Precambrian granites . . . it is no wonder that most of the older metasediments and recrystallized plutonic rocks of the region have lost part or all of the radiogenic argon accumulated before the intrusion of the young granites. . . .

One must not oversimplify the pre-1,900 m.y. record of the Baltic Shield. The 2,200–2,300 and 2,500–2,600 m.y. peaks of Figure 15.8 may represent events occurring at those times or earlier events whose apparent ages have been reduced by loss of argon during reheating. These peaks are less certain indicators of age than the loss lines are of events at 2,700, 1,900, and 1,650 m.y.

AGES FROM STRONTIUM/RUBIDIUM RATIOS

Rubidium 87 is more abundant than potassium 40, but it decays to strontium 87 rather slowly (Table 15.2), and the mass spectrometer used for its determination is less sensitive than that used for argon. On balance, one might expect the Ar40/K40 and Sr87/Rb87 methods to be about equally effective, and they do commonly lead to similar ages (see Figure 15.10).

The Sr87/Rb87 method has one advantage. The radiogenic Sr87 appears to stay in or near the source mineral even after mild metamorphism, as shown by a comparison of the analysis of a rock with analyses of its rubidium-bearing constituents mica, hornblende, and feldspar. Such analyses permit checks on strontium/rubidium ages similar to the loss-line checks on lead/uranium ages.

PRECISION AND ACCURACY OF DETERMINATIONS OF GEOLOGIC AGE

Statisticians make a distinction between precision and accuracy. The term **precision** refers to the scatter, or lack of it, among repeated

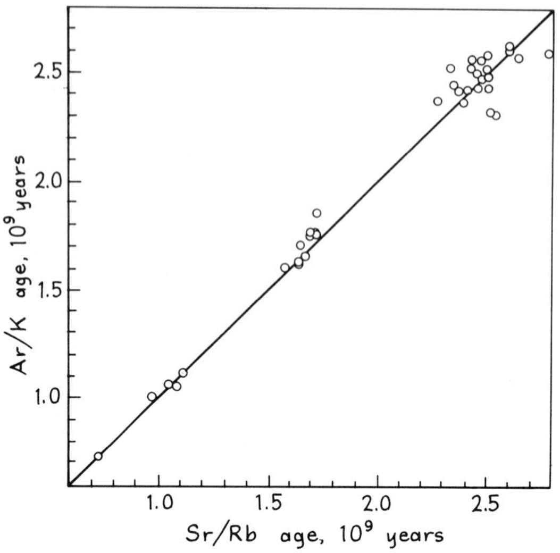

FIGURE 15.10
Concordance of Ar/K and Sr/Rb ages, shown by data for Minnesota Precambrian rocks. (After S. S. Goldich and others, *Minnesota Geol. Survey Bull.* 41, 1961.)

determinations of what is thought to be a single value, such as the age of the biotite in a granite, determined by the argon/potassium method. The **accuracy** of the determinations, however, is a measure of their deviation from the true age, if that can be discovered.

Before comparing precision and accuracy we must have clearly in mind the kinds and causes of variation or error in the numbers that represent the age of a mineral occurrence. **Analytical errors** are those made during chemical treatment and analysis. **Sampling errors** are variations from the average composition that result from the selection of the mineral sample, which may, for example, be made up of hundreds of little crystals of zircon or flakes of mica. The two groups of errors are statistically similar, for both are discovered through repeated determinations on substances as they now exist. The probable analytical error can be calculated if a number of determinations are available. If the frequencies are plotted, a bell-shaped curve is commonly obtained. For example, 40 out of 100 determinations might be exactly 100 m.y., 80 within the range 98–102 m.y., and all 100 between 95 and 105 m.y., with a mean of 100 m.y. The bell-shaped curve would then be very high and narrow, with a standard deviation from the mean smaller than ±2 m.y. One feels intuitively that the mean, 100 m.y., is probably within 2 m.y. of the true value for the sample —that is, that analytical precision equals analytical accuracy. But was the analyzed sample a fair sample? In order to answer this question, one collects multiple samples and prepares them for analysis, commonly with great labor. Then one treats the analyses of the different samples statistically to obtain a new mean and a standard deviation that applies to both analytical and sampling errors.

Even numerous samples of a radioactive mineral, however, are not likely to give the true age by simple analysis for parent and daughter isotopes. Allowances for **contamination** and **leakage** should be made. It is standard procedure, in analyses for radiogenic lead or argon, to make allowances for the amounts of nonradiogenic Pb206, Pb207, Pb208, and Ar40 indicated by the presence of other, wholly nonradiogenic lead or argon isotopes. Leakage from the radioactive hourglass is allowed for if the uranium-lead loss line is used, and error that is the result of recent leakage is by-passed in the Pb207/Pb206 method. In one way or another, more or less satisfactory estimates of the first four types of error are frequently available.

Systematic errors are those that have similar effects on whole arrays of determinations. One kind of systematic errors is not included in any of the previous groups: those in the decay constants. The constants have been revised several times; those now in use are not all identical in Russia and the United States. A hundred determinations with a mean of 900 m.y. and a standard deviation of ±18 m.y. might be changed to a hundred determinations with a mean of 950 m.y. and a standard deviation of ±19 m.y. as a result of a change in a decay constant. All other ages based on the same decay pair would be affected in exactly similar fashion.

In order to have geological application, a mineral age must be shown to have some specified relation to the age of a rock. The mineral may be older than the rock, contemporaneous with it, or younger. Some of the thousands of little zircons in a granite may, after being detrital in a sedimentary rock, have been incorporated into the granite without melting and without restarting the radioactive clock.

A large zircon in a pegmatite may have formed in a crack or solution cavity produced at a late date, during a revival of pegmatitic activity. Even if the zircon crystals in a particular pegmatite were formed at the same time as all the other minerals in that rock, some other pegmatites in the district may have been formed at a very different time. These possibilities are examples of those that must be considered by persons who wish to date rocks by the ages of radioactive minerals. Every occurrence must be considered a special problem, to be solved individually.

The analytical variations for some samples have been studied rather thoroughly. One study involved lepidolite samples from five rocks, each analyzed in more than one laboratory, the number varying from two to four. The mean determined ages ranged from 100 to 2,760 m.y.; the standard deviations at any one laboratory were mostly below 4 per cent, and the differences between the means obtained at different laboratories were also mostly less than 4 per cent. Many lead and Ar40/K40 ages probably have equally good laboratory reproducibilities; some are somewhat better. Variability between samples (sampling error) is not so well known; here contamination and leakage may be involved. The Sr87/Rb87 ages of different samples of lepidolite from a pegmatite at Pala, California, determined in a single laboratory, varied, for unknown reasons, from 107 to 116 m.y. . . .

AGES OF MINERALS IN STRATIFIED ROCKS

The ages of most stratified rocks cannot be determined directly from radiometric ratios. Such a ratio yields the time elapsed since the crystallization of a mineral containing uranium, thorium, or potassium (accompanied by rubidium). In sedimentary rocks, unfortunately, most minerals containing these elements occur as clastic grains in which the radiometric clocks were started long before sedimentation. One or two sedimentary potassium minerals deserve consideration, but most sedimentary sequences must be dated radiometrically from the ages of interbedded tuffs or other volcanic rocks or, less satisfactorily, from the ages of intrusive plutonic rocks. Useful volcanic and plutonic rocks are rather rare. Whole systems, including the Silurian and practically all of the Carboniferous, lack, at this writing (1964), usable dates. The few available radiometric ages of Cambrian and later fossiliferous rocks are, obviously, of minor value to the stratigrapher. Nevertheless, these dates make a consistent pattern that is useful in the solution of such problems as a local rate of sedimentation or a general rate of evolution per million years. After more and better-distributed dates have accumulated, it may become possible to estimate in years the lengths of most or all geologic periods, from the Cambrian up.

Two sedimentary rocks, three sedimentary minerals, four volcanic minerals, and one type of volcanic rock have yielded radiometric ages of greater or lesser value.

SEDIMENTARY SUBSTANCES USED FOR DATING

The two sedimentary rocks that have been used for dating are uranium-bearing black shale and a dark, fine-grained, uranium-bearing Scandinavian rock locally called kolm. The many Pb206/U238 ages for kolm are different from the Pb207/U235 ages for the same samples, and the pairs of values do not plot on a loss line. A Tennessee black shale looks more promising, but not conclusively so. Neither of these materials will be considered further here.

The three sedimentary minerals that have been used for radiometric ages, sylvite (potassium chloride), glauconite (iron-potassium silicate), and a potassium-bearing clay mineral, have commonly been dated from the argon/potassium and strontium/rubidium ratios, but at least two occurrences have been dated from the Ca40/K40 ratio. Most age-determinations for sedimentary rocks are based on Ar40/K40 ratios for glauconites. All three minerals have given some amazingly reasonable determinations of age, but each has an inherent defect that makes it an unsatisfactory guide to true age, at least in the present state of knowledge concerning it.

Sylvite, which has been dated by the argon/potassium and calcium/potassium methods, is soluble in water. Its recrystallization is therefore very easy and commonly also hard to recognize. Each recrystallization gives the radiometric clock a new start. Both concordant and discordant sylvite ages have been reported in the U.S.S.R. A Ca40/K40 age of 228 ± 7 m.y. was found for an apparently unrecrystallized Lower Permian sample and an age of 620 ± 20 m.y. for a Lower Cambrian sample. The Ar40/K40 age was slightly lower for the Permian material and very much lower for the Cambrian material. The Ca40/K40 Russian ages are consistent with those of volcanic and plutonic rocks, to be discussed later, and should be kept in mind, but the calcium/potassium method has been used too little to be relied on.

Glauconite, the principal radioactive sedimentary mineral used for dating, seems to have crystallized on the sea floor as sand-sized pellets (greensand) that got their chemical constituents largely from adjacent clay particles and even incorporated the remains of such particles. The clastic source material (clay) may have contained, at the time of deposition, radiogenic argon 40 and strontium 87, and these isotopes may not have escaped completely during the formation of glauconite; as a result, the determined glauconite ages may be high. On the other hand, since lower Paleozoic glauconites usually contain more potassium than later glauconites, this mineral can, perhaps, gain potassium long after its first crystallization. The result might be low argon/potassium ages, especially for the more ancient glauconites.

The third radioactive sedimentary mineral, a potassium-bearing clay, has the defects of glauconite in exaggerated degree. It will not be considered further here.

VOLCANIC SUBSTANCES USED FOR DATING

The four volcanic minerals that have been used for dating stratified rocks are biotite, potassium feldspar, zircon, and monazite, all of which occur as crystals in tuffs. Monazite has been used only in an Ordovician sample that also contained zircon.

The most widespread tuffs, and hence those that are stratigraphically the most useful, are the high-silicon rhyolitic ashes, products of the explosive outbursts of viscous magmas. These tuffs commonly contain a few shiny black biotite crystals, uncommonly a few zircons. If the biotite crystals are still fresh, they give a usable argon/potassium age. If enough zircons can be concentrated from a tuff, they may give usable lead/uranium ages. Whole-rock samples of a few potassium-rich non-fragmental lavas, analyzed for potassium and radiogenic (or total?) argon, have provided data for age calculations.

SAMPLE DATES FOR THE CRETACEOUS SYSTEM

The amount of scatter and some other facts about sedimentary radiometric ages become apparent from a sample graph. The example, Figure 15.11, is a rough graph of the apparent radiometric ages of rocks assigned to the upper and middle stages of the Cretaceous System. Argon/potassium ages only are listed, partly because they are much the most numerous and partly to eliminate variations due to the method used. The Cretaceous stages are listed in order at the left, with the highest stage at the top. The stratigraphic positions of the analyzed samples are given as closely as possible; if only the stage is known, the age is plotted in the middle of the space. The uncertainties as to radiometric age or stage assignment that were indicated by some analysts are not shown in the graph. Circles mark mean ages for stages.

A general trend is clear, especially for the stage means, from smaller numbers at the top to larger ones near the bottom. The scatter, however, is very large. Cenomanian dates range from 70 to 128 m.y., Middle Albian from 94 to 142. The scatter is too great for us to have much confidence in the individual ages. A single apparent radiometric age, chosen at random, would make an inadequate age datum and, from the stratigraphic point of view, would be greatly inferior to a guide fossil. The scatter can be reduced by elimination of some kinds of data. Glauconite dates show the widest scatter, from 70 to 128 m.y. in the Cenomanian and from 94 to 142 m.y. in the Middle Albian. We might eliminate the glauconite dates, even though we should, at the same time, lose all the dates derived directly from sedimentary rocks. As the whole-rock vol-

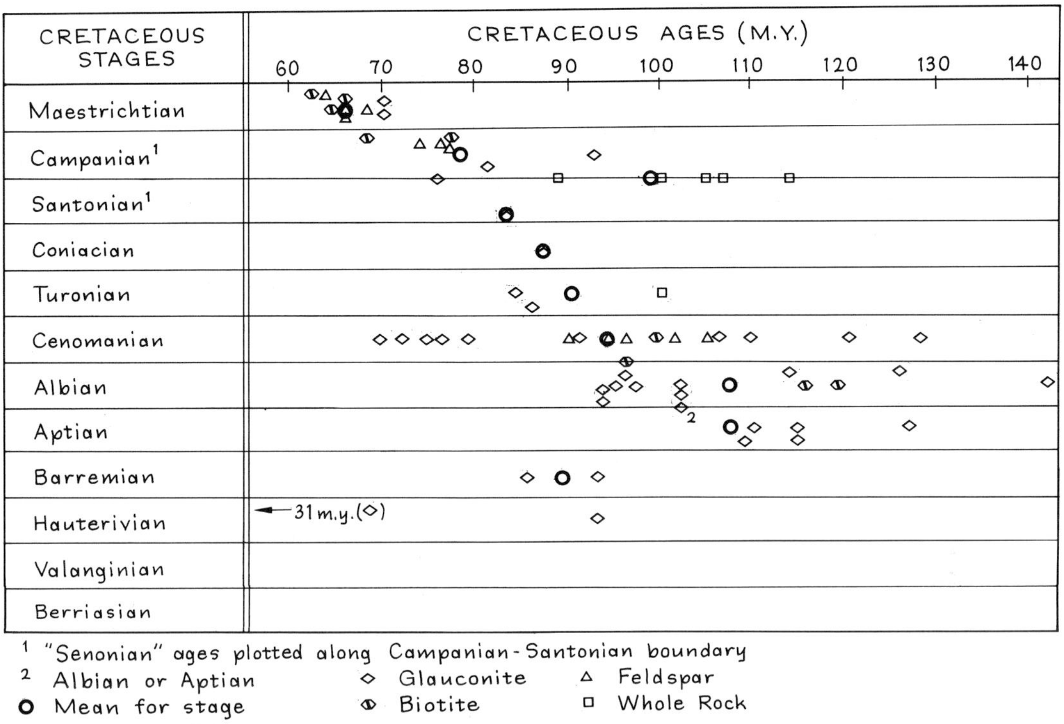

FIGURE 15.11
Cretaceous Ar/K ages. (Data mostly from C. F. Davidson, Liverpool and Manchester, *Jour. Geology*, 1960; J. F. Evernden and others. *Geochim. et Cosmochim. Acta*, 1961; G. A. Kazakov and N. I. Polevaya, *Geochemistry*, 1958; and R. E. Folinsbee and others, 1961.)

canic ages also show considerable scatter, from 89 to 114 m.y. for the "Senonian," we might set them aside too. We should have left only a few ages for samples of biotite and potassium feldspar from volcanic rocks. These remaining ages make a regular progression, consistent with stratigraphic position, from 63–67 m.y. for the Maestrichtian through 75–76 m.y. for the Campanian and 93–96 m.y. for the Cenomanian to 115–119 m.y. for the Albian.

Lower Paleozoic glauconite ages are markedly lower than those for volcanic rocks. Because of this divergence and the glauconite scatter at most horizons, we should probably ignore glauconite ages (and the few other ages for sedimentary rocks) in constructing a radiometric age scale for the fossiliferous rock systems.

AGE SCALE FOR STRATIFIED ROCKS

The use of radiometric volcanic ages, supplemented by plutonic ones, makes possible a rather clean-cut, though tentative, age scale for Cambrian and younger rocks. Such a scale is shown in Figure 15.12. In this figure, stratigraphic position in the standard geologic column is plotted vertically. Ages in years are plotted horizontally, from zero at the left to 600 m.y. at the right. For each of the forty-nine ages, a cross shows stratigraphic position plotted against age in years. Cenozoic volcanic ages are so numerous that the crosses interfere with one another at the upper left, and some crosses stand for two or more rock ages. The pre-Cretaceous ages are both sparser and less precise; for most of them the analytical and stratigraphic uncertainties are large enough to show on the graph. The analytical uncertainty (commonly the standard deviation) is indicated by the length of the horizontal bar of the cross. The stratigraphic uncertainty is shown by the length of the vertical bar.

The tentative age scale in Figure 15.12 is the oblique straight line; it was fitted by alternate inspections and adjustments. The geological periods, which were largely established on changes in the fossil marine faunas, were first

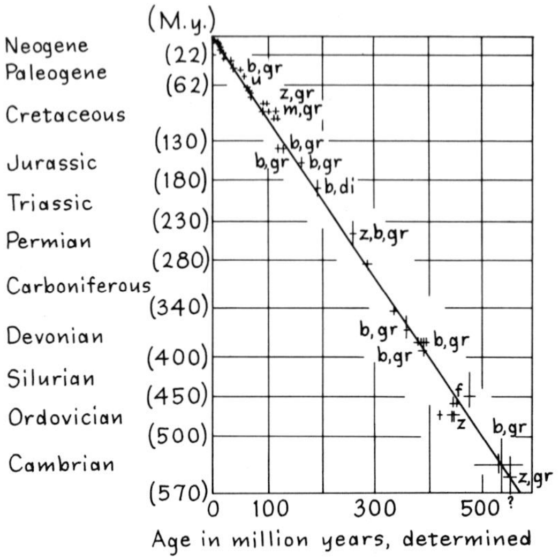

FIGURE 15.12
Biotite, feldspar, zircon, and monazite ages of fossil-controlled volcanic and plutonic rocks. Ordinates determined qualitatively by stratigraphic position but with period lengths uncertain below the Cretaceous, adjusted to bring crosses close to the diagonal straight line. Most ages in the Kulp list (1961), including Kulp Nos. 2, 5–9, 11, 13, 14, 17–19, 24, 30, 32, 33, 35, 42, 43, 45, 50, 52, 53, 55, 59, 63, 65, 68, 73, 75–77, 80, 81, 84, 85. *Cross*, single or mean age; *elongated vertical bar*, stratigraphic uncertainty; *elongated horizontal bar*, analytical uncertainty; *unlettered*, biotite from tuff, Ar/K age; *f*, feldspar from tuff, Ar/K age; *z*, zircon from tuff, Pb/U age; *b,di*, biotite from diabase, Ar/K age; *b,gr*, plutonic biotite, Ar/K age; *m,gr*, plutonic monazite, Pb/U age; *z,gr*, plutonic zircon, Pb/U age; *u*, ore uraninite, Pb/U age; *z,b,gr*, nearly identical plutonic zircon and biotite ages.

plotted with equal lengths of 50 m.y. Several departures from this rule became necessary if the crosses were to be close to the oblique straight line. The base of the Neogene is now scaled at 22 m.y., the base of the Paleogene at 62 m.y., and the base of the Cretaceous at 130 m.y. Finally, the vertical spaces for the Carboniferous and Devonian were increased to the equivalent of 60 m.y. and the Cambrian to 70 m.y.

The greatest stratigraphic uncertainties in Figure 15.12 are for the rather numerous examples of intrusive rocks. Fourteen intrusive rocks are involved: twelve quartz plutonites, one diabase, and one ore-vein. In the pre-Cretaceous part of the array the intrusives provide about half of the ages (10 out of 21). The stratigraphic uncertainties of these intrusives vary considerably. Among the least uncertain are the *z,gr* and *m,gr* mid-Cretaceous dates, for granitic rocks in southern California and Lower California, respectively. . . .

Below the Cretaceous the available volcanic and plutonic ages are sparse. They fit the oblique straight line of Figure 15.12 rather well because the diagram is the result of the adjustment of period lengths to a stratigraphically consistent set of radiometric ages. In the future, new radiometric dates will no doubt make further adjustments of period lengths necessary. Changes, large or small, should be welcomed as improvements on the present-day reasonable guesses.

An important horizon that does not yet have a well-established radiometric age is the base of the Cambrian. Most of the data are consistent with the age of 570 m.y. shown in Figure 15.12. . . .

RELATIVE PRECISION OF RADIOACTIVE AGES AND FOSSIL CORRELATIONS

If, by radiometric dating, the range of Neogene ages is from 1 (or 3) to 22 m.y., if that of Paleogene ages is 22–62 m.y., and if that of Cretaceous ages is 62–130 m.y., should these numbers be used as new bases for the definition of the Neogene, Paleogene, and Cretaceous Periods? Or should stratigraphers stick exclusively to the definition of a period as the time of deposition of the rocks of the sedimentary system? This is a real problem in connection with plutonic rocks. Only a few batholiths are closely dated stratigraphically. Before making a decision, one should compare the uncertainties of radiometric ages and fossil correlations. For a radiometric age-determination, the indicated uncertainty, such as the ±7 m.y. in 228 ± 7 m.y., is usually the standard deviation for the mass-spectrometer readings, without any provision for the non-analytical errors discussed on previous pages. These other errors are likely to be at least as great as the uncertainty of the mass-spectrometer readings, making, for the example given, a total uncertainty of at least ±14 m.y., or 6 per cent. For an estimate of the uncertainty in fossil correlations we can go to the uncertainty in the age of the base of the Jurassic System. That uncertainty [is] estimated to be of the order of 1 or 2 m.y., a figure that is about 1 per cent of a typical Jurassic age. On the other hand, as recently as the decade 1950–1960, competent stratigraphic paleontologists, when dealing with poor fossil specimens from mildly metamorphosed terrains, have made errors of approximately one geologic period in the ages of rocks in the western United States. Such errors can be compared with the apparent argon/potassium error of about one billion years for a pegmatite at Pacoima, California. We can only decide to use all the information available in making any specific age-determination.

REFERENCES

Ahrens, L. H., 1955, The convergent lead ages of the oldest monazites and uraninites (Rhodesia, Manitoba, Madagascar, and Transvaal): Geochim. et Cosmochim. Acta, v. 7, p. 294–300.

Davis, G. L., and others, 1960, The ages of rocks and minerals: Carnegie Inst. Washington Year Book 59, p. 147–158.

Gastil, Gordon, 1960, The distribution of mineral dates in time and space: Jour. Sci., v. 258, p. 1–35.

Holmes, Arthur, 1960, A revised geological time-scale: Edinburgh Geol. Soc. Trans., v. 17, p. 183–216.

Hsu, K. J., George Edwards, and W. A. McLaughlin, 1963, Age of the intrusive rocks of the southeastern San Gabriel Mountains, California: Geol. Soc. America Bull., v. 74, p. 507–512.

Knopf, Adolph, 1957, Measuring geologic time: Sci. Monthly, v. 85, p. 225–236.

Kulp, J. Laurence, 1961, Geologic time scale: Science, v. 133, p. 1105–1114.

Kulp, J. Lawrence, and others, 1961, Geochronology of rock systems: New York Acad. Sci. Annals, v. 91, p. 150–594.

Lowdon, J. A., and others, 1963, Age determinations by the Geological Survey of Canada: Geol. Survey Canada Paper 62-17, p. 1–122.

Silver, L. T., C. R. McKinney, Sarah Deutsch, and J. Bolinger, 1963, Precambrian age determinations in the western San Gabriel Mountains, California: Jour. Geology, v. 71, p. 196–214.

Stieff, L. R., and T. W. Stern, 1961, Graphic and algebraic solutions of the discordant lead-uranium age problem: Geochim. et Cosmochim. Acta, v. 22, p. 176–199.

Wetherill, G. W., 1956, Discordant uranium-lead ages, I: Am. Geophys. Union Trans., v. 37, p. 320–326.

16

Age of Meteorites and the Earth

CLAIRE PATTERSON
1956

From *Geochimica et Cosmochimica Acta*, vol. 10, pp. 230–237, 1956. Reprinted with permission of the author and Pergamon Press, Inc.

It seems we now should admit that the age of the earth is known as accurately and with about as much confidence as the concentration of aluminium is known in the Westerly, Rhode Island granite. Good estimates of the earth's age have been known for some time. After the decay-constant of U^{235} and the isotopic compositions of common earth-leads were determined by Nier, initial calculations, such as Gerling's, roughly defined the situation. Approximately correct calculations were made by Holmes and by Houtermans on the basis of bold assumptions concerning the genesis of lead ores. Subsequent criticism of these calculations created an air of doubt about anything concerning common leads and obscured the indispensable contributions which these investigators made in establishing the new science of the geochemistry of lead isotopes. When the isotopic composition of lead from an iron meteorite was determined, we were able to show that a much more accurate calculation of the earth's age could be made, but it still was impossible to defend the computation. Now, we know the isotopic compositions of leads from some stone meteorites and we can make an explicit and logical argument for the computation which is valid and persuasive.

The most accurate age of meteorites is determined by first assuming that meteorites represent an array of uranium-lead systems with certain properties, and by then computing the age of this array from the observed lead pattern. The most accurate age of the earth is obtained by demonstrating that the earth's uranium-lead system belongs to the array of meteoritic uranium-lead systems.

The following assumptions are made concerning meteorites: they were formed at the same time; they existed as isolated and closed systems; they originally contained lead of the same isotopic composition; they contain uranium which has the same isotopic composition as that in the earth. On the basis of these assumptions various leads might be expected to evolve as a result of different original U/Pb ratios in separate meteorites, and an expression* for any pair of leads derived from such an array is:

$$\frac{R_{1a} - R_{1b}}{R_{2a} - R_{2b}} = \frac{(e^{\lambda_1 T} - 1)}{k(e^{\lambda_2 T} - 1)} \qquad (1)$$

where $R_1 = Pb^{207}/Pb^{204}$ and $R_2 = Pb^{206}/Pb^{204}$ for leads from different meteorites a and b, $k = U^{238}/U^{235}$ today (137.8), $\lambda_1 = U^{235}$ decay-constant (9.72×10^{-10} yr^{-1}), $\lambda_2 = U^{238}$ decay-constant (1.537×10^{-10} yr^{-1}), and T = age of the array.

TABLE 16.1
The isotopic compositions of lead in meteorites

Meteorite	Pb composition		
	206/204	207/204	208/204
Nuevo Laredo, Mexico	50.28	34.86	67.97
Forest City, Iowa	19.27	15.95	39.05
Modoc, Kansas	19.48	15.76	38.21
Henbury, Australia	9.55	10.38	29.54
Canyon Diablo, Arizona	9.46	10.34	29.44

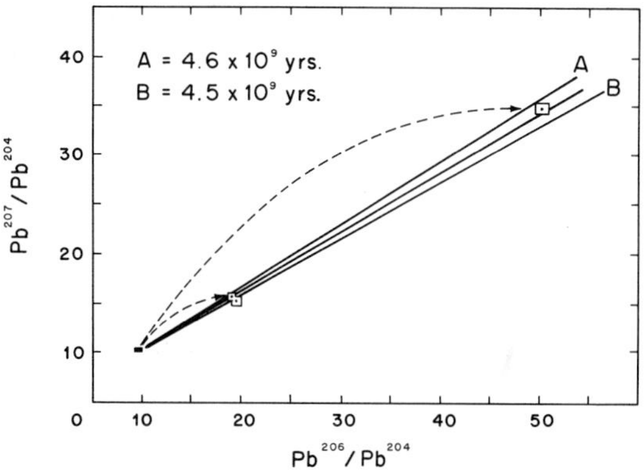

FIGURE 16.1
The lead isochron for meteorites and its estimated limits. The outline around each point indicates measurement error.

The isotopic compositions of leads isolated from three stone and two iron meteorites are listed in Table 16.1 (Patterson, 1955). Because the radiogenic and nonradiogenic leads may ocur in different mineral environments in a stone meteorite and the sample dissolution procedures may be chemically selective, the lead ratios for the first three meteorites in Table 16.1 have estimated errors from the absolute of about 2%. The lead ratios for the last two meteorites in Table 16.1 have estimated errors from the absolute of about 1%.

These leads cover an extreme range in isotopic composition and satisfy expression (1), yielding, within experimental error, a unique value of T. This is illustrated in Figure 16.1, where it is shown that the Pb^{206}/Pb^{204} and Pb^{207}/Pb^{204} ratios from meteorite leads lie on a straight line whose slope corresponds to an age of 4.55×10^9 yr. The dotted lines indicate how stone meteorite leads have evolved. It is clear that the assumptions of the age method are justified by the data. Errors in the lead data and in the decay-constants contribute about equally to the overall error in the calculated age, which amounts to about 1½%. The age for the meteorite array is calculated to be $4.55 \pm 0.07 \times 10^9$ yr.

The assumptions have not been shown to be unique. The data can be explained by other qualifying or even contradictory assumptions. Most of these can be excluded as improbable. One common criticism should be mentioned: the time of a process of division or agglomeration of meteoritic material (without differentiation) cannot be distinguished by this age method. It seems probable that any such process of division or agglomeration would be accompanied by chemical differentiation. Any meteorite which had a differentiation history after its initial formation would fall off the isochron. The five meteorites in Table 16.1 represent a most extreme range of differentiation which occurred during the initial process of formation. This criticism is not serious as far as meteorities are concerned, since if it were valid the lead-lead isochron would date

* A similar form of this expression was first used by A. Nier in 1939. F. Houtermans has termed the expression an "isochron." References for the constants are: (k) M. Inghram, Manhattan Project Tech. Sev., Div. 2, Gaseous Diffusion Project, v. 14, chap. V, p. 35 (1946); (λ_1, λ_2) E. Fleming, A. Ghiorso, and B. Cunningham, *Phys. Rev.*, v. 88, p. 642 (1952).

the ocurrence of differentiation processes; however, it is important with respect to the age of the earth and will be mentioned later.

At the present time, the next most accurate meteorite age is determined by the A^{40}/K^{40} method. The argon ages of six stone meteorites, three of them determined by Wasserburg and Hayden (1955), and three of them determined by Thomson and Mayne (1955), are listed in Table 16.2. The age of *Forest City* has been redetermined without change by Reynolds and Lipson (1955). Two sets of ages are calculated on the basis of the two reasonable limits of the e^-/β^- branching ratio.

The 0.085 branching ratio is the value obtained by studies of old potassium minerals dated by uranium-lead techniques. The 0.125 branching ratio is the value obtained by counting techniques and by direct measurements of the amounts of decay products. The difference between the two values can be accounted for by systematic loss of radiogenic argon in the old potassium minerals. If one assumes that a fixed amount of about 20% of radiogenic argon is lost from all stone meteorites, i.e. using a branching ratio of about 0.10, then there is agreement of lead and argon ages for the same stone and an indication that the stones have existed as cold and solid bodies since they were formed. Argon meteorite ages different from the ones mentioned here have been reported by Gerling (1951), and Pavlova, Gerling, and Rik (1954). Since errors in the data presented by Gerling and Pavlova cannot be evaluated with any certainty, we cannot be concerned by differences between ages calculated by them and ages calculated from other data. Because of logarithmic behaviour, values for calculated ages of these old samples are insensitive to changes in the e^-/β^- branching ratio. For this reason only disagreements of about 15% between A^{40}/K^{40} and Pb^{207}/Pb^{206} meteoritic ages can be accounted for by a twofold change in the branching ratio. Large age differences must therefore be reconciled on the basis of other experimental errors. Measurements of the amounts of nonradiogenic argon in radiogenic and nonradiogenic argon mixtures are subject to large uncertainties, and for the first four meteorites in Table 16.2, nonradiogenic argon corrections were small. For the last two meteorites in Table 16.2, nonradiogenic argon corrections were extremely large and the errors in calculated age are excessive. The isotope dilution determination of potassium, used by Wasserburg and Hayden, is nearly an absolute method, while the flame-photometric determination of potassium, used by Thomson and Mayne, requires a natural absolute standard which they did not use.

The age of meteorites has been determined by the Sr^{87}/Rb^{87} method. The concentrations of rubidium and strontium and the isotopic compositions of strontium have been determined in two stone meteorites by Schumacher (1955). The Rb/Sr ratio in one stone was so low that any change in isotopic composition of strontium due to radioactivity would be within experimental error. The Rb/Sr ratio in the other stone (Forest City, Iowa) was con-

TABLE 16.2
A^{40}/K^{40} ages of meteorites

Meteorite	Age × 10^9		Investigators
	($e^-/\beta^- = 0.085$)	($e^-/\beta^- = 0.125$)	
Beardsley, Kansas	4.8	4.2	Wasserburg and Hayden
Holbrook, Arizona	4.8	4.2	Wasserburg and Hayden
Forest City, Iowa	4.7	4.1	Wasserburg and Hayden Reynolds and Lipson
Akabu, Transjordan	4.4	3.8	Thomson and Mayne
Brenham Township, Kansas	4	3	Thomson and Mayne
Monze, Northern Rhodesia	2	2	Thomson and Mayne

siderably higher and sufficient to cause a 10% difference in the relative abundance of Sr^{87} when the isotopic compositions of strontium from both stones were compared.

The value for the decay-constant of Rb^{87} is in question at the present time. Reported values range from 4.3 to 6.7×10^{10} yr for the half-life. Part of the difficulty in the counting techniques of measuring the half-life arises from the fact that the frequency of β^{-}s at the low end of the energy spectrum increases rapidly with no appearance of a maximum. Measurements of decay products in terrestrial rubidium minerals dated by uranium-lead technique involve errors of open chemical systems. Schumacher's experiment probably constitutes an ideal case of the geological measurement of the half-life of Rb^{87}, since the ages have been determined by lead methods and the possibility of open chemical systems are remote. His methods of measurement are at least as accurate as the radiometric methods. One would therefore use his data to calculate the half-life of Rb^{87}, using the Pb-Pb isochron age of meteorites. The half-life of Rb^{87}, as determined by these data, is 5.1×10^{10} yr, and is probably the most reliable value at present. The half-life determined by the geological method on terrestrial minerals (5.0×10^{10} yr) agrees well with this.

Because of the overwhelming abundance of nonradiogenic helium in iron meteorites and the large errors associated with the determination of the concentrations of uranium and thorium in iron and stone meteorites, the age of meteorites by the helium method is not accurate to much better than an order of magnitude (Paneth et al., 1953; Dalton et al., 1953). It has been reported that iron meteorites and the metal phases of stone meteorites were outgassed of helium as of about 5×10^{8} yr ago, while the silicate phases of stone meteorites were not (Reasbeck and Mayne, 1955). Such an event would be highly significant and would require detailed evolutionary theory for meteorites. Recent neutron activation (Reed and Turkevich) and nuclear emulsion (Picciotto) analyses of iron meteorites show that the concentrations of uranium in these bodies are very low, and that the uranium concentrations used for helium age calculations of iron meteorites may be erroneously high. The question is unresolved at present, but it seems reasonable to believe that investigations of meteoritic helium will become vitally important to cosmic-ray studies and may be decisive in meteorite evolution theory, but cannot be used for accurate meteorite-age calculations at the present time.

The Canyon Diablo lead listed in Table 16.1 was isolated from troilite where the U^{238}/Pb^{204} ratio was shown by direct analysis to be 0.025 (Patterson et al., 1953). This ratio is accurate to at least an order of magnitude, and it is so small that no observable change in the isotopic composition of lead could have resulted from radioactive decay after the meteorite was formed. Since stone meteorites were cold and solid during their lifetime, it is unlikely that lead transport could have occurred between iron and stone meteoritic phases if they existed in one body. This iron-meteorite lead is therefore primordial and represents the isotopic composition of primordial lead at the time meteorites were formed. Using the isotopic composition of primordial lead and the age of meteorites, expressions can be written for a representative lead which is derived today from any system belonging to the meteoritic array:

$$Pb^{206}/Pb^{204} = 9.50 + 1.014\ U^{238}/Pb^{204} \quad (2)$$

$$Pb^{207}/Pb^{204} = 10.36 + 0.601\ U^{238}/Pb^{204} \quad (3)$$

If any two of the three ratios above can be independently measured in the earth's uranium lead system, and they satisfy expressions (2) and (3), then this system belongs to the meteoritic array and must have its age. Two of the ratios can be measured in a sample of earth lead, but the problem of choosing such a sample is complex because the ratio of uranium to lead varies widely in different rocks and minerals whose ages are short compared to the age of the earth.

One approach is to partition the earth's crust into separate chemical systems of uranium and lead and consider their interactions. Such systems may range from minerals to geochemical cycles. Nearly all of the lead-isotope data concerns either minerals in which the uranium-to-lead ratio is very high (uraninites, etc.) or minerals in which this ratio is essentially zero (galenas). The approximate times of formation of some galenas have been determined, and of these, two dozen or so lately formed galenas may be used as a measure of earth lead (*Nuclear Geology*, 1954, H. Faul, ed.). The isotopic compositions of lead in some recent oceanic sediments have also been determined (Patterson, Goldberg, and Inghram, 1953), and these may be used as a measure of earth lead.

Any of these samples will be improper or biased if they are derived from a system of uranium and lead which is only partially closed and is subject to slow but appreciable transport from other systems with different U^{238}/Pb^{204} ratios. In this respect, the sample which may represent the system of largest mass is probably the more reliable. One sample of oceanic sediment lead probably represents more material than a dozen galenas. The isotopic composition of this sediment lead is $Pb^{206}/Pb^{204} = 19.0$ and $Pb^{207}/Pb^{204} = 15.8$, which satisfies expressions (2) and (3) surprisingly well. It is doubtful if these figures are grossly biased, since a few measurements of uranium and the isotopes of lead in rocks with widely different U^{238}/Pb^{204} ratios indicate rather good mixing to be the first-order effect on the isotopic composition of lead in the earth's crust (Patterson, Tilton, and Inghram, 1955).

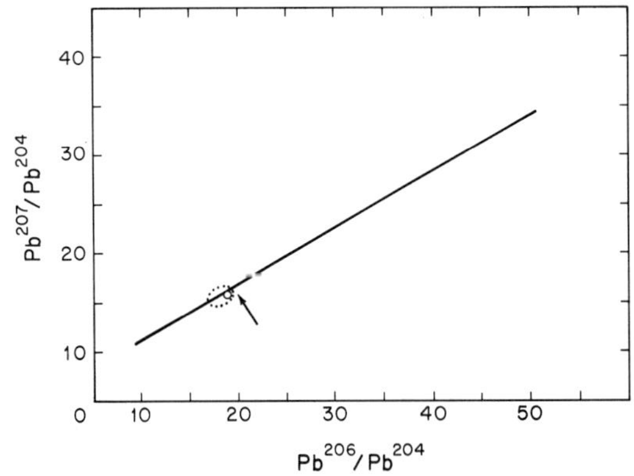

FIGURE 16.2
The relationship between common earth leads and the meteoritic lead isochron

Independent of the absolute abundances of lead isotopes, a rough measure of the rates of change of the lead-isotope abundances in the earth's crust may be obtained from the isotopic composition of galenas of different ages. These rates of change are defined by the ratios of uranium and thorium to lead in the material from which the galenas are derived. From the observed rate of change of Pb^{206}, the U^{238}/Pb^{204} ratio in the earth's crust is found to be 10 (Collins, Russell, and Farquhar, 1953). This value satisfies expression (2) and (3) for sedimentary lead with unexpectedly good agreement.

In Figure 16.2 it is shown that oceanic sediment lead (open circle) falls on the meteoritic lead isochron. Most of the lately formed galenas fall within the dotted outline, although a few are widely aberrant. The position of a lead along the isochron is determined by the U^{238}/Pb^{204} ratio in the system from which the lead evolves. The arrow indicates the position on the isochron which sediment lead should occupy as predicted by the isotopic evolution of dated ore leads. Independently measured values for all three ratios adequately satisfy expressions (2) and (3), and therefore the time since the earth attained its present mass is $4.55 \pm 0.07 \times 10^9$ yr.

If the earth is a late agglomeration without differentiation of meteoritic material then it can have any age less than meteoritic material. Rather than arguing that such a process would be accompanied by chemical differentiation (and a change of the U/Pb ratio), it seems reasonable to believe instead that such a late agglomeration process would be less probable than one where both meteorites and the earth were formed at the same time. It is a fact that extreme chemical differentiation occurred during the process which led to the mechanical isolation of the mass of material of which the earth is made, and since changes in this mass were accompanied by chemical differentiation, the Pb/Pb meteorite isochron age properly refers to the time since the earth attained its present mass.

SUMMARY

Within experimental error, meteorites have one age as determined by three independent radiometric methods. The most accurate method (Pb^{207}/Pb^{206}) gives an age of $4.55 \pm 0.07 \times 10^9$ yr. Using certain assumptions which are apparently justified, one can define the isotopic evolution of lead for any meteoritic body. It is found that earth lead meets the requirements of this definition. It is therefore believed that the age for the earth is the same as for meteorites. This is the time since the earth attained its present mass.

REFERENCES

Collins, C., R. Russell, and R. Farquhar, 1953, Canadian Jour. Phys., v. 31, p. 402.

Dalton, J., F. Paneth, P. Reasbeck, S. Thomson, and K. Mayne, 1953, Nature, v. 172, p. 1168.

Faul, H., ed., 1954, Nuclear geology: New York, John Wiley and Sons.

Gerling, E., and T. Pavlova, 1951, Akad. Nauk SSSR Doklady, v. 77, p. 85.

Gerling, E., and K. Rik, 1954, Meteorika, v. 11, p. 117.

Paneth, F., K. Chackett, P. Reasbeck, E. Wilson, J. Dalton, J. Golden, G. Martin, E. Mercer, and S. Thomson, 1953, Geochim. et Cosmochim. Acta, v. 3, p. 257.

Patterson, C., H. Brown, G. Tilton, and M. Inghram, 1953, Phys. Rev., v. 92, p. 1234.

Patterson, C., E. Goldberg, and M. Inghram, 1953, Geol. Soc. America Bull., v. 64, p. 1387.

Patterson, C., 1955, Geochim. et Cosmochim. Acta, v. 7, p. 151.

Patterson, C., G. Tilton, and M. Inghram, 1955, Science, v. 121, p. 69.

Picciotto, E., Nuclear Physics Centre, University of Brussells, manuscript.

Reynolds, J., and J. Lipson, Epipoleological Society, Spring 1955 meeting, U.C.L.A.

Reasbeck, P., and K. Mayne, 1955, Nature, v. 176, p. 186.

Reed, G., and A. Turkevitch, Institute for Nuclear Studies, University of Chicago, manuscript.

Schumacher, E., National Research Council conference on nuclear processes in Geologic Settings (communicated by H. Urey and M. Inghram), September 1955 meeting, Pennsylvania State University. (Copies of his manuscript are available.)

Thomson, S., and K. Mayne, 1955, Geochim. et Cosmochim. Acta, v. 7, p. 169.

Wasserburg, G., and R. Hayden, 1955, Phys. Rev., v. 97, p. 86.

Wasserman, G., National Research Council conference on nuclear processes in Geologic Settings, September 1955 meeting, Pennslyvania State University.

17

Radiocarbon Dating

W. F. LIBBY

1961

Radiocarbon dating had its origin in a study of the possible effects that cosmic rays might have on the earth and on the earth's atmosphere. We were interested in testing whether any of the various effects which might be predicted could actually be found and used. Initially the problem seemed rather difficult, for ignorance of billion-electron-volt nuclear physics (cosmic-ray energies are in this range) was so abysmal at the time (and, incidentally, 14 years later is still so abysmal) that it was nearly impossible to predict with any certainty the effects of the collisions of the multi-billion-volt primary cosmic radiation with air.

FORMATION OF RADIOCARBON

However, in 1939, just before the war, Serge Korff of New York University and others discovered that the cosmic rays produce secondary neutrons in their initial collisions with the top of the atmosphere. The neutrons were found by sending counters, designed to be sensitive to neutrons, up to high altitudes, and they were found to have an intensity which corresponded to the generation of about two neutrons per second for each square centimeter of the earth's surface.

Whereas it was extremely difficult to predict the types of nuclei that might be produced by the billion-volt primary cosmic rays, the neutrons, being secondaries, were in the million-volt energy range and, therefore, subject to laboratory tests. So at this point the question was: What will million-electron-volt neutrons do if liberated in the air? The answer to this question was already available—in fact, Korff noted in one of the papers announcing the discovery of the neutrons that the principal way in which the neutrons would disappear would be by forming radiocarbon. The reaction involved is a simple one. Oxygen is essentially inert to neutrons, but nitrogen is quite

From *Science*, vol. 133, pp. 621–629, 1961. Reprinted with permission of the author and the American Association for the Advancement of Science.

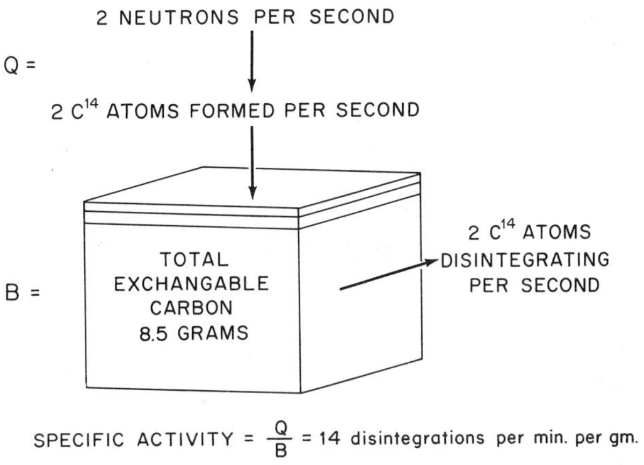

FIGURE 17.1
Radiocarbon genesis and mixing

reactive. Nitrogen-14, the abundant nitrogen isotope, reacts essentially quantitatively to form carbon-14 with the elimination of a proton. It also reacts about 1 per cent of the time to produce tritium (radioactive hydrogen); this is another story, leading to a method of dating water and wine.

TABLE 17.1
Make-up of the carbon reservoir. (Grams of carbon per square centimeter of surface.) According to Anderson and Libby and W. W. Rubey

	Anderson and Libby	Rubey
Ocean "carbonate"	7.25	6.95
Ocean, dissolved organic	0.59	0.78
Biosphere	0.33	
Humus	0.20	0.125
Atmosphere	0.12	
Total	8.5	7.9

To return to radiocarbon dating, knowing that there are about two neutrons formed per square centimeter per second, each of which forms a carbon-14 atom, and assuming that the cosmic rays have been bombarding the atmosphere for a very long time in terms of the lifetime of carbon-14 (carbon-14 has a half-life of about 5600 years), we can see that a steady-state condition should have been established, in which the rate of formation of carbon-14 would be equal to the rate at which it disappears to reform nitrogen-14. This allows us to calculate quantitatively how much carbon-14 should exist on earth (see Figure 17.1); and since the two atoms per second per square centimeter go into a mixing reservoir with about 8.5 grams of carbon per square centimeter, this gives an expected specific activity for living matter of 2.0/8.5 disintegrations per second per gram of carbon.

The mixing reservoir consists not only of living matter, which dilutes the radiocarbon, but of the dissolved carbonaceous material in the oceans, which can exchange carbon with the atmospheric carbon dioxide and thus dilute it. In fact, the ocean is the larger part of the diluting carbon reservoir (see Table 17.1). For each square centimeter of the earth's surface, there are about 7.25 grams of carbon dissolved in the ocean in the form of carbonate, bicarbonate, and carbonic acid, and the biosphere itself contains about 0.33 gram per square centimeter of surface. Adding all the elements of the reservoir, we get a total of 8.5 grams of diluting carbon per square centimeter, and the two carbon-14 atoms disintegrating every second should be contained in 8.5 grams of carbon. Thus, the specific activity of living carbon should be that number. We find this to be the actual value observed, to within about 10 per cent (see Table 17.2). Of course, the times for mixing of all parts of the reservoir must be short as compared to the average lifetime of radiocarbon, 8000 years. The time for mixing of the oceans is the longest, about 1000 years on the average.

This is interesting, for it means that the present intensity of the cosmic radiation (unless there have been canceling errors in our calculations) corresponds to the average intensity over the last 8000 years, the average life of carbon-14. It tells us, also, that the ocean is mixed nearly perfectly to its bottom depths in 8000 years. This we know because we included all of the dissolved carbon in the sea. Also, direct measurement of the carbonate and bicarbonate in deep ocean water confirms this. These conclusions could be false if errors in the very different quantities—the intensity of the cosmic rays and the mixing rate and depths of the oceans—should happen just to cancel one another. Since these factors are so unrelated, we believe this to be very unlikely and conclude that the agreement between the predicted and observed assays is encouraging evidence that the cosmic rays have indeed remained constant in intensity over many thousands of years and that the mixing time, volume, and composition of the oceans have not changed either.

We are in the radiocarbon-dating business as soon as this has been said, for it is clear from the set of assumptions that have been given that organic matter, while it is alive, is in equilibrium with the cosmic radiation—that is, all the radiocarbon atoms which disintegrate in our bodies are replaced by the carbon-14 contained in the food we eat, so that while we are alive we are part of a great pool which contains the cosmic-ray-produced radiocarbon. The specific activity is maintained at the level of about 14 disintegrations per minute per gram by the mixing action of the biosphere and hydrosphere. We assimilate cosmic-ray-produced carbon-14 atoms at just the rate that the carbon-14 atoms in our bodies disappear to form nitrogen-14. At the time of death, however, the assimilation process stops abruptly. There is no longer any process by which the carbon-14 from the atmosphere can enter our bodies. Therefore, at the time of death the radioactive disintegration process takes over in an uncompensated manner and, according to the law of radioactive decay, after 5600 years the carbon that was in our bodies while we were alive will show half the specific carbon-14 radioactivity

TABLE 17.2
Activity (in disintegrations per minute per gram) of samples from the terrestrial biosphere

Source	Geomagnetic latitude	Absolute specific activity
White spruce, Yukon	60°N	14.84 ± 0.30
Norwegian spruce, Sweden	55°N	15.37 ± 0.54
Elm wood, Chicago	53°N	14.72 ± 0.54
Fraxinus excelsior, Switzerland	49°N	15.16 ± 0.30
Honeysuckle leaves, Oak Ridge, Tenn.	47°N	14.60 ± 0.30
Pine twigs and needles (12,000-ft alt.), Mount Wheeler, N.M.	44°N	15.82 ± 0.47
North African briar	40°N	14.47 ± 0.44
Oak, Sherafut, Palestine	34°N	15.19 ± 0.40
Unidentified wood, Teheran, Iran	28°N	15.57 ± 0.31
Fraxinus mandshurica, Japan	26°N	14.84 ± 0.30
Unidentified wood, Panama	20°N	15.94 ± 0.51
Chlorophora excelsa, Liberia	11°N	15.08 ± 0.34
Sterculia excelsa, Copacabana, Bolivia (9000-ft alt.)	1°N	15.47 ± 0.50
Ironwood, Majuro, Marshall Islands	0°	14.53 ± 0.60
Unidentified wood, Ceylon	2°S	15.29 ± 0.67
Beech wood, Tierra del Fuego	45°S	15.37 ± 0.49
Eucalyptus, New South Wales, Australia	45°S	16.31 ± 0.43
Seal oil from seal meat from Antarctica	65°S	15.69 ± 0.30
Average		15.3 ± 0.1

that it shows now. Since we have evidence that this has been true for tens of thousands of years, we should expect to find that a body 5600 years old would be half as radioactive as a currently living organism. This appears to be true. Measurements of old artifacts of historically known age have shown this to be so within the experimental errors of measurement.

INITIAL RESEARCH

The research on radiocarbon dating was carried out in several stages. In the first place, my collaborator, E. C. Anderson, and I had to determine whether the living material actually had the radioactivity expected. At that time we had no measurement techniques sufficiently sensitive to detect the radio-activities involved directly because these levels are quite low. Later we developed methods for making the measurement, but at that time we did not have them, so we used the method of concentrating the heavy isotope of carbon. An apparatus for this purpose had been built by and was being used by A. V. Grosse of Temple University, then of the Houdry Process Corporation at Marcus Hook, Pennsylvania. Grosse was concentrating the carbon-13 isotope for medical tracer purposes and kindly agreed to try to concentrate some biological methane for the test so crucial to our research. We had to use biological, as contrasted with petroleum, methane, for we had at this point arrived at a distinction between living and dead organic chemicals. We had both "dead" methane and "living" methane in the sense that methane from oil wells in which the oil has been long buried would be expected to be entirely free from radiocarbon while the methane made from the disintegration of living organic matter should contain radiocarbon with an activity of 14 disintegrations per minute per gram of carbon. The task was to take this living methane and concentrate it in the isotope separation column to see whether the heavily enriched product was radioactive. Happily for our research, it was found to be so, and to about the expected degree. The material used was methane gas from the sewage disposal plant of the city of Baltimore.

The second stage of the research was the development of methods of measurement sufficiently sensitive to eliminate the use of this $10,000 thermal-diffusion isotope column, which was so expensive to operate that it cost thousands of dollars to measure the age of a single mummy. Obviously, radiocarbon dating would have been an impractical method of measuring archeological ages if this phase of the research had been unsuccessful.

COUNTING TECHNIQUE

The counting method developed involves measuring the radioactivity of the carbon directly. We convert the samples by chemical methods into a suitable form—carbon dioxide or acetylene gas or even solid carbon—which then is placed inside a Geiger or proportional counter, where it itself constitutes the gas or lies on the inner counter wall. This is possible because carbon as lampblack is an electrical conductor, and the gases carbon dioxide and acetylene are satisfactory counter gases. In this way a maximum count rate is achieved.

The counter itself is shielded from the background radiations in order to accentuate the carbon-14 count. A typical shield is shown in Figure 17.2. It consists of 8 inches of iron to absorb the radiations from terrestrial sources, such as uranium, thorium, and potassium. The cosmic rays, however, which consist at sea level largely of μ-mesons, penetrate the thick iron shield readily, and whereas the count rate in the absence of the shield is about 500 counts per minute, the rate is decreased to about 100 counts per minute by the iron shield. This remaining activity, due in main part to μ-mesons, has to be removed. In order to do this, we surround the counter, with the carbon dating sample in it, with a complete layer of Geiger counters in tangential contact with one another and wire them so that when any one of these counters counts, the central counter with the dating sample is turned off for about one thousandth of a second. In this way the μ-mesons are eliminated from the record, so the background radiation comes down to something between 1 and 6 counts per minute, depending on the details of counter and shield design. This is for a counter of about 1 liter volume, capable of holding up to 5 grams of carbon with counting rates of 75 counts per minute for living carbon, 37.5 counts for 5600-year-old carbon, and 18.7 and 0.7 count, respectively, for 11,200-year-old and 56,000-year-old carbon.

After we had developed a technique for measuring natural carbon relatively inexpensively with the requisite accuracy, our next job was to determine whether the following assumption was sound: that the variation of radiocarbon production due to the variation of the cosmic rays with latitude (which is very strong indeed) would be wiped out by the movement of the winds and the ocean currents in the 8000-year lifetime of carbon-14. The plan was to measure living materials from various places on earth and to see whether they had the same radiocarbon content per gram of carbon. These data on the natural abundance of radiocarbon in the earth were presented by E. C. Anderson for his doctoral thesis at the University of Chicago. They showed no appreciable differences, even though the samples came from places varying in latitude from near the South Pole to near the North Pole (Table 17.2). At the present time, 10 years later, no evidence for variation has been found except in areas of extensive carbonate deposits where the surface waters may carry a considerable amount of old carbon dissolved, and thus reduce the carbon-14 level below the world-wide average for the biosphere-atmosphere-ocean pool as a whole. Fortunately, such conditions are relatively rare and generally easily recognized.

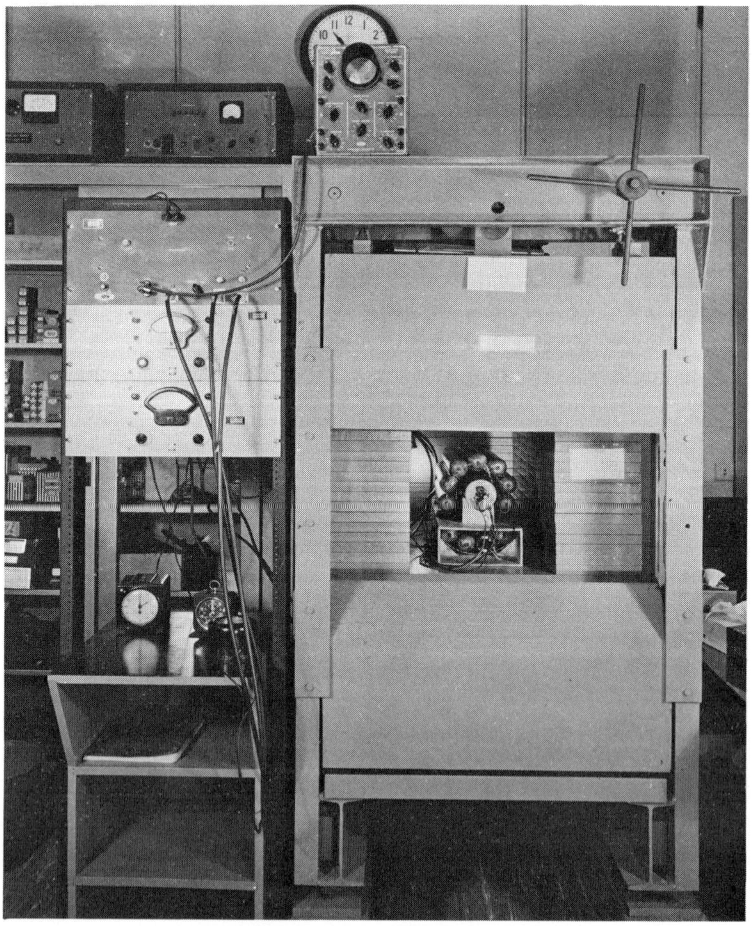

FIGURE 17.2
Radiocarbon counting apparatus

DATING TECHNIQUE

After the study of the natural occurrence of radiocarbon, the next stage was to see whether we had a method of dating artifacts of a known age, a problem which led us to mummies. J. R. Arnold joined us at this stage. We had a decay curve drawn which predicted, with no unknown factors and no adjustable constants, the specific activity of ancient organic matter. And so the question was to see whether it worked. The first thing we had to do, of course, was to get the materials for measurement. This was done by enlisting the cooperation of the American Anthropological Association and the Geological Society of America. Geologists have been quite interested in the results of this dating technique from the beginning, even though its reach in time is short for many of their problems. A committee of advisers, consisting of Donald Collier, Richard Foster Flint, Frederick Johnson, and Froelich Rainey, was appointed to select the samples for us and to help us collect them. These gentlemen worked hard for several years, assisting and collecting the samples and advising us.

The research in the development of the dating technique consisted of two stages—dating of samples from the historical and the prehistorical epochs, respectively. Arnold and I had our first shock when our advisers informed us that history extended back only for 5000 years. We had thought initially that we would be able to get samples all along the curve, back to 30,000 years before the present; we would put the points in, and then our work would be finished. You read statements to the effect that such and such a society or archeological site is 20,000 years old. We learned rather abruptly that these numbers, these ancient ages, are not known accurately; in fact, the earliest historical date that has been established with any real certainty is about the time of the 1st Dynasty in Egypt. So we had, in the initial stages, the opportunity to check against samples of known age, principally Egyptian artifacts, and in the second stage we had to go into the great wilderness of prehistory to see whether there were elements of internal consistency which would lead one to believe that the method was sound or not.

For the prehistoric period, members of our committee set up a network of problems which were designed to check, in as many ways as possible, points of internal consistency. They set out about a dozen major projects, and we collected samples from each of these projects and worked hard and measured them; similar measurements are still going on. . . .

CURVE FOR SAMPLES OF KNOWN AGE

Figure 17.3 shows the curve of "knowns"—the results obtained for samples of known age as compared to the carbon-14 decay curve drawn with the value of 14 disintegrations per minute (the value for living matter) taken as unity and with a half-life of 5568 ± 30 years. The half-life itself was measured in 1949 in collaboration with A. G. Engelkemier, W. H. Hamill, and M. G. Inghram and found to be 5580 ± 45 years, a value which, when combined with independent values of 5589 ± 75 obtained by W. M. Jones and 5513 ± 165 obtained by W. W. Miller, R. Ballentine, W. Bernstein, L. Friedman, A. O. Nier, and R. D. Evans, gave 5568 ± 30 by weighting according to the inverse square of the errors quoted. Remeasurements are now being made, by Mann at the National Bureau of Standards in Washington and by Olson at the University of Uppsala.

The knowns are in two main groups—those measured by us at the University of Chicago and those measured by Miss Ralph at the University of Pennsylvania, labeled (C) and (*P*), respectively. One sample, "Pompei," was measured by E. A. Olson and W. S. Broecker of the Lamont Geological Observatory.

The oldest samples of known age measured were "Hemaka" and "Zet" from the 1st Dynasty in Egypt. Both were wood found in the subterranean brick structures of the 1st Dynasty tombs of the Vizier Hemaka and of King Zet, both at Saqqara. Hemaka was contemporaneous with King Udimu, and both tombs were generally agreed to date from 4900 ± 200 years before the present. The next oldest samples were cedar wood from the upper chamber of the Southern Pyramid of Sneferu at Dahshur. The next sample, marked "Sesostris," is a very interesting one. It is a part of the deck of the funeral ship which was placed in the tomb of Sesostris III of Egypt and is now in the Chicago Museum of Natural History. It is about 20 feet long and six feet wide and is quite an imposing object, complete with paddles. The next sample is "Aha-nakht." It consists of wood, probably cedar, from the outer sarcophagus of Aha-nakht, at El Bersheh. It was found in the tomb, which was covered with earth. The coffin was presumably excavated by the natives at the same time as the El Bersheh coffin obtained for the British Museum by E. A. W. Budge, after 1895.

As we proceed up the curve, the next sample is the heartwood of one of the largest redwood trees ever cut. The tree was known as the "Centennial Stump," felled in 1874. There were 2905 rings between the innermost (and 2802 rings between the outermost) portion of the sample and the outside of the tree. Therefore, the known mean age, determined according to the tree-ring method of Douglas, was 2928 ± 51 years, as of the time it was cut. This is an interesting point, as it shows that, in the heartwood of the *Sequoia gigantea* at least, the sap is not in chemical equilibrium with the cellulose and other large molecules of the tree. In other words, the carbon in the central wood was deposited there about 3000 years ago, although the tree itself was cut just a few years ago. The next sample, which is marked "Tayinat," is from a house in Asia Minor which was burned in 675 B.C. It was wood from the floor of a central room in a large *hilani* ("palace") of the "Syro-Hittite" period in the city of Tayinat in northwest Persia. Its known age is 2625 ± 50 years.

The next sample is the linen wrapping of one of the Dead Sea scrolls, the Book of Isaiah, which was found in Palestine a few years ago (Figure 17.4). The next sample, labeled "Pompei," was carbonized bread from a house of ancient Pompeii; still looking like an overdone roll, it was charred by the volcanic ashes that buried the city in 79 A.D., roughly 1880

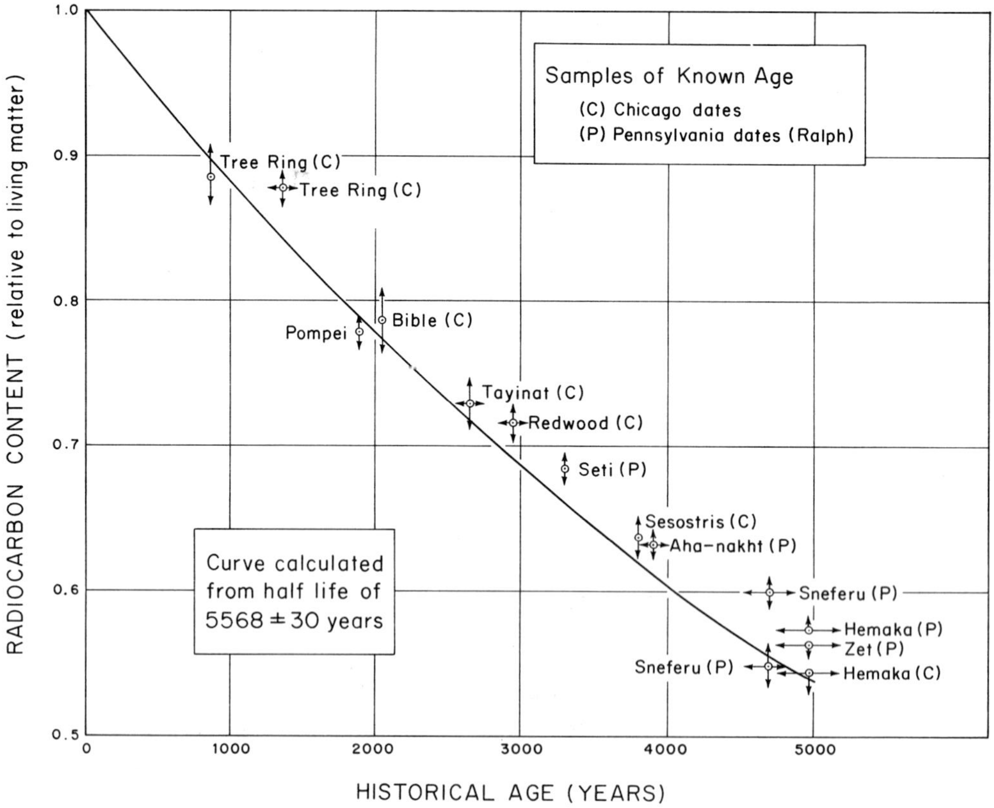

FIGURE 17.3
Curve of knowns

years ago. The other samples are wood, dated by the Douglas tree-ring-counting technique. When results from these samples are taken all together, the agreement with the predicted radiocarbon content seems to be satisfactory. The errors are given as the counting errors (standard deviations) only.

FIGURE 17.4
Linen wrapping, 1917 ± 200 years old, of the Book of Isaiah, one of the Dead Sea scrolls

It is certainly possible that the decay curve, which is drawn on the basis of a half-life of 5568 years, could be drawn somewhat differently. However, it is well to know that all radiocarbon dates published today have been calculated on this half-life, and in order to avoid confusion we should be careful about changing the basis of the calculation of radiocarbon ages before the evidence for a change in half-life is definite. The curve of knowns seems to indicate that a slightly longer half-life might be permissible. However, there are other possible explanations of a deviation of the curve of knowns from the theoretical curve. We all await the results of the half-life researches of Mann and Olsson with great interest.

PERTURBATIONS

It has been observed that fossil carbon dioxide from the combustion of coal and oil, after about 1870, began to dilute the biosphere and to reduce the radiocarbon content, and that the trend continued until 1954, when the explosion of atomic devices reversed it. The carbon-14 introduced by the neutrons produced in the explosions more than compensated for the reduction by the fossil carbon—a reduction which at that time had amounted, in the Northern Hemisphere, to about 3 percent of the primeval level as far back as it has been possible to measure it, from tree rings. H. L. de Vries and Hans E. Suess have been particularly active in research on this point. It was Suess, in fact, who discovered that fossil carbon dioxide had been reducing this specific activity in recent biospheric material, since 1870.

Broecker and Olson have made careful studies of the carbon-14 content of ancient woods as well. And the general result is that there appear to have been, prior to 1870, only very minor variations, of the order of 1 percent or less, in the radiocarbon content of living matter. The recent perturbations are of no great concern for archeologists and geologists now living. Of course, in the future it will be difficult to correct for the period when these perturbations were active; that is, 5000 years from now there may be some difficulty in understanding why, for a period of a century or so, beginning in 1870, the radiocarbon level was so perturbed. However, the written records may well explain the anomaly; in fact, radiocarbon dating as such may not be needed to establish historical fact.

DATING THE LAST ICE SHEET

After the curve of knowns had been drawn, the next step in the research was to test in the great periods of prehistory to see whether the dates obtained were reasonable. Perhaps the most interesting single general result for this prehistoric period is the time in which the last ice sheet moved down to cover the northern part of the United States and the European continent. The result, 11,400 ± 200 years, has now been well established by the radiocarbon technique. The radiocarbon dates for this cataclysmic development show that it happened simultaneously in Europe and in North America and that the phenomenon was very widespread, and that it had a tremendous impact on the living habits of people the world over. The oldest sign of man in northern Europe and in England is younger than this, presumably because of the thoroughness with which the glacier removed all sorts of human artifacts. Therefore, the oldest of the Scandinavian, the English, and the North American occupation sites are all about 10,400 years old, dating back, presumably, to the time when the ice sheet receded.

In Figure 17.5 are plotted, for the Americas, the number of occupation sites versus age. It is quite clear that there is an abrupt discontinuity at about 10,400 years. In Europe, however, if instead of examining sites in the northern regions we look at sites in the Mediterranean basin, there is no discontinuity, and evidences of human occupation extend back as far as the radiocarbon dating technique can reach—50,000 years or so. There seems to be some contrast between this and the situation in the Americas, where, as shown in Figure 17.5, one sees a decided difference in the total number of sites in preglacial times. In view of the fact that it is known that extensive areas of the Americas were not glaciated by the last ice sheet, this raises something of a question. There is, of course, the definite possibility that this is pure accident, and it even seems possible that we do now have human sites in the Americas which are definitely older than 10,400 years. However, the weight of the evidence seems to indicate that something in the nature of a discontinuity occurred at that time. Most of the sites that are older than 10,400 years are equivocal in one way or another. . . . This is not true in Southern Europe and Asia Minor. One of the most remarkable of the sites in Europe is the Lascaux Cave in Central France, which has the beautiful paintings on the walls, showing the ancient animals in such authentic style as to demonstrate the remarkable advancement of the culture of the people at that time. These paintings are presumably older than 15,000 years, the age determined for the charcoal found in the soil of the cave. Around Asia Minor and in the areas of the Middle East there is no scarcity of materials which date back as far as radiocarbon dating can reach, and there is considerable evidence that the sites are human sites.

IN GEOLOGY, OCEANOGRAPHY AND METEOROLOGY

In addition to its use in the work on human history, radiocarbon dating has been used for geological purposes to a considerable extent. Of course, the time span of radiocarbon is so short, as compared to the history of the earth, that most geological problems are outside the

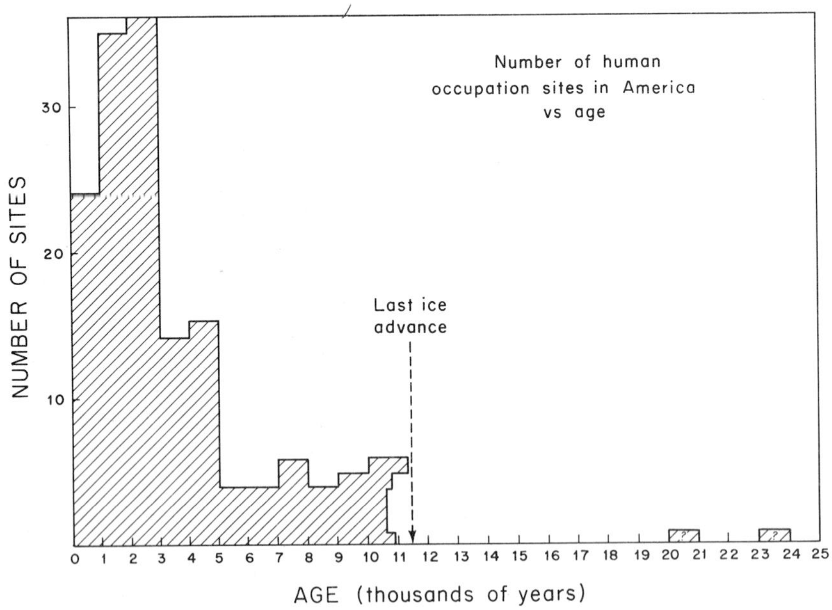

FIGURE 17.5
Number of human sites in the Americas plotted against age

reach of the technique. But recent history and recent events do fall within its scope, and there have been a number of investigations, in particular the sorting out and measuring of the chronological events of the recent ice ages—that is, the relative times of arrival of the various ice advances and the periods of time between them, the points of simultaneity, and the identification of particular moraines with particular advances. On these points, small and perhaps relatively unimportant as they are, the geologists have found radiocarbon dating to be of some use.

In oceanography, the great question of the rate of mixing of the oceans has yielded to the radiocarbon technique to a considerable extent, particularly in the hands of Suess and of Broecker and Olson—Suess particularly in the Pacific and Olson and Broecker in the Atlantic. They have shown that the Pacific mixes relatively less rapidly, the turnover time being something between 1500 and 2000 years, whereas the Atlantic mixes relatively more rapidly, at a rate about twice this, or with a 750- to 1000-year turnover time. It is clear from these researches that the fundamental assumption of radiocarbon dating, that the reservoir of the sea must be counted as a diluent for the cosmic-ray carbon-14, is valid. Further, it has been shown by Suess that there will be opportunities of measuring the deep ocean currents. He finds evidence for velocities and directions of the deep ocean currents in the Pacific corresponding to a requirement of some hundreds of years for the passage northward along the bottom.

In meteorology, radiocarbon dating has been of some use. It has been interesting to observe the changes in the radiocarbon content in living matter near large industrial centers where the rate of production of carbon dioxide from coal and oil was highest, and also to observe the dissemination of the radioactive carbon made by atomic explosions in the atmosphere. From these things we know that world-wide mixing occurs. We observe the effects of changes generated very largely in the Northern Hemisphere quite clearly in the Southern Hemisphere, though they are reduced somewhat in intensity. This is the first time that there has been clear and incontrovertible evidence for such a world-wide circulation, and on a time scale of a very few years; such evidence is particularly clear in the case of the bomb-test carbon-14.

IN ARCHEOLOGY

Of course, the main use of radiocarbon dating is in archeology and the investigation of the history of man through the use of chemistry, for most ancient men did not write, and we have no written records except in Egypt, in Asia Minor, and in limited areas of Central America. Yet it is perfectly clear that 10,000 and more years ago people lived in a way that indicates they rivaled modern man in intelligence and capabilities. We have just to look at their handiwork to see this. The paintings in the Lascaux Cave, the handiwork of the ancient Indians in North America—particularly the basketry and the very skillfully made arrowheads—attest to their great capabilities. Where they came from perhaps we do not know, but we do know that they were very intelligent and very capable people.

[In the spring of 1960], on Santa Rosa Island off the coast of California, friends of mine found a 6-foot skeleton, 10,400 years old, to judge by the radiocarbon measurements of Broecker of Lamont Geological Observatory on some charcoal found next to the skeleton. This is the same 10,400-year date which we have observed so often and which now marks the early evidence of man in Santa Rosa Island; the Lindenmeier site in Colorado; the Clovis site; the Lamus Cave in eastern Nevada on the Utah-Nevada border, continuously occupied from the time of the melting of the last glacier 10,400 years ago down to the time when modern man came into the area; the Fort Rock Cave in Oregon, where the most beautiful basketry of ancient man was discovered—grass rope woven into sandals of beautiful shape and design, 300 pairs of them neatly stacked just as though in a community shoe store 9000 years old; and several other sites in the Americas. We see in this the evidences that man has been a long time learning to *write* history but has been *making* history for many thousands and perhaps tens of thousands of years.

In Central Europe the element of simultaneity, which is revealed by the radiocarbon dates for the people who did not write or leave records, establishes conflicts and clashes between cultures which are interesting to examine and speculate upon. The Neanderthal man and the Cro-Magnon man did not stay long together. The Neanderthal man disappeared, and the Cro-Magnon man won; he may have been the man who painted the beautiful Lascaux Cave paintings, as I understand it from the archeologists.

We learn various details about the ancient peoples. For example, in the time of Hammurabi, the Babylonian king, there was an accurate calendar, but we have been uncertain about the correlation of this calendar with our own. This calendar of the Babylonians was a very good one, but there is an uncertainty which, as I understand it, concerns the identification of a particular eclipse as we calculate it backwards in time in order to arrive at a correlation with our own calendar. Therefore, careful measurements were made on a portion of a house about 4000 years old that was precisely dated by the Babylonian calendar. In this case, a serious attempt was made to test the limit of sensitivity of the radiocarbon dating method. The sample of wood came from a beam from the roof of this house in Nippur, which bore a clear and legible date according to the Hammurabian calendar. The beam was divided into three equal portions; these were carefully measured (the total measurement time was three months), and the results for the three portions were then coordinated to obtain a definite answer as to which of the two most likely correlations of the Christian and Babylonian calendars was correct. We concluded that the younger of the two possible calendars was strongly favored and that the odds against the other being correct were something like 9 to 1.

With the advancement of the radiocarbon dating technique and the consequent increase in accuracy, at least of the relative dates, it is possible to do more of these difficult jobs of pinpointing past events in time so as to drive back history into prehistoric periods and to more clearly delineate what really did happen in the development of man. Determination of the chronology of ancient civilizations may be said to be the main archeological problem and task of radiocarbon dating. As the technique is developed further and more fully and is more widely used, it should be possible to excavate and utilize sites which are now hardly more than dark spots in some remote area. Charcoal is one of the best materials for radiocarbon dating, provided adequate care is taken to see that intrusive rootlets and humic acids are removed before measurements are made.

We intend, at the University of California, Los Angeles, to attempt to make a portable radiocarbon dater which will allow us to work in the field with the archeologists and geologists and thus to obtain dates which, though not as accurate as those which would be obtained in the laboratory, may be useful enough to serve as guides during the digging. The problem is to find a truck that will carry the rather heavy equipment over rough country. If this effort is successful, it will be a development which will bring the carbon daters and the archeologists and geologists even closer together. Of all the rewards of research, none is greater than that of meeting people in different fields and finding interests in common. It will be most refreshing and rewarding for the radiocarbon daters to go out and share, at least vicariously, in the great thrill of an archeological dig.

ACCURACY OF THE RESULTS

The many people who have contributed to the development of the radiocarbon dating technique (several of whom I have mentioned but many of whom I have been unable to mention) are largely responsible for whatever success it has had. We now have several thousand radiocarbon dates throughout the fields of archeology, geology, meteorology, oceanography, and other areas. From examination of the results it is possible to form an opinion as to the general reliability and general weaknesses of the method. I am sure that Arnold would agree with me in saying that it has lived up to our fondest hopes.

It was clear from the beginning that there would be difficulties about the samples. Anyone knows that it is possible to get dirt into solid matter which is lying in the ground, even if it is there only for a brief period, let alone many thousands or tens of thousands of years. The saving aspect of the situation, however, is that it is very much more difficult to mix molecules in such a way that they cannot be separated chemically, particularly in the case of substances such as charcoal and wood and cloth, and even, in certain instances, limestone and shale. One can separate and distinguish the contaminant from the original material and in this way disclose the real radiocarbon content. The researches of a number of people have validated the assumption that it is possible and that, indeed, it is not too difficult to obtain authentic samples in the field. In general, the samples may have to be inspected with some care under a relatively high-powered glass and then, possibly, treated with properly chosen chemicals. But all of these things can be done, with techniques that are no more difficult than those used by the average hospital technician, and a sample can be obtained which should give authentic radiocarbon dates. The dating technique itself is one which requires care, but which can be carried out by adequately trained personnel who are sufficiently serious about it. It is something like the discipline of surgery—cleanliness, care, seriousness, and practice. With these it is possible to obtain radiocarbon dates which are consistent and which may indeed help roll back the pages of history and reveal to mankind something more about his ancestors and thus, perhaps, about his future.

BIBLIOGRAPHY

American Journal of Science, 1959, Am. Jour. Sci. Radiocarbon Supp., v. 1.

———, 1960, Am. Jour. Sci. Radiocarbon Supp., v. 2.

Libby, W. F., 1959, Radiocarbon dating (2d ed.): Chicago, University of Chicago Press.

18

Corals and the History of the Earth's Rotation

S. K. RUNCORN

1967

From *Sea Frontiers*, vol. 13, pp. 4–12, 1967.

In 1963, J. W. Wells, a distinguished student of fossil corals, had an idea of great importance to geophysicists. He suggested that tiny growth rings visible on the external surface or epitheca of the skeletons of fossil corals which lived in Devonian times 370 million years ago [Figures 18.1 and 18.2] were each put down in one day. These ridges were about one five hundredths of an inch thick. Much broader bands are also seen on coral skeletons and have long been supposed to be yearly bands analogous to the annual rings in trees. Thus Wells was able to count the number of days in the year in Devonian times and obtained a value of 400. As there are strong grounds to suppose that the length of the year has remained unaltered, Wells' result indicates that the day was then 22 hours and thus the earth's rotation has gradually slowed down, since the Devonian, to its present speed of one rotation in 24 hours. In making his bold suggestion that corals faithfully record the passage of day and night, Wells had remarkably little to support his speculation. T. F. Goreau had indeed shown that the modern coral secretes calcium carbonate for its skeleton at a greater rate during the day than the night and of course it has long been known that a diurnal rhythm is present as its tentacles are extended during the night rather than in the day. Further, a very few measurements on the growth of modern corals in the Bahamas suggest rates of about 1 to 4 inches a year—not inconsistent with the thickness of the ridges Wells believed to be daily growth increments.

DAYS ARE LENGTHENING

The rate at which the earth turns is a geophysical quantity of much importance, and the modern invention of extremely accurate clocks—atomic and crystal clocks—has enabled the geophysicist to observe that in the fall the day shortens by a thousandth of a second and lenghens correspondingly in the spring. This is due to meteorological effects and does not affect the average length of the day in the long run. Before this invention of very accurate clocks, the astronomers possessed another very ingenious way of checking whether the earth was rotating always at the same speed, and they concluded that it was not. Their most important discovery was that the day was lengthening by two-thousandths of a second each century. This extraordinarily small change was detected by observing the movement of the sun, Mercury, Venus and the moon across the sky over the centuries, just as if they were the hands of a gigantic clock. It is found that the hands of this celestial clock formed by sun, Mercury, Venus, gradually move ahead of the invisible hand stretching from the earth which makes one revolution in the course of a day. Astronomers concluded that the cause was a gradual slowing down, of the earth clock, that is, the day was lengthening by two-thousandths of one second in a century. The moon clock too was gaining on the earth clock but not by as much as the sun, making allowance for the fact that the moon makes 13.4 revolutions of the celestial sphere during one revolution by the sun. These remarkable discoveries were made not only by observatories during the last few centuries but by studies of the places from which the Greeks and Babylonians saw eclipses. The track of the belt of total eclipses depends on the exact positions of the sun and moon. In fact, it was Edmund Halley, the discoverer of the famous comet, who 250 years ago first showed in this way that the moon appeared to be speeding up in its motion.

TIDES SLOW THE SPINNING EARTH

The explanation of these facts was first given by the philosopher, Emmanuel Kant, who pointed out that the ocean tides should be slowing the earth down, much as one might slow down a spinning wheel by a friction band—the tides being thought of as a fluid layer which remain more or less heaped up along the line joining the moon to the earth, while the earth spins within. It is known now that this is the true explanation of the lengthening of the day. George H. Darwin, Charles Darwin's son, drew a further conclusion. The tides are causing the earth to lose angular momentum; but the most fundamental law of physics says this quantity cannot disappear. Actually the momentum lost by the earth is transferred to the moon, with the effect that the moon moves away from the earth at a rate of 5 yards a century and the month lengthens by 1/25 of a second each century. As the age of the earth-moon system is estimated at 4,600 million years and the moon's distance from the earth is 250,000 miles, this rate of retreat, assuming it has always been the same, implies that the earth and moon were close together early in their history. On this Darwin founded his famous theory of the moon being formed by the fission of an original planet, assuming that the Pacific basin is the place from which the moon was torn.

It is therefore clear that a measurement of the length of the month in the past can be used, by a simple calculation, to determine the length of the day in the past and vice versa, assuming of course that the only cause of changes in the rotation of the earth is the action of the tides.

Returning now to the fossil corals, we see that an excellent way of finding out whether Wells was correct in interpreting what he saw as daily and annual growth layers would be to find also a monthly band on corals. This equally remarkable discovery was made by Dr. C. T. Scrutton in 1965, who showed that on other Devonian corals there are bands containing on the average 30.6 of the supposedly daily growth lines. He interpreted these as monthly growth bands. It would, of course, be very valuable if we knew that modern corals also showed daily, monthly and yearly growth bands and that they gave the correct values of 29.5 and 365.25 days in the month and year respectively. But at present such studies are only just beginning and for the present moment the geophysicist must rather ask: do the values of Scrutton and Wells make sense? Because the month and day are related as explained above, it is possible to check their values.

From their two values it is possible to determine the average rate at which the angular momentum of the earth is decreasing as a result of tidal action since the Devonian, and the rate so calculated . . . is exactly that which the astronomers find from their observations over the last few hundred or thousand years. If this is not just a lucky coincidence, then it is strong evidence that the bands palaeontologists see on corals are really the day, month and year of Devonian times.

WHERE WAS THE MOON?

With this information we are able to retrace Darwin's argument and find to our astonishment that the earth and moon were in contact not at the origin of the earth but more recently, perhaps two billion years ago. A grave puzzle exists, therefore, as to where the moon was in the first 2.6 billion years of the earth's existence. This difficulty was first recognized by L. B. Slichter, before the data on corals became available, on the basis of the astronomically determined value of the present rate of retreat of the moon from the earth. It was then, however, perfectly possible to get out of the difficulty by supposing that the average rate of retreat of the moon in the past was several times less than it is now. After all, the melting of the polar ice caps since the end of the last Pleistocene glaciation has caused sea level to rise, and our knowledge of the theory

FIGURE 18.1
Coarse annuli and finer lines on fossil corals from the Middle Devonian. A study of these ridges shows whether the earth's rotation was faster in this age, 370 million years ago. *Left to right: Disphyllum* sp. (Iowa), *Eridophyllum archaici* (New York), and *Heliophyllum halli* (New York). (Courtesy of J. W. Wells.)

FIGURE 18.2
Daily growth ridges of fossil corals. *Above*, a coral of Silurian age from Ludlow, England; *Below*, a coral of Jurassic age from Oxfordshire, England. (British Museum of Natural History.)

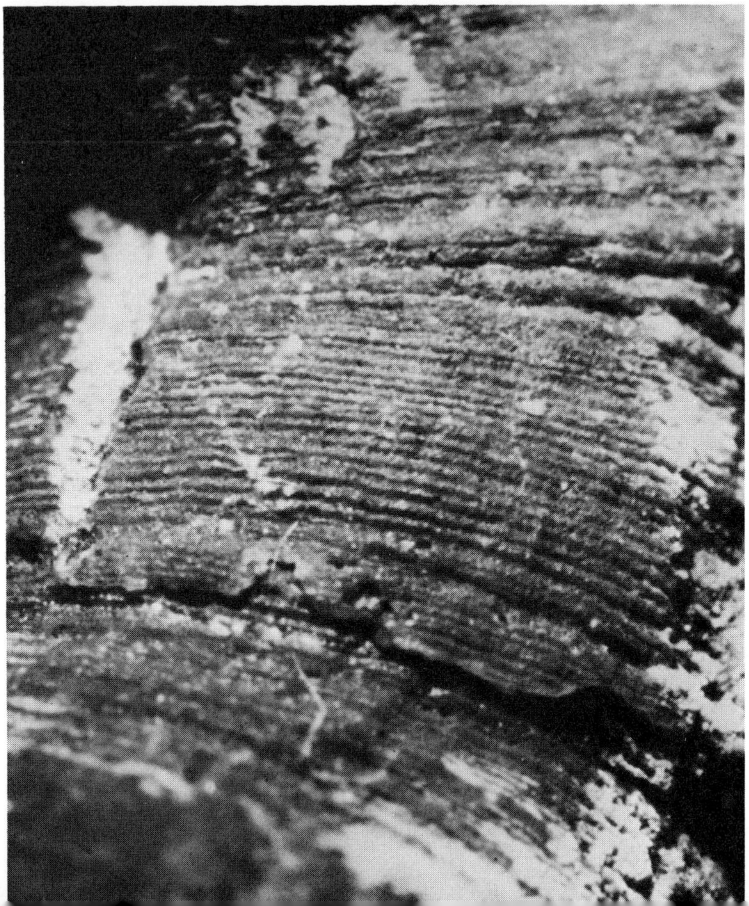

of tides and especially their frictional action on the earth's rotation is not yet good enough to be confident that this action has not changed. We do know that tidal energies are dissipated largely in shallow seas, such as the Bering Straits, and so a change in sea level might be supposed to have a large influence on the rate of the moon's retreat. But a few measurements are worth more than much theoretical calculation in most of the complicated problems in nature and we see that the corals appear to show that the present rate of retreat is representative of that over 370 million years. Thus the puzzle of the moon's origin is now one of the most challenging in science.

Was Darwin right, except that the moon's expulsion from the earth was so relatively recent? I find this difficult to believe in the face of evidence that sediments were being laid down in quiet waters about this time, for instance the great Belt series of rocks in Glacier National Park. Is it conceivable that the moon could have been so close—raising huge tides—despite the record preserved in these rocks showing ripple marks and other indications of relatively quiet depositional conditions not unlike those found in rocks of recent times? Or was the moon in the asteroid belt perhaps, and coming close to the earth was it captured, as recently suggested by Gerstenkorn? It seems very unlikely that the moon could have come near the earth with such a speed and moving in such a direction for this to have happened by accident. Let us remember the extraordinarily elaborate and accurate guidance which rocket experts currently use to put satellites in orbit round the earth and the moon. Or can it be that the moon did not exist in the first half of the earth history but gradually formed from a dust ring round the earth, as Professor H. Berlage suggested years ago?

One more piece of information of great value to the student of the history of the earth can be obtained from the corals. It is well known that a ballet dancer can spin faster if she pulls in her arms close to her body. So the earth if it gradually contracts will spin faster, or if it expands will spin slower. The length of the day, therefore, can be changed other than by the action of the tides. But if we have both the length of the day and the length of the month, we can find how the day would have changed had there been no tidal slowing down of the earth.

IS THE EARTH SHRINKING OR EXPANDING?

Many theories of the earth's evolution have been put forward. Sir Harold Jeffreys, among others, attributes the crumpled mountain ranges, such as the Rockies, to a slow shrinkage of the earth due to its cooling. If the interior of the earth contracts, its skin or crust will have to crumple as a drying out apple does. Some scientists on the other hand have sought to explain the cracks in the ocean floor by an expansion of the earth, between a half and one millimeter a year, according to Prof. K. M. Creer and Dr. L. Egyed. Others, Professor F. A. Vening Meinesz, Professor H. C. Urey and I, have argued that the crumpling long observed by geologists in the great mountain ranges of the continents and the recent discoveries by oceanographers of the rifts in the ocean ridges are the results of great flow systems in the earth's mantle, which, because the earth is apparently "solid," were not formerly suspected. The development of these flow systems suggests that the heavier elements in the earth, which now has an iron core 2,000 miles in radius, have gradually sunk to the center, causing the earth to spin faster in consequence.

From Wells' and Scrutton's counts I conclude that some of the wilder theories of the earth's evolution, such as that the earth has increased in radius by 40% in the last 200 million years, are definitely wrong and we look forward to the refinement of the observations on corals to find out which of these various theories of the earth's evolution is true. If the earth were proved to have gradually expanded, this would be of profound significance for physicists, for the only explanation of expansion is to suppose that the constants of nature, particularly the gravitational constant, are not unchanging but slowly alter their values as the universe expands.

We see, therefore, that from considering the

tiny lines on the skeleton of an animal which lived 370 million years ago we are led to the consideration of profound problems of cosmology, the evolution of the earth, and the formation of the moon. But for progress in such fields, reliable measurements of the length of the day and month in other geological times are of vital importance. We are, of course, only at the beginning of a new subject; observations on corals of other geological periods are now being made in Newcastle, based on a more reliable physical method of doing the counting to eliminate any bias in the observer. The marine biologist is now faced with an extremely exciting challenge to study corals afresh with these measurements in mind. Exactly how does the moon affect growth in marine life? Is the grunion laying its eggs in the sand on the beaches of California at spring tide, and the hatching of the eggs at the next high tide two weeks later, a valid illustration of the reasonableness of supposing an influence of the moon on the coral's growth? At any rate, the supposed existence of clocks in marine animals raises profoundly interesting biological questions. Finally, the work challenges us again with the need to obtain a better understanding of the action of tides.

The extraordinary interplay in this subject of biology, astronomy, palaeontology, oceanography and geophysics is perhaps the best argument for doing research in it.

19

Classification and Correlation

W. J. ARKELL
1956

For the stratigrapher, the Jurassic is the very well and fountain of his subject. It was on the Jurassic rocks that William Smith, Father of Historical Geology, founded the science of stratigraphy, enunciated the law of superposition, identified fossils with particular strata, and named the classic formations. It was on Jurassic rocks that Oppel founded modern zonal stratigraphy and named the classic zones. It was for Jurassic rocks that d'Orbigny introduced the first scheme of stages. All these concepts became part of the fabric of stratigraphical geology the world over. . . .

THE UNITS OF CLASSIFICATION

In order to be able to begin to describe or discuss a geological system it is necessay to have a classification. For all fossiliferous sedimentary systems three separate classifications have grown up, based on different concepts and requirements and built up of different kinds of units. Each has its place and all three are interdependent, but they should not be mixed. On the first system the rocks are divided into Formations, on the second into Zones, on the third into Stages. It is essential to have a clear understanding of the nature, advantages and limitations of each kind of unit.

FORMATIONS

A formation is a convenient lithological rock unit in a particular area and the basis of geological mapping. It is essentially defined by lithology, but that in turn may be sometimes influenced by abundance of certain kinds of fossils to such an extent that the fossils determine the formation; for example, corals, sponges, or oysters may build a large part of the rock. Typical formations in the English Jurassic are the Lias, Inferior Oolite, Forest Marble, Oxford Clay, Coral Rag, Portland Stone, Purbeck Beds; in France the Calcaire

From *Jurassic Geology of the World* by W. J. Arkell, pp. 3–13. Oliver & Boyd Ltd., 1956. Reprinted with permission of the publisher.

de Caen, Oolithe Miliaire and Choin; in Germany the Einbeckhäuser Plattenkalk and Serpulite. The size and scope of the formations are as varied as the names. This is not surprising, since most of them go back to the beginnings of geology: in England most of them were named by William Smith between 1799 and 1815. They are still, however, the basis of all classification and the ultimate court of appeal for settling problems of zonal succession and correlation. Any attempt to standardize them, or modify them in any way, would be disastrous; and such attempts would be futile, for units of classification for modern purposes are provided by the zones and stages.

Groupings into units of higher rank in this same scale are equally arbitrary, inconsistent and heterogeneous, having arisen at different times as a convenience. They too have their uses and historical claims to freedom from 'reform.' But they grade into formations and like them are strictly limited geographically. In the other direction, formations can be subdivided to any extent required.

In Britain and other European countries the formation names in geological literature have historical associations and antiquity and a consequent individuality which makes them useful and easy to remember. It is not so with many formations recently introduced in some other parts of the world. A superabundance of formation names (which by themselves convey nothing) can choke the literature and build a formidable barrier between writer and reader.

ZONES

Palaeontologically the old formations are often too comprehensive and also inconsistent in content from place to place. The need for time-planes independent of lithology and geography, so that rocks may be correlated more satisfactorily, led to the concept of the Zone.

The hallmark of a zone is the assemblage of guide fossils, of which one is selected as index species and gives its name to the zone. These are supposed to have lived, for practical purposes, contemporaneously, wherever they occur.

Like so many fundamental concepts, the zone is a subject of unending controversy. There are many kinds of zone: faunizones based on assemblages of fossils, biozones based on the evolutionary duration of a species, teilzones based on the local presence of a species, and so on. (For a full exposition see Arkell, 1933.) But over and above these considerations there is uncertainty as to the basic concept of the zone: whether as originally conceived by Oppel it was a stratum or bed, or a time-interval, or an abstract combination of the two,—a hypothetical column of sediment (probably nowhere actually existing) representing the time of duration of the index species on the assumption of continuous sedimentation at some unknown average rate.

British geologists have always envisaged a zone as a bed or stratum, a tangible object accessible to the hammer, though differing lithologically from place to place. Consequently some have thought it necessary to construct a parallel terminology to express the time units to which the various kinds of zones correspond. The need to keep time and rock distinct in our thoughts is obvious, and to the extent that this elaborate terminology has led to clarification of thought it has served a useful purpose. But beyond that it is unnecessary. No one uses it, nor ever will.

That Oppel himself fully appreciated the time element cannot be doubted (Schindewolf, 1950). The fact that he nowhere defined a zone, nor made it clear whether his zones were strata or time intervals, may be taken to mean that he visualized zones from both aspects at once. The argument that a zone must be one or the other is sterile. A zone is much more than a mere bed or stratum, or a formation, because it is an abstraction and a generalization: it is in theory *any* bed, stratum, or formation deposited in any part of the world during the period in which the index fossils lived. To mention a concrete example: the Mariae Zone is part of the Oxford Clay in the south of England and part of the Lower Calcareous Grit in the north of England and the marls of Mount Hermon in Syria, but we do not know whether it exists in Japan, because no comparable fauna has been found there. Wherever it is, the Mariae Zone is a bed or part of a formation, but this does not express its whole entity: it transcends all local occurrences, and the factor which enables it to do this is the time element in the concept. Anything deposited *during the critical period of time* is part of the zone.

In practice zones have their limitations because for various reasons no fossils fulfil perfectly all the requirements of zonal indices, namely, ease of identification, combined with short vertical and universally wide horizontal range. The best zone fossils are often the most difficult to identify, because their short vertical range depends on subtle characters undergoing rapid evolution, and, owing to the existence of ecological and palaeogeographical barriers and provinces, no fossils are evenly distributed over the whole earth. It is therefore necessary to construct a separate zonal column for each faunal province.

The degree of refinement of the zonal scale that may be possible depends on a number of local factors, not the least of them the lithological. Given ideal lithology and abundance of suitable fossils, a high degree of refinement may be achieved in a restricted area, but the more the area is enlarged the more the refinements break down. This has obvious explanations, which have been discussed elsewhere (Arkell, 1933, pp. 30–35). . . .

Experience has now shown that minute subdivisions, such as those made by Buckman in the English Lias, are not recognizable even in other European countries, but that over wide areas only the general faunal succession such as is expressed by Oppel's zones and a few subzones can be recognized. This, moreover, is true even for the Lias, which is by far the most favourable part of the Jurassic for zonal subdivision and correlation over long distances. For the Upper Jurassic even Oppel's zones are often too small to be recognized outside Europe.

STAGES

Just as it is convenient to group together formations into [Groups and] Series, so it is convenient to group like zones together and reduce the numbers for practical purposes, and above all to have a grouping which enables several zones to be correlated in a general way over long distances when the zones individually are too precise. Such groupings of zones are [time stratigraphic subdivisions called] Stages. They transcend zones horizontally as well as vertically and provide a stratigraphical unit of wider use, adapted to inter-continental comparisons and correlations. Whereas the individual zone cannot be recognized beyond the area of occurrence of its index species or typical fauna, a stage can be followed all over the world by a series of overlapping correlations and by the general grade of evolution of its critical fauna.

The hallmarks of a stage-name are that it is based on the name of a place or district and has the termination -ian (in French -ien). Names in this form began to be coined for formations in France during the second quarter of the nineteenth century by Brongniart, Marcou and d'Orbigny, but it was not until 1850 that d'Orbigny introduced for the Jurassic and Cretaceous his standard set of stages which are still used to this day. To attempt to unravel and revert to the ancient terms and meanings of before 1850 would produce chaos, for before that date knowledge of stratigraphy was so primitive that no clear definition of a stage-name was possible, nor was there any clear conception of the requirements of the future. (For example Brongniart's Oxfordien, 1829, also used by Marcou before 1850, covered the whole Middle Jurassic, and Bathonien was first used in 1843 as synonymous with the German Dogger.)

D'Orbigny's scheme of 1850 was based on the classical areas of northwest and central Europe, and with a few modifications it has stood the test of a century. . . . It contains a convenient number of stages, neither too many nor too few, and is by far the best scheme yet devised for classification on a world scale.

From the Hettangian up to the Middle Kimeridgian these stages can be recognized all over the world, but after that the scheme breaks down owing to regional differentiation of faunas. The terms Portlandian and Purbeckian are applicable only to NW. Europe, except that Purbeckian faunas extend to Savoy and Portlandian to Greenland and perhaps central Russia. In Russia and the Arctic there is otherwise a completely separate ammonite fauna, for which the stage-name Volgian has to be used. Over all the rest of the

STANDARD SCHEME OF STAGES

Upper Jurassic
- Purbeckian (Purbeck, Dorset, England)
- Portlandian (Portland, Dorset, England)
- Kimeridgian (Kimeridge, Dorset, England)
- Oxfordian (Oxford, England)

Middle Jurassic
- Callovian (Callovium = Kellaways, Wiltshire, England)
- Bathonian (Bath, Somerset, England)
- Bajocian (Bajoce = Bayeux, Normandy, France)

Lower Jurassic
- Toarcian (Toarcium = Thouars, Deux-Sèvres, France)
- Pliensbachian (Pliensbach, near Boll, Württemberg, Germany)
- Sinemurian (Sinemurium = Semur, Côte d'Or, France)
- Hettangian (Hettange, Lorraine, France)

world the presumed equivalents of these late Jurassic stages have nothing in common with either NW. Europe or Russia and are known as the Tithonian.

Vast numbers of other stages have been proposed by different authors but their very numbers proclaim their futility. . . .

The principles, or rules, on which the names now used have been chosen have been explained at length elsewhere (Arkell, 1946). They are a compromise between priority, suitability and usage. On the whole these self-imposed rules have been adhered to, but a few decisions then made have had to be reconsidered in the light of seven years' further experience. Purbeckian has been reinstated as a separate stage instead of merging it in the Portlandian as advocated by Haug, a procedure likely to cause confusion; and Berriasian has been adopted for the lowest stage of the Cretaceous, in conformity with almost universal modern usage. Although Oppel's Tithonian is not named after a place, it is too late to abolish it after a hundred years of continuous use. . . .

INTERPRETATION OF THE STAGES

As units of the single world scale of classification Stages must be based on zones. As now used they are essentially groupings of zones, but they transcend zones both vertically and horizontally.

At the time d'Orbigny promulgated his scheme of stages, however, although he was the first to use the term zone, the zonal concept current to-day had not been born. It derives essentially from Oppel (1856–63). D'Orbigny listed certain ammonites supposed to be characteristic of each stage, but at that early date the specific names he used (all referred to the single genus *Ammonites*) so often had quite different meanings from those attaching to them to-day, and so many were wrongly used, or ambiguous, or assigned to two stages, or included as the result of incorrect stratigraphical information, that any attempt to interpret the stages primarily by means of these lists of ammonites leads to chaotic results.

The formations, on the contrary, had been defined all over western Europe and were especially well known in the areas after which d'Orbigny named the stages. It was essentially on formations that the stages were based.

A process akin to translation is therefore necessary to render the stages as defined by d'Orbigny on the basis of formations into the stages as used in modern stratigraphy, which must be defined on the basis of zones. Fortunately d'Orbigny gave a more or less clear definition of each stage in terms of formations at some type locality or type area. It is generally a simple matter now to establish the zones represented in those formations at the type locality, and thus to arrive at a satisfactory definition of the contents of each stage.

D'Orbigny's type localities, however, are not always precisely those from which the stage-name was derived. For instance, he defined the Callovian and Oxfordian stages, not in accordance with successions at Kellaways and Oxford, where no comprehensive exposures existed, but on the cliffs of the Yorkshire coast, which had been fully described stratigraphically and palaeontologically by Phillips. The terms Kellaways (or Kelloway) Rock and Oxford Clay have since been proved to have been wrongly applied in Yorkshire, but nevertheless it is better at this late date to accept d'Orbigny's definitions although based on Phillips' errors. . . .

When a new fauna is found elsewhere, not present or not detected at the type locality, it falls readily into place if it comes between two zones already in the same stage, but if it falls at the boundary between two stages it has to be classed according to its nearest palaeontological affinities. In practice, surprisingly few difficulties have arisen on this score.

The possibility of describing and analysing a geological system as a whole, all over the world, depends primarily on availability of a single universal language for use in classification. This language the stages provide. Their great value for this purpose is impaired if different countries introduce their own scheme of stages. Those recently proposed, for instance,

TABLE 19.1
Standard stages and ammonite zones of the Jurassic of N.W. Europe

Series	Stages	Zones
Upper Jurassic	Purbeckian	[No ammonites]
	Portlandian	*Titanites giganteus* *Glaucolithites gorei* *Zaraiskites albani*
	Kimeridgian	*Pavlovia pallasioides* *Pavlovia rotunda* *Pectinatites pectinatus* *Subplanites wheatleyensis* *Subplanites* spp. *Gravesia gigas* *Gravesia gravesiana* *Aulacostephanus pseudomutabilis* *Rasenia mutabilis* *Rasenia cymodoce* *Pictonia baylei*
	Oxfordian	*Ringsteadia pseudocordata* *Decipia decipiens* *Perisphinctes cautisnigrae* *Perisphinctes plicatilis* *Cardioceras cordatum* *Quenstedtoceras mariae*
Middle Jurassic	Callovian	*Quenstedtoceras lamberti* *Peltoceras athleta* *Erymnoceras coronatum* *Kosmoceras jason* *Sigaloceras calloviense* *Proplanulites koenigi* *Macrocephalites macrocephalus*
	Bathonian	*Clydoniceras discus* *Oppelia aspidoides* *Tulites subcontractus* *Gracilisphinctes progracilis* *Zigzagiceras zigzag*
	Bajocian	*Parkinsonia parkinsoni* *Garantiana garantiana* *Strenoceras subfurcatum* *Stephanoceras humphriesianum* *Otoites sauzei* *Sonninia sowerbyi* *Ludwigia murchisonae* *Tmetoceras scissum* *Leioceras opalinum*

Series	Stages	Zones
Lower Jurassic	Toarcian	*Lytoceras jurense* *Hildoceras bifrons* *Harpocenas falcifer* *Dactylioceras tenuicostatum*
	Pliensbachian	*Pleuroceras spinatum* *Amaltheus margaritatus* *Prodactylioceras davoei* *Tragophylloceras ibex* *Uptonia jamesoni*
	Sinemurian	*Echioceras raricostatum* *Oxynoticeras oxynotum* *Asteroceras obtusum* *Euasteroceras turneri* *Arnioceras semicostatum* *Arietites bucklandi*
	Hettangian	*Schlotheimia angulata* *Psiloceras planorbis*

for New Zealand, are not true stages, since they are not definable in terms of zones and are not applicable outside New Zealand. They are in reality Series, or groups of formations. An independent scale of classification for the Jurassic rocks of New Zealand was a necessity and these names will no doubt be invaluable as a basis for further work in that country; but in this book the terminations -ian, -an will be reserved for stages in the old sense, which can be defined palaeontologically and used virtually in any part of the world.

Those geologists who like to keep time terms separate from rock terms consider a stage a rock term and an age its equivalent time-term. . . .

THE GUIDE FOSSILS OF THE JURASSIC

It is a commonplace that for the three Mesozoic systems ammonites provide incomparably the best zonal index fossils. For the four requirements of the ideal index fossil—short vertical range, wide horizontal range, independence of facies, and ease of recognition—the ammonites score heavily over all other fossils, except perhaps for ease of recognition. On the first two requirements (the most important) they have no serious rivals. Marine pelecypods have been found in recent years to have much longer ranges than had sometimes been supposed: single species in Europe alone often range through four or five stages and many ammonite zones. This makes them of little value for correlation in spite of the great geographical extension of some of them, which may exceed that of many ammonites. It is illuminating to find the limestone escarpment of Jebel Tuwaiq in central Arabia strewn with some of the same species of pelecypods as may be picked up in the English Cotswolds—*Pholadomya, Homomya, Mactromya, Ceromyopsis,* etc.; but whereas in the Cotswolds the limestones enclosing them are Bajocian, in the Jebel Tuwaiq they are Upper Bathonian and Callovian.

Gastropods are sometimes useful locally, where ammonites are rare or non-existent, but they too have long ranges, some species occurring through four stages.

Brachiopods are also helpful locally, but over wider areas they are disqualified because of their colonial habits, heavy dependence on facies and frequent homoeomorphy.

On the third requirement, independence of facies, most groups of fossils take low marks and even ammonites are not entirely successful here. The types of facies in which ammonites are seldom found are coral reef and current-bedded rocks. This is not the place to enter into the wide fields of speculation concerning the mode of life of ammonites, but there is much to be said for the hypothesis of Termier

& Termier (1951) that many bred in loose mud among marine vegetation, which on decaying could have produced the iron and sulphur that went to make the iron pyrites in which large numbers of ammonites in clays and shales are so often preserved.

The clay milieu which was so favourable to many ammonites seems to have been inimical to others, such as Stephanocerataceae, which are usually linked with limestone deposits (Arkell, 1952, pp. 83–4). The great variety of forms and apertural modifications among ammonites strongly suggests that there were adaptations to almost every kind of niche, excepting always coral reefs and the distributaries of deltas. In addition their floating shells were probably carried far and wide after death, like Nautilus shells at the present day, by winds and currents. Drifted specimens therefore may come to the rescue of stratigraphers in unlikely places.

BIBLIOGRAPHY

Arkell, W. J., 1933, The Jurassic system in Great Britain: London, Oxford University Press.

———, 1946, Standard of the European Jurassic: Geol. Soc. America Bull., v. 57, p. 1.

———, 1951–55, Monograph of the English Bathonian ammonites (parts 1–5, in progress): London, Palæontographical Society.

Buch, L. von, 1837 (1839), Über den Jura in Deutschland: Kgl. Akad. Wiss. Berlin Abh., 1837, p. 49.

Oppel, A., 1856–58, Die Juraformation Englands, Frankreichs und des südwestlichen Deutschlands: Stuttgart.

———, 1862–63, Über jurassische Cephalopoden: Mus. kgl. Bayerischen Staates Paläont. Mitt., v. 3, p. 127.

———, 1865, Die tithonische Etage: Deutsche Geol. Gesell. Zeitschr., v. 17, p. 535.

Orbigny, A. d', 1842–51, Paléontologie française, Terrains jurassiques, Céphalopodes: Paris.

Schindewolf, O. H., 1950, Grundlagen und Methoden der paläontologischen Chronologie: Berlin.

SECTION IV

EARTH'S AIR, WATER, AND CLIMATE

And the waters prevailed
and were increased greatly upon the earth.

GENESIS

What was the earth like just after completion of its condensation from the third dust cloud out from the solar disc perhaps 4.6 to 4.8 aeons ago? The best inferences we can make suggest that it was a heterogeneous agglomeration of siliceous and ferruginous matter, probably somewhat less dense (and therefore larger) than now, but having a surface temperature of no more than a few hundred degrees Kelvin. This primeval earth probably had little or no atmosphere, and therefore had little or no water vapor from which a hydrosphere could condense. It was not differentiated internally, nor was there any surficial segregation of light and heavy rocks into higher-standing continents and downward-sagging ocean basins.

Section IV is concerned with the origin and the nature of the earth's early atmosphere and water, the motions brought about in each as a consequence of the earth's rotation and its thermal gradient from equator to poles, and the way these and other components interact to produce climate and to establish a record of climatic history for the earth. Thus it sets the stage for discussion of the differentiation of the solid earth in Section V, and for much of what follows.

Reading Selection 20 was originally published in 1844 by the philosopher Herbert Spencer. Spencer clearly recognized, even at that early date, the necessary interreaction between atmospheric and biospheric evolution, which he called the theory of reciprocal dependence. Spencer, of course, could not have foreseen the refinements that would eventually be made on his ideas. Although they were contrary to the scientific dogma of his time, current thinking both vindicates and extends his bold insights.

This historical background provides a good perspective against which to view present concepts of atmospheric and hydrospheric evolution, summarized by W. W. Rubey, Director of the Lunar Science Institute, in Reading Selection 21. This paper, "Geologic History of Sea Water," was Rubey's presidential address to the Geological Society of America. Only the abstract of this epoch-making and exacting paper is reprinted here, but advanced students will want to study the entire meticulously documented work, as well as Rubey's 1955 paper listed in the Supplemental Reading. Rubey shows that geochemical balance and the record of the rocks seem to require an internal source for, and the gradual accumulation of, the volatile substances that make up our atmosphere and hydrosphere.

Biophysicist P. H. Abelson, director of the Carnegie Institution's Geophysical Laboratory, then departs from Rubey's synthesis with a paper titled "Chemical Events on the Primitive Earth" (Reading Selection 22). Abelson starts by reviewing likely limits for the nature of the early atmosphere and hydrosphere, rejecting the methane-ammonia model for the primitive atmosphere in favor of Rubey's model, wherein the earth's volatile envelope consists predominantly or exclusively of components formerly occluded within the earth. He considers likely gas equilibria in terms of the simple thermodynamics of free-energy change (ΔF) and probable aqueous and gaseous concentrations in terms of moles (M) and atmospheres. He concludes with a discussion of the kinds of organic molecules that might have arisen within the early hydrosphere as a result of high-energy ultraviolet (UV) irradiation, polymerization, and other processes. The last half of Abelson's discussion can be omitted, as it does not relate directly to the theme of this section; however, it provides such a useful transition to Section VI that it should be read and reread when that section is reached. There, Abelson tells briefly how HCN from irradiation of the primitive atmosphere, NH_3 from degradation of the products of HCN, and CH_2O produced by hydrolysis of CO from volcanic sources might react to produce a variety of amino acids, fatty acids, sugars, and the important enzyme ferredoxin, all essential steps in the kind of chemical evolution that might have led to biogenesis.

Given an atmosphere and hydrosphere of a certain composition on a rotating globe with a latitudinal temperature gradient, what kinds of motions will be generated? What might be the effects on such motions of the surface differentiation of the globe into continents and ocean basins, and of their changing configurations in the past? How might that totality of motion, thermal gradient, and surface configuration interact to produce climatic conditions that would be reflected in the kinds of sedimentary rocks and organisms preserved at different times and places in the geologic past? Fundamental to all such questions is the Coriolis effect—a consequence of the law of the conservation of angular momentum—whereby freely moving masses at or above the earth's surface are deflected to the right in the northern hemisphere and to the left in the southern hemisphere. A concise explanation of that phenomenon is Reading Selection 23, from *The Earth Sciences* by physiographer A. N. Strahler of Columbia University.

Proceeding from Strahler's discussion of the Coriolis effect, meteorologist Edward Lorenz of the Massachusetts Institute of Technology considers the general circulation of the atmosphere (Reading Selection 24). He shows how thermally circulating air, deflected by the Coriolis effect, can give rise to the well-defined subtropical trade winds and to the prevailing westerly winds of the middle latitudes, as well as to numerous local eddies. The major components of the circulating atmosphere thus are visualized as great energy and moisture transport mechanisms. Linked to the sea they help to generate its circulation, and the circulating atmosphere and sea together control the heat and moisture budget of the earth. The combination of circulating sea and atmosphere, with variations in solar radiation and the configuration and relief of the land masses and water bodies, generates climate. For a simpler and more traditional discussion of the general circulation of the atmosphere, and for reference to the polar easterlies, consult the paper by Wexler (1955) under Supplemental Reading. Having been written before all the new complexities were discovered, it presents a much more generalized picture of atmospheric circulation, and one which still seems to be broadly valid. That simpler scheme is very briefly outlined in Reading Selection 25.

The dependence of oceanic on atmospheric circulation is discussed in Reading Selection 25, by University of California geophysicist Walter Munk. Munk finds that the circulation of the oceans, like that of the atmosphere, is complex and changes rapidly in detail. As is also true of the atmosphere, however, the large-scale and long-term pattern is reasonably regular and predictable, which offers hope for paleoclimatologic and paleo-oceanographic reconstruction.

The theory of climate and its application to the geologic past is introduced in Reading Selection 26, "Facets of Climate," by the leading climatologist H. E. Landsberg of the University of Maryland. Landsberg very simply and briefly presents some of the observations and experiments that can provide insights into the factors determining weather and climate and their variations with geologic time. In Sections IX and X it will become apparent that the concepts here so fleetingly touched upon have important implications for earth history.

A highly recommended paper in the Supplemental Reading is the difficult but excellent "Theoretical Paleoclimatology" by Mitchell (1965). He examines the problem of climatic variation in terms of the dynamic theory of world climate and the general atmospheric and oceanic circulation. He looks at the probable responses of climate to various influences, such as changes in the solar constant, variations in atmospheric CO_2, volcanic dust, and air-sea interactions; and he discusses probable time scales for such responses, both in general and for the specific case of Quaternary glaciation. His examination reveals that, although much is still uncertain, some limits can now be placed on conjecture, and that more abundant data and improved data processing offer bright prospects for future progress in paleoclimatology. Additional information on the principles and procedures of paleoclimatology is given in papers in the two volumes edited by Nairn (1961, 1964).

The paper by von Arx (1957) is also of special interest because it shows how three-dimensional or pencil-and-paper models may be made to approximate oceanic circulation for the hemispheres on either side of the equator—given a known or inferred distribution of land and a specific axis of rotation. An interesting laboratory exercise is to prepare similar models for specific episodes in the geologic past where data permit reasonably detailed paleogeographic, paleobiogeographic, and paleoclimatologic inferences of regional extent. The simple "dishpan model" described in the short paper by Landsberg (Reading Selection 26) can be adapted for this purpose.

Supplemental Reading

Brown, Harrison, 1952, Rare gases and the formation of the earth's atmosphere, *in* G. P. Kuiper, ed., The atmosphere of the earth and planets (2d ed.): Chicago, University of Chicago Press, p. 258–266.

Coriolis, G., 1835, Sur les équations du mouvement relatif des systèmes de corps: École Polytech. Jour., v. 15, p. 142–154.

Eady, E. T., 1964, The general circulation of the atmosphere and oceans, *in* D. R. Bates, ed., The planet earth: Long Island City, N.Y., Pergamon Press, p. 141–163.

Guilluly, James, A. C. Waters, and A. O. Woodford, 1968, Principles of geology (3d ed.): San Francisco, W. H. Freeman and Company, 687 p. (chap. 22).

Hadley, G., 1735, Concerning the cause of the general tradewinds: Royal Soc. [London] Philos. Trans., v. 39, p. 58–62.

Holland, H. D., 1964, On the chemical evolution of the terrestrial and Cytherean atmospheres, *in* P. J. Brancazio and A. G. W. Cameron, eds., The origin and evolution of atmospheres and oceans: New York, John Wiley and Sons, p. 86–100.

Kuiper, G. P., 1952, Planetary atmospheres and their origin, *in* G. P. Kuiper, ed., The atmospheres of the earth and planets (2d ed.): Chicago, University of Chicago Press, p. 306–405.

Livingstone, D. A., 1963, The sodium cycle and the age of the ocean: Geochim. et Cosmochim. Acta, v. 27, p. 1055–1069.

Mitchell, J. M., Jr., 1965, Theoretical paleoclimatology, *in* H. E. Wright, Jr., and D. G. Frey, eds., The Quaternary of the United States: Princeton, N.J., Princeton University Press, p. 881–901.

Nairn, A. E. M., ed., 1961, Descriptive paleoclimatology: New York, John Wiley and Sons, Interscience Publications, 380 p.

———, ed., 1964, Problems in paleoclimatology: New York, John Wiley and Sons, Interscience Publications, 705 p.

Rasool, S. I., and W. E. McGovern, 1966, Primitive atmosphere of the earth: Nature, v. 212, p. 1225–1226.

Revelle, Roger, 1955, On the history of the oceans: Jour. Marine Research, v. 14, p. 446–461.

Rubey, W. W., 1951, Geologic history of sea water: Geol. Soc. America Bull., v. 62, p. 1111–1148.

———, 1955, Development of the hydrosphere and atmosphere, with special reference to the probable composition of the early atmosphere: Geol. Soc. America Spec. Paper 62, p. 631–650.

Stommel, H., 1955, The anatomy of the Atlantic: Scientific American Offprint 810, 7 p.

von Arx, W. S., 1957, An experimental approach to problems in physical oceanography, *in* L. H. Ahrens, ed., Physics and chemistry of the earth, v. 2: New York, Pergamon Press, p. 1–29.

Wexler, Harry, 1955, The circulation of the atmosphere: Scientific American, Sept. 1955, p. 114–124.

20

Remarks upon the Theory of Reciprocal Dependence

in the Animal and Vegetable Creations, as Regards its Bearing upon Paleontology

HERBERT SPENCER
1844

From *The London, Edinburgh, and Dublin Philosophical Magazine and Journal of Science*, vol. 24, pp. 90–94, 1844.

Upon perusing an article which some time since appeared in the Philosophical Magazine explanatory of M. Dumas' views respecting the peculiar relationship that exists between plants and animals, in so far as their action upon the atmosphere is concerned, it occurred to me that the doctrine there set forth involved an entirely new and very beautiful explanation of the proximate causes of progressive development.

In unfolding the several results of the theory and exhibiting its application in the solution of natural phænomena, M. Dumas adverts to the fact, that not only do the organisms of the vegetable kingdom decompose the carbonic acid which has been thrown into the atmosphere by animals, but that they likewise serve for the removal of those extraneous supplies of the same gas that are being continually poured into it through volcanos, calcareous springs, fissures, and other such channels. It is to the corollary deducible from this proposition, respecting the alterations that have taken place in the composition of that atmosphere, that attention is requested.

If it had been found that during the past epochs of the world's existence animals had always borne such a proportion to plants as to ensure the combustion of the whole of the carbon assimilated by them from the air, or in other words, if the carbon-reducing class had always been exactly balanced by the carbon-consuming class, it would then follow, that as the gas decomposed in the one case was wholly recomposed in the other, the only change that could have taken place in the character of the atmosphere would have been a deterioration resulting from the continual influx of carbonic acid from the above-mentioned sources. Such, however, were not the conditions of the case, for it is manifest, not only from the nature of existing arrangements, but likewise from the records of the world's history, that the vegetable kingdom has always had such a preponderance as to accumulate a much larger supply of carbon than could be consumed by animals. . . .

The fact of there having been a larger abstraction of carbon from the atmosphere by the decomposition of its carbonic acid gas than has ever been returned to it, will, however, be most distinctly proved by a reference to purely geological data. The vast accumulations of carbonaceous matter contained in the numerous coal basins distributed over the surface of the globe—the large proportion of bitumen existing in many of the secondary deposits, to say nothing of the uncombined carbon which must be diffused through a great part of the strata composing the earth's crust, bear palpable witness to the truth of the position. All such combustible material has been originally derived from the air, and the fact of its remaining to the present day unoxidized and bidding fair to continue in the same condition (setting aside human agency) for an indefinite period, strongly favours the conclusion that the carbon of which it is composed has been permanently reduced from the gaseous combination in which it previously appeared.

If then it be conceded that the carbonic acid which during past eras escaped out of the earth has been continually undergoing the process of de-carbonization, it follows as an apparently legitimate consequence, that its remaining constituent, the oxygen, being thus constantly liberated and effused into the atmosphere, now exists in that medium in a larger proportion than it originally did, and that it has from the commencement of vegetable life to the present day been ever on the increase. . . .

Assuming then that the proposed theory, supported as it is by the fact that the constituents of the atmosphere are *not in atomic proportions*, and borne out likewise by the foregoing arguments, is correct, let us mark the inferences that may be drawn respecting the effects produced upon the organic creation.

Superior orders of beings are strongly distinguished from inferior ones by the warmth of their blood. A low organization is uniformly accompanied by a low temperature, and in ascending the scale of creation we find that, setting aside partial irregularities, one of the most notable circumstances is the increase of heat. It has been further shown, by modern discoveries, that such augmentation of temperature is the direct result of a greater consumption of oxygen; and it would appear that a quick combustion of carbonaceous matter through the medium of the lungs was the one essential condition to the maintenance of that high degree of vitality and nervous energy without which exalted psychical or physical endowments cannot exist.

Coupling this circumstance with the theory of a continual increase in the amount of atmospherical oxygen, we are naturally led to the conclusion that there must of necessity have been a gradual change in the character of the animate creation. If a rapid oxidation of the blood is accompanied by a higher heat and a more perfect mental and bodily development, and if in consequence of an alteration in the composition of the air greater facilities for such oxidation are afforded, it may be reasonably inferred that there has been a corresponding advancement in the temperature and organization of the world's inhabitants.

Now this deduction of abstract reasoning we know to be in exact accordance with geological observations. An inspection of the records of creation demonstrates that such change has taken place, and although remains have from time to time been found which prove that beings of an advanced development existed at an earlier period than was previously supposed, still the broad fact is not by any means invalidated. A retrospective view of the various phases of animal life, tracing it through the extinct orders of mammalia, saurians, fishes, crustacea, radiata, zoophytes, &c., shows distinctly that whatever may have been the oscillations and irregularities produced by incidental causes, the average aspect nevertheless indicates the law of change alluded to, seeing that there appears to have been an æra in which the earth was occupied exclusively by cold-blooded creatures requiring but little oxygen; that it was subsequently inhabited by animals of superior organization consuming more oxygen, and that there has since been a continual increase of the hot-blooded tribes and an apparent diminution of the cold-blooded ones.

Bearing in mind therefore the undoubted relationship that exists between the consumption of oxygen on the one hand and the degree of vitality and height of organization on the other, it would appear extremely probable that there is some connexion between the supposed change in the vital medium, and the increased intensity of life and superiority of construction that has accompanied it. Whether the alteration that has taken place in the constitution of the atmosphere is to be looked upon as the *cause* of this gradual development of organic existence, or whether it is to be regarded as an arrangement intended to prepare the earth for the reception of more perfect creatures, are points which need not now be entered upon. The question at present to be determined is, whether the alleged improvement in the composition of the air has really happened, and if so, whether that improvement has had anything to do with the changes that have taken place in the characteristics of the earth's inhabitants.

[*** We have inserted the foregoing communication because the inquiry to which it relates is one of extreme interest, and our correspondent's reasoning may excite attention to the subject; but we doubt whether his inferences are warranted by the known facts of Chemistry and Palæontology: we fear that his generalizations are at least premature. —EDIT.]

21

Geologic History of Sea Water

WILLIAM W. RUBEY

1951

From *Geological Society of America Bulletin*, vol. 62, pp. 1111–1112, 1951. Abstract: reprinted with permission of the author and the Geological Society of America.

Paleontology and biochemistry together may yield fairly definite information, eventually, about the paleochemistry of sea water and atmosphere. Several less conclusive lines of evidence now available suggest that the composition of both sea water and atmosphere may have varied somewhat during the past; but the geologic record indicates that these variations have probably been within relatively narrow limits. A primary problem is how conditions could have remained so nearly constant for so long.

It is clear, even from inadequate data on the quantities and compositions of ancient sediments, that the more volatile materials—water, carbon dioxide, chlorine, nitrogen, and sulfur—are much too abundant in the present atmosphere, hydrosphere, biosphere, and in ancient sediments to be explained, like the commoner rock-forming oxides, as the products of rock weathering alone. If the earth were once entirely gaseous or molten, these "excess" volatiles may be residual from a primitive atmosphere. But if so, certain corollaries should follow about the quantity of water dissolved in the molten earth and the expected chemical effects of a highly acid, primitive ocean. These corollaries appear to be contradicted by the geologic record, and doubt is therefore cast on this hypothesis of a dense primitive atmosphere. It seems more probable that only a small fraction of the total "excess" volatiles was ever present at one time in the early atmosphere and ocean.

Carbon plays a significant part in the chemistry of sea water and in the realm of living matter. The amount now buried as carbonates and organic carbon in sedimentary rocks is about 600 times as great as that in today's atmosphere, hydrosphere, and biosphere. If only 1/100 of this buried carbon were suddenly added to the present atmosphere and ocean, many species of marine organisms would probably be exterminated. Furthermore, unless CO_2 is being added continuously to the atmosphere-ocean system from some source other than rock weathering, the present rate of its subtraction by sedimentation would, in only a few million years, cause brucite to take the place of calcite as a common marine sediment. Apparently, the geologic record shows no evidence of such simultaneous extinctions of many species nor such deposits of brucite. Evidently the amount of CO_2 in the atmosphere and ocean has remained relatively constant throughout much of the geologic past. This calls for some source of gradual and continuous supply, over and above that from rock weathering and from the metamorphism of older sedimentary rocks.

A clue to this source is afforded by the relative amounts of the different "excess" volatiles. These are similar to the relative amounts of the same materials in gases escaping from volcanoes, fumaroles, and hot springs, and in gases occluded in igneous rocks. Conceivably, therefore, the hydrosphere and atmosphere may have come almost entirely from such plutonic gases. During the crystallization of magmas, volatiles such as H_2O and CO_2 accumulate in the remaining melt and are largely expelled as part of the final fractions. Volcanic eruptions and lava flows have brought volatiles to the earth's surface throughout the geologic past; but intrusive rocks are probably a much more adequate source of the constituents of the atmosphere and hydrosphere. Judged by the thermal springs of the United States, hot springs (carrying only 1% or less of juvenile matter) may be the principal channels by which the "excess" volatiles have escaped from cooling magmas below.

This mechanism fails to account for a continuous supply of volatiles unless it also provides for a continuous generation of new, volatile-rich magmas. Possibly such local magmas form by a continuous process of selective fusion of subcrustal rocks, to a depth of several hundred kilometers below the more mobile areas of the crust. This would imply that the volume of the ocean has grown with time. On this point, geologic evidence permits differences of interpretation; the record admittedly does not prove, but it seems consistent with, an increasing growth of the continental masses and a progressive sinking of oceanic basins. Perhaps something like the following mechanism could account for a continuous escape of volatiles to the earth's surface and a relatively uniform composition of sea water through much of geologic time: (1) selective fusion of lower-melting fractions from deep-seated, nearly anhydrous rocks beneath the unstable continental margins and geosynclines; (2) rise of these selected fractions (as granitic and hydrous magmas) and their slow crystallization nearer the surface; (3) essentially continuous isostatic readjustment between the differentiating continental masses and adjacent ocean basins; and (4) renewed erosion and sedimentation, with resulting instability of continental margins and mountainous areas and a new round of selective fusion below.

22

Chemical Events on the Primitive Earth

PHILIP H. ABELSON
1966

From *Proceedings of the National Academy of Sciences*, vol. 55, pp. 1365–1372, 1966. Reprinted with permission of the author and the National Academy of Sciences.

During the past 15 years, many workers employing a variety of energy sources have demonstrated the abiologic production of a large number of biologically interesting substances from many simple starting materials. Most of the experiments, however, have had a curious deficiency. While designed to elucidate origin of life on earth, they do not take into account a body of geologic information.

In this paper the nature of the primitive atmosphere and ocean is considered in the light of geologic and geophysical information. The hypothesis of an early methane-ammonia atmosphere is found to be without solid foundation and indeed is contraindicated. Geologists favor an alternative view—that genesis of air and oceans is a result of planetary outgassing. Some consequences of this view are examined. Volatiles from outgassing interacted with the alkaline crust to form an ocean having a pH 8–9 and to produce an atmosphere consisting of CO, CO_2, N_2, and H_2. Radiation interacting with such a mixture yields HCN as a principal product. Ultraviolet irradiation of HCN solutions at pH 8–9 yields amino acids and other important substances of biologic interest.

The nature of the earth's environment limited the kinds of compounds that might have accumulated in a soup. Arguments concerning feasible components support the view that amino acids and proteins preceded sugars and nucleic acids.

If the methane-ammonia hypothesis were correct, there should be geochemical evidence supporting it. What is the evidence for a primitive methane-ammonia atmosphere on earth? The answer is that there is *no* evidence for it, but much against it. The methane-ammonia hypothesis is in major trouble with respect to the ammonia component, for ammonia on the primitive earth would have quickly disappeared.

The effective threshold for degradation by ultraviolet radiation is 2,250 A. A quantity of ammonia equivalent to present atmospheric nitrogen would be destroyed in ~30,000 years.

Small amounts of ammonia would be reformed, but this process is unimportant in comparison to the destruction.

If large amounts of methane had ever been present in the earth's atmosphere, geologic evidence for it should also be available. Laboratory experiments show that one consequence of irradiating a dense, highly reducing atmosphere is the production of hydrophobic organic molecules which are adsorbed by sedimenting clays. The earliest rocks should contain an unusually large proportion of carbon or organic chemicals. This is not the case.

The composition of the present atmosphere with respect to the gases neon, argon, krypton, and xenon is crucial. Neon is present on earth to an extent about 10^{-10} that of cosmic abundance [1], and similarly argon, krypton, and xenon are relatively absent. It seems likely that if xenon of atomic weight 130 could not accumulate, other volatile light constituents such as hydrogen, nitrogen, methane, and carbon monoxide would also be lost at the same time. The concept that the earth had a dense methane-ammonia atmosphere is not supported by geochemistry, and it is contraindicated by the scarcity of xenon and krypton in our present atmosphere.

Understanding the evolution of our present atmosphere does not require *ad hoc* assumptions. Geological evidence suggests that the atmosphere evolved as a result of outgassing of the earth. This process has been discussed by a number of investigators, including Rubey [2, 3], Holland [4], and Berkner and Marshall [5].

The geologic record shows that volcanism and associated outgassing have been going on for more than 3,000 million years. Rubey [2] has emphasized that the composition of volcanic gases is similar to that of the volatile substances that must be accounted for at or near the surface of the earth. These major volatile substances are H_2O, $16{,}700 \times 10^{20}$ gm; C as CO_2, 921×10^{20} gm; and N_2, 43×10^{20} gm.

Studies of the composition of volcanic gases by Shepherd and others have shown that water and CO_2 are the major volatiles produced by outgassing. These gases are accompanied by a significant amount of reducing potential in the form of hydrogen. One can estimate the amount of reducing power brought to the surface of the earth through outgassing by making a balance sheet of the oxidized and reduced chemicals in the atmosphere, biosphere, and sedimentary rocks. This estimate does not take into account gain or loss of hydrogen from the top of the atmosphere.

Most of the carbon is present in sedimentary rocks as carbonate. Part is also present as reduced carbon. Rubey estimates that the organic carbon has a composition 68×10^{20} gm C, 25×10^{20} gm O, and 9.6×10^{20} gm H. To burn this material to $CO_2 + H_2O$ would require 235×10^{20} gm O_2.

Most of the organic carbon present in the sediments appears to have been derived from photosynthetic organisms, presumably forming organic matter from $CO_2 + H_2O$. In the process, 235×10^{20} gm O_2 would be liberated. Hutchinson [6] points out that the quantity of atmospheric and fossilized oxygen that can be recognized is much less than this. Assuming that all the sulfate of the sea and the sediments represents oxidized sulfide and that oxygen has been fossilized in the production of ferric from ferrous iron, he calculates the total free and fossil oxygen to be

Free in atmosphere	12×10^{20} gm
Sulfate in sea and sediments	47×10^{20} gm
As ferric iron derived from ferrous	14×10^{20} gm
Total	73×10^{20} gm

This leaves 162×10^{20} gm O_2 to be accounted for. Rubey [2] suggested that the most probable explanation for the discrepancy is that an appreciable amount of the carbon released from volcanoes was in the form CO. Hutchinson points out that other reducing gases such as H_2 are also possible, and cites Cotton [7].

One can estimate the nature of the reducing gases. The major amount of magma accompanying volcanism is basaltic in composition and contains ferrous silicates. Holland [4] has provided an estimate of the equilibrium relations between H_2O and basalt, and CO_2 and basalt, using a simplified system which approaches basalt in composition. His calculation is based on the quaternary invariant point in the system MgO-FeO-Fe_2O_3-SiO_2 at 1255°C. At this temperature and an estimated P_{O_2} of $10^{-7.1}$ atm, $P_{H_2O}/P_{H_2} = 105$ and $P_{CO_2}/P_{CO} = 37$.

These ratios correspond to values observed at Kilauea by Eaton and Murata [8], which were $P_{H_2O}/P_{H_2} = 137$ and $P_{CO_2}/P_{CO} = 31$. Assuming that the discrepancy in the balance sheet for oxygen can be accounted for by H_2 and CO emitted from volcanoes, and using Holland's estimate of the ratios of P_{H_2O}/P_{H_2} and P_{CO_2}/P_{CO}, one can obtain values for the amounts of these gases which have reached the surface during outgassing. The values are H_2, 19×10^{20} gm, and CO, 17×10^{20} gm.

One can obtain another estimate for the amounts of H_2 and CO using the known amounts of volatiles now at the surface and the ratios of H_2O/H_2 and CO_2/CO quoted by Holland. The values obtained by these different routes are H_2, 16×10^{20} gm, and CO, 14×10^{20} gm. Thus the amounts of H_2 and CO accompanying the water and CO_2 are of the right magnitude to account for the reduced carbonaceous matter found in the sedimentary rocks.

The nature of the primitive atmosphere was to a large degree determined by the ocean-atmosphere interaction, and the pH of the primitive ocean is crucial. Most of the present components of the crust probably reached the surface in the form of basalt. The igneous rocks gradually disintegrate in the presence of water to form partially ionized products. In effect, silicate minerals are salts of strong bases and weak acids, and in dissolving form mildly alkaline solutions. If pulverized basalt is added to water, the pH immediately rises to about 9.6 [9].

Within a short time after outgassing began, there would be sufficient water to form extensive lakes. Rainstorms would begin to occur, accompanied by a weathering process which would bring alkaline waters back to the lakes. These rivers would carry Na^+, Ca^{++}, and clay minerals much as do the rivers of today. These waters would have a pH somewhat less than 9.6, for their pH would be lowered toward 8 by CO_2 and other acid gases. During the initial phases of weathering, the pH of the ocean may have been higher than it is today. At present only about 28 per cent of the surface is available for weathering and most of the continental exposures are sedimentary rocks. These are not so alkaline as are basalts. Sillén [10] has emphasized the buffering capacity of the huge amounts of silicates that have been weathered. The buffering system of weathered silicates and ocean has tended to maintain the pH of the ocean at about 8–9 since outgassing began.

The major products of outgassing were quickly removed from the atmosphere. Water condensed, CO_2 was dissolved in water and converted to carbonate, and other acid gases were converted to nonvolatile salts. The residual gases to be accounted for are CO, N_2 and H_2. The oceanic buffering system affected the distribution of CO. Carbon monoxide is slightly soluble in water and slowly reacts to produce formic acid [11].

The equilibrium between carbon monoxide in the atmosphere and in the ocean is governed by

$$CO_{(g)} + \overline{OH} \rightleftarrows \overline{HCO}_{2(aq)} \qquad \Delta F = -9.6 \text{ kcal.}$$

Most CO would be converted to formate.

Assuming that the proportions of volatiles have not changed with time and that $16{,}600 \times 10^{20}$ gm H_2O and 17×10^{20} gm CO have reached the surface, the concentration of formate would amount to 0.035 *M*. If the reducing capacity represented by the H_2 were employed in producing CO, the initial concentration of formate might have been as great as 0.6 *M*. Correspondingly, the partial pressure of CO could have been as high as 0.06 atm.

Water vapor was another important component of the atmosphere. Its partial pressure at low altitudes was determined largely by the atmospheric temperature at the surface of the earth. The amount of water vapor at high altitudes was governed by the temperature profile above the earth. It is likely that the temperature of the primitive atmosphere decreased rapidly with height to reach a minimum. In the present atmosphere the temperature distribution is complicated by the effects of oxygen and ozone. The temperature drops from 289°K at the surface to 214°K at 14 km, then rises due to effects of ozone before dropping again to 178°K at 86 km [12]. In the primitive atmosphere with little oxygen present, there was only one temperature minimum. Very low temperatures might have been reached at altitudes not much greater than 20 km. This low-temperature region would limit the fraction of moisture in the region above the temperature minimum.

Most of the nitrogen that has reached the

surface of earth is now in the atmosphere. From a small value the nitrogen content has gradually increased to its present amount.

Hydrogen is an important component of volcanic gases. Its abundance in the atmosphere would be governed in part by hydrogen escape, which is sharply dependent on the temperature at the top of the atmosphere. The abundance of hydrogen would also be governed by chemistry occurring at the top of the atmosphere. This too is influenced by temperature. A well-considered calculation of the temperature of the ionosphere of the primitive earth would be an important contribution. However, that is beyond the scope of this paper. Crude guidance is obtained from measurements of the present atmosphere. Above the minimum at 86 km, temperatures rise to 800°K at 140 km, 1200°K at 180 km, and to higher temperatures, e.g., ~1500°K, above that. In a primitive atmosphere possessing a different composition, the temperature would not be the same. However, at the top of the atmosphere where energetic radiations from the sun impinge and where chemical events of interest occur, the temperature would have been elevated.

The reaction $CO_2 + H_2 \rightleftharpoons CO + H_2O$ is of importance. At 25°C this reaction has a $\Delta F = +6.831$ kcal [13]. However, at such temperatures the equilibrium time is about 10^{20} years. At 1200°K the reaction proceeds rapidly [14] and $\Delta F = \sim 0$.

The composition of gases at the top of the atmosphere was governed by thermodynamic relationships existing at the higher temperatures. It was also influenced by the action of the cold trap in limiting the partial pressure of H_2O. These conditions combined to favor production of CO from $CO_2 + H_2$. As a result, carbon monoxide was at one time a major component of the earth's atmosphere.

Above the earth the principal agent causing radiation-induced transformations is ultraviolet radiation and this acts at the top of the atmosphere where temperatures are high. An electric discharge producing high temperatures and short ultraviolet radiation provides a situation qualitatively similar to the terrestrial circumstances. By conducting the discharge in a vessel with a cold trap, one can improve the similarity to nature. The cold trap maintains a low partial pressure of H_2O and serves to remove complex molecules produced by radiation.

To obtain an indication of the kinds of chemicals that might be synthesized, Dr. T. C. Hoering and I have conducted experiments under such conditions. Starting mixtures, with pressures measured in centimeters of Hg, were (1) N_2, 8; CO, 8; H_2, 2; (2) N_2, 4; CO, 4; H_2, 4; (3) N_2, 2; CO, 4; H_2, 6; (4) N_2, 2; CO, 4; H_2, 24. The principal product formed in the last three mixtures was HCN and H_2O. Small amounts of CH_4 and CO_2 were also made. In the first mixture, CO_2 was the major product, with HCN and H_2O second. The products were analyzed by T. C. Hoering in a mass spectrometer. Thus it was simple to look for formaldehyde and for the unexpected. No formaldehyde was detected, which meant that if made, it was present in amounts no more than about 10^{-3} those of HCN. Similarly, other products such as nitriles, acids, and hydrocarbons would have been seen. When hydrogen is not present, the principal products from $N_2 + CO$ or CO alone are CO_2 and C_3O_2. This reaction was studied by Harteck, Groth, and Faltings [15]. We also studied other mixtures. If the cold finger is not refrigerated, water is present in the gas phase. Yields of interesting products such as HCN are small. In summary, irradiation of a variety of mixtures of CO, N_2, H_2 produces HCN as the major product and little else except C_3O_2, CO_2, and H_2O.

In the natural situation any formaldehyde would tend to be destroyed. CH_2O is unstable and it decomposes to $CO + H_2$. The reaction is rapid at 500°C [16]. Formaldehyde if produced at the top of the atmosphere would not survive the temperatures or radiation there; CH_2O is decomposed by quanta of wavelengths as long as 3650 A [17].

Any surviving formaldehyde which reached the alkaline ocean would be subject to further attenuation. Formaldehyde undergoes disproportionation to methyl alcohol plus formic acid. In addition, CH_2O reacts rapidly with HCN, amines, and amino acids at room temperatures at pH 8–9. Experiments made in the last century showed that formaldehyde in lime water yields sugarlike substances. Suppose that a small amount of a carbohydrate were formed. This product would also be subject to rapid degradation and attenuation. First there is the well-known browning reaction. In addition, carbohydrates such as glucose combine readily with amina acids to form nonbiologic products. This reaction proceeds at room temperature, and even at 0°C there is a noticeable reaction in a week. At pH 8–9, amino acids and free carbohydrates are simply incompatible. Reaction between them leaves whatever is present in excess. As will be seen, synthesis of amino acids is relatively much more favored than synthesis of carbohydrates. In addition, substances such as glycine and alanine are very stable and hence could accumulate. Thus it is unlikely that the primitive ocean ever contained more than traces of free glucose, free ribose, or deoxyribose.

This discussion of limitations on the production and preservation is illustrative of similar arguments which can be made with respect to important constituents of any primitive "thick soup." For instance, arginine is adsorbed by sedimentary clay as are chlorophyll and prophyrins. Fatty acids form insoluble salts with magnesium and calcium, and hence would be removed from the soup. At least five major factors limit the kinds of compounds that might have accumulated in the primitive ocean.

First, there are limitations on what can be made by inorganic means; second, all organic matter degrades spontaneously with time; third, some substances are readily destroyed by radiation; fourth, many compounds would have been removed from the ocean by precipitation or absorption; fifth, there are serious chemical incompatibilities among the constituents of living matter, and some of the components of the soup would react to form nonbiologic substances. In view of these limitations, one is challenged to seek a series of steps toward life that are compatible with the environment.

What kind of prebiologic chemistry is there that can occur at ordinary temperatures, in dilute solutions at pH 8.0? How can one form carbon-carbon bonds under these circumstances? Among simple substances, three methods are notably feasible. One is condensation of aldehydes. A second is condensation of aldehydes with HCN. A third is polymerization of HCN. I have indicated that formaldehyde would not be produced in quantity and it is easily destroyed. In contrast HCN can be readily produced and is stable at high temperatures. In slightly alkaline solution, HCN combines with itself to yield a number of interesting compounds.

The reactions involved are importantly sensitive to pH. Thus a 1 *M* solution of HCN having a pH 4.6 will not polymerize. Polymerization does not occur at very high pH. However, the reaction proceeds well at pH 8–9. Thus the range of pH likely in the primitive ocean is also a favorable one for polymerization of HCN. With solutions 0.1 *M* in HCN + cyanide, the reaction occurs rapidly at 100°C, more slowly at 25°C. A major product is the tetramer:

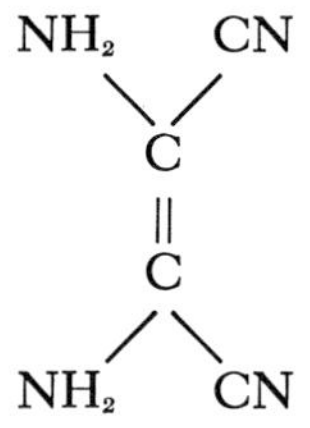

This reaction has long been known, and it has further been found that on hydrolysis this tetramer gives small yields of glycine. Oró and Kamat [18] have also noted production of small amounts of alanine and aspartic acid when 2.2 *M* cyanide solutions were heated at 70°C for 25 days.

Production of glycine from HCN has been noted in this laboratory. However, yields can be strikingly improved by radiation, and polymerization of dilute cyanide solutions can be made to occur at ambient temperatures. When solutions containing HCN at pH 8–9 are irradiated with 2,536-Å radiation and the product mixture is hydrolyzed, glycine, alanine, serine, aspartic acid, and glutamic acid result. The relative yields of the acids depend on time of irradiation. With short irradiations, yields are low and glycine is prominent. With longer times, yields are better and the larger amino acids are more prominent. At very long times, yields decrease. The ultraviolet radiation speeds the polymerization of HCN and, in view of the products obtained, must cause internal rearrangements including disproportionation. Production of amino acids from solutions 0.002–0.10 *M* in cyanide have been noted. After irradiation the solutions were hydrolyzed with 6 *M* HCl. The resultant amino acids were determined by E. Hare using an amino acid analyzer. In one instance, 1 mmole HCN gave rise to the following amounts of amino acids (μmole): 30.0 gly, 3.5 ser, 0.9 ala, 0.8 asp.

Others have studied the production of interesting substances from cyanide. These include Oró [19], who produced adenine. Additional important roles involving cyanide and its products have been discovered. From irradiation of aqueous HCN, cyanamide is produced [20]. Cyanamide in turn has the important facility of bringing about peptide synthesis from amino acids in dilute solution under the influence of ultraviolet radiation [21, 22]. Other dehydrating reactions of great biologic interest are also facilitated in a similar way [23].

One difficulty that must be considered is that HCN is subject to hydrolysis. The rate of reaction is such that HCN decomposes to $NH_4OH + HCOOH$ in about 10 years at 25°C and about 70 years at 15°C [24]. At the same time, the production of HCN is limited. Assuming formation of cyanide requires photolysis of nitrogen, and assuming an over-all efficiency of 10 per cent of the quanta available, one obtains a production rate of the order of 4×10^{14} gm/year. Even in the early stages of the ocean when the volume was less than, e.g., 10^{22} ml, the resultant solution would be quite dilute ($\sim 10^{-4}$ *M* in HCN).

A dehydrating mechanism for resynthesis of HCN might have been available. We have already seen one example. It is possible that silicates could do the job even better. The energy involved in dehydration reactions is in the range 0 to perhaps 10 kcal/mole. On the other hand, typical quanta of visible light represent $\sim$50 kcal/mole. If visible light were harnessed to reform HCN from NH_4COOH, a large amount of HCN would be available for synthetic activities.

Formate would be a consequence of volcanic outgassing. The ammonia produced by hydrolysis of HCN would be available for recycling. As an example, let us examine the production of serine. The net chemical reaction is

$$5HCN + 7H_2O \rightarrow \underset{\text{Serine}}{C_3H_7O_3N} + 4NH_3 + 2CO_2.$$

If the dehydration system were working, the product ammonia would be combined with more formate.

Given a dehydration mechanism utilizing cyanamide or some other agent, the step to an enzyme is relatively short. Eck and Dayhoff [25] have developed some interesting arguments about ferredoxin which are relevant.

Ferredoxin is an unusually simple protein containing only 55 amino acid residues. It occurs in primitive anaerobic organisms, both photosynthetic and nonphotosynthetic. The functions of ferredoxin are basic to cell chemistry. The enzyme participates in oxidation, reduction, energy transfer, fixation of nitrogen, formation of ATP, and synthesis of pyruvate [26].

Eck and Dayhoff have made an analysis of amino acid content and structure of the enzyme. They find that it contains an unusual proportion of glycine, alanine, serine, aspartic acid, and cysteine. From a study of the sequence of amino acids in ferrodoxin, the authors are led to the conclusion that the original molecule was based on a repeating sequence of alanine, serine, aspartic acid, and glycine. These amino acids are those which are produced most readily from HCN.

When one examines the processes of biosynthesis, he is impressed by how few mechanisms and basic building blocks are involved. Pyruvate, acetate, and carbonate are key chemicals in the synthesis of amino acids. In some microorganisms these three sources can furnish almost all the carbon in serine, glycine, cysteine, alanine, valine, leucine, isoleucine, lysine, aspartic acid, threonine, methionine, glutamic acid, proline, [and] arginine. All three of these carbon sources were present in the primitive ocean. Pyruvate and acetate result from degradation of serine. Snell [27] points out that the reaction

$$\underset{\text{Serine}}{CH_2OHCHNH_2COOH} + H_2O \rightarrow \underset{\text{Pyruvate}}{CH_3COCOOH} + NH_3$$

proceeds to the right. From pyruvate and from malonic acid, acetate can be derived.

The principal processes required to synthesize the 14 amino acids are condensations (such as those involving pyruvate, carbonate, and acetate in the Krebs cycle), hydrogenation, and transfer of NH_3. Furthermore, given condensation and hydrogenation, one has a mechanism for producing fatty acids. Formate would be a convenient source of hydrogen. Simple receptors for solar radiation might have helped speed the condensation reactions. Thus one can visualize that natural conditions might have favored synthesis of increasingly complex molecules from the simple but versatile substances available.

REFERENCES AND NOTES

1. Harrison Brown, in *The Atmospheres of the Earth and Planets* (Chicago: University of Chicago Press, 1952), p. 258.
2. W. W. Rubey, *Geol. Soc. America Bull.*, v. 62, p. 1111 (1951).
3. W. W. Rubey, *Geol. Soc. America Spec. Paper* 62, p. 631 (1955).
4. H. D. Holland, in *Petrologic Studies—A Volume in Honor of A. F. Buddington*, ed. A. E. J. Engel, H. L. James, and B. F. Leonard (Boulder, Colo.: Geological Society of America, 1962), p. 447.
5. L. V. Berkner and L. C. Marshall, *Jour. Atmos. Sci.*, v. 22, p. 225 (1965).
6. G. E. Hutchinson, in *The Earth as a Planet*, ed. G. P. Kuiper (Chicago: The University of Chicago Press, 1954), p. 371.
7. C. A. Cotton, *Nature*, v. 154, p. 399 (1944).
8. J. P. Easton and K. J. Murata, *Science*, v. 132, p. 925 (1960).
9. For a discussion of the *p*H of water in contact with silicate minerals, see R. E. Stevens and M. K. Carron, *Am. Mineralogist*, v. 33, p. 31 (1944).
10. L. G. Sillen, in *Oceanography* (AAAS Pub. 67), ed. Mary Sears (Washington, D.C.: American Association for the Advancement of Science, 1961), p. 549.
11. G. E. K. Branch, *Am. Chem. Soc. Jour.*, v. 37, p. 2316 (1915).
12. International Council of Scientific Unions, Committee on Space Research, *COSPAR International Reference Atmosphere*, 1961, compiled by H. Kallmann-Bijl et al. (Amsterdam: North-Holland Publishing Co., 1961).
13. *JANAF* (Joint Army–Navy–Air Force) *Interim Thermochemical Tables* (Midland, Michigan: Thermal Laboratory, The Dow Chemical Co., 1960), v. 1 and 2.
14. W. M. Graven and F. J. Long, *Am. Chem. Soc. Jour.*, v. 76, p. 2602 (1954).
15. P. Harteck, W. Groth, and K. Faltins, *Zeitschr. Elektrochemie*, v. 44, p. 621 (1938).
16. C. J. M. Fletcher, *Royal Soc. [London] Proc.*, ser. A, v. 146, p. 357 (1934).
17. Carleton Ellis and A. A. Wells, *The Chemical Action of Ultraviolet Rays* (revised and enlarged edition by F. F. Heyroth) (New York: Reinhold Publishing Corp., 1941), p. 417.
18. J. Oro and S. S. Jamat, *Nature*, v. 190, p. 442 (1961).
19. J. Oro, *Nature*, v. 191, p. 1193 (1961).
20. A. Schimpl, R. M. Lemmon, and M. Calvin, *Science*, v. 147, p. 149 (1965).
21. G. Steinman, R. M. Lemmon, and M. Calvin, *Science*, v. 147, p. 1574 (1965).
22. C. Ponnamperuma and E. Peterson, *Science*, v. 147, p. 1572 (1965).
23. G. Steinman, R. M. Lemmon, and M. Calvin, *[U.S.] Natl. Acad. Sci. Proc.* v. 52, p. 27 (1964).
24. A. L. Peiker, thesis presented to the Graduate Committee, Trinity College, June, 1927 cited in V. K. Krieble, F. C. Duennebier, and E. Colton, *Am. Chem. Soc. Jour.*, v. 65, p. 1479 (1943).
25. R. V. Eck and M. O. Dayhoff, *Science*, v. 152, p. 363 (1966).
26. D. I. Arnon, *Science*, v. 149, p. 1460 (1965).
27. E. E. Snell, in *The Origins of Prebiological Systems and of Their Molecular Matrices*, ed. Sidney W. Fox (New York: Academic Press, 1965), p. 203.

23

The Coriolis Effect

ARTHUR N. STRAHLER

1963

Abridgement of pp. 32–34, including fig. 2.17, 2.18, and 13.9 on p. 231, from *The Earth Sciences* by Arthur N. Strahler.

Perhaps the most remarkable of the persistent physical effects resulting from the earth's rotation is the tendency of all particles of matter in motion on the earth's surface to be deflected toward the right with respect to their compass direction of motion in the Northern Hemisphere and toward the left in the Southern Hemisphere. Termed the *Coriolis effect*, after the nineteenth-century French mathematician G. G. Coriolis, who first analyzed it, the phenomenon is not a simple mechanical force, such as gravitation or centripetal force, but rather the apparent, or fictitious, effect of a number of forces that act upon any particle set in motion on the earth's spherical surface.

Without attempting to give a full mathematical explanation, two basic aspects of the deflective effect can be considered in order to gain some understanding of the causes. To begin with, Newton's first law of motion states that, when any particle is set in motion, it will follow a straight line unless compelled to change its path by some external force. In this case the straight-line path is fixed in space with respect to the stars. Now, there is no place on the surface of the turning globe where a horizontal path of travel of finite length can maintain its geographic orientation with respect to the parallels and meridians and at the same time remain fixed in space. To show why adherence to the first law of motion tends to result in a turning of a moving particle toward the right of its initial path, a large globe and a long piece of string can be used as a demonstration apparatus (Figure 23.1). Attach the string to a point across the room, some 20 or 30 feet away. Holding the string taut, place the free end so as to touch the globe on, say, the 40th parallel of latitude as designated by P_1 in Figure 23.1. The string must be exactly tangent to the selected parallel and must lie in the same plane as the parallel. When so fixed, the string represents a true eastward compass direction, which is the desired initial direction of motion, but it is also in the plane of a great circle tangent to the parallel. Mark on the globe a segment of line, designated 1 in the enlarged diagram of Figure 23.1, representing a travel distance of, say, 300 miles. Next place the end of the string at P_2, the end of the first segment, and rotate the globe eastward through 5° of longitude, then add a second line segment in the new compass direction taken by the taut string. Repeat this operation until the globe has rotated through 30°. The six segments of line will represent very crudely the type of curved path taken by the object as it attempts to maintain its original direction in space at the same time that it is following a horizontal path on the earth's surface to which it is held by gravity. The experiment can be repeated at any northern latitude and with any initial starting direction. It will yield the same result: a travel path curving to the right of the initial direction of motion. In the Southern Hemisphere a curving to the left of the direction of initial motion will result; along the equator, whether due eastward or westward no tendency will be found for the path to curve either left or right. The actual path followed by a moving object subjected to normal frictional forces is only very slightly curved compared with the demonstration path. Only an earth satellite free of the frictional effect of the earth's atmosphere will hold the plane of its path fixed in space as the earth turns beneath it.

Whereas the foregoing analysis has been solely one of the geometry of lines generated by moving points, the second principle involved in the Coriolis effect concerns masses in motion. It is a requirement of dynamics of moving masses that the *angular momentum* of any object moving over the surface of the rotating earth be maintained constant, provided that no outside forces are applied. The principle may be demonstrated by tying a small weight to a piece of string and then starting the weight swinging in a circle in such a way that the string wraps itself around your finger, shortening the radius continuously until the string is all wound up. (Do not add to this motion once it has been started.) Notice that, as the string shortens, the rate of turning speeds up rapidly, even though no added impulse has been given. Now, the angular momentum of the moving weight is equal to the

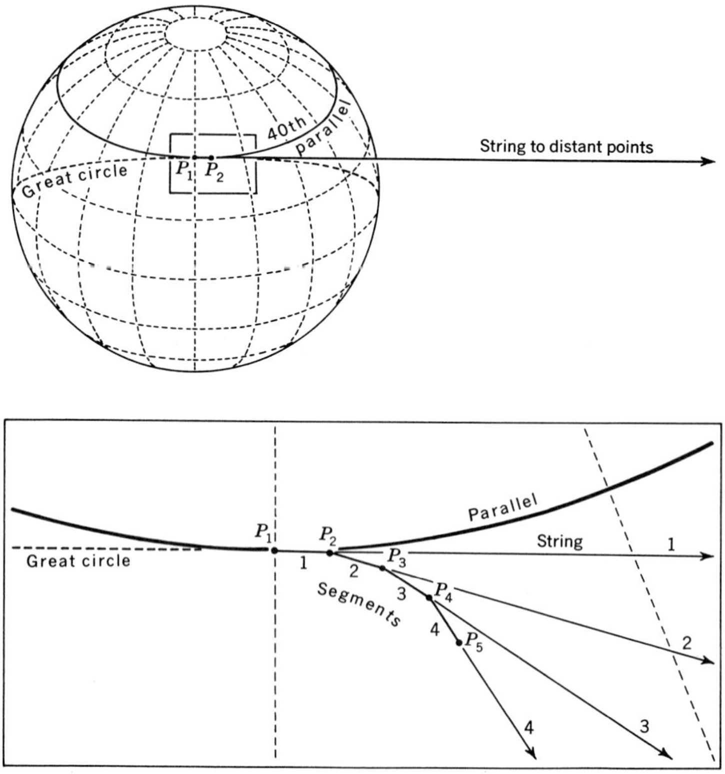

FIGURE 23.1
Eastward deflection of a moving object due to earth rotation

product of its mass, radius of turning, and linear velocity in the circular path. Because the momentum must remain constant if no outside forces are brought to bear, the linear velocity of the weight must increase as the radius shortens.

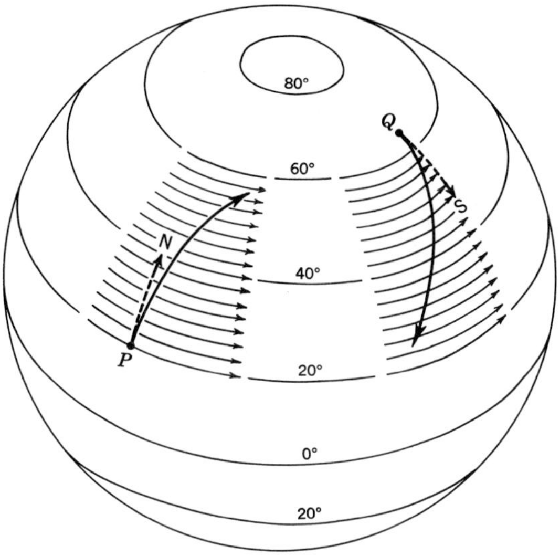

FIGURE 23.2
The Coriolis effect. An object starting northward from *P* will cross parallels of progressively lower linear velocities, whereas an object starting southward from *Q* will cross progressively faster moving parallels.

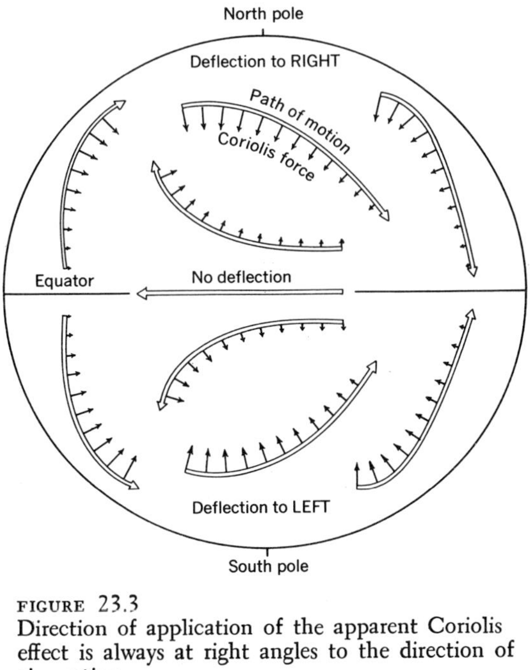

FIGURE 23.3
Direction of application of the apparent Coriolis effect is always at right angles to the direction of air motion.

Apply this principle of conservation of angular momentum to an object moving northward along a meridian in the Northern Hemisphere, that is, toward higher latitudes (Figure 23.2). Suppose that the particle is given a starting impulse due north from point *P*. As the particle travels northward, it crosses successively smaller circles of latitude, which means that the radius of its rotation is becoming shorter. To maintain its angular momentum, the particle must increase its velocity, and it therefore travels eastward faster than the parallels of latitude over which it is moving. Its actual path will therefore be curved toward the right. If the initial direction of travel is south from point *Q* (Figure 23.2), the radius of the circle of motion of the particle becomes longer as it crosses successively larger parallels. The particle therefore slows down and lags behind the earth. The path is again curved, and there is also a turning to the right when one faces in the direction of the motion. In the Southern Hemisphere the curvature will be to the left.

The effect of the principle of momentum conservation is at its maximum for motion in a north-south direction, but becomes less effective as the direction changes toward east-west, and will be zero for east-west motion following a parallel of latitude.

Two variables affect the magnitude of the Coriolis effect acting on a given mass: linear velocity and latitude. The effect increases directly with velocity, so that, if velocity is doubled, the deflecting effect is doubled. The effect varies in intensity from zero on the equator to a maximum at either pole (Figure 23.3), the relation to latitude being mathematically the same as that for the increase in rate of turning of the Foucault pendulum with latitude; that is, the effect is directly proportional to the sine of the latitude. . . . A third cause of variation could be a change in angular velocity of rotation, but in the case of the earth this rate is a constant. The following equation expresses the factors controlling the Coriolis effect as an acceleration in units of centimeters per second squared:

$$\text{Coriolis effect} = V\, 2\Omega \sin \phi$$

where V is the linear velocity in centimeters per second, Ω is the angular velocity of rotation in radians per second, and ϕ is the latitude in degrees.

24

The Circulation of the Atmosphere

EDWARD N. LORENZ
1966

From *American Scientist*, vol. 54, no. 4, pp. 402–420, 1966. Reprinted with permission of the author and the Society of the Sigma Xi.

If a fluid is subjected to non-uniform heating, a circulation will ordinarily develop. One of the problems of greatest concern to the fluid dynamicist is that of deducing from the basic laws of physics the circulation which will take place in a particular fluid system when it is heated in a particular fashion. Even for some of the simplest systems—for example, a tank of water insulated on the bottom and sides and cooled at the top—the problem is but partially solved.

The atmosphere itself is a special fluid, and it is heated more strongly by the sun in equatorial and tropical latitudes than in temperate and especially polar latitudes. It must therefore possess a circulation. One of the dreams of the theoretical meteorologist has been the deduction of this circulation from basic principles, given such quantities as the mass, radius, and angular velocity of the earth, the total mass and composition of the atmosphere, and the intensity and spectral distribution of the radiation from the sun.

Actually there is some question as to whether the meteorologist can really deduce the circulation. He could undoubtedly do so if he could determine the general solution of the mathematical equations which represent the physical laws. But the exact equations are too complicated to be handled by any known method, and some simplifying approximations are essential. The meteorologist is already familiar with the general features of the circulation, and this knowledge will in all probability influence him in choosing among the many available approximations. For example, in many theoretical studies the complete three-dimensional distribution of the atmospheric variables—presure, temperature, wind, moisture—is represented by the two-dimensional distributions of these variables at a few chosen levels, the values occurring between these levels being obtained by interpolation. But the number and spacing of the levels is generally based upon previous knowledge of the true atmospheric structure. In view of such circumstances, many meteorologists regard their task as that of explaining or accounting for the circulation as it is observed, rather than deducing it from basic considerations.

Before we consider how one might account for the observed circulation, let us attempt to put ourselves on a more nearly equal footing with the theoretical meteorologist by looking at some of its principal features. One of the first things to be noticed is that the total circulation is composed of identifiable circulation systems of widely differing horizontal scales. We shall first examine some of the smaller-scale systems, and then progress toward the larger ones.

Perhaps the smallest-scale system to be dignified by a special name is the dust devil. These whirling columns of dust-laden air typically reach heights of a few hundred feet, but over hot deserts they sometimes extend half a mile upward. The dust serves only to make them visible; vortices of this size often form where no dust is available, and presumably many such vortices are invisible for each one which can be seen. If a person should be struck by one, he would probably experience nothing more than a sudden gust of wind. In fact, when an unexpected gust is encountered, it is frequently a portion of a dustless dust devil. The opposing motion a few yards away may remain undetected.

Despite their general inconsequential effect upon human activity, these small systems are so numerous that collectively they comprise a significant element in the total circulation of the atmosphere. Their most obvious motion is rotary, but they also contain powerful upward currents. The dust which they raise will fall back to the ground when the circulation wanes, but in the meantime they are an effective mechanism for conveying heat from the ground to higher levels.

Occurring in many sizes, but ordinarily larger than dust devils, are cumulus clouds. Within and directly underneath the clouds the currents are mainly upward, and the compensating downward currents occur largely in and directly below the drier spaces between the clouds. Particularly in tropical latitudes, cumulus cloud circulations are one of the principal mechanisms for conveying water from the earth's surface up to higher levels in the atmosphere.

The most fully developed cumiliform clouds, the cumulonimbus, generally contain showers, and often thunderstorms. In extreme cases they are ten miles deep. In that event hail is likely, and tornado funnels may reach from the main cloud mass down to the ground.

The tornado bears a superficial resemblance to the dust devil, but the energy for maintaining it appears to come from the cloud above rather than the ground below. It is the most violent of storms, and has received much study because of its devastating effect upon human life and property. Nevertheless, tornadoes are not a very important element in the total circulation simply because there are so few of them; if a gram of air could be picked at random from the atmosphere, the probability that it would be taken from a tornado is about one in 10^{12}.

Individual cumulus clouds are seldom randomly distributed, but tend to be organized into systems of larger scale. Figure 24.1 is a photograph of a radar scope, showing a long line of thunderstorms extending across eastern Oklahoma. The display is arranged in the form of a map, the location of the radar being represented by the center of the large bright spot. The line extending northward from this spot is a reference line. The storms appear to the southeast.

Ordinary clouds, whose droplets are typically a hundredth of a millimeter or so in diameter, are transparent to radar rays. Only those clouds containing raindrops (or snowflakes, or hailstones), whose diameters often exceed a millimeter, show up on the scope. This particular scope is designed so that different intensities of the reflected radar signal, resulting from different intensities of rain, show up as different shadings. The brightest spots within the line indicate the heaviest rain—in this case, thunderstorms. About twenty of these storms are organized into a line about two hundred miles long.

Lines of thunderstorms or heavy rain frequently form portions of still larger systems. Figure 24.2 is another radar photograph, which shows a tropical hurricane as it strikes southern Florida. The bright areas are again rain, but this radar does not differentiate between intensities. The dry central eye is plainly visible. Surrounding it is a very wet eye wall composed of towering cumulonimbus clouds, and a complex of spiral rain bands whose individual structures are somewhat like that of the line shown in Figure 24.1.

Photographing complete storms in visible light has recently been made possible by the satellite. Figure 24.3 shows a storm over the north Atlantic. The area covered by the photograph is nearly a thousand miles square. The storm, which is not of tropical origin, looks very much like the tropical storm of Figure 24.2. It should be noted, however, that in Figure 24.3 we are seeing clouds rather than rain. We may assume that rain is falling from some of the heavier clouds, but altogether the storm contains far less water than its tropical counterpart.

To display a larger system in a single picture we may combine information obtained from different geographical locations. Some interesting results have been obtained by piecing together successive photographs from a single satellite, but most of our composite descriptions of the atmosphere are in the form of weather maps.

Figure 24.4 is a northern hemisphere map for a particular late winter day. The lines are isobars—lines of constant pressure, after the pressure has been reduced to sea level by a standard procedure. The relation between the pressure field and the field of motion is given to a first approximation by the geostrophic wind law. This law, which is often lesson number one to the meteorology student, states that the air moves parallel to the isobars, traveling clockwise about a high pressure area and counterclockwise about a low pressure area in the northern hemisphere, and in the opposite sense in the southern hemisphere. The direction of the geostrophic wind at sea level is indicated in Figure 24.4 by arrows attached to the isobars.

Those who have had experience with nonrotating fluids may be more familiar with motion at right angles to the isobars, toward lower

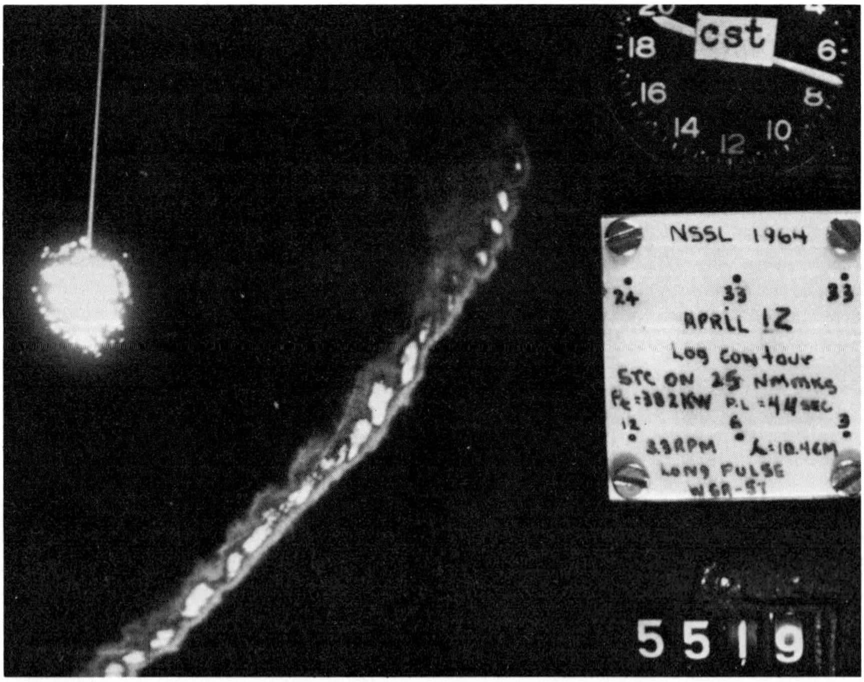

FIGURE 24.1
A line of thunderstorms. At 1918 C.S.T., April 12, 1964, as seen by the WSR-57 radar of the National Severe Storms Laboratory, Environmental Science Services Administration, U.S. Department of Commerce, Norman, Oklahoma. North is to the top and the maximum range is 120 miles. (Photo by Charles Clark, reproduced with the permission of ESSA.)

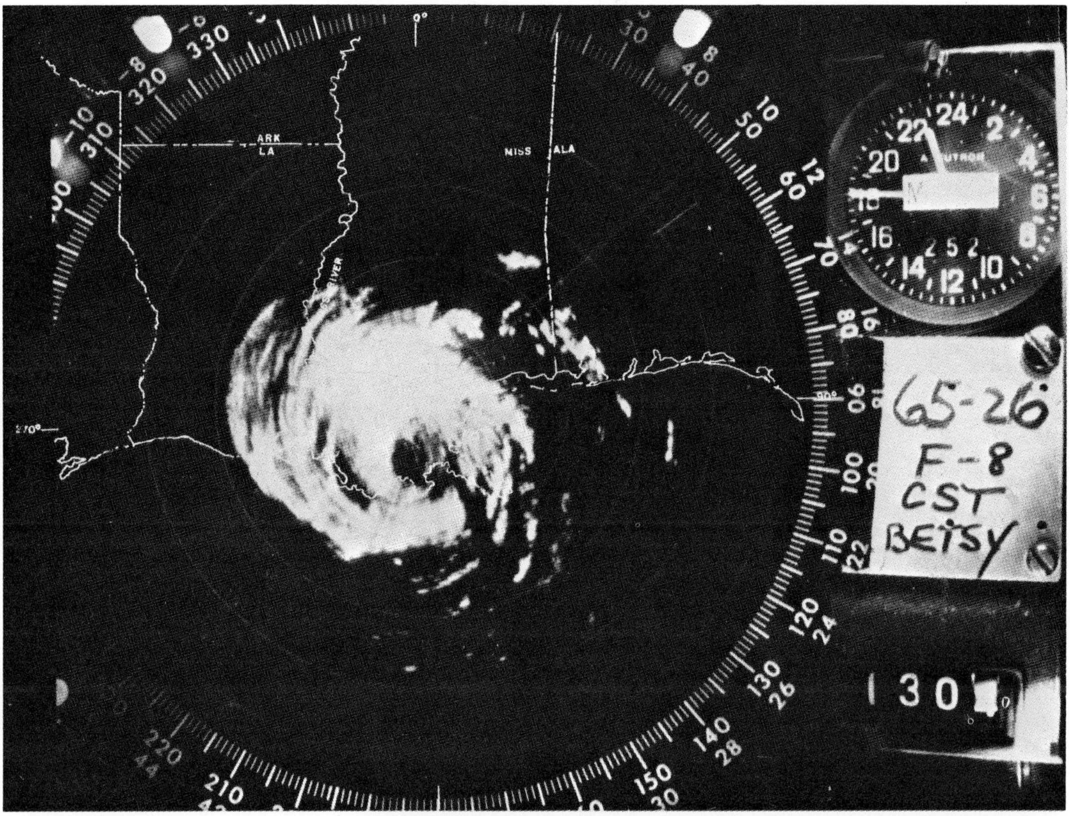

FIGURE 24.2
Hurricane Betsy. At 0427 E.S.T., September 8, 1965, as seen by the WSR-57 radar of the United States Weather Bureau at Miami, Florida. (U.S. Weather Bureau photo, reproduced through courtesy of the American Meteorological Society.)

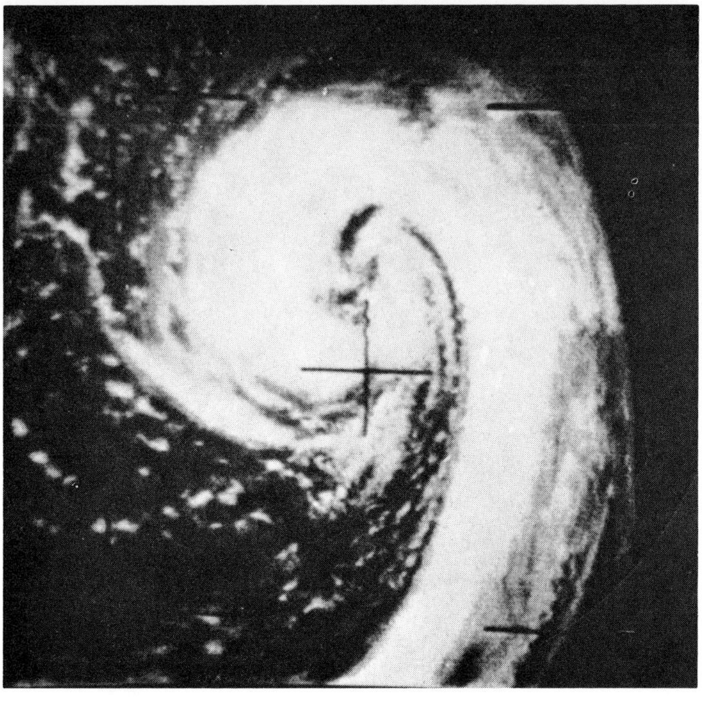

FIGURE 24.3
A North Atlantic storm. Centered at 48°N, 22°W, at 1402 G.M.T., June 11, 1964, as seen by the TIROS VII weather satellite. (NASA photo reproduced through courtesy of Aracon Geophysics Co.)

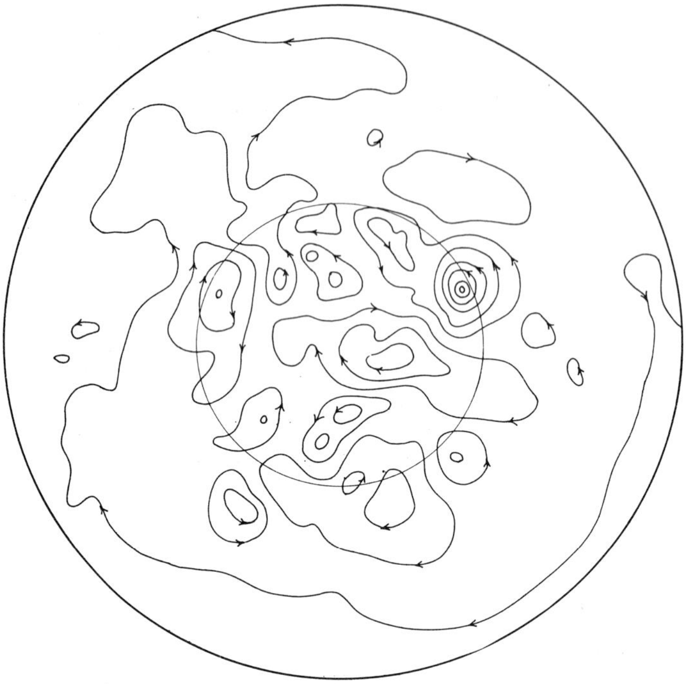

FIGURE 24.4
Northern Hemisphere weather maps at sea level. At 1230 G.M.T., March 15, 1952. *Outer circle,* equator; *inner circle,* forty-fifth parallel; *heavy lines,* isobars; *arrows,* direction of geostrophic wind. (Isobar positions based upon U.S. Weather Bureau analysis.)

FIGURE 24.5
Northern Hemisphere weather map at 30,000 feet elevation. At 1000 G.M.T., March 15, 1952. Lines have same meanings as in Figure 24.4. (Isobar positions based upon U.S. Weather Bureau analysis.)

pressure. Such motion will occur, for example, when the pressure force, which is directed toward lower pressure, is balanced by the force of friction, which opposes the motion. Throughout most of the atmosphere, however, friction is a minor force, and the pressure force is ordinarily balanced by the Coriolis force—the deflecting force resulting from the earth's rotation—which acts at right angles to the motion. Near the ground, friction assumes a more important role, and the wind tends to have a small component toward lower pressure superposed upon the geostrophic component. A mathematical demonstration that the forces must be nearly in balance would be extremely involved; it is simply a matter of observation that the forces do tend to balance for the most part.

Referring to Figure 24.4 we observe that in lower latitudes a belt of easterly winds nearly encircles the globe. These easterlies are the familiar trade winds—the steadiest of the global currents. In connection with the trades we often hear of the prevailing westerlies in middle latitudes, but in Figure 24.4 we see no globe-encircling belt of westerlies. If we measure the wind at a sufficient number of points in middle latitudes, and then average these measurements, we shall find a resultant wind from the west, so that the prevailing westerlies are indeed present, but only in a statistical sense. They are not present at all locations at one time, nor are they present at all times at one location. The more obvious feature in middle latitudes is the great number of anticyclones and cyclones—the centers of high and low pressure with their accompanying clockwise and counterclockwise vortices. We have seen examples of cyclones in the radar and satellite photographs.

Figure 24.5 is similar to Figure 24.4 except that it presents the conditions at an elevation of about 30,000 ft. The low-latitude easterlies are less prominent than at sea level, but the middle-latitude westerlies are much more pronounced, and form a belt which encircles the globe. Cyclones and anticyclones are still present, but to some extent they have been replaced by troughs and ridges—lines along which the pressure is lower or higher than at adjacent longitudes. The strongest winds, indicated in Figure 24.5 by the most closely packed isobars, form a relatively narrow continuous current which nearly encircles the polar regions; this is the now familiar jet stream. Winds as high as 200 miles per hour are not uncommon there.

The maps in Figures 24.4 and 24.5 present conditions on a single day, but the flow which they illustrate is for the most part typical of the general behavior of the atmosphere. Important features which are not present or not clearly revealed are tropical hurricanes, which are confined mainly to the summer or autumn hemisphere, and the intertropical convergence zone, a rather narrow region extending virtually around the globe where currents from the northern and southern hemispheres converge and rise, and in doing so bring about rather heavy cumulus convection, with frequent thunderstorms.

The motions of global scale—the trade winds and the prevailing westerlies at low levels, the upper-level westerlies which culminate in the jet stream, and the intertropical convergence zone—form what is ordinarily called the general circulation of the atmosphere. The migratory cyclones and anticyclones and the accompanying upper-level troughs and ridges, and at lower latitudes the tropical hurricanes, are usually classified as secondary circulations. There is not complete agreement, however, as to how the general circulation should be defined; I personally prefer to regard at least the existence of cyclones and anticyclones, and some of their collective statistical properties, as basic characteristics of the general circulation.

Having noted some of the principal features of the circulation of the atmosphere, let us see to what extent they can be accounted for. We shall first examine some features of global scale. Proposed explanations for the trade winds date back several centuries, but Hadley (1735) was the first to recognize the significance of the earth's rotation, and his ideas have become a familiar part of meteorological history.

Hadley assumed that the excess solar heating in lower latitudes over that in higher latitudes would bring about a general rising motion in lower latitudes and sinking in higher latitudes, the circuit being completed by a general equatorward motion near the earth's surface and a poleward motion aloft. He argued that there would be no reason for systematic eastward or westward motion if the earth were not rotating. He noted, however, that the surface of a rotating earth moves more rapidly toward the east in low latitudes than in high latitudes, in an absolute sense. Air moving directly equatorward across some middle latitude would therefore, in trying to conserve its absolute eastward velocity, arrive at lower latitudes with a westward motion relative to the earth—thus the trade winds.

Hadley's numerical calculations indicated that the air would acquire much higher westward speeds than those actually observed, and he attributed the lower speeds to the frictional drag between the air and the earth's surface. He then noted that this same drag would continually slow down the rotation of the earth, unless counteracted by an equal and opposite drag somewhere else; this he assumed to occur in the latitudes of the prevailing westerlies. To account for the westerlies he argued that the air which had reached low latitudes and risen to higher elevations would, upon returning poleward, acquire an eastward motion relative to the earth, thus becoming the upper-level westerlies. Upon sinking in higher latitudes it would form the prevailing westerlies, after which it would again move equatorward, completing the circuit.

It is easy enough in the light of today's knowledge to find fault with Hadley's reasoning. For one thing, the equatorward or poleward moving air tends to conserve its absolute angular momentum rather than its absolute velocity, and Hadley's assumption to the contrary caused his numerical calculations to be too small by a factor of two. The tendency of the air to conserve its angular momentum is identical with what we now call the eastward component of the Coriolis force. But Hadley preceded Coriolis by a century, and it is perhaps to his credit that he was as nearly correct as he was. Moreover, his quantitative error does not invalidate his subsequent reasoning, which is entirely qualitative; his assumption concerning friction was simply that it would reduce the strength of the trade winds to what it is observed to be from what it would be otherwise.

A more general criticism of Hadley's work is that it fails to demonstrate that the circulation must assume its observed form in preference to some other, since it lacks the necessary quantitative treatment. It may be shown that in a thermally forced system the warmer air must rise and the colder air must sink in some over-all sense, or, more precisely, that the temperature and the upward motion must be positively correlated, but the correlation need not be perfect nor even very high. Hadley assumed, without justification, that all of the rising air was warmer than all of the sinking air, and his subsequent conclusions were therefore not demanded by the physical laws.

Nevertheless, as an essentially correct account of what does take place, as opposed to what must take place, Hadley's work went virtually unchallenged for nearly two centuries. Once the dynamical effect of the earth's rotation had been properly expressed in mathematical form (e.g., by Coriolis, 1835) it was possible to replace the qualitative reasoning by quantitative computations, and ultimately a number of theoreticians attempted to do so. As we have already noted, the exact equations proved to be so complex that numerous simplifications were required. Thus, as in Hadley's paper, the presence of oceans and continents was generally neglected. Within the framework of such simplifications, the early quantitative results (e.g., Oberbeck, 1888) generally confirmed Hadley's work.

We may reword Hadley's arguments concerning the frictional drag in terms of absolute angular momentum, by saying that angular momentum (regarded as positive if the motion is eastward) is transferred from the earth to the atmosphere in the latitudes of the trade winds, and from the atmosphere to the earth in the latitudes of the prevailing westerlies. Since the earth is to a large extent a solid, it does not acquire any differential rotation thereby, but the atmosphere, being a fluid, would continue to speed up (in the absolute sense) in low latitudes and slow down in high latitudes, were it not for some mechanism for conveying angular momentum from low to high latitudes within the atmosphere. Hadley's picture contains such a mechanism since the poleward moving air aloft carries with it more eastward angular momentum than the equatorward moving air below. Nevertheless, other mechanisms are physically possible.

A feature of Hadley's paper which was characteristic of much of the ensuing work is that the large-scale currents were assumed to behave quite independently of any secondary circulations. As one familiar with the high seas, Hadley was well aware of the violent storms which were often encountered, but he presumably looked upon them as irrelevant as far as the maintenance of the trade winds was concerned. Later investigators recognized the potential importance of the secondary circulations, but tended to regard them as a sort of large-scale turbulence, which could be suitably incorporated into the mathematical equations by choosing larger coefficients of viscosity and thermal conductivity than would otherwise be demanded. Since the appropriate values of these coefficients were not known in any case, the inclusion of storms would not invalidate any results which had been previously arrived at.

But sooner or later all theories are challenged, and Jeffreys (1926) eventually proposed that the secondary circulations were actually responsible for maintaining the global currents. This idea was not well received by those who based their reasoning upon turbulence theory; turbulence should tend to smooth out the temperature field by conveying heat from latitudes of high to those of low temperature; likewise, it should tend to create a state of solid rotation by conveying angular momentum from latitudes of high to those of low angular velocity. Jeffreys was proposing that, unlike turbulence, the secondary circulations conveyed angular momentum in the opposite direction.

For a number of years Jeffreys' ideas were no more than alternatives to Hadley's. Then, following World War II, Starr (1948) observed that upper-level troughs and ridges whose axes possessed a general northeast-southwest orientation were of the proper shape to convey angular momentum northward. In Figure 24.5 a ridge of this sort extends northeastward from the high-pressure center marked with an "X," in the lower right portion of the map. To the east of this ridge, the isobars intersect the 45th parallel nearly at right angles; the air therefore crosses the parallel from almost due north, and carries no angular momentum with it, except that which it possesses as a result of rotating with the earth. To the west of the ridge, the air crosses from the southwest rather than the south, and therefore carries considerable additional angular momentum. The result of this exchange of air across the 45th parallel is therefore a net removal of angular momentum from the south side to the north. Starr felt that throughout middle latitudes in the northern hemisphere, troughs and ridges of this shape were more prevalent than their mirror images, which would transport angular momentum in the opposite direction.

By 1950 routine upper-level wind observations in the northern hemisphere were of sufficient quantity and quality to put Starr's ideas to test. The calculations clearly indicated that the secondary systems, and particularly the upper-level troughs and ridges, transported enough angular momentum across the 30th parallel to maintain the prevailing westerlies north of there against the dissipative effects of friction (Starr and White, 1951). A decade later southern hemisphere observations were plentiful enough to yield a similar result (Obasi, 1963). Thus Hadley's account of the circulation was finally overthrown, not because of any fatal error in his reasoning, but because it failed to agree with observations which after more than two centuries had finally become available.

Close to the equator Hadley's ideas fared better. Air does appear to rise near the equator, notably in the intertropical convergence zone, and move toward the poles aloft, but it generally sinks and returns equatorward while still in the subtropics. The resulting closed circuits, which are confined mainly to the equatormost thirty degrees of either hemisphere, and which can convey significant amounts of angular momentum across the 15th parallels, are now known as the Hadley cells. Across the 30th parallels, and into the regions of the prevailing westerlies, the required momentum transport is accomplished by other means—the secondary systems.

Does this revised picture of the circulation explain why the trade winds and the prevailing westerlies exist, and why they are found in their observed locations? I feel that it does not, even though it reveals the immediate cause. We have simply replaced the problem of explaining these currents by the equally formidable problem of explaining why the upper-level troughs and ridges assume the orientations which they do, rather than essentially north-south orientations without much transport of momentum. Before attacking this problem we must consider a more basic question: why do we have secondary circulations at all?

There are many contributing factors. For one thing, the oceans and continents and the mountains and plains are rather irregularly distributed over the earth, and any circulation temporarily showing no variations with longitude could not maintain such a condition. Nevertheless, theoretical studies aimed at determining the effect of the irregularities of the earth's surface indicate that the variations with longitude which they demand are far less pronounced than the variations actually observed. There should therefore be some other explanation.

Although some meteorologists (Eady, 1950) had previously suggested that the secondary circulations formed as a result of the instability of the circulation which would otherwise prevail, I feel that the meteorological world was first made aware of the significance of instability by a laboratory device best known as the "dishpan." The relevant experiments were performed at the University of Chicago in the early 1950's (Fultz, *et al.*, 1959). Although the complete apparatus was rather elaborate and expensive, one of the principal elements was an ordinary dishpan. This was placed on a rotating turntable and filled to a depth of a few centimeters with water. The pan was heated near its rim by a heating coil, and in some cases was cooled near its center by a spray of water from below. The dishpan was supposed to simulate a hemisphere of the earth, the heating and cooling simulated the heating and cooling of the atmosphere in equatorial and polar regions, the rotation simulated the rotation of the earth, and it was hoped that the resulting circulation in the dishpan would simulate the circulation of the atmosphere.

One feature of the atmosphere prominently lacking in most of the dishpan experiments was the irregularity of the bottom surface, which would have been needed to simulate oceans and continents, or mountains and plains. Within the limits of experimental control, the input was perfectly symmetric with respect to the axis of rotation, and one might have anticipated that the resulting circulation would be symmetric also.

Figure 24.6 shows a nearly symmetric circulation which developed in one experiment. The photograph is a time exposure of the free surface of the water, upon which particles of a tracer have been sprinkled; the moving particles therefore appear as streaks, and the lengths of the streaks indicate the speed of the flow. The camera rotates with the dishpan, so that only the motion relative to the pan is revealed.

There is a single large vortex, whose center is near the center of the pan. Altogether the flow bears considerable resemblance to the circulation envisioned by Hadley.

Figure 24.7 shows a circulation obtained in an experiment where the external conditions are the same as before, except that the turntable rotates more rapidly. Here the symmetry is gone, and in addition to one concentrated elliptical vortex there are troughs and ridges bearing considerable resemblance to those found on upper-level weather maps. There is a fairly well developed jet stream, indicated by the longest streaks, which extends fairly close to the rim at some longitudes.

Sometimes a dye is introduced into the water to reveal the circulation at greater depths. When troughs and ridges occur at the free surface, small vortices resembling the migratory cyclones and anticyclones on weather maps are frequently found below.

Thus a symmetric input sometimes brings about a symmetric flow, and sometimes not. The rather abrupt transition from the type of flow pictured by Hadley to the type of flow more closely resembling the true atmospheric behavior, as the speed of rotation passes some critical value, strongly suggests that the asymmetries, when they occur, are the result of instability. That is, symmetric flow appears to be a mathematical possibility for any rate of rotation, in the sense that it is a solution of the mathematical equations governing the flow. For the higher rates of rotation, however, it appears to be unstable; asymmetric disturbances of small amplitude superposed upon a symmetric flow would ultimately develop into major features of the circulation.

The phenomena of stability and instability play a fundamental role in many of the sciences. The transition from stable to unstable motion is typified by the spinning top, which

FIGURE 24.6
Motion at free surface of water in differentially heated dishpan. Rotating at 1.9 rpm, after statistically steady state has been attained. Radius 19.5 cm, depth of water 4.2 cm. (Photo through courtesy of D. Fultz.)

FIGURE 24.7
Motion at free surface of water in dishpan heated as in Figure 24.6. Rotating at 3.8 rpm, after statistically steady state has been attained. (Photo through courtesy of D. Fultz.)

continues to stand on its point if it spins rapidly, but falls over if it spins too slowly, even though a slowly spinning or even a stationary top standing on its point is a mathematical solution of the equations governing the motion of the top. There is thus an analogy between the spinning top and the rotating dishpan, one of the obvious differences being that whereas the top is unstable when it spins slowly, the dishpan is unstable when it rotates rapidly.

How about the real atmosphere? Is the presence of secondary systems an instability phenomenon? We have noted that some asymmetries are to be expected in any case, but that they need not be so pronounced as the asymmetries actually observed. It therefore appears likely that secondary systems of the observed intensity, and particularly the migratory ones, occur because simpler circulation patterns, although mathematically possible, are unstable.

This conclusion has gained further support from one of the most recent innovations in theoretical meteorology—numerical simulation of the circulation, first introduced by Phillips (1956). Numerical simulation is an outgrowth of another recent development-numerical weather prediction. Here one attempts to forecast the weather by solving the system of equaions governing the behavior of the atmosphere. We have already noted that some approximations are essential; in particular, because the equations are nonlinear, numerical methods of integration must be used to obtain time-dependent solutions. The initial conditions represent the present weather, and the solution is extended over the range of the forecast—most frequently one or two days.

In numerical simulation the equations are solved by the same methods, but the initial conditions need not represent any known weather situation, and the solution is extended over a period of months or even years. The numerical solutions are then treated as data, and various statistics are computed from them. The investigator hopes that these statistics will be representative of the general solution of the equations, just as the climatologist hopes that the statistics which he computes from weather records will be representative of the long-term climate.

Figure 24.8 shows a particular sea-level weather map generated by Smagorinsky (1965) in his numerical experiments. As in

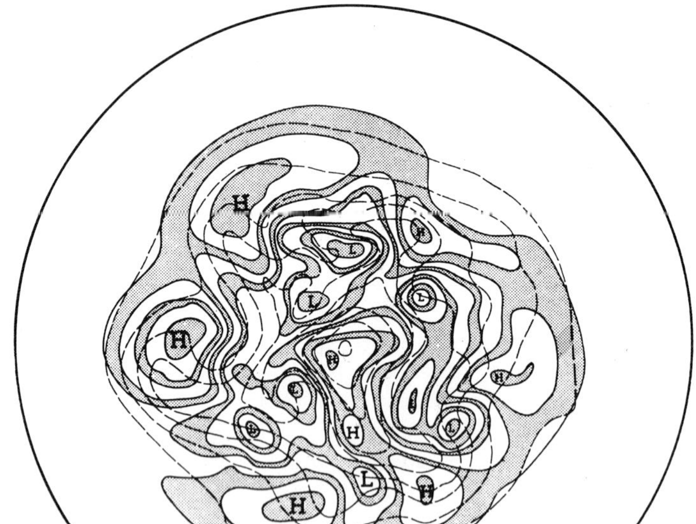

FIGURE 24.8
Northern Hemisphere weather map at sea level. Generated in numerical experiment by Smagorinsky, et al. (1965). Shading is between alternate isobars; additional dashed lines are isotherms. (Figure reproduced through courtesy of *Monthly Weather Review*.)

the real atmosphere (Figure 24.4), there is a nearly unbroken belt of trade winds in the lower latitudes, while the prevailing westerlies occur only in a statistical sense, and cyclones and anticyclones are abundant. Evidently the experiment does a creditable job of simulating the atmosphere.

The equations used in numerical simulation may be simplified to the extent of omitting all the inhomogeneities of the earth's surface, and suppressing the annual and diurnal variability of the heating. In this case steady-state symmetric solutions may be found numerically. Here there is no need to postulate that the symmetric flow is unstable; its ability may be tested by choosing initial conditions representing the symmetric flow plus a small asymmetric perturbation, and then solving the equations numerically. Within a few days the simulated circulation acquires secondary systems resembling those in the real atmosphere.

I therefore feel that the existence of secondary circulations—the cyclones and anticyclones and the troughs and ridges—has been reasonably well accounted for. How can we now explain the preferred orientation of the trough and ridge lines, as we must if we are to explain the trade winds and the prevailing westerlies? I do not know of any simple qualitative arguments like Hadley's or any simple mathematical demonstrations which accomplish this end.

Nevertheless, in all the major experiments in numerical simulation of the circulation, the trough and ridge lines show a preference for the proper orientations, and the trade winds and the prevailing westerlies appear in the proper latitudes. In a sense, then, these global currents are explained; they are demanded by the system of equations which governs the atmosphere.

Some persons, however, would not find such an explanation very satisfying. They would argue that since the real atmosphere does obey the governing equations, and since trade winds and prevailing westerlies do occur, we know even without examining the equations that they demand the presence of trade winds and prevailing westerlies. To these persons the numerical experiments are little more than a demonstration that we are using realistic equations, and handling them properly.

Yet mathematical solutions do constitute acceptable explanations for many physical phenomena. What is lacking in this instance is a real physical insight into the mechanism through which the troughs and ridges acquire their typical orientation. If there is a simple process which could readily be described in a qualitative manner, it has so far been obscured by the complexity of the total problem.

Having satisfied ourselves reasonably well that the existence of middle-latitude cyclones is the result of instability, can we make the same statement about tropical hurricanes, which in some respects are so similar? It would be natural to assume that hurricanes develop because of the instability of the undisturbed trade winds, but we have yet to demonstrate that this is so. We have not shown that the low-latitude flow is unstable with respect to disturbances having the dimensions of tropical hurricanes, and hurricanes have not appeared in the numerical simulations of the total circulation. In this sense the simulations are less realistic than we should wish. Moreover, we are not sure why hurricanes do not appear.

A very promising recent suggestion (Ooyama, 1962; Charney and Eliassen, 1963) is that we are not properly taking into account the cumulus clouds which are present in the trade wind belts before a hurricane begins to develop. From the macroscopic point of view, a mass of atmosphere filled with cumulus clouds is a different fluid from a mass of air which is either entirely saturated or entirely unsaturated with water vapor. In a cumulus-filled atmosphere a slight over-all increase in moisture does not cause a large unsaturated region to become suddenly saturated; it simply increases the percentage of the atmosphere occupied by the clouds, and reduces the spaces between the clouds. Our failure to simulate hurricanes numerically may thus arise because we are trying to make them develop in the wrong fluid.

Likewise, it is not known how great a role hurricanes play in maintaining the currents of larger scale. This lack of knowledge results largely from the lack of enough representative observations in the vicinity of hurricanes. Indeed, meteorologists who have been asked what would aid them most in furthering the purely theoretical study of hurricanes have frequently wished for more detailed observations. Evidently they have not expected to deduce the features which they have not yet observed. If we some day find that hurricanes are instrumental in maintaining the low-latitude circumpolar currents, just as the middle-latitude cyclones are instrumental in maintaining the prevailing westerlies, and if in addition we find that hurricanes cannot be properly explained without taking cumulus convection into account, we shall have established a close interrelation between three widely different scales of motion in tropical latitudes.

REFERENCES

Charney, J. G., and A. Eliassen, 1963, On the growth of the hurricane depression: Jour. Atmos. Sci., v. 21, p. 68–75.

Coriolis, G., 1835, Sur les équations du mouvement relatif des systemes de corps: Ecole Polytech. Jour., v. 15, p. 142–154.

Eady, E. T., 1950, The cause of the general circulation of the atmosphere: Royal Meteorol. Soc. Centenary Proc., p. 156–172.

Fultz, D., R. R. Long, G. V. Owens, W. Bohan, R. Kaylor, and J. Weil, 1959, Studies of themal convection in a rotating cylinder with some implications for large-scale atmospheric motions: Am. Meteorol. Soc. Meteorol. Mon., 104 p.

Hadley, G., 1735, Concerning the cause of the general trade-winds: Royal Soc. [London] Philos. Trans., v. 39, p. 58–62.

Jeffreys, H., 1926, On the dynamics of geostrophic winds: Royal Meteorol. Soc. Quart. Jour., v. 52, p. 85–104.

Lorenz, E. N., 1963, The predictability of hydrodynamic flow: New York Acad. Sci. Trans., ser. 2, v. 25, p. 409–432.

Obasi, G. O. P., 1963, Poleward flux of atmospheric angular momentum in the southern hemisphere: Jour. Atmos. Sci., v. 20, p. 516–528.

Oberbeck, A. 1888, Uber die Bewegungserscheinungen in der Atmosphäre: Kgl. Preusse Akad. Wiss. Sitzungsber., 1888, p. 383–395 and 1129–1138.

Ooyama, K., 1962, A dynamical model for the study of tropical cyclone development: Am. Meteorol. Soc. Bull., v. 43, p. 666.

Phillips, N. A., 1956, The general circulation of the atmosphere—a numerical experiment: Roy. Meteorol. Soc. Quart. Jour., v. 82, p. 123–164.

Smagorinsky, J., S. Manabe, and J. L. Holloway, 1965, Numerical results from a nine-level general circulation model of the atmosphere: Monthly Weather Rev., v. 93, p. 727–768.

Starr, V. P., 1948, An essay on the general circulation of the earth's atmosphere: Jour. Meteorology, v. 5, p. 39–43.

Starr, V. P., and R. M. White, 1951, A hemispherical study of the atmospheric angular-momentum balance: Royal Meteorol. Soc. Quart. Jour., v. 77, p. 215–225.

25

The Circulation of the Oceans

WALTER MUNK
1955

Everybody knows the difference between climate and day-to-day weather. It is less known that a similar distinction applies also to the currents of the oceans. Until recently we were aware only of the broad, average features of the ocean movements—the "climatic" circulation. But modern studies have disclosed a fine structure which is superposed on this climate and which shifts from day to day in an unbelievably mercurial manner. If 10 vessels strategically placed in the Gulf Stream were to measure the currents and make a "weather map" of the Stream next Tuesday, the map would differ from the one for Friday. Not long ago we watched a freighter carefully holding a course which according to the climatic chart should have speeded it on its way to Europe by taking advantage of the Gulf Stream. Actually the ship was bucking a two-knot countercurrent; the Gulf Stream was 100 miles off its usual path!

The vagaries of the ocean currents were practically unknown until the last world war, when new techniques and more detailed mapping disclosed that currents in the Atlantic were not as steady or predictable as the earlier climatic maps had suggested. The upshot is that oceanographers have now become interested in two kinds of maps: the climatic map, which shows the average currents over a large area for a year, and the "synoptic" map, which is like a daily or weekly weather report, showing how the currents change from one week to the next. The currents look quite different in the two charts. In the synoptic picture they are narrow, winding and fast; in the climatic picture they are smooth, broad and slow.

Both charts have their uses. If you want to study a long-term phenomenon such as the transport of sediments by currents off the coast of a continent, the climatic chart will be the one you need. On the other hand, if you are piloting a ship or submarine, you will find the synoptic chart much more useful.

Oceanographers have mapped the general circulation of all the world's oceans, relying mainly on a method which is like that for

From *Scientific American,* vol. 193, no. 3, pp. 96–104 (*Scientific American* Offprint 813).

determining air currents in the atmosphere; that is, the currents are deduced from pressure fields in the sea, which in turn are indicated by measurements of water salinity and temperature. [Figure 25.1] summarizes what we know about the climatic circulation of the oceans' surface (the top 1,000 feet).

Is there any system to this complex circulation pattern—any clue to how it may be produced? I think there is, and [Figure 25.2] is an attempt to analyze the chief elements of the picture. Suppose we plot the currents that should appear in an idealized rectangular ocean responding to the known winds that blow over the world at the various latitudes. (To simplify things we take into account only the east-west components of the wind system, disregarding "details" such as the winds blowing around the Bermuda high.) The circulation in this schematic ocean then divides into several gyres (rings) corresponding to the wind belts—a counterclockwise gyre in the subpolar region, a clockwise circulation in the subtropical belt above the equator, a narrow gyre on each side of the equator and a counterclockwise gyre in the subtropical region below the equator. In each gyre there is a strong, persistent current on the western side (due, as we shall see, to the rotation of the earth) and a compensating drift in the central and eastern portion.

With some imagination we can recognize this pattern in the three major ocean basins of the earth. The strong western current appears as the Gulf Stream in the North Atlantic, the Kuroshio in the North Pacific, the Brazil current in the South Atlantic, the Agulhas in the Indian Ocean, and possibly the East Australia current in the South Pacific. The current driven by the strong west winds in the "roaring forties" of the Southern Hemisphere flows not in a gyre but right around the globe, because no continent stands in its path; this is the mighty Antarctic circumpolar current.

The ocean-current gyres in our picture correspond closely not only to the wind systems but also to chemical and biological properties of the ocean regions. Each subtropical gyre, for example, encloses a sea which is relatively warm, salty, poor in phosphates, low in biological activity and blue in color (blue is the desert color of the sea). At the boundaries of the gyre these conditions change sharply. And the center of each gyre, near the western shore, is an unusually stable environment. The best known such region is the Sargasso Sea in the Atlantic, named after its sargassum, or gulfweed. Very possibly the six other similar regions in the world—the centers of the subtropical gyres in other oceans—will be found to have like populations of floating sea life with narrow environmental tolerances; that remains to be explored.

The precise mechanism whereby the winds produce the circulation gyres is complex and not clear. First of all, the action of wind upon water is itself a complicated matter. Wind can move water simply by frictional force as it slides over the surface, even when the surface is smooth. It must also accelerate the motion of water when it picks up spray and throws it down again, particularly during hurricanes, when so much water is pulled up into the air that the "boundary" between the sea and the air is lost. Another important means by which wind drives ocean water is its pressure on the waves as it sweeps over rough water—just as wind blowing over a field bends the blades of grass because pressure is higher on the windward sides than on the lee sides. It turns out that the important elements in the response of water to wind are not the large waves that rock boats and make people seasick, but the tiny bumps, the ripples. If we could cover the North Atlantic with oil and smooth these ripples, the Gulf Stream would lose an appreciable part of its strength. The importance of these tiny waves is surprising.

How do the driving winds produce the great circulations (gyres) that we see in the oceans? During the last 10 years a theory has been developed. We start with a situation where no land barrier stands in the way of the wind-driven water. The currents will then flow in a great circle around the earth, as they do around the Antarctic Continent [Figure 25.3]. Things get more complicated when we intro-

FIGURE 25.1
Climatic circulation in the ocean basins. Arrows show the present picture of the average currents. Equatorial countercurrent, which is present in all the oceans, lies five degrees north of the geographic equator.

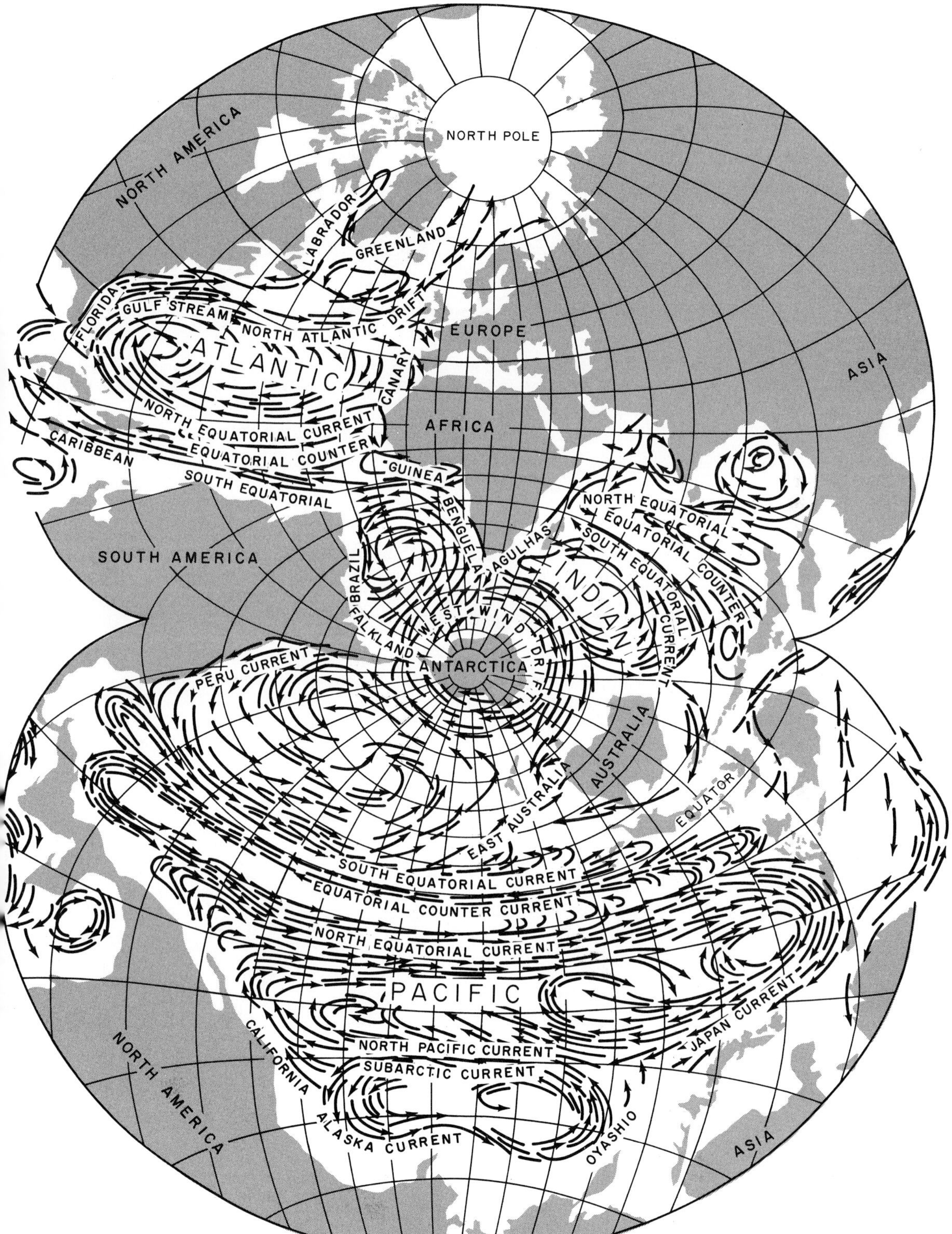

NORTH POLE
NORTH AMERICA
LABRADOR
GREENLAND
FLORIDA
GULF STREAM
NORTH ATLANTIC DRIFT
EUROPE
ASIA
ATLANTIC
CANARY
NORTH EQUATORIAL CURRENT
AFRICA
CARIBBEAN
EQUATORIAL COUNTER
GUINEA
SOUTH EQUATORIAL
BENGUELA
NORTH EQUATORIAL
EQUATORIAL
SOUTH AMERICA
AGULHAS
SOUTH EQUATORIAL
COUNTER
BRAZIL
INDIAN
WEST WIND DRIFT
CURRENT
FALKLAND
ANTARCTICA
PERU CURRENT
AUSTRALIA
EAST AUSTRALIA
EQUATOR
SOUTH EQUATORIAL CURRENT
EQUATORIAL COUNTER CURRENT
NORTH EQUATORIAL CURRENT
PACIFIC
JAPAN CURRENT
CALIFORNIA
NORTH PACIFIC CURRENT
SUBARCTIC CURRENT
NORTH AMERICA
ALASKA CURRENT
OYASHIO
ASIA

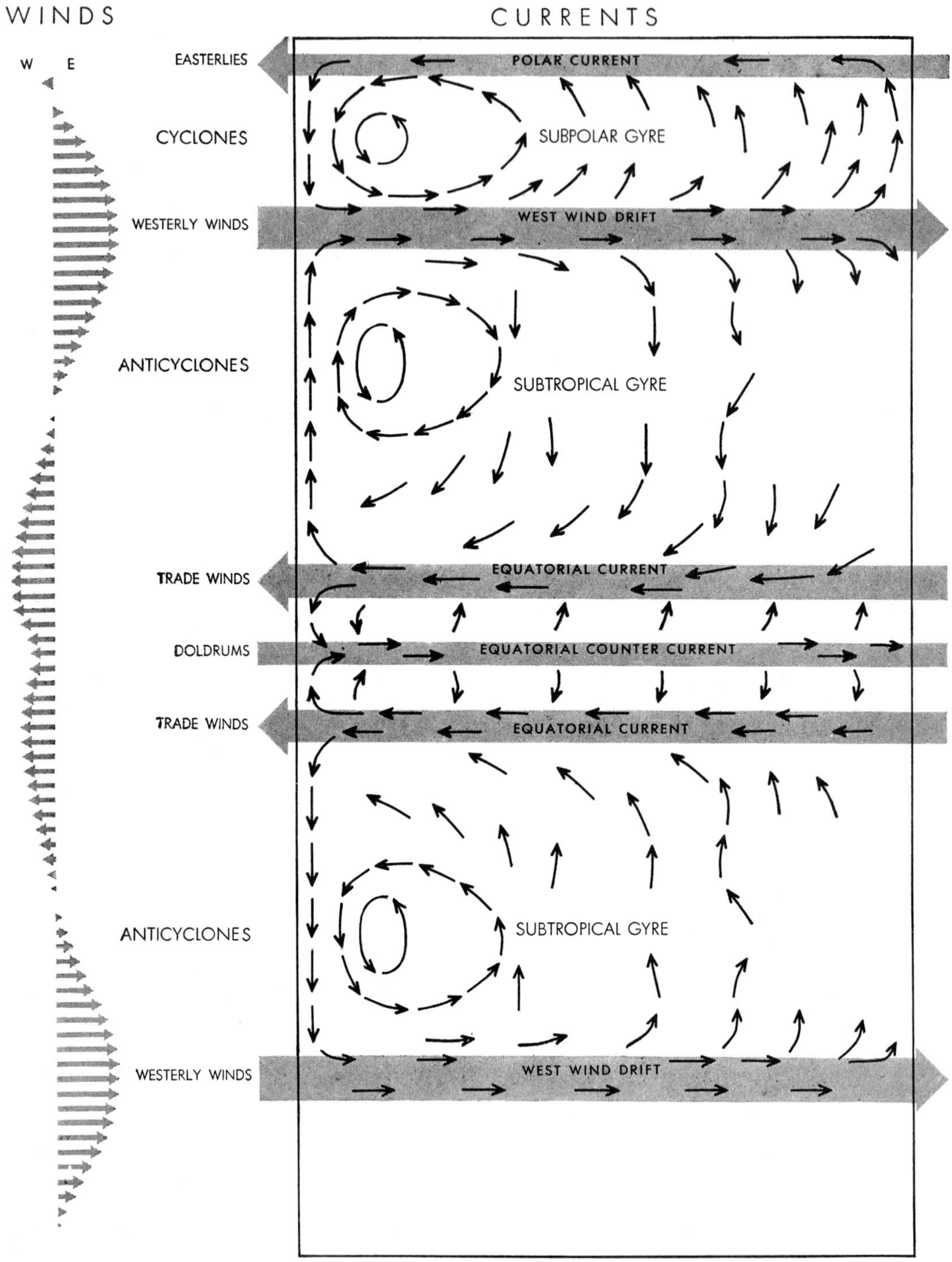

FIGURE 25.2
Idealized ocean. Rectangular in shape and subject only to the horizontal wind forces shown by the broad gray arrows, it would have the circulation patterns traced by the black arrows. Approximate relative velocities of surface winds are indicated at left.

duce land masses. Suppose we erect barriers and make an enclosed sea. Now if winds blow only from the west and have equal force at all latitudes in this sea, there can be no rotary circulation or currents . . . The wind will simply pile up water on the eastern side of the sea. But if the wind is stronger at some latitudes than at others, the stronger will overpower the weaker and the water will begin to circulate. The circulation will be even stronger, of course, if the winds at different latitudes blow in opposite directions. To this effect we must now add the effect of the earth's rotation. The turning of the earth toward the east exerts a torque on the ocean circulation, with the result that the center is displaced toward the west and the currents are intensified on the western side.

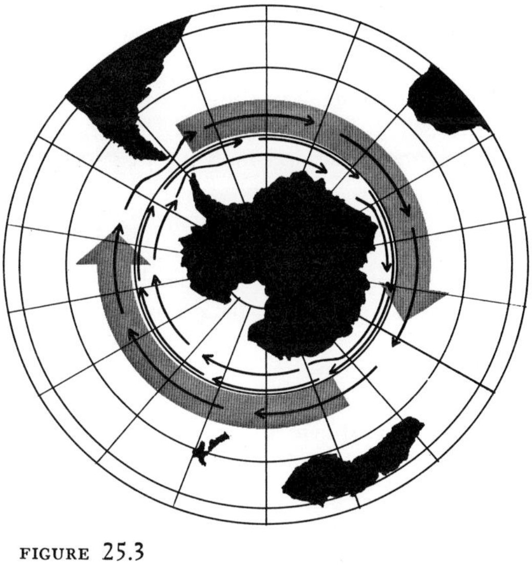

FIGURE 25.3
Antarctic circulation. It is relatively simple because no land barriers prevent the waters from responding to the prevailing west winds. West-to-east current rings continent.

In general the great wind-driven currents in the world's oceans do fit this model and the theory derived from it. The boundaries of the major currents are where they should be in relation to wind systems, and the strong western currents also appear where they should. Moreover, the theory has received some support from a laboratory model simulating ocean circulations. William von Arx, of the Woods Hole Oceanographic Institution, performed these experiments with a rotating basin shaped like a roulette wheel—essentially a hemisphere turned inside out. His "oceans" consist of a thin film of water clinging in an equilibrium distribution over the surface of the whirling basin, and winds are blown on the water from nozzles on vacuum cleaners. Von Arx projects the Northern Hemisphere into this basin, with the North Pole at the low point in the center. Potassium permanganate crystals are placed in the center, and when ink is introduced into the water, it reacts with the chemical to show the flow patterns in different colors. Von Arx's model faithfully reproduces the gyres of the North Atlantic and the North Pacific, including the intense western currents. The model is especially interesting because the topography and winds can be varied to show possible circulations of the oceans in the past, when conditions were different; for instance, one can investigate how the Gulf Stream might have behaved at a time when there was a separation between North and South America in the place of the present Isthmus of Panama.

It must not be supposed that the theory about how the ocean circulations are produced is fully confirmed by these observations and experiments. There are many inconsistencies; in particular, some of the circulation in the oceans of the Southern Hemisphere refuses to fit into the pattern pictured by the theory.

This is where we stand, then, on the climatic circulation. The era of measurement of the synoptic circulation, or day-to-day ocean weather, began with the recent invention of certain new techniques and instruments, notably (1) the radio location method called "loran," (2) the instrument for rapidly measuring temperatures at various depths which is called the "bathythermograph," and (3) an instrument, invented by von Arx and named the "geomagnetic electrokinetograph," which determines the motion of ocean water by measuring the electric potentials induced in it because of its movement through the earth's magnetic field.

Resurveying the Gulf Stream with these techniques, Columbus O'Donnell Iselin and his collaborators at Woods Hole discovered that the Stream was narrower and much faster than had been thought. As their instruments and techniques improved, the current because even narrower and faster. They also found that the position and direction of the current varied from one cruise to the next. A five-ship expedition called Operation Cabot was organized by the U.S. Navy Hydrographic Office in 1950 to study the Gulf Stream more closely. This cruise detected a most important and dramatic phenomenon: the Gulf Stream meandered off the usual course to form a loop 250 miles long! Within two days the loop broke off and separated as an independent eddy. The eddy then gradually weakened.

It is estimated that this single eddy injected some 10 million million tons of subarctic water from the North Atlantic into the subtropical Atlantic. Obviously such an immense transport of water, with its content of living organisms, must be of considerable importance to the biology of the sea. Possibly similar eddies of water from the south break off toward the north, injecting subtropical water into the colder part of the ocean.

Frederick Fuglister of Woods Hole, an artist who has been in oceanographic work since the war, later discovered some other unsuspected characteristics of the Gulf Stream. Plotting currents by means of temperature gradients measured with the bathythermograph, he found a pattern which suggested that the Gulf Stream consists of a number of long, narrow, separate ribbons, or filaments. They are not continuous over thousands of miles; as a rule one will peter out and another will start somewhere else. In other words, it appears that the concept of a single, continuous Gulf Stream all the way from Florida to Europe must be abandoned. Rather one must visualize the Stream as composed of high-speed filaments of current separated by countercurrents. L. V. Worthington of Woods Hole, using all the modern tools, has substantially confirmed this picture with detailed cross-section studies. In one 30-mile cross section he found three separate major filaments, each flowing at better than three miles per hour. Gunther Wertheim, also of Woods Hole, further demonstrated the complexity and variability of the Gulf Stream by discovering that the transport of water by the Florida current section of the Stream doubled from one month to the next! He computed the movement of water from measurements of electric potential between Havana and Key West, made by attaching electrodes to the Western Union telegraph cable between those points.

Fuglister has satisfied himself that the Japanese current also can be interpreted as consisting of filaments; in fact almost everywhere we look the ocean weather seems extremely fickle. Henry Stommel, monitoring radio drift buoys near Bermuda, found the currents highly changeable; every sudden waxing or waning of the winds set up rotary currents.

My interpretation of the new look with regard to the ocean weather is something like this. The motion of water in the open sea is highly irregular and variable. If we release a drift buoy, we can expect the current to carry it something like half a mile in an hour, but the velocity and the direction will be quite different from one day to the next. This unsteady motion—the "noise" of the ocean circulation—represents in some way the response of the sea to the multiplicity of shocks it receives from the wind blowing on its surface. The response is not simple, and the underlying laws have not yet been recognized. The transient ocean weather, unlike the slow climatic circulation, apparently has no blow-by-blow counterpart in the circulation of the atmosphere.

The fine structure of the ocean currents can be tied in with the climatic circulation only in a general way. It evidently results from the fact that the broad circulation cannot dissipate all the energy received by the ocean from the wind, but just why the fine structure takes the forms it does is a problem awaiting further exploration.

BIBLIOGRAPHY

Iselin, C. O'D., and Frederick C. Fuglister, 1948, Some recent developments in the study of the Gulf Stream: Jour. Marine Research, v. 7, no. 3, p. 317–329.

Stommel, Henry, 1954, Circulation in the North Atlantic Ocean: Nature, v. 170, no. 4411, p. 886–888.

Wertheim, Gunther K., 1954, Studies of the electrical potential between Key West, Florida, and Havana, Cuba: Am. Geophys. Union Trans., v. 35, no. 6, p. 872–882.

26

Facets of Climate

H. E. LANDSBERG
1960

Climate is part of our environment. It is an entity abstracted from the ever-changing weather. With topography and natural resources it is a basic element of our surroundings. Climate governs the flora and exercises a profound influence on the fauna. It rules the water supplies, determines our clothing, housing and, even to some extent, our health.

Long before the time of written history, man had been concerned with climate. His struggles with daily life and his migrations reflected the importance of this factor. Crude attempts at measurements antedate the present era. The Greek philosophers were well aware of the fact that climatic conditions had a relation to solar elevation above the horizon. That the inclination of the sun's rays with the horizontal influenced the temperature was well known to them. It gave rise to the name "climata" (or inclinations). The steeper an angle the sun's rays make with the surface of the earth, the higher are the temperatures. The greater their slant, the cooler it gets. Thus, the geographic latitude becomes a main cause for climatic differences.

We can demonstrate this very easily by observing the temperature of a flat surface on a calm, sunny day. This temperature follows the solar elevation above the horizon. We can also readily see that slopes to the south get warmer than slopes toward the north. Just as we can note the diurnal pattern, it is also easy to follow the annual course of temperature. This difference between summer and winter is again following the changing elevation of the sun. But here it becomes almost immediately obvious that other causes enter into shaping the march of temperature. The highest and lowest values do not any more coincide with the extremes of solar elevation. Instead they lag behind. This lag is a function of many factors but one of them is the influence of the oceans. At places far inland, the lag is short. At the coast or on islands it is long.

The distribution of land and sea on the earth exercises a very profound influence on the climate. The sun, by heating the earth

From *The Science Teacher*, vol. 27, no. 2, pp. 6–12, 1960. Reprinted with permission of the author and the National Science Teachers Association.

near the equator more than at the poles, sets up the energy differences responsible for the general atmospheric circulation. But water masses and solid earth react differently to the heat transactions. Because of mobility a thicker layer of water gets involved than in the case of solid earth. In fact, the annual variation penetrates ten times deeper into the water than into the soil. This solid layer heats quickly and cools quickly. The large water masses take longer to heat, [and store] heat in summer [and act as a thermal reservoir] in winter. [Thus,] oceans furnish heat to the air in winter, but are relatively cool surfaces in summer. This again causes important regular variations in the general circulation. On an extended scale this is seen in the monsoons which blow from land to sea in winter and then from sea to land in the summer.

These large-scale phenomena can now be studied and, to some extent, be duplicated in the laboratory. If one heats the fluid in a slowly rotating dish-pan with a heat source at the rim and cools it in the center, a circulation analogous to that in the earth's atmosphere is set up—easterly flow near the rim (= equator), westerly flow with eddies in the middle zone (= moderate latitudes), and easterlies again near the center (= pole). Dr. Dave Fultz of The University of Chicago has performed an excellent series of experiments showing these effects. One can also duplicate the disturbances created in the flow of [air by] an obstacle (= mountain).

These experiments help us in a better understanding of the great variety of climates. In their world distribution these climates are an outgrowth of the general circulation. If the earth's surface were uniform and smooth, climatic conditions would be simple and readily predictable. The problems arise from the infinite mosaic of landscape and distribution of water surfaces. These often create notable climatic variations within a climatic zone. These small-scale patterns, often called microclimates, can be studied everywhere. They reflect such distinctions as the differences of nighttime temperatures between a city and its suburbs, or a valley and a hill. On an even smaller scale one can note them within a garden, around a hedge, or between the north and south side of a house. Sometimes they are well reflected in the type of flowers that will grow or the dates on which they will start blooming.

But climate is more than temperature. It includes the many elements which make up the day-to-day weather. Hence precipitation, atmospheric pressure, wind direction and

FIGURE 26.1
Visible hurricane formation (Hazel). About 1000 miles in diameter, it covers more than a million square miles. This is equal to about two-fifths of the area of the United States. The horizon extends almost 3000 miles from Oklahoma to Mexico. Photograph taken by Aerobee rocket over Texas and the Southwest. Fired from White Sands, New Mexico. (Upper left of earth photo shows hurricane spiral pattern.)

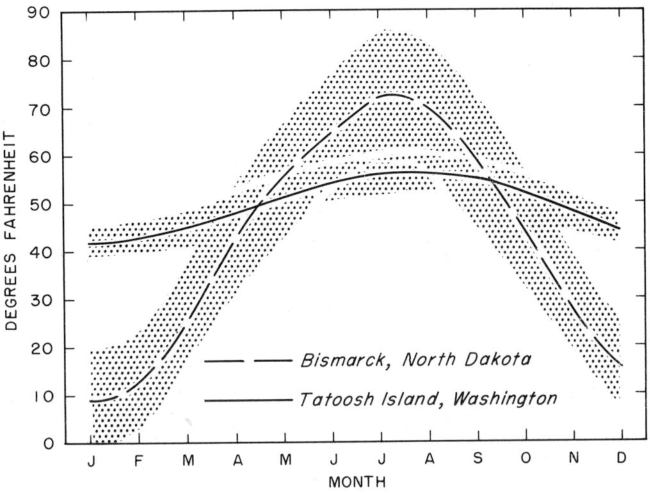

FIGURE 26.2
Mean annual temperature curves for a location in a maritime climate (Tatoosh Island) and one in a continental climate (Bismarck). The shaded zone indicates the average daily temperature range. Note that both annual and daily swing are much larger in mid-continent than at the coast.

speed, cloudiness, and special events such as thunderstorms are part of the climate. In weather studies and weather forecasting we treat these factors individually in a day-to-day fashion at many places simultaneously. In contrast, climatology deals with them as statistical collectives. . . .

As in any other physical science, we like to think about the possibilities of predicting future events. The oldest method in climatology has been to follow the lead of astronomy and search for cycles. Two such cycles are very prominent: One is 24 hours long, the other 365 days. These correspond to the axial rotation of the earth and the revolution around the sun. Not even these, however, show very precise repetitions in climatological data. Although there is a good chance to have the lowest temperature of the day about an hour before sunrise and the highest two hours after noon, there are many days on which these two events take place hours before or after these times. In the annual course of events, the coldest month of the year in the moderate latitudes of the Northern Hemisphere is usually January but a few times February, December, or even March may play that role. Similarly in summer, we can never be positive whether July or August will turn out to be warmer. In rainfall, some areas have pronounced dry and wet seasons but nowhere do these occur with clock-like precision.

Nonetheless the search for cyclical events has been carried on with determination by climatologists. It has been a very frustrating hunt. Perhaps we are—as it happens often in science—following the wrong trail. Yet one would expect some elements of regularity in a thermodynamic system operating within fixed geographic boundaries and dimensions. With long series of data on punched cards, new attempts have been made to find hidden periodicities—hidden because they are certainly not immediately obvious. Powerful statistical methods that were originally developed in World War II to find sounds from submerged submarines in the welter of oceanic noise have found use in this problem. It is the procedure of power spectrum analysis, which is a form of generalized harmonic analysis. This indicates what general rhythms are contained in a time series of data. If we take some of our longer climatic records in our regions and subject them to this treatment a few facts emerge. One is that there is a slight tendency for repetitiousness in the interval from 5 to 7 days, and another around 12 to 20 days. These are not too pronounced but they seem to be real. The shorter period is probably connected with long waves in the westerly winds which dominate the moderate latitudes. These are probably somewhat analogous to standing waves of fluid dynamics in a closed system. Usually there are 3 to 5 such waves around the hemisphere. They are migrating around the earth so that each locality gets under the influence of one every few days. Occasionally, these waves show some precision and for a month or so we may have the experience that it will rain always on the same day of the week. Then the rhythm may disappear and another one take its place. How they change and why they change is still a puzzle. The longer cycle of around two weeks has something to do with the meridional exchange of energy between lower and higher latitudes. This too takes place in a pulsating form but the length of the rhythm is irregular and changes in the pulse rate are not yet within our predictive grasp.

If we look at longer time intervals about the same picture emerges from the analysis. In this area, much has been said and written about the climatic influence of varying solar conditions. These are often expressed in terms of sunspots. These manifestations of solar activity themselves are irregular. On an average the length of one cycle is 11 years but it can vary from 8 to 18 years. There is ample evidence for solar influences on terrestrial atmospheric events, especially in the ionosphere but as we come close to the surface the relations become very tenuous. The power spectrum analysis of data in the eastern United States shows a slight rhythm around 11 years. It accounts for less than 5 per cent of the over-all variability of temperature.

The closest connections to solar influences have always been noted in the tropics and for elements which integrate conditions over large areas. Among these are lake levels and river flows. If we arrange, for example, the river discharge of the Nile River according to sunspots over the period of eight cycles one can note that there is some variation within the cycle with a tendency for low discharges the year before sunspot minimum. Again less than 20 per cent of the variability is accounted for by the possible rhythmical contribution of the sunspot variation. Without knowledge of what causes the sunspots we can predict their

FIGURE 26.3
Dust storm. (Courtesy Environmental Science Services Administration.)

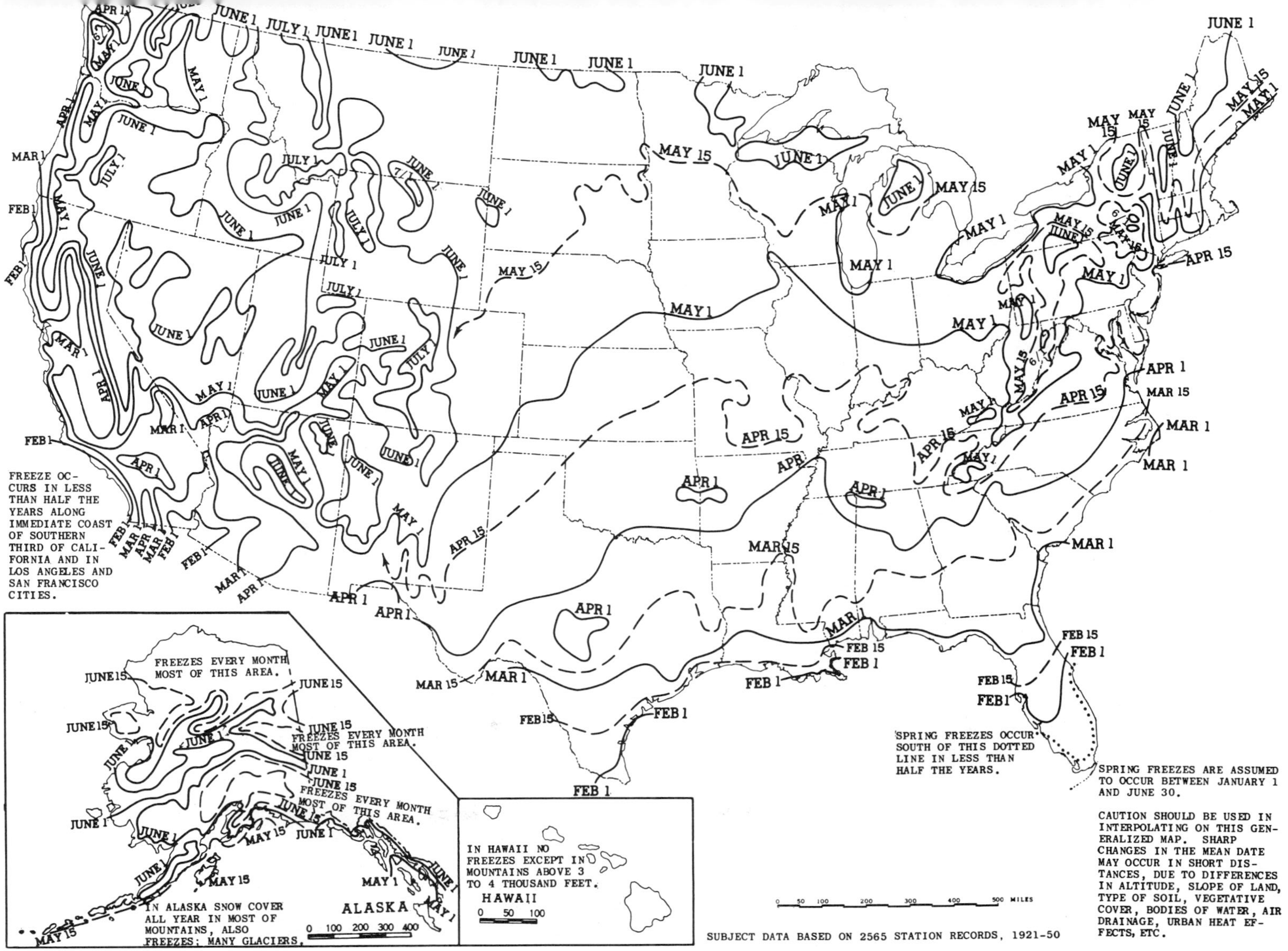

FIGURE 26.4
Average date of last daily minimum temperature of 32°F in spring.

changes only by statistical methods. Thus there is presently little chance of using this only partially predictable element to presage a terrestrial condition, which seems to follow these sunspots to a very limited degree. In spite of this lack of success the fascination of the problem remains.

We are equally puzzled by climatic fluctuations of still longer duration. These are measured in decades, centuries, and millenia. At one time climatologists deemed climate to be essentially invariant, at least over the span of a human life. The records we have accumulated definitely show that this is not so. There are slow secular trends. [During the first fifty years of this century], for example, there [was] a gradual warming over the globe. It [was not] uniform. In the Arctic it [was] more pronounced than in moderate latitudes or in the southern hemisphere. In the eastern United States it [was] 1 or 2 degrees Fahrenheit. The winters, in particular, [became] warmer. In the Arctic the warming led to a gradual melting of the ice. Some scientists have even visualized a complete melting of the polar ice caps. Until we know what causes the warming process, this is only speculation. In fact, there is [now (1960) evidence] that the warming trend [has come to an end]. Of course, geological evidence shows that the whole earth has had a warmer climate for epochs counted in hundreds of millions of years. We also know that there have been ice ages. The last major glaciation showed a number of stages of advancing and retreating ice sheets. In North America, the latest continental glacier formation began to recede 11,000 years ago. So the question is: Are we now in an interglacial stage or are we slipping completely out of the ice age? Until the effects can be traced back to their causes, this question cannot be answered unequivocally. Some scientists believe that terrestrial phenomena are responsible for the large-scale climatic changes—possibly the formation of mountains and volcanic eruptions. Others think that astronomical conditions cause the changes—among them fluctuations in path elements of the earth's orbit, axial wobble, cosmic dust clouds between sun and earth, and possible changes in the output of solar energy and related phenomena.

For the latest fluctuations there are some arguments that man and his activities has had an influence. In the last century this was a

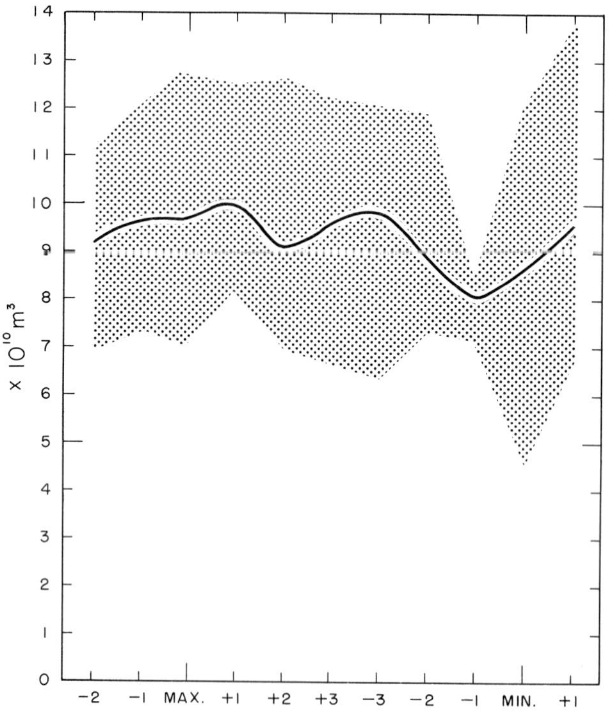

FIGURE 26.5
Curve showing the average annual discharge (in 10 billions of cubic meters) of the Nile River during the past 8 sunspot cycles. The years within the cycle are indicated as abscissas. The shaded area around the curve shows how widely the river discharges have varied in individual years from the mean value.

claim made for deforestation and cultivation. No proof for large-scale changes can be given although local changes can be attributed to these activities. Over the last few decades, however, another element has entered. Through various man-made combustion processes large amounts of carbon dioxide have entered the atmosphere. This gas is a good absorber of infrared radiation. It intercepts part of the outgoing long-wave radiation from earth to space. An increase of this gas in the atmosphere would lead to a gradual warming. The period for which we have sufficiently accurate air analyses is too short to be sure of this increase in carbon dioxide. During the International Geophysical Year 1957–1958 the carbon dioxide concentration was checked at a worldwide network of stations. It is hoped that this will continue into the future so that close surveillance can be kept of this important constituent of the atmosphere.

Many sciences can point with pride to the solid doctrines that have been built. Questions have been answered and discoveries leading to better understanding have been made. In climatology, as in other phases of atmospheric science, many puzzles still remain. There are more questions than answers. These stay as a challenge to human imagination. Here is a vast domain still to be conquered. . . .

SECTION V

THE DIFFERENTIATION OF THE SOLID EARTH

What was solid earth has become sea,
and solid ground has issued from the bosom of the waters.

Ovid, METAMORPHOSES

How did the present configuration of lands and seas come about? What effect has their evolution had on the past circulation of hydrosphere and atmosphere, on paleoclimatology, and on the succession of rocks and life forms on earth? It would take many volumes to follow the controversy that has raged over these and related questions. A once-prevalent concept held that the earth had seen only relatively trivial cyclic modifications of its surface features, and that the basic features, the continents and ocean basins, had not undergone major changes since the beginning of earth history. Today we have a variety of dramatically evolving models to choose from (or blend into new combinations), involving continental accretion, convection in the earth's mantle, sea-floor spreading, and drifting (together and apart again) of "floating" crustal plates of vast dimensions.

Reading Selection 27, though now somewhat dated, is still a broadly valid discussion of the present internal structure of the earth, deduced from its physical properties as inferred from earthquake data. It was written by K. E. Bullen, the eminent Australian National University seismologist. Bullen shows how the two classes of seismic waves that travel through the body of the earth are reflected and refracted at its main internal boundaries, thus defining roughly concentric inner and outer cores, a four-layered mantle, and the crust; and how the disappearance within the outer core of the secondary or shear waves (which vibrate at right angles to the direction of movement) demonstrates that the outer core has the properties of a fluid. These and other data lead to inferences about the density, compressibility, rigidity, material composition, and likely pressures and temperatures of the several concentric shells of the earth—a subject further elaborated in a paper by E. C. Robertson (1966, Supplemental Reading).

Records of the history of the earth, however, are located almost entirely in that portion of the total mass (less than one percent) that makes up the outer crust (a term carried over from the long-outmoded concept of an early surficial crustification of a once completely molten globe). Bullen's paper, therefore, is logically followed by G. P. Woollard's concise discussion of crustal geophysics (Reading Selection 28). Geophysicist Woollard of the University of Hawaii leads the reader through the various principles of crustal physics to concepts of crustal structure based on refraction seismology, gravity data, and earthquake records. He also discusses the concept of *isostasy*, which holds that the lighter materials of continents and mountains "float" like icebergs in hydrostatic equilibrium on the plastic mantle materials beneath, and that the ocean basins lie low because they are floored with rocks of greater density.

Background of this sort is essential to considering the problem of convection in the earth's mantle, a process that is involved in many current explanations of crustal differentiation. Reading Selection 29, by physicist Peter J. Brancazio of the Goddard Institute for Space Studies, focuses on the convection problem and the difficulties that arise from a lack of information about the viscosity of the mantle. If convection should prove to be a valid mechanism, however, it would make more credible a number of other hypothetical processes in earth history which otherwise encounter difficulties. Brancazio then considers several lines of reasoning which lead him to the conclusion that convection cells probably do, in fact, exist within the earth's mantle.

Assuming the validity of the convection theory, the late Harry H. Hess of Princeton University next presents a provocative picture of the evolution of ocean basins (Reading Selection 30). Here we see an excellent example of the mixture of liberating insight with individually nondiscriminating but converging lines of evidence that is so characteristic of the best writings in theoretical geology. The result is a testable model of sea-floor spreading—the first clear enunciation of that concept—where mantle material conveyed upward in mid-oceanic convection centers expands, spreads laterally at rates of up to six centimeters per year, in both directions, and eventually sweeps the older parts of the ocean floor beneath the continents. As Hess shows, this model is also quantitatively adequate to explain the present volumes of continental material and sea water; and, as we shall see, it has stimulated, and been supported by, some of the most exciting inquiries in modern geology.

Hess's interpretation assumes the existence of continental drift, although of a passive sort: the continental fragments ride piggyback on the tops of convection cells. Another way of looking at the data suggests incomplete early differentiation of the continental matter (called sial, from *si*licon and *al*uminum, because of the prevalence of alkali-aluminum silicates) with continuing accretion at both base and periphery through time. This interpretation is presented by A. E. J. and Celeste Engel of the University of California. Their paper, "Continental Accretion and the Evolution of North America" (Reading Selection 31), does not reject continental drift; but it does not depend upon it either. North America gives the best picture of peripheral accretion. Some continents (Australia and Antarctica, for example) may have grown in one direction only, and others may have had several accretion centers (Africa, for instance). In North America the rate of growth seems to have been roughly linear. It was also apparently accompanied by broad trends through time in the kinds of sediments deposited; and it was essentially completed by the beginning of Paleozoic time.

But why not continental drift? Major difficulties arise in formulating a detailed model of how continental drift might work. The best discussions of the difficulties are reluctantly relegated to the Supplemental Reading. Among these are two papers by G. J. F. MacDonald of the University of California, dealing with the deep structure of continents as it bears on continental structure and drift. MacDonald (1964, 1965) considers observations of gravity and heat-flow that imply structural and chemical differences extending beneath continents and ocean basins to depths of several hundred kilometers. Under such conditions, thin "rafts" of continental sial cannot simply sail over a universal layer of sima (from *si*licon and *ma*gnesium, to denote the heavier ferromagnesian rocks that lie beneath the sial and form the floor of the ocean basins). Hypotheses of continental drift must overcome this difficulty. Other difficulties are pointed out by Maxwell (1968), who asks: How can the continents drift away from all mid-ocean ridges unless the earth is expanding? Yet we do not see the amount of increase in length of day that we would expect to see if the earth were expanding; and what little increase we do see is easily accounted for by the retardation of the earth's rate of rotation as a consequence of tidal friction.

Nevertheless, the idea of convection currents in the mantle continues to appeal to many geologists as a possible explanation for otherwise seemingly inexplicable events. This appeal is illustrated by an instructive example, which also shows how quantitative limitations on geological conjecture can be established where knowledge is inadequate, but where a definition of limits is still needed. In Reading Selection 32, "Atlantic Sediments, Erosion Rates, and the Evolution of the Continental Shelf," James Gilluly balances data on erosion rates and areas, on the volume of sediments, and on tectonic history, to conclude that subsidence of the Atlantic coast of the United States requires a thinning of the crust in that region as a result of convection currents moving landward beneath the Moho (Mohorovičić discontinuity, interpreted as denoting the base of the crust).

The question of the existence or nonexistence of mantle convection and continental drift was long a seemingly inexhaustible source of the creative controversy that geologists enjoy so much. But then, dramatically, analysis of a critically focused regional survey brought resolution seemingly within reach. That survey was of a portion of the Mid-Atlantic Ridge southwest of Iceland, made in 1963 by the U.S. Naval Oceanographic Office. Its analysis was reported by F. J. Vine of Princeton University in 1966 (see Supplemental Reading), and similar results have been obtained in other areas since then. In a fascinating bit of geophysical detective work, Vine correlated the mirror-image symmetry that is found between patterns of linear magnetic anomalies on either side of the ridge with the sequence of normal and reversed polarity events known for the last 3.6 million years. This and other aspects of the problem are described in Reading Selection 33, a lucid paper entitled "Reversals of the Earth's Magnetic Field," by Allan Cox, G. Brent Dalrymple, and Richard R. Doell, of Stanford University and the U.S. Geological Survey. Cox, Dalrymple, and Doell first carefully establish the paleomagnetic framework from which the interpretation of reversals emerges. Then they suggest how this can be applied to the dating of deep-sea sediments, to the correlation between marine and continental sequences, and, finally, to testing the hypothesis of sea-floor spreading.

Despite the difficulties remaining to be explained, it now appears that geological and geophysical evidence and opinion have converged to the degree that most earth scientists now hold that the burden of proof rests on those who would deny continental drift, rather than the reverse. This viewpoint, and the rationale behind it, is summarized in Reading Selection 34, by geochronologist P. M. Hurley of the Massachusetts Institute of Technology. He follows a good historical summary with a marshalling of the evidence in favor of continental drift, including records of glaciation in the southern hemisphere; floral affinities between now widely separated land masses; the consistency and displacements of the earth's seismic, volcanic, and heat-flow belts; paleomagnetic and geochronologic indications of sea-floor spreading; and the matching of age belts, petrographic zones and mineralized belts across the Atlantic. This evidence converges to imply a contiguous grouping of the continents in late Paleozoic time. Stratigraphic evidence suggests that the Atlantic Ocean began to open up from south to north in the Triassic and that the Indian Ocean began to do so in the Permian. As for the mechanics of the spreading, Hurley supports the idea that the crust of the earth moves apart above the rising limbs of the convection cells, and that the sinking limbs pull the surface together and toward the region of sinking. When the ocean floor moves toward a sinking zone within an ocean it forms an island arc; when it moves beneath a continent it forms a mountain chain. Motion may take place immediately beneath the upper mantle at depths of 100–200 kilometers, where low seismic velocities indicate that the temperature of the rocks approaches the melting point. But if that is true, then why are there not great recent mountain chains facing one another across the Atlantic Ocean, the very paradigm of sea-floor spreading above an active convection cell?

That question finds its answer in what has come to be called plate tectonics—a concept that has emerged from a succession of papers (Wilson, 1965; Vine, 1966; Sykes, 1967; Oliver and Isacks, 1967; Le Pichon, 1968; and others) written since the beginning of the Upper Mantle Project of the International Council of Scientific Unions in 1962. Excellent syntheses dealing with that concept have been written by Morgan (1968) and Knopoff (1969), but the paper chosen to introduce it here is "A New Class of Faults and Their Bearing on Continental Drift" (Reading Selection 35), by J. Tuzo Wilson, the eminent geophysicist and Principal of Erindale College of the University of Toronto. In that unusually perceptive paper, Wilson was the first to point out that there is something very peculiar about the succession of offsets normal to the mid-ocean ridges and their branches—that, among other things, earthquake epicenters occur along them only between the points that appear to be offset. Their peculiarities might be explained if the offsets were inherited from original lines of weakness roughly perpendicular to those along which formerly contiguous continents had been rifted apart, reflecting the shape of the initial break. The offsets would thus be zones of transformation from one kind of mobile zone to another; but their real motion should be opposite to the apparent motion implied by the offset parts of the ridge. Such transform faults, as Wilson called them, "cannot exist unless there is crustal displacement, and their existence would provide a powerful argument in favor of continental drift and a guide to the nature of the displacements involved." Moreover, Wilson adds, the earth's great mobile belts—actively growing mountains, mid-ocean ridges, and faults of great horizontal displacement—are all interconnected, defining a number of large crustal blocks, or plates, which may interact at the margins but are essentially rigid and inactive within their boundaries. Plates that are drifting apart may ride over or under other plates, causing crustal engulfment along their overlapping fronts and the generation of new crust in their wakes. Such a system, of course, answers one of Maxwell's major objections to drift by simply not requiring that the continents drift away from all mid-ocean ridges simultaneously. Finally, Wilson suggests some tests of his hypotheses involving projections of the transform faults to the old coast lines and determination of the directions of seismic motions. He winds up with the provocative suggestion that the greatest of "transcurrent faults," the San Andreas, may actually be an enormous transform fault.

Wilson's visionary suggestions were followed in close succession not only by the discovery of the bilateral magnetic symmetry of the mid-ocean ridges but also by the discovery—from the study of first motions of earthquakes—that the direction of real motion along transform faults was, in fact, as Wilson had hypothesized it should be (see Sykes, 1967, in the Supplemental Reading).

The essence of the new plate tectonics (or "new global tectonics"), as seen by Wilson and its other expositors as this book goes to press, is that the surface of the earth is made up of a relatively small number (six to twenty or more) of rigid but interacting plates. The boundaries of these plates are defined by major zones of earthquakes and faulting—the mid-ocean rises where new crust is made; the deep sea trenches, below and landward from which crustal material is dragged back down into the upper mantle (the Benioff zones) and landward from which mountain systems arise; and big faults along which crust is neither created nor destroyed. These large rigid plates slide over a weak zone of incipient melting at a depth of roughly 100 kilometers. Where they jostle one another earthquakes occur, defining their margins. Crust is created or destroyed and mountains are folded up only at these margins. Crustal shortening or extension does not appear within a given plate. Most, if not all, offsets in the mid-ocean ridges are not transcurrent faults as they appear at first glance, but transform faults—a product of the shape of the initial break between continents, and with a motion in the direction opposite to the offset. On such a model, the plate of which North America is a part has only its western boundary coincident with what we normally consider the continental margin. The eastern boundary is the Mid-Atlantic Ridge!

The crustal mobility called for by the new plate tectonics must involve mantle motions, but the nature of those motions remains in dispute. W. J. Morgan (1968, see Supplemental Reading) sees the location of mid-ocean rises as not necessarily fixed by deep thermal sources but determined by the yet unexplained motion of the plates (not all of which need move). He hypothesizes that, where a formerly joined plate separates into two parts along a line of weakness, mantle material wells up along the zone of separation to produce a succession of dikes which are then repeatedly split into subequal halves along their hot, and therefore weak, mid-portions as the new crustal plates drift apart. That would explain the mirror-image pattern of striped magnetic anomalies on opposite sides of active oceanic ridges—a pattern having a regularity difficult to account for otherwise. Knopoff (1969, see Supplemental Reading) finds great difficulty in extrapolating heat-flow data from the earth's surface to get an idea of the temperature distribution below the moving plates. The upper mantle is more heterogeneous than was once believed, and, as MacDonald has pointed out, the crustal plates are not detached from the mantle below. We may no longer visualize the crust as independent of the mantle, floating on it like an array of icebergs. Thermally driven convection currents thus appear to Knopoff to be no more than a plausible mechanism.

The new plate tectonics involves a revolution in the earth sciences that is still in its germinal stages and which promises eventually to throw much new light on earth history. The student should watch for new sources of information to further supplement the Reading Selections and the Supplemental Reading; and he should seek out and consider alternatives to the various hypotheses and mechanisms already proposed.

Supplemental Reading

Bateman, P. C., and J. P. Eaton, 1967, Sierra Nevada batholith: Science, v. 158, p. 1407–1417.

Berry, W. B. N., and A. J. Boucot, 1967, Continental stability—a Silurian point of view: Jour. Geophys. Research v. 72, p. 2254–2265.

Dietz, R. S., 1962, Ocean basin evolution by sea floor spreading: Oceanog. Soc. Japan Jour., Twentieth Anniv. Vol., p. 4–14.

Donn, W. L., B. D. Donn, and W. G. Valentine, 1965, On the early history of the earth: Geol. Soc. America Bull., v. 76, p. 287–306.

Emery, K. O., and M. L. Natland, 1952, Our shrinking globe—a discussion: Geol. Soc. America Bull., v. 63, p. 1069–1072.

Fisher, R. L., and Roger Revelle, 1955, The trenches of the Pacific: Scientific American Offprint 814, 7 p.

Heiskanen, W. A., 1955, The earth's gravity: Scientific American Offprint 812, 6 p.

Jeffreys, Harold, 1964, How soft is the earth?: Royal Astron. Soc. Quart. Jour., v. 5, no. 1, p. 10–22.

Kennedy, G. C., 1959, The origin of continents, mountain ranges, and ocean basins: Am. Scientist, v. 47, p. 491–504.

Knopoff, Leon, 1969, The upper mantle of the earth: Science, v. 163, p. 1277–1287.

Le Pichon, Xavier, 1968, Sea-floor spreading and continental drift: Jour. Geophys. Research, v. 73, p. 3661–3697.

MacDonald, G. J. F., 1964, The deep structure of continents: Science, v. 143, p. 921–929.

———, 1965, Continental structure and drift: Royal Soc. [London] Philos. Trans., ser. A, v. 258, p. 215–227.

Martin, Henno, 1961, The hypothesis of continental drift in the light of recent advances of geological knowledge in Brazil and in South West Africa (seventh A. L. du Toit Memorial Lecture): Geol. Soc. South Africa Quart. News Bull., v. 56, annexure, 47 p.

Maxwell, J. C., 1968, Continental drift and a dynamic earth: Am. Scientist, v. 56, p. 35–51.

Morgan, W. J., 1968, Rises, trenches, great faults, and crustal blocks: Jour. Geophys. Research, v. 73, p. 1959–1981.

Oliver, Jack, and Bryan Isacks, 1967, Deep earthquake zones, anomalous structures in the upper mantle, and the lithosphere: Jour. Geophys. Research, v. 72, p. 4259–4275.

Robertson, E. C., 1966, The interior of the earth: U.S. Geol. Survey Circ. 532, 10 p.

Sykes, L. R., 1967, Mechanism of earthquakes and nature of faulting on the mid-oceanic ridges: Jour. Geophys. Research, v. 72, p. 2131–2153.

Tobin, D. G., and L. R. Sykes, 1968, Seismicity and tectonics of the northeast Pacific Ocean: Jour. Geophys. Research, v. 73, p. 3821–3845.

Urey, H. C., 1953, On the origin of continents and mountains: [U.S.] Natl. Acad. Sci. Proc., v. 39, p. 933–946.

Vine, F. J., 1966, Spreading of the ocean floor—new evidence: Science, v. 154, p. 1405–1415.

Wilson, J. T., 1950, On the growth of continents: Royal Soc. Tasmania Papers and Proc., v. 84, p. 85–111.

———, 1963, Continental drift: Scientific American Offprint 868, 16 p.

———, 1966, Did the Atlantic close and then reopen?: Nature, v. 211, p. 676–681.

27

The Interior of the Earth

K. E. BULLEN
1955

Each year 10 or more major earthquakes shake the earth. The energy released in any of them is about a thousand times as much as in the Bikini atomic bomb of July 1946; the Assam earthquake of August, 1950, had about 100,000 times that energy. The waves set up by these convulsions travel through the whole interior of the earth, including the core, and their paths are bent and shaped by the changing properties of the earth's internal structure. Thus the seismic waves bear clues of the regions they traverse, and from the story they tell when they are received at our seismological stations on the surface it is possible to infer a picture of the interior. In effect the seismologist X-rays the earth, even if at times he sees through a glass, darkly.

Seismology has lifted our notions about the interior of our planet from the realm of wild speculation to the stage of scientific measurement and well-reasoned inferences. Combined with certain astronomical observations, laboratory experiments on rocks at high pressures, and the application of modern theoretical physics, it gives us a basis for learning something about the various conditions in the deep interior—its layered structure, the materials, their physical state, the pressures, and so on. In addition, observations made by geologists at the earth's outer surface can be useful in restricting allowable hypotheses.

Serious study of earthquakes did not start until about 200 years ago. In 1750, a writer in the *Philosophical Transactions* of the Royal Society of London apologized to "those who are apt to be offended at any attempts to give a natural account of earthquakes." But observations of earthquake effects accumulate from about that date on. Late in the nineteenth century, seismology began to emerge as a real quantitative science when the Englishman John Milne constructed in Japan a seismograph suitable for world-wide use. The seismograph was later developed further, notably by E. Wiechert in Germany, by Prince Galitzin in Russia, and by Hugo Benioff of the California Institute of Technology.

The release of elastic strain energy at the

From *Scientific American*, vol. 193, no. 3, pp. 56–61, with minor emendations by the author.

source, or "focus," of an earthquake produces waves which radiate in all directions from the focus. In 1897, R. D. Oldham of England identified on seismograms three main types of seismic waves: (1) primary waves (P waves), which are compression-and-expansion waves like those of sound; (2) secondary waves (S waves), in which earth particles vibrate at right angles to the direction of wave travel, analogously to light waves; and (3) surface waves, which travel over the earth's surface and give information on structure near the surface. The P waves travel through both solid and fluid parts of the earth; the S waves only through solid. In solid regions, the S waves travel at about two thirds of the speed of P waves. The speed of both varies with depth in the earth; for example, the P waves travel at 8½ miles per second, their maximum speed, at a depth of 1,800 miles, and at about three miles per second in rocks near the earth's surface. Because of changing properties, the path of the waves' travel usually curves upward. When the waves arrive at a boundary between layers they may be refracted or reflected, and on reaching the earth's outer surface they are reflected downward again. At a boundary, an incident P or an S wave may give rise to both P and S waves. Thus any one seismogram from a particular earthquake may show many distinct phases, each associated with a different type of path or P or S wave character. A typical seismogram illustrating several phases is shown in Figure 27.1.

With this kind of evidence, Oldham showed, in 1906, that the earth has a large central core; and in 1914, Beno Gutenberg, then in Germany, located the boundary of the core at 1,800 miles below the earth's surface. Since the radius of the whole earth is about 4,000 miles, the central core has a radius of some 2,200 miles. The "mantle" is the part of the earth outside the core (Figure 27.2).

The discovery of the core came about from the observation of shadow zones where P waves are relatively subdued. Consider P waves issuing from a major earthquake with its focus at the South Pole. The waves would be observed at the surface throughout the Southern Hemisphere, and up to 15 degrees above the equator (*i.e.*, up to the latitude of Guatemala) in the Northern Hemisphere. But between the latitudes of Guatemala and Winnipeg little indication of P waves would be received. Then, from a latitude of 52 degrees north to the North Pole, the waves would come in again strongly. The whole of the U.S. would thus be part of a "shadow zone" for that earthquake. On examination, it was seen that the existence of such shadow zones requires the presence of a central core which would bend sharply downwards the seismic rays striking it from above, somewhat after the manner in which light rays from a stick in water are bent at the water surface.

One of the great labors of seismologists during the first 40 years of this century was to evolve reliable tables for the times of travel of P and S waves along the various phases of their routes. In 1930, Sir Harold Jeffreys of the

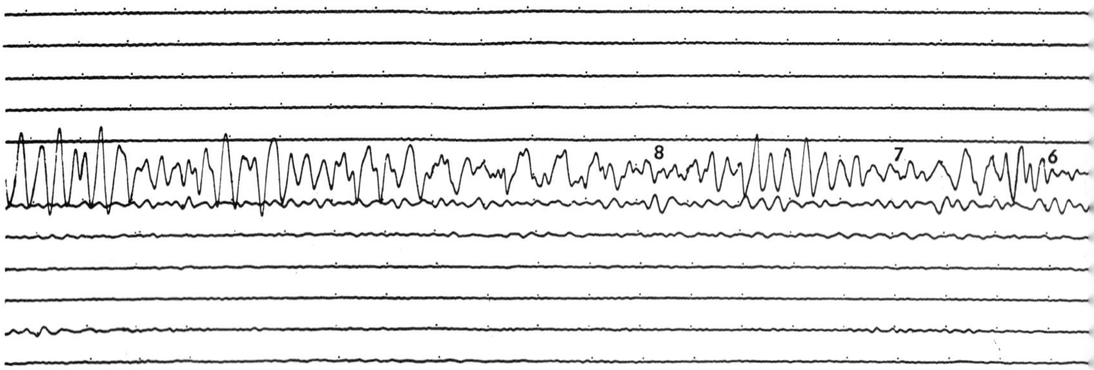

FIGURE 27.1
Seismogram of an earthquake on the Kamchatka Peninsula in Siberia. Recorded at the Lamont Geological Observatory. The separate lines are actually part of a continuous spiral trace, going from right to left, on a circular drum. The interval between successive dots is one

University of Cambridge, suspecting that the existing "travel-time tables" contained large errors, began a long series of revisions. The author of this article was associated with Jeffreys in this work from 1931 to 1939.

The Jeffreys-Bullen tables of 1940 are now used in preparing the International Seismological Summary. They agree fairly well, in the main, with travel times derived about the same time by Gutenberg and Charles F. Richter at the California Institute of Technology. The travel-time tables are of cardinal importance for charting the structure of the earth's interior. It is possible to deduce from the tables the velocities of P waves throughout the earth and S waves throughout the mantle. Studying the variations of velocity with depth, one can chart different layers and locate boundaries.

With the new tables Jeffreys calculated that Gutenberg's measurement, placing the boundary of the central core at 1,800 miles below the earth's surface, was correct within three or four miles. At least the outer part of the core is judged to be molten. S waves do not pass through it, and its fluid character is established by other evidence, including data on the tidal deformation of the solid earth and astronomical data on the movements of the earth's poles. H. Takeuchi of Japan has calculated that this region is at most one 300th as rigid as the material at the bottom of the mantle.

The use of the terms "solid" and "fluid" in connection with the huge pressures prevailing in the earth's interior is sometimes questioned. The term "solid" in this context means simply that the elastic behavior of the material in question can be described by equations which match those applying to ordinary solids in normal laboratory conditions. These equations involve the use of two coefficients: "incompressibility," which is the measure of resistance to pressure, and "rigidity," signifying resistance to shearing stress. In the case of a fluid, the resistance to shear is negligible. This is why a fluid does not transmit S waves.

The whole of the mantle (apart from the oceans and pockets of magma in volcanic regions) is essentially solid because it transmits S as well as P waves. In 1909, the Croatian seismologist A. Mohorovičić, studying a Balkan earthquake, discovered an important discontinuity (boundary) now known to be some 20 miles below the earth's surface in continental areas. The part of the earth above the Mohorovičić discontinuity has come to be called the crust. But nowadays the term "crust" has only a conventional meaning. According to seismic evidence the crust is less rigid than the material deep in the mantle.

The crust differs from the underlying mantle in the fact that P and S waves travel in it more slowly and more irregularly. This irregularity makes detailed charting of the crust difficult. The work is being pursued vigorously, however, by the study of surface waves, of P and S waves from near earthquakes (near the recording stations), of waves from large man-made explosions (such as the one on Helgoland in 1947), and by seismic probings with dynamite, as in oil prospecting. One important

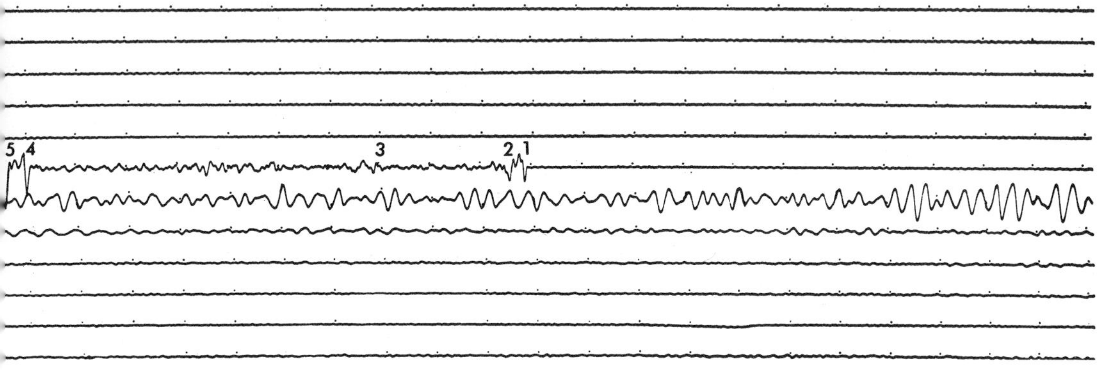

minute. The first disturbance recorded was the P wave designated by the number *1*. Then followed the multiply reflected P waves *2* and *3*. S waves begin at position *4*, followed by multiply reflected waves at *5*, *6*, and *7*. Surface waves start at *8*.

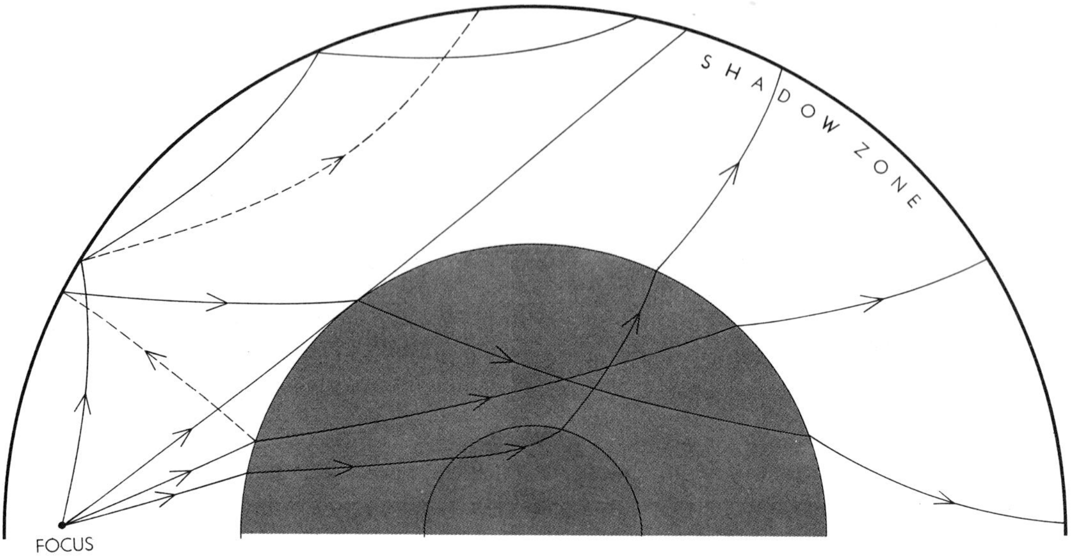

FIGURE 27.2
Earthquake waves are bent and reflected as they travel from their source. *Solid lines*, P waves; *dotted lines*, S waves formed by reflection. The only P waves that can get into the shadow zone are those which enter the inner core and are sharply bent.

discovery has been that the crust is much thinner under the oceans than under the continents.

Several distinct concentric regions have now been identified in the earth. In 1936, Miss I. Lehmann of Denmark discovered that the core is not uniform, but consists of at least two different parts. Looking closely at the relatively minor P waves that emerge in the shadow zone at the surface, she inferred that these waves are bent sharply upward by an inner core inside which P waves travel significantly faster than in the outer core. Her proposal later received support from work by Gutenberg, Richter, and Jeffreys. The inner core has a radius of some 800 miles.

On the basis of work on density variations, the writer has divided the body of the earth into seven regions, called A, B, C, D, E, F, and G (Figure 27.3). The A region is the crust. The rest of the mantle below is divided into B, C, and D, with D subdivided into D′ and D″. Some of the divisions are tentative because of certain uncertainties in estimates of velocity gradients. The outer part of the core is called E, and the inner part, G. Between the inner and outer core Jeffreys finds a layer F, some 80 miles thick, where the velocity of P waves declines sharply (Figure 27.4). Gutenberg has not found this layer, but has said that his data do not exclude its existence.

How can we estimate the pressures, densities, and other physical characteristics of matter at various depths in the body of the earth? The velocities of P and S waves depend on the density, compressibility, and rigidity of the materials through which they pass, but they do not provide enough information to give values of all three quantities. There are, however, indirect clues which help us to arrive at estimates—information on the earth's mass and moment of inertia, high-pressure experiments on rocks, mathematical theories of elasticity and gravitational attraction.

By such means the writer has estimated that the earth's density increases gradually from 3.3 grams per cubic centimeter just below the crust to 5½ grams per c.c. at the bottom of the mantle, then jumps suddenly to 9½ grams at the top of the core, and thereafter increases steadily to 11½ grams at the bottom of the outer core (Figure 27.5).

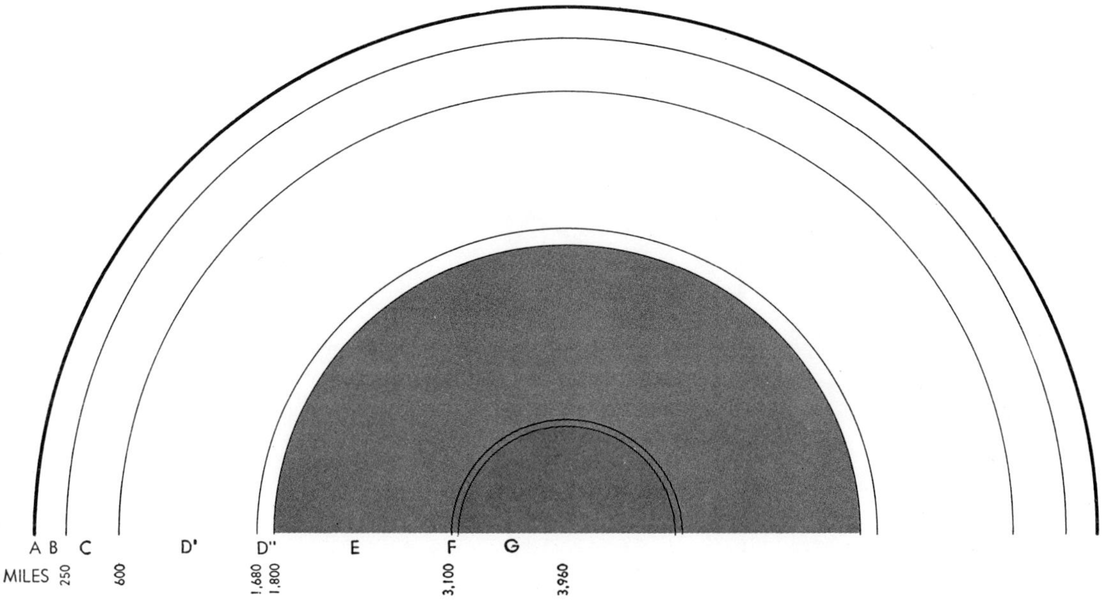

FIGURE 27.3
Earth's cross section is divided into distinct layers through which seismic waves travel at different speeds. *Light gray*, outer core; *dark gray*, inner core. Layer A is the thin crust of the earth.

A related calculation gave the increase in pressure with depth in the earth. At the bottom of the Pacific Ocean the pressure is about 800 atmospheres. Only 200 miles down in the mantle the pressure is already 100,000 atmospheres—as great as the highest pressure so far produced in the laboratory. At the base of the mantle, 1,800 miles down, the pressure reaches the immense figure of 1⅓ million atmospheres, and at the center of the earth it is nearly four million atmospheres.

Next the calculations yielded the surprising finding that the rigidity of the material in the mantle increases with depth until, at the mantle's base, it is nearly four times that of steel in ordinary conditions. Below, in the outer core, the seismic evidence shows that the rigidity sinks to practically zero, meaning that the material is essentially fluid (Figure 27.6).

Perhaps the most important fruits of this series of calculations have been the findings on compressibility. In spite of the sharp changes in density and in rigidity at the boundary between the mantle and the core, the compressibility of the material does not change substantially at the boundary, according to the calculations. This finding led the writer to examine the theoretical effect of pressure on the compressibilities of materials likely to be present in the earth at pressures of a million atmospheres or more. Taking into account a variety of evidence, the conclusion was that bounds could be set to the changes of compressibility inside the core.

Following this line of argument, it seems highly probable that the inner core, unlike the outer core, is solid in the sense defined. The idea that the inner core is solid, suggested by the writer in 1946 and since developed, would explain the speeding up of P waves when they penetrate into the inner core. Calculation indicates that the inner core is probably at least twice as rigid as steel at ordinary pressures.

On the same line of evidence we can also estimate, as we could not before, the density of the inner core. At the center of the earth the density is probably between 12½ and 18 grams per cubic centimeter.

What is the deep interior of the earth made of? For many years there have been good grounds for believing that much of the mantle below the crust consists of ultrabasic rock such

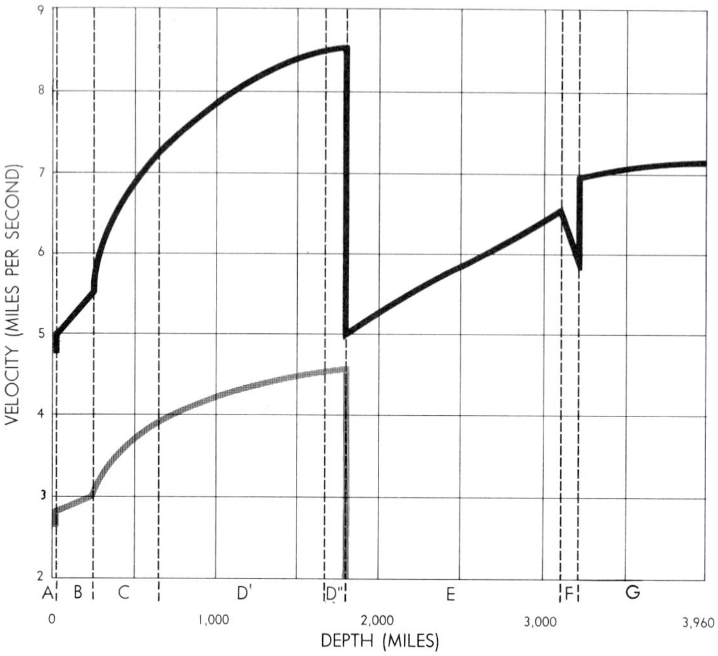

FIGURE 27.4
Seismic wave speeds vary with depth. *Black line*, velocities of P waves (as derived by Jeffreys in 1939); *gray line*, velocities of S waves. Both change abruptly at core, or *E* layer, and the S wave disappears.

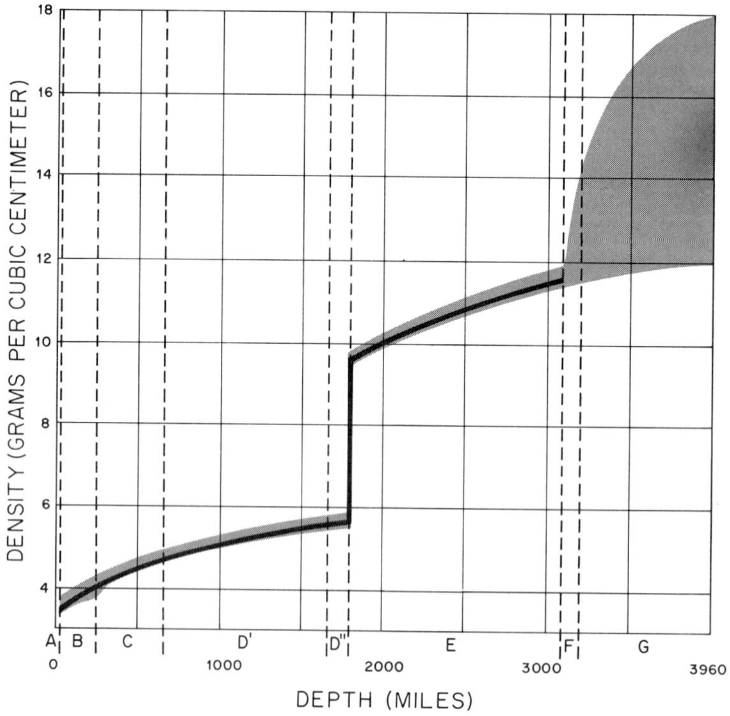

FIGURE 27.5
Density of the earth's material increases with depth. *Solid line*, the most probable value at each depth; *gray region*, the probable range of uncertainty.

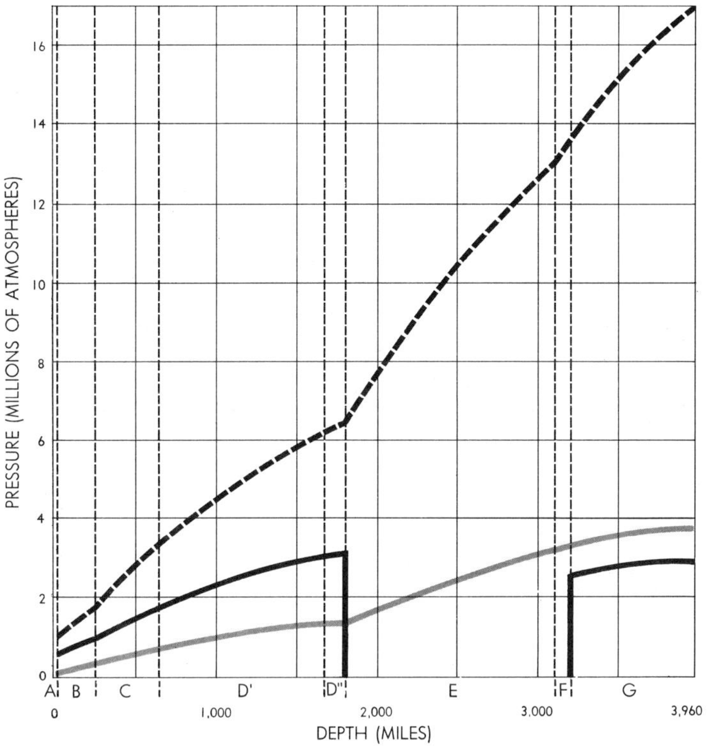

FIGURE 27.6
Elasticity of the earth's interior. *Gray line,* pressure; *dotted black line,* incompressibility; *solid black line,* rigidity.

as magnesium-iron silicate. The region B seems to be principally composed of a material like the known mineral olivine. C appears to be a transition region where the composition may change and where there may also be a change of crystalline form. The region D′ may contain several distinct phases, such as silica, magnesia, and iron oxide. Inside the region D″, the lowest 150 miles of the mantle, the composition is probably variable, but there is as yet no widely accepted agreement on what materials would have gravitated to this depth.

The composition of the central core has lately become the subject of extremely interesting new conjectures. It had long been assumed that the core consists largely of iron or nickel-iron, and this view was supported by analysis of meteorites, believed to be pieces of an exploded planet resembling the earth. But in 1941, W. Kuhn and A. Rittmann put forward the radical idea that compressed hydrogen made up the core. This theory, while contradicted by weighty arguments, gave rise to new investigations based on the idea that under increasingly high pressures the material at the base of the earth's mantle might suddenly jump in density. Thus the outer core may consist not of uncombined iron or nickel but of a high-density modification of the material in the mantle just above it. This theory is highly controversial. On balance of probability the present evidence appears to favor a compromise: namely, that the outer core contains both uncombined iron and some material of appreciably smaller atomic number.

An interesting aspect of the new theory is that it makes plausible the idea that the planets Mars, Venus, Mercury, and Earth are all of the same primitive overall composition. Jeffreys and the writer had shown that the earth cannot have the same overall composition as the other planets if its core is markedly different from the mantle in composition. According to calculations by W. H. Ramsey of England and the writer, the observed masses and diameters of Mars and Venus, and the oblateness of Mars, would be accounted for fairly well by the theory that they are composed of terrestrial materials modified by pressure at depth.

The earth's inner core probably consists principally of nickel and iron.

Estimates of the temperatures in the interior of the earth are much less certain than estimates of pressure. In deep mines the temperature rises at the rate of about 30 degrees Centigrade per mile as one descends. If it rose at this rate all the way down to the core the temperature in the center of the earth would exceed 100,000 degrees. Actually, it is practically certain that the rate of increase is very much less in the depths of the earth. Present estimates of the temperature at the center lie mainly between 2,000 to 6,500 degrees. It is fairly clear that the increase of temperature in the earth's interior is dwarfed by the increase in pressure.

BIBLIOGRAPHY

Bullen, K. E., 1965, An introduction to the theory of seismology (3d ed.): Cambridge University Press.

Gutenberg, B., ed., 1954, The internal constitution of the earth: New York, Dover Publications.

Jeffreys, Sir Harold, 1950, Earthquakes and mountains: New York, John Wiley and Sons.

———, 1962, The earth (4th ed.): Cambridge University Press.

28

The Crust of the Earth

G. P. WOOLLARD

1960

That the earth has an internal structure not unlike that of a liquid-center golf ball is known from the travel times and types of seismic waves that are transmitted through it from earthquake shocks. As indicated in Figure 28.1, in gross form this structure can be described as a thin outer crust 5 to 65 kms thick, an underlying mantle about 2900 km thick, and a central liquid core at whose center at a depth of about 5100 km there appears to be an inner solid core. The crust, which is the subject of this paper, is of particular interest as it constitutes the surface upon which man lives. The stability, mineral composition, surface relief, and evolutionary changes of the crust all have a direct bearing upon man's activities, wealth, and even life itself, as brought out by the disastrous earthquakes in Chile [in 1960].

GENERAL DESCRIPTION OF CRUST

Basically, the crust can be thought of as floating upon the underlying mantle layer as though it were supported by a liquid. Actually, the mantle rock material is solid, but like most materials subject to long-term stress it appears to yield by plastic flow to the variations in pressure imposed by changes in weight of the overlying crust. This phenomenon of plastic flow of solid material can be observed in a short-period experiment by placing a heavy hammer upon the surface of a barrel of solid tar. Given sufficient time the hammer will not only sink into the tar but eventually will sink to the bottom of the barrel. The same tar, struck a blow with the hammer, would show no visible imprint although the surface might be locally shattered as if it were glass. Therefore, the factor of time is an important one in considering all tectonic processes involving the crust, and the complex folding of normally brittle rocks that is observed in many mountain ranges is evidence that the earth's crust itself has undergone considerable plastic deformation over the years.

From *The Science Teacher,* vol. 27, no. 5, pp. 6–11, 1960. Reprinted with permission of the author and the National Science Teachers Association.

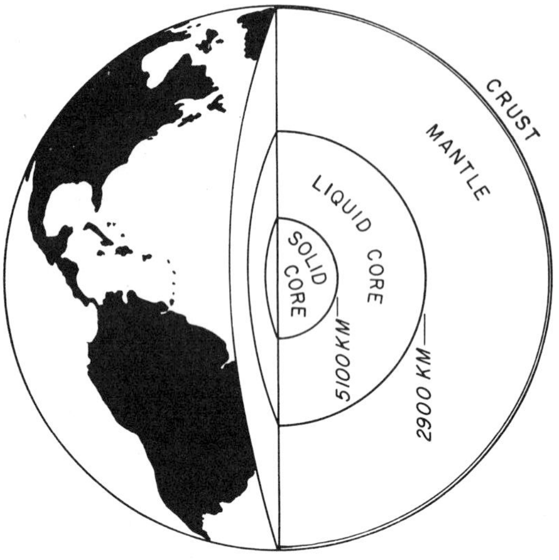

FIGURE 28.1
Cutaway section of earth showing basic internal structure

The concept that the crust is in effect floating upon the underlying plastic mantle material, i.e., displaces its own weight in the mantle layer, is not a new one, but there was little or no proof to support this concept until recently. As long ago as 1855, Sir George Airy advanced the idea of a floating crust to explain why the gravitational attraction of mountainous masses on a plumb bob is invariably less than that which was computed. This conclusion is also substantiated by gravity measurements. For example, it is observed that if one allows for the gravitational effect of changes in latitude (change in earth radius and the outward centrifugal force), change in elevation, and the gravity effect of the included mass of material above the mean surface of the earth (geoid) represented by sea level, the theoretically computed values depart from the actual variations in gravity in a systematic manner that is dependent upon elevation. This departure is referred to as the Bouguer gravity anomaly in recognition of the French scientist by that name. He did pioneer gravity work (1740) in the Andes Mountains at the time of the famed expeditions of the French Academy to Lapland and what was then Peru (now Ecuador) to determine whether the earth was really flattened at the poles rather than at the equator, as some scientists thought at that time.

The Bouguer anomaly values show an inverse relationship to elevation and suggest a compensating negative mass at depth whose gravity effect offsets that of the surface mass distribution. This phenomenon, known as isostasy, implies that at some depth below the surface all terrestrial columns exert equal pressure. This situation, as visualized by Sir George Airy, was analogous to the pressure exerted on the bottom of a harbor filled with shipping. As any floating body, in accordance with Archimedes' principle, displaces its own weight of the supporting medium, the bottom pressure everywhere will be the same whether a ship is overhead or not, or whether the vessel is a light rowboat or a deeply laden cargo vessel. Under this concept of isostasy the crust should be thicker beneath the continents than beneath the oceans, and beneath mountains there should be downward projecting "roots" analogous to those associated with icebergs floating in the sea. The amount of root beneath a mountain would thus be directly proportional to the height of the mountain.

An alternate interpretation for isostasy, however, had been advanced by the Archdeacon Pratt in 1854. It visualized the mountains as standing high because they are composed of lower density material. This is sometimes referred to as the "dough" theory of isostasy in that it implies the crust of the earth has risen to varying elevations in response to some internal mechanism affecting its density, analogous to having varying amounts of yeast in different batches of bread dough on a table top. For years geologists debated not only the merits of these two different theories concerning the crust, but also the reality of the phenomenon of isostasy itself. It was not until the techniques of exploration seismology, as used for mapping subsurface geologic structure in the hunt for favorable locations for the entrapment of oil, were adopted to the study of the crust that the problem was resolved.

SEISMOLOGICAL STUDY OF THE CRUST

The seismological study of the crust dates from 1910 when a Yugoslav seismologist, Mohorovičić, announced that studies of the travel times for a local earthquake in southeastern Europe showed that there was a change in seismic velocity from about 5.7 to 8.0 km/sec at a depth of about 50 kms.

This velocity discontinuity, now known as the Mohorovičić discontinuity, or more familiarly as the "Moho," is one of the earth's most consistent seismic horizons. As its depth appears to vary directly with the surface elevation, and also appears to confirm the conclusion reached from the study of gravity data and the deflections of the plumb bob that the crust appears to be floating and in a state of hydrostatic equilibrium, the "Moho" has been adopted as a seismic marker for defining the base of the crust.

Although the "Moho" was discovered through the analysis of earthquakes wave travel-time data, this method of study is neither as efficient nor as reliable as that based upon explosive seismological techniques which permit one to carry out controlled experimental studies of the crust. The following description, therefore, of current seismic methods of crustal study is confined to explosion seismology.

The seismological study of the crust using explosions depends upon the physical laws of optics and particularly the refraction and reflection of compressional sound waves generated by an explosion. By controlling the time of an explosion and knowing accurately the distances from the point of the explosion to a series of seismic wave detectors and the time of arrival of the wave front at each, it is possible to determine both the internal structure and thickness of the crust. The seismic-reflection method of depth determination is identical to that embodied in the use of the Fathometer for the determination of the depth of water at sea. A sound pulse is generated by an explosion, and the time it takes a reflected pulse (echo) to return is a direct gauge of the distance to the reflecting horizon. The reliability of the method is dependent upon a knowledge of the velocity with which sound is transmitted through the intervening medium. If the crust of the earth were a layer of homogeneous material, the reflection technique would adapt itself very well to the measurement of variations in crustal thickness. The earth's crust, however, is far from homogeneous. In most areas it is composed of from two to four layers, but the number of layers and their velocity characteristics change from place to place. To adequately map any such structure, it is best to use a technique which will permit the velocity of each layer and its thickness to be determined. This can be done by using what is known as the seismic refraction method. In this method the arrival times of the explosive sound pulse are recorded at varying distances out to some distance approximately four times the depth that is to be investigated. Instead of timing a vertically or near vertically reflected echo, the times recorded are those for sound that has traveled a predominantly horizontal path between the shot point and the detectors. These travel times, when plotted as a function of the distance from the point of explosion (shot point) to the various detectors, thus give a graph composed of segments of straight lines whose slopes are the reciprocal of the velocity at which the sound was transmitted in each layer. If the crust were composed of homogeneous material, the travel-time plot would define a single straight line.

The refraction method is based upon Snell's Law for refracted light. Its successful application depends upon the layering within the crust being essentially horizontal and the fact that the deeper layers have a progressively higher velocity than the material above them. At each velocity layer interface, the energy that is critically refracted (refracted at 90°) into the underlying layer will travel along the boundary interface as a new source of energy radiating sound waves back towards the surface in accordance with Huygen's principle. If the velocity of the underlying layer is less than that of the overlying material, however, the energy incident upon the boundary will be refracted downward in accordance with Snell's Law, and no energy will be returned to the surface by a refracted path until higher speed material is encountered. Fortunately, the geology of the crust is such that it is density-layered with the deeper material not only having a higher density but also a higher seismic velocity. Under these conditions there is upward refraction at each boundary, and the existence of layering is apparent on the travel-time graph by a change in the slope value of the graph. In Figure 28.2 a schematic representation is shown depicting the relation between the travel-time graph data and the subsurface velocity structure for a three-layer situation. The seismic record (seismogram) shown contains all of the pertinent data concerning time. The shot instant which was relayed by radio to the central recording site is transferred directly to a galvanometer whose deflection defines this event on the seismogram, which is a moving recording strip of photographic paper. Each detector, which consists of a spring-mounted magnetic mass with a high moment of inertia inside of a coil, is likewise connected to a recording galvanometer through an amplifying circuit. Upon the arrival of the seismic wave front at the detector, a differential movement occurs between the coil mounted in the core and the spring-mounted high inertia core that induces a current in the coil. It is this signal which marks the arrival of sound pulse on the seismogram. Time lines are put on the seismogram at .001 second intervals through the use of a driven tuning fork or other device that can be relied upon to break a beam of light at fixed intervals.

Depth determinations are based entirely upon the optical ray theory. The basic depth equation for a two-layer situation, for example, is

$$h = \frac{TV_1}{2 \cos i}$$

where T is the V_2 layer zero-distance time intercept value (see Figure 28.2), h the thickness of the upper V_1 layer, i the angle of the incident ray refracted a 90° along the V_1—V_2 layer interface, and V_1 the velocity in the surface layer. The values of V_1 and V_2 are taken directly from the graph, as in the value T. The angle of incidence for the ray refracted at 90° at V_1—V_2 interface is determined from Snell's Law, which states

$$\frac{V_1}{V_2} = \frac{\text{sin incident ray}}{\text{sin refracted ray}}$$

As the refracted ray is specified for 90° and the sine of 90° = 1, the ratio of the velocity values V_1 and V_2 determined from the travel-time graph define the incident ray. The only unknown, therefore, is h, the thickness of the upper layer having a velocity V_1. Where several layers are involved, equations similar to the one given above are used.

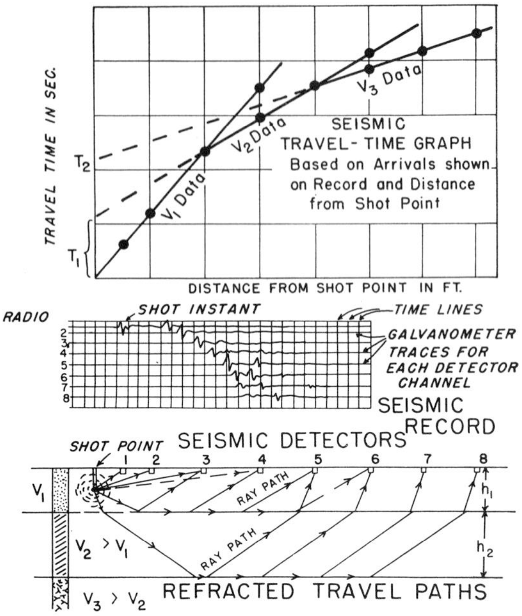

FIGURE 28.2
Seismic travel-time plot, seismogram, and depth section

The accuracy of the seismic refraction method where it has been checked by drilling in oil field exploration work is well within ten per cent, and there is every reason to believe that the method gives a similar degree of reliability in the study of the crust.

RESULTS OF CRUSTAL SEISMIC MEASUREMENTS

Most of the measurements of crustal structure by the explosive seismic method have been done since the end of World War II. The program of measurements has not been restricted to any one continent or ocean and has been literally world-wide in scope. As a result we now have a better idea about the structure of the crust and how it varies in thickness with changes in surface relief. In the oceans, for example, we find that the crust is relatively thin (5 to 6 kms) and that it has a rather simple velocity structure of either one or two layers with velocity values in the range 6.4 to 6.7 km/sec. On the continents, on the other hand, the thickness of the crust at sea level is about 34 kms, and it thickens as the surface elevation increases up to values in the range 55

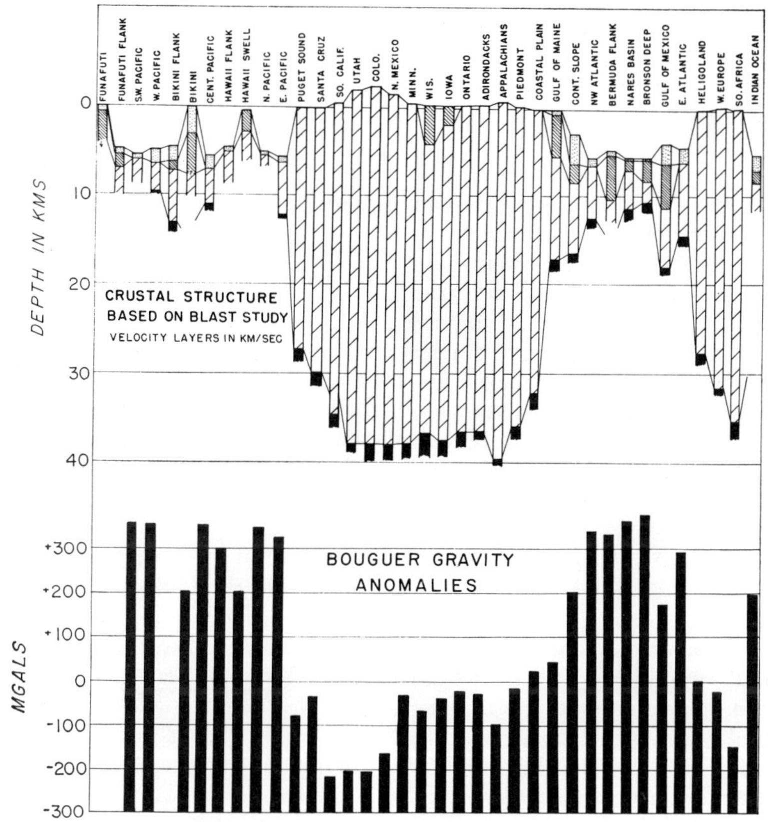

FIGURE 28.3
Seismic sections of crust and related Bouguer gravity anomalies

to 65 kms beneath the high mountains. The internal structure also varies considerably with a single layer indicated in some areas and several layers in other areas. The velocity values vary from about 5.4 to 6.2 km/sec at the surface to as much as 7.6 km/sec near its base. The only factor that appears to be common to both the continents and the oceans is the velocity of the underlying mantle rock which everywhere appears to be characterized by a velocity of about 8.0 km/sec.

RELATION BETWEEN GRAVITY ANOMALIES AND SEISMIC MEASUREMENTS

As already mentioned, there is a systematic inverse relationship between Bouguer gravity anomalies and the surface elevation that Sir George Airy attributed to variations in crustal thickness on the assumption that the crust floats upon the mantle. That this concept in gross form is substantiated by the seismic measurements is shown in Figure 28.3, representing a compilation of gravity and seismic data in the same areas from different parts of the world. From Figure 28.3 and the results of laboratory and field measurements of the seismic velocities and density values associated with different kinds of rocks, we can reach the following general conclusions concerning the crust: (1) the crust has a mean density of about 2.86 gm/cc; and the underlying mantle a density of about 3.32 gm/cc; (2) the crust does appear to float upon the mantle; (3) the surface elevation is directly related to crustal thickness, and the freeboard to root ratio for average crustal conditions is about 1:6.7. There are, however, significant departures from these over-all generalizations. For example, we know that the crust does vary in mean density from the normal value of 2.87 gm/cc over fairly large areas. Where the density is greater than normal, the surface elevation is less and the crustal thickness less than normal. Conversely, where the mean density is less than the normal value, the surface elevation is higher and the crustal thickness greater than normal. These conclusions have been demonstrated by both seismic measurements and the analysis of associated gravity data. The cause for these departures in crustal composition are as yet not understood, and they do not appear to be related to observable surface-geologic features except in the case of granitic batholiths which appear to be characterized by both a subnormal density and seismic velocity.

REGIONAL VERSUS LOCAL ISOSTATIC COMPENSATIONS

Another factor associated with the crust beside its thickness and composition is its strength and ability to sustain variations in load associated with local changes in topography. In this connection, it is useful to think of the crust as being like a sheet of ice on a lake. When one steps out on a sheet of ice over a lake it frequently can be seen to bend down like an elastic sheet. The ice does not break although it is obviously deformed over a wide area by our weight. This constitutes regional isostatic compensation as the added weight is in part carried by the strength of the ice and in part displaces the underlying water over a wide area. If the strength of the ice were exceeded and the ice broke, however, one would end up floating in the underlying water. This would constitute local isostatic compensation as now one's weight is sustained only in terms of the density differential between ourselves and the water, with our head representing freeboard topography and the rest of our body the compensating root. Although local compensation applies to all major topographic features, there are many smaller features, such as the Bighorn Mountains of Wyoming, that appear to be regionally compensated and without underlying roots. Although such areas can be recognized from analytical studies of gravity data, present knowledge of the strength of the crust is still too limited to permit one to gauge exactly how much load can be sustained through regional compensation rather than through local compensation. A rough rule of thumb, though, is that if the width of the topographic feature does not exceed three times the probable thickness of the crust for the region as a whole, it is probably regionally compensated.

PHYSICAL-CHEMICAL RELATIONS

Another phenomenon of interest that is related to the crust is that in many areas, such as the Gulf Coast, the deep exploration work for oil indicates that here there has been an accumulation of about 50,000 feet (15 kms) of sedimentary rock material—sand, silt, and mud. As the structural attitude of this material shows that the Gulf Coast area has been progressively sinking as the material was deposited, one is confronted with the problem of how 15 kms of material can be added to the top of the crust and have the surface sink instead of rise as would be predicted from Archimedes' principle. Obviously the crust must be mechanically deformed in such areas or some phenomenon is operative that results in a thinning of the crust by attrition at its lower boundary that keeps pace with the addition of material at the surface. One theory that has been proposed in connection with the latter explanation (Kennedy, 1959) is that the mantle material immediately beneath the crust is composed of the rock eclogite and that the basal portion of the crust is composed of basalt. Eclogite can undergo a reversible polymorphic phase transformation to a lower density form which is basalt, with changes in either temperature or pressure. The addition of surface sediments under this hypothesis increases the pressure and automatically thins the crust by inducing the reverse of this transformation. One area where it should be possible to test this hypothesis on a continental-wide scale is Antarctica, where the superimposed load of ice is the equivalent of over one km of sedimentary rock material.

Another physical-chemical phase transformation that has been considered in connection with the crust is the transformation of the high-density rock peridotite to the lower density form serpentine, on the assumption that

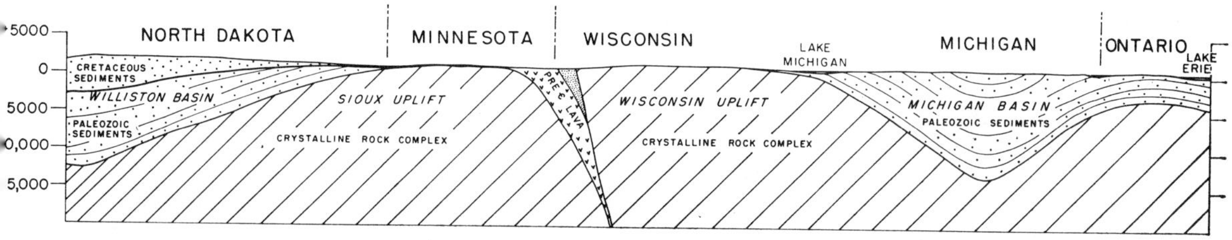

FIGURE 28.4
Geologic section from North Dakota-Canadian boundary to Michigan-Ontario boundary

the mantle material is composed of peridotite. This transformation, which is also reversible, is dependent upon the addition of water and a temperature of less than 500°C. It has been proposed (Hess, 1955) as an explanation for the long-term rise of plateau regions, such as the Colorado Plateau where the incised meanders of the Colorado Canyon suggest that the surface has risen over a mile in recent geologic time.

INSTABILITY OF THE CRUST

It is clear from the evidence of the surface geology that the continental crust has not only been subject to tremendous upheavals, fracturing, and horizontal movement, but also periods of subsidence allowing great inundations of the seas. Some areas, as Wisconsin, appear to have had almost a continuous history of domal uplift over the past 400 million years. Adjacent areas, as the peninsula of Michigan and Illinois on the other hand, have had a history of almost continuous subsidence. Figure 28.4 shows the difference in level of the crystalline rock surface on a line from North Dakota across Minnesota, Wisconsin, and Michigan. The explanation for these differences in crustal behavior in adjacent areas is not known. They might be related to vertical convectional flow in the underlying mantle induced by heat flow from the central core of the earth. Such convection currents conceivably might pile up crustal material at points of downflow and thin the crust at points of upward and outward movement, or have the reverse effect in bulging the crust upward over points of upflow and dragging it down at points of downflow. The latter explanation has

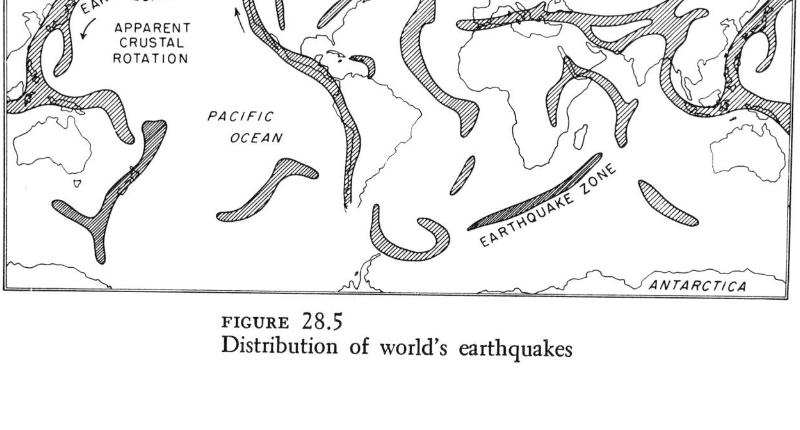

FIGURE 28.5
Distribution of world's earthquakes

been advanced by Ewing (1960 Vetlesen Lecture) to account for the Mid-Atlantic Ridge which extends almost the entire length of the Atlantic Ocean.

That the crust is subject to large-scale torsional forces which have been a dominant horizontal component that presumably are also related to movement in the underlying mantle is evidenced by the pattern of the world's earthquake belts. These show areas of localized shear and horizontal movement which in the case of California has resulted in a gross displacement of over 150 miles northward of the coastal area relative to the rest of the continent in recent geologic time. In Japan the evidence is that the coastal area is moving to the south. These observations, therefore, suggest that the entire Pacific Ocean Basin is rotating in a counter-clockwise direction. This appears to be further substantiated, as shown in Figure 28.5, by the "ring of fire" defined by both earthquakes and volcanic activity that mark the boundary of this, the earth's largest crustal feature.

CONCLUSION

In conclusion it can be said that the problems of the crust are many, and our knowledge of the basic phenomena related to it is still so limited that crustal study can be expected to remain an intriguing branch of scientific study for some time to come. Perhaps when we know more about the crust we shall be able to unravel the problem of the origin of the continents and the ocean basins. At the moment, the theories on the origin of these features range from one having a primordial oceanic crust with the continents growing by accretion from nuclei of oceanic volcanic islands to major variations in crustal thickness being the result of convectional flow on a gigantic scale at an early stage in the earth's history. Another problem that might be resolved through further study of the crust is that of continental drift. Certainly the geologic evidence suggests that several of the now existing continents may have been at one time part of a larger mass. The evidence, however, is far from convincing and implies a mobility that is difficult to reconcile with physical theory unless it can also be proved that the earth's crust as a whole is free to migrate as an independent entity about the earth which it encloses.

BIBLIOGRAPHY

Ewing, W. M., 1960, The mechanics of the mid-ocean ridge and rift: Vetlesen Lecture, 1960. [A lecture given by Professor Ewing at ceremonies for the presentation of the Vetlesen Prize, established for achievement in the earth sciences. Professor Ewing was the first recipient of the prize, which was given to him for his work in oceanography.]

Hess, H. H., 1955, Serpentines, orogeny and epeirogeny, *in* Arie Poldervaart, ed., Crust of the earth: Geol. Soc. America Spec. Paper 62, p. 391–408.

Kennedy, George C., 1959, The origin of the continents, mountain ranges, and ocean basins: Am. Scientist, v. 47, p. 491–504.

29

Convection in the Earth's Mantle

PETER J. BRANCAZIO

1964

The question of the existence of convection currents in the mantle of the earth has been the cause of a considerable amount of controversy. In recent years, a rather extensive body of observations has been built up purporting to give evidence in favor of the convection hypothesis. The bulk of this evidence is impressive although not really conclusive; there are at the same time some rather nagging discrepancies. However, the major barrier against the general acceptance of the convection hypothesis seems to be the lack of an adequate theoretical description of the currents themselves. A good part of the difficulty here is tied up with our lack of knowledge of the properties of the mantle material.

The significance of convection in the mantle with respect to the origins of the oceans and the atmosphere is that convection currents, if they exist, would undoubtedly represent very important mechanisms for bringing water and gases from the interior to the surface. In this article, we will review the present situation with regard to the convection hypothesis by summarizing the present state of the theory and discussing some of the evidence for and against the existence of convection currents. We will then consider the role of convection with regard to degassing processes.

THEORY OF CONVENTION CURRENTS

The general picture of convention currents in the mantle suggests that convective overturn of the mantle material occurs intermittently. That is, a sufficient temperature gradient ΔT must be built up before convection can occur; once this ΔT is reached, there is a half-turn of the mantle material so that the hot material rises to the surface and the cold material sinks. At this point, convection stops until radioactive heating in the interior and cooling at the surface have established a ΔT sufficient to trigger a new overturn. The usual value taken for the velocity of the current is on the order

From *The Origin and Evolution of Atmospheres and Oceans*, edited by Peter J. Brancazio and A. G. W. Cameron, pp. 64–73. John Wiley & Sons, Inc., 1964. Reprinted with permission of the author and the publisher.

of 1–10 cm/yr near the surface, with a value of perhaps 100 cm/yr in the interior (Runcorn, 1962). Griggs (1939) has estimated that it should take 60 million years to complete one overturn, and about 500 million years to set up a ΔT sufficient to trigger a new overturn.

Chandrasekhar (1953) has solved the idealized problem of convection in a fluid confined to a spherical shell under the influence of a radial gravitational field. The results show that the convection cells are roughly as wide as they are deep, and thus as the ratio of the inner radius to the outer radius of the shell increases, the cells will become smaller in size and will increase in number.

However, when we attempt a solution on the basis of a more realistic picture of conditions in the mantle, formidable difficulties are encountered. First of all, we should not picture the mantle as an homogeneous fluid. In actuality, the mantle material has a finite strength, and the physical properties vary with depth. Another difficulty is that the heat sources are themselves in motion. Finally, one of the more critical parameters is the viscosity, and there is considerable debate as to what value to use in calculations. Suggested values range from 10^{22} gm/cm-sec, based on the postglacial uplift of Fennoscandia (Gutenberg, 1959), to 10^{26} gm/cm-sec, based on the time response of the nonequilibrium bulge of Earth that results from deceleration due to tidal friction (MacDonald, 1963). As an example of how one's choice of a viscosity value can crucially affect the discussion, let us look at the calculation usually given to establish whether convection is possible. By equating the viscous and buoyant forces, we obtain as a condition for convection (Runcorn, 1962):

$$g\rho\alpha\,\Delta T = \frac{\mu v}{r^2}$$

where g = acceleration of gravity
ρ = density
α = thermal coefficient of volume expansion
ΔT = temperature difference between rising and falling columns
μ = viscosity
v = velocity of convection current
r = depth of mantle, taken from surface of the earth.

Taking $g = 10^3$ cm/sec², $\rho = 5$ gm/cm³, $\alpha = 2 \times 10^{-5}$/C°, $v = 10$ cm/yr, and $r = 1.5 \times 10^8$ cm, we obtain

$$\Delta T = 1.5 \times 10^{-22}\,\mu$$

The next step in this argument is to obtain the heat flow rate to the surface based on the calculated ΔT. If 10^{22} gm/cm-sec is used for μ, the calculated heat flow is not very different from the observed value, whereas if 10^{26} gm/cm-sec is used, the calculated heat flow is much too large. This argument can be (and has been) used by both sides in the dispute. Its validity, however, depends entirely on the validity of the viscosity determinations.

A major shortcoming of the lack of a realistic theoretical picture is that we are unable to decide with any certainty the number, size, and location of the convection cells. This severely limits the testability of the hypothesis. It is not certain whether the cells would extend from the core to the crust. The region of the earth's interior from 200 to 900 km depth is marked by a very rapid increase in density. If this is due to a change in composition, then the existence of this region indicates the absence of full-scale convection. On the other hand, if there is a phase change in this region, the currents will not be greatly affected.

In addition, it was shown by Elsasser (1963) that convection currents may necessarily be confined to the upper few hundred kilometers of the mantle. Assuming a certain temperature distribution, he showed that the viscosity of the mantle material should increase with depth, and that the viscosity should vary by a factor of 10^2 to 10^3 from the top of the mantle to the bottom. On this basis, the flow would be expected to be concentrated near the top of the mantle.

We will now go on to look at some of the evidence that has been presented with regard to the convection hypothesis. We will begin with some of the more indirect lines of evidence.

MISCELLANEOUS GEOLOGICAL EVIDENCE

The theory predicts that overturn should occur intermittently. We might expect that there would be some indication of this in the geological record. In fact, there is considerable evidence for the episodic nature of geological activity. Gastil (1960) has conducted a survey of the radioactive ages of rocks from all continents and found several peaks in the graph of the number of rocks vs. age. These age peaks are indicative of periodic upsurges in geologic activity.

Birch (1951) has shown that the density of the mantle, when reduced to surface temperature and pressure conditions, is essentially constant from 900 km depth down to the core. Thus the mantle appears to be homogeneous in composition and phase in this region, as would be expected if convection systems were in operation.

It is a common view that the secular variations of the geomagnetic field result from convection currents in the earth's core (Gutenberg, 1959). Bullard (1949) has shown that if these currents do in fact exist in the core, the heat transferred out of the core is more than can be transferred through the mantle by conduction. On this basis, if there is convection in the core, there must also be convection in the mantle.

It is now generally accepted that the crust of the earth is in isostatic equilibrium. Thus we have a picture of the crust "floating" on the mantle, which indicates that at least a part of the mantle is plastic and capable of flow. In fact, the existence of the so-called low-velocity layer has been well established (Gutenberg, 1959); this is a region from about 60 km depth down to 250 km in which the material is of relatively low rigidity. The existence of the low-velocity layer is not in itself evidence for convection, but it is significant in that it demonstrates that mantle material can have a low enough rigidity to permit flow.

Related to the existence of isostatic equilibrium is the problem of explaining gravity anomalies found at various points on the earth. Vening Meinesz has pointed out that many negative gravity anomalies are associated with the trenches near island arcs (Heiskanen and Vening Meinesz, 1958). He suggests that such trenches are places where currents descend into the mantle. We would expect crustal thickening here; however, Worzel and Shurbet (1955), on the basis of seismic measurements, found no such thickening. In addition, Ewing and Heezen (1955) found low-density sediments in the bottom of the Puerto Rico trough and showed that these sediments could account for the gravity anomaly.

A most intriguing line of thought is that which relates the surface topography of the earth to convection currents in the mantle. Following an analysis by Prey, Vening Meinesz (1962) analyzed the surface features of the earth in terms of spherical harmonics and found that several terms, notably the 3rd, 4th, and 5th order terms, are particularly strong. However, Chandrasekhar (1953), in his solution of the problem of convection in a spherical shell, found that for a shell with the dimensions of the earth's mantle, the 3rd, 4th and 5th harmonics of convective flow would be dominant. It is thus suggested that the surface features of the earth are a function of the convection currents in the mantle. Vening Meinesz has extended the topography analysis to the 31st order and accounted for the stronger orders by a refinement of the picture of convection in the mantle to include six or seven layers of rotating cells stacked in the mantle.

One criticism of this picture is offered by MacDonald (1963), who feels that the gravitational potential of the earth should also show the same harmonics if topography is indeed a result of convection. Kaula (1963) has shown that there is a negligible correlation between topographic and geodesic harmonics.

CONTINENTAL DRIFT

The hypothesis of continental drift . . . is closely related to the convection hypothesis. For if it can be shown that continental drift has in fact taken place, then convection currents would be the most likely mechanism for supplying the force to move the continents. It should be noted, however, that theories for continental drift without convection currents have been proposed (Heezen, 1962); these generally speculate that the earth is expanding through one process or another. Nevertheless, we will proceed to consider some of the evidence for continental drift.

Historically, the first piece of evidence suggesting continental drift was the observation of the remarkable correspondence between the coastlines of Africa and South America. There have been several discoveries of correspondence between geological or geographic features on opposite sides of oceans; for example, Wilson (1962) has noted the strong similarities in structure and age of the Great Glen Fault in Scotland and the Cabot Fault on the northeastern coast of North America.

In addition, considerable climatological evidence has been gathered indicating that there has been relative motion between the continents and the geographic poles. For example, such climatological anomalies as glaciation at the Equator in Africa and coal deposits, coral reefs, and petrified trees in polar regions have been observed (Durham, 1962; Opdyke, 1962). On the other hand, Axelrod (1963) has studied the distribution of flora during the eras when the continents were supposedly at different latitudes, and he states that the climates suggested by the fossil flora are inconsistent with the proposed latitudes of the continents. Perhaps the paleotemperature measurements now being made on the basis of the O^{18}/O^{16} ratios for various fossils will provide a better approach to this problem.

Perhaps the strongest line of evidence for continental drift results from the paleomagnetic data of Runcorn et al. (1962). The basic assumptions made are that (1) rocks acquire an essentially permanent magnetization upon formation, so that the direction of the magnetization in the rock gives the direction of the magnetic field at the time of formation; and (2) that the earth's magnetic field has always been essentially a dipole. On this latter point, MacDonald (1963) has pointed out that there have apparently been reversals in the field, and there may well have been intervals during which the field was not dipolar. At any rate, Runcorn and his co-workers have looked at rocks of the same age and from the same continents and have found that the directions of magnetization point to a specific location for the magnetic pole, without a great deal of error. From this information, they have plotted polar wandering curves; on comparing the curves for different continents, a divergence is exhibited which indicates that the continents have moved relative to one another. Runcorn suggests that there has been no substantial motion of the continents since the Middle Tertiary.

As can be seen, there is some attractive evidence in favor of continental drift; yet continental drift has many geological implications which have yet to be accounted for (Heezen, 1962). Verifiction of the continental drift hypothesis would constitute a strong argument for the existence of convection currents in the mantle.

EVIDENCE FROM THE OCEAN FLOOR

During recent years, the ocean floors have been the subject of rather intense study. This research has produced evidence for convection which is considerably more direct than what has been presented thus far.

One of the undersea features which has been the subject of recent study is the Mid-Atlantic Ridge, which lies along the length of the Atlantic Ocean, midway between the continents; it is, in fact, part of a worldwide system of midoceanic ridges. The most interesting feature of the ridge is the deep rift running along the center of the ridge. Furthermore, the vast majority of earthquake epicenters in the Atlantic Ocean lie within a narrow belt that coincides with the rift. Also, the rate of heat flow from the interior of the earth is five to six times higher than average along the ridge (Heezen, 1962).

Another anomalous structure to be found on the ocean floor is the East Pacific Rise. This is a bulge in the ocean floor which runs roughly parallel to the Coast of South America, meeting the North American continent at lower California. This structure has been found to have on its crest a heat flow rate eight times greater than normal; shallow earthquakes seem to be common along the crest, and the crust has been shown to be thinner than usual along the rise.

All of this information can be fitted into a relatively consistent picture, assuming the existence of convection currents, as follows: both the Mid-Atlantic Ridge and the East Pacific Rise lie over regions where rising convection currents come to the surface. The rising hot material would be a source of earthquake activity, and would account for the anomalously high heat-flow rates. As the rising currents reach the surface of the mantle, they turn and flow horizontally under the crust; this action would tend to produce tension in the crust in the vicinity of the rising currents. This tension is exhibited in the thinning of the crust over the East Pacific Rise and in the development of the central rift along the Mid-Atlantic Ridge. This mechanism also accounts for the numerous fracture zones that are found lying perpendicular to the axes of both the Ridge and the Rise.

This description is not without its inadequacies. For example, the lack of a rift valley in the vicinity of the East Pacific Rise needs to be explained. A possible explanation for this is that the Mid-Atlantic Ridge is a product of an older, well-developed convection system, while the East Pacific Rise is a result of the early stages of development of a new convection cell. In fact, Hess (1962) estimates that the East Pacific Rise is less than 100 million years old. He also points out that there is evidence for the existence of an ancient trans-Pacific ridge; this ridge apparently began to subside about 100 million years ago, and has almost completely disappeared except for a belt of atolls and guyots stretching across the Pacific.

Another problem is to find the areas where the convection currents turn and sink into the mantle. We would expect to find in such locations low heat flow and compression in the crust, coupled with extensive earthquake activity. Oceanic trenches generally have such properties, but there does not seem to be a consistent worldwide picture linking the regions of rising currents to the regions of sinking currents.

On the other hand, the observations of heat flow rates constitute a thorny problem for the anticonvectionists. In view of the differences between the continental and oceanic crust, it came as quite a surprise when it was noted that the heat-flow rates for continents and oceans were essentially the same (Gutenberg, 1959). The picture was even more confused by the discovery of localized regions of abnormally high or low heat flow such as we have just described. This situation is much more easily accounted for if convection, rather than conduction, is the major heat transfer mechanism for the earth.

An additional argument for convection is the relatively thin layer of sediments found in ocean basins. Based on calculations on the rate of deposition of sediments and the indication that this rate may not have varied since the Miocene, Hess (1962) calculates that the present layer of sediments was built up in 200 to 300 million years. This seems to indicate that the ocean floor has been swept clean periodically by overturns of the mantle. As further evidence for the periodic regeneration of the ocean floor, Hess points to the relatively small number of volcanoes found in the oceans.

CONVECTION, DEGASSING, AND THE ORIGIN OF THE OCEANS

There has apparently been little discussion of the effect of convection currents on the degassing of the interior. Clearly convection would be important, for through this mechanism a great deal more of the mantle would be in a position to provide gases for the exterior. For a solid earth, only the upper layers of the mantle are likely to be degassed. Quantitative studies are difficult to make for several reasons, however. Without knowing the dimensions of the convection cells, we cannot tell how much mantle material will be available for degassing. In addition, the mechanisms by which gases escape from the mantle, enter the crust, and then escape to the atmosphere are difficult to specify. Finally, we must know the distribution of the gas-producing elements (uranium, thorium, potassium, etc.) in the mantle.

In this vein, an interesting calculation has been made by Hess (1962) in which he shows that the oceans may have resulted from the transfer of water from the mantle to the crust via convection. Hess gives evidence that the oceanic crust contains a layer of serpentinized peridotite directly beneath the sediments. He assumes that this layer has been serpentinized by water carried up by rising convection currents. At the point where the convection currents bend downward, the crust is also bent downward and into a region of higher temperature. Here the serpentine layer is dehydrated and the water enters the ocean. Hess assumes that the transfer of water to the crust occurs all along the 25,000-km length of the oceanic ridge system. He also assumes a current velocity of 1 cm/yr and takes this to mean that a layer 1 cm thick is formed on each side of the ridge each year. Based on seismic velocity measurements, he estimates the water content of the uprising materials, and from this determines that approximately 0.4 km^3 of water leave the mantle in this manner per year. Assuming that this rate has been the same for 4×10^9 yr, and subtracting the water still remaining in the serpentine layer, he obtains a value of 1.3×10^9 km^3 of water released from the mantle over geologic time. This is approximately the volume of water now present in the oceans. We might argue that the evidence as to the level of the sea over geologic history indicates that the volume of the ocean has not changed appreciably, but this is not a valid argument because we would expect the oceanic crust to adjust isostatically to the additional weight of new water; thus changes in sea level are not necessarily good indicators of changes in the volume of the ocean.

CONCLUSIONS

The situation with regard to convection is somewhat confused at present. The weight of the evidence (most of which is indirect) tends to be in favor of the convection hypothesis, but acceptance is hampered by the lack of a good theoretical description, or at least a consistent worldwide picture of where the currents rise and fall. The evidence against convection is not particularly formidable; perhaps the best argument against convection is that the viscosity of the mantle may be too high. A clear-cut determination of the viscosity of the mantle would certainly tip the balance one way or another. . . .

It is realized that convection currents would play a significant role in the formation of the oceans and atmosphere. However, because of the many uncertainties involved, a clear understanding of the effect of convection on degassing has not yet been attained.

REFERENCES

Axelrod, D., 1963, Fossil floras suggest stable, not drifting continents: Jour. Geophys. Research, v. 68, p. 3257.

Birch, F., 1951, Remarks on the structure of the mantle, and its bearing upon the possibility of convection currents: Am. Geophys. Union Trans., v. 32, p. 533.

Bullard, E. C., 1949, The magnetic field within the earth: Royal Soc. (London) Proc., ser. A, v. 197, p. 433.

Chandrasekhar, S., 1953, The onset of convection by thermal instability in spherical shells: Philos. Mag., v. 44, no. 233, p. 1129.

Durham, J. W., 1962, The drifting continents: Nat. History, v. 71, no. 4, p. 30.

Elsasser, W. M., 1963, Early history of the earth, *in* J. Geiss and E. D. Goldberg, eds., Earth science and meteorites: New York, John Wiley and Sons, Interscience.

Ewing, M., and B. C. Heezen, 1955, Puerto Rico trench topography and geophysical data, *in* Arie Poldervaart, ed. Crust of the earth: Geol. Soc. America Spec. Paper 62, p. 255.

Gastil, G. 1960, The distribution of mineral dates in time and space: Am. Jour. Sci., v. 258, p. 1.

Griggs, D. T., 1939, A theory of mountain-building: Am. Jour. Sci., v. 237, p. 611.

Gutenberg, B., 1959, Physics of the earth's interior: New York, Academic Press.

Heezen, B. C. 1962, The deep-sea floor, *in* S. K. Runcorn, ed., Continental drift: New York, Academic Press.

Heiskanen, W. A., and F. A. Vening Meinesz, 1958, The earth and its gravity field: New York, McGraw-Hill.

Hess, H. H., 1962, History of ocean basins, *in* A. E. J. Engle, H. L. James, and B. F. Leonard, eds., Petrologic studies—a volume in honor of A. F. Buddington: Boulder, Colo., Geological Society of America, p. 599.

Kaula, W. M., 1963, Elastic models of the mantle corresponding to variations in the external gravity field: Jour. Geophys. Research, v. 68, p. 4967.

MacDonald, G. J. F., 1963, The internal constitution of the inner planets and the moon: Space Sci. Rev., v. 2, p. 473.

Menard, H. W., 1960, The East Pacific Rise: Science, v. 132, p. 1737.

Opdyke, N. D., 1962, Palaeoclimatology and continental drift, *in* S. K. Runcorn, ed., Continental Drift: New York, Academic Press.

Runcorn, S. K., 1962, Palaeomagnetic evidence for continental drift and its geophysical cause, *in* S. K. Runcorn, ed., Continental drift: New York, Academic Press.

Vening Meinesz, F. A., 1962, Thermal convection in the earth's mantle, *in* S. K. Runcorn, ed., Continental drift: New York, Academic Press.

Wilson, T., 1962, Cabot fault, an Appalachian equivalent of the San Andreas and Great Glen faults and some implications for continental displacement: Nature, v. 195, p. 135.

Worzel, J. L., and G. L. Shurbet, 1955, Gravity anomalies at continental margins, *in* Arie Poldervaart, ed., Crust of the earth: Geol. Soc. America Spec. Paper 62, p. 87.

30

History of Ocean Basins

H. H. HESS
1962

The birth of the oceans is a matter of conjecture, the subsequent history is obscure, and the present structure is just beginning to be understood. Fascinating speculation on these subjects has been plentiful, but not much of it predating the last decade holds water. Little of Umbgrove's (1947) brilliant summary remains pertinent when confronted by the relatively small but crucial amount of factual information collected in the intervening years. Like Umbgrove, I shall consider this paper an essay in geopoetry. In order not to travel any further into the realm of fantasy than is absolutely necessary I shall hold as closely as possible to a uniformitarian approach; even so, at least one great catastrophe will be required early in the Earth's history.

PREMISES ON INITIAL CONDITIONS

Assuming that the ages obtained from radioactive disintegrations in samples of meteorites approximate the age of the solar system, then the age of the Earth is close to 4.5 aeons. The Earth, it is further assumed, was formed by accumulation of particles (of here unspecified character) which initially had solar composition. If this is true, then before condensation to a solid planet the Earth lost, during a great evaporation, a hundred times as much matter as it now contains. Most of this loss was hydrogen. An unknown but much smaller amount of heavier elements was lost to space as well. The deficiency of the atmosphere in the inert gases points clearly to their loss. Urey (1957) suggests loss of nitrogen, carbon, and water, and perhaps a considerable proportion of original silicate material. He also points out that the lack of concentration of certain very volatile substances at the Earth's surface indicates that it never had a high surface temperature. This low temperature more or less precluded escape of large amounts of material after the Earth condensed and suggests that the loss occurred when the material forming

From *Petrologic Studies—A Volume in Honor of A. F. Buddington,* edited by A. E. J. Engel, Harold L. James, and B. F. Leonard, pp. 599–620. The Geological Society of America, 1962. Reprinted with permission of the author and the publisher.

the Earth was very much more dispersed so that the escape velocity from its outer portion was comparatively low. The condensation was rapid, and some light elements and volatile compounds were trapped within the accumulated solid material of the primordial Earth. I will assume for convenience and without too much justification that at this stage the Earth had no oceans and perhaps very little atmosphere. It is postulated that volatile constituents trapped within its interior have during the past and are today leaking to the surface, and that by such means the present oceans and atmosphere have evolved.

THE GREAT CATASTROPHE

Immediately after formation of the solid Earth, it may have contained within it many short-lived radioactive elements; how many and how much depends on the time interval between nuclear genesis and condensation. The bricketted particles from which it was made might be expected to have a low thermal conductivity at least near its surface as suggested by Kuiper (1954). The temperature rose, lowering the strength and perhaps starting partial fusion. The stage was thus set for the *great catastrophe* which it is assumed happened forthwith. A single-cell (toroidal) convective overturn took place (Figure 30.1) (Vening Meinesz, 1952), resulting in the formation of a nickel-iron core, and at the same time the low-melting silicates were extruded over the rising limbs of the current to form the primordial single continent (Figure 30.1). The single-cell overturn also converted gravitational energy into thermal energy (Urey, 1953). It is postulated that this heat and a probably much larger amount of heat resulting from the energy involved in the accumulation of the Earth were not sufficient to produce a molten Earth. The great quantitative uncertainties in this assumption can be gauged from MacDonald's analysis (1959).

The proposed single-cell overturn brought about the bilateral asymmetry of the Earth, now possibly much modified but still evident in its land and water hemispheres. After this event, which segregated the core from the mantle, single-cell convection was no longer possible in the Earth as a whole (Chandrasekhar, 1953).

The critical question now facing us is what percentage of the continental crustal material and of the water of the oceans reached the surface in the *great catastrophe*. On the basis that continental material is still coming to the surface of the Earth from the mantle at the rate of 1 km^3/year, accepting Sapper's (1927, p. 424) figure on the contribution of volcanoes over the past 4 centuries, and assuming uniformitarianism, this means 4×10^9 km^3 in 4 aeons or approximately 50 per cent of the continents. So we shall assume that the other half was extruded during the catastrophe. The percentage of water is much harder to estimate. Rapid convective overturn might be much less efficient in freeing the water as compared to the low-melting silicates. The water might be expected to be present as a monomolecular film on grain surfaces. The low-melting silicate droplets could coagulate into sizable masses as a result of strong shearing during the overturn. On the other hand, shearing that would break down solid crystals to smaller size might increase their surface

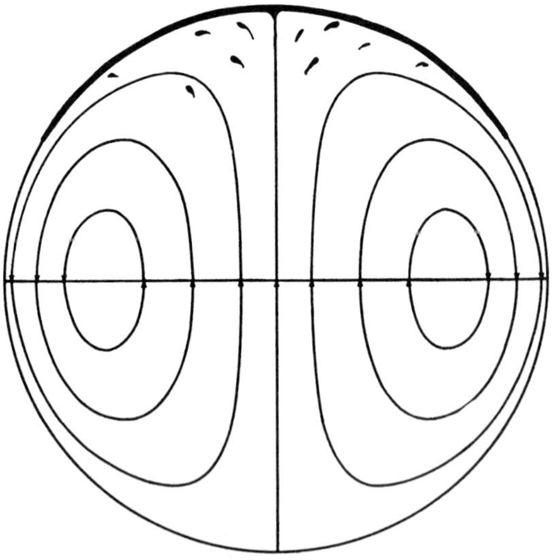

FIGURE 30.1
Single-cell (toroidal) convective overturn of earth's interior. (After Vening Meinesz.) Continental material extruded over rising limb but would divide and move to descending limb if convection continued beyond a half cycle.

areas and actually inhibit freeing of water films. The best guess that I can make is that up to one-third of the oceans appeared on the surface at this time.

It may be noted that a molten Earth hypothesis would tend toward the initial formation of a thin continental or sialic layer uniformly over the Earth with a very thin uniform world-encircling water layer above it. Later it would require breaking up of this continental layer to form the observed bilateral asymmetry. With the present set of postulates this seems to be a superfluous step. Bilateral asymmetry was attained at the start, and it would be impossible ever to attain it once a core had formed, unless George H. Darwin's hypothesis that the moon came out of the Earth were accepted.

We have now set the stage to proceed with the subject at hand. Dozens of assumptions and hypotheses have been introduced in the paragraphs above to establish a framework for consideration of the problem. I have attempted to chose reasonably among a myriad of possible alternatives, but no competent reader with an ounce of imagination is likely to be willing to accept all of the choices made. Unless some such set of confining assumptions is made, however, speculation spreads out into limitless variations, and the resulting geopoetry has neither rhyme nor reason.

TOPOGRAPHY AND CRYSTAL COLUMNS

If the water were removed from the Earth, two distinct topographic levels would be apparent: (1) the deep-sea floor about 5 km below sea level, and (2) the continental surface a few hundred meters above sea level. In other words, the continents stand up abruptly as plateaus or mesas above the general level of the sea floor. Seismic evidence shows that the so-called crustal thickness—depth to the M discontinuity—is 6 km under oceans and 34 km under continents on the average. Gravity data prove that these two types of crustal columns have the same mass—the pressure at some arbitrary level beneath them, such as 40 km, would be the same. They are in hydrostatic equilibrium. It is evident that one cannot consider the gross features of ocean basins independent of the continental plateaus; the two are truly complementary.

Whereas 29 per cent of the Earth's surface is land, it would be more appropriate here to include the continental shelves and the slopes to the 1000-m isobath with the continents, leaving the remainder as oceanic. This results in 40 per cent continental and 60 per cent oceanic crust. In 1955 I discussed the nature of the two crustal columns, which is here modified slightly to adjust the layer thickness to the more recent seismic work at sea (Raitt, 1956; Ewing and Ewing, 1959) (Figure 30.2). A drastic change, however, has been made in layer 3 of the oceanic column, substituting partially serpentinized peridotite for the basalt of the main crustal layer under the oceans as proposed elsewhere (Hess, 1959a). Let us look briefly into the facts that seemed to necessitate this change.

That the mantle material is peridotitic is a fairly common assumption (Harris and Rowell, 1960; Ross, Foster, and Myers, 1954; Hess, 1955). In looking at the now-numerous seismic profiles at sea the uniformity in thickness of layer 3 is striking. More than 80 per cent of the profiles show it to be 4.7 ± 0.7 km thick.

Considering the probable error in the seismic data to be about ± 0.5 km, the uniformity may be even greater than the figures indicate. It is inconceivable that basalt flows poured out on the ocean floor could be so uniform in thickness. Rather, one would expect them to be thick near the fissures or vents from which they were erupted and thin or absent at great distance from the vents. The only likely manner in which a layer of uniform thickness could be formed would be if its bottom represented a present or past isotherm, at which temperature and pressure a reaction occurred. Two such reactions can be suggested: (1) the basalt to eclogite inversion (Sumner, 1954; Kennedy, 1959), and (2) the hydration of olivine to serpentine at about 500°C (Hess, 1954). The common occurrence of peridotitic inclusions in oceanic basaltic volcanic rocks (Ross, Foster, and Myers, 1954) and absence of eclogite inclusions lead the writer to accept postulate (2). Furthermore, the dredging of serpentinized peridotites from fault scarps in the oceans (Shand, 1949), where the displacement on the faults may have been sufficient to expose layer 3, adds credence to this supposition. This choice of postulates is made here and will control much of the subsequent reasoning. The seismic velocity of layer 3 is highly variable; it ranges from 6.0 to 6.9 km/sec and averages near 6.7 km/sec, which would represent peridotite 70 per cent serpentinized (Figure 30.3).

MID-OCEAN RIDGES

The Mid-Ocean Ridges are the largest topographic features on the surface of the Earth. Menard (1958) has shown that their crests closely correspond to median lines in the oceans and suggests (1959) that they may be ephemeral features. Bullard, Maxwell, and Revelle (1956) and Von Herzen (1959) show that they have unusually high heat flow along their crests. Heezen (1960) has demonstrated that a median graben exists along the crests of the Atlantic, Arctic, and Indian Ocean ridges and that shallow-depth earthquake foci are concentrated under the graben. This leads him to postulate extension of the crust at right angles to the trend of the ridges. Hess (1959b) also emphasizes the ephemeral character of the ridges and points to a trans-Pacific ridge that has almost disappeared since middle Cretaceous time, leaving a belt of atolls and guyots that has subsided 1–2 km. Its width is 3000 km and its length about 14,000 km (Figure 30.4). The present active mid-ocean ridges have an average width of 1300 km, crest height of about 2½ km, and total length of perhaps 25,000 km.

The most significant information on the structural and petrologic character of the ridges comes from refraction seismic information of Ewing and Ewing (1959) (Figure 30.5) on the Mid-Atlantic Ridge, and Raitt's (1956) refraction profiles on the East Pacific Rise. The sediment cover on the Mid-Atlantic Ridge appears to be thin and perhaps restricted to material ponded in depressions of the topography. On the ridge crest, layer 3 has a seismic velocity of from 4 to 5.5 km/sec instead of the normal 6 to 6.9 km/sec. The M discontinuity is not found or is represented by a transition from layer 3 to velocities near 7.4 km/sec. Normal velocities and layer thicknesses, however, appear on the flanks of ridges.

Earlier I (1955, 1959b) attributed the lower velocities (*ca.* 7.4 km/sec) in what should be mantle material to serpentinization, caused by olivine reacting with water released from below. The elevation of the ridge itself was thought to result from the change in density (olivine 3.3 g/cc to serpentine 2.6 g/cc). A 2-km rise of the ridge would require 8 km of complete serpentinization below, but a velocity of 7.4 km/sec is equivalent to only 40 per cent of the rock serpentinized. This serpentinization would have to extend to 20-km depth to

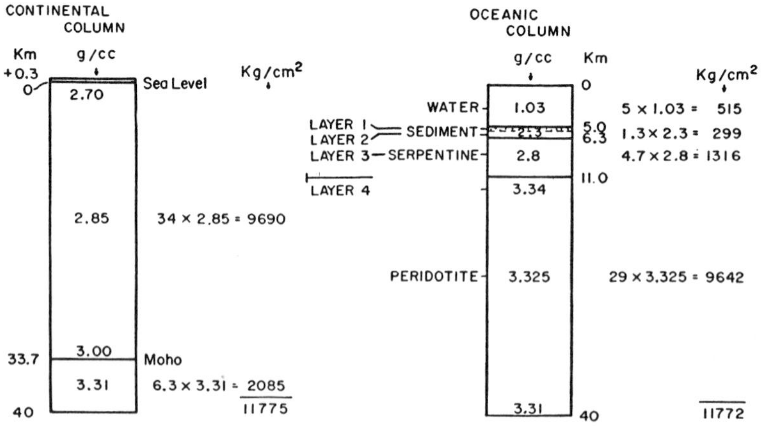

FIGURE 30.2
Balance of oceanic and continental crustal columns

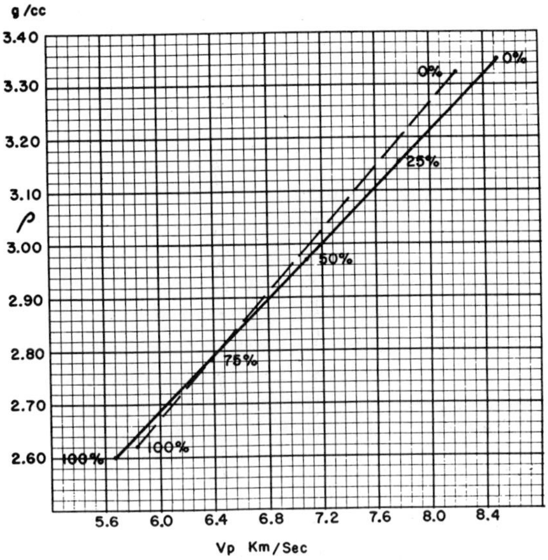

FIGURE 30.3
Relationship between seismic velocity, density, and per cent serpentinization. *Solid curve,* room temperature and pressure; *Dashed curve,* estimated temperature and pressure at 15 km depth. Curves based on measurements in laboratory by J. Green at the California Research Laboratory, La Habra, with variable temperatures up to 200°C and pressures up to 1 kilobar. The 100 per cent serpentinized sample measured by F. Birch at Harvard at pressures from 0 to 10 kilobars at room temperature (Hess, 1959a).

produce the required elevation of the ridge. This reaction, however, cannot take place at a temperature much above 500°C, which, considering the heat flow, probably exists at the bottom of layer 3, about 5 km below the sea floor, and cannot reasonably be 20 km deep. Layer 3 is thought to be peridotite 70 per cent serpentinized. It would appear that the highest elevation that the 500°C isotherm can reach is approximately 5 km below the sea floor, and this supplies the reason for uniform thickness of layer 3 (Figure 30.6).

CONVECTION CURRENTS IN THE MANTLE AND MID-OCEAN RIDGES

Long ago Holmes suggested convection currents in the mantle to account for deformation of the Earth's crust (Vening Meinesz, 1952; Griggs, 1939; 1954; Verhoogen, 1954; and many others). Nevertheless, mantle convection is considered a radical hypothesis not widely accepted by geologists and geophysicists. If it were accepted, a rather reasonable story could be constructed to describe the evolution of ocean basins and the waters within them. Whole realms of previously unrelated facts fall into a regular pattern, which suggests that close approach to satisfactory theory is being attained.

As mentioned earlier a single-cell convective overturn of the material within the Earth could have produced its bilateral asymmetry, segregating the iron core and primordial continents in the process. Since this event only multicell convection in the mantle has been possible. Vening Meinesz (1959) analyzed the spherical harmonics of the Earth's topography up to the thirty-first order. The peak shown in the values from the third to fifth harmonic would correlate very nicely with mantle-size convection currents; cells would have the approximate diameter of 3000 to 6000 km in cross section (the other horizontal dimension might be 10,000–20,000 km, giving them a banana-like shape).

The lower-order spherical harmonics of the topography show quite unexpected regularities. This means that the topography of a size smaller than continents and ocean basins has a greater regularity in distribution than previously recognized.

Paleomagnetic data presented by Runcorn (1959), Irving (1959), and others strongly suggest that the continents have moved by large amounts in geologically comparatively recent times. One may quibble over the details, but the general picture on paleomagnetism is sufficiently compelling that it is much more reasonable to accept it than to disregard it. The reasoning is that the Earth has always had a dipole magnetic field and that the magnetic poles have always been close to the axis of the Earth's rotation, which necessarily must remain fixed in space. Remanent magnetism of old rocks shows that position of the magnetic poles has changed in a rather regular manner with time, but this migration of the poles as measured in Europe, North America, Australia, India, etc., has not been the same for each of these land masses. This strongly indicates independent movement in direction and amount of large portions of the Earth's surface with respect to the rotational axis. This could be most easily accomplished by a convecting mantle system which involves actual movement of the Earth's surface passively riding on the upper part of the convecting cell. In this case at any given time continents over one cell would not move in the same direction as continents on another cell. The rate of motion suggested by paleomagnetic measurements lies between a fraction of a cm/yr to as much as 10 cm/yr. If one were to accept the old evidence, which was the strongest argument for continental drift, namely the separation of South America from Africa since the end of the Paleozoic, and apply uniformitarianism, a rate of 1 cm/yr results. This rate will be accepted in subsequent discussion. Heezen (1960) mentions a fracture zone crossing Iceland on the extension of the Mid-Atlantic rift zone which has been widening at a rate of 3.5 m/1000 yrs/km of width.

The unexpected regularities in the spherical harmonics of the Earth's topography might be attributed to a dynamic situation in the present Earth whereby the continents move to positions dictated by a fairly regular system of convection cells in the mantle. Menard's theorem that mid-ocean ridge crests correspond to median lines now takes on new meaning. The mid-ocean ridges could represent the traces of the rising limbs of convection cells, while the circum-Pacific belt of deformation and volcanism represents descending limbs. The Mid-Atlantic Ridge is median because the continental areas on each side of it have moved away from it at the same rate—1 cm/yr. This is not exactly the same as continental drift. The continents do not plow through oceanic crust impelled by unknown forces; rather they ride

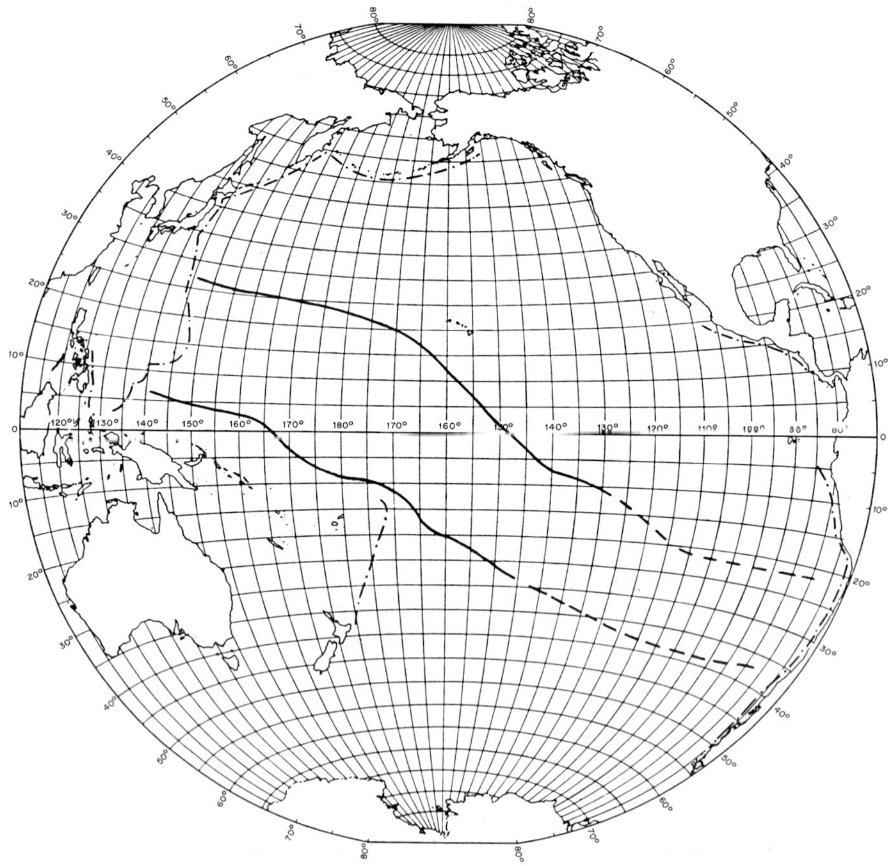

FIGURE 30.4
Former location of a Mid-Pacific Mesozoic ridge

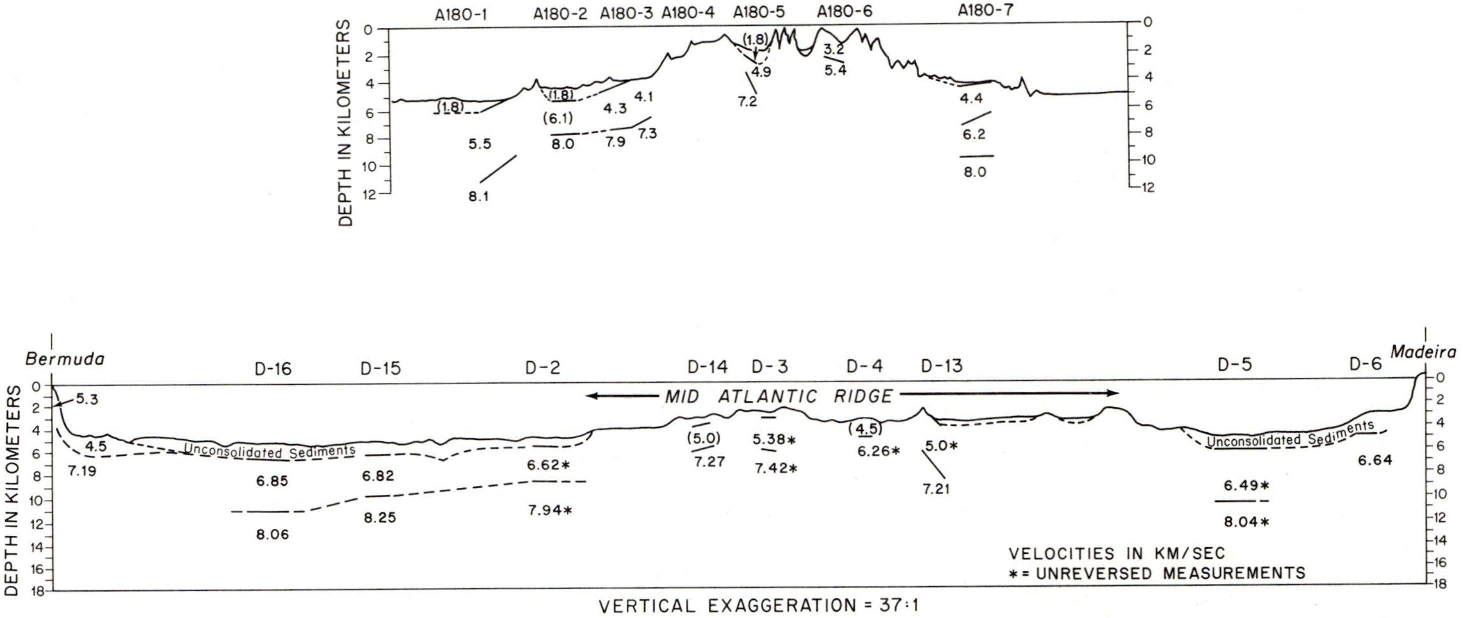

FIGURE 30.5
Seismic profiles on the Mid-Atlantic Ridge. (By Ewing and Ewing, 1959.)

passively on mantle material as it comes to the surface at the crest of the ridge and then moves laterally away from it. On this basis the crest of the ridge should have only recent sediments on it, and recent and Tertiary sediments on its flanks; the whole Atlantic Ocean and possibly all of the oceans should have little sediment older than Mesozoic (Figure 30.7). Let us look a bit further at the picture with regard to oceanic sediments.

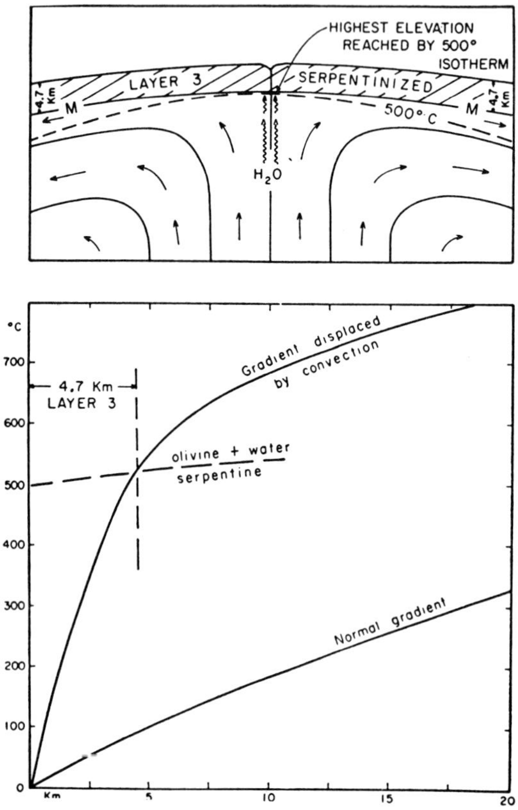

FIGURE 30.6
Serpentinization above the 500°C isotherm. Diagram portrays highest elevation that 500°C isotherm can reach over the rising limb of a mantle convection cell, and expulsion of water from mantle which produces serpentinization.

Looking over the reported data on rates of sedimentation in the deep sea, rates somewhere between 2 cm and 5 mm/1000 yrs seem to be indicated. Writers in the last few years have tried hard to accept the lowest possible rate consistent with the data in order to make the thickness jibe with the comparatively thin cover of sediment on the ocean floor indicated by Seismic data. Schott's figures for the Atlantic and Indian oceans as corrected by Kuenen (1946) and further corrected by decreasing the number of years since the Pleistocene from 20,000 years to 11,000 years indicate a rate of 2 cm/1000 yrs. Hamilton's (1960) figures suggest 5 mm/1000 yrs. A rate of 1 cm/1000 yrs would yield 40 km in 4 aeons or 17 km after compaction, using Hamilton's compaction figures. A 5-mm rate would still give 8.5 km compacted thickness instead of 1.3 km as derived from seismic data. This 1 order of magnitude discrepancy had led some to suggest that the water of the oceans may be very young, that oceans came into existence largely since the Paleozoic. This violates uniformitarianism to which the writer is dedicated and also can hardly be reconciled with Rubey's (1951) analysis of the origin of sea water. On the system here suggested any sediment upon the sea floor ultimately gets incorporated in the continents. New mantle material with no sedimentary cover on it rises and moves outward from the ridge. The cover of young sediments it acquires in the course of time will move to the axis of a downward-moving limb of a convection current, be metamorphosed, and probably eventually be welded onto a continent.

Assuming a rate of 1 cm/1000 yrs one might ask how long, on the average, the present sea floor has been exposed to deposition if the present thickness of sediment is 1.3 km. The upper 0.2 km would not yet have been compacted and would represent 20 million years of deposition. The remaining 1.1 km now compacted would represent 210 million years of accumulation or in total an average age of the sea floor of 260 million years. Note that a clear distinction must be made between the age of the ocean floor and the age of the water in the oceans.

In order to explain the discrepancy between present rate of sedimentation in the deep sea and the relatively small thickness of sediment on the floor of the oceans, many have suggested that Pleistocene glaciation has greatly increased the rate of sedimentation. The writer is skeptical of this interpretation, as was Kuenen in his analysis (1946)*. Another discrep-

* The Mohole test drilling off Guadalupe Island in 1961 suggest a rate of sedimentation in the Miocene of 1 cm/1000 yrs or a little more.

ancy of the same type, the small number of volcanoes on the sea floor, also indicates the apparent youth of the floor. Menard estimates there are in all 10,000 volcanic seamounts in the oceans. If this represented 4 aeons of volcanism, and volcanoes appeared at a uniform rate, this would mean only one new volcano on the sea floor per 400,000 years. One new volcano in 10,000 years or less would seem like a better figure. This would suggest an average age of the floor of the ocean of perhaps 100 to 200 million years. It would account also for the fact that nothing older than late Cretaceous has ever been obtained from the deep sea or from oceanic islands.

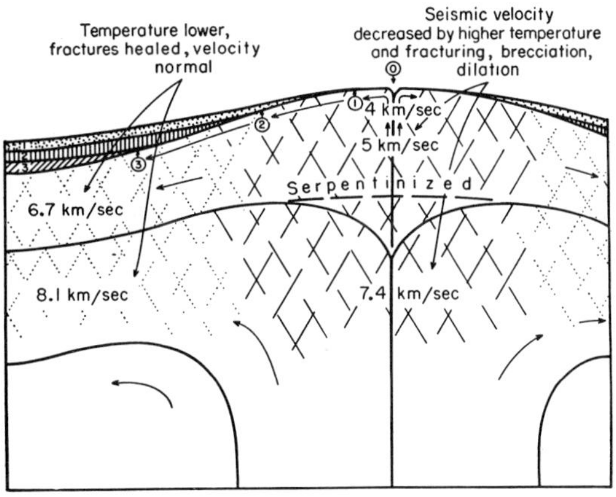

FIGURE 30.7
Overlap of ocean sediments on the ridge, and fracturing where convective flow changes. Diagram represents the apparent progressive overlap of ocean sediments on a mid-ocean ridge, which would actually be the effect of the mantle moving laterally away from ridge crest; and the postulated fracturing where convective flow changes direction from vertical to horizontal. Fracturing and higher temperature could account for the lower seismic velocities on ridge crests, and cooling and healing of the fractures with time, the return to normal velocities on the flanks.

Still another line of evidence pointing to the same conclusion relates to the ephemeral character of mid-ocean ridges and to the fact that evidence of only one old major ridge still remains on the ocean floor. The crest of this one began to subside about 100 million years ago. The question may be asked: Where are the Paleozoic and Precambrian mid-ocean ridges, or did the development of such features begin rather recently in the Earth's history?

Egyed (1957) introduced the concept of a great expansion in size of the Earth to account for apparent facts of continental drift. More recently Heezen (1960) tentatively advanced the same idea to explain paleomagnetic results coupled with an extension hypothesis for mid-ocean ridges. S. W. Carey (1958) developed an expansion hypothesis to account for many of the observed relationships of the Earth's topography and coupled this with an overall theory of the tectonics of the Earth's crust. Both Heezen and Carey require an expansion of the Earth since late Paleozoic time (*ca.* 2×10^8 years) such that the surface area has doubled. Both postulate that this expansion is largely confined to the ocean floor rather than to the continents. This means that the ocean basins have increased in area by more than 6 times and that the continents until the late Paleozoic occupied almost 80 per cent of the Earth's surface. With this greatly expanded ocean floor one could account for the present apparent deficiency of sediments, volcanoes, and old mid-ocean ridges upon it. While this would remove three of my most serious difficulties in dealing with the evolution of ocean basins, I hesitate to accept this easy way out. First of all, it is philosophically rather unsatisfying, in much the same way as were the older hypotheses of continental drift, in that there is no apparent mechanism within the Earth to cause a sudden (and exponential according to Carey) increase in the radius of the Earth. Second, it requires the addition of an enormous amount of water to the sea in just the right amount to maintain the axiomatic relationship between sea level-land surface and depth to the M discontinuity under continents, which is discussed later.

MESOZOIC MID-PACIFIC RIDGE

In the area between Hawaii, the Marshall Islands, and the Marianas scores of guyots were found during World War II. It was supposed that large numbers of them would be found elsewhere in the oceans. This was not the case. The Emperor seamounts running north-northwest from the west end of the Hawaiian chain are guyots, a single linear group of very large ones. An area of small guyots is known in the Gulf of Alaska (Gibson, 1960). There are a limited number in the Atlantic Ocean north of Bermuda on a line between Cape Cod and the Azores, and a few east of the Mid-Atlantic Ridge; other than these only rare isolated occurrences have been reported.

Excluding the areas of erratic uplift and depression represented by the island arcs, lines can be drawn in the mid-Pacific bounding the area of abundant guyots and atolls (Figure 30.4), marking a broad band of subsidence 3000 km wide crossing the Pacific from the Marianas to Chile. The eastern end is poorly charted and complicated by the younger East Pacific Rise. The western end terminates with striking abruptness against the eastern margin of the island-arc structures. Not a single guyot is found in the Philippine Sea west of the Marianas trench and its extensions, although to the east they are abundant right up to the trenches.

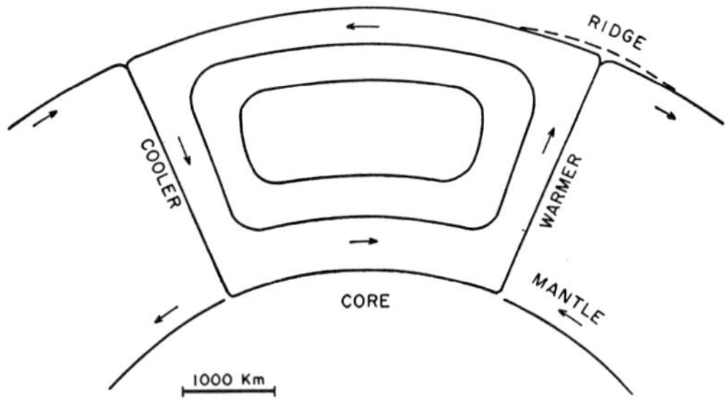

FIGURE 30.8
Possible geometry of a mantle convection cell

Fossils are available to date the beginning of the subsidence, but only near the axis of the old ridge. Hamilton (1956) found middle Cretaceous shallow-water fossils on guyots of the Mid-Pacific mountains, and Ladd and Schlanger (1960) reported Eocene sediments above basalt at the bottom of the Eniwetok bore hole. It should also be noted that atolls of the Caroline, Marshall, Gilbert, and Ellice islands predominate on the southern side of the old ridge, whereas guyots greatly predominate on the northern side. Hess (1946) had difficulty in explaining why the guyots of the mid-Pacific mountain area did not become atolls as they subsided. He postulated a Precambrian age for their upper flat surfaces, moving the time back to an era before lime-secreting organisms appeared in the oceans. This became untenable after Hamilton found shallow-water Cretaceous fossils on them. Looking at the same problem today and considering that the North Pole in early Mesozoic time, as determined from paleomagnetic data from North America and Europe, was situated in southeastern Siberia, it seems likely that the Mid-Pacific mountain area was too far north for reef growth when it was subsiding. The boundary between reef growth and nonreef growth in late Mesozoic time is perhaps represented by the northern margins of the Marshall and Caroline islands, now a little north of 10°N, then perhaps 35°N. Paleomagnetic measurements from Mesozoic rocks, if they could be found within or close to this area, are needed to substantiate such a hypothesis.

The old Mesozoic band of subsidence is more than twice as wide as the topographic rise of present-day oceanic ridges. This has interesting implications regarding evolution of ridges which are worth considering here. Originally I attributed the rise of ridges to release of water above the upward-moving limb of a mantle convection cell and serpentinization of olivine when the water crossed the 500-degree C isotherm. As mentioned above, this hypothesis is no longer tenable because the high heat flow requires that the 500-degree C isotherm be at very shallow depth. The topographic rise of the ridge must be attributed to the fact that a rising column of a mantle convection cell is warmed and hence less dense than normal or descending columns. The geometry of a mantle convection cell (Figure 30.8) fits rather nicely a 1300-km width assuming that the above effect causes the rise.

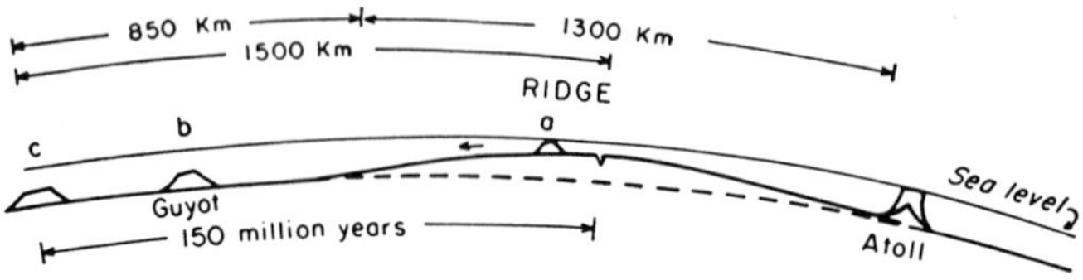

FIGURE 30.9
Postulated migration with time of volcanic peaks, guyots, and atolls, from a ridge crest to the flanks

Looking now at the old Mesozoic Mid-Pacific Ridge with the above situation in mind, volcanoes truncated on the ridge crest move away from the ridge axis at a rate of 1 cm/yr. Eventually they move down the ridge flank and become guyots or atolls rising from the deep-sea floor. Those 1000 km from the axis, however, were truncated 100 million years before those now near the center of the old ridge (Figure 30.9). On this basis it would be very interesting to examine the fauna on guyots near the northern margin of the old ridge or to drill atolls near the southern margin to see if the truncated surfaces or bases have a Triassic or even Permian age. At any rate the greater width of the old ridge and its belt of subsidence compared to present topographic ridges could be explained by the above reasoning.

Turning to a reconsideration of the Mid-Atlantic Ridge it appears that layer 3, with a thin and probably discontinuous cover of sediments, forms the sea floor. The dredging of serpentinized peridotite from fault scarps at three places on the ridge (Shand, 1949) points to such a conclusion. The abnormally low seismic velocity, if this is layer 3, might be attributed to intense fracturing and dilation where the convective flow changes direction from vertical to horizontal. The underlying material, which ordinarily would have a velocity of 8 km/sec or more, has a velocity approximately 7.4 km/sec partly for the same reason but also because of its abnormally high temperature (Figure 30.7). The interface between layer 3 and the 7.4 km/sec material below is thus the M discontinuity. The increase in velocity of layer 3 to about 6.7 km/sec and of the sub-Moho material to 8 km/sec as one proceeds away from the ridge crest may be attributed to cooling and healing of the fractures by slight recrystallization or by deposition from solution in an interval of tens of millions of years.

DEVELOPMENT OF THE OCEANIC CRUST (LAYER 3) AND THE EVOLUTION OF SEA WATER

Assuming that layer 3 is serpentinized peridotite, that the water necessary to serpentinize it is derived by degassing of the rising column of a mantle convection cell, and that its uniform thickness (4.7 ± 0.5 km) is controlled by the highest level the 500°C isotherm can reach under these conditions, we have a set of reasonable hypotheses which can account for the observed facts (Figure 30.6).

The present active ridge system in the oceans is about 25,000 km long. If the mantle is convecting with a velocity of 1 cm/yr a vertical layer 1 cm thick of layer 3 on each side of the ridge axis is being formed each year. The material formed is 70 per cent serpentinized, based on an average seismic velocity of 6.7 km/sec, and this serpentine contains 25 per cent water by volume. If we multiply these various quantities, the volume of water leaving the mantle each year can be estimated at 0.4 km^3. Had this process operated at this rate for 4 aeons, 1.6×10^9 km^3 of water would have been extracted from the mantle, and this less 0.3×10^9 km^3 of water now in layer 3 equals 1.3×10^9 km^3 or approximately the present volume of water in the oceans. (The estimate of how much of the present Mid-Ocean Ridge system is active is uncertain. That fraction of the system with a median rift was used in this estimate. The whole system is approximately 75,000 km long. The velocity of 1 cm/yr is also uncertain. If it were 0.35 cm/yr, as Heezen mentions for widening of the Iceland rift, this coupled with a 75,000 km length of the ridge system would give the required amount of water for the sea in 4 aeons.)

The production of layer 3 by a convective system and serpentinization must be reversed over the downward limbs of convection cells. That is, as layer 3 is depressed into the downward limb it will deserpentinize at 500°C and release its water upward to the sea. Thus the rate of entry of juvenile water into the ocean will equal the rate of acquisition of water from the mantle to form layer 3 over the rising limbs of convection cells.

It is not at present possible to check against the record the assumption that the process outlined went far back to the beginning of geologic history at a uniform rate. If Africa and South America moved away from each other at the rate of 2 cm a year they would have been adjacent to each other about 200 million years ago. Presumably this was the beginning of the convection cells under the present ridge. The assumption of a rate of movement for convection of 1 cm/yr was based on the above situation because the geologic record suggests splitting apart near the end of the Paleozoic Era. The convection cells under the Mesozoic Mid-Pacific Ridge ceased to function about 100 million ago inasmuch as the crest is known to have begun to subside at this time. It must have taken at least 150 million years at 1 cm/yr for the flanks of the ridge to spread to a width of 3000 km, and possibly the convection cells were in operation here for several times this long. The East Pacific Rise (Figure 30.10) crosses the Mesozoic ridge at right angles and presumably did not come into existence until recent times, but certainly less than 100 million years ago. No evidence of older ridges is found in the oceans, suggesting that convection is effective in wiping the slate clean every 200 or 300 million years. This long and devious route leads to the conclusion that the present shapes and floors of ocean basins are comparatively young features.

RELATIONSHIP OF THICKNESS OF CONTINENTS TO DEPTH OF THE SEA

In Figure 30.2 the balance of oceanic and continental columns is portrayed. The layer thicknesses are derived from seismic profiles, and the densities are extrapolated from seismic velocities and petrologic deduction (Hess, 1955). Gravity measurements during the past half century have shown that the concept of isostasy is valid—in other words that a balance

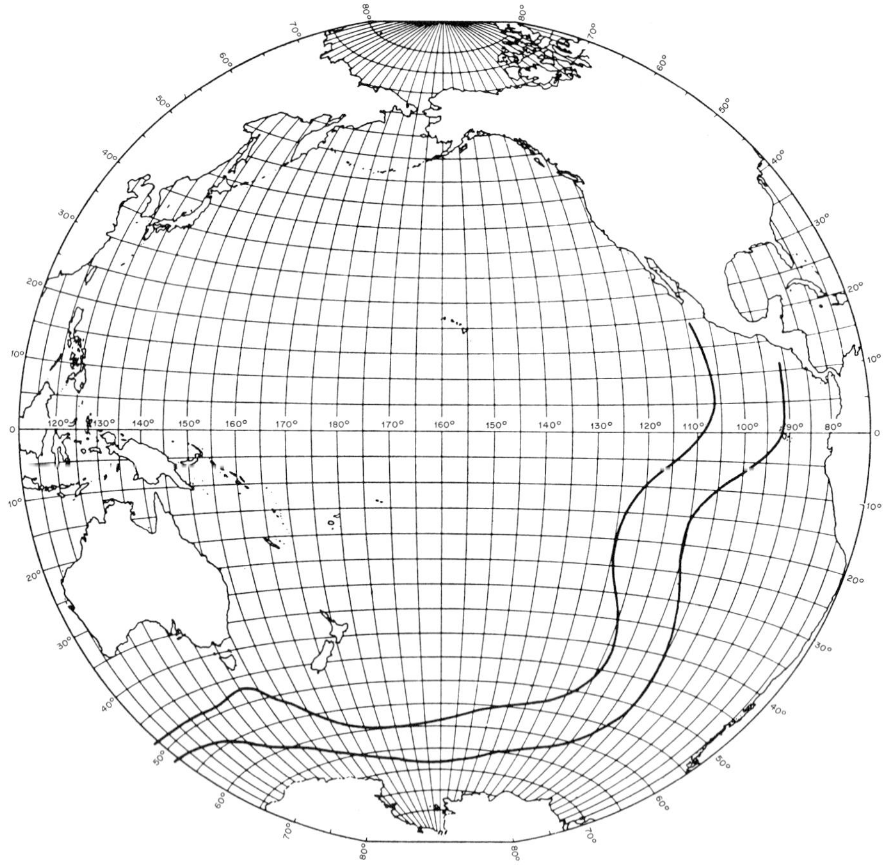

FIGURE 30.10
Approximate outline of East Pacific Rise. Possibly represents an oceanic ridge so young that it has not yet developed a median rift zone and pre-Rise sediments still cap most of its crest.

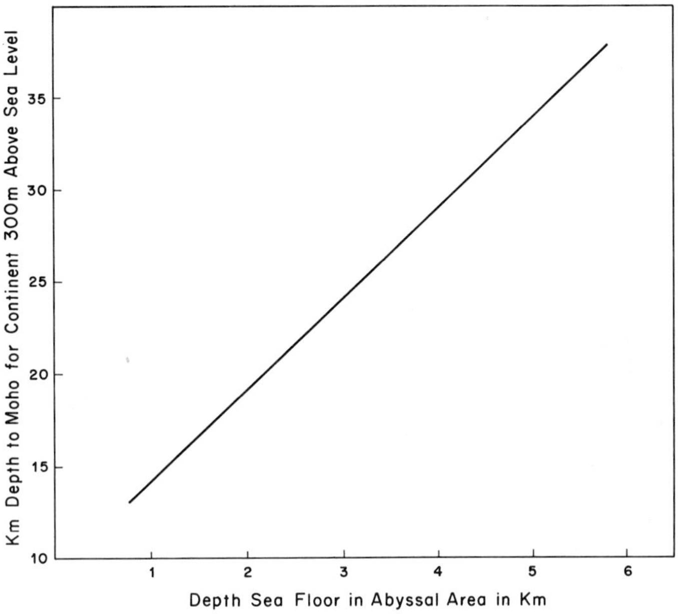

FIGURE 30.11
Graph portraying depth to the Mohorovičić discontinuity under continents *vs.* depth of abyssal areas in oceans. Computed from balance of crustal columns.

does exist. The oceanic column is simpler than the continental column and less subject to conjecture with regard to layer thicknesses or densities. The main uncertainty in the continental column is its mean density. Given the thickness of the crust, this value was derived by assuming that the pressure at 40 km below sea level under the continents equalled that for the same depth under the oceans, or 11,775 kg/cm². The mean density of the continental crust then becomes 2.85 g/cc. The latitude that one has for changing the numerical values in either of the two columns is small. The error in the pressure assumed for 40 km depth is probably less than 1 per cent.

The upper surface of the continent is adjusting to equilibrium with sea level by erosion. But as material is removed from its upper surface, ultimately to be deposited along its margins in the sea, the continent rises isostatically. If undisturbed by tectonic forces or thermal changes it will approach equilibrium at a rate estimated by Gilluly (1954) as 3.3×10^7 yrs half life. It is thus evident that, if the oceans were half as deep, the continents would be eroded to come to equilibrium with the new sea level, they would rise isostatically, and a new and much shallower depth to the M discontinuity under continents would gradually be established. A thinner continent but one of greater lateral extent would be formed inasmuch as volume would not be changed in this hypothetical procedure. The relationship between depth of the oceans, sea level, and the depth to the M discontinuity under continents is an axiomatic one and is a potent tool in reasoning about the past history of the Earth's surface and crust.

The oft-repeated statement that amount of water in the sea could not have changed appreciably since the beginning of the Paleozoic Era (or even much further back) because the sea has repeatedly lapped over and retreated from almost all continental areas during this time interval is invalid because the axiomatic relationship stated in the last paragraph would automatically require that this be so regardless of the amount of water in the sea.

One can compute the pressure at 40 km depth for an ocean with 1, 2, 3, or 4 km of water and equate this to continental columns for the same pressure at 40 km, distributing the amount of crustal material (density 2.85 g/cc) and mantle material (density 3.31 g/cc) in such proportion that balance is established. This computation is shown graphically in Figure 30.11. Assuming, as has been done in this chapter, that the oceans have grown gradually with time, one must suppose that the continents were much thinner in the early Precambrian. This could possibly be recognizable in the difference of tectonic pattern in very old terrains as compared to present continental structure.

If there is gradual increase of water in the sea one may ask why continents are not eventually flooded and why are there not continental-type areas now a kilometer or more below sea level. No extensive areas of this sort are found. Part of the answer might lie in the generation of new continental material at a rate equivalent to eruption of new water. An increase of depth of the sea by 1 km allows thickening of the continents by about 5 times this amount, which would be several times in excess of the estimated 1 km^3 per year extraction of magma from the mantle. Even if this were an underestimate there is no reason why continents might not extend laterally rather than grow thicker. The answer seems to be that there is more than enough energy in the crustal regime of the Earth to thicken the continents to an extent that they are maintained somewhat above the equilibrium level (Figure 30.12). A continent will ride on convecting mantle until it reaches the downward-plunging limb of the cell. Because of its much lower density it cannot be forced down, so that its leading edge is strongly deformed and thickened when this occurs. It might override the downward-flowing mantle current for a short distance, but thickening would be the result as before.

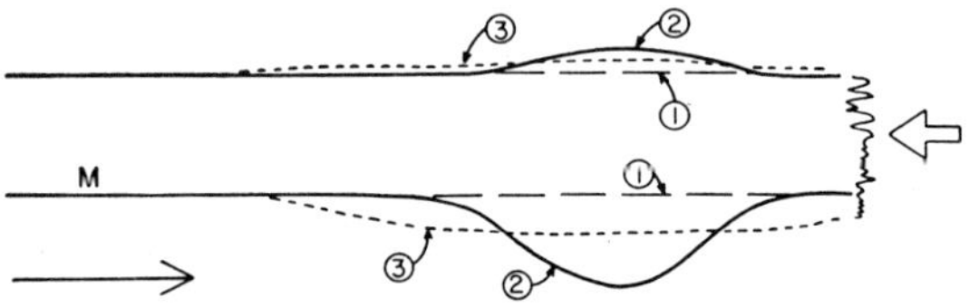

FIGURE 30.12
Diagram to illustrate thickening of a continent by deformation. Initially a mountain system and much larger root are formed, but both spread laterally with time and isostatic adjustment.

The Atlantic, Indian, and Arctic oceans are surrounded by the trailing edges of continents moving away from them, whereas the Pacific Ocean is faced by the leading edges of continents moving toward the island arcs and representing downward-flowing limbs of mantle convection cells or, as in the case of the eastern Pacific margin, they have plunged into and in part overridden the zone of strong deformation over the downward-flowing limbs.

RECAPITULATION

The following assumptions were made, and the following conclusions reached:

(1) The mantle is convecting at a rate of 1 cm/yr.
(2) The convecting cells have rising limbs under the mid-ocean ridges.
(3) The convecting cells account for the observed high heat flow and topographic rise.
(4) Mantle material comes to the surface on the crest of these ridges.
(5) The oceanic crust is serpentinized peridotite, hydrated by release of water from the mantle over the rising limb of a current. In other words it is hydrated mantle material.
(6) The uniform thickness of the oceanic crust results from the maximum height that the 500°C isotherm can reach under the mid-ocean ridge.
(7) Seismic velocities under the crests of ridges are 10–20 per cent lower than normal for the various layers including the mantle, but become normal again on ridge flanks. This is attributed to higher temperature and intense fracturing with cooling and healing of the fractures away from the crest.
(8) Mid-ocean ridges are ephemeral features having a life of 200 to 300 million years (the life of the convecting cell).
(9) The Mid-Pacific Mesozoic Ridge is the only trace of a ridge of the last cycle of convecting cells.
(10) The whole ocean is virtually swept clean (replaced by new mantle material) every 300 to 400 million years.
(11) This accounts for the relatively thin veneer of sediments on the ocean floor, the relatively small number of volcanic seamounts, and the present absence of evidence of rocks older than Cretaceous in the oceans.
(12) The oceanic column is in isostatic equilibrium with the continental column. The upper surface of continents approaches

equilibrium with sea level by erosion. It is thus axiomatic that the thickness of continents is dependent on the depth of the oceans.

(13) Rising limbs coming up under continental areas move the fragmented parts away from one another at a uniform rate so a truly median ridge forms as in the Atlantic Ocean.

(14) The continents are carried passively on the mantle with convection and do not plow through oceanic crust.

(15) Their leading edges are strongly deformed when they impinge upon the downward moving limbs of convecting mantle.

(16) The oceanic crust, buckling down into the descending limb, is heated and loses its water to the ocean.

(17) The cover of oceanic sediments and the volcanic seamounts also ride down into the jaw crusher of the descending limb, are metamorphosed, and eventually probably are welded onto continents.

(18) The ocean basins are impermanent features, and the continents are permanent although they may be torn apart or welded together and their margins deformed.

(19) The Earth is a dynamic body with its surface constantly changing. The spherical harmonics of its topography show unexpected regularities, a reflection of the regularities of its mantle convection systems and their secondary effects.

Here, the writer has attempted to invent an evolution for ocean basins. It is hardly likely that all of the numerous assumptions made are correct. Nevertheless it appears to be a useful framework for testing hypotheses relating to the oceans. It is hoped that the framework with necessary patching and repair may eventually form the basis for a new and sounder structure.

REFERENCES CITED

Bullard, E. C., A. E. Maxwell, and R. Revelle, 1956, Heat flow through the deep sea floor: Advances in Geophysics, v. 3, p. 153–181.

Carey, S. W., 1958, The tectonic approach to continental drift: Symposium, University of Tasmania, Hobart, 1956, p. 177–358.

Chandrasekhar, S., 1953, The onset of convection by thermal instability in spherical shells: Philos. Mag., ser. 7, v. 44, p. 233–241.

Egyed, L., 1957, A new dynamic conception of the internal constitution of the Earth: Geol. Rundschau, v. 46, p. 101–121.

Ewing, J., and M. Ewing, 1959, Seismic-refraction profiles in the Atlantic ocean basins, in the Mediterranean Sea, on the Mid-Atlantic Ridge and in the Norwegian Sea: Geol. Soc. America Bull., v. 70, p. 291–318.

Gilluly, J., 1954, Geologic contrasts between continents and ocean basins, *in* Arie Poldervaart, ed., Crust of the earth: Geol. Soc. America Spec. Paper 62, p. 7–18.

Gibson, W. M., 1960, Submarine topography in the Gulf of Alaska: Geol. Soc. America Bull., v. 71, p. 1087–1108.

Griggs, D., 1939, A theory of mountain building: Am. Jour. Sci., v. 237, p. 611–650.

———, 1954, Discussion, Verhoogen, 1954: Am. Geophys. Union Trans., v. 35, p. 93–96.

Hamilton, E. L., 1956, Sunken islands of the Mid-Pacific mountains: Geol. Soc. America Mem. 64, 98 p.

———, 1960, Ocean basin ages and amounts of original sediments: Jour. Sed. Petrology, v. 30, p. 370–379.

Harris, P. G., and J. A. Rowell, 1960, Some geochemical aspects of the Mohorovičić discontinuity: Jour. Geophys. Research, v. 65, p. 2443–2460.

Heezen, B. C., 1960, The rift in the ocean floor: Scientific American, v. 203, p. 98–110.

Herzen, R. von, 1959, Heat flow values from the southern Pacific: Nature, v. 183, p. 882–883.

Hess, H. H., 1946, Drowned ancient islands of the Pacific Basin: Am. Jour. Sci., v. 244, p. 772–791.

———, 1954, Serpentines, orogeny and epeirogeny, *in* Arie Poldervaart, ed., Crust of the earth: Geol. Soc. America Spec. Paper 62, p. 391–408.

———, 1955, The oceanic crust: Jour. Marine Research, v. 14, p. 423–439.

———, 1959a, The AMSOC hole to the Earth's mantle: Am. Geophys. Union Trans., v. 40, p. 340–345; (1960, Am. Scientist, v. 47, p. 254–263).

———, 1959b, Nature of the great oceanic ridges: Internat. Oceanog. Cong. Preprints, p. 33–34, AAAS, Washington, D.C.

Irving, E., 1959, Paleomagnetic pole positions: Royal Astron. Soc. Geophys. Jour., v. 2, p. 51–77.

Ladd, H. S., and S. O. Schlanger, 1960, Drilling operations on Eniwetok Atoll: U. S. Geol. Survey Prof. Paper 260Y, p. 863–903.

Kennedy, G. C., 1959, The origin of continents, mountain ranges and ocean basins: Am. Scientist, v. 47, p. 491–504.

Kuenen, Ph. H., 1946, Rate and mass of deep-sea

sedimentation: Am. Jour. Sci., v. 244, p. 563–572.
Kuiper, G., 1954, On the origin of the lunar surface features: [U.S.] Natl. Acad. Sci. Proc., v. 40, p. 1096–1112.
MacDonald, G. J. F., 1959, Calculations on the thermal history of the Earth: Jour. Geophys. Research, v. 64, p. 1967–2000.
Menard, H. W., 1958, Development of median elevations in the ocean basins: Geol. Soc. America Bull., v. 69, p. 1179–1186.
———, 1959, Geology of the Pacific sea floor: Experientia, v. 15, no. 6, p. 205–213.
Raitt, R. W., 1956, Seismic refraction studies of the Pacific Ocean Basin: Geol. Soc. America Bull., v. 67, p 1623–1640.
Ross, C. S., M. D. Foster, and A. T. Myers, 1954, Origin of dunites and olivine rich inclusions in basaltic rocks: Am. Mineralogist, v. 39, p. 693–737.
Rubey, W. W., 1951, Geologic history of sea water: Geol. Soc. America Bull., v. 62, p. 1111–1148.
Runcorn, S. K., 1959, Rock magnetism: Science, v. 129, p. 1002–1011.
Sapper, K., 1927, Vulkankunde: Stuttgart, Engelhorn, 358 p.
Shand, S. J., 1949, Rocks of the Mid-Atlantic Ridge: Jour. Geology, v. 57, p. 89–92.
Sumner, J. S., 1954, Consequences of a polymorphic transition at the Mohorovičić discontinuity (Abstract): Am. Geophys. Union Trans., v. 35, p. 385.
Umbgrove, J. H. F., 1947, The pulse of the Earth (2d ed.): The Hague, Martinus Nijhoff, 359 p.
Urey, H. C., 1953, Comments on planetary convection as applied to the Earth: Philos. Mag., ser. 7, v. 44, p. 227–230.
———, 1957, Boundary conditions for theories of the origin of the solar system, *in* L. H. Ahrens, ed., Physics and chemistry of the earth, v. 2: New York, Pergamon Press, p. 46–76.
Vening Meinesz, F. A., 1952, The origin of continents and oceans: Geol. en Mijnbouw, n. ser., v. 14, 373–384.
———, 1959, The results of development of the Earth's topography in spherical harmonics up to the 31st order, provisional conclusions: Koninkl. Nederlandse Akad. Wetensch. Proc., ser. B, v. 62, p. 115–136.
Verhoogen, J., 1954, Petrologic evidence on temperature distribution in the mantle of the Earth: Am. Geophys. Union Trans., v. 35, p. 50–59.

31

Continental Accretion and the Evolution of North America

A. E. J. ENGEL
CELESTE G. ENGEL

1964

From *Advancing Frontiers in Geology and Geophysics: a Volume in Honour of M. S. Krishnan*, edited by A. P. Subramaniam and S. Balakrishna, pp. 17–37e. Indian Geophysical Union, 1964. Reprinted with permission of the authors and the publisher.

Among the current and popular hypotheses of continental origins and evolution, two predominate. One postulates a thin crust of continental (granitic) rock formed very early in the earth's history, during relatively rapid differentiation of the earth into core, mantle and crust (Vening Meinesz, 1952; Deer, 1958), and subsequent break up of this primordial granitic crust into continents, migration of the continents, buckling, cycles of erosion, sedimentation, and volcanism.

According to the other hypothesis, the primordial differentiation was less complete—a differentiation of the earth into protocore, protomantle, and oceanic (basaltic) crust. The continents have been derived secondarily, throughout geologic time, by continuing terrestrial differentiation. The essential constituents of the continents, the oceans, and the atmosphere were supplied during secular growth of an iron-rich core, and through partial melting and degassing of the mantle. Volatiles and alkali-aluminium silicates repeatedly moved upward from the mantle in both magma and hydrothermal fluids (Rubey, 1951; 1955). According to this hypothesis the sources of energy have been derived from gravitational processes, and from radioactive disintegrations, particularly of short-lived nuclei such as potassium-40 (Birch, 1954, 1958; MacDonald, 1959). There is ample evidence of complementary surficial differentiation, and other such processes may be readily inferred in the absence of direct evidence. They include repeated cycles of weathering and sedimentation, deep burial of sediments, their metamorphism and partial melting, and permeation of the crust by the resulting granitic melts, especially along great linear mountain belts. The major crustal cycles, it is argued, tend to reoccur at unstable interfaces of any pre-existing continents and oceanic crust. Successive cycles are believed to have resulted in successive sheaths of granite and granitized sediments, welded to the pre-existing, accreting, continental plate (Wilson, 1953, p. 204).

In essence, either hypothesis, and each of

the innumerable variants of the two, includes the supposition that the relatively thick, infinitely complicated patches of granitic crust result from an efficient differentiation; and from localized, surficial concentrations in the continents of alkali-aluminium silicates, the so-called sial. The hypotheses differ mainly with regard to the causes, time or times, processes, and rates of continental differentiation.

The first stated concept envisages little change with time in the total *area* of sialic crust. But there is an important implied change in the progressive increases in total thickness of the continents. The second hypothesis suggests that both the area and thickness of continents have increased in a series of episodes, which if integrated through time reflect a linear increase in both continental *thickness and area.*

An increase in thickness of sial with time appears to be required if the presently prevailing concepts of a continuously degassing earth are valid (Rubey, 1951; Holland, 1962). For if the oceans have grown in volume and depth throughout geologic time, continents would necessarily have to grow progressively thicker to maintain isostatic (hydrostatic) equilibrium. This is a fundamental requirement of isostasy as Hess (1962) and Gilluly (1955) have emphasized. The present differences in surface elevation of continents and ocean basins must reflect differences in density of sial (plus any associated sima) compared to basalt plus sea water. If the oceans were only half as deep thick continents would be eroded to come to equilibrium with this lower sea level. Gradually, with approach toward isostatic equilibrium between these continents and the ocean basins, the depth of the Mohorovičić discontinuity under the continents would be reduced to a fraction of the present depth.

One result of erosion of any thickness sial is the transportation and deposition of the eroded, sialic detritus in troughs along the margins of continents. This relationship of positive, relatively thick, sialic blocks, contributing to marginal geosynclines has been observed and described in detail since the pioneer studies of Dana (1873), Hall (1883), Haug (1900), and Jones (1938). The concept of an unstable, tectonically active geosyncline marginal to continents is now deeply embedded in our geologic thinking. Complementary to the geosynclinal phase, and as a culmination of it, is the orogenic phase, the orogeny in turn reconstituting the geosynclinal pile and welding it to the pre-existing continent.

Hence, there has been a progressive evolution and expansion of the geosynclinal concept into one of continental accretion. Much of the evidence for, and controversies about, continental accretion have emanated from North America. Fortunately, the integration of detailed field mapping and age dating programs

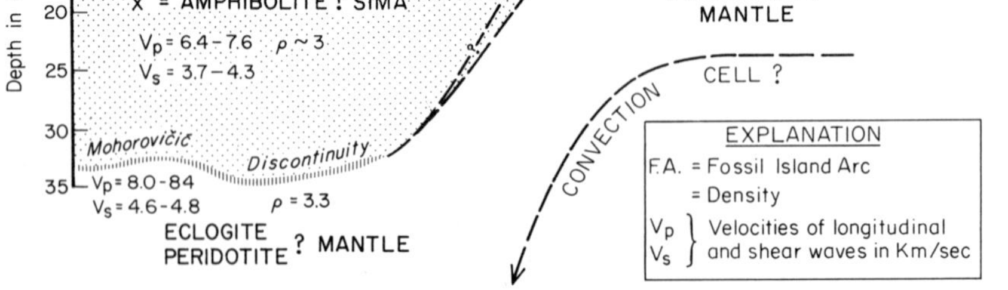

FIGURE 31.1
Generalized vertical section through the earth's crust. Shows the inferred relations of the Americas or Asia to the Pacific Ocean.

in North America permit a continuing and progressively more rigorous evaluation of the accretion concept. This paper is a brief discussion of the geological features of North America, which have both fostered the concept of continental accretion and perplexed all but its most zealous adherents. . . .

MAJOR CRUSTAL FEATURES

The base of the crust is now defined by the seemingly abrupt Mohorovičić discontinuity in the velocity of elastic waves in the earth (Gutenberg, 1955; Press, 1961). Above this discontinuity the velocities of V_L (longitudinal) and V_S (shear) waves are less than 7 and 3.5 km/sec, respectively. At the discontinuity, in the earth's mantle, V_L and V_S rise abruptly to about 8 and 4.5 km/sec, respectively. The abrupt increase in velocity at the discontinuity seems to reflect the occurrence of rocks that are progressively more dense, more degassed, and richer in ferro-magnesian silicates. Typical of such "mafic" rocks are the peridotite and eclogite presumed to form the upper mantle. The interrelations of these rocks in the crust and upper mantle are shown in Figure 31.1.

Typical oceanic crust lies under more than 4000 meters of water and is only 5 to 7 kilometers thick. Dredge hauls, seismic data, and studies of oceanic islands suggest that the predominant rock is basalt, and possibly hydrated peridotite (serpentinite). Over the basalt lies a surprisingly thin blanket of muds and calcareous oozes (1 kilometer thick, or less), in places interfingering with submarine lava and debris flows (Ewing and Ewing, 1959; Raitt, 1956; Heezen, 1962).

Near and under most island arcs and their associated trenches, in water from 1500 to 3000 meters deep, the crust thickens to intermediate values of 12 to 25 kilometers (Officer, et al, 1957; Talwani, et al, 1959; Adams, 1962). Most island arcs are dominated by basalt, but peridotite (from the mantle?) and igneous rocks intermediate between basalt and granite also occur. Most of the older, deeply eroded island arcs have granitic cores, and their primitive sediments include fragments of granite, potassium-rich feldspar, and quartz (Schmidt, 1957; Liechti, and others, 1960; Australasian Petroleum Co. Proprietary 1961).

All of the exposed continental crust and most of the crust that lies under 2000 meters of water is from 20 to 60 kilometers thick, averaging about 35 kilometers. In general, the thickness of continental crusts reflects topography; that is, many mountain ranges appear to have roots of crustal rock projecting downward into the mantle, whereas most great basins very crudely define areas of thinner crust (Figure 31.1). Apparently the boundary between crust and mantle is not only a seismic discontinuity but also a level of compensation. Columns of crustal rock (or rock plus water) of equal cross-sectional area are of roughly equal mass. The crust seems to float in approximate hydrostatic (isostatic) equilibrium on the mantle (Heiskanen and Vening Meinesz, 1958; Wollard, 1959).

The predominant rock of continental crusts is widely referred to as granitic. In most areas where erosion has stripped away the surficial blanket of flat-lying shelf sediments, 30 to 90 per cent of the exposed rock is granitic (Table 31.1). The frequent use of granitic as a synonym for continental crust probably is valid as a first approximation for the crust to depths of about 12 to 15 kilometers (Press, 1961). But this generalization should not blur the facts that (1) parts of the crust as large as 2×10^5 cubic kilometers may consist entirely of rock of a very different type such as quartzite, basalt, carbonate, or anorthosite, and (2) the finer scale structural features of the crust are extremely complicated (Noble, 1941; Brown and Engel, 1956).

Below 12 to 15 kilometers in the continents, petrogenic theory and geophysical observations suggest by analogy, that rocks of intermediate to basaltic composition occur. The base of the continental crust is presumed to be metamorphosed basalt and the top of the mantle eclogite, or peridotite.

ANTIQUITY OF CONTINENTS AND OCEANS

We find, as noted above, two quite dissimilar kinds of crust—a thin, relatively dense, basaltic ocean crust and a much thicker, lighter, granitic crust. The island arcs seem to be a significant, transitional evolutionary feature of intermediate thickness and composition, commonly but not invariably formed at the continental—oceanic interface.

The oldest rock complexes of North America and other continents ($> 2.5 \times 10^9$ years) have their closest analogues in the island arcs. This is, of course, one of the main reasons for postulating continental accretion and differentiation from crust of oceanic type and mantle. But before pursuing this matter, brief additional reference should be made to the oceans.

Although the oldest continental fragments are at least 2.5 to 3 billion years old, almost nothing is known of the history of oceanic crust prior to the Cretaceous period (100 million years ago). Actually 100 million years is the age not of the oceanic crust but of sediments dredged from seamounts rising from the ocean floor. The oldest known basalt from existing oceanic crust was emplaced less than 50 million years ago, although many seamounts must be Cretaceous or older (Hamilton, 1956). Our enormous ignorance of the early history of the oceanic crusts reflects the cost, the logistical problems involved in oceanographic investigations—major impediments to all studies of crustal evolution.

Possibly, there may be little more of early crustal history to read directly from the rocks of the oceans. Many students of mountain building and most contemporary geologists who endorse the theory of continental drift postulate the continuing existence of large convection cells in the mantle to make the mountains, and move the continents (Vening Meinesz, 1962; Chamalaun and Roberts, 1962). They argue that the measured rates of oceanic sedimentation (1 to 2 cm/1000 Years) and the extremely thin skin of sediments in the oceans indicate that the oceanic environment cannot have been stable for more than the last 150 to 200 million years. Hess has suggested that the earlier oceanic crusts, with their accumulated record of sedimentary and organic evolution, have been swept laterally against and reconstituted into continental margins by convection cells (Hess, 1962).

There is, however, considerable evidence that large bodies of sea water have existed for over 3.2 billion years, that they have supported life for over 2.6 billion years (Macgregor, 1940; Holmes, 1954; Aldrich et al, 1956); and that hypersaline seas evolved in restricted basins at least 1.4 billion years ago (Brown and Engel, 1956; Blackadar and Frazer, 1960, p. 6). But this evidence has been extracted by the hammer-carrying geologist from exposures of the marine rocks deposited, and now exposed, on the continents. Until more sophisticated sampling of the crust has been accomplished . . . the paleoceanographer must turn to his landlubber colleagues and the more accessible rocks of the continents for source material in writing the history of the sea.

TABLE 31.1
Approximate percentage of granitic and pre-existing rocks exposed in geologic provinces of North America. The data are based on point counts of 320 geologic maps, at scales of 1:12,000 to 1:500,000.

Provinces	Age $\times 10^9$ yrs.	Basic volcanics	Felsic volcanics	Sedimentary rock	Peridotite*	Diorite and quartz diorite	Granitic rock**	Other
Superior, Wyoming, and Slave	(2.5–3.2)	12	0.1	5	0.1	—	76	4
Churchill	(1.8–2.5)	6	0.5	18	trace	1	70	4
Central	(1.4–1.8)	3	20	2	trace	0.01	70	5
Grenville	(1.0–1.8)	3	4	20	trace	0.01	66	6
Appalachian and Pacific	(0.0–1.0)	5	4	46	0.1	16	24	5

* Island-Arc (Alpine) type.
** Includes quartz-monzonite, granodiorite, quartz porphyry and gneisses pervasively veined by granite.

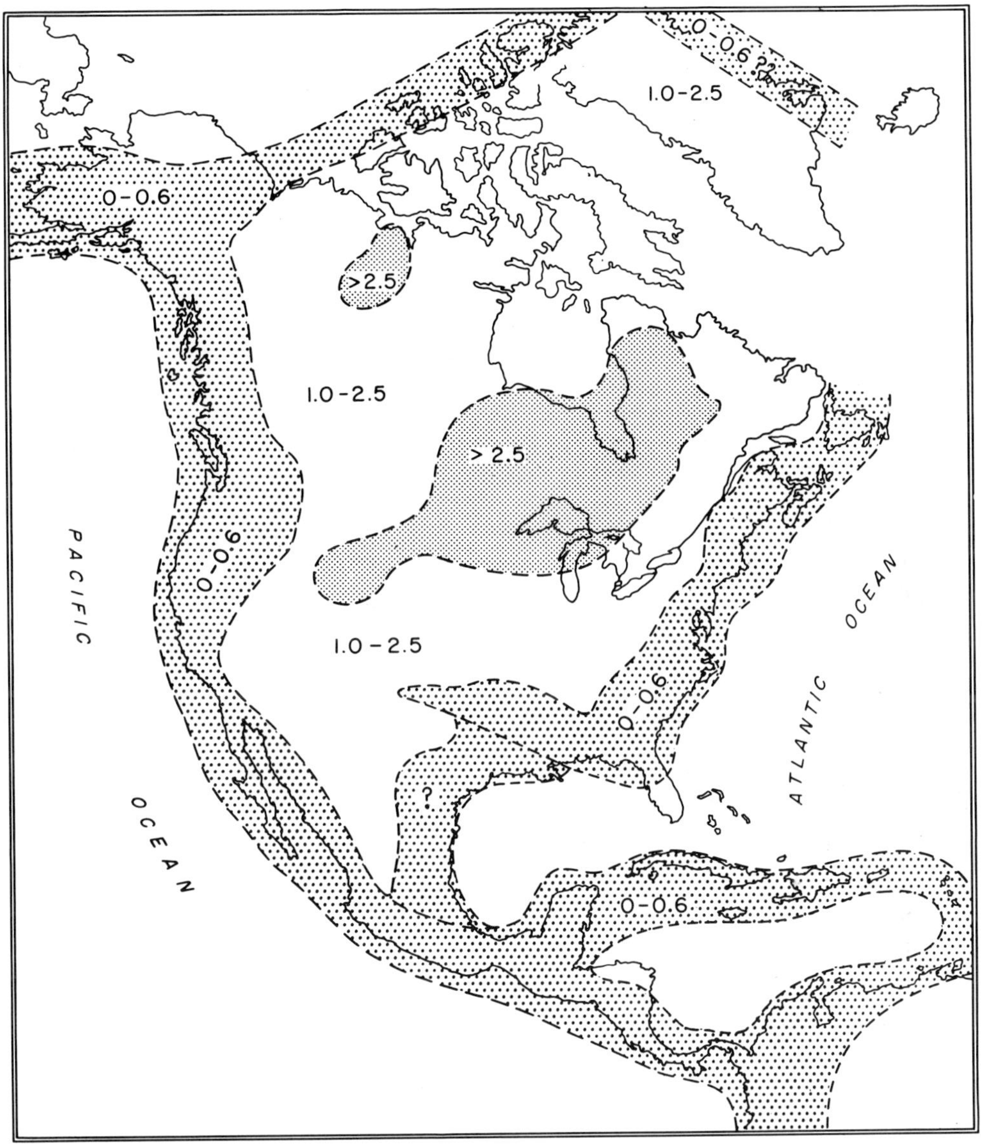

FIGURE 31.2
Gross patterns and ages of geologic provinces in North America. Defined by major granite-forming, mountain-building events.

CONTINENTAL FEATURES

The concept of an initially molten earth led field geologists of a generation ago to seek exposures of the primordial chilled crust. They found the continents to consist instead of a complicated, yet recognizable, succession, of volcanic-sedimentary and mountain-forming events that culminate in great granite-forming episodes. In the deeply eroded but now stable continental platforms the succession of metamorphosed sediments and volcanics, variously obliterated by younger granites, appears to reach backward in time almost indefinitely. Because of the overlap of events, the ultimate beginnings of continents seemed to be largely or wholly obliterated.

Hutton, the pioneer British geologist,

noted: "In the economy of the World, I can find no traces of a beginning, no prospect of an end."

His conclusion has frequently been echoed by field geologists who have reconnoitered the cores of the continents. But new techniques and new approaches are producing exciting and revealing data. Patterson and his colleagues seem to have established the age of the earth at 4.5 billion years (Patterson 1956). The chronologic succession of visible, widespread continental events is either established or closely bracketed in absolute years; and the properties of the earth that cannot be directly observed and sampled are being measured with increasing accuracy.

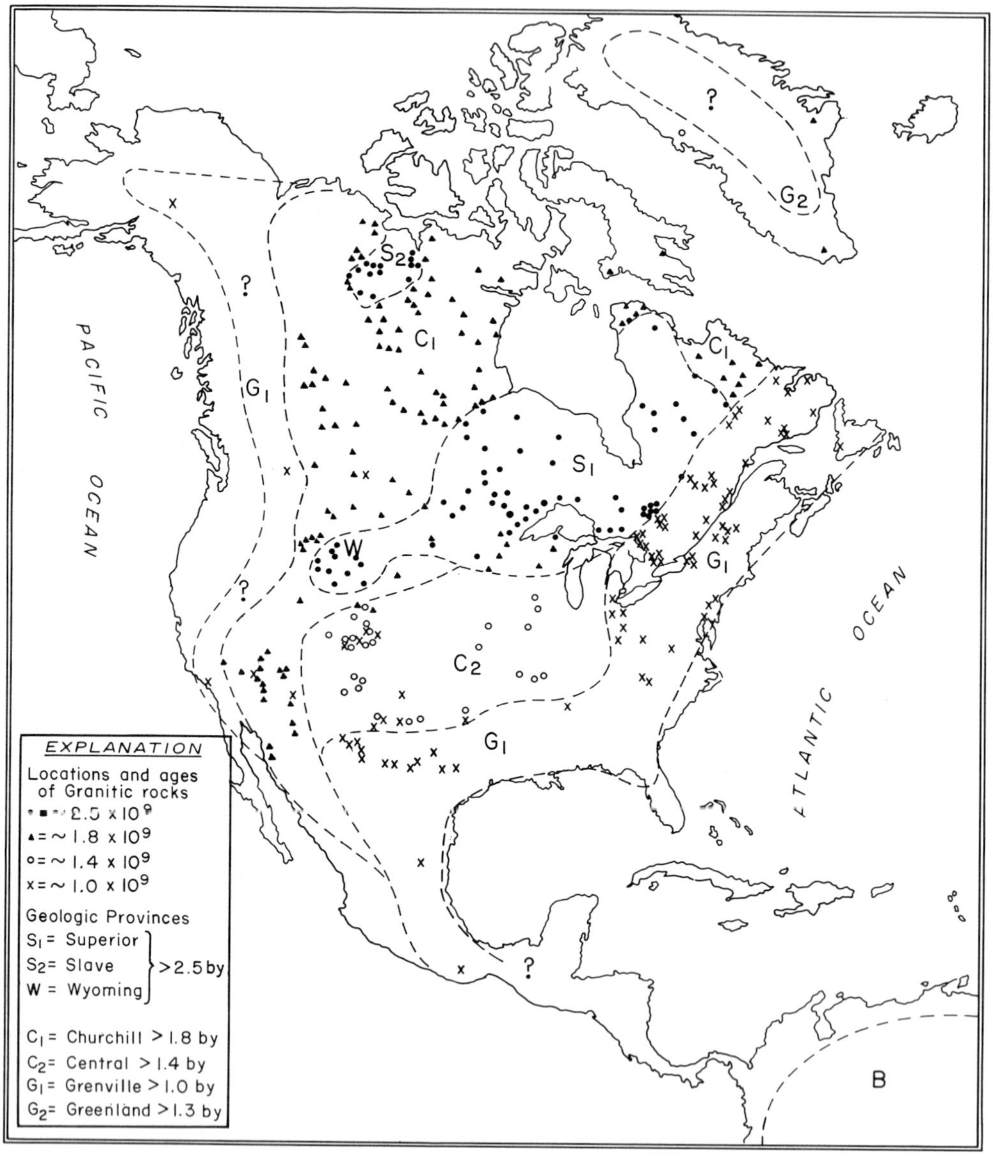

FIGURE 31.3
Localities at which major granite-forming events of a billion or more years ago have been dated. Each point marks the site of one radiometric age determination, or of several closely spaced age determinations. These determinations, together with data from geologic field studies, define the areal extent of Precambrian provinces.

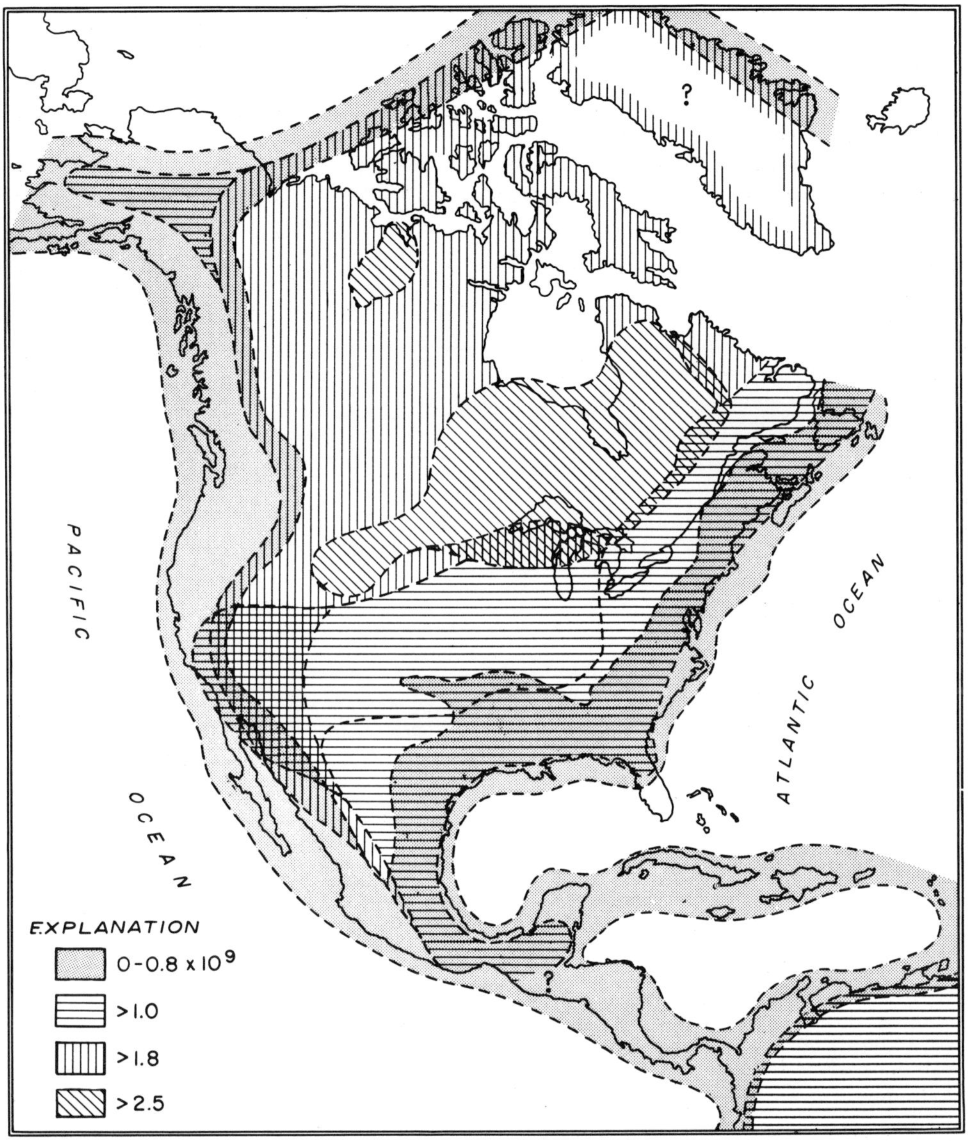

FIGURE 31.4
Some examples of known and readily inferred overlap of successively formed geologic provinces. Defined by major granite-forming events.

Throughout, the concept of continental accretion of North America has survived and flourished. Accretion and secular differentiation of North America from basaltic and more mafic crust and mantle are suggested by three major, complementary features: (1) the striking analogy between the oldest rock complexes in the heart of North America and rocks of the island arcs; (2) the progressive, secular differentiation of igneous and sedimentary rocks in successively formed geologic provinces, from rocks typically oceanic in character to rocks more characteristically continental; (3) the crudely zonal patterns of successive, major, granite-forming and related continent-forming events, as manifest in decipherable rock provinces.

This zonal pattern of rock provinces is

broadly generalized in Figure 31.2, and is shown in greater detail in Figures 31.3 and 31.4. These maps indicate the decrease in the ages of the designated geologic provinces outward from a central nucleus.

North America, stripped of its thin blanket of younger (0.5×10^9 years) platform sediments, has a core 6 times older than its margins. As noted previously, the oldest rock complexes in the continental core are those characteristic of island arcs and oceanic margins. Younger provinces include various dilutions of continental and oceanic types (Tables 31.1 and 31.2). In general the younger the province, the greater its continental characteristics, as though the successively younger cycles in the outward accretion were increasingly dominated by contributions from the expanding, granitic continent itself. Today's continuing outward spread of North America may be reflected in the accumulation of thick prisms of debris largely of continental type in the Gulf of Mexico (Ewing et al, 1962; Shepard et al, 1960), Baja California (Hamilton, 1961), the pacific Basin and Range Province (Shepard and Emery, 1941), the Gulf of Alaska (Shor 1962,) (Menard 1955) and so on.

GEOLOGIC CYCLES

Although the provinces delimited in Figures 31.2, 31.3, and 31.4 are infinitely complicated, each is defined by a series of justaposed, variously impinging, and complementary geological "cycles." Most cycles are punctuated by at least one great granite-forming event. The granites tend to be localized along sinuous mountain belts, the sites of maximum crustal instability, and are emplaced at the culmination of one or more major sedimentary or sedimentary-volcanic episodes. The rock products of any cycle reflect the nature and stability of the crust during the cycle. Major stages in the mountain-building cycles are as follows:

(1) Erosion of the crustal highs and sedimentation in adjacent crustal troughs, basins and platforms (the larger crustal troughs, deeply filled with sedimentary and volcanic debris, are called geosynclines).
(2) Volcanism, at various intervals and sites, but concentrated and intense during the evolution of most geosynclines.
(3) Deformation of the thicker volcanic-sedimentary piles in the geosynclines and

TABLE 31.2
Approximate percentages of sedimentary rock types in rock sequences deposited prior to the major granite-forming event in each of the geological provinces of North America

Provinces	Age $\times 10^9$ yrs.	Carbonate	Quartzite*	Sandstone and shale**	Arkose and conglomerate	Graywacke argillite†	High rank graywacke and tuff‡	Other
Superior, Wyoming, and Slave	(2.5–3.2)	trace	2	5	7	15	70	1
Churchill and Central	(1.4–2.5)	1	15	15	20	35	10	4
Grenville (Quebec and E. Ontario)	(1.0–1.8)	2	10	25	18	35	5	5
Grenville (New York and S.E. Ontario)	(1.0–1.8)	18	15	20	15	25	5	2
Appalachian and Pacific	(0–0.6)	7	12	45	10	20	5	1
Average recent sediment	(0–0.6)	8	15	54	10	5	4	2

* More than 70% quartz.
** Na/K less than 0.7, average 0.3.
† Na/K less than 1.2, greater than 0.3, average 0.8; ratio of sedmient to associated volcanic = 10.
‡ Na/K greater than 1.2, average 1.4; ratio of sediment to associated volcanic = 5.

recrystallization and partial melting of their depressed keels and of the subjacent mantle.
(4) Engulfment of much of the geosynclinal pile by the partial melt, predominantly granitic but ranging in composition from mafic to granitic. This is the major, widely dated, granite-forming "event" on which the "age" assigned each continental province shown in Figures 31.2, 31.3, and 31.4 is based.
(5) Rise of the resulting, commonly elongate, thickened, and granitized mountain range, and its erosion, perhaps as a stage in a new superimposed or adjacent, crustal cycle. Each cycle results in further crustal differentiation toward more sialic assemblages (Tables 31.1, 31.2, and 31.3).

Complementary to the great mountain-building, granite-forming cycles are the rise and fall of adjacent continental platforms and shelves. The depressed portions of these areas acquire widespread blankets of well-sorted and weathered sediments, the so-called platform and shelf sediments. Obviously, the sediments differ in physical and chemical properties according to their source, the agents of transportation, and the sites of deposition, and the entire milieu changes throughout the immediate sedimentary cycle and the encompassing crustal cycle. Consequently, vital clues to crustal history and continental evolution may be drawn from evidence of secular changes in kinds and patterns of sediments and associated volcanics.

OLDEST CONTINENTAL ROCKS

The oldest rocks, and consequently the first clearly recognisable events in North America, are in the Superior-Wyoming and Slave provinces (the latter in the region of Great Slave Lake in Canada, Figures 31.2 and 31.3). In these areas a major granite-forming event occured about 2.5 billion years ago (Lowdon, 1961; Gast et al, 1958; Goldich et al, 1961). The granites largely engulf the oldest mappable rocks, a series of volcanic-graywacke sequences (Pettijohn, 1943). We have noted that in many respects these volcanic-sedimentary rocks are strikingly like rocks known to form on and adjacent to evolving island arcs. They are made up of basaltic lavas, mafic ash falls, slides and slumps of slightly weathered mafic debris, volcanic ejecta, and high rank graywacke (Pettijohn, 1943). There also are peridotites (from the mantle?) and siliceous iron-bearing sediments.

Some of the volcanic-graywacke suites appear to have their closest analogues in recently emergent volcanic archipelagoes such as the Aleutians and Kurils (Byers, 1959; Coats 1962; Goryatchev, 1962; Yerokhov, 1960). Other suites, while consisting largely of basalt and graywacke, include fragments of alkali and silica-rich porphyries, and granite (Bass 1961). Many of the graywackes also contain minerals common only in granitic (Continental) terranes, especially potassium-rich feldspar and micas, zircons, monazites, and abundant quartz. There is thus distinct evidence in these ancient sediments of detrital contributions from pre-existing granitic, hence continental, source areas—some sort of protocontinent that formed the nucleus of North America well over 2.5 billion years ago.

The oldest recognizable rocks on other continents are similar island-arc-like complexes (Macgregor, 1951; Wilson, 1958; Krishnan, 1960, p. 104; Simonen, 1960). In describing the ancient Bulawayan complex of South Africa (2.5×10^9 years), Macgregor (1951) writes: "The general picture presented by these rocks in one of volcanic islands scattered over an area exceeding 3000 miles from north to south and 200 miles from east to west, with gently-sloping volcanic cones of Hawaiian type and explosive andesitic volcanos rising above the sea, as thick flows of pillowy lava spread out on the ocean floor."

Some of the ancient graywackes include granitic pebbles, or clastic grains of minerals characteristic of granite. In South Africa pegmatitic granites that cut another pre-existing volcanic-graywacke sequence have been dated as 3.2 billion years old (Nicholaysen, 1962; Allsopp, 1961). Polkanov and Gerling report an age of 3.5 billion years for a granitic gneiss from the Kola Peninsula (1961). If these ages prove to be "firm" they establish the existence of granitic rocks—patches of continental crust —no more than a billion years after the origin of the earth.

There is no impelling reason to assume that all continents were nucleated simultaneously, but these data suggest the possibility of at least one, and perhaps several, volcanic sedimentary cycles in North America preceding those now mapped in the Superior-Wyoming and Slave provinces.

The data are consistent with the view that the continents were formed from a predominantly volcanic-basaltic crust not unlike that now found in the Atlantic and Pacific Oceans. Initial differentiation could have occurred largely through the weathering of oceanic volcanics, the metamorphism and partial melting of resulting sediments and their basaltic floors, or a combination of these processes superimposed upon a suite of magmatic differentiates (Bowen, 1928). Granitic rock is erupted by existing Pacific volcanoes but in relatively small amount (Peterson and Goldberg, 1962). Granitic rocks also appear in the deeply eroded parts of many Mesozoic and younger island arcs (Coats, 1962).

The nature of the intial, granite-forming events remains conjectural. There are limits to the classic view—that geologic events of the past may be explained by observable, contemporary earth processes and products. The formation of the earth 4.5 billion years ago was a cataclysmic event. So in lesser degree may have been the formation of a first granitic crust.

For example, astrogeologists argue that the early impaction of giant meteorites fostered or furthered the differentiation of early granitic crust by producing great pools of lava (Urey, 1952; Dietz, 1961). Certainly the largest mafic lava pools that we observe frozen in the crust (the stratiform sheets) show internal differentiation into more mafic and granitic types (Wager and Deer, 1939; Buddington, 1940; Hess, 1960).

Only one province in North America younger than the Superior-Wyoming and Slave provinces—the Pacific province—is dominated by rocks characteristic of, and largely indigenous to, the island arcs and crust of oceanic type. Pettijohn (1943) first emphasized the dominance of graywackes in the Superior province. Succeeding workers (Clark and Stearn, 1960, p. 264) have suggested that the ancient island arcs of the Superior-Wyoming and Slave provinces emerged adjacent to stable shelves and shelf sediments, now effaced by erosion. The argument may be inverted. For in the last 2.5 billion years of geologic time it is the stable continental shelves and their highly differentiated, winnowed blankets of sediments that have best resisted obliteration. The virtual absence of earlier stable shelves on continents suggests that none existed that were equivalent to contemporary shelves in thickness, composition, and stability. Instead, prior to 2.5 billion years ago patches of granitic crust were either (1) very much thinner than later granitic crust or (2) relatively small in area, hence unable to resist the dynamic and thermal processes that recurred in the underlying mantle.

Whatever the primordial facts, the contemporary vista suggests that it is impossible for basalt-graywake suites of the Superior-Wyoming and Slave type to evolve on a well-defined continent, 20th Century model. The average composition of the crust on emergent North America between 2.8 and 3 billion years ago (prior to the emplacement of granite) was far closer to that of basalt than the crust of North America is today (Table 31.1). This fact is also apparent by inspection of Tables 31.2 and 31.3. The data assembled in these tables were obtained by point counting the per cent by area, (and then calculating the volume per cent) of the several sedimentary and rock types in 320 mapped areas in the geologic provinces of North America. Obviously a count of this type represents only a first approximation of the relative amounts of each sedimentary type deposited. Nevertheless it is clear from this study that the sediments of the Superior-Wyoming and Slave provinces are very different in total composition from the sediments formed in the Churchill and in each succeeding Province of North America in the last 2.5 billion years (Tables 31.2 and 31.3). The trend is obvious. The ratios of residuate sediments to non-residuate types, and of carbonates to non-carbonates increase in a general way toward the present. There exists of course a complementary decrease in the ratio of high rank greywackes to shales plus non-wacke type sandstones. There has been continental growth and differentiation. This does not mean that there have been no temporary reversals or partial foundering of granitic crust. But the gross trend has important implications for studies of geochemical cycles and the so called geochemical balance, in which the compositions of the average modern sediments, of the average contemporary crust, and so on are commonly employed as secular constants (Goldschmidt, 1954, p. 47; Wickman, 1954).

The age of the Superior-Wyoming and Slave provinces is defined by waves of granitic rocks that largely engulfed the volcanic-graywacke complexes some 2.5 billion years ago. These granitic rocks constitute three-fourths of these provinces as they are now mapped (Table 31.1). Geophysical data indicate that they persist to depths of at least 12 to 15 kilometers in the crust. Downward-projecting keels of the graywacke-volcanic complexes appear to reach a depth equivalent to the width of the exposed complex (Innes, 1960).

Actually, only a small fraction of the so-called granitic rocks are, strictly speaking, granite. The "granitic" terranes include abundant diorites, quartz diorites, and granodiorite and in most localities these rocks appear to have been emplaced in sequence, the most mafic first, followed by the more granitic types. Characteristically, diorites and quartz diorites are largely indigenous to volcanic-graywacke terranes and are among the first deep-seated igneous rocks emplaced in such terranes. The fact that granitic rocks are so abundant and widespread in the Superior-Wyoming and Slave provinces at the 2.5 billion year level suggests that many of these granites are regenerated, partial melts from pre-existing crust of intermediate character, formed either in preceding cycles or through cataclysmic events. One of the major, unresolved problems in continental evolution is whether abundant granite can evolve as a magmatic differentiate from basaltic magma of the oceanic types; or whether most granite is a product of either (1) partial melting of geosynclinal roots or (2) assimilation of sialic constituents by perhaps superheated, more basic magma types.

The granite-forming event of 2.5 billions years ago is significant in that it indicates the development for the first time in North America of a thick, stable, and resistant granitic crust. Thereafter, this crust (the Superior-Wyoming and Slave provinces) persisted either above sea level or as a partially immersed but stable platform. Observations of mass and crustal buoyancy suggest that for 2.5 billion years the continental crust of the Superior-Wyoming and Slave provinces has been at least 20 or more kilometers thick.

It is tempting to speculate on the intial areal extent of the 2.5 billion year continental crust. Almost surely the Superior-Wyoming and Slave provinces were more extensive than is now apparent. This suggestion is readily inferred from studies of younger provinces. All of these overlap pre-existing provinces by 20 per cent, to as much as 60 per cent (Figure 31.4). Specifically, the succession of volcanic-sedimentary and granite-forming events that define the Appalachian province (0.2 to 0.8×10^9 yr) overlap the Grenville province (1×10^9 yr) by about 60 per cent (Figure 31.4). Similarly in the western part of North America there is wide overlap and near-obliteration of older provinces by a succession of younger provinces dated at 0.1, 0.4, 1.0, and 1.8 billion years ago. The most recent cycle of volcanism, sedimentation, and orogeny culminating in the Coast Ranges and the Sierra Nevada (Pacific province) overlaps pre-existing provinces by at least 40 per cent. Probably the overlap is much greater. But the plutonic, volcanic and sedimentary products of Coast Range and Sierran orogenies at about 100 million years ago have completely obliterated or covered pre-existing rock provinces throughout most of Alaska, western Canada, United States and Mexico. In fact, inspection of Figure 31.3 brings out a very striking relationship; that definite relicts of Precambrian crust are not uncommon within 300 miles of the coast in most areas of North America except in the region of very youngest orogeny (the Pacific Province). We may infer that Precambrian continental rocks once existed, and may lie buried as relicts in many portions of western North America now represented by the blank spaces of Figure 31.3.

Other features which suggest that the Superior-Wyoming and Slave provinces were formerly more extensive than they are now include (1) their broad but stubby forms, and (2) the angular intersections of their mountain belts with those of enveloping provinces. In general, the younger the mountain belt and province, the more elongate the form. These relations suggest that the fossilized mountain belts that form the older provinces have been sliced off and reincorporated in succeeding mountain-building, granite-forming episodes.

A complementary or alternative reason for the decrease in width to length ratios of the geologic province (and orogenic belts?) with decreasing age may be found in the inferred secular increase in thickness of the sial. If the earlier formed parts of sial were appreciably thinner, they would have been much weaker and hence incapable of withstanding orogenic pulses induced by convection or other mountain forming processes. With progressive thickening, and resultant strengthening of the continents, the geosynclinal and mountain building forces are necessarily most effective along the narrow, potentially weak interfaces between thickened sial and thinner oceanic crust, and presumably in the oceanic crust. Whether mountain chains have extended into, or across oceans at intervals in geologic time is a major enigma. But the mid-Atlantic ridge and East Pacific rise both appear to obliquely intersect and die out at continental borders (Menard, 1961; Heezen, 1962).

Mountain belts formed within continents, such as the Rocky Mountains and the Urals are minority types, probably because of the great strength and resistance to deformation of Continental crust 35 or more kilometers thick. This interpretation seems further supported by [their constituent] relatively unfolded wedges and blocks of sial, either flat topped, or in the form of "trap doors" (Thom, 1955; Chamberlin, 1940).

Actually, recent detailed mapping of the edges of the Superior-Wyoming and Slave provinces proves that parts of these older provinces have been sliced off and reincorporated in succeeding, mountain-building, granite-forming episodes. Blurred vestiges of rocks in the Superior province can be traced southeast across the "Grenville front" into the much younger (1.0×10^9 yr) Grenville province, where they are all but obliterated by super-imposed events (Osborne and Morin, 1962; Phemister, 1960). Recent work also suggests that the Superior and Slave provinces were originally either joined or were separated by only a very narrow belt of island arc or oceanic-type crust. Hence the relict Superior-Wyoming and Slave provinces tell us that 2.5 billion years ago thick granitic crust comprised an area at least 20 per cent that of present day North America. But the data suggest that the extent of (thinner?) granitic crust may have been greater—equivalent to perhaps one-fourth or more of the present area of the continent.

SUCCEEDING PROVINCES AND EVENTS

The evolution of successive geologic provinces in North America is characterized by several features. (1) Most of the volcanic-sedimentary series show a progressive increase in the increments of continental debris, much of it extensively weathered and differentiated. (2) Relicts of the pre-existing provinces behave as stable, neutral, or slightly negative plates and basins into which well-sorted clastics and chemical and biochemical precipitates are desposited as broad, thin blankets and thicker prisms. (3) The associated volcanics include higher percentages of alkali and silica-rich types than the volcanics of pre-existing provinces. These generalizations are drawn from data in Tables 31.1, 31.2, and 31.3, obtained by the point count of some 320 maps of areas in the several provinces.

Although the data in Tables 31.1, 31.2, and 31.3 are crude approximations, the trends are obvious. For example, in the Churchill province, which partially encircles and partly separates the Superior-Wyoming and Slave provinces, the pre-granitic volcanic-sedimentary complexes include abundant graywacke and pillowed basalt. But lavas and tuffs of intermediate and rhyolitic (granitic) composition are common and widespread. Arkoses—that is, sandstones largely composed of disintegrated granites—appear in many sedimentary sequences. So do carbonate layers and well-sorted, cross-bedded quartz rich sandstones, although they commonly constitute only a small fraction of the total sedimentary record (Armstrong, 1960).

During the evolution of the Churchill province (1.8 to 2.5×10^9 years ago), epicontinental seas covered large areas of the Superior-Wyoming and Slave provinces. In these seas, in large shallow basins, the first well defined miogeosynclinal and shelf sediments formed

(Stockwell, 1962). These include well-sorted cross-bedded quartzose sandstones, potassium-rich shales, and carbonate sediments. A feature of these old carbonate sediments in North America and other continents is the rare appearance of fossil algal reefs and colonies. Indeed, one algal limestone in South Africa predates the emplacement of granite 2.4 billion years ago, although there are no unequivocal examples of metazoan fossils prior to about 600 million years ago (Figure 31.5).

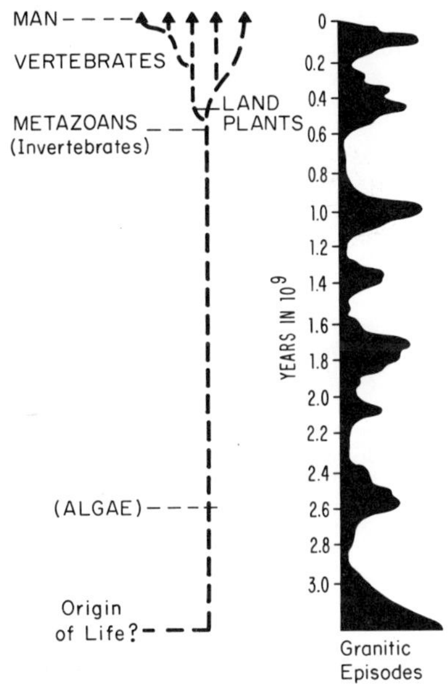

FIGURE 31.5
Schematic representation of organic evolution and occurrence of major granite-forming episodes of North America

The granite-forming events that culminated in the development of the Churchill province about 1.8 billion years ago extended into Greenland and as far southwest as the Gulf of California (Figure 31.3). It is not clear whether the Churchill province ever enveloped the Superior-Wyoming and Slave provinces on the southeast, nor are the relative extents and interrelations of the Churchill and Central provinces well understood. But it does seem clear that by 1.8 billion years ago the Churchill province was nearly 1.5 times larger than the relict Superior-Wyoming and Slave provinces; that is almost encircled them; and that with them it comprised an area almost half that of present-day North America. The data also permit the conclusion that the Churchill province was much larger in extent than it is today.

The Central province is poorly exposed, but much of what we see in rare outcrops and scattered drill holes seems unique and exciting. Bass (verbal communication) has noted the seeming predominance of intermediate-to-rhyolite volcanics and potassium-rich granite in which there is little evidence of solid state deformation. Most granites of other provinces are deformed, presumably by mountain-making forces that accompanied their emplacement. Other unique aspects of many parts of the Central province are the scarcity of sedimentary rocks and the date of the major, granite-forming event, about 1.4 billion years ago (Tilton et al, 1962; Aldrich, et al, 1957). This great magmatic event and the much more recent Pacific event interrupt a series of granitic episodes that apparently otherwise occurred with some regularity every 600 to 800 million years (Figures 31.3 and 31.5).

The unique features of the sparsely exposed and drilled parts of the Central province raise the question whether the exposed parts of the Canadian shield per se are a true reflection of the characteristics of all of the Precambrian crust of North America. Certainly there are striking differences in structural features, and composition, between known Precambrian rocks of the Central province, and the Canadian shield; and these differences seem to require processes that differ greatly in degree if not in kind. The data suggest that about 1.4 billion years ago the entire central and southwestern part of the United States was a gigantic puddle or blister of granite, with perhaps a very thin sedimentary skin.

If the Central province evolved by differentiation at a continental-oceanic interface, the processes were uniquely efficient and complete. For typical granitie and rhyolitic volcanics in the central province contain as much as 7.0 weight per cent K_2O and have a K_2O/Na_2O ratio > 1.0. Typical granitic rocks evolving at continental-oceanic interfaces are sodic, with a ratio of K_2O/Na_2O of < 1.0. Moreover in the circum-pacific the ratio K_2O/Na_2O in granitic and volcanic rocks of major orogenic episodes tends to increase from the edge of the ocean basin per se inward into areas of typically continental crust (Moore, 1959; Sugimara, 1961; Wasserburg et al, 1963).

TABLE 31.3
Estimated composition of average sediments at three periods during the evolution of North America

	3.2–2.5 × 10^9 yrs. ago	2.5–1.8 × 10^9 yrs. ago	0.6 × 10^9 yrs. ago to present
SiO_2	66.0	65.2	58.8
Al_2O_3	14.5	14.1	13.6
Fe_2O_3	1.4	1.7	3.5
FeO	3.9	2.9	2.1
MgO	2.2	2.3	2.7
CaO	2.8	3.1	6.0
Na_2O	3.0	2.8	1.2
K_2O	1.4	2.6	2.9
Other*	4.8	5.3	9.2

* H_2O+, H_2O-, CO_2, CaS, TiO_2, P_2O_5.

These relations, coupled with the scarcity of gneissic features and meta-sedimentary rocks in the known parts of the Central Province suggest that it may largely represent a refusion and further differentiation of pre-existing continental crust at least 1.8 billion years old.

The Grenville province is developed along the entire eastern and southern parts of North America (Figure 31.3). There it seems to form a great sheath extending from Labrador to Mexico (Engel and Engel, 1953; Wasserburg et al, 1962; Fries et al, 1962). It may also appear in the southern part of Greenland and extend southward into Central America. Its pre-granitic, volcanic-sedimentary sequences vary widely in composition. The best known, in southeast Ontario (Engel, 1956), southwest Quebec (Osborne and Morin, 1962), and New York includes thick clean carbonate beds, quartzites and at least locally—an evaporite sequence with gypsum. Anorthosites form scattered massifs of highly controversial origin and age.

During the evolution of the Grenville province, algae flourished in widespread shallow shelf seas that invaded parts of the Central, Churchill, and Superior-Wyoming and Slave provinces. Carbonate formations are widespread in both the geosynclinal and the shelf sediments. Indeed, with quartzites and potassium-rich shales, they commonly predominate over sediments of the microbreccia graywacke type (Tables 31.2 and 31.3). Dolomite predominated over limestone at this time, but the ratio was reversed about 500 million years ago (Tables 31.2 and 31.4). The average sediment thus shows an increase in well-weathered and sorted types over primitive graywacke types, with increases in the ratios of potassium to sodium, of ferric iron oxide to ferrous iron oxide, of calcium to magnesium, of calcite to dolomite, and of carbonates to clastics in which there are free carbon and sulfides (Tables 31.2, 31.3, and 31.4).

TABLE 31.4
Estimated secular variation in the composition of carbonate sediments and in the ratio of carbonates to clastics

Clastics / Carbonate	Dolomite $CaMg(CO_3)_2$ / Limestone $CaCO_3$	Age in years
1000:1	3:1	> 1.8 × 10^9
30:1	3:2	1.0–1.8 × 10^9
15:1	1:4	< 0.6 × 10^9

The granite-forming episodes that climaxed the Grenville era emplaced potassium-rich silicate fluids throughout at least 20 per cent of North America. A major unresolved question is whether an analogue to the Grenville event occurred in western North America. A tenuous association of granite (dated 10^9 yrs) at Pikes Peak and geologic features near Los Angeles and in southeastern Alaska suggest Grenville granite-forming events and sediments at these places (Aldrich et al, 1958; Silver, L.T., verbal communication; Wasserburg and Eberlein, 1962). But as previously noted the succeeding, complex series of sedimentary-volcanic and granite-forming events along the entire western coast have all but obliterated the earlier record. This is true to a lesser extent in eastern North America. Geochronologic sleuthing indicates that there the Appalachian

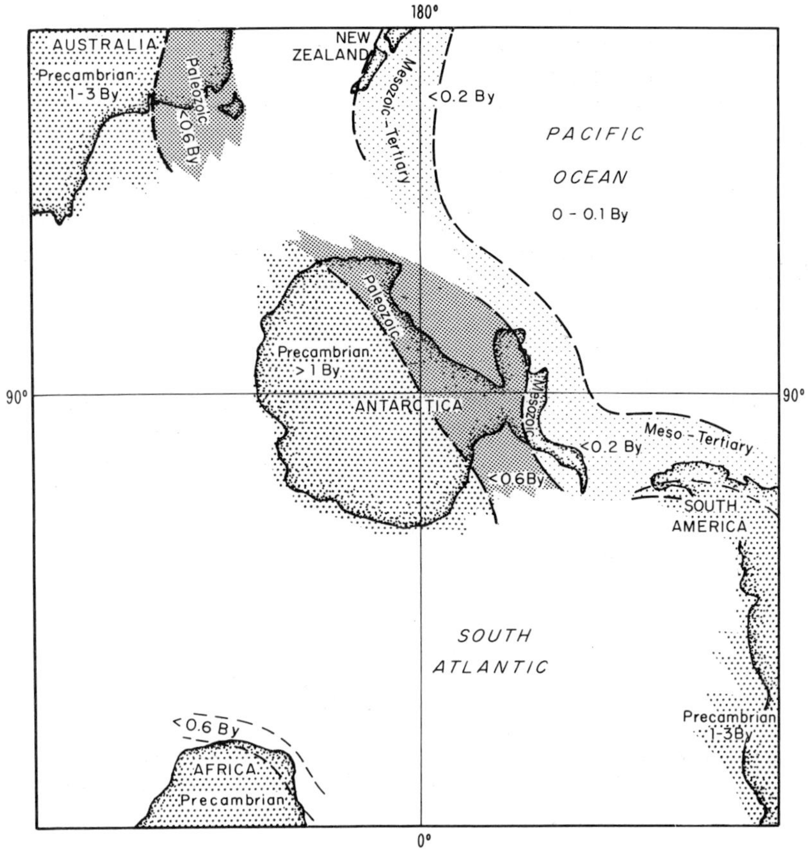

FIGURE 31.6
Unidirectional patterns of successive orogenic and granite-forming episodes in parts of the southern hemisphere

province is built largely upon the Grenville (Figure 31.4; Tilton et al, 1960; Long and Kulp, 1962). The encircling patterns of these young Applachian, Pacific, and Greenlandian provinces are perhaps the most striking example of province overprinting, and of the instability of the continental edges, during the last 600 million years (Figures 31.2 and 31.4).

The relatively young Appalachian, Pacific and Greenlandian provinces are known in considerable detail and the constituent rocks are described at length in most textbooks of historical geology and stratigraphy. Several of their broad features are especially pertinent here. (1) They form very young, elongate sheaths to the continents. (2) They are built in part on pre-existing older provinces but include constituents from fringing island arcs (Kay, 1951) or other positive crustal blocks not now apparent (Pettijohn, 1960, p. 452). (3) Both the Appalachian and the Greenlandian provinces appear to have once projected outward beyond the existing continental crust into the oceanic basin (Figure 31.2). This suggests that continents may have pulled apart, or that mobile belts extended from one continent to another across the ocean floor (Gastil, 1960 p. 162)

OTHER CONTINENTS AND CONTINENTAL DRIFT

There are grounds for postulating the continental accretion of North America, but what of the patterns of provinces and mountain belts on other continents? The data seem too fragmentary to justify extended speculation. One thing is clear. Young evolving(?) island arcs and mountain belts are by no means ubiquitous at continental-oceanic margins. They are found throughout much of the Pacific, the Carribbean, and the Arctic and Antarctic oceans. In contrast, the perimeters of the Atlantic and Indian oceans largely lack island arcs and young coastal mountains. Parts of the granitic, continental crusts of Greenland, India, Western Australia, and eastern South America—a billion or more years old—appear to merge abruptly into thin, basaltic, oceanic crust (Figure 31.6).

This fact, together with the near-fit of some continental outlines, extensive but not entirely convincing paleoclimatological and paleomagnetic data, and the interruptions of mountain belts and old sial at the edges of the continents, has kept Wegener's hypotheses of continental drift alive and kicking (Runcorn et al, 1952; Hess, 1962). There is clearly a crude fit between the edges of the continents that face the Atlantic and the Indian Oceans. This has prompted some geologists to suggest that the present continents dispersed from a common super-continent and drifted across the present Atlantic and Indian oceans. The time-of-drift that fits best with diverse geologic events and data is about 150 to 200 million years ago. But it is difficult to reconcile the interpretation of continental drift and continental accretion. If North America broke away from Europe and Africa and drifted west less than 200 million years ago, we would expect accretion to be largely unidirectional from east to west. Otherwise, the Grenville and Appalachian mountain belts must have evolved in the heartland of the parent continent prior to the drift.

There appear to be examples of unidirectional continental accretion, although some of these are not easily reconciled with the postulated drift. One example is the Australian-Antarctic region indicated in Figure 31.7. Geologists familiar with the Australia-New Zealand region have frequently postulated the "eastward migration of geosynclines," and of the continental-oceanic interface. The evidence is suggestive (Everdon and Richards, 1962; Joplin, 1962, p. 52; Wasserberg et al, 1963; Hess, 1955, p. 389) although there seem to be serious objections (Standard, 1961). Both the dramatic aspects of, and apparent conflicts between, the hypotheses of continental accretion and continental drift endow them with an aura of excitement and controversy that only more accurate and complete data will resolve.

RATES OF GROWTH

Several possible rates of continental growth of North America are implied by the data. A plot of the relict areas of each province (including the known overlap) against time suggests a linear growth rate (Figure 31.8). Hurley and his colleagues have argued that a linear rate of continental growth is borne out by comparisons of the ratio Sr^{87}/Sr^{86} with the geological age of granitic rocks (1962). They estimate an

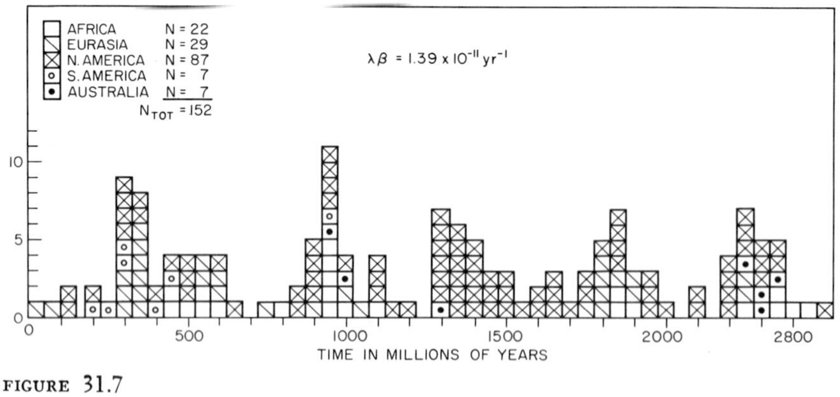

FIGURE 31.7
Distribution in time and by continent of 152 Rb-Sr age determinations. Indicates the world-wide episodic nature of granite-forming events (from Aldrich, Wetherill, Bass, Tilton, and Davis, 1960). Plots of hundreds of age determinations using Ar^{40}-K^{40}, Pb-Pb, U-Th-Pb, show correlative peaks (Gastil, 1960a).

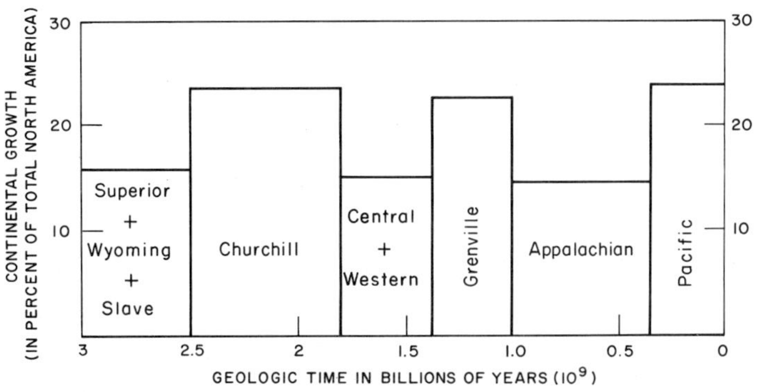

FIGURE 31.8
Graphic representation of the crudely linear rate of continental growth. Indicated by the known extent and overlap of successively formed geologic provinces. Geologic evidence permits extensive variations from this pattern.

average growth rate of about 7000 square kilometers per million years, operative over most of geologic time. Their geochemical calculations are suggestive but not conclusive. Wide deviations from linearity are consistent with the data at hand; these include waxing and waning periods of continental growth, as suggested by Tatsumoto and Patterson (1963) and the previously noted explosive early growth, with recurrent, lesser granite-forming eposides every 300 to 800 million years. In considerations of continental growth, a distinction seems necessary between areal extent of continents, and their thickness and volume. Conceivably, existing continents cover either no greater (or even less?) area than that of a thin primordial, sial formed over 3.2×10^9 years ago. But our contemporary concepts of degassing of the earth, and leaching of alkalis from the mantle suggest that there has been a secular increase in the total volume and thickness of sial, complementary to an increase in volume and depth of oceans.

SUMMARY

The oldest decipherable rock complexes within North America (more than 2.5×10^9 years old) are largely basaltic volcanics and graywacke. Recent and modern analogues are the island arcs formed along and adjacent to the unstable interface of continental and oceanic crusts. The major interfacial reactions (orogenies) incorporate pre-existing sial, oceanic crust, and mantle into crust of a more continental type. Incipient stages of continental evolution, more than 3×10^9 years ago, remain obscure. They may involve either a cataclysmic granite-forming event or a succession of volcanic-sedimentary and granite-forming cycles. Intermediate and recent stages of continental evolution, as indicated by data for North America, involve accretion of numerous crustal interfaces with fragments of adjacent continental crust and their partial melting, reinjection, elevation, unroofing, and stabilization. Areas of relict provinces defined by ages of granites suggest that continental growth is approximately linear. But the advanced differentiation found in many provinces and the known overlaps permit wide deviation from linearity in the direction of a more explosive early or intermediate growth.

Mountain-building, granite-forming events instrumental in continental evolution are episodic, possibly periodic on a worldwide scale.

The trend of continental evolution, although episodic and at least intermittently reversible, involves increases in (1) the ratio of thickened, stable continent to unstable island arc and ocean; (2) the ratio of continental volume to eroded sediments; (3) the ratio of residuate sediments to graywacke; and (4) the ratio of biochemical precipitates to clastics.

Secular changes in the composition of average sediment on and eroded from North America include increases in the ratios of Fe_2O_3/FeO, K/Na, and Ca/Mg. Specific sediments exhibit little sęcular change in composition but show critical changes in proportions and in the geography of their environments. Secular distributions on North America of arc-type ultrabasics, pillow basalts, quartz diorites, and other rocks largely indigenous to crustal interfaces and oceanic crust form a series of crudely arcuate zones. These migrate outward with time from the continental core to the present continental margins.

REFERENCES CITED

Adams, R. D., 1962, Thickness of the earth's crust beneath the Campbell Plateau: New Zealand Jour. Geology and Geophysics, v. 5, p. 74–85.

Aldrich, L. T., G. W. Wetherill, M. N. Bass, G. R. Tilton, and G. L. Davis, 1960, Mineral age measurements and earth history: Carnegie Institution Ann. Rept. Dept. of Terrestrial Magnetism, 1959–1960, p. 208–220.

Aldrich, L. T., G. W. Wetherill, and G. L. Davis, 1957, Occurrence of 1350 million-year old granitic rocks in western United States: Geol. Soc. America Bull., v. 68, p. 655–656.

———, 1956, Determination of radiogenic Sr^{87} and Rb^{87} of an interlaboratory series of lepidolites: Geochim. et Cosmochim. Acta, v. 10, p. 238–240.

Allsopp, H. L., 1961, Rb-Sr age measurements of total rocks and separated-mineral fractions from old granite of the Central Transvaal: Jour. Geophys. Research, v. 66, no. 5, p. 1499–1508.

Armstrong, H. S., 1960, Marbles in the "Archean" of the southern Canadian Shield, *in* Pre-Cambrian stratigraphy and correlations: Internat. Geol. Cong. 21st Sess. Rept., pt. 9, p. 7–20.

Australasian Petroleum Company Proprietary, 1961, Geological results of petroleum exploration in Western Papua: Jour. Geol. Soc. Australia, v. 8, pt. 2, 113 p.

Bass, M. N., 1961, Regional tectonics of part of the southern Canadian Shield: Jour. Geology, v. 69, p. 668–702.

Birch, A. F., 1954, Heat from radioactivity, *in* H. Faul, ed., Nuclear geology: New York, John Wiley and Sons, p. 148–174.

———, 1958, Differentiation of the mantle: Geol. Soc. America Bull., v. 69, p. 483–485.

Blackadar, R. G. and R. G. Fraser, 1960, Precambrian geology of arctic Canada; A summary account: Geol. Survey Canada Paper 60-8, 24 p.

Bowen, N. L., 1928, Evolution of igneous rocks: Princeton, N.J., Princeton University Press, 334 p.

Brown, J. S., and A. E. J. Engel, 1956, Revision of Grenville stratigraphy and structure in the Balmat-Edwards district, northwest Adirondacks, New York: Geol. Soc. America Bull., v. 67, p. 1599–1622.

Buddington, A. F., 1940, Some petrological concepts and the interior of the earth: Am. Mineralogist, v. 28, p. 119–140.

Byers, F. M., 1959, Geology of Umnak and Bogoslof Islands, Aleutian Islands, Alaska: U.S. Geol. Survey Bull. 1028-L, p. 267–369.

Chamalaun, T., and P. H. Roberts, 1962, The theory of convection in spherical shells and its application to the problem of themal convection in the earth's mantle, *in* S. K. Runcorn, ed., Continental drift: New York, Academic Press, p. 171–197.

Chamberlin, R. T., 1950, Diastrophic behavior around the Bighorn Basin: Jour. Geology, v. 48, p. 673–716.

Clark, T. A., and C. W. Stearn, 1960, The geologic evolution of North America: New York, Ronald Press, 434 p.

Coats, R. R., 1962, Magma type and crustal structure in the Aleutian Arc, *in* The crust of the Pacific Basin: Am. Geophys. Union Mon. 6, p. 92–109.

Dana, J. D., 1873, On the results of the earth's contraction from cooling, including a discussion of the origin of mountains: Am. Jour. Sci., ser 3., v. 5, p. 423–443.

Deer, L. R., 1958, Beneath the earth's crust: Adv. Sci., v. 15, p. 31–46.

Dietz, R. S., 1961, Vredefort ring structure; Meteorite impact scar: Jour. Geology, v. 69, p. 499–516.

Engel, A. E. J., 1965, Apropos the Grenville, *in* J. E. Thomson, ed., The Grenville problem, (Royal Soc. Canada Spec. Pub.) Toronto Press, p. 74–98.

Engel, A. E. J., and Celeste G. Engel, 1953, The Grenville series in the northwest Adirondack Mountains; Part I, General features of the Grenville series: Geol. Soc. America Bull., v. 64., p. 1013–1048.

Evernden, J. F., and J. R. Richards, 1962, Potassium-argon ages in eastern Australia: Geol. Soc. Australia Jour., v. 9, pt. 1, p. 1–49.

Ewing, J. I., and W. M. Ewing, 1959, Seismic-refraction measurements in the Atlantic Ocean Basins, in the Mediterranean Sea, on the Mid-Atlantic Ridge, and in the Norwegian Sea: Geol. Soc. America Bull., v. 70, p. 291–317.

Ewing, J. I., J. L. Worzel, and W. M. Ewing, 1962, Sediments and oceanic structural history of the Gulf of Mexico: Jour. Geophys. Research, v. 67, p. 2509–2527.

Fries, C., Jr., R. Schmitter, P. R. Damon, and D. E. Livingston, 1962, Rocas Precambricas de edad Greenvilliana de la parte central de Oaxaca en el sur de Mexico, *in* Estudios Geochronologicos de Rocas Mexicanas: Univ. Nac. Auton. Mexico Inst. Geologia Bull., 64, p. 55–69.

Gast, P. W., L. J. Kulp, and L. E. Long, 1958, Absolute age of early Precambrian rocks in the Bighorn Basin of Wyoming and Montana: Am. Geophys. Union Trans., v. 39, p. 322–334.

Gastil, G., 1960a, The distribution of mineral dates in time and space: Am. Jour. Sci., v. 258, p. 1–35.

———, 1960b, Continents and mobile belts in the light of mineral dating, *in* Pre-Cambrian stratigraphy and correlations: Internat. Geol. Cong. 21st Sess. Rept., pt. 9, p. 162–169.

Gilluly, J., 1955, Geologic contrast between continents and ocean basins, *in* Arie Poldervaart, ed., Crust of the earth: Geol. Soc. America Spec. Paper 62, p. 7–18.

Goldich, S. S., A. O. Nier, H. Baadsgaard, J. H. Hoffman, and H. W. Krueger, 1961, The

Precambrian geology and geochronology of Minnesota: Minnesota Geol. Survey Bull., v. 41, 193 p.

Goldschmidt, V. M., 1954, Geochemistry: Oxford, Clarendon Press, 730 p.

Goryachev, A. V., 1962, On the relationship between geotectonic and geophysical phenomena of the Kuril-Kamchatka folding zone at the junction zone of the Asiatic Continent with the Pacific Basin, *in* The crust of the Pacific Basin: Am. Geophys. Union Mon. 6, p. 41–49.

Gutenberg, B., 1955, Wave velocities in the earth's crust, *in* Arie Poldervaart, ed., Crust of the earth: Geol. Soc. America Spec. Paper 62, p. 19–34.

Hall, J., 1883, Contributions to the geological history of the American Continent: Am. Assoc. Adv. Sci. 31st Mtg. Proc., p. 29–69.

Hamilton, E. L., 1956, Sunken islands of the Mid-Pacific Mountains: Geol. Soc. America Mem. 64, 97 p.

Hamilton, W., 1961, The origin of the Gulf of California: Geol. Soc. America Bull., v. 72, p. 1307–1318.

Harrison, J. M., and K. E. Eade, 1957, Proterozoic in Canada, *in* James E. Gill, ed., The Proterozoic in Canada (Royal Soc. Canada Spec. Pub. 2): Toronto, University of Toronto Press, p. 3–9.

Haug, E., 1900, Les geosynclinaux et les aires continentales: Soc. géol. France Bull., v. 28, p. 617–711.

Hayes, W. C., 1961, Guidebook to the geology of the St. Francois Mountain area: Missouri Geol. Survey and Water Resources Rept. Inv. 26, 137 p.

Heezen, B. C., 1962, The deep sea floor, *in* S. K. Runcorn, ed., Continental drift: New York, Academic Press, p. 235–288.

Heiskanen, W. A., and F. A. Vening Meinesz, 1958, The earth and its gravity field: New York, McGraw-Hill, 470 p.

Hess, H. H., 1955, Serpentine, orogeny and epeirogeny, *in* Arie Poldervaart, ed., Crust of the earth: Geol. Soc. America Spec. Paper 62, p. 391–408.

———, 1960, Stillwater igneous complex, Montana: Geol. Soc. America Mem. 80, 230 p.

———, 1962, History of ocean basins, *in* A. E. J. Engel, J. L. James, and B. F. Leonard, eds., Petrologic studies—a volume in honor of A. F. Buddington: Boulder, Colo., Geological Society of America, p. 599–620.

Holland, H. D., 1962, Model for the evolution of the earth's atmosphere, *in* A. E. J. Engel, H. L. James, and B. L. Leonard, eds., Petrologic studies—a volume in honor of A. F. Buddington: Boulder, Colo., Geological Society of America, p. 447–477.

Holmes, A., 1954, The oldest dated minerals of the Rhodesian Shield: Nature, v. 173, p. 612–614.

Hurley, P. M., H. Hughes, G. Faure, H. W. Fairbairn, and W. H. Pinson, 1962, Radiogenic strontium-87 model of continent formation: Jour. Geophys. Research, v. 67, no. 13, p. 5315–5334.

Innes, M. J. S., 1960, Gravity and isostasy in northern Ontario and Manitoba: Dominion Observatory Pub. 6, p. 261–338.

Jones, O. T., 1938, On the evolution of a geosyncline: Geol. Soc. London Quart. Jour., v. 4, p. 60–110.

Joplin, Germaine A., 1962, An apparent magmatic cycle in the Tasman geosyncline: Geol. Soc. Australia Jour., v. 9, pt. 1, p. 51–70.

Kay, G. M., 1951, North America geosynclines: Geol. Soc. America Mem. 48, 143 p.

Krishnan, M. S., 1960, The geology of India and Burma: Madras, Higginbothams Ltd., 604 p.

Liechti, P., F. W. Roe, and N. S. Haile, 1960, The geology of Sarawak, Brunei, and the western part of North Borneo: Geol. Survey Borneo Bull. 3, v. 1, 360 p.

Long, L. E., and L. J. Kulp, 1962, Isotopic age study of the metamorphic history of the Manhattan and Reading Prongs: Geol. Soc. America Bull., v. 73, p. 969–996.

Lowdon, J. A., 1961, Age determination by the Geological Survey of Canada: Geol. Survey Canada Paper 61–17, 127 p.

MacDonald, G. J. F., 1959, Chrondrites and the Chemical composition of the earth, *in* P. H. Ableson, ed., Researches in geochemistry: New York, John Wiley and Sons, p. 476–494.

Macgregor, A. A., 1940, A Pre-Cambrian algal limestone in Southern Rhodesia: Geol. Soc. South Africa Trans., v. 43, p. 9–15.

———, 1951, Some milestones in the Precambrian of Southern Rhodesia: Geol. Soc. South Africa Trans., v. 54, p. 27–71.

Menard, H. W., 1955, Deep-sea channels, topography, and sedimentation: Am. Assoc. Petroleum Geologists Bull., v. 39, p. 236–255.

———, 1961, The East Pacific Rise: Science, v. 132, no. 3441, p. 1737–1746.

Moore, J. G., 1959, The quartz diorite boundary line in the western United States: Jour. Geology, v. 67, p. 198–210.

Nicholaysen, L. O., 1962, Stratigraphic interpretation of age measurements in southern Africa, *in* A. E. J. Engel, H. L. James, and B. L. Leonard, eds., Petrologic studies—a volume in honor of A. F. Buddington: Boulder, Colo., Geological Society of America, p. 569–598.

Noble, L. F., 1941, Structural features of the Virgin Spring area, Death Valley, California: Geol. Soc. America Bull., v. 52, p. 941–999.

Officer, C. B., J. I. Ewing, R. S. Edwards, and H. R. Johnson, 1957, Geophysical investigations in the eastern Caribbean-Venezuelan Basin, Antilles Island Arc, and Puerto Rico Trench: Geol. Soc. America Bull., v. 68, p. 359–378.

Osborne, F. F., and M. Morin, 1962, Tectonics of part of the Grenville Subprovince, *in* J. S. Stevenson, ed., The tectonics of the Canadian Shield (Royal Soc. Canada Spec. Pub. 4):

Toronto, University of Toronto Press, p. 118–143.
Patterson, C., 1956, Age of meteroites and the earth: Geochim. et Cosmochim. Acta, v. 10, p. 230–237.
Peterson, M. N., and E. D. Goldberg, 1962, Feldspar distributions in South Pacific pelagic sediments: Jour. Geophys. Research, v. 67, p. 3477–3492.
Pettijohn, F. J., 1943, Archean sedimentation: Geol. Soc. America Bull., v. 54, p. 925–972.
———, 1960, Some contributions of sedimentology to tectonic analysis, *in* Structure of the earth's crust and deformation of rocks: Internat. Geol. Cong. 21st Sess. Rept., pt. 19, p. 446–454.
Phemister, T. C., 1960, The nature of the contact between the Grenville and Temiskaming Subprovinces in the Sudbury District of Ontario, Canada, *in* The granite gneiss problem: Internat. Geol. Cong. 21st Sess. Rept., pt. 15, p. 108–119.
Polkanov, A. A., and E. K. Gerling, 1961, Geochronology and geological evolution of the Baltic Shield and its folded margins: Akad. Nauk. SSSR Lab. Geol. Dokembriya Trudy, no. 15, p. 7–102.
Press, Frank, 1961, The earth's crust and upper mantle: Science, v. 133, no. 3463, p. 1455–1463.
Raitt, R. W., 1956, Crustal thickness of the Pacific Ocean Basin: Geol. Soc. America Bull., v. 67, p. 1623–1639.
Rubey, W. H., 1955, Development of the hydrosphere and atmosphere, with special reference to probable composition of the early atmosphere, *in* Arie Poldervaart, ed., Crust of the earth: Geol. Soc. America Spec. Paper 62, p. 136–650.
Runcorn, S. K., 1962, Paleomagnetic evidence for continental drift and its geophysical cause, *in* S. K. Runcorn, ed., Continental drift: New York, Academic Press, p. 1–40.
Schmidt, R. G., 1957, Geology of Saipan, Mariana Islands; Petrology of the volcanic rocks: U.S. Geol. Survey Prof. Paper 280-B, p. 127–174.
Shepard, R. P., and K. O. Emery, 1941, Submarine topography off the California coast: Geol. Soc. America Spec. Paper 31, 171 p.
Shepard, F. P., F. B. Phleger, and T. H. Van Andel, 1960, Recent sediments, northwest Gulf of Mexico: Am. Assoc. Petroleum Geologists Spec. Volume, 286 p.
Shor, G. G., 1962, Seismic refraction studies off the coast of Alaska: Seismol. Soc. America Bull., v. 52, p. 37–57.
Simonen, A., 1960, Pre-Cambrian stratigraphy of Finland, *in* Pre-Cambrian stratigraphy and correlations: Internat. Geol. Cong. 21st Sess. Rept., pt. 9, p. 141–153.
Standard, J. C., 1961, Submarine geology of the Tasman Sea: Geol. Soc. America Bull., v. 72, p. 1777–1788.
Stockwell, C. H., 1962, A tectonic map of the Canadian Shield, *in* J. S. Stevenson, ed., The tectonics of the Canadian Shield (Royal Soc. Canada Spec. Pub. 4): Toronto, University of Toronto Press, p. 6–15.
Sugimura, A., 1961, Regional variations of the K_2O/Na_2O ratios of volcanic rocks in Japan and environs: Geol. Soc. Japan Jour., v. 67, p. 292–300.
Talwani, M., G. Sutton, and J. Worzel, 1959, A crustal section across the Puerto Rico Trench: Jour. Geophys. Research, v. 64, p. 1545–1555.
Thom, W. R., Jr., 1955, Wedge uplifts and their tectonic significance, *in* Arie Poldervaart, ed., Crust of the earth: Geol. Soc. America Spec. Paper 62, p. 369–376.
Tatsumoto, M., and C. Patterson, 1964, Age studies of zircon and feldspar concentrates from Great Lakes Region river sands and from the Franconia sandstone: Jour. Geology, v. 72, p. 232–242.
Tilton, G. R., G. W. Wetherill, and G. L. Davis, 1962, Mineral ages from the Wichita and Arbuckle Mountains, Oklahoma, and the St. Francis Mountains, Missouri: Jour. Geophys. Research, v. 67, p. 4011–4020.
Tilton, G. R., G. W. Wetherill, G. L. Davis, and M. N. Bass, 1960, 1000 million-year-old minerals from the eastern United States and Canada: Jour. Geophys. Research, v. 65, p. 4173–4179.
Urey, H. C., 1952, The planets: New Haven, Yale University Press, 352 p.
Vening Meinesz, F. A., 1952, The origins of continents and oceans: Geol. Mijnbouw, n.s., v. 14, p. 373–384.
———, 1962, Thermal convection in the earth's mantle, *in* S. K. Runcorn, ed., Continental drift: New York, Academic Press, p. 145–176.
Wager, L. R., and W. A. Deer, 1939, Geological investigations in east Greenland; Part 3, Petrology of the Skaergaard intrusion, Kangerdlugssuq, East Greenland: Medd. Grønland, v. 105, 335 p.
Wasserburg, G. J., and G. D. Eberlein, 1962, Age of the Birch Creek schist and some batholithic instrusions in Alaska: Geol. Soc. America Ann. Mtg. Program, 1962.
Wasserburg, G. J., G. W. Wetherill, and L. A. Wright, 1959, Ages in the Precambrian terrane of Death Valley, California: Jour. Geology, v. 67, p. 702–708.
Wasserburg, G. J., G. W. Wetherill, L. T. Silver, and P. Y. Flawn, 1962, A study of the ages of the Precambrian of Texas: Jour. Geophys. Research, v. 67, p. 4021–4047.
Wasserburg, G. J., H. Craig, H. W. Menard, A. E. J. Engel, and Celeste G. Engel, 1963, Age and composition of the Bounty Islands and Seychelles Islands granite: Jour. Geology, v. 71, no. 6, p. 785–789.

32

Atlantic Sediments, Erosions Rates, and the Evolution of the Continental Shelf

Some Speculations

JAMES GILLULY

1964

The isopach map of the Atlantic Continental Shelf and Slope by Drake, Ewing, and Sutton (1959) supplies data fundamental to many geological problems. It permits an estimate of the volume of offshore sediment and shows a rough approximation of the form of the offshore basins and the presence of a nearly continuous median ridge separating an inner group of deep basins from an outer group.

Seismic evidence suggests that the basement on which the sediments lie is continuous from the Piedmont seaward. It is assumed, therefore, that the sediment is chiefly younger than Triassic, but inasmuch as several troughs of Triassic sediment are overlapped by the formations of the Coastal Plain, a larger proportion of offshore sediment may be of Triassic age than would be inferred from maps of the Piedmont province.

The map thus furnishes a basis for comparing the average rate of Mesozoic and Cenozoic erosion with that of the present. It also gives clues as to the origin of the Continental Shelf and the Mesozoic and Cenozoic history of the Atlantic Ocean.

VOLUME OF SEDIMENTS

Very slight extrapolation of the trends of the isopachs determined by Drake, Ewing, and Sutton (1959, Fig. 29) makes possible a rough estimate of the volume of sediments on the Shelf and Slope between lat. 37° 30′ N. (near the Virginia–North Carolina border), and a line trending southeast from a point on the Nova Scotia coast near lat. 45° N. As the seaward limit, I have taken an extrapolation of the 5000-foot isopach north of lat. 40° N., and the 10,000-foot isopach and its extrapolation on strike to the south of that parallel (Figure 32.1). Thus at the cutoff on the seaward side, sediment thicknesses are still great. The omitted seaward extensions, if included, would notably increase the volume of sediment measured

From *Geological Society of America Bulletin*, vol. 75, pp. 483–492, 1964. Reprinted with permission of the author and the Geological Society of America.

and accordingly the rate of erosion here deduced; the present estimates are thus very conservative.

By planimetry, the mapped area of Triassic and younger sedimentary rocks on the Coastal Plain, Continental Shelf and Slope is about 190,000 mi². The volume as computed from the 0-, 1000-, 5000-, 10,000-, and 15,000-foot isopachs is approximately 280,000 mi³. The porosity of the sediment is greater than that of the source rock, which included both more compacted older sediment and a considerable volume of crystalline rock. A mean density of 2.3 for the present sediments seems reasonable; if the source bedrock had a mean density of 2.65, the present volume of sediments represents about 245,000 mi³ of bedrock.

Because the interface between sediments and basement is continuous from that exposed at the Fall Line to the Shelf edge throughout the map area of Drake, Ewing, and Sutton (1959), it seems reasonable to conclude, as these authors imply, that nearly all this sediment is of Triassic and younger age.

Although there are a few marls in the exposed rocks of the Coastal Plain, there are no true limestones in the latitudes here considered; probably the offshore sediments are likewise predominantly noncalcareous. Thus the sediments were supplied primarily by the suspended and traction loads, rather than the dissolved load, of the streams emptying into the Atlantic, with minor contributions from shore erosion.

SOURCE AREA

To estimate the average rate of erosion implied by the measured volume of sediment, we must make assumptions as to both time of accumulation and source area. The time we can assume to be about 225 m. y., the usually accepted estimate for the span since the beginning of the Triassic (Holmes, 1960). The source area is considerably more uncertain. Because the general trend of the isopachs determined by Drake, Ewing, and Sutton (1959) is roughly parallel to the coast, and the width of the shelf is roughly constant both northeast and southwest of the map area, no very great convergence or divergence of sediment seems to have occurred during its accumulation. Therefore the segment of the continent directly inshore from the mapped area probably supplied most of the sediment.

The landward limit of the source area is

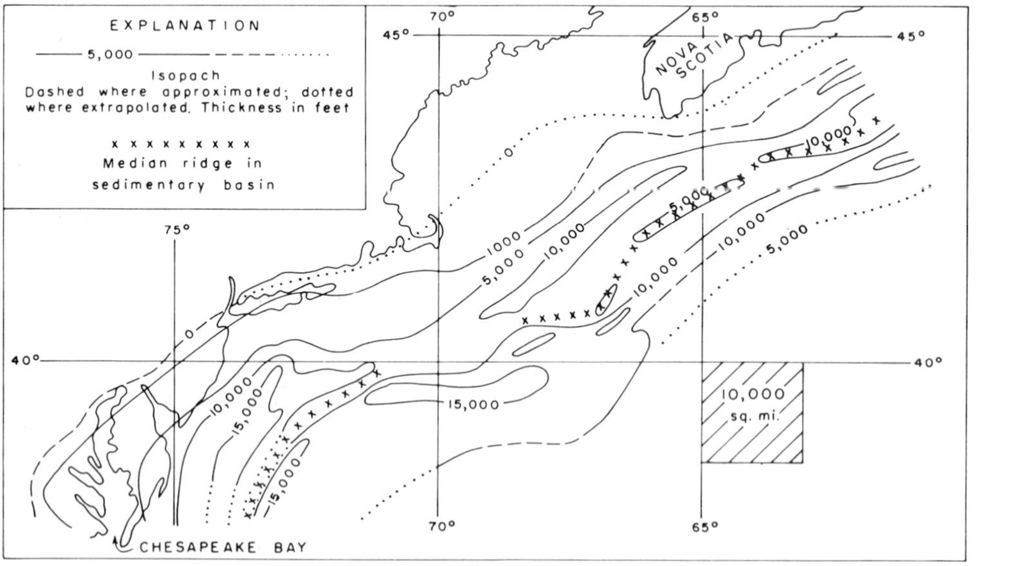

FIGURE 32.1
Isopach map of sediments of the Atlantic Coastal Plain, Continental Shelf, and Continental Slope. (Slightly modified and somewhat extrapolated from Figure 29 of Drake, Ewing, and Sutton, 1959.)

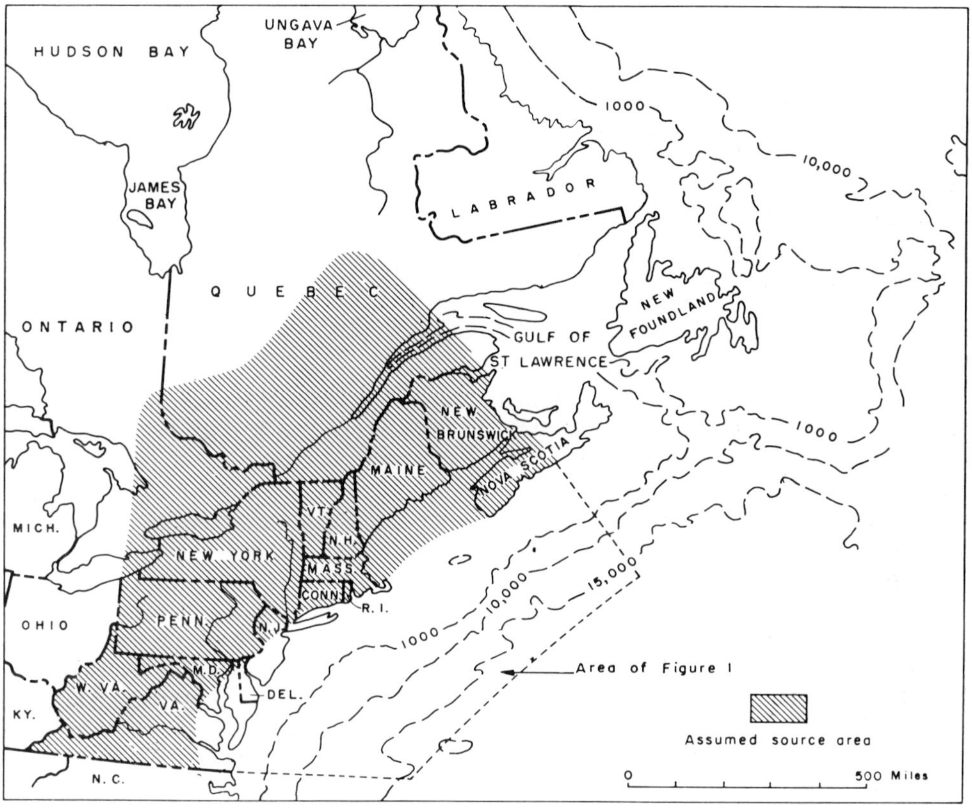

FIGURE 32.2
Assumed source area for sediments of the Coastal Plain, Continental Shelf, and Continental Slope between Chesapeake Bay and Nova Scotia

highly uncertain. The volume of Mesozoic and Cenozoic sediment in the Gulf of Mexico implies nearly as great a rate of supply during Mesozoic and Cenozoic time (mainly via the Mississippi River) as that of the present (Gilluly, 1955). The Rocky Mountain Cretaceous geosynclinal sea extended eastward almost to the Mississippi River. The Mississippi now drains more country than it did prior to the glacial diversion of the Missouri and Ohio rivers and thus the Atlantic drainage in the area of the St. Lawrence divide probably did not head much farther inland than it does today. Clearly, much of the headwater extension of the St. Lawrence drainage was due to Pleistocene diversions. I therefore assume that the ancestral St. Lawrence headed no farther west than Lake Erie and thus arbitrarily delimit the hypothetical source area as shown on Figure 32.2, by lines roughly normal to the coast at either end of the mapped area.

This area includes Virginia and all the coastal States to the northeast, most of New Brunswick, and parts of Ontario, Quebec, and Nova Scotia. The boundary extends along the zero isopach of Figure 32.1, and inland along the south border of Virginia, west border of West Virginia, Pennsylvania, and New York, the divide between the drainage of the St. Lawrence and that of James Bay as far as the Ungava Bay divide, from which point it trends southeastward to the coast in central Nova Scotia. The submarine contours of Figure 32.2 show that the northeastern boundary assigns relatively much greater segments of the Shelf off Labrador, Cape Breton Island, and Newfoundland to a relatively much smaller source area in Quebec, Labrador, and Newfoundland. From the standpoint of estimation of erosion rates in the area of our concern, the boundary is conservative. The St. Lawrence drainage has probably emptied about where it now does since well back in the Tertiary, so that the sedimentation area of our concern has probably not received its full quota of St. Lawrence sediment. The rate of denudation arrived at in this paper is thus probably lower than the true one.

The source area thus arbitrarily arrived at is about 510,000 mi².

PRESENT EROSION RATE

The hypothetical source area is now drained mainly by the St. Lawrence and by the rivers included by Dole and Stabler (1909) in their North Atlantic Group. Dole and Stabler estimated (p. 84) that the North Atlantic streams are now carrying enough suspended sediment to lower their drainage basins 0.000,20 inch per year. The St. Lawrence now carries so little suspended load that its drainage basis is lowered only 0.000,005 inch per year on this account, although clearly the present regimen of the St. Lawrence is highly abnormal because of the settling basins of the Great Lakes. I have therefore considered the rate estimated by Dole and Stabler for the "North Atlantic" streams the one to be tested for the entire source area.

Dole and Stabler made no effort to estimate the traction load of the streams, and even now few data are available. Some data gathered by Corbel (1959) show traction loads of several streams to range from 2 to 300 per cent of the suspended load; except in alpine environments he found the traction load to be generally 5–15 per cent of the suspended. For my rough estimates I assume a traction load 10 per cent of the suspended, or one equivalent to 0.000,020 inch of denudation per year.

The dissolved load, which I assume did not contribute to the offshore sediments appreciably, but of course did aid in denudation of the source area, is such as to lower the drainage basins of the North Atlantic Group 0.000,68 inch per year and the St. Lawrence basin 0.000,60 inch per year (Dole and Stabler, 1909); I assume 0.000,64 inch per year as the average.

In summary, the approximate rate of denudation of the assumed source area at present is:

By suspended load	0.000,20 in/yr
By traction load	0.000,02 in/yr
Total clastic sediments	0.000,22 in/yr
By dissolved load (assumed lost to general oceanic circulation	0.000,64 in/yr

Total erosion is thus equivalent to 0.000,86 inches per year.

COMPARISON OF PRESENT EROSION RATE WITH AVERAGE OF MESOZOIC AND CENOZOIC TIME

If the present rate of denudation were applicable to the assumed source area of 510,000 mi² for 225 m. y., the clastic sediment transported would aggregate 390,000 mi³ of material of the density of the source rock. Allowing for increased porosity, the resulting, less-consolidated sediment would occupy perhaps 450,000 mi³. This volume is to be compared with the 280,000 mi³ actually found in the adjacent Coastal Plain, Continental Shelf, and Continental Slope. The ostensible average rate of erosion from the beginning of the Triassic to the present would thus be 62 per cent of the present rate, or 0.000,136 inch per year.

Actually, I think the inferred average rate is highly conservative and that the true rate may have been fully equal to that of the present. The computation neglects several probably significant factors that would increase the inferred rate; neglected factors of the opposite tendency do not seem very weighty.

NEGLECTED FACTORS WHOSE OMISSION DECREASES THE COMPUTED RATE

The arbitrary assumptions that were used in the preceding estimates neglect several noteworthy items: (1) reworking of Coastal Plain sediments; (2) probable overestimate of source area; [and] (3) omission of the wedge of sediment offshore from the mapped area in computing the volume of erosion products.

REWORKING OF COASTAL PLAIN SEDIMENTS

Without question, there has been considerable reworking of the Coastal Plain sediments; some of the measured sediment has been reworked, perhaps more than once. The areas now covered by Triassic, Cretaceous, or Miocene strata obviously did not supply sediment to the Triassic, Cretaceous, or Miocene deposits respectively; instead, they and areas adjacent to them (now denuded) were recipients of sediments for part of the time we are considering. In other words, for long periods the source area was considerably smaller than I have assumed, and much of the sediment measured in the offshore area has been transported more than once. Both factors lead to an underestimate of the average rate of past erosion.

The Triassic is still represented on the Coastal Plain and Piedmont by deposits aggregating nearly 20,000 mi^3, as deduced from the Paleotectonic folio (McKee and others, 1959). These deposits have been included in the sediment volumes just considered. Certainly Triassic rocks were formerly much more extensive and voluminous. Sanders (1963) has suggested that the now-separated basins of New Jersey and Connecticut were originally parts of a single fault trough, and that other large areas of New York and Massachusetts once contained Triassic sediments. Presumably this implies comparable expansions of the Triassic sediments of Nova Scotia and of the Piedmont of Pennsylvania, Maryland, and Virginia and thus the source area during perhaps 15 m. y. of Late Triassic time would have been much restricted, perhaps by as much as 50,000 mi^2, and the volume of Triassic sediments since reworked might be as great as 100,000 mi^3. Correction for the first factor, the restriction of the source area, would only result in perhaps a 2 per cent adjustment in the rate of erosion deduced and may be neglected in computations so rough as these. But the correction implied by the volume of reworked Triassic sediments might be as great as 30 per cent and even if the volumes implied by Sanders are too high, the correction must still be considerable. If we assume that only 50,000 mi^3 of Triassic rocks was reworked and add this amount to the 280,000 mi^3 measured on the Coastal Plain and offshore prism the average rate of denudation would be not 62 per cent, but 73 per cent of the present rate. If Sanders' reconstruction were accepted the average rate deduced would be still higher.

Similar corrections may be needed for Jurassic modifications of source area and for reworking of Jurassic sediments, but there is no basis for evaluating them.

Cretaceous history, however, does imply the need of some corrections. An extreme view of Cretaceous paleogeography is that of Johnson (1931) who thought that the Cretaceous Coastal Plain sediments at one time covered most of the folded Appalachians. Were this true, the volume of reworked sediment (and the area necessarily eliminated as a source during much of Cretaceous time) would be very great. Johnson's theory would demand deposition and later stripping of sediment from a belt 125–200 miles wide—surely more than enough to accommodate the difference between the present rate of erosion and the average deduced for the Mesozoic and Cenozoic. In other words, if Johnson had been correct, we would have to infer erosion rates for most of this time notably higher than those of the present.

Johnson's theory seems, however, to be purely deductive; no direct evidence of so wide a former extent of the Coastal Plain formations has been presented. Groot (1955) has shown that some, at least, of the Cretaceous formations were supplied from nearby Piedmont sources and could never have extended very much farther northwest than they now do.

The figures derived do require a correction for reworking of Cretaceous rocks, but far less correction than Johnson's theory would demand. As a rough guess, a wedge 20 miles wide and 500 feet thick at the butt (an average thickness of exposed Coastal Plain formations of Cretaceous and later ages) along the coast might approximate the volume of the reworked sediments of the Coastal Plain. Such a volume would add nearly 1000 mi^3 to the aggregate sediment and diminish the source area by some part of, perhaps 20,000 mi^2; but these corrections would be only a very small fraction of that computed. Any reasonable estimate seems to me only a few times as large. In view of the crudeness of all these estimates, I believe the correction for reworked Cretaceous and Tertiary sediments would probably be less than 5 per cent of the computed average.

By thus considering restrictions of the source area at various times and reworking of sediments, we would arrive at an average rate for Mesozoic and Cenozoic erosion between 80 and 90 per cent of the present rate as computed by Dole and Stabler (1909).

POSSIBLE DIVERSITY OF SEDIMENT FROM POSTULATED SOURCE AREA TO OTHER DEPOSITION SITES

Nearly one third of the hypothetical source area lies in the present drainage basin of the St. Lawrence River. Absence of Mesozoic and Cenozoic sediments, glacial drainage modifications, and isostatic rebound make it impossible to evaluate the persistence or position of the Atlantic-Arctic drainage divide during pre-Recent time. Continued rebound should enlarge St. Lawrence drainage at the expense of the James Bay and Ungava Bay tributaries; perhaps this relation was the normal one in nonglacial times. The great volume of post-Triassic sediments of the Mississippi Embayment and the eastward extent of the Rocky Mountain Cretaceous into Minnesota and Iowa make it highly improbable that the source area assumed for the Atlantic sediments should be extended significantly into the present Mississippi drainage.

The St. Lawrence now discharges about 200 miles to the northeast of the Shelf section considered, and almost certainly did so for much of Tertiary and perhaps even Cretaceous time. The great width and volume of the shelf northeast, east, south, and southwest of Newfoundland (Figure 32.2) suggest a tremendous contribution of sediment from the St. Lawrence to that area—much of the St. Lawrence sediment must have accumulated there. Nevertheless, some St. Lawrence sediment has probably been carried into our area by longshore and other currents, and thus, for my rough estimates (and to be conservative as to past erosion rates) I have drawn the end boundaries of the "source area" about normal to the coast.

My computations may, indeed, have given too much weight to the part of the area in the St. Lawrence drainage and thus may have erred on the side of conservatism. Perhaps, instead of supplying 30 or 35 per cent of the computed volume of sediment, as implied by Figure 32.2, the St. Lawrence drainage supplied only 20 or 25 per cent. Correcting for such an over-estimate of source area would surely bring the hypothetical average erosion rate to within 90 per cent of the rate computed by Dole and Stabler, perhaps even to 95 per cent.

OMISSION OF OFFSHORE SEDIMENTS

The volume of sediment computed from the planimetry is highly conservative: it neglects a voluminous wedge of sediment offshore from the mapped area. For half the length of the mapped strip this wedge has a base height of 10,000 feet and for the other half, 5,000 feet; although it feathers out, it is unlikely to do so in less than 100 miles. If we include such a wedge, the volume to be added to that measured is nearly 50,000 mi^3, a correction of another 10 per cent.

NEGLECTED FACTORS WHOSE OMISSION INCREASES THE COMPUTED RATE

Among the possible factors whose omission tends to increase the computed rate of denudation are: (1) possible carbonates in the coastal and shelf sediments; (2) coastal erosion by the sea; [and] (3) possible inclusion of pre-Triassic sediments in the measured volume of deposits.

POSSIBLE PRESENCE OF CARBONATE SEDIMENTS

In the area here considered, the Coastal Plain sediments include a few marl units, but they are so subordinate that their omission does not affect the crude computations the data permit.

Possibly in the presumably milder climate of Cretaceous and early Tertiary time effective limestone deposition occurred farther north than at present, but a correction for such additions seems of a second order.

COASTAL EROSION

Coastal erosion by waves and currents contributes steadily to the sediment. The amount contributed is difficult to evaluate from Atlantic coastal data, but Kuenen (1950, p. 234) has estimated that the global average contribution of sediment by coastal erosion is less than 1 per cent of that supplied by the rivers. For our rough estimates, such a correction is negligible.

POSSIBLE INCLUSION OF PRE-TRIASSIC SEDIMENTS

The whole thesis of this paper is based on the postulate that all the sediment overlying the apparently continuous basement is of Triassic or younger age. This assumption seems to me safe for the area as far offshore as the median ridge in the basement; beyond that it is increasingly doubtful. The uniformity of seismic properties throughout the map area seem to me, however, to justify the assumption as a working hypothesis; the reader who rejects the hypothesis will of course reject the entire argument.

CLUES TO DEPTH OF EROSION OF THE SOURCE AREA

Our estimates can be checked by determining whether the depths of subaerial erosion here inferred from the sedimentary record are at all consonant with the geology of the postulated source area. To the depth of erosion deduced by extrapolating the present suspended and traction loads of the streams (3300 feet) it is necessary to add the depth corresponding to the solution load. At the present rate of 0.000,64 inch per year, the denudation by solution during 225 m.y. would be 11,600 feet. The total of traction, suspension, and solution loads at present rates would be 16,300 feet or almost 3.1 miles.

An estimate of the depth of erosion permitted by the geology observable at present is difficult. Chamberlin (1910), in his study of the folded Appalachians of Pennsylvania, drew sections of restored folds and by measuring the area between the base of the Pottsville Formation and the "Kittatinny" surface deduced an average denudation of 3 miles between Tyronne and Harrisburg, in postfolding (Permian?) time. If we include the volumes of Pottsville and younger rocks, and the large areas reduced below the "Kittatinny" surface, we see that in this one area the theoretical erosion during 225 m.y. at present rates and the actual depth of denudation suggested by the geology agree remarkably.

Erosion would almost surely have been slower over much of the crystalline areas; on the other hand many of these were unquestionably covered by greater or lesser thicknesses of Paleozoic sedimentary rocks at the close of the Appalachian revolution. With so many uncertainties, it seems reasonable to me to accept an average rate of denudation for Mesozoic and Cenozoic time not very different from that of the present.

DISCUSSION

The data and computations presented are of course speculative. Nevertheless when combined with the more definite information from the Gulf of Mexico (Weaver, 1950; 1955; Murray and others, 1952; Gilluly, 1955) they strongly suggest that present rates of erosion are not 10 times higher than the average of those of the geologic past (Barrell, 1917; Kuenen, 1950, p. 168); I think it most unlikely that the present rates are even twice as high—the most conservative figure suggested by Kuenen (1946, p. 571). I believe the evidence suggests that the average rate of denudation for Triassic and younger time along the Atlantic seaboard and the rate of denudation deduced by Dole and Stabler for the present are not significantly different: the present rate is probably only a few per cent higher. When data comparable to those of Drake, Ewing, and Sutton for Atlantic coastal and offshore sediments become available for the wide Continental Shelf off Newfoundland a much more definite estimate will be possible.

The facts that the shelf and slope retain a continental crust beneath the sediment, even though this crust thins seaward as Drake, Ewing, and Sutton show, and that the surface of the basement was in Triassic and earlier time one of subaerial erosion, go far to prove the reality of a former "Appalachia"—a landmass it has become increasingly popular to discredit. The shelf, without doubt, was variably emergent during parts of Paleozoic time and a source of sediment for the Appalachian geosyncline.

These facts throw some light on the origin of the Continental Shelf. Inasmuch as no sediment is likely to be more than two thirds as dense as the subcrustal material displaced, patently no amount of accumulating sediment can depress a surface of active sedimentation below its original level by purely isostatic forces. The old surface of subaerial erosion of Appalachia was thus not changed into a submarine surface of deposition merely by being loaded with sediment. Some subcrustal process must have brought about the submergence; isostatic adjustment to a growing sedimentary load would of course operate to continue the sinking.

The Continental Shelf, therefore, is not due primarily to subsidence of an offshore area under a load of fluvial sediments discharged at the shore, as conceived by Kuenen (1950). The subsidence preceded much of the sedimentary loading. The loading must indeed have induced further subsidence, but it cannot account for the 5000 feet of differential sinking of the landward troughs with respect to the median rise, on the seaward side of which even deeper basins occur. Five thousand feet of sediment cannot account for the difference in basement elevation between basin and rise when both columns are overlain by the same depths of water. The still greater subsidence of the troughs seaward of the median ridge is even harder to attribute to isostasy, for here the upper surface of the sediment in the troughs is in deep water, well down the Continental Slope.

Possibly fluctuations in the position of the shore line because of eustatic shifts, both Pleistocene and older, have modified the relations of inner and outer troughs and median ridge. But these structures must owe their primary forms to subcrustal processes, with sedimentation adding only secondary modifications. The seismic speeds presented by Drake, Ewing, and Sutton do not suggest that the outer troughs contain much basalt. It seems unlikely that the offshore troughs are strongly eugeosynclinal, even though several seamounts there are doubtless volcanoes.

For the former Appalachia to have subsided the sialic crust beneath it must have been thinned. Inasmuch as subaerial erosion can only reduce the crust to sea level, the thinning must have been subcrustal. The sial thins steadily southeastward and most abruptly beneath the Continental Slope (Drake, Ewing, and Sutton, 1959, Fig. 28), although there is no very marked change in its seismic properties and the presedimentary surface appears continuous with that of the Piedmont. The continuity of the upper surface of the basement and the general similarity of the seismic properties of the crust from the Piedmont to the Continental Slope suggest that the whole crust is sial. The M discontinuity here separating this sial from the mantle is almost surely not a phase transition, but a compositional boundary. This conclusion is also in accord with considerable experimental work (*i.e.*, Yoder and Tilley, 1962). The crustal thinning must then be due to subcrustal processes that involve not phase transformations but mass transfer. I think this is a strong argument for subcrustal flowage and erosional thinning of the sial by movements at its base. That such processes exist is suggested by many other phenomena described by Vening-Meinesz (1934; 1948), Ampferer (1941; 1944), Kraus (1951), Gilluly (1955; 1963), Hess (1962), Wilson (1963), and Kaitera (1963).

The origin of currents in the outer mantle is perhaps convectional, but a consideration of scale (Hubbert, 1937; Maillet and Parans de Ceccaty, 1937) shows that during millions of years any large-volume density differences, however generated, will inevitably tend to equalize by flow. Here it is important to reiterate a fact pointed out by Lawson (1932) and recently elaborated by Kaitera (1963): Once a coast has been established isostasy necessitates a subcrustal flow from ocean basin to beneath the continent to compensate for the mass eroded from the continent and deposited in the sea. Of course such a motion might be too deep to influence the crust directly, although the considerable variation of immediately sub-Moho seismic velocities from place to place suggests otherwise. The coastal zone as a whole is a zone of torque about a horizontal axis, with (1) the continent tending to flow out over the ocean floor, (2) the floor near the coast being depressed by both this continental spreading and by the increasing load of sediment, and (3) a continent-trending flow in the mantle compensating for the mass transferred. The folded basement of the Atlantic sediments suggests that the continent-trending flow is close enough beneath the sial to deform it and to crowd the sedimentary prism against the continental mass. The basins and swells are too large to have been caused directly by drag; they may have been produced by instabilities generated or maintained by the postulated landward flow. According to this interpretation, the Continental Shelf is due to a complex of factors—sedimentation, isostatic response to loading, and subcrustal flow. I suggest that the thinning of the crust toward the foot of the Continental Slope is a result of subcrustal erosion by the mantle current, localized by the sedimentary load.

The relationships discussed do not seem to require either a drastic change in the volume of the sea in Cretaceous time, as has been suggested to account for the Pacific guyots, or a late date for the birth of the Atlantic. The postulated westward drift of America from the Mid-Atlantic Ridge (Ampfere, 1941; Runcorn, 1962; Hess, 1962; Wilson, 1963) seems to be permitted but not compelled by the evidence. A critical point here is the volume of pelagic sediment in the North Atlantic on both sides of the Mid-Atlantic Ridge. After the volume of these sediments has been as well determined as that in the area covered by Drake, Ewing, and Sutton in their important paper, we may be able to give a firmly based interpretation as to the age of the ocean and of its sediments and as to the erosion rates of the geologic past.

SUMMARY

The volume of Triassic and younger sediment on and offshore from the Atlantic coast between Virginia and Nova Scotia can be estimated from the isopach map by Drake, Ewing, and Sutton (1959) of Atlantic coastal and offshore sediments. This volume is compared with that which would have been derived from the probable source area at present rates of erosion. It is found that the average rate of erosion in Triassic and later time was probably not less than three fourths and perhaps equal to the present rate.

The arrangement of the sedimentary troughs identified by Drake, Ewing, and Sutton suggests that the Continental Shelf was formed in part by isostatic sinking of the offshore crust beneath the sedimentary load supplied by the rivers. But the presence of a nearly continuous median ridge in the sedimentary basin suggests that isostatic sinking is not alone responsible for the downwarp and in fact could not suffice to bring it about. The density of the sediment must be less than two thirds that of the subcrustal material displaced. If the basement had been originally horizontal or sloping uniformly seaward, the basin landward of the median ridge must have sunk by a mechanism other than isostatic depression beneath an additional 5000 feet of sediment, for the seafloor is roughly at the same depth over both ridge and inner basin. This differential depression of the basement, as well as the sinking of a former land area to form such basins, requires thinning of the crust; it is here suggested that subcrustal erosion by currents beneath the M discontinuity caused the thinning. Possibly the median ridge and the basins are due partly to instabilities produced by such currents, although they seem too large to be attributed to drag.

REFERENCES CITED

Ampferer, Otto, 1941. Gedanken über das Bewegungsbild des atlantischen Raumes: Akad. Wiss. Wien Sitzungsber., Math.-Naturw. Kl., ser. I, v. 150, p. 19–36.

———, 1944, Vergleich der tektonischen Wirksamkeit von Kontraktion und Unterstromung: Geol. Gesell. Wien Mitt., v. 35, p. 107–123.

Barrell, Joseph, 1917, Rhythms and the measurements of geologic time: Geol. Soc. America Bull., v. 28, pt. 3, p. 745–904.

Chamberlin, R. T., 1910, The Appalachian folds of central Pennsylvania: Jour. Geology, v. 18, p. 228–251.

Corbel, J., 1959, Vitesse de l'erosion: Zeitschr. Geomorphologie, n. f., v. 3, no. 1, p. 1–28.

Dole, R. B., and Herman Stabler, 1909, Denudation, *in* Papers on the conservation of water: U.S. Geol. Survey Water-Supply Paper 234, p. 78–93.

Drake, C. L., Maurice Ewing, and G. H. Sutton, 1959, Continental margins and geosynclines—the east coast of North America north of Cape Hatteras, *in* L. H. Ahrens, ed., Physics and chemistry of the earth, v. 3: New York, Pergamon Press, p. 110–198.

Gilluly, James, 1955, Geologic contrasts between continents and ocean basins, *in* Arie Poldervaart, ed., Crust of the earth: Geol. Soc. America Spec. Paper 62, p. 7–18.

———, 1963, The tectonic evolution of the western United States: Geol. Soc. London Quart. Jour., v. 119, p. 133–174.

Groot, J. J., 1955, Sedimentary petrology of the Cretaceous sediments of northern Delaware in relation to paleogeographic problems: Delaware Geol. Survey Bull. 5, 157 p.

Hess, H. H., 1962, History of ocean basins, *in* A. E. J. Engel, H. L. James, and B. F. Leonard, eds., Petrologic studies—a volume in honor of A. F. Buddington: Boulder, Colo., Geological Society of America, p. 599–620.

Holmes, Arthur, 1960, A revised geological time scale: Edinburgh Geol. Soc. Trans., v. 17, pt. 3, p. 183.

Hubbert, M. K., 1937, Theory of scale models applied to the study of geologic structures: Geol. Soc. America Bull., v. 48, p. 1459–1519.

Johnson, D. W., 1931, A theory of Appalachian geomorphic evolution: Jour. Geology, v. 39, p. 497–508.

Kaitera, Pentti, 1963, Sea pressure as a factor shaping the Earth's crust: Terra, yr. 75, no. 4, p. 342–347.

Kraus, Ernst, 1951, Die Baugeschichte der Alpen, v. 2 (Neozoikum): Berlin, Akademie-Verlag, 489 p.

Kuenen, P. H., 1946, Rate and mass of deep-sea sedimentation: Am. Jour. Sci., v. 244, p. 563–572.

———, 1950, Marine geology: New York, John Wiley and Sons, 568 p.

Lawson, A. C., 1932, Insular arcs, foredeeps, and geosynclinal seas of the Asiatic coast: Geol. Soc. America Bull., v. 43, p. 353–381.

Maillet, R., and R. Parans de Ceccaty, 1937, Le physicien devant la tectonique: Paris, 2nd World Petroleum Congress.

McKee, E. D., S. S. Oriel, K. B. Ketner, M. E. MacLachlan, J. W. Goldsmith, J. C. MacLachlan, and M. R. Mudge, 1959, Paleotectonic maps of the Triassic System: U.S. Geol. Survey Misc. Geol. Inv. Map I-300.

Murray, G. E., and others, 1952, Sedimentary volumes in Gulf Coastal Plain of United States and Mexico: Geol. Soc. America Bull., v. 63, p. 1157–1228.

Runcorn, S. K., 1962, Paleomagnetic evidence for continental drift and its geophysical cause, *in* S. K. Runcorn, ed., Continental drift: New York, Academic Press, p. 1–40.

Sanders, J. E., 1963, Late Triassic tectonic history of northeastern United States: Am. Jour. Sci., v. 261, p. 501–524.

Vening Meinesz, F. A., 1934, Report of the gravity expedition in the Atlantic of 1932 and the interpretation of the results, v. 2: Delft, Netherlands Geodetic Commission, 208 p.

———, 1948, Major tectonic phenomena and the hypothesis of convection currents in the earth: Geol. Soc. London Quart. Jour., v. 103, p. 191–207.

Weaver, Paul, 1950, Variations in history of continental shelves: Am. Assoc. Petroleum Geologists Bull., v. 34, p. 351–360.

———, 1955, Gulf of Mexico, *in* Arie Poldervaart, ed., Crust of the earth: Geol. Soc. America Spec. Paper 62, p. 269–278.

Wilson, J. T., 1963, Hypothesis of earth's behavior: Nature, v. 198, no. 4884, p. 925–929.

Yoder, H. S., Jr., and C. E. Tilley, 1962, Origin of basalt magmas, an experimental study of natural and synthetic rock systems: Jour. Petrology, v. 3, p. 342–564.

33

Reversals of the Earth's Magnetic Field

ALLAN COX
G. BRENT DALRYMPLE
RICHARD R. DOELL

1967

When molten volcanic rocks cool and solidify, the magnetic minerals in them are magnetized in the direction of the earth's magnetic field. They retain that magnetism, thus serving as permanent magnetic memories (much like the magnetic memory elements of a computer) of the direction of the earth's field in the place and at the time they solidified. In 1906 the French physicist Bernard Brunhes found some volcanic rocks that were magnetized not in the direction of the earth's present field but in exactly the opposite direction. Brunhes concluded that the field must have reversed. Although his observations and conclusion were accepted by some later workers, the concept of reversals in the earth's magnetic field attracted little attention. In the past few years, however, it has been definitely established that the earth's magnetic field has two stable states: it can point either toward the North Pole as it does today or toward the South Pole, and it has repeatedly alternated between the two orientations.

There was no basis in theory for anticipating this characteristic of the earth's magnetic field. Moreover, theory on the whole subject of the earth's magnetism is so rudimentary that the mechanism of reversal is still far from being understood. Nevertheless, the magnetic memory of volcanic rocks, together with the presence in the same rocks of atomic clocks that begin to run just when their magnetism is acquired, has made it possible to draw up a time scale that shows no fewer than nine reversals of the earth's field in the past 3.6 million years [Figure 33.1]. This time scale is a valuable tool for dating events in the earth's history and may help earth's history and may help earth scientists to deal with such large questions as how much the continents have drifted.

The earth's magnetic field is the field of an axial magnetic dipole, which is to say that it is equivalent to the external field of a huge bar magnet in the core of the earth aligned approximately along the planet's axis of rotation (or to the external field of a uniformly magnetized sphere or of a loop of electric current in the

From *Scientific American,* vol. 216, no. 2, pp. 44–54.

plane of the Equator). The lines of force in such a field are directed not toward the geographic poles but toward the magnetic poles, and the angle at any point between true north and the direction of the field is called the declination. The lines of force are also directed, except at the Equator, toward or away from the center of the earth, and the angle above or below the horizontal is called the inclination. It is along these lines of force that the memory elements in volcanic rocks have been oriented.

The memory elements themselves are magnetic "domains": tiny bodies in which magnetism is uniform. These bodies consist of various iron and titanium oxides that can be recognized quite easily under the microscope because, unlike most rock-forming minerals, they are opaque to transmitted light and are excellent reflectors of incident light.

At high temperatures the iron and titanium oxides are nonmagnetic. They become magnetic only after they cool to a critical point called the Curie temperature, which for the common minerals in volcanic rocks may be as high as 680 degrees centigrade or as low as about 200 degrees, depending on chemical composition. These temperatures are well below those at which rocks crystallize (about 1,000 degrees C.), so that it is clear that rocks are not magnetized by the physical rotation and orientation in the earth's field of previously magnetized grains in the molten lava, as was once thought. As the minerals begin to cool through the Curie temperature, even the earth's weak field of less than one gauss is adequate to partly magnetize them. That is because this initial magnetization is "soft," like that of iron or ordinary steel, both of which are easily magnetized by weak magnetic fields. As the rocks continue to cool, the minerals undergo a second abrupt change: the initially soft magnetism acquired in the earth's field is frozen in and becomes "hard," like the magnetism of a man-made permanent magnet.

The pertinent question for the geophysicist is how well these magnetic memory elements function as recorders of the earth's field. Do they record its direction accurately? The most direct way to assess the accuracy of volcanic rocks as recorders is to measure the magnetism of such rocks that flowed out and cooled recently in places where the magnetic field that existed at the time of flow is known. We have made such measurements on three lava flows that formed on the island of Hawaii in the years 1907, 1935 and 1955.

To obtain samples of undisturbed rock from the solid parts of a lava, a hollow cylindrical diamond drill is generally used. From five to eight cylindrical "cores" are taken from each lava flow to obtain a representative magnetic direction for the entire flow rather than for one isolated sample; each core's orientation with respect to the horizontal and to true north is accurately recorded before it is removed [Figure 33.2]. Back in the laboratory the sample's magnetic vector is determined with a magnetometer [Figure 33.3]. The results of the measurements on the three formations indicate that lava flows record the direction of the earth's magnetic field with an accuracy of several degrees [Figure 33.4], which is ample for most geophysical applications.

If rock magnetism is to provide a record of the ancient earth's field, the magnetic record must also be stable. Is the magnetism of rocks soft like that of iron and ordinary steel or is it hard like that of permanent magnets? This question of stability is so critical that laboratory tests to deal with it have become an integral part of paleomagnetic research. The usual technique is to place a sample from a rock formation in a kind of magnetic "washing machine," subject it to a rapidly alternating magnetic field and determine the amount of magnetism that survives. The natural magnetism of most volcanic rocks turns out to be comparable in stability to the magnetism of the hardest permanent magnets. Once the magnetic hardness of the rocks from a given flow is established, the magnetic cleaning process can be used to strip away from each sample whatever soft magnetism has been acquired (from such sources as lightning strokes) since the rock solidified, leaving only the hard magnetism that reflects the direction of the original ambient field.

It is clear, then, that paleomagnetism is accurate and stable enough to provide information about past states of the earth's magnetic

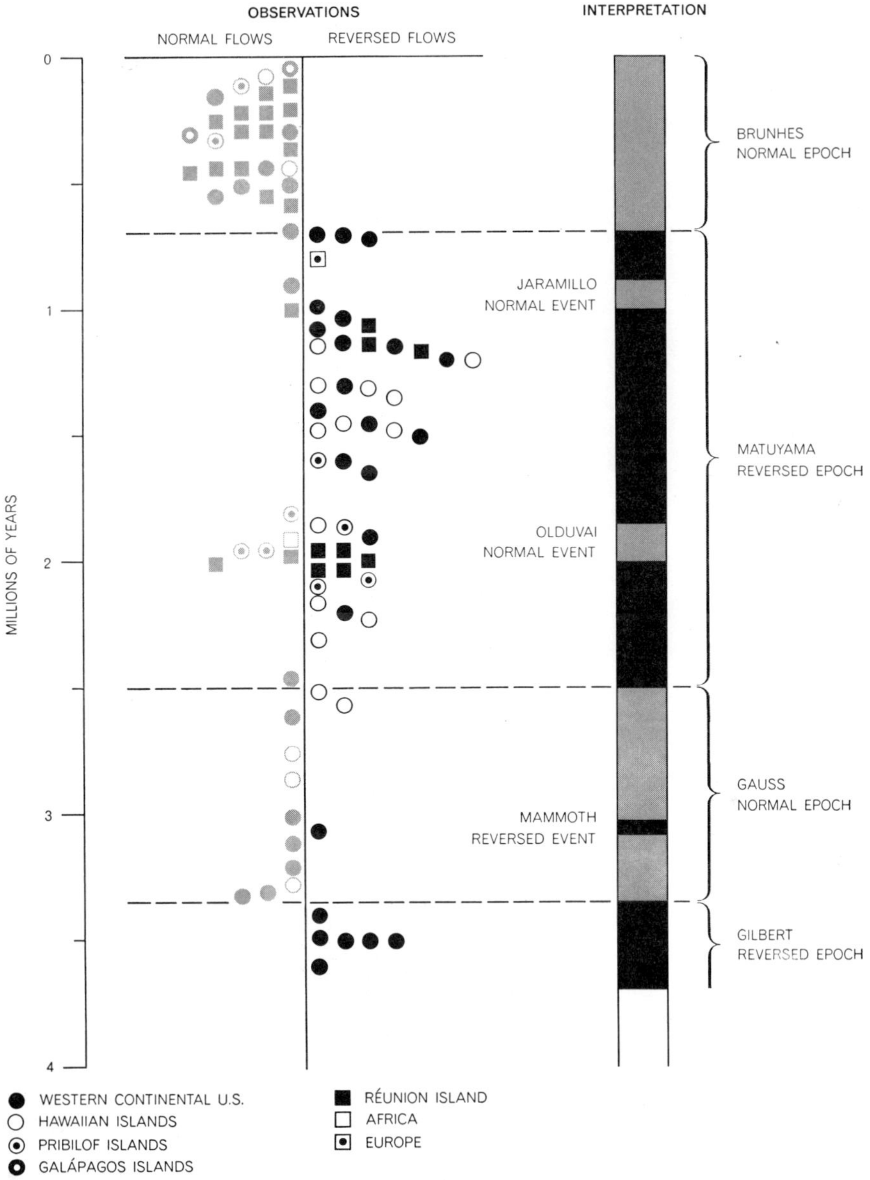

FIGURE 33.1
Time scale for reversals of the earth's magnetic field. Established on the basis of paleomagnetic data and radiometric age obtained for nearly 100 volcanic formations in both hemispheres. Here the flows with *normal* and *reversed* magnetism are arranged by their age (*left*). It is clear that the data fall into four principal time groupings, or geomagnetic polarity "epochs," during which the field was entirely or predominantly of one polarity. Superimposed on the epochs are shorter polarity "events."

field. In assessing such information one must of course take into consideration the movement of rock masses that takes place over a period of geologic time; the deviation of a sample's magnetism from the direction of the present field could reflect mountain-building, warping along faults or continental drift. Our studies of magnetic reversal have been restricted, however, to relatively young rocks and to volcanic formations we can be fairly sure are still oriented as they were when they solidified.

We begin our paleomagnetic research on the island of Hawaii, where we had tested the technique and where the superb lava flows exposed on the flanks of volcanoes provide magnetic records going back about half a million years. We collected samples from 107 of these flows and found that their declination

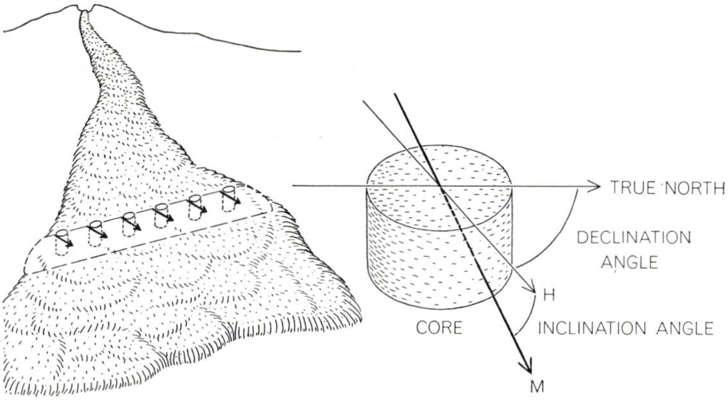

FIGURE 33.2
Samples for paleomagnetic studies are cores drilled from volcanic formations. The direction of magnetization (*M*) is expressed as the declination angle between true north and the horizontal projection (*H*) of *M* and the inclination angle of *M* above or below horizontal.

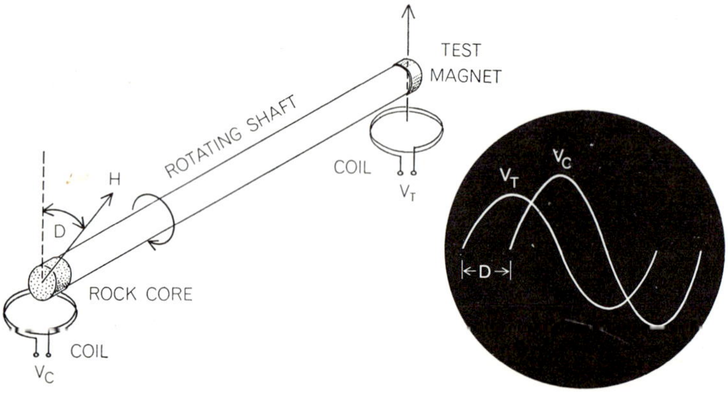

FIGURE 33.3
Core mounted on a magnetometer. As the shaft rotates, electrical signals (V_C and V_T) are induced in the coils by the core and a test magnet and can be displayed on an oscilloscope. The intensity and direction of the core's magnetism are determined by comparing the magnitudes of the signals and their phase shift, which is equal to the declination (*D*).

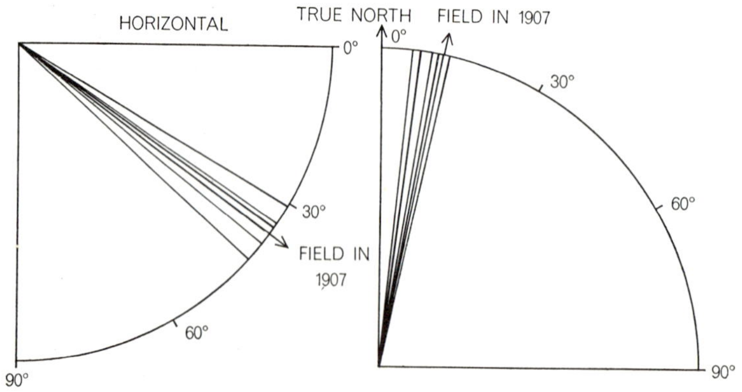

FIGURE 33.4
Angles of inclination (*left*) and declination (*right*) of six cores from a 1907 Hawaiian lava flow cluster about the known angles of the 1907 field. Although angles obtained from individual cores vary, the average values are accurate measures of the historic field.

angles clustered at around 10 degrees east of true north and their inclination angles at around 30 degrees below the horizontal. This was just about what we expected on the basis of the dipole nature of the earth's field.

Studies of other young volcanic rocks along the eastern edge of the Pacific ocean basin have yielded similar results. At the high latitude of the Pribilof Islands in the Bering Sea the magnetic vectors of the lava flows are inclined steeply downward, as one would expect for a dipole field in high latitudes, whereas in the Galápagos Islands on the Equator the magnetic vectors are almost horizontal. Measurements in many parts of the world indicate that during the time spanned by these young lava flows (roughly half a million years) the earth's field was essentially dipolar and was aligned as it is today.

Quite different results are obtained when paleomagnetic techniques are applied to somewhat older lava flows. Only about half of these flows are magnetized in the same direction as the younger ones; the remainder are magnetized in the opposite direction. For example, some volcanic rocks at middle latitudes in the Northern Hemisphere are magnetized toward the south and upward, rather than toward the north and downward [Figure 33.5]. In recent years this "antiparallel" magnetism has been found in thousands of samples of volcanic rock from all over the world by scores of investigators working independently. Sampling has been particularly intensive in the range of ages between 3.5 million years ago and the present, and the paleomagnetic results obtained are always remarkably similar. The magnetic vectors fall into two groups: "normal" vectors nearly parallel to the present field of the earth and "reversed" ones that are nearly opposite. Most of the data are clustered within 30 degrees of these two directions, with very few vectors oriented in intermediate directions [Figure 33.6].

The immediate implication is that the earth's magnetic field has indeed reversed its direction in the past. Brunhes so interpreted his results in France in 1906, although he cautiously restricted field-reversal to the area from which he collected his samples. In 1929 Motonori Matuyama also found evidence that the field had reversed, but he too restricted his conclusions to the area in Japan from which his samples had come. The accumulating evidence that reversed magnetic directions are invariably opposite to the present field direction at the sampling site led in time to the hypothesis that the sample reversals are not local but global; in other words, that the entire field reverses.

An important alternative explanation must be considered before the field-reversal hypothesis can be accepted. The alternative is that rocks magnetized in reverse may possess some special mineralogical property that causes them to become so magnetized in a normal field. The existence of such "self-reversal" in rocks was suggested in 1950 by John Graham, then at the Carnegie Institution of Washington's Department of Terrestrial Magnetism, as an explanation for the occurrence of both normal and reversed magnetism in rock samples that had formed simultaneously. Graham's suggestion stimulated the French physicist Louis Néel to examine the problem from the viewpoint of solid-state physics, and Néel soon discovered several ways in which self-reversal might occur. Experimental confirmation came almost immediately. At the Philips Research Laboratories in the Netherlands, E. W. Görter synthesized an iron-chromium-manganese compound that underwent self-reversal, and S. Uyeda and T. Nagata of the University of Tokyo found a self-reversing volcanic rock.

It is thus apparent that at least some volcanic rocks are not infallible magnetic recorders. Like laboratory recorders that are hooked up backward, they sometimes record a signal that is not only wrong but is wrong by exactly 180 degrees. If all reversed magnetism could be explained in this way, the experimental evidence for reversals in the earth's magnetic field would vanish. An obvious experiment is to heat and then cool rock samples in a known field and measure their acquired magnetization. This operation has been performed on many hundreds of rock samples with reversed magnetism, and fewer than 1 per cent have turned out to be self-reversing.

Therefore the laboratory evidence favors the field-reversal hypothesis. Like many rock-forming processes, however, the acquisition of natural magnetism cannot be reproduced with complete fidelity in the laboratory. The missing ingredient is time, and for certain of the theoretical self-reversing processes this ingredient is crucial. For example, John Verhoogen of the University of California at Berkeley has shown theoretically that whereas certain iron oxides containing impurities of aluminum, magnesium or titanium would be magnetized normally when cooled rapidly in a normal magnetic field, the magnetism could be reversed as the atoms in the cooled oxide reordered themselves toward an equilibrium distribution. The calculated time required for this self-reversal is on the order of 100,000 to a million years, so that it could hardly be reproduced in the laboratory. The theoretical studies by Néel and Verhoogen showed that the fact that self-reversal is rare in the laboratory does not make it safe to conclude that it is equally rare in nature. How, then, could one determine the geophysical significance of reversed magnetism? Two main lines of experimental attack have been pursued during the past decade, each closely related to one of the two proposed reversal-producing processes.

One approach was to search for a correlation between the magnetism of rocks and their mineralogy. Even though self-reversals may not always be reproducible in the laboratory, if all reversed magnetism is due to a process occurring on the mineralogical level, rocks with reversed magnetism should be somehow different from those with normal magnetism; chemical processes being the same the world over, the unique mineralogical properties associated with reversed magnetism should appear in rocks from all over the world.

This approach has been pursued most actively by P. M. S. Blackett at the Imperial College of Science and Technology in London and Rodney Wilson at the University of Liverpool. In some sequences of rocks Wilson has found a correlation between reversed magnetism and mineralogical properties, but in other rocks he finds no such correlation. Like Wilson, we have occasionally noted a correlation between mineralogy and magnetism within a sequence from one locality, but such a local correlation may well stem from the tendency of volcanic flows to occur in pulses. Between two successive pulses separated by a long time interval the mineralogical character of the lavas commonly changes; if the polarity of the earth's field also happens to change in this interval, there will be an apparent correlation between mineralogy and polarity. In short, mineralogical investigations have not yielded evidence that all or even most reversed magnetism is produced by self-reversal.

The second experimental approach followed from an implication of the field-reversal theory: If the earth's magnetic field alternates between intervals when it is normal and intervals when it is reversed, the geologic ages of normal and reversed rocks should fall into corresponding intervals. Data bearing on the age and magnetism of rocks should provide a yes-or-no answer to the validity of the field-reversal theory and, if the theory is valid, should yield a time scale for reversals. Matuyama had noted in 1929 that the geologic age of all the rocks with reversed magnetism in Japan was early Pleistocene (about a million years ago), whereas younger rocks invariably had normal magnetism. The strongest possible evidence in support of the field-reversal theory would be to extend Matuyama's study to show that rocks from all parts of the world, regardless of mineralogy, occur in similar normal and reversed sequences that are time-dependent.

The difficulty lay in finding a sufficiently precise method for establishing the age relations of normal and reversed rocks. Many techniques that yield fairly precise age relations when applied to older rocks are based on plant and animal fossils; these techniques begin to break down when applied to the past million years or so because of the slow rate at which evolution proceeds and the time required for plant and animal migrations. A solution that suggested itself was some kind of radioactive clock, and our search quickly narrowed to the potassium-argon clock first suggested in 1940 by Robley D. Evans of the Massachusetts Institute of Technology and now widely applied in geological investigations. . . .

[Radiogenic] argon will not accumulate as long as the rock is in a molten state, so for volcanic rocks the potassium-argon clock is started only when the rock solidifies.

The amount of potassium 40 in a sample is usually determined by measuring all the potassium in the sample by standard chemical methods and then calculating the potassium 40 from its known relative abundance. The

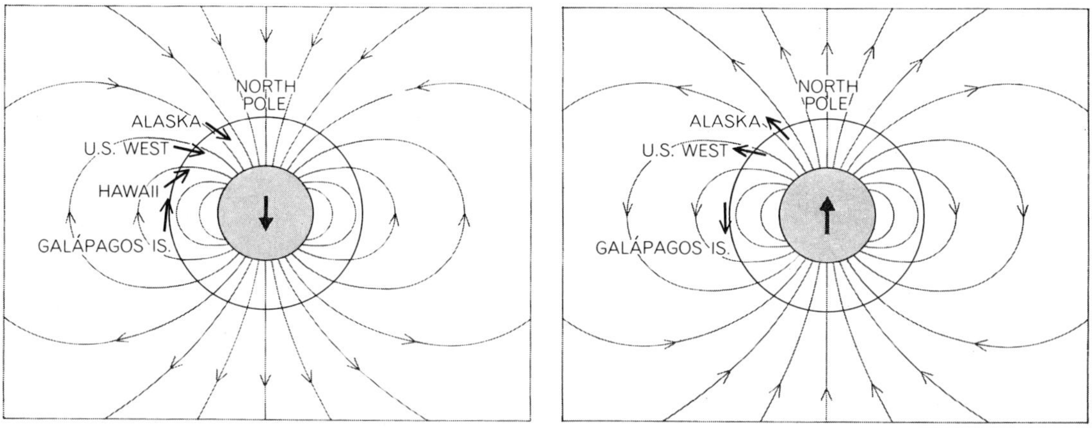

FIGURE 33.5
Inclination angles. From flows in Alaska, the U.S. West (California, Idaho, and New Mexico), the island of Hawaii, and the Galápagos Islands. Shown by the black arrows. The flows range up to three million years in age. The angles fall into two distinct groups: a "normal" group aligned with the earth's present field, that of a bar magnet pointed toward the South Pole (*left*), and a "reversed" group appropriate to an oppositely oriented field (*right*). All the flows on Hawaii had normal magnetism.

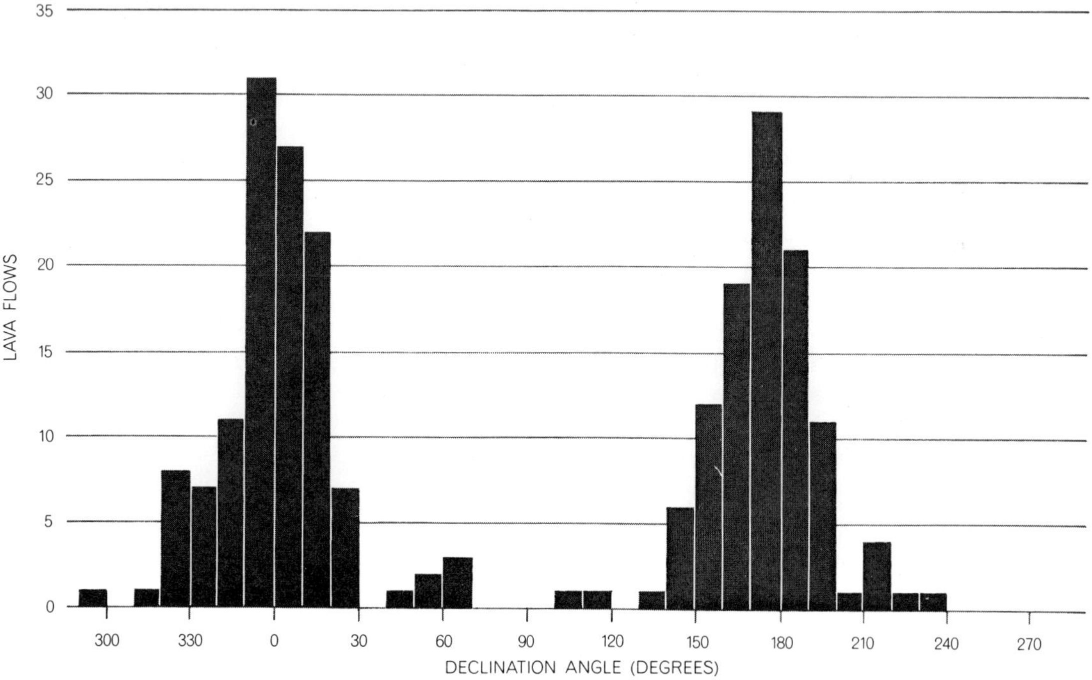

FIGURE 33.6
Declination angles. From 229 flows up to three million years old in Alaska, the western U.S., Hawaii, and the Galápagos Islands. They display a similar twofold grouping: northerly (normal) and southerly (reversed). Intermediate directions are seldom observed.

argon determination is more difficult because the amounts are extremely small. In a typical 10-gram sample of basalt a million years old the amount of argon 40 from potassium 40 is 10^{-9} (.000000001) gram, and the accuracy of the dating depends on the accuracy with which this argon can be measured. A sample of the rock or mineral is placed in a gas-extraction apparatus and melted to release the accumulated argon 40. Reactive gases such as oxygen, nitrogen and water are removed. During the extraction a known amount of isotopically enriched argon, called the tracer, is mixed with the gas from the sample, so that the final argon gas consists of three components: the argon 40 whose amount is to be determined; the tracer, which is mostly argon 38 but which also contains some argon 36 and argon 40, and contaminating argon from the atmosphere, for which a correction must be made. This argon mixture is analyzed with a mass spectrometer that gives the relative amounts of the three isotopes of argon. Knowing the amount of the enriched tracer and its isotopic composition, and the relative composition of atmospheric argon and of the total gas mixture, one can calculate the amount of argon derived from potassium 40. This information is used with the results of the potassium analysis to determine the age of the rock.

For the reversal problem the potassium-argon method has several distinct advantages over other dating methods. It can be applied to a wide variety of volcanic rocks. It is also the only dating method that can be applied in the range from a few thousand to several million years ago. And, as we have noted, the potassium-argon clock starts to run at exactly the same time the magnetic record is frozen into a volcanic rock.

The potassium-argon dating method has now been successfully applied to rocks from nearly 100 magnetized volcanic formations with ages ranging from the present back to 3.6 million years [Figure 33.1]. This work has been done primarily by ourselves at the U.S. Geological Survey laboratory in Menlo Park, Calif., and by Ian McDougall, D. H. Tarling and F. H. Chamalaun at the Australian National University. Relevant data have also been contributed by M. Rutten of the University of Utrecht and by C. S. Grommé, R. L. Hay, J. F. Evernden and G. H. Curtis of the University of California at Berkeley. The rocks that were investigated came from different parts of the world and are of different types, so that the available data come from heterogeneous sources.

As Figure 33.1 shows, the ages of these magnetically normal and magnetically reversed rocks are well grouped in distinct sequences, leaving little room for doubting the reality of geomagnetic field reversals. To explain them by self-reversal would require an unreasonable kind of coincidence involving synchronous worldwide changes in the nature of the processes by which minerals are formed and magnetized.

Four major normal and reversed sequences are defined by the paleomagnetic and radioactive-clock data for the past 3.6 million years. We call these major groupings geomagnetic polarity epochs and have named them for people who made significant contributions to our knowledge of the earth's magnetic field. Superimposed on the polarity epochs are brief fluctuations in magnetic polarity with a duration that is an order of magnitude shorter. We call these occasions polarity events and have named them for the localities where they were first recognized.

The polarity events are important for theories of the earth's magnetism because they emphasize the irregular nature of reversals of the earth's field. The first polarity event to be discovered was the "Olduvai" normal event, which is recorded in a flow in Olduvai Gorge in Tanzania that was investigated in 1963 by Grommé and Hay. At first the Olduvai flow was thought to lie within the "Gauss" normal polarity epoch and hence was not recognized as an anomaly. When better dating of the epochs placed the date of the Olduvai flow within the "Matuyama" reversed epoch, it appeared to be an unexplained anomaly in an otherwise coherent picture.

The explanation that the Olduvai result represents a brief, worldwide fluctuation in polarity was first advanced by us after we discovered in the Pribilof Islands three lava flows that are normally magnetized, like the Olduvai flow, and that have similar ages of about 1.9 million years. These flows were sandwiched between reversed flows that gave slightly older and slightly younger ages, providing the evidence that confirmed the existence of polarity events. Since then we have recognized and named two additional events: a reversed one that was recorded 3,050,000 years ago at Mammoth, Calif., and a normal one recorded about 900,000 years ago in some rocks near Jaramillo Creek in New Mexico. The Jaramillo event was recently confirmed by Chamalaun and McDougall in their study of lava flows on Réunion Island in the Indian Ocean, where they also found two additional flows that represent the Olduvai event.

Only rarely does a sequence of lava flows succeed in capturing a record of a polarity transition. This indicates that the time required for a complete change of the earth's magnetic field from one polarity to another is amazingly short; our best estimate of the transition time is 5,000 years. This is based on the ratio between the number of lava flows that happen to have recorded the earth's field during a transition and the number of flows with clearly defined normal or reversed directions. An indirect estimate of this kind is necessary because the potassium-argon dating method is unable to resolve age differences as small as 5,000 years. On the scale of geologic time, polarity transitions appear to be almost instantaneous, and they therefore provide sharp time markers indeed.

The idea that the earth's magnetic field reverses at first seems so preposterous that one immediately suspects a violation of some basic law of physics, and most investigators working on reversals have sometimes wondered if the reversals are really compatible with the physical theory of magnetism. The question is meaningful only within the context of a broader question: Why does the earth have a magnetic field? Geophysicists are simply not sure. After centuries of research the earth's magnetic field remains one of the best-described and least-understood of all planetary phenomena. The only physical mechanism that has been proposed as the basis of a tenable theory is the mechanism of a magneto-hydrodynamic dynamo. According to this theory, which has been developed primarily by Walter M. Elsasser, now at Princeton University, and Sir Edward Bullard of the University of Cambridge, the molten iron-and-nickel core of the earth is analogous to the electrical conductors of a dynamo. Convection currents in the core supply the necessary motion, and the resulting electric currents create a magnetic field. The entire regenerative process presumably began with either a stray magnetic field in the earth's formative period or with small electric currents produced by some kind of battery-like action.

The mathematical difficulties of this theory are immense. It is impossible to predict what the intensity of the earth's field should be or whether it fluctuates or remains stationary. Certainly the theory is in too rudimentary a state for one to predict whether reversals should or should not occur or should occur only under certain conditions. On the other hand, complete mathematical solutions have been obtained for simple theoretical models of dynamos, and these models do show spontaneous reversals of magnetic field; some of the models show sequences of reversals that are strikingly similar to the geomagnetic polarity time scale. These results at least demonstrate that magnetic reversals are possible in self-regenerating dynamos. The fact remains that observations are leading theory in this area of investigation, and any complete theory of geomagnetism will eventually have to accommodate the observed reversals of the field.

Meanwhile geologists are applying the reversal time scale to establish age relations among rocks they would be hard put to date any other way. An especially important application is in determining the ages of deep-sea sediments, which are very difficult to date beyond the short range of 200,000 years. It has long been recognized that fine-grained sediments may become magnetized in the earth's field as they drift slowly downward in quiet water. Recently C. G. A. Harrison and B. M. Funnell of the Scripps Institution of Oceanography and N. D. Opdyke and D. E. Hayes and their colleagues at the Lamont Geological Observatory of Columbia University have observed magnetic reversals in the sediments of deep-sea cores [Figure 33.7]. In one core in particular (from the Bellingshausen Sea near Antarctica) Opdyke and Hayes found a polarity record going back to the "Gilbert" epoch, or 3.6 million years, in which the pattern of reversals is remarkably similar to the pattern of our polarity time scale. Even the brief polarity events are clearly discernible. These findings confirm the reversal time scale determined from volcanic rocks and suggest that polarity studies can provide a method for determining rates of sedimentation and for establishing worldwide correlations among various deep-sea sediments, two problems that have long perplexed oceanographers. Magnetic studies are also helping to establish stratigraphic links between marine and continental rocks. Magnetic-reversal stratigraphy has shown, for example, that sediments of glacial origin on Iceland and at the bottom of the Bellingshausen Sea were both deposited at about the end of the "Gauss" normal polarity epoch, or about 2.5 million years ago—a fact of considerable importance for Pleistocene geology.

Reversals may explain certain puzzling magnetic anomalies characteristic of many oceanic areas, particularly those adjacent to the mid-ocean rises, or ridges. These anomalies are parallel bands, extending for hundreds and even thousands of miles, in which the intensity of the earth's magnetic field is higher or lower than the average for the region. It is easy to see how the presence of normal and reversed magnetized rock formations in the crust of the earth, which would add to and subtract from the earth's main dipole field, could account for such findings. Many of the magnetic-anomaly patterns, however, display a striking symmetry around the crests of certain mid-ocean ridges [Figures 33.8 and 33.9] that is difficult to explain on the basis of familiar volcanic processes.

Recently F. J. Vine, now at Princeton University, and J. H. Matthews of the University of Cambridge have pointed out that ideas advanced by Harry H. Hess of Princeton and by the Canadian geophysicist J. Tuzo Wilson to account for certain characteristics of ocean basins and their margins and also for the drifting of continents may shed light on the symmetrical anomalies. Hess and Wilson had suggested that convection currents in the earth's mantle, the layer below the crust, may bring material up to form a mid-ocean ridge and then move the material outward, away from the ridge. If successive bands solidified and were magnetized during successive polarity epochs, Vine and Matthews reported, the symmetry of the patterns could be explained on this basis. So could the particular spacing of the bands along the mid-Atlantic ridge, for example, provided that the sea floor is spreading at the rate of about one centimeter per year [Figure 33.10]. This rate is consistent with earlier estimates by Wilson. Although the hypothesis of sea-floor spreading seems to be inconsistent with some other lines of evidence and has been resisted by many oceanographers and geologists, the magnetic evidence seems to reinforce it.

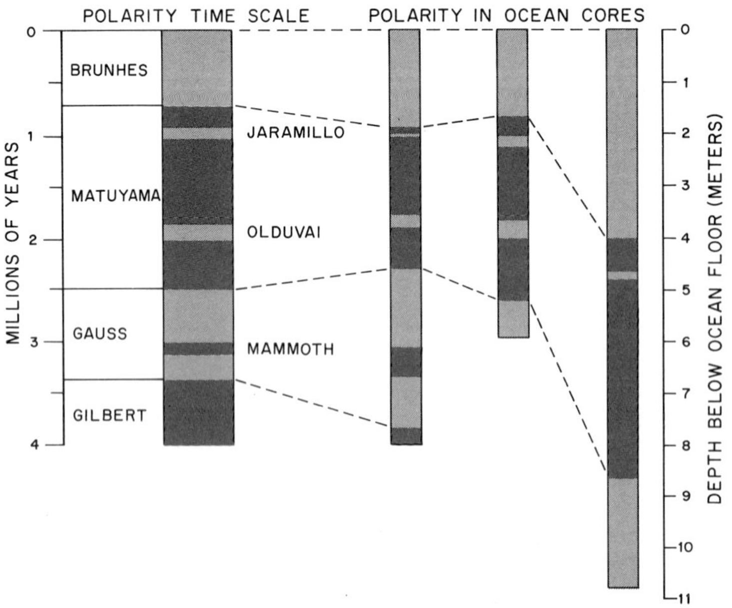

FIGURE 33.7
Deep-sea sediments confirm the field-reversal time scale. Magnetic particles become oriented in the direction of the earth's field as they settle through the water; a core that samples many layers of sediments may record a series of normal (*dark gray*) and reversed (*light gray*) epochs and events. Here cores from Antarctic waters are correlated with the time scale.

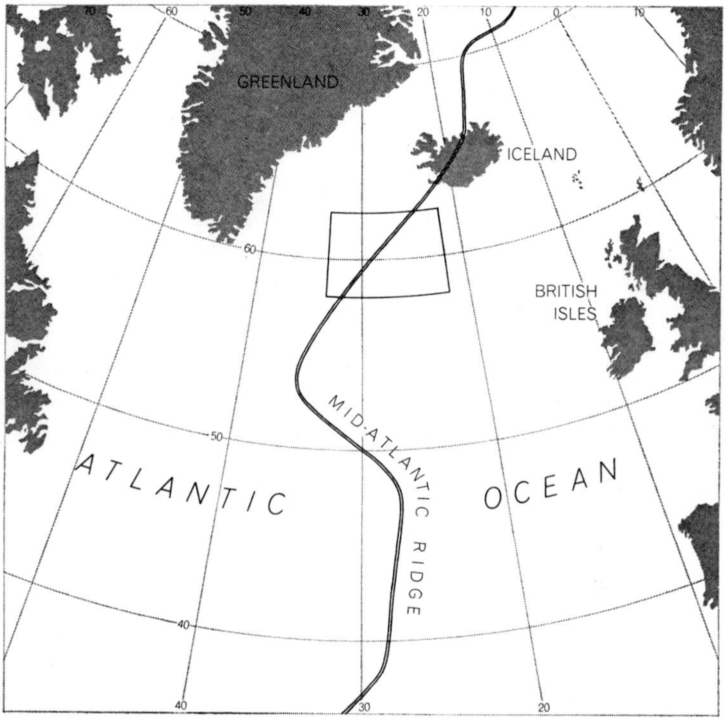

FIGURE 33.8
Areas of discovery of symmetrical magnetic anomalies. These are on ocean floors, particularly along mid-ocean rises. One pattern was mapped in an area (*outlined*) on the mid-Atlantic Ridge.

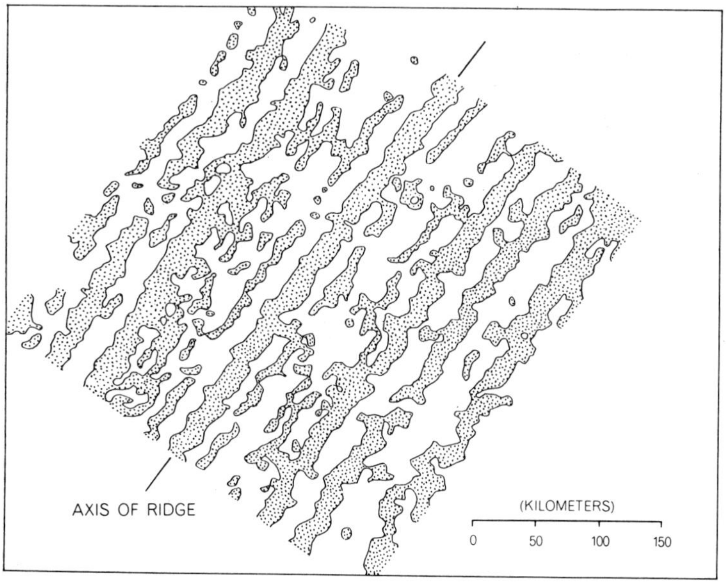

FIGURE 33.9
Magnetic anomaly pattern in the area delineated on the map in Figure 33.8 shows striking symmetry. The parallel bands in which the earth's field is stronger (*stippled*) or weaker (*white*) than the regional average are oriented along the ridge's axis. The magnetic bands are presumably produced by bands of rock with normal and reversed magnetism.

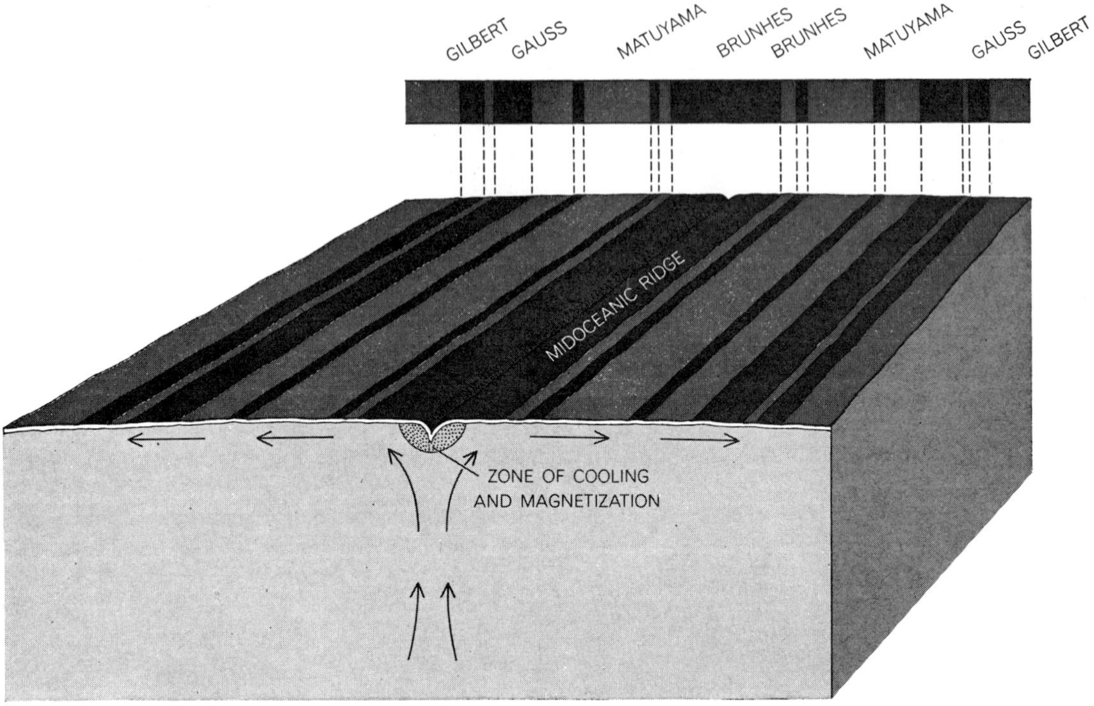

FIGURE 33.10
Spreading of the ocean floor. This could explain the magnetic-anomaly patterns. According to one theory (*see text*) convection currents bring molten material up under the mid-ocean ridge, where it cools, becomes magnetized, and then spreads laterally away from the ridge. Symmetrical bands of normal and reversed rocks would be produced by the combined effect of field reversal and spreading.

Reversals of the earth's magnetic field may even have implications for the history of life on our planet. R. J. Uffen of the University of Western Ontario pointed out in 1963 that if the magnetic field of the earth disappears or is greatly attenuated during a reversal in polarity, the earth would lose some of its magnetic shielding against cosmic rays, with the resulting increase in radiation dosages, mutation rates should increase. Paleomagnetic evidence for the behavior of the earth's field during polarity transitions is fragmentary, but there are indications that the field may be only about a fifth as intense as in normal times. Uffen argues on paleontological grounds that rates of evolution were exceptionally high at times when the earth's magnetic field was undergoing many changes in polarity, although the support for this conclusion in the paleomagnetic record is rather weak. Cores examined by Opdyke and Hayes do provide some support for Uffen's theory in that major changes in the assemblages of microfossils appear near two of the magnetic-polarity changes. Much additional information is needed, however, before it will be possible to judge the extent to which field reversals may have affected life on the earth.

BIBLIOGRAPHY

Cox, Allan, and Richard R. Doell, 1960, Review of paleomagnetism: Geol. Soc. America Bull., v. 71, no. 6, p. 645–768.

Cox, Allan, Richard R. Doell, and G. Brent Dalrymple, 1964, Reversals of the earth's magnetic field: Science, v. 144, no. 3626, p. 1537–1543.

Hamilton, E. I., and L. H. Ahrens, 1965, Applied geochronology: New York, Academic Press.

Irving, E., 1964, Paleomagnetism and its application to geological and geophysical problems: New York, John Wiley and Sons.

Rikitake, Tsuneji, 1965, Electromagnetism and the earth's interior: New York, American Elsevier.

34

The Confirmation of Continental Drift

PATRICK M. HURLEY
1968

From *Scientific American*, vol. 218, no. 4, pp. 52–64.

As recently as five years ago the hypothesis that the continents had drifted apart was regarded with considerable skepticism, particularly among American investigators. Since then, as a result of a variety of new findings, the hypothesis has gained so much support that its critics may now be said to be on the defensive. The slow acceptance of what is actually a very old idea provides a good example of the intensive scrutiny to which scientific theories are subjected, particularly in the earth sciences, where the evidence is often conflicting and where experimental demonstrations are usually not possible.

As long ago as 1620 Francis Bacon discussed the possibility that the Western Hemisphere had once been joined to Europe and Africa. In 1668 P. Placet wrote an imaginative memoir titled *La corruption du grand et du petit monde, où il est montré que devant le déluge, l'Amérique n'était point séparée des autres parties du monde.* . . . Some 200 years later Antonio Snider was struck by the similarities between American and European fossil plants of the Carboniferous period (about 300 million years ago) and proposed that all the continents were once part of a single land mass. His work of 1858 was called *La Création et Ses Mystères Dévoilés*. . . .

By the end of the 19th century geology had come seriously into the discussion. At that time the Austrian geologist Eduard Suess had noted such a close correspondence of geological formations in the lands of the Southern Hemisphere that he fitted them into a single continent he called Gondwanaland. (The name comes from Gondwana, a key geological province in east central India.) In 1908 F. B. Taylor of the U.S. and in 1910 Alfred L. Wegener of Gemany independently suggested mechanisms that could account for large lateral displacements of the earth's crust and thus show how continents might be driven apart. Wegener's work became the center of a debate that has lasted to the present day.

Wegener advanced a remarkable number of detailed correlations, drawn from geology and

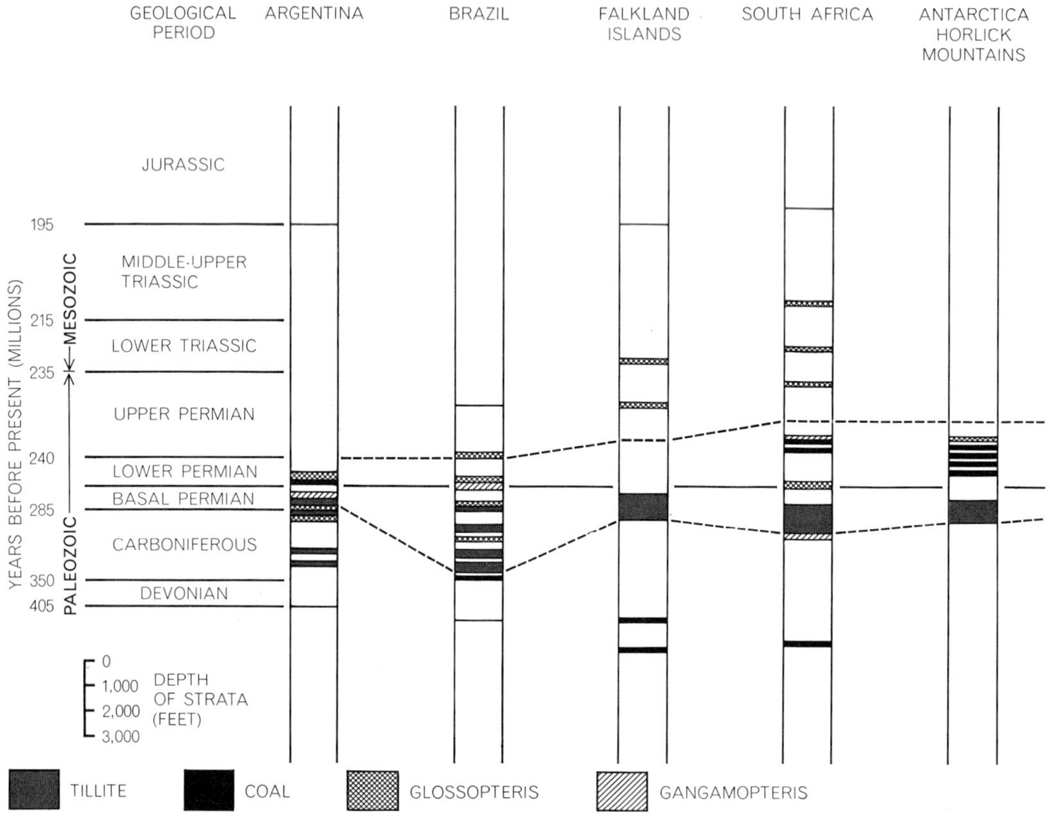

FIGURE 34.1
Gondwana succession. The name given to a late Paleozoic succession of land deposits found in South America, Africa, Antarctica, India, and Australia. The succession contains beds of tillite (glacial rubble), coal deposits, and a diversity of plants arranged in such a way that perhaps 200 million years ago the different areas must have been a single land mass known

paleontology, indicating a common historical record on the two sides of the Atlantic Ocean. He proposed that all the continents were joined in a single vast land mass before the start of the Mesozoic era (about 200 million years ago). Wegener called this supercontinent Pangaea. Today the evidence favors the concept of two large land masses: Gondwanaland in the Southern Hemisphere and Laurasia in the Northern.

In the Southern Hemisphere an additional correlation was found in a succession of glaciations that took place in the Permian and Carboniferous periods. These glaciations left a distinctive record in the southern parts of South America, Africa, Australia, in peninsular India and Madagascar and, as has been discovered recently, in Antarctica. The evidence of glaciations is compelling. Beds of tillite—old, consolidated glacial rubble—have been studied in known glaciated regions and are unquestioned evidence of the action of deep ice cover. In addition many of the tillites rest on typically glaciated surfaces of hard crystalline rock, planed flat and grooved by the rock-filled ice moving over them.

This kind of evidence has been found throughout the Southern Hemisphere. In all regions the tillites are found not only in the same geological periods but also in a sequence of horizontal beds bearing fossils of identical plant species. This sequence, including the geological periods from the Devonian to the Triassic, is called the Gondwana succession. The best correlations are apparent in the Permocarboniferous beds, where two distinctive plant genera, *Glossopteris* and *Gangamopteris*, reached their peak of development. These

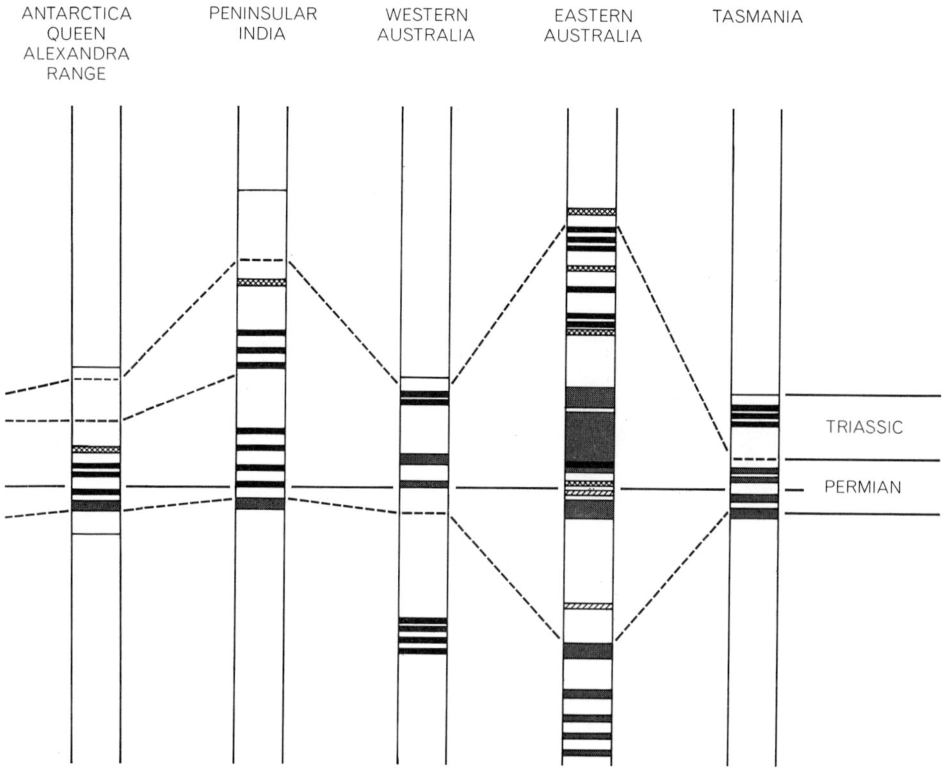

as Gondwanaland, or at the very least a closely associated mass connected by land bridges. Only two of several major plant genera are plotted here: *Glossopteris* and *Gangamopteris.* The depths of the various deposits have been arbitrarily aligned between the lower and the basal Permian.

plants were so abundant that they gave rise to the Carboniferous coal measures, which are commonly interbedded in the Gondwana succession [Figure 34.1].

The South African geologist Alex L. du Toit and others have sought out and mapped these Gondwana sequences so diligently that today they provide the strongest evidence not only that these continental areas were joined in the past but also that they once wandered over or close to the South Pole. It is inconceivable that the complex speciation of the Gondwana plants could have evolved in the separate land masses we see today. It takes only a narrow strip of water, a few tens of miles wide at the most, to stop the spread of a diversified plant regime. The Gondwana land mass was apparently a single unit until the Mesozoic era, when it broke into separate parts. Thereafter evolution proceeded on divergent paths, leading to the biological diversity we observe today on the different continental units.

Wegener and Du Toit published their work in the 1920's and 1930's. The debate for and against drift became polarized largely between geologists of the Southern Hemisphere and the leaders of geophysical thought in the Western Hemisphere. Eminent geophysicists such as Sir Harold Jeffreys of the University of Cambridge voiced strong oppposition to the hypothesis on the grounds that the earth's crust and its underlying mantle were too rigid to permit such large motions, considering the limited energy thought to be available.

Not all felt this way, however. In the late 1930's the Dutch geophysicist F. A. Vening Meinesz proposed that thermal convection in the earth's mantle could provide the mechanism. His ideas were supported by his gravity surveys over the deep-sea trenches and the adjacent island arcs of the western Pacific. The results implied that some force was maintaining the irregular shape of the earth's surface against its natural tendency to flatten out. Presumably the force was somehow related to thermal convection. Arthur Holmes of the University of Edinburgh added his weight to the argument in favor of the hypothesis, and he was followed by S. W. Carey of Tasmania, Sir Edward Bullard and S. K. Runcorn of Britain, L. C. King of South Africa, J. Tuzo Wilson of Canada and others. The historical and dynamical characteristics of the earth now engaged the attention of many more geophysicists, and today the interplay of all branches of geology and geophysics generates the excitement of a new frontier area.

CONTINENTS AND OCEANS

Although the general nature of the earth's crust is familiar to most readers, it is worth reviewing and summarizing some of its major features while asking: How do these features look in the context of continental drift? The earth's topography has two principal levels: the level of the continental surface and the level of the oceanic plains. The elevations in between represent only a small fraction of the earth's total surface area. What maintains these levels? Left alone for billions of years, they should reach equilibrium at an average elevation below the present sea level, so that the earth would be covered with water. Instead we see sharp continental edges, new mountain belts, deep trenches in the oceans—in short, a topography that appears to have been regularly rejuvenated.

The continental areas are a mosaic of blocks that are roughly 1,000 kilometers across and have ages ranging from about 3,000 million years to a few tens of millions. In Africa there appear to be several ancient nuclear areas, or cratons, surrounded by belts of younger rocks. Most of the younger belts have an age of 600 million years or less, contrasting sharply with an age of 2,000 million to 3,000 million years for the cratons.

A closer look at the younger belts tells us that although much of the material is apparently new, there are large blocks that have the same age as the cratons. It looks as if the earth's surface has been warped and folded around the ancient continental masses, catching up segments of the crust and intruding younger igneous rocks into the folds. In some places the ancient material has been altered beyond recognition, but elsewhere it has been left fairly undisturbed and its antiquity can be determined by radioactive-dating methods. These composite belts are termed zones of rejuvenation. When they are eroded down to sea level, all we see, as far as topography is concerned, is another part of the continental platform. Geological mapping, however, reveals the belt structure clearly. A closer look at the cratons shows us that they too have the structure of preexisting mountain belts that have been carved into segments, with the younger material always cutting across the older structural pattern.

We see the process in action today. Our young mountain belts have not been eroded to sea level but show high elevations that are clearly apparent; we do not need geological surveys to observe them. It is only when we see the global distribution of these mountain belts on land areas, together with the distribution of rifts and their associated ridges under the oceans, that we begin to perceive the possibility that vast motions of the earth's surface may be their cause [Figure 34.2].

The earth is also encircled by belts of geological activity in the form of volcanoes, earthquakes and high heat flow, and observable motions in the form of folded rocks and the large displacements known as faults. In recent years the direction of displacements that are not observable on the surface has been deduced by the study of seismic waves arriving at various points on the earth's surface from earthquakes. It is now possible to tell the direction of slippage in the zones of rupture within the solid rocks of the earth's near-surface regions, so that the directions of the forces can be obtained.

If one looks at a map such as [that of Figure 34.2], one is immediately struck by the large scale and systematic distribution of these lines of geologic activity. Some of the systems are coherent over distances of several thousand kilometers. This immediately suggests the large-scale motion of material in the

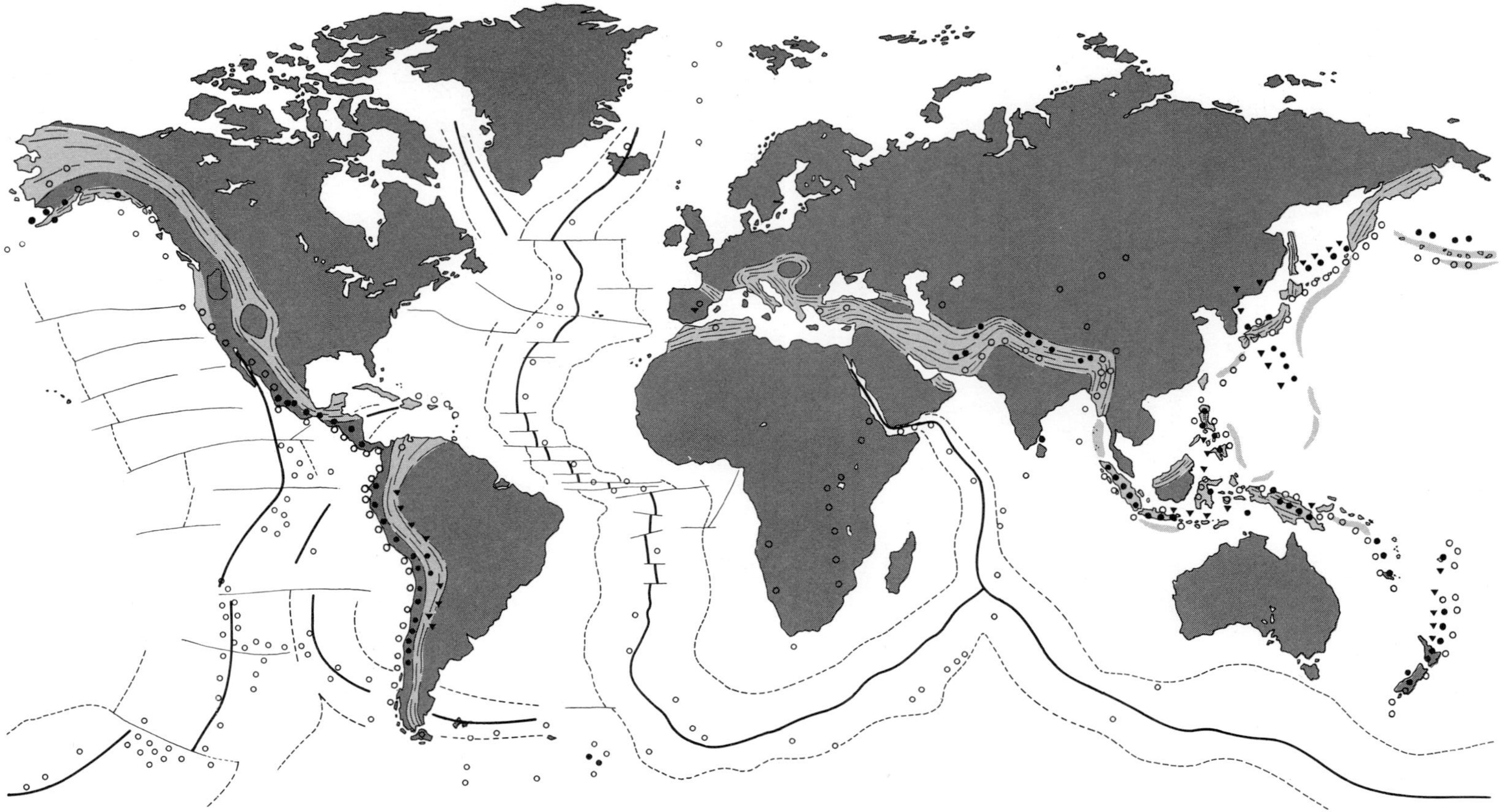

FIGURE 34.2
Worldwide geological patterns support continental drift. They provide evidence that the major land masses have been driven apart by a slow convection process that carries material upward from the mantle below the earth's crust. *Heavy lines,* crests of oceanic ridges that are now believed to coincide with upwelling regions—these ridges are crossed by large transcurrent fracture zones; *broken lines,* approximate limits of the oceanic rises; *light gray areas,* worldwide pattern of recent mountain belts, island arcs, deep trenches, earthquakes, and volcanism that apparently mark the downwelling of crustal material. The downwelling seems to coincide with the occurrence of deep earthquakes (*triangles*) and earthquakes of intermediate depth (*solid dots*). Upwelling zones seem to coincide only with shallow earthquakes (*open dots*).

earth's interior. It does not, however, necessarily imply motions extending a similar distance into the interior. It is possible to have sheets of rigid material supporting stresses and fracturing over great distances if the underlying material is less rigid.

The topography of the ocean floors has been rapidly revealed in the past two decades by the sonic depth recorder. The principal systems of ridges and faults have been mapped in considerable detail by such oceanographers as Bruce C. Heezen and Maurice Ewing of Columbia University and H. W. Menard of the Scripps Institution of Oceanography. The layers of sediment on the sea floor have also been explored by such methods as setting explosive charges in the water and recording the echoes. It became a great puzzle how in the total span of the earth's history only a thin veneer of sediment had been laid down. The deposition rate measured today would extend the process of sedimentation back to about Cretaceous times, or 100 to 200 million years, compared with a continental and oceanic history that goes back at least 3,000 million years. How could three-quarters of the earth's surface be wiped clean of sediment in the last 5 per cent of terrestrial time? Furthermore, why were all the oceanic islands and submerged volcanoes so young? The new oceanographic investigations were presenting questions that were awesome to contemplate.

In the early 1960's Harry H. Hess of Princeton University and Robert S. Dietz of the U.S. Coast and Geodetic Survey independently proposed that the oceanic ridge and rift systems were created by rising currents of material which then spread outward to form new ocean floors. On this basis the ocean floors would be rejuvenated, sweeping along with them the layer of sedimentary material. If such a mechanism were at work, no part of the ocean basins would be truly ancient. Although this radical hypothesis had much in its favor, it appeared farfetched to most.

TRACKING THE SHIFTING POLES

During this time a group of physicists and geophysicists were studying the directions of magnetism "frozen" into rocks in the hope of tracing the history of the earth's magnetic field. When an iron-bearing rock is formed, either by crystallization from a melt or by precipitation from an aqueous solution, it is slightly magnetized in the direction of the earth's magnetic field. Unless this magnetism is disturbed by reheating or physical distortion it is retained as a permanent record of the direction and polarity of the earth's magnetic field at the time the rock was formed. By measuring the magnetism in rocks of all ages from different continents, it has been possible to reconstruct the position of the magnetic pole in the past history of the earth. Great impetus was given to this study by P. M. S. Blackett and Runcorn, who with others soon found that the position of the pole followed a path going backward in time that was different for each continent [Figure 34.3].

The interpretation of this effect was that the continents had moved with respect to the present position of the magnetic pole, and that since the paths were different for each land mass, they had moved independently. Because it was unlikely that the magnetic pole had wandered very far from the axis of the earth's rotation, or that the axis of rotation had changed position with respect to the principal mass of the earth, it was concluded that the continents had moved over the surface of the earth. Moreover, since the shift in latitude of the southern continents was generally southward going backward in time, the motions were in accord with the older evidence pointing toward a Gondwanaland in the south-polar regions. In short, the magnetic evidence supported not only the notion of continental drift but also the general locations from which the continents had moved within the appropriate time span.

This was still not enough to sway the preponderance of American scientific opinion. Finally, at the annual meeting of the Geological Society of America in San Francisco in 1966, came the blows that broke the back of the opposition. Several papers put forward startling new evidence that related the concepts of ocean-floor spreading and continental drift, the cause of the oceanic-ridge and fault systems and the direction and time scale of the drift motions. In addition, the development of new mechanisms explaining displacement along

FIGURE 34.3
North magnetic pole. It appears to have wandered inexplicably during the past few hundred million years (*heavy lines above*), on the basis of "fossil" magnetism measured in rocks of various ages in various continents. The diagram is based on one by Allan Cox and Richard R. Doell of the U.S. Geological Survey. The pole could hardly have followed so many different tracks simultaneously; evidently it was the continents that wandered. K. M. Creer of the University of Newcastle upon Tyne found that the tracks could be brought together if South America, Africa, and Australia were grouped in the late Paleozoic as shown below.

faults brought into agreement some of the formerly contradictory seismic evidence.

In the study of rock magnetism it was observed that the earth's magnetic field not only had changed direction in the past but also had reversed frequently. In order to study how frequently and when the reversals occurred three workers in the U.S. Geological Survey—Allan Cox, G. Brent Dalrymple and Richard R. Doell—carefully measured the magnetism in samples of basaltic rocks that they dated by determining the amount of argon 40 in the rocks formed by the decay of radioactive potassium 40. They noted a distinct pattern of reversals over some 3.6 million years. Their finding was soon confirmed when Neil D. Opdyke and James D. Hays of Columbia University found the same pattern in going downward into older layers in oceanic sediments. It was thus established that the polarity of the magnetic field had universally reversed at certain fixed times in the past.

Meanwhile an odd pattern of magnetism in the rocks of the ocean floors had been detected by Ronald G. Mason and Arthur D. Raff of the Scripps Institution of Oceanography. Using a shipborne magnetometer, they found that huge areas of the ocean floor were magnetized in a stripelike pattern. Putting together these patterns, the discovery of magnetic reversals and Hess's idea that the oceanic ridges and rifts were the site of rising and spreading material, F. J. Vine, now at Princeton, and D. H. Matthews of the University of Cambridge proposed that the hypothesis of the continuous creation of new ocean floors might be tested by examining the magnetic pattern on both sides of an oceanic ridge. The extraordinary discovery that the pattern was symmetrical with the ridge was demonstrated by Vine and Tuzo Wilson, who studied the two sides of a ridge next to Vancouver Island.

The history of the magnetic field going back into the past was laid out horizontally in the magnetism of the rocks of the sea floor going away from the ridge in both directions. It appeared that new hot material was rising from the rift in the center of the ridge and becoming magnetized in the direction of the earth's field as it cooled; it then moved outward, carrying with it the history of magnetic reversals. Since the dates of the reversals were known, the distance to each reversed formation gave the rate of spreading of the ocean floor [Figure 34.4].

This important pice of work was quickly followed up by James R. Heirtzler, W. C. Pitman, G. O. Dickson and Xavier Le Pichon of Columbia, who have now shown that the ridges of the Pacific, Atlantic and Indian oceans all exhibit similar patterns. In fact, these workers have detected recognizable points in the history of magnetic reversals back about 80 million years, or in the Cretaceous period, and have drawn isochron lines, or lines of equal age, over huge strips of the ocean floors. Hence it is now possible to date the ocean floors and perceive the direction and rate of their lateral motion simply by conducting a magnetic survey over them. The implications for the study of drifting continents are immediately apparent.

These and other new findings do not unequivocally call for continental drift. It might be possible to have sea-floor spreading without drifting continents. Nonetheless, the directions and rates of motion for both sea-floor spreading and continental drift are entirely compatible. Above all, the principal objection to a hypothesis of continental movement has been removed.

Looking back, it is interesting to observe how each new piece of evidence presented in the past was met by counterevidence. Wegener's reconstruction, for example, was countered by numerous geologists who took exception to his detailed arguments. The arguments for the Permocarboniferous Gondwana glaciations were countered by Daniel I. Axelrod of the University of California at Los Angeles and others in this country. They contended that most species of fossil plant tend to be restricted to zones of latitude that hold for the continents in their present position, a fact that

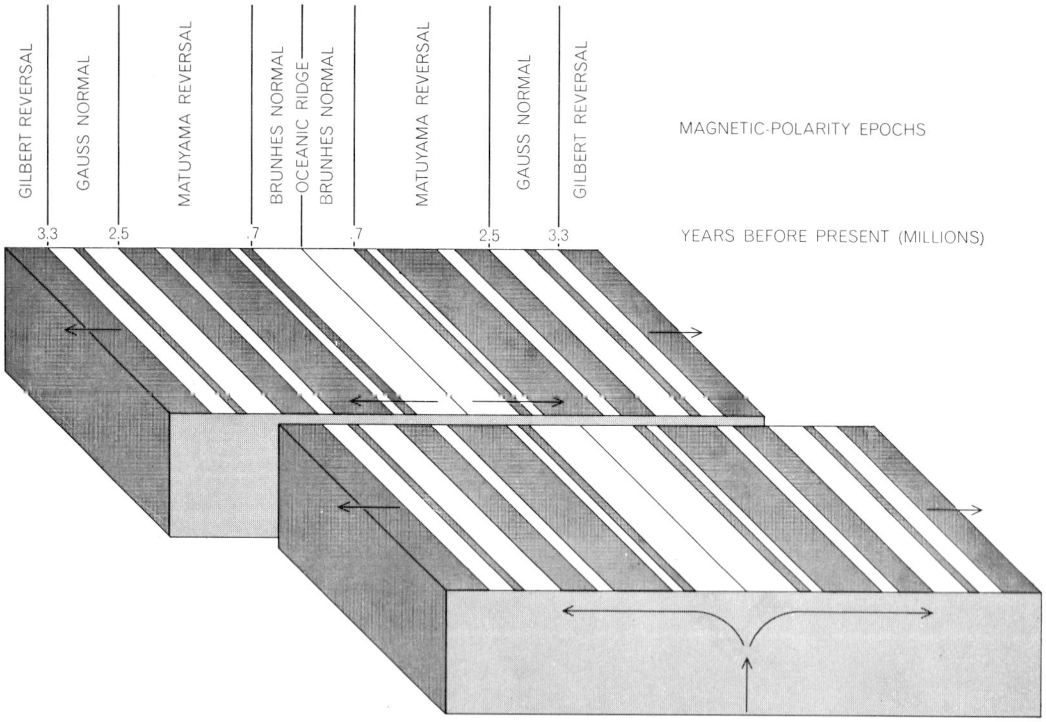

FIGURE 34.4
Evidence for sea-floor spreading. Obtained by determining the polarity of fossil magnetism in rocks lying on both sides of oceanic ridges. *White*, rocks of normal, or present-day, polarity; *gray*, rocks of reversed polarity. The displacement of the two blocks represents a transcurrent fracture zone. The symmetry suggests that the rocks welled up in a molten or semimolten state and gradually moved outward. The diagram is based on studies by a number of workers.

is hard to reconcile with the presumed pattern of glaciation. The idea that the great Gondwana land masses drifted in latitude has also been opposed by F. G. Stehli of Case Western Reserve University; his studies suggest that ancient fauna were most diverse at the Equator, and that the Equator defined in this way has not shifted.

ANOTHER TEST OF THE HYPOTHESIS

Any hypothesis must be tested on all points of observational fact. The balance of evidence must be strongly in its favor before it is even tentatively accepted, and it must always be able to meet the challenge of new observations and experiments. My own interest in the problem of continental drift was stimulated at a 1964 symposium in London sponsored by the Royal Society and arranged by Blackett, Bullard and Runcorn. At that time Bullard and his University of Cambridge associates J. E. Everett and A. G. Smith presented an elegant study of the geographic matching of continents on both sides of the North and South Atlantic. They had employed a computer to produce the best fit by the method of least squares. Instead of using shorelines, as had been done in earlier attempts, they followed the lead of S. W. Carey; he had chosen the central depth of the continental slope as representing the true edge of the continent.

The fit was remarkable [Figure 34.5]. The average error was no greater than one degree over most of the boundary. My colleagues and I at the Massachusetts Institute of Technology now began to think of further testing the fit by comparing the sequence and age of rocks on opposite sides of the Atlantic.

Radioactive-dating techniques for determining the absolute age of rocks had reached a point where much could be learned about the age and history of both the ancient cratonic regions and the younger rejuvenated ones. For such purposes two techniques can be used in combination: the measurement of strontium 87 formed in the radioactive decay of rubidium 87 in a total sample of rock, and the measurement of argon 40 formed in the decay of potassium 40 in minerals separated from the rock. A collaborative effort was arranged between our geochronology laboratory and the University of São Paulo in Brazil (in particular with G. C. Melcher and U. Cordani of that institution). We also enlisted the aid of field geologists who had been working on the west coast of Africa (in Nigeria, the Ivory Coast, Liberia and Sierra Leone) and on the east coast of Brazil and Venezuela. The São Paulo group made the potassium-argon measurements of the Brazilian rock samples; we did the rubidium-strontium analyses on samples from all locations.

European geochronologists (notably M. Bonhomme of France and N. J. Snelling of Britain) had done pioneering work on the Precambrian geology of former French and British colonies and protectorates in West Africa. Of special interest to us at the start was the sharp boundary between the 2,000-million-year-old geological province in Ghana, the Ivory Coast and westward from these countries, and the 600-million-year-old province in Dahomey, Nigeria and east. This boundary heads in a southwesterly direction into the ocean near Accra in Ghana. If Brazil had been joined to Africa 600 million years ago, the boundary between the two provinces should enter South America close to the town of São Luís on the northeast coast of Brazil. Our first order of business was therefore to date the rocks from the vicinity of São Luís.

To our surprise and delight the ages fell into two groups: 2,000 million years on the west and 600 million years on the east of a boundary line that lay exactly where it had been predicted. Apparently a piece of the 2,000-million-year-old craton of West Africa had been left on the continent of South America.

In subsequent work on both sides we have found no incompatibilities in the age of many geological provinces on both sides of the South Atlantic [Figure 34.6]. Furthermore, the structural trends of the rocks also agree, at least where they are known. Minerals characteristic of individual belts of rocks are also found in juxtaposition on both sides; for example, belts of manganese, iron ore, gold and tin seem to follow a matching pattern where the coasts once joined.

Can such comparisons be made elsewhere? To some extent, yes. Unfortunately the rifting

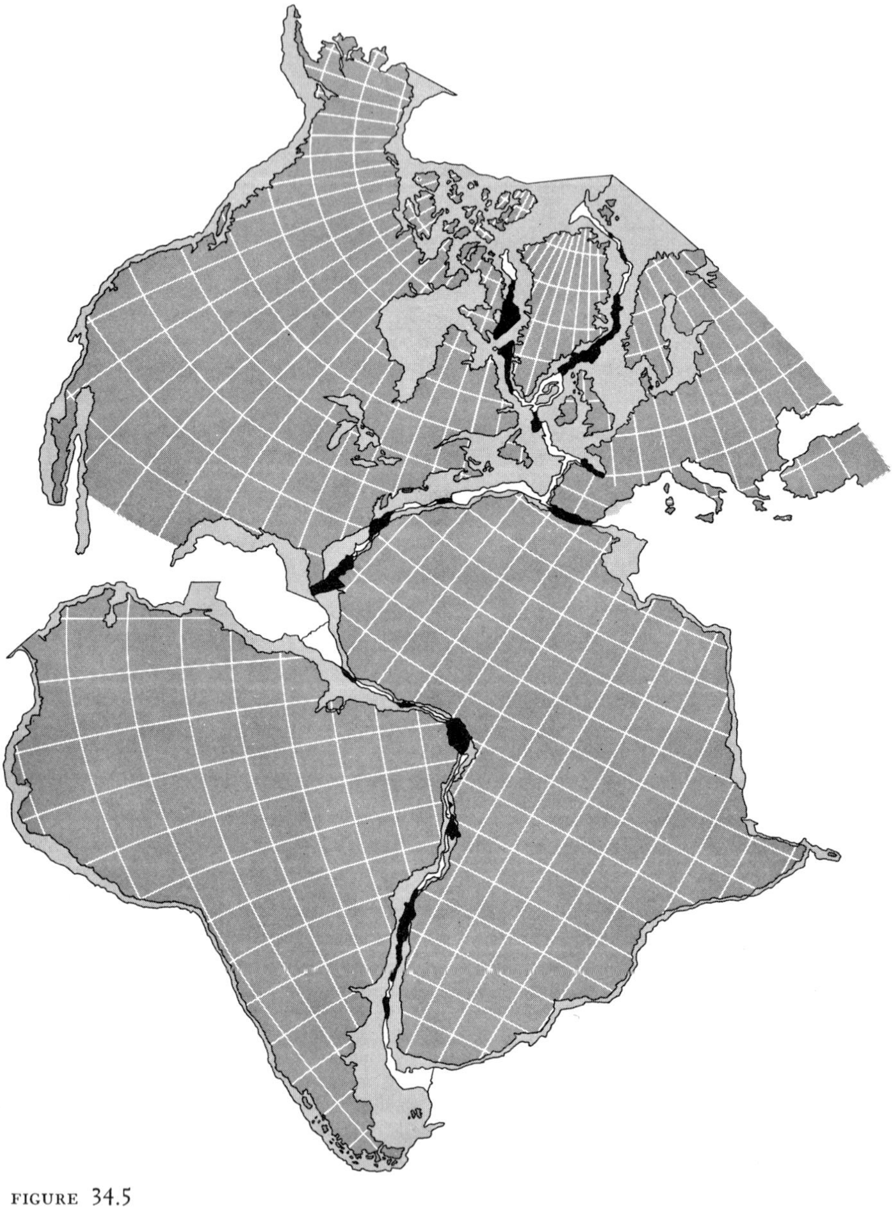

FIGURE 34.5
Fit of continents. Optimized and error-tested on a computer by Sir Edward Bullard, J. E. Everett, and A. G. Smith of the University of Cambridge. Over most of the boundary the average mismatch is no more than a degree. The fit was made along the continental slope (*light gray*) at the 500-fathom contour line. The regions where land masses, including the shelf, overlap are black; gaps are white.

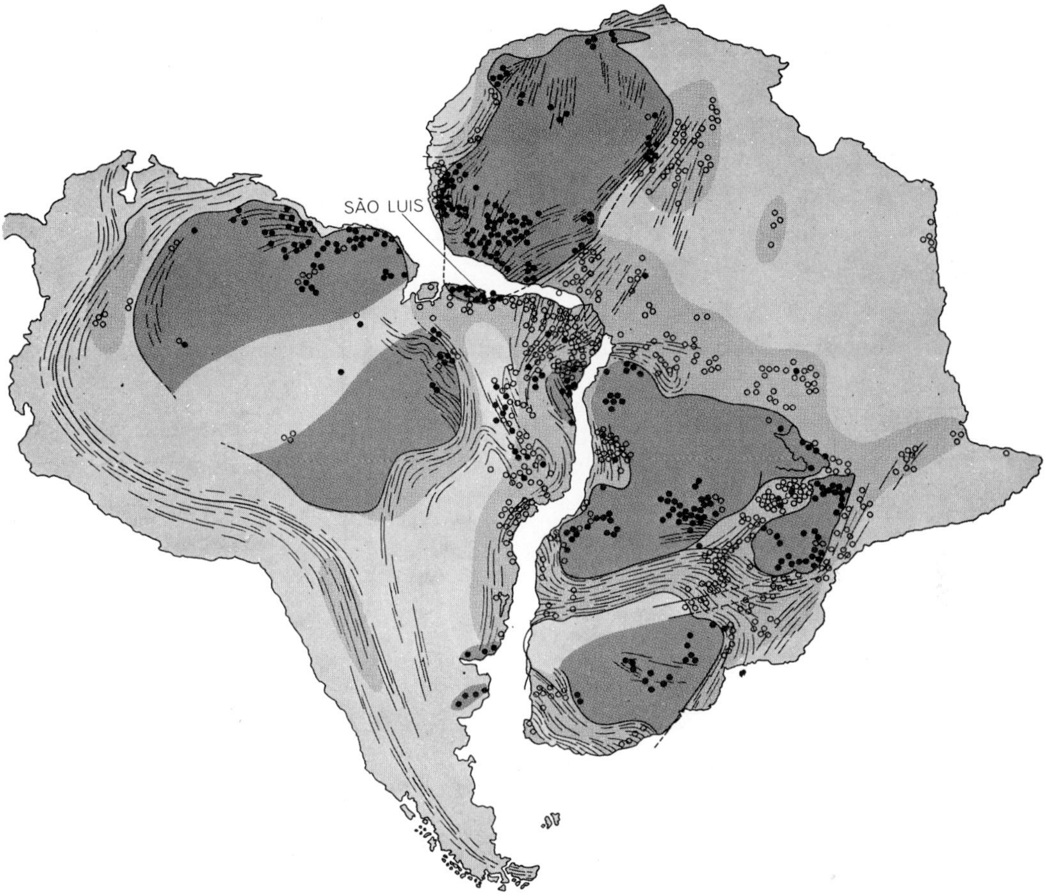

FIGURE 34.6
Tentative matching of geological provinces of the same age. Shows how South America and Africa presumably fitted together some 200 million years ago. *Dark areas,* ancient continental blocks, called cratons, that are at least 2,000 million years old; *light areas,* younger zones of geological activity—mostly troughs filled with sediments and volcanic rocks that were folded, compressed, and intruded by hot materials, forming granites and other rock bodies. Much of this activity was 450 million to 650 million years ago, but some of it goes back 1,100 years. Dots show the sites of rocks dated by many laboratories, including the author's at the Massachusetts Institute of Technology: *solid dots,* rocks older than 2,000 million years; *open dots,* younger rocks. The region near São Luís is part of an African craton left stranded on the coast of Brazil.

process by which a continent breaks up seems to be guided by zones of rejuvenation between cratons, as if these zones were also zones of weakness deep in the crust. It is necessary for the break to have transected the structure of the continent, cutting across age provinces, if one is to get a close refitting of the blocks. In the North Atlantic this is not the case, but the continental areas on both sides were simultaneously affected by an unmistakable oblique crossing of a Paleozoic belt of geological activity [Figure 34.7]. Actually the belt covers the region of the Appalachian Mountains and the Maritime Provinces of North America, with an overlap along the coast of West Africa, and then splits into two principal belts: one extending through the British Isles and affecting the Atlantic coast of Scandinavia and Greenland and the other turning eastward into Europe. There is a superposition of at least four periods of renewed activity affecting the various parts of this complex. All four are represented on both sides of the North Atlantic, making this correlation extremely difficult to explain unless the continents were once together.

My colleagues H. W. Fairbairn and W. H. Pinson, Jr., and I, as well as other workers, have made age measurements in the northern Appalachians and Nova Scotia for many years, and we have found all four periods well represented in New England. The earliest period of activity (which Fairbairn has named Neponset) is dated about 550 million years ago; it is seen in some of the large rock bodies in eastern Massachusetts and Connecticut, in the Channel Islands off the northern coast of France, in Normandy, Scotland and Norway. The next-oldest period (the Taconic) was about 450 million years ago and is found on the western edge of New England and in parts of the British Isles. The next period, going back about 360 million years, is strongly represented in the entire span of the Appalachians and Nova Scotia (where it is called the Acadian) and in England and Norway (where it is called the Caledonian). Finally, about 250 million years ago, the activity seemed to move into southern Europe and North Africa, where it has been called the Hercynian. This activity, however, also extended into New England; much of southern Maine, eastern New Hampshire, Massachusetts and Connecticut show rocks of this age. Here the event is called the Appalachian.

Farther south the Lower Paleozoic section

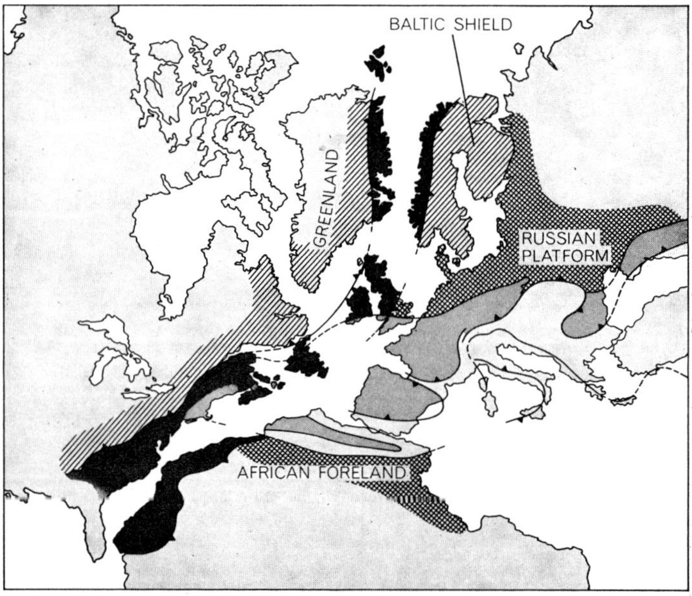

FIGURE 34.7
Matching of North Atlantic regions. Matching is more difficult here than in the South Atlantic. This tentative, pre-drift reconstruction of a portion of Laurasia depends on matching ancient belts of similar geological activity. *Dark gray belt* represents the formation of sediment-filled troughs and folded mountains in the early and middle Paleozoic (470 million to 350 million years ago); *medium gray belt* was formed in the late Paleozoic (350 million to 200 million years ago). The latter belt overlapped the region of the former in the northern Appalachians and in southern Ireland and England, but diverged eastward in Europe. Four distinct and superimposed periods of geological activity occur on both sides of the present North Atlantic, providing strong evidence for a previous juncture.

of the northwest coast of Africa (Senegal) appears to continue under the younger coastal sediments of Florida. This African belt shows large rock units with ages equivalent to the Neponset, and also evidence of the younger events.

THE FITTING OF ANTARCTICA

The recent extensive geological surveys in Antarctica have been highly rewarding in reconstructing Gondwanaland. Prior to the end of the Permian period the younger parts of western Antarctica were not yet formed. Only eastern Antarctica was present, including the great belts of folded rocks that form the Transantarctic Mountains. These consist of two geosynclines, or sediment-filled troughs: the inner Eopaleozoic and the outer Paleozoic [Figure 34.8]. The inner belt includes late Precambrian and early Cambrian sediments, which were folded and invaded by igneous rocks during late Cambrian or early Ordovician times (about 500 million years ago). Thus the inner belt is similar in age to the widespread event in the rest of Gondwanaland. It is marked by Cambrian fossil Archaeocyathida, organisms that formed barrier reefs. These coral-like structures are found transecting sediments in bodies known as bioherms. The outer belt, farther within western Antarctica, is a

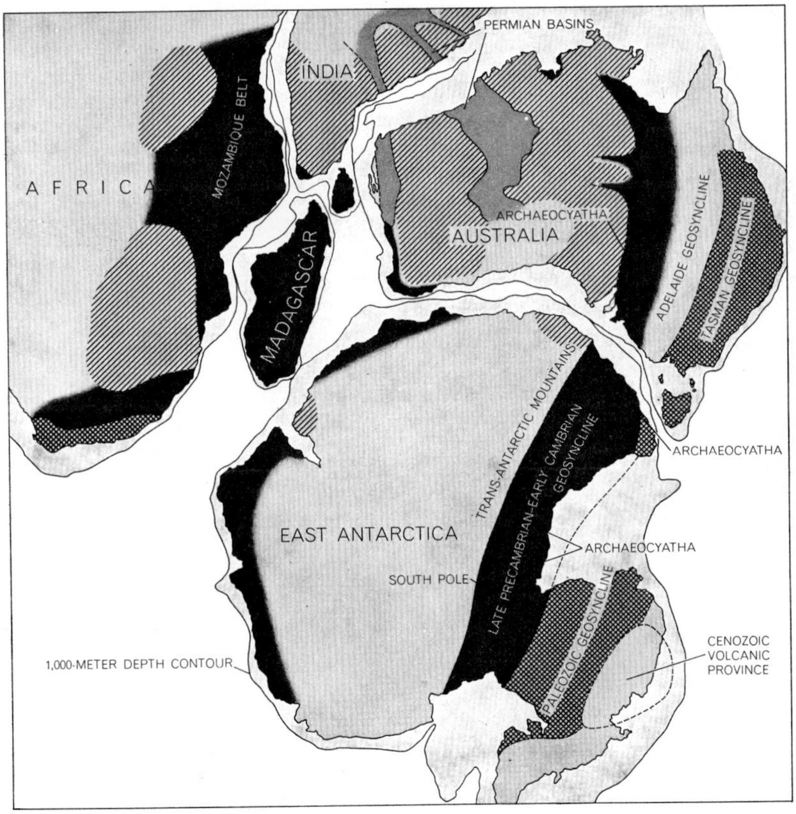

FIGURE 34.8
Part of Gondwanaland. Tentative reconstruction brings together East Antarctica, Africa, Australia, Madagascar, India. The fit is at the 1,000-meter depth contour of the continental slope. Late Precambrian and Paleozoic geosynclines, or sediment-filled troughs, in eastern Australia are correlated in age and location with similar troughs along the Transantarctic Mountains. The deep Permian basins of northwest Australia match those of India. Glacial deposits, fauna, and metal ores provide other correlations.

geosyncline filled with Lower Paleozoic sediments. Like the northern Appalachians, it was deformed and invaded by igneous rocks in the middle and late Paleozoic. Later it was covered with a quite representative Gondwana succession, with its galcial deposits, coal and diverse plants.

There seems to be a similar record of events in eastern Australia. The bioherms of Cambrian Archaeocyathida are found in a belt extending northward from Adelaide and mark the edge of an early geosyncline filled with sediments including late Precambrian and Cambrian ones. Later in time, and farther to the east, great thicknesses of Silurian and Lower Devonian sediments accumulated in the Tasman trough. Compression and igneous intrusion occurred in this Tasman geocyncline mostly late in the Early Devonian to the Middle Devonian (about 350 million years ago). The later cover of sediments includes a Gondwana succession similar to the one in Antarctica.

There is also strong evidence for a juncture between Australia and India, particularly in the Permian basins of sedimentation of the two continental blocks and in Gondwana sequences of coal and plants. Limestone beds containing the same Productid shells are found in the upper layers of the sequence on both sides. A correlation also exists between the banded iron ores of Yampi Sound in northwestern Australia and the similar ores of Singhbhum in India.

Figure 34.8 is a reconstruction of Gondwanaland based on the evidence we have discussed so far. The three land masses—Antarctica, Australia and India—have been fitted together not at their present shorelines but where the depth of the surrounding ocean reaches 1,000 meters. As can be seen, the fit of the edges is good. The detailed fit of this assemblage into the southeastern part of Africa is still debated because most of the edges lack structures that cut across them. Nevertheless, I have included the edge of Africa in the map to show how it might possibly fit on the basis of limited age data from Antarctica.

This arrangement of land masses in the late Paleozoic is extremely tentative. It is now up to the geochronologists to test each juncture more closely for correlations in geologic age, and up to the field geologists to match structure and rock type. One particularly interesting fit may be forthcoming in a study of the boundaries of shallow and deep marine glacial deposits, and of the land tillites around what appears to be the start of an oceanic basin at the time Antarctica was breaking away. This attempt to establish the former position of Antarctica, which is being made by L. A. Frakes and John C. Crowell of the University of California, may set in place the key piece in the puzzle. A detailed correlation of fossil plants in Antarctica with those of the adjacent land masses, which has been undertaken by Edna Plumstead of the University of Witwatersrand, is similarly limiting the possible position of the blocks.

THE AGE OF THE ATLANTIC

When did Gondwanaland begin to break up? One of the best pieces of evidence for the start of the opening of the South Atlantic is the age of offshore sediments along the west coast of Africa. Drilling through these sediments down to the ancient nonsedimentary rocks shows that the layer of sediments is quite young: not older than the middle Mesozoic (about 160 million years ago). If the South Atlantic had been in existence for a major part of geologic time, the continent of Africa would unquestionably have developed a large shelf of sediments along the entire length of its western margin. The continental shelf would consist of sediments dating all the way back to the time of the ancient cratons. This is not the case. It looks as though the rift started from the northern edge of western Africa in the middle Triassic and slowly opened to the south until the final separation occurred in the Cretaceous. The east coast of Africa, on the other hand, apparently started to open earlier, in the Permian.

With the acceptance of sea-floor spreading and continental drift the global problems of geology are beginning to be solved. Although the train of thought on such matters is not universally accepted in detail, it is something like the following. Continental areas appear to have greater strength, to a depth of 100 kilometers or so, than ocean basins do, so that they tend to maintain themselves as buoyant masses that are not destroyed by sinking motions. They can, however, be ruptured. Rising material pushes the surface apart; sinking material pulls the surface together and toward the region of sinking. Therefore if a sinking zone is established in an oceanic region, the continents will move toward the zone, and if a rising zone is established under a continent, the continent will split apart and the parts will move away from the zone. When the ocean floor moves toward a sinking zone in an oceanic region, it forms a deep trench bordered by volcanoes, chains of islands or elongated land masses such as the Philippines and Japan. When an ocean floor moves toward a continent, it appears to pass under the continental border, forming a great mountain chain. The mountain chain may be in part piled-up material that was already present and in part volcanic material that rose as the ocean swept its load of sediment, underlying volcanic rock and the continental shelf itself toward and under the edge of the continent. The process leads to a melting of underlying rock and to the intrusion of new volcanic material. The west coast of South America is a good example.

Another example is the thrust of India into Eurasia that formed the Himalayas. It has long been known that there was a large body of water between Africa and Urasia and that a great thickness of sediments was deposited there at some time during the past 200 million years. This body is known as the Tethys Sea. It was located north of Arabia and extended from the former location of the Atlas Mountains to east of the Himalayas. As I have mentioned, it appears that Gondwanaland not only broke up but also moved northward, with India and Africa pushing up into Eurasia. This motion apparently caused the buckling up of sediments in the Tethys Sea, giving rise to the mountain ranges that now form a contorted chain from the western Atlas range through the Mediterranean, the western Alps, the Caucasus and the Himalayas.

The way the present mountain systems of the earth fall along great circles suggests that the motions in the earth's interior have a large-scale coherence, of the order of the dimensions of the earth itself. The prevailing explanation stems from a new lead in seismology: a zone in the earth at a depth of 100 or 200 kilometers has been found to transmit seismic waves more slowly than the layers above and below it and to absorb seismic energy more strongly. This low-velocity zone is generally thought to consist of a material whose strength is reduced because a small amount of it is molten or because its temperature is approaching the melting point. The surface of the earth may therefore move around on this low-strength layer like the skin of an onion. It is believed the earth loses heat partly by conduction outward and partly by convection currents in the relatively thin layer above the weak zone. These currents, as they have been depicted by Walter M. Elsasser of Princeton and Egon Orowan of M.I.T., form rather flat convection cells.

A hypothesis that is currently popular is that the mechanism of spreading at the oceanic ridges involves the intrusion of hot material into ruptures near the surface. This material is the same as that in the low-velocity zone, lubricated by partly molten rock. A small proportion of the intruded material actually loses some of its melted fraction upward, giving rise to volcanoes and creating a thin layer (about five kilometers thick) of volcanic rock at the surface. The masses of intruded material cool as they move sideways from the central ridge, which is overlain by the thin layer of volcanic rock. This results in the observed distribution of seismic velocities at various depths, helps to explain why the flow of heat to the surface decreases with distance from the ridge and accounts for the pattern of magnetic reversals. At the sinking end of the convection cell this relatively rigid block of mantle material with its thin cover of basalt (plus a thin cover of new sediment) moves downward on an inclined plane.

It is clear where these concepts will lead. If folded mountain belts are the "bow waves" of continents plowing their way through ocean floors and ramming into other continents, we can use them to show us the relative directions of motion prior to the last great drift episode. If we look at the pre-drift Paleozoic mountain belts, such as the Appalachian belt of North America, the Hercynian of Europe and the Ural of Asia, we find that they are located *internally* in the great continental masses of Gondwanaland and Laurasia. This suggests that these pre-drift supercontinents had been formed by the inward motion of several separate blocks, which came together before they broke apart. Geologists have a new game of chess to play, using a spherical board and strange new rules.

BIBLIOGRAPHY

Blackett, P. M. S., Sir Edward Bullard, and S. K. Runcorn, eds., 1965, A symposium on continental drift—organized for the Royal Society: Royal Soc. [London] Philos. Trans., ser A, v. 258, p. vii–322.

Runcorn, S. K., ed., 1962, Continental drift: New York, Academic Press.

Vine, F. J., 1966, Spreading of the ocean floor—new evidence: Science, v. 154, no. 3755, p. 1405–1415.

Wegener, Alfred, 1924, The origin of continents and oceans: London, Methuen.

35

A New Class of Faults

and Their Bearing on Continental Drift

J. TUZO WILSON
1965

From *Nature,* vol. 207, pp. 343–347, 1965. Reprinted with permission of the author and Macmillan (Journals) Ltd.

TRANSFORMS AND HALF-SHEARS

Many geologists [1] have maintained that movements of the Earth's crust are concentrated in mobile belts, which may take the form of mountains, mid-ocean ridges or major faults with large horizontal movements. These features and the seismic activity along them often appear to end abruptly, which is puzzling. The problem has been difficult to investigate because most terminations lie in ocean basins.

This article suggests that these features are not isolated, that few come to dead ends, but that they are connected into a continuous network of mobile belts about the Earth which divide the surface into several large rigid plates (Figure 35.1). Any feature at its apparent termination may be transformed into another feature of one of the other two types. For example, a fault may be transformed into a mid-ocean ridge as illustrated in Figure 35.2A. At the point of transformation the horizontal shear motion along the fault ends abruptly by being changed into an expanding tensional motion across the ridge or rift with a change in seismicity.

A junction where one feature changes into another is here called a transform. This type and two others illustrated in Figures 35.2B and C may also be termed half-shears (a name suggested in conversation by Prof. J. D. Bernal). Twice as many types of half-shears involve mountains as ridges, because mountains are asymmetrical whereas ridges have bilateral symmetry. This way of abruptly ending large horizontal shear motions is offered as an explanation of what has long been recognized as a puzzling feature of large faults like the San Andreas.

Another type of transform whereby a mountain is transformed into a mid-ocean ridge was suggested by S. W. Carey [2] when he proposed that the Pyrenees Mountains were compressed because of the rifting open of the Bay of Biscay (presumably by the formation of a

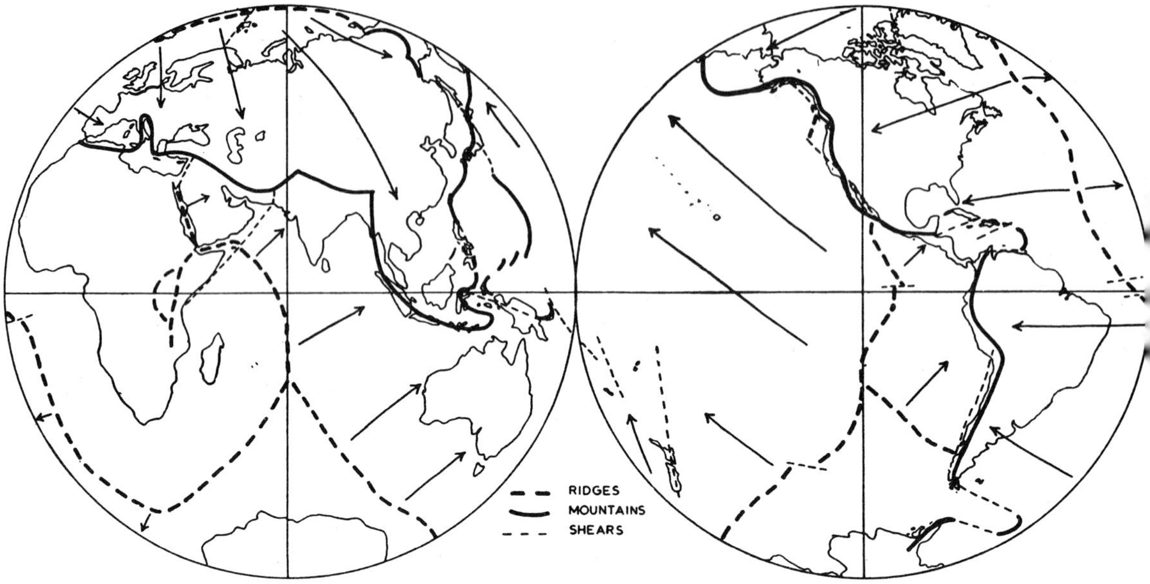

FIGURE 35.1
Sketch map illustrating the present network of mobile belts around the globe. Such belts comprise the active primary mountains and island arcs in compression (*solid lines*), active transform faults in horizontal shear (*light dashed lines*), and active mid-ocean ridges in tension (*heavy dashed lines*).

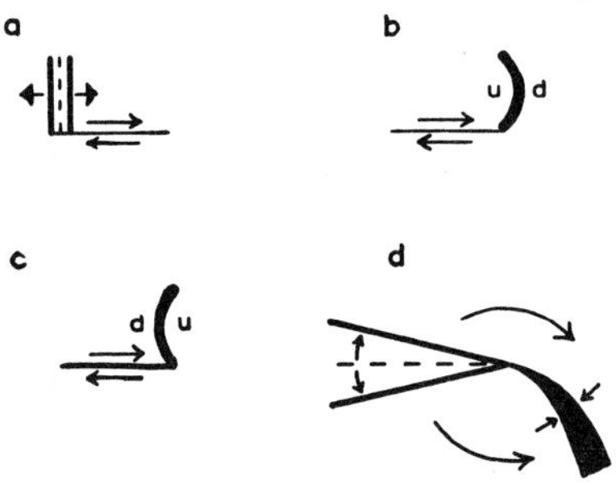

FIGURE 35.2
Diagram illustrating the four possible right-hand transforms: *a*, ridge to dextral half-shear; *b*, dextral half-shear to concave arc; *c*, dextral half-shear to convex arc; *d*, ridge to right-hand arc.

mid-ocean ridge along its axis). The types illustrated are all dextral, but equivalent sinistral types exist.

In this article the term 'ridge' will be used to mean mid-ocean ridge and also rise (where that term has been used meaning mid-ocean ridge, as by Menard [3] in the Pacific basin). The terms mountains and mountain system may include island arcs. An arc is described as being convex or concave depending on which face is first reached when proceeding in the direction indicated by an arrow depicting relative motion (Figures 35.2 and 35.3). The word fault may mean a system of several closely related faults.

TRANSFORM FAULTS

Faults in which the displacement suddenly stops or changes form and direction are not true transcurrent faults. It is proposed that a separate class of horizontal shear faults exists which terminate abruptly at both ends, but which nevertheless may show great displacements. Each may be thought of as a pair of half-shears joined end to end. Any combination of pairs of the three dextral half-shears may be joined giving rise to the six types illustrated in Figure 35.3. Another six sinistral forms can also exist. The name transform fault is proposed for the class, and members may be described in terms of the features which they connect (for example, dextral transform fault, ridge-convex arc type).

The distinctions between types might appear trivial until the variation in the habits of

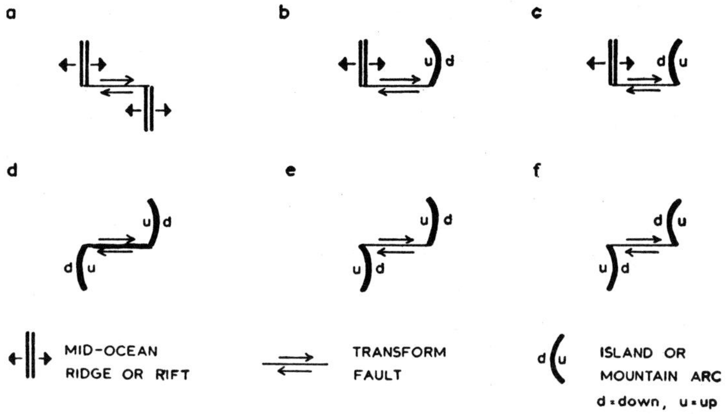

FIGURE 35.3
Diagram illustrating the six possible types of dextral transform faults: *a*, ridge to ridge type; *b*, ridge to concave arc; *c*, ridge to convex arc; *d*, concave arc to concave arc; *e*, concave arc to convex arc; *f*, convex arc to convex arc. Note that the direction of motion in *a* is the reverse of that required to offset the ridge.

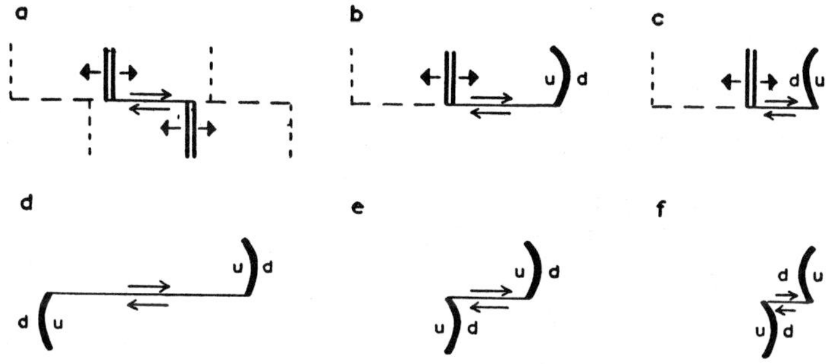

FIGURE 35.4
Diagram illustrating the appearance of the six types of dextral transform faults shown in Figure 35.3 after a period of growth. *Dashed lines*, traces of former positions now inactive, but still expressed in the topography.

growth of the different types is considered as is shown in Figure 35.4. These distinctions are that ridges expand to produce new crust, thus leaving residual inactive traces in the topography of their former positions. On the other hand oceanic crust moves down under island arcs absorbing old crust so that they leave no traces of past positions. The convex sides of arcs thus advance. For these reasons transform faults of types A, B, and D in Figure 35.4 grow in total width, type F diminishes and the behaviour of types C and E is indeterminate. It is significant that the direction of motion on transform faults of the type shown in Figure 35.3A is the reverse of that required to offset the ridge. This is a fundamental difference between transform and transcurrent faulting.

Many examples of these faults have been reported and their properties are known and will be shown to fit those required by the constructions above. If the class as a whole has not heretofore been recognized and defined, it is because all discussions of faulting, such as those of E. M. Anderson, have tacitly assumed that the faulted medium is continuous and conserved. If continents drift this assumption is not true. Large areas of crust must be swallowed up in front of an advancing continent and re-created in its wake. Transform faults cannot exist unless there is crustal displacement, and their existence would provide a powerful argument in favour of continental drift and a guide to the nature of the displacements involved. These proposals owe much to the ideas of S. W. Carey, but differ in that I suggest that the plates between mobile belts are not readily deformed except at their edges.

The data on which the ensuing accounts are based have largely been taken from papers in two recent symposia [4, 5] and in several recent books [3, 6, 7] in which many additional references may be found.

NORTH ATLANTIC RIDGE TERMINATION

If Europe and North America have moved apart, an explanation is required of how so large a rift as the Atlantic Ocean can come to a relatively abrupt and complete end in the

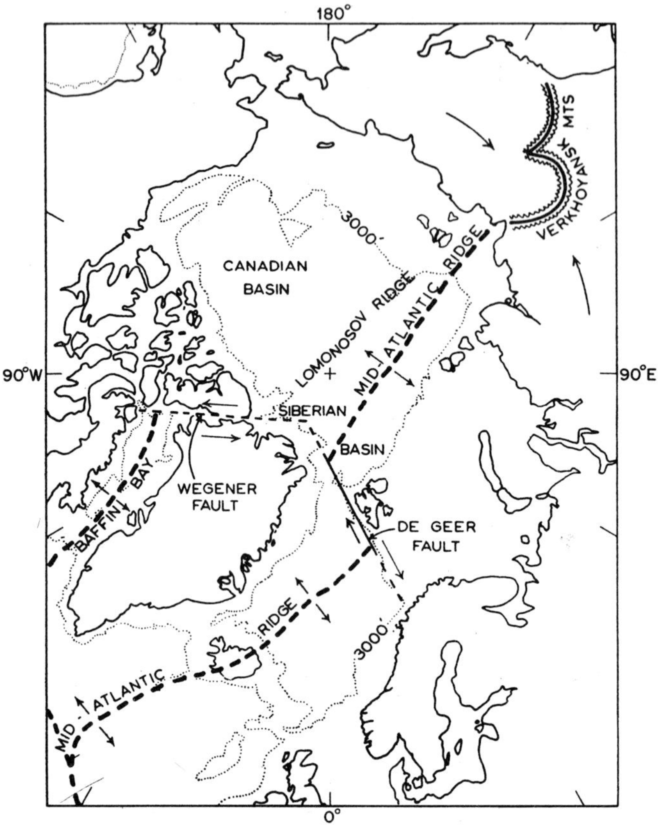

FIGURE 35.5
Sketch map of the northern termination of the Mid-Atlantic Ridge. This involves two large transform faults (Wegener and De Geer faults) and transformation into the Verkhoyansk Mountains.

cul-de-sac of the Arctic Sea. Figure 35.5 illustrates one possible explanation.

Wegener [8] suggested that the strait between Greenland and Ellesmere Island was formed by a fault, here postulated to be a sinistral transform fault (ridge-ridge type). Wegmann [9] named another between Norway, Spitsbergen and Greenland, the De Geer line, which is here regarded as a dextral transform fault (ridge-ridge type). The extension of the Mid-Atlantic ridge across the Siberian basin was traced by Heezen and Ewing [10], while Wilson [11] proposed its transform into the Verkhoyansk Mountains by rotation about a fulcrum in the New Siberian Islands. In accordance with the expectations from Figure 35.4A earthquakes have been reported along the full line of the De Geer fault in Figure 35.5, but not along the dashed older traces between Norway and Bear Island and to the north of Greenland. The Baffin Bay ridge and Wegener fault are at present quiescent. W. B. Harland [10] and Canadian geologists have commented on the similarities of Spitsbergen and Ellesmere Island.

EQUATORIAL ATLANTIC FRACTURE ZONES

If a continent in which there exist faults or lines of weakness splits into two parts (Figure 35.6), the new tension fractures may trail and be affected by the existing faults.

The dextral transform faults (ridge-ridge type) such as *AA′* which would result from such a period of rifting can be seen to have peculiar features. The parts *AB* and *B′A′* are older than the rifting. *DD′* is young and is the only part now active. The offset of the ridge which it represents is not an ordinary faulted displacement such as a transcurrent fault would produce. It is independent of the distance through which the continents have moved. It is confusing, but true, that the direction of motion along *DD′* is in the reverse direction to that required to produce the apparent offset. The offset is merely a reflexion of the shape of the initial break between the continental blocks. The sections *BD* and *D′B′* of the fault are not now active, but are intermediate in age and are represented by fracture zones showing the path of former faulting.

Figure 35.7 shows that the Mid-Atlantic ridge and the fracture zones in the equatorial Atlantic may well be a more complex example of this kind. If so the apparent offsets on the ridge are not faulted offsets, but inherited from the shape of the break that first formed between the coasts of Africa and the Americas. Figure 35.7 is traced from Heezen, Bunce, Hersey and Tharp [12] with additions to the north from Krause [13]. The fracture zones are here held to be right-hand transform faults and not left-hand transcurrent faults as previously stated. If the fracture zones can be traced across the Atlantic and are of the type postulated, then the points where they intersect the opposite coasts are conjugate points which would have been together before rifting.

It seems possible that the old fault in Pennsylvania and the offset of the Atlantic Coast described by Drake and Woodward [14] are of the same nature, although it is suggested that it is not usual for a fracture zone to follow a line of seamounts, and that the fracture zone may extend eastward, not south-east.

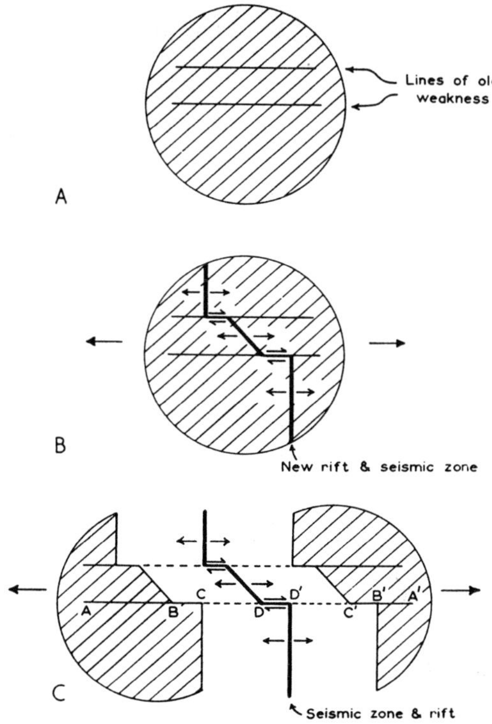

FIGURE 35.6
Diagram illustrating three stages in the rifting of a continent into two parts. This could represent South America and Africa. There will be seismic activity along the heavy lines only.

A POSSIBLE EXPLANATION OF THE TERMINATION OF THE CARLSBERG RIDGE

Another type of transform fault is found in the Indian Ocean (Figure 35.8). If the Indian Ocean and Arabian Gulf opened during the Mesozoic and Cenozoic eras by the northward movement of India, new ocean floor must have been generated by spreading of the Carlsberg ridge. This ends abruptly in a transcurrent fault postulated by Gregory [15] off the east coast of Africa. A parallel fault has been found by Matthews [16] as an offset across the Carlsberg ridge and traced by him to the coast immediately west of Karachi. Here it joins the Ornach-Nal and other faults [17] which extend into Afghanistan and, according to such descriptions as I can find, probably merge with the western end of the Hindu Kush. This whole fault is thus an example of a sinistral transform fault (ridge-convex arc type).

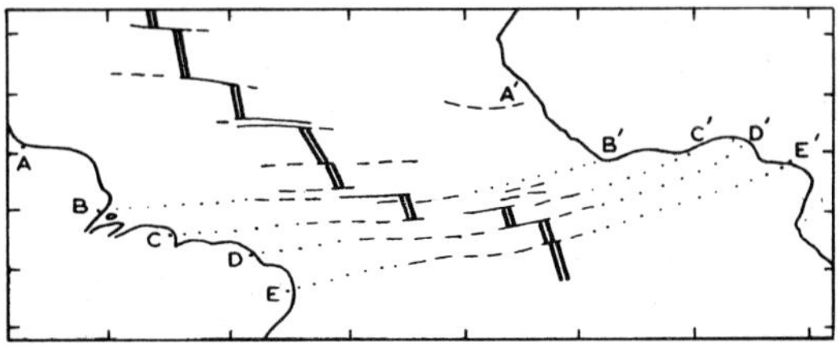

FIGURE 35.7
Sketch (after Krause and Heezen et al.) showing how the Mid-Atlantic Ridge is offset to the left by active transform faults which have dextral motions if the rift is expanding (see Figure 35.4, *a*). *Double vertical lines,* mid-ocean ridge; *solid horizontal lines,* active fault; *dashed lines,* inactive fault trace; *dotted lines,* hypothetical extension of fault.

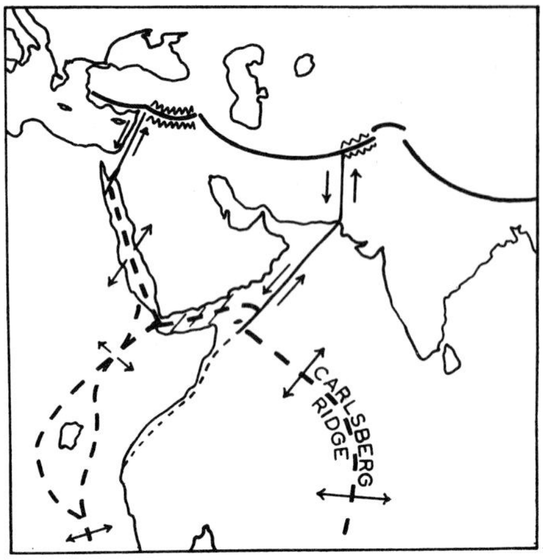

FIGURE 35.8
Sketch illustrating the end of the Carlsberg mid-ocean ridge by a large transform fault (ridge to convex arc type) extending to the Hindu Kush, the end of the rift up the Red Sea by a similar transform fault extending into Turkey and the still younger East African rifts.

At a later date, probably about Oligocene time according to papers quoted by Drake and Girdler [18], the ridge was extended up the Red Sea and again terminated in a sinistral transform fault (ridge-convex arc type) that forms the Jordan Valley [19] and terminates by joining a large thrust fault in south-eastern Turkey (Z. Ternek, private communication). The East African rift valleys are a still later extension formed in Upper Miocene time according to B. H. Baker (private communication).

The many offsets in the Gulf of Aden described by Laughton [20] provide another example of transform faults adjusting a rift to the shape of the adjacent coasts.

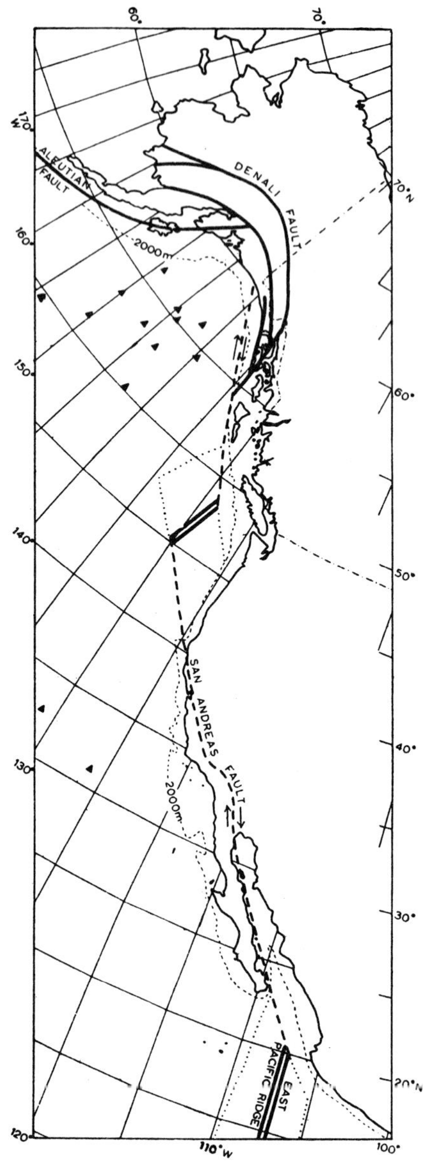

FIGURE 35.9
Sketch map of the west coast of North America showing major structural features. These include the approximate location of a submarine thrust fault along the Aleutian trench, the Denali faults (after St. Amand), the San Andreas and another large transform fault (after Benioff), and part of the East Pacific ridge and another mid-ocean ridge (after Menard).

POSSIBLE RELATIONSHIPS BETWEEN ACTIVE FAULTS OFF THE WEST COAST OF NORTH AMERICA

This tendency of mid-ocean ridges to be offset parallel to adjacent coasts is thought to be evident again in the termination of the East Pacific ridge illustrated in Figure 35.9. The San Andreas fault is here postulated to be a

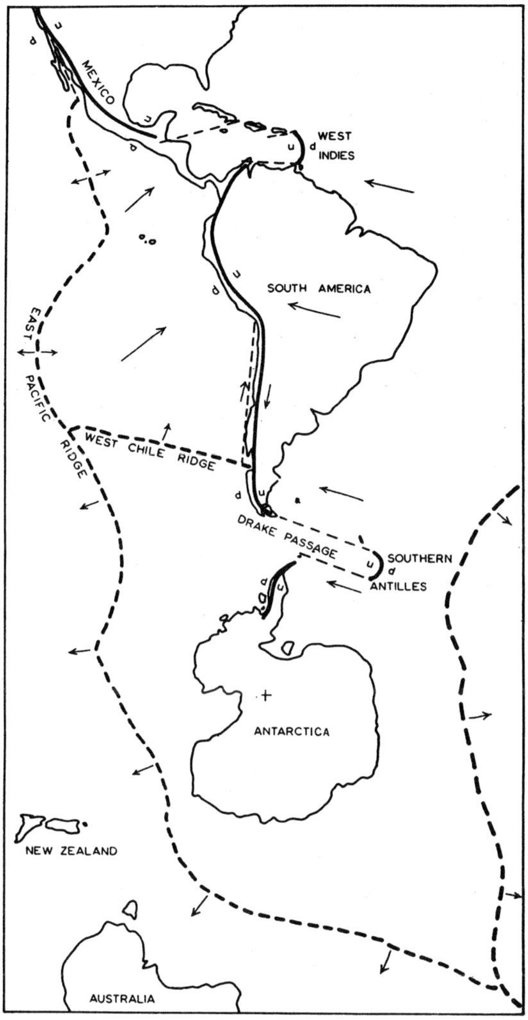

FIGURE 35.10
Sketch map of Mexico, South America, Antarctica, and part of the mid-ocean ridge system. This illustrates that the great loop of the ridge about Antarctica can grow only by increasing in diameter. *Heavy dashed lines,* mid-ocean ridges; *light dashed lines,* transform faults.

dextral transform fault (ridge-ridge type) and not a transcurrent fault. It connects the termination of the East Pacific ridge proper with another short length of ridge for which Menard [3] has found evidence off Vancouver Island. His explanation of the connexion—that the mid-ocean ridge connects across western United States—does not seem to be compatible with the view that the African rift valleys are also incipient mid-ocean ridges. The other end of the ridge off Vancouver Island appears to end in a second great submarine fault off British Columbia described by Benioff [7] as having dextral horizontal motion.

In Alaska are several large faults described by St. Amand [21]. Of the relations between them and those off the coast he writes: "If the two systems represent one consistent system, some interesting possibilities arise. One that the San Andreas and Alaska Complex is a gigantic tear fault, along which the Pacific Basin is being slid, relatively speaking under the Alaska Mainland, and the Bering Sea. On the other hand, if the whole system is a strike-slip fault having consistent right-lateral offset, then the whole of the western north Pacific Basin must be undergoing rotation."

St. Amand was uncertain, but preferred the latter alternative, whereas this interpretation would favour the former one. Thus the Denali system is considered to be predominantly a thrust, while the fault off British Columbia is a dextral transform fault.

At a first glance at Figure 35.9 it might be held that the transform fault off British Columbia was of ridge-concave arc type and that it connects with the Denali system of thrust faults, but if the Pacific floor is sliding under Alaska, the submarine fault along the Aleutian arc that extends to Anchorage is more significant. In that case the Denali faults are part of a secondary arc system and the main fault is of ridge-convex arc type.

FURTHER EXAMPLES FROM THE EASTERN PACIFIC

If the examples given from the North and Equatorial Atlantic Ocean, Arabian Sea, Gulf of Aden and North-west Pacific are any guide, offsets of mid-ocean ridges along fracture zones are not faulted displacements, but are an inheritance from the shape of the original fracture. The fracture zones that cross the East Pacific ridge [22] are similar in that their seismicity is confined to the offset parts between ridges. An extension of this suggests that the offsets in the magnetic displacements observed in the aseismic fracture zones off California may not be fault displacements as has usually been supposed, but that they reflect the shape of a contemporary rift in the Pacific Ocean. More complex variants of the kind postulated here seem to offer a better chance of explaining the different offsets noted by Vacquier [7] along different lengths of the Murray fracture zone than does transcurrent faulting. If the California fracture zones are of this character and are related to the Darwin rise as postulated by Hess, then the Darwin rise should be offset in a similar pattern.

The southern Andes appear to provide an example of compression combined with shearing. The compressional features are obvious. The existence of dextral shearing is also well known [23]. It is suggested that the latter may be due to the transformation of the West Chile ridge into a dextral transform fault (ridge-convex arc type) along the Andes which terminates at the northern end by thrusting under the Peruvian Andes (Figure 35.10).

The observation that there is little seismicity and hence little movement south of the point where the West Chile ridge intersects the Andes can be explained if it is realized that the ridge system forms an almost complete ring about Antarctica, from which expansion must everywhere be directed northwards. This may explain the absence of an isthmus across Drake Passage.

It would also appear that the faults at the two ends of the South Antilles and West Indies arcs are examples of dextral and sinistral pairs of transform faults (concave-concave arc types). According to Figure 35.4 both these arcs should be advancing into the Atlantic and inactive east-west faults should not be found beyond the arcs.

This article began by suggesting that some aspects of faulting well known to be anomalous according to traditional concepts of transcurrent faults could be explained by defining a new class of transform faults of which twelve varieties were shown to be possible.

The demonstration by a few examples that at least six of the twelve types do appear to exist with the properties predicted justifies investigating the validity of this concept further.

It is particularly important to do this because transform faults can only exist if there is crustal displacement and proof of their existence would go far towards establishing the reality of continental drift and showing the nature of the displacements involved.

REFERENCES

1. W. H. Bucher, *The Deformation of the Earth's Crust* (Princeton, N.J.: University Press, 1933).
2. S. W. Carey, *Royal Soc. Tasmania Proc.*, v. 89, p. 255 (1955).
3. H. W. Menard, *Marine Geology of the Pacific* (New York: McGraw-Hill Book Co., 1964).
4. P. M. S. Blackett, E. C. Bullard, and S. K. Runcorn, eds., "A Symposium on Continental Drift—Organized for the Royal Society," *Royal Soc. [London] Philos. Trans.*, ser. A, v. 258, p. vii–322.
5. P. M. Hurley, ed., *Advances in Earth Sciences* (Cambridge, Mass.: M.I.T. Press, 1966).
6. *The Sea* (v. 2), ed. M. N. Hill (New York: Interscience, 1963).
7. In *Continental Drift*, ed. S. K. Runcorn (New York: Academic Press, 1963).
8. A. Wegener, *The Origin of Continents and Oceans* (New York: E. P. Dutton and Co., 1924).
9. C. E. Wegmann, *Medd. om Grønland*, v. 144, no. 7, (1948).
10. In *Geology of the Arctic* (v. 1), ed. O. Rausch (Toronto: University of Toronto Press, 1961).
11. J. Tuzo Wilson, *Nature*, v. 198, p. 925 (1963).
12. B. C. Heezen, E. T. Bunce, J. B. Hersey, and M. Tharp, *Deep-Sea Research*, v. 11, p. 11 (1964).
13. D. C. Kraus, *Science*, v. 146, p. 57 (1964).
14. C. L. Drake and H. P. Woodward, *New York Acad. Sci. Trans.*, ser. II, v. 26, p. 48 (1963).
15. J. W. Gregory, *Geog. Jour.*, v. 56, p. 13 (1920).
16. D. H. Matthews, *Nature*, v. 198, p. 950 (1963).
17. *Hunting Survey Corporation, Reconnaissance Geology of Part of West Pakistan*, p. 365 (Toronto, 1960).
18. C. L. Drake and R. W. Girdler, *Geophys. Jour.*, v. 8, p. 473, (1964).
19. A. M. Quesnell, *Geol. Soc. London Quart. Jour.*, v. 114, p. 1 (1958).
20. A. S. Laughton, *Royal Soc. [London] Philos. Trans.*, ser. A, v. 259, no. 1099, p. 150.
21. P. St. Amand, *Geol. Soc. America Bull.*, v. 68, p. 1343 (1957).
22. L. B. Sykes, *Jour. Geophys. Research*, v. 68, p. 5999 (1963).
23. P. St. Amand, *Los Terremotos de Mayo: Chile, 1960* (China Lake, Calif.: Michelson Laboratory, U.S. Naval Ordnance Test Stations *NOTS* TP2701, 1961).

PART TWO

THE GEOLOGIC RECORD

SECTION VI

THE PRIMITIVE EARTH

But somewhere, beyond Space and Time,
Is wetter water, slimier slime!

Rupert Brooke, HEAVEN

This section includes a group of papers that deal with concepts of the origin and early evolution of life on earth, and with the interactions between biologic evolution and the separate but related evolutions of lithosphere, atmosphere, and hydrosphere. Unless the first organisms came here from some other inhabited planet (which only puts off the question), life on earth resulted either from natural processes or from a supernatural event. Experiments by Redi, Spallanzani, and Pasteur once seemed to demonstrate that life could not arise spontaneously, leaving the problem outside the domain of science until a few decades ago. Now the combined efforts of geologists, biologists, and biochemists have reopened the question, but with emphasis on an evolutionary origin, and with experiments and observations that delimit it in ways susceptible to scientific inquiry. In the broadest terms, it now appears that life arose from a continuum of chemical evolution more than 3.2 aeons ago. It is believed that the atmosphere then contained CO_2, CO, H_2O, N_2, and traces of other gases, but no oxygen near the earth's surface; and that the waters in which life arose, although salty, contained little or no sulfate ion and were probably somewhere between ten and thirty percent of their present volume.

When the interior of the earth attained temperatures high enough to initiate the differentiation of core and mantle, the escape of volatiles to the surface would have started (or accelerated) the growth of atmosphere and hydrosphere, resulting in the beginning of a sedimentary record. Within that early volatile envelope, chemical evolution energized by ultraviolet radiation paved the way for the origin of life. Once biologic processes were introduced, the sedimentary record could never be the same again. With the evolution of an organism that could make its own foodstuffs (an autotroph) and, eventually, of an oxygen-producing photoautotroph, new influences were involved in the evolution of atmosphere, hydrosphere, and lithosphere. Interactions among these major components of the evolving earth, and between them and the biosphere, eventually gave rise to conditions that led to the emergence of differentiated multicellular animal life (the Metazoa), at or near the beginning of Paleozoic time—although just when, how, why, and from what antecedents are matters of vigorous discussion.

It is instructive to begin our survey of these problems with Thomas Henry Huxley's masterful 1870 presidential address to the British Association for the Advancement of Science, "Biogenesis and Abiogenesis" (Reading Selection 36). He traces the ideas and researches of Lucretius, Goethe, Harvey, Redi, Buffon, Needham, Spallanzani, Pasteur, Schulze and Schwann, Helmholtz, Tyndall, Darwin, and others—leading to the consensus in his time that life came only from previous life (an origin he called *biogenesis*) and not by spontaneous generation (which he called *abiogenesis*). The portion of his paper reproduced here, however, concludes by disclaiming denial of the possibility that spontaneous conversion from nonliving to living had ever taken place in the past or ever would take place in the future. Had it been given Huxley to observe the early days of the earth he "should expect to be a witness to the evolution of living protoplasm from not living matter." Many would call this biogenesis now, abandoning the term abiogenesis or reserving it to designate the production of organic molecules by nonvital processes. For those who are priority conscious, however, the word biopoesis is available, coined by N. W. Pirie in 1954 to denote the origin of life without regard to the mode of origin. (Biosynthesis has also been used to denote the origin of life without prejudice as to means, but it has another more commonly accepted meaning.) Since it now seems certain that life initially arose from nonliving matter as a consequence of evolutionary processes, the terminology need not detain us.

The man most responsible for reopening the scientific investigation of the origin of life was another great British biologist, J. B. S. Haldane. In his paper titled "The Origins of Life" (Reading Selection 37), he considers four possible ways in which life may have originated on earth and discusses the evidence (as of 1954) for and against each possibility. In the end, he ventures the judgment that life most probably began as a result of chemical evolution in an oxygen-poor environment. Metastable organic compounds might thus be produced, eventually giving rise to catalytically active molecules capable of replicating themselves. Life could begin when arrays of self-reproducing polymers became enclosed within semipermeable membranes. Haldane supposes, however, that probably no version of an evolutionary origin of life is without merit, nor, for that matter, is any one version wholly right. Each subhypothesis may include something of value for the final synthesis, whatever that may turn out to be.

Great advances have been made since Haldane wrote. Scientists in many laboratories are now busy generating organic molecules that are possible precursors to other more complex molecules from which living organisms may have arisen. They are also trying to synthesize these more advanced molecules—and perhaps life itself. However, a test-tube biogenesis would by no means prove that the pathways and combinations observed were the only ones from which life might have originated, but only that such a route, among others, was possible. Other scientists are searching in the most ancient sedimentary rocks both for morphological and biogeochemical records of earliest life and for evidence of the antecedent chemical evolution that gave rise to it. Having reached the point, therefore, where we are working seriously at questions of the origins of life, and even on the remote but finite possibility of detecting life on other planetary bodies in our solar system, it is well to consider what attributes a structure must have before it can properly be called living, or once-living.

That question is tackled from the modern viewpoint by biologist Daniel Mazia of the University of California in Reading Selection 38, titled "What is Life?" Mazia makes the point that living things are self-making, self-sustaining, kind-conserving things. Survival in the biological sense requires a conservation of character in the face of a continuous flux of matter. Living things, however, not only grow and reproduce but also mutate and reproduce mutations, thus bringing about evolutionary change. In fact, morphology is one of the best criteria for recognizing either living or once living things—discriminate because complex, but hard to quantify or define. The force of morphological evidence rests on the multiplicity of converging clues, rather than on the diagnostic nature of single criteria. Functional morphology applies at the deepest level, but we badly need a better mathematics of form. Mazia turns, then, to molecular biology, which has been given the job of translating survival into molecular terms. Here we are involved with the cell, the cytoplasm, various proteins (including different specific enzymes for each biochemical reaction), the genome (sume of hereditary material), the nucleic acid molecules that carry and transmit the genetic code (DNA), and the translation of instructions given by the DNA to make new genomes. Viewed thus, a cell is a device for maintaining and propagating a genome: the cytoplasm provides the goods and services, and the genome makes copies of itself. Biochemistry reveals powerful clues to the existence of life in the form of the very large molecules that are so characteristic of organisms. In the ultimate analysis, however, the boundary between living and nonliving seems blurred, even though the domains on either side are quite different.

What events might allow a thing to cross the blurred boundary between nonliving and living? Life cannot originate spontaneously without a preceding chemical evolution to provide the essential building blocks. Reading Selection 39, by Nobel laureate Melvin Calvin of the University of California, approaches this question from two directions: first, by studying the biochemical components of ancient sediments, particularly their molecular architecture; and second, by attempting "to reconstruct the possible sequence of chemical events that could have occurred before the existence of living things on the face of the earth." After demonstrating how various organic molecules of biological importance can be produced by nonvital processes, he shows that dehydration condensations of such molecules could lead to the formation of polysaccharides, polypeptides, proteins, polynucleotides and nucleic acids. Moreover, he finds that dehydration processes of possible importance for biogenesis can take place in quite dilute aqueous solutions of already synthesized precursor molecules in the presence of expectable catalysts. All that remains is for those things to be packaged in the right way for there to be a unit capable of self-replication and information transfer—a living organism. The paper by Eglinton and Calvin (1967) in the Supplemental Reading adds useful information about the methods and instrumentation employed in these researches.

But puzzling questions remain: Why should life as we know it be constituted as it is? Might it have been possible for life to have originated in different patterns in this or in other galaxies? Why not silicon instead of carbon as the central element, or ammonia instead of water as the liquid phase? These and other questions are the subject of Reading Selection 40, by another Nobel laureate, George Wald of Harvard University. Bearing the same title as Haldane's earlier paper "The Origins of Life," Wald's essay was presented at the centenary celebration of the U.S. National Academy of Sciences in 1964. Inasmuch as anaerobic processes underlie all other forms of metabolism, Wald reasons, they are probably primitive. This affirms Haldane's judgment that the first life forms were probably anaerobic. Wald then suggests steps by which oxygen-producing green-plant photosynthesis might have emerged, subsequently generating the conditions under which oxidative metabolism could arise. He specifies the limiting conditions for biogenesis: (1) an atmosphere neither too thin, nor so dense as to screen out energizing radiation; (2) an environmental temperature generally within the limits between which water remains liquid; (3) water, which floats when it freezes; (4) an external source of energy; and (5) shielding from light of wave lengths less than 3000 angstroms, which destroys biological macromolecules, denatures proteins, and depolymerizes nucleic acids. Oxygen would have been inimical to the origin of life because synthesized organic molecules would have been oxidized by it. On the other hand, oxygen is needed for the most efficient and largest energy conversions; hence it is among the special elements essential to the fullest development of life.

Wald then argues that the structural and bonding properties of hydrogen, oxygen, nitrogen, and carbon make them the most likely candidates for the central molecules of living things. They are the four smallest elements that stabilize with 1, 2, 3, and 4 electrons, and, being small, they make the tightest bonds and the most stable molecules. Oxygen, nitrogen, and carbon, in addition, are the only elements that regularly form double and triple bonds. Silicon, sulfur, and phosphorous cannot replace carbon, oxygen, and nitrogen because they form looser, less stable compounds susceptible to disruption by lone electrons. Ammonia, moreover, cannot substitute for water because of its low temperature range as a liquid (from −33.4° to −77.7°C), the fact that it contracts and sinks on freezing, and the fact that it does not yield O_2 on splitting but only relatively inert nitrogen. Considering the repeated independent selection of similar molecules for similar purposes in known biochemical evolution, Wald hypothesizes, life wherever found is likely to be basically similar to that on earth. It might use either right- or left-handed amino acids and sugars, but it would probably be consistent in the use of one or the other. Wald's conclusion: natural selection operates everywhere; we can know and understand our universe and our origins.

Had there been room for still another paper on the origin of life, I would have chosen that by biochemists S. L. Miller, of the University of California, and N. H. Horowitz, of the California Institute of Technology's Jet Propulsion Laboratory (1966, see Supplemental Reading). Theirs is an informative and critical summary of current work in many laboratories on the nonvital synthesis of a variety of compounds of biological interest under supposed primitive earth conditions. Although experimental work is still lacking in a number of important areas, the results imply that large quantities of organic compounds similar to those of living organisms could have been (and probably were) synthesized on the primitive earth.

Clues to the differentiation of the earth are needed to test such concepts, and some important ones are provided by a thoughtful analysis of the structure of the Barberton Mountain Land of southeastern Africa by geologist A. E. J. Engel of the University of California (Reading Selection 41). That region includes the oldest sedimentary rocks yet known on earth. The basaltic and peridotitic lavas associated with its rocks are essentially identical geochemically to the similar rocks of presently active island-arc regions, which presumably arise directly from the mantle. This continuity of type, especially the relative scarcity in even the oldest lavas of the radioactive nuclides of potassium, uranium, and thorium, implies that the mantle of the earth was already differentiated from the core by about 3.2–3.5 aeons ago. From this and other evidence we can also infer that a substantial hydrosphere and atmosphere had accreted by that time, and that the continental and oceanic regions of the earth were beginning to separate, or had separated, from one another.

Finally, in Reading Selection 42, the editor of this volume integrates material treated in the preceding papers, plus additional information, to construct a model of the interacting evolutions of biosphere, atmosphere, hydrosphere, and lithosphere of the primitive earth. Geochronological data imply a major melting event about 3.5 to 3.6 aeons ago. This may have started, or added conspicuously to, atmospheric and hydrospheric growth. It may also have been connected with the segregation, or completion of segregation, of core and mantle. Quantities of water and an oxygen-poor atmosphere thus became available for chemical evolution under the energizing influence of ultraviolet radiation. Following chemical evolution leading to biogenesis, a sequence of important steps in biochemical evolution can be visualized as interacting with atmospheric and lithospheric evolution to bring about a gradual increase of oxygen in the hydrosphere and atmosphere. That, then, would have set the stage for the evolution of the nucleated, aerobic, mitosing cell —and, at or near the beginning of the Paleozoic, the appearance of the Metazoa. Views contradictory to those developed here will be found under Supplemental Reading in papers by Glaessner, Hough, and Davidson. Davidson (1965) in particular disagrees with most other geologists and geochemists about the postulated lack of oxygen in the early atmosphere, and even with the evidence from which it has been induced. He presents an alternate interpretation which denies any major changes in the nature of crustal sediments, atmosphere, or hydrosphere throughout geologic time.

An interesting alternative hypothesis for the origin of the Metazoa is that of Peter K. Weyl of the State University of New York, outlined in his paper on "Precambrian Marine Environment and the Development of Life" (Reading Selection 43). Weyl argues that the development of a density gradient in the upper 300 meters of the sea could lead to a concentration of oxygen-producing phytoplankton at depths between about 50 and 150 meters: hence a layer rich in oxygen, overlain and underlain by waters with little or no free oxygen, and shielded from ultraviolet radiation. In such a layer, he suggests, pelagic Metazoa may have arisen. When a more general diffusion of oxygen was attained, the previously planktonic Metazoa were able to occupy the shallow shelf waters, "find" the bottom, and become shell-bearing benthos. Before this time, shelly exoskeletons would have had the disadvantage of weighting down their planktonic bearers, causing them to sink below the oxygen-rich layer into an inhospitable, oxygen-poor environment. Now we must seek the evidence that will either enhance or reduce our confidence in this model, or in alternative models —or in some combination of models, for those that are consistent with present knowledge of the geologic record are by no means mutually exclusive.

Section VI concludes with a pair of papers on the problem of reconstructing a meaningful pre-Paleozoic history. The first (Reading Selection 44), by H. L. James, Chief Geologist of the U.S. Geological Survey since 1965, describes how the conventional interpretation of the pre-Paleozoic rocks was thrown into confusion both by the discrediting of criteria once thought applicable to their arrangement in a time sequence, and by refinements in—and invalid uses of—radiometric dating. Nevertheless, James concludes, by using radiometric ages in combination with the same ordering criteria as apply to younger rocks, we can expect, eventually, to decipher a meaningful history for much of the first seven-eighths of the geologic record—not as detailed as for later geologic time, but rich in its own way.

In Reading Selection 45, paleontologist M. F. Glaessner of the University of Adelaide considers the biological criteria available for constructing a pre-Paleozoic time scale. Although the low degree of diversification attained by pre-Paleozoic organisms detracts from their stratigraphic resolving power, assessment of their possible uses as time markers is now generating much interest. In his discussion, Glaessner also gives us a good review of the current state of pre-Paleozoic biostratigraphy, the kinds of fossils that are found, the problems that beset recognition of the lower limit of the Paleozoic, and the important work now being done on those problems in the U.S.S.R. and elsewhere.

A few refinements are necessary to put Glaessner's conclusions in perspective for this volume. As he notes, the Vendian strata of the U.S.S.R., which may be transitional from Proterozoic to Paleozoic, contain both the stromatolite *Conophyton* and representatives of the earliest well-authenticated Metazoa—a combination which Cloud (1968) has argued is not known to exist, and whose possible lack of overlap might be used to define the Proterozoic-Paleozoic boundary. Glaessner's observation is correct, but its implications are not. The Metazoa to which he refers are recorded (as of March 1969) only from the upper Vendian and the *Conophyton* only from one locality (in East Sayan) in the lower Vendian. (In fact, some Russian stratigraphers exclude the *Conophyton*-bearing beds from the Vendian and associate them with the underlying Riphean). These Metazoa, moreover, occur above a pair of tillites, whereas the *Conophyton* occurs only below possible lateral equivalents of the tillites. This adds force to the suggestion, made now by a number of workers, that the tillites (where demonstrable) might serve as an operational marker zone in recognizing the biologically defined boundary between the uppermost Proterozoic and the basal Paleozoic. We may be approaching a critical test. If a pair of tillite horizons should prove to be truly widespread at the hypothesized Proterozoic-Paleozoic transition, then the occurrence of *Conophyton* above or of Metazoa below such tillites would seem to invalidate the use of the terminal ranges of these forms in defining the boundary. On the other hand, the longer the search continues without unequivocal demonstration of such a conflict, the more confidence we may feel in defining the Proterozoic-Paleozoic boundary as the base of the range-zone of Metazoa and the top of the range-zone of *Conophyton*.

Supplemental Reading

Abelson, P. H., 1956, Paleobiochemistry: Scientific American Offprint 101, 7 p.

———, 1957, Effects of ultraviolet light on the "primitive environment": Carnegie Inst. Washington Yearbook, v. 56, p. 179–185.

Barghoorn, E. S., and S. A. Tyler, 1965, Microorganisms from the Gunflint chert: Science, v. 147, p. 573–577.

Berkner, L. V., 1965, History of major atmospheric components: [U.S.] Natl. Acad. Sci. Proc., v. 53, p. 121–125.

Cloud, P. E., Jr., 1968, Pre-Metazoan evolution and the origins of the Metazoa, *in* Ellen T. Drake, ed., Evolution and ecology: New Haven, Conn., Yale University Press, p. 1–72.

Cloud, P. E., Jr., and P. H. Abelson, 1961, Woodring Conference on major biologic innovations and the geologic record: [U.S.] Natl. Acad. Sci. Proc., v. 47, p. 1705–1712.

Davidson, C. F., 1965, Geochemical aspects of atmospheric evolution: [U.S.] Natl. Acad. Sci. Proc., v. 53, no. 6, p. 1194–1205.

Deering, R. A., 1962, Ultraviolet radiation and nucleic acid: Scientific American Offprint 143, 8 p.

Eglinton, Geoffrey, and Melvin Calvin, 1967, Chemical fossils: Scientific American Offprint 308, 13 p.

Glaessner, M. F., 1961, Pre-Cambrian animals: Scientific American Offprint 837, 8 p.

Hough, J. L., 1958, Fresh-water environment of deposition of Precambrian banded iron formations, Lake Superior district: Jour. Sed. Petrology, v. 28, p. 414–430.

James, H. L., 1954, Sedimentary facies of iron formation: Econ. Geology, v. 49, p. 235–293.

King, P. B., 1964, Geology of the central Great Smoky Mountains, Tennessee: U.S. Geol. Survey Prof. Paper 349-C, 148 p.

Kuznetsov, S. I., M. V. Ivanov, and N. N. Lyalikova, 1963, Introduction to geological microbiology: New York, McGraw-Hill, 252 p. (A translation from the Russian.)

Lotze, Fr., and K. Schmidt, eds., 1966, Präkambrium—erster Teil—nördliche Halbkugel: Stuttgart, Ferdinand Enke Verlag, 388 p.

Miller, S. L., and N. H. Horowitz, 1966, The origin of life, *in* C. S. Pittendrigh and others, eds., Biology and the exploration of Mars: [U.S.] Natl. Acad. Sci.–Natl. Research Council Pub. 1296, p. 41–69.

Muehlberger, W. R., R. E. Dennison, and E. G. Lidiak, 1967, Basement rocks in continental interior of United States: Am. Assoc. Petroleum Geolgists Bull., v. 51, p. 2351–2380.

Pirie, N. W., 1953, Ideas and assumptions about the origin of life: Discovery, v. 14, p. 238–242.

———, 1957, Some assumptions underlying discussion on the origins of life: New York Acad. Sci. Annals, v. 69, p. 369–376.

Rankama, Kalervo, ed., 1963–1967, The Precambrian (v. 1–3): New York, John Wiley and Sons, Interscience Publications, 279, 454, and 325 p.

Ross, C. P., 1959, Geology of Glacier National Park and the Flathead region, northwestern Montana: U.S. Geol. Survey Prof. Paper 269, 125 p.

Rutten, M. G., 1962, The geological aspects of the origin of life on earth: New York, American Elsevier, 146 p.

Sprigg, R. C., 1947, Early Cambrian (?) jellyfishes from the Flinders Ranges, South Australia: Royal Soc. South Africa Trans., v. 71, p. 212–224.

Tyler, S. A., and E. S. Barghoorn, 1954, Occurrence of structurally preserved plants in Precambrian rocks of the Canadian Shield: Science, v. 119, p. 606–608.

Van Hise, C. R., 1901, The iron-ore deposits of the Lake Superior region: U.S. Geol. Survey Ann. Rept. 21, p. 305–434.

White, W. S., and J. C. Wright, 1954, The White Pine copper deposit, Ontonagon County, Michigan: Econ. Geology, v. 49, p. 675–716.

36

Biogenesis and Abiogenesis

T. H. HUXLEY
1870

. . . I shall endeavour to put before you the history of the rise and progress of a single biological doctrine; and I shall try to give some notion of the fruits, both intellectual and practical, which we owe, directly or indirectly, to the working out, by seven generations of patient and laborious investigators, of the thought which arose, more than two centuries ago, in the mind of a sagacious and observant Italian naturalist.

It is a matter of everyday experience that it is difficult to prevent many articles of food from becoming covered with mould; that fruit, sound enough to all appearance, often contains grubs at the core; that meat, left to itself in the air, is apt to putrefy and swarm with maggots. Even ordinary water, if allowed to stand in an open vessel, sooner or later becomes turbid and full of living matter.

The philosophers of antiquity, interrogated at to the cause of these phenomena, were provided with a ready and a plausible answer. It did not enter their minds even to doubt that these low forms of life were generated in the matters in which they made their appearance. Lucretius, who had drunk deeper of the scientific spirit than any poet of ancient or modern times except Goethe, intends to speak as a philosopher, rather than as a poet, when he writes that "with good reason the earth has gotten the name of mother, since all things are produced out of the earth. And many living creatures, even now, spring out of the earth, taking form by the rains and the heat of the sun." The axiom of ancient science, "that the corruption of one thing is the birth of another," had its popular embodiment in the notion that a seed dies before the young plant springs from it; a belief so widespread and so fixed, that Saint Paul appeals to it in one of the most splendid outbursts of his fervid eloquence: "Thou fool, that which thou sowest is not quickened, except it die."

The proposition that life may, and does, proceed from that which has no life, then, was held alike by the philosophers, the poets, and the people, of the most enlightened nations,

Presidential address to the British Association for the Advancement of Science, 1870. From *Discourses Biological and Geological* by T. H. Huxley, pp. 229–257. D. Appleton & Company, 1896.

eighteen hundred years ago; and it remained the accepted doctrine of learned and unlearned Europe, through the Middle Ages, down even to the seventeenth century.

It is commonly counted among the many merits of our great countryman, Harvey, that he was the first to declare the opposition of fact to venerable authority in this, as in other matters; but I can discover no justification for this widespread notion. After careful search through the "Exercitationes de Generatione," the most that appears clear to me is, that Harvey believed all animals and plants to spring from what he terms a "*primordium vegetale*," a phrase which may nowadays be rendered "a vegetative germ"; and this, he says, is "*oviforme*," or "egg-like"; not, he is careful to add, that it necessarily has the shape of an egg, but because it has the constitution and nature of one. That this "*primordium oviforme*" must needs, in all cases, proceed from a living parent is nowhere expressly maintained by Harvey, though such an opinion may be thought to be implied in one or two passages; while, on the other hand, he does, more than once, use language which is consistent only with a full belief in spontaneous or equivocal generation. In fact, the main concern of Harvey's wonderful little treatise is not with generation, in the physiological sense, at all, but with development; and his great object is the establishment of the doctrine of epigenesis.

The first distinct enunciation of the hypothesis that all living matter has sprung from pre-existing living matter, came from a contemporary, though a junior, of Harvey, a native of that country, fertile in men great in all departments of human activity, which was to intellectual Europe, in the sixteenth and seventeenth centuries, what Germany is in the nineteenth. It was in Italy, and from Italian teachers, that Harvey received the most important part of his scientific education. And it was a student trained in the same schools, Francesco Redi—a man of the widest knowledge and most versatile abilities, distinguished alike as scholar, poet, physician, and naturalist—who, just two hundred and two years ago, published his "Esperienze intorno alla Generazione degl' Insetti," and gave to the world the idea, the growth of which it is my purpose to trace. Redi's book went through five editions in twenty years; and the extreme simplicity of his experiments, and the clearness of his arguments, gained for his views, and for their consequences, almost universal acceptance.

Redi did not trouble himself much with speculative considerations, but attacked particular cases of what was supposed to be "spontaneous generation" experimentally. Here are dead animals, or pieces of meat, says he; I expose them to the air in hot weather, and in a few days they swarm with maggots. You tell me that these are generated in the dead flesh; but if I put similar bodies, while quite fresh, into a jar, and tie some fine gauze over the top of the jar, not a maggot makes its appearance, while the dead substances, nevertheless, putrefy just in the same way as before. It is obvious, therefore, that the maggots are not generated by the corruption of the meat; and that the cause of their formation must be a something which is kept away by gauze. But gauze will not keep away aëriform bodies, or fluids. This something must, therefore, exist in the form of solid particles too big to get through the gauze. Nor is one long left in doubt what these solid particles are; for the blowflies, attracted by the odour of the meat, swarm round the vessel, and, urged by a powerful but in this case misleading instinct, lay eggs out of which maggots are immediately hatched, upon the gauze. The conclusion, therefore, is unavoidable; the maggots are not generated by the meat, but the eggs which give rise to them are brought through the air by the flies.

These experiments seem almost childishly simple, and one wonders how it was that no one ever thought of them before. Simple as they are, however, they are worthy of the most careful study, for every piece of experimental work since done, in regard to this subject, has been shaped upon the model furnished by the Italian philosopher. As the results of his experiments were the same, however varied the nature of the materials he used, it is not wonderful that there arose in Redi's mind a presumption, that, in all such cases of the seeming production of life from dead matter, the real explanation was the introduction of living germs from without into that dead matter. And thus the hypothesis that living matter always arises by the agency of pre-existing living matter, took definite shape; and had, henceforward, a right to be considered and a claim to be refuted, in each particular case, before the production of living matter in any other way could be admitted by careful reasoners. It will be necessary for me to refer to this hypothesis so frequently, that, to save circumlocution, I shall call it the hypothesis of *Biogenesis;* and I shall term the contrary doctrine—that living matter may be produced by not living matter—the hypothesis of *Abiogenesis.*

In the seventeenth century, as I have said, the latter was the dominant view, sanctioned alike by antiquity and by authority; and it is interesting to observe that Redi did not escape the customary tax upon a discovered of having to defend himself against the charge of impugning the authority of the Scriptures; for his adversaries declared that the generation of bees from the caracase of a dead lion is affirmed, in the Book of Judges, to have been the origin of the famous riddle with which Samson perplexed the Philistines:—

"Out of the eater came forth meat,
And out of the strong came forth sweetness."

Against all odds, however, Redi, strong with the strength of demonstrable fact, did splendid battle for Biogenesis; but it is remarkable that he held the doctrine in a sense which, if he had lived in these times, would have infallibly caused him to be classed among the defenders of "spontaneous generation." "Omne vivum ex vivo," "no life without antecedent life," aphoristically sums up Redi's doctrine; but he went no further. It is most remarkable evidence of the philosophic caution and impartiality of his mind, that although he had speculatively anticipated the manner in which grubs really are deposited in fruits and in the galls of plants, he deliberately admits that the evidence is insufficient to bear him out; and he therefore prefers the supposition that they are generated by a modification of the living substance of the plants themselves. Indeed, he regards these vegetable growths as organs, by means of which the plant gives rise to an animal, and looks upon this production of specific animals as the final cause of the galls and of, at any rate, some fruits. And he proposes to explain the occurrence of parasites within the animal body in the same way.

It is of great importance to apprehend Redi's position rightly; for the lines of thought he laid down for us are those upon which naturalists have been working ever since. Clearly, he held *Biogenesis* as against *Abiogenesis;* and I shall immediately proceed, in the first place, to inquire how far subsequent investigation has borne him out in so doing.

But Redi also thought that there were two modes of Biogenesis. By the one method, which is that of common and ordinary occurrence, the living parent gives rise to offspring which passes through the same cycle of changes as itself—like gives rise to like; and this has been termed *Homogenesis.* By the other mode, the living parent was supposed to give rise to offspring which passed through a totally different series of states from those exhibited by the parent, and did not return into the cycle of the parent; this is what ought to be called *Heterogenesis,* the offspring being altogether, and permanently, unlike the parent. The term Heterogenesis, however, has unfortunately been used in a different sense, and M. Milne-Edwards has therefore substituted for it *Xenogenesis,* which means the generation of something foreign. After discussing Redi's hypothesis of universal Biogenesis, then, I shall go on to ask how far the growth of science justifies his other hypothesis of Xenogenesis.

The progress of the hypothesis of Biogenesis was triumphant and unchecked for nearly a century. The application of the microscope to anatomy in the hands of Grew, Leeuwenhoek, Swammerdam, Lyonnet, Vallisnieri, Réaumur, and other illustrious investigators of nature of that day, displayed such a complexity of organisation in the lowest and minutest forms, and everywhere revealed such a prodigality of provision for their multiplication by germs of one sort or another, that the hypothesis of Abiogenesis began to appear not only untrue, but absurd; and, in the middle of the eighteenth century, when Needham and Buffon took up the question, it was almost universally discredited.

But the skill of the microscope makers of the eighteenth century soon reached its limit. A microscope magnifying 400 diameters was a *chef d'œuvre* of the opticians of that day; and, at the same time, by no means trustworthy. But a magnifying power of 400 diameters, even when definition reaches the exquisite perfection of our modern achromatic lenses, hardly suffices for the mere discernment of the smallest forms of life. A speck, only 1/25th of an inch in diameter, has, at ten inches from the eye, the same apparent size as an object 1/10000th of an inch in diameter, when magnified 400 times; but forms of living matter abound, the diameter of which is not more than 1/40000th of an inch. A filtered infusion of hay, allowed to stand for two days, will swarm with living things among which, any which reaches the diameter of a human red blood-corpuscle, or about 1/3200th of an inch, is a giant. It is only by bearing these facts in mind, that we can deal fairly with the remarkable statements and speculations put forward by Buffon and Needham in the middle of the eighteenth century.

When a portion of any animal or vegetable body is infused in water, it gradually softens and disintegrates; and, as it does so, the water is found to swarm with minute active creatures, the so-called Infusorial Animalcules, none of which can be seen, except by the aid of the microscope; while a large proportion belong to the category of smallest things of which I have spoken, and which must have looked like mere dots and lines under the ordinary microscopes of the eighteenth century.

Led by various theoretical considerations which I cannot now discuss, but which looked promising enough in the lights of their time, Buffon and Needham doubted the applicability of Redi's hypothesis to the infusorial animalcules, and Needham very properly endeavoured to put the question to an experimental test. He said to himself, If these infusorial animalcules come from germs, their germs must exist either in the substance infused, or in the water with which the infusion is made, or in the superjacent air. Now the vitality of all germs is destroyed by heat. Therefore, if I boil the infusion, cork it up carefully, cementing the cork over with mastic, and then heat the whole vessel by heaping hot ashes over it, I must needs kill whatever germs are present. Consequently, if Redi's hypothesis hold good, when the infusion is taken away and allowed to cool, no animalcules ought to be developed in it; whereas, if the animalcules are not dependent on pre-existing germs, but are generated from the infused substance, they ought, by and by, to make their appearance. Needham found that, under the circumstances in which he made his experiments, animalcules always did arise in the infusions, when a sufficient time had elapsed to allow for their development.

In much of his work Needham was associated with Buffon, and the results of their experiments fitted in admirably with the great French naturalist's hypothesis of "organic molecules," according to which, life is the indefeasible property of certain indestructible molecules of matter, which exist in all living things, and have inherent activities by which they are distinguished from not living matter. Each individual living organism is formed by their temporary combination. They stand to it in the relation of the particles of water to a cascade, or a whirlpool; or to a mould, into which the water is poured. The form of the organism is thus determined by the reaction between external conditions and the inherent activities of the organic molecules of which it is composed; and, as the stoppage of a whirlpool destroys nothing but a form, and leaves the molecules of the water, with all their inherent activities intact, so what we call the death and putrefaction of an animal, or of a plant, is merely the breaking up of the form, or manner of association, of its constituent organic molecules, which are then set free as infusorial animalcules.

It will be perceived that this doctrine is by no means identical with *Abiogenesis*, with which it is often confounded. On this hypothesis, a piece of beef, or a handful of hay, is dead only in a limited sense. The beef is dead ox, and the hay is dead grass; but the "organic molecules" of the beef or the hay are not dead, but are ready to manifest their vitality as soon as the bovine or herbaceous shrouds in which they are imprisoned are rent by the macerating action of water. The hypothesis therefore must be classified under Xenogenesis, rather than under Abiogenesis. Such as it was, I think it will appear, to those who will be just enough to remember that it was propounded before the birth of modern chemistry, and of the modern optical arts, to be a most ingenious and suggestive speculation.

But the great tragedy of Science—the slaying of a beautiful hypothesis by an ugly fact—which is so constantly being enacted under the eyes of philosophers, was played, almost immediately, for the benefit of Buffon and Needham.

Once more, an Italian, the Abbé Spallanzani, a worthy successor and representative of Redi in his acuteness, his ingenuity, and his learning, subjected the experiments and the conclusions of Needham to a searching criticism. It might be true that Needham's experiments yielded results such as he had described, but did they bear out his arguments? Was it not possible, in the first place, he had not completely excluded the air by his corks and mastic? And was it not possible, in the second place, that he had not sufficiently heated his infusions and the superjacent air? Spallanzani joined issue with the English naturalist on both these pleas, and he showed that if, in the first place, the glass vessels in which the infusions were contained were hermetically sealed by fusing their necks, and if, in the second place, they were exposed to the temperature of boiling water for three-quarters of an hour, no animalcules ever made their appearance within them. It must be admitted that the experiments and arguments of Spallanzani furnish a complete and a crushing reply to those of Needham. But we all too often forget that it is one thing to refute a proposition, and another to prove the truth of a doctrine which, implicitly or explicitly, contradicts that proposition; and the advance of science soon showed that though Needham might be quite wrong, it did not follow that Spallanzani was quite right.

Modern Chemistry, the birth of the latter half of the eighteenth century, grew apace, and soon found herself face to face with the great problems which biology had vainly tried to attack without her help. The discovery of oxygen led to the laying of the foundations of a scientific theory of respiration, and to an examination of the marvellous interactions of organic substances with oxygen. The presence of free oxygen appeared to be one of the conditions of the existence of life, and of those singular changes in organic matters which are known as fermentation and putrefaction. The question of the generation of the infusory animalcules thus passed into a new phase. For what might not have happened to the organic matter of the infusions, or to the oxygen of the air, in Spallanzani's experiments? What security was there that the development of life which ought to have taken place had not been checked or prevented by these changes?

The battle had to be fought again. It was needful to repeat the experiments under conditions which would make sure that neither the oxygen of the air, nor the composition of the organic matter, was altered in such a manner as to interfere with the existence of life.

Schulze and Schwann took up the question from this point of view in 1836 and 1837. The passage of air through red-hot glass tubes, or through strong sulphuric acid, does not alter the proportion of its oxygen, while it must needs arrest, or destroy, any organic matter which may be contained in the air. These experimenters, therefore, contrived arrangements by which the only air which should come into contact with a boiled infusion should be such as had either passed through red-hot tubes or through strong sulphuric acid. The result which they obtained was that an infusion so treated developed no living things, while, if the same infusion was afterwards exposed to the air, such things appeared rapidly and abundantly. The accuracy of these experiments has been alternately denied and affirmed. Supposing them to be accepted, however, all that they really proved was that the treatment to which the air was subjected destroyed *something* that was essential to the development of life in the infusion. This "something" might be gaseous, fluid, or solid; that it consisted of germs remained only an hypothesis of greater or less probability.

Contemporaneously with these investigations a remarkable discovery was made by Cagniard de la Tour. He found that common yeast is composed of a vast accumulation of minute plants. The fermentation of must, or of wort, in the fabrication of wine and of beer, is always accompanied by the rapid growth and multiplication of these *Torulæ*. Thus, fermentation, in so far as it was accompanied by the development of microscopical organisms in enormous numbers, became assimilated to the decomposition of an infusion of ordinary animal or vegetable matter; and it was an obvious suggestion that the organisms were, in some way or other, the causes both of fermentation and of putrefaction. The chemists, with Berzelius and Liebig at their head, at first laughed this idea to scorn; but in 1843, a man then very young, who has since performed the unexampled feat of attaining to high eminence alike in Mathematics, Physics, and Physiology —I speak of the illustrious Helmholtz—reduced the matter to the test of experiment by a method alike elegant and conclusive. Helmholtz separated a putrefying or a fermenting liquid from one which was simply putrescible or fermentable by a membrane which allowed the fluids to pass through and become intermixed, but stopped the passage of solids. The result was, that while the putrescible or the fermentable liquids became impregnated with the results of the putrescence or fermentation which was going on on the other side of the membrane, they neither putrefied (in the ordinary way) nor fermented; nor were any of the organisms which abounded in the fermenting or putrefying liquid generated in them. Therefore the cause of the development of these organisms must lie in something which cannot pass through membranes; and as Helmholtz's investigations were long antecedent to Graham's researches upon colloids, his natural conclusion was that the agent thus intercepted must be a solid material. In point of fact, Helmholtz's experiments narrowed the issue to this: that which excites fermentation and putrefaction, and at the same time gives rise to living forms in a fermentable or putrescible fluid, is not a gas and is not a diffusible fluid; therefore it is either a colloid, or it is matter divided into very minute solid particles.

The researches of Schroeder and Dusch in 1854, and of Schroeder alone, in 1859, cleared up this point by experiments which are simply refinements upon those of Redi. A lump of cotton-wool is, physically speaking, a pile of many thicknesses of a very fine gauze, the fineness of the meshes of which depends upon the closeness of the compression of the wool. Now, Schroeder and Dusch found, that, in the case of all the putrefiable materials which they used (except milk and yolk of egg), an infusion boiled, and then allowed to come into contact with no air but such as had been filtered through cotton-wool, neither putrefied, nor fermented, nor developed living forms. It is hard to imagine what the fine sieve formed by the cotton-wool could have stopped except minute solid particles. Still the evidence was incomplete until it had been positively shown, first, that ordinary air does contain such particles; and, secondly, that filtration through cotton-wool arrests these particles and allows only physically pure air to pass. This demonstration has been furnished within the last year by the remarkable experiments of Professor Tyndall. It has been a common objection of Abiogenists that, if the doctrine of Biogeny is true, the air must be thick with germs; and they regard this as the height of absurdity. But nature occasionally is exceedingly unreasonable, and Professor Tyndall has proved that this particular absurdity may nevertheless be a reality. He has demonstrated that ordinary air is no better than a sort of stirabout of excessively minute solid particles; that these particles are almost wholly destructible by heat; and that they are strained off, and the air rendered optically pure, by its being passed through cotton-wool.

It remains yet in the order of logic, though not of history, to show that among these solid destructible particles, there really do exist germs capable of giving rise to the development of living forms in suitable menstrua. This piece of work was done by M. Pasteur in those beautiful researches which will ever render his name famous; and which, in spite of all attacks upon them, appear to me now, as they did seven years ago, to be models of accurate experimentation and logical reasoning. He strained air through cotton-wool, and found, as Schroeder and Dusch had done, that it contained nothing competent to give rise to the development of life in fluids highly fitted for that purpose. But the important further links in the chain of evidence added by Pasteur are three. In the first place he subjected to microscopic examination the cotton-wool which had served as strainer, and found that sundry bodies clearly recognisable as germs, were among the solid particles strained off. Secondly, he proved that these germs were competent to give rise to living forms by simply sowing them in a solution fitted for their development. And, thirdly, he showed that the incapacity of air strained through cotton-wool to give rise to life, was not due to any occult change effected in the constituents of the air by the wool, by proving that the cotton-wool might be dispensed with altogether, and perfectly free access left between the exterior air and that in the experimental flask. If the neck of the flask is drawn out into a tube and bent downwards; and if, after the contained fluid has been carefully boiled, the tube is heated sufficiently to destroy any germs which may be present in the air which enters as the fluid cools, the apparatus may be left to itself for any time and no life will appear in the fluid. The reason is plain. Although there is free communication between the atmosphere laden with germs and the germless air in the flask, contact between the two takes place only in the tube; and as the germs cannot fall upwards, and there are no currents, they never reach the interior of the flask. But if the tube be broken short off where it proceeds from the flask, and free access be thus given to germs falling vertically out of the air, the fluid, which has remained clear and desert for months, becomes, in a few days, turbid and full of life.

These experiments have been repeated over and over again by independent observers with entire success; and there is one very simple mode of seeing the facts for one's self, which I may as well describe.

Prepare a solution (much used by M. Pasteur, and often called "Pasteur's solution") composed of water with tartrate of ammonia, sugar, and yeast-ash dissolved therein. Divide it into three portions in as many flasks; boil all three for a quarter of an hour; and, while the steam is passing out, stop the neck of one with a large plug of cotton-wool, so that this also may be thoroughly steamed. Now set the flasks aside to cool, and, when their contents are cold, add to one of the open ones a drop of filtered infusion of hay which has stood for twenty-four hours, and is consequently full of the active and excessively minute organisms known as *Bacteria*. In a couple of days of ordinary warm weather the contents of this flask will be milky from the enormous multiplication of *Bacteria*. The other flask, open and exposed to the air, will, sooner or later, become milky with *Bacteria*, and patches of mould may appear in it; while the liquid in the flask, the neck of which is plugged with cotton-wool, will remain clear for an indefinite time. I have sought in vain for any explanation of these facts, except the obvious one, that the air contains germs competent to give rise to *Bacteria*, such as those with which the first solution has been knowingly and purposely inoculated, and to the mould-*Fungi*. And I have not yet been able to meet with any advocate of Abiogenesis who seriously maintains that the atoms of sugar, tartrate of ammonia, yeast-ash, and water, under no influence but that of free access of air and the ordinary temperature, re-arrange themselves and give rise to the protoplasm of *Bacterium*. But the alternative is to admit that these *Bacteria* arise from germs in the air; and if they are thus propagated, the burden of proof that other like forms are generated in a different manner, must rest with the assertor of that proposition.

To sum up the effect of this long chain of evidence:—

It is demonstrable that a fluid eminently fit for the development of the lowest forms of life, but which contains neither germs, nor any protein compound, gives rise to living things in great abundance if it is exposed to ordinary air; while no such development takes place, if the air with which it is in contact is mechanically freed from the solid particles which ordinarily float in it, and which may be made visible by appropriate means.

It is demonstrable that the great majority of these particles are destructible by heat, and that some of them are germs, or living particles, capable of giving rise to the same forms of life as those which appear when the fluid is exposed to unpurified air.

It is demonstrable that inoculation of the experimental fluid with a drop of liquid known to contain living particles gives rise to the same phenomena as exposure to unpurified air.

And it is further certain that these living particles are so minute that the assumption of their suspension in ordinary air presents not the slightest difficulty. On the contrary, considering their lightness and the wide diffusion of the organisms which produce them, it is impossible to conceive that they should not be suspended in the atmosphere in myriads.

Thus the evidence, direct and indirect, in favour of *Biogenesis* for all known forms of life must, I think, be admitted to be of great weight.

On the other side, the sole assertions worthy of attention are that hermetically sealed fluids, which have been exposed to great and long-continued heat, have sometimes exhibited living forms of low organisation when they have been opened.

The first reply that suggests itself is the probability that there must be some error about these experiments, because they are performed on an enormous scale every day with quite contrary results. Meat, fruits, vegetables, the very materials of the most fermentable and putrescible infusions, are preserved to the extent, I suppose I may say, of thousands of tons every year, by a method which is a mere application of Spallanzani's experiment. The matters to be preserved are well boiled in a tin case provided with a small hole, and this hole is soldered up when all the air in the case has been replaced by steam. By this method they may be kept for years without putrefying, fermenting, or getting mouldy. Now this is not because oxygen is excluded, inasmuch as it is now proved that free oxygen is not necessary for either fermentation or putrefaction. It is not because the tins are exhausted of air, for *Vibriones* and *Bacteria* live, as Pasteur has shown, without air or free oxygen. It is not because the boiled meats or vegetables are not putrescible or fermentable, as those who have had the misfortune to be in a ship supplied with unskilfully closed tins well know. What is it, therefore, but the exclusion of germs? I think that Abiogenists are bound to answer this question before they ask us to consider new experiments of precisely the same order.

And in the next place, if the results of the experiments I refer to are really trustworthy, it by no means follows that Abiogenesis has taken place. The resistance of living matter to heat is known to vary within considerable limits, and to depend, to some extent, upon the chemical and physical qualities of the surrounding medium. But if, in the present state of science, the alternative is offered us,—either germs can stand a greater heat than has been supposed, or the molecules of dead matter, for no valid or intelligible reason that is assigned, are able to re-arrange themselves into living bodies, exactly such as can be demonstrated to be frequently produced in another way,—I cannot understand how choice can be, even for a moment, doubtful.

But though I cannot express this conviction of mine too strongly, I must carefully guard myself against the supposition that I intend to suggest that no such thing as Abiogenesis ever has taken place in the past, or ever will take place in the future. With organic chemistry, molecular physics, and physiology yet in their infancy, and every day making prodigious strides, I think it would be the height of presumption for any man to say that the conditions under which matter assumes the properties we call "vital" may not, some day, be artifically brought together. All I feel justified in affirming is, that I see no reason for believing that the feat has been performed yet.

And looking back through the prodigious vista of the past, I find no record of the commencement of life, and therefore I am devoid of any means of forming a definite conclusion as to the conditions of its appearance. Belief, in the scientific sense of the word, is a serious matter, and needs strong foundations. To say, therefore, in the admitted absence of evidence, that I have any belief as to the mode in which the existing forms of life have originated, would be using words in a wrong sense. But expectation is permissible where belief is not; and if it were given me to look beyond the abyss of geologically recorded time to the still more remote period when the earth was passing through physical and chemical conditions, which it can no more see again than a man can recall his infancy, I should expect to be a witness of the evolution of living protoplasm from not living matter. I should expect to see it appear under forms of great simplicity, endowed, like existing fungi, with the power of determining the formation of new protoplasm from such matters as ammonium carbonates, oxalates and tartrates, alkaline and earthy phosphates, and water, without the aid of light. That is the expectation to which analogical reasoning leads me; but I beg you once more to recollect that I have no right to call my opinion anything but an act of philosophical faith.

37

The Origins of Life

J. B. S. HALDANE
1954

From *New Biology* (vol. 16), pp. 12–27. Penguin Books Ltd., 1954. Reprinted with permission of the publisher.

Living organisms exist on our planet today, and have existed for over 500 million years. But whether the earth's surface was once wholly molten or whether, as is now often suggested, it was formed by a hail of solid particles coming down at great speeds, the conditions at some time in the past were very unsuited for life. It is therefore thought that life on earth had a beginning. Until 300 years ago it was generally believed that life was constantly arising from dead matter. When Redi, Spallanzani, and Pasteur showed that there was no evidence for such an event, and when even the smallest organisms were found to be chemically very complicated, the problem of the origin of life became really acute. Most of the suggestions as to its origin can be classified as follows:

(1) Life has no origin. Matter and life have always existed. When stars become habitable, they are colonized by 'seeds' of life from interstellar space, perhaps spores of bacteria or simple plants. These may have been driven out of planetary atmospheres by radiation pressure, as Arrhenius suggested, or even launched into space by intelligent beings.

(2) Life originated on our planet by a supernatural event, that is to say an event of a kind incapable of description in the terminology of natural science, and *a fortiori* incapable of prediction or control by man.

(3) Life originated from 'ordinary' chemical reactions by a slow evolutionary process.

(4) Life originated as the result of a very 'improbable' event, which however was almost certain to happen given sufficient time, and sufficient matter of suitable composition in a suitable state.

(3) and (4), as we shall see, grade into one another; but I state them in extreme forms.

Hypothesis (1) does not seem to me impossible, in our present state of knowledge. The universe may have had no beginning. I do not think it had. Further, if it had no beginning, some parts of it may at all times have been in the condition of the parts which we know, and have included some niches where life was possible. Bondi (1952), Hoyle, and Gold have recently put forward the view that the universe has always, on the whole, been much as it is now, associated with the further hypothesis that matter is constantly arising 'out of nothing.' Ambarzumian (1953) finds no need for this latter hypothesis, though agreeing that in some parts of the universe conditions have always been similar to those known to us. On such a view life is presumably coeternal with matter. If it turns out that hypothesis (3) will not work, and that hypothesis (4) demands an event which had an extremely small chance of happening anywhere on earth in four thousand million years, then hypothesis (1) will have to be considered seriously.

Hypothesis (2), in any form compatible with known facts, is somewhat different from the ideas of the author of the first chapter of the book of Genesis. When, according to him, the Lord said: 'Let the waters bring forth abundantly the moving creature that hath life,' it was not suggested that waters did not still do so. The stress in the divine command was perhaps on 'abundantly.' A supernatural origin of life appears as a much greater miracle to us than it did 3,000 or even 200 years ago. Hypothesis (2) is unverifiable except by revelation from a witness of the event. Unless one is fully convinced that one of the existing accounts of it is such a revelation, it should not be accepted till (1), (3), and (4) have been disproved or shown to be highly improbable.

Bernal and Pringle have both supported hypothesis (3), and Pirie has on the whole done so. I am still more lukewarm, and think that hypothesis (4) must be taken seriously, for the following reason. The theory of instructions to machines is being rapidly developed in connexion with electronic calculators. You can impress on a punched tape instructions to a machine to calculate π to 2,000 decimal places; or to go on moving in a prescribed direction at a prescribed height until it gets within a specified distance of an electric conductor, and then to explode, and so on. Can one give a machine an instruction to make another one like itself also provided with a copy of these instructions? If so, as long as the parts needed to construct another such machine are available, the machine will go on reproducing its like, and so will its progeny. Von Neumann (1951) on the basis of a theorem due to Turing, claims to have proved that such a machine can be constructed from a finite number of parts of about twelve different kinds. If he is right, such a machine would have a considerable claim to be alive, even if it had to wander about hunting for ready-made Meccano parts as we have to wander about hunting for ready-made amino-acids and vitamins, as well as foodstuffs which are merely energy sources. Nobody has yet calculated the minimum number of parts of such a machine. This calculation will be of great interest. If, for example, it turned out to be bigger than the number of atoms in a bacillus, the mechanistic theory of life would have been logically disproved.

If the parts could be fairly simple molecules of three types of which I shall write later, we shall see that these may have been fairly readily available in the past. If the minimum number of such parts needed turns out to be some smallish number n_1, we can accept hypothesis (3). Once the parts were there, they would certainly get put together by chance in the right configuration in a few seconds or centuries, as by mere shuffling you will get the letters ACEHIMN to spell 'machine' once in 5040 trials on an average. If the number is a large one n_2, it may turn out that, under the probable physical and chemical conditions, 'biopoesis' would only be expected to occur on the earth's surface once in several hundred million years. If it is a still larger one, n_3, we shall be able to say that, unless hypothesis (1) or (2) is true, it is excessively improbable that there is any life anywhere except on earth within the range of our best telescopes. The theory that the earth is unique in being an abode of life is of course also compatible with hypothesis (2) though hardly with (1). My objection to it is perhaps irrational.

Of course the arrangement of the parts is very relevant to any such calculation. A simple example will show the kind of calculation one can make. Nucleic acids appear to consist of alternate purine and pyrimidine nucleotides arranged in a chain. In desoxyribose nucleic acid the purine is either adenine or guanine, the pyrimidine either cytosine or thymine. The average molecular weight of a link in the chain is about 300. There are clearly 2^n possible types of chain n units long. A gram is 6×10^{23} times the mass of an H atom, the sun's mass is 2×10^{33} gm, that of our galaxy is about 10^{11} times that of the sun. There are at least 10^{6} galaxies within range of the best telescopes (i.e. from which light which started since the early Cambrian has yet had time to reach us). Their mass is about that of 1.2×10^{74}, or 2^{246} H atoms. It follows that if one each of all the sorts of nucleic acid molecule with 245 links in the chain, or molecular weights up to 73,500, could be made, their joint mass would be that of the known part of the universe. Some nucleic acids have molecular weights of at least half a million. If it could be shown that one and only one nucleic acid of molecular weight 100,000, and no smaller one, could reproduce itself, then even if nucleotides and catalysts to condense them were available we should have to abandon hypotheses (3) and (4), and turn to (1) or (2). I think this is most unlikely. But the number 10^{74} or 2^{246} is not large in this sort of context. It is, e.g., the number of possible 'words' of 173 letters.

Now let us come down to earth again. Haldane (1929) produced some hypotheses which, thanks to Oparin on the one hand, and Horowitz and Urey on the other, are actually 'orthodox' both in the U.S.S.R. and the U.S.A., a fact which, I confess, makes me somewhat sceptical of them. There was little free oxygen in the earth's primitive atmosphere. It probably contained hydrogen, ammonia, and methane like those of the great planets. Haldane thought it contained carbon dioxide rather than methane. Here he was probably wrong. But methane and ammonia were only discovered in the atmospheres of Jupiter, Saturn, and Uranus after he wrote the article. Under the influence of ultraviolet solar radiation, metastable* organic molecules were formed. Haldane suggested that they were formed directly, Pringle that they were formed by the partial oxidation of hydrocarbons by small amounts of oxygen, ozone, or peroxides, formed by the ultraviolet radiation. In either case solar energy was stored in these molecules. It was further suggested that the energy so stored was the source used by the first living organisms, and that photosynthesis within a living cell followed later, and the complete oxidation of organic molecules only began after photosynthetic plants had produced a good deal of free oxygen. These suggestions, particularly the suggestion that metastable organic compounds were formed until 'before the origin of life they must have accumulated till the primitive oceans reached the consistency of hot dilute soup,' are generally accepted. They may well be incorrect, as Madison (1953) argues.†

Haldane's reason for regarding anaerobic life as primitive, against Pringle and Madison, was as follows. The biochemical mechanisms concerned in anaerobic metabolism are very similar in all organisms where they have been investigated. Thus glucose is broken down to ethanol and carbon dioxide in yeast by nearly

* A metastable molecule means one which can liberate free energy by a transformation, but is stable enough to last a long time unless it is activated by heat, radiation, or union with a catalyst. For example, trinitrotoluene is highly metastable; a kilogram of it liberates a lot of energy. Glucose is mildly metastable, but will liberate some energy if turned into ethanol and carbon dioxide. Yeast cells use this energy. Most organic molecules are metastable.

† Since I wrote this article, Madison's (1953) paper has reached me. I am not going to comment on it as it deserves, since its intellectual digestion will take me a month or so. He opens with a valuable review of the literature since 1917. I only wish that he would not write 'Haldane proposes,' meaning 'Haldane proposed in 1929.' Even protozoa appear to be capable of learning, that is to say changing their behaviour as a result of experience. So am I.

He vigorously attacks the notion that the primitive ocean was full of organic molecules, though this has now gained the powerful support of Urey, whose opinion on the chemistry of the primitive earth is worth a lot more than mine; and comes down in favour of the theory that the first organisms were autotrophic, obtaining their free energy by oxidizing sulphides, and using it to reduce carbonates. Here he comes near to Pringle's view. Following Blum, whose book I fear I have not read, he seems to regard ATP as something formed at a very early stage in the origin of life. Later in this article I suggest that much simpler molecules containing phosphate chains may have preceded it.

I am not sure that Madison's definitions of 'life' and 'organism' would stand up very well were Pirie's criticism directed to them. But I cordially recommend his article, if only as an antidote to my own.

the same set of enzymes which convert it to lactic acid in our muscles. But the systems concerned in oxidation are very different. Most of the oxidation in vertebrates is by the 'citric acid cycle'; but this is unimportant or even absent in many simpler organisms, and a fair number of these can live permanently without any oxygen. Haldane therefore regarded anaerobic life as more primitive than aerobic life, and postulated a primitive reducing atmosphere before the composition of the atmospheres of the outer planets was known.

We have some notion as to when photosynthesis began. Sulphur consists of two isotopes, S^{32} and S^{34}. The ratio of light to heavy sulphur in early pre-Cambrian sulphides and sulphates is about 22.1. In sea-water sulphate it is about 21.8, in Cretaceous FeS_2 it is 23.0. About eight hundred million years ago a process began which very gradually increased the amount of S^{32} in sulphides, and diminished it in sulphates. The only known process which would do this is the oxidation of sulphur or hydrogen sulphide to sulphate by bacteria, and its reduction again by plants and other bacteria. Thode, Macnamara, and Fleming (1953) put the origin of sulphur oxidizing bacteria eight hundred million years back, and suggest that this 'predates the beginning of large scale photosynthesis.' Their graphs suggest that the amount of oxygen in the air has increased a good deal since the Cambrian. If this argument is valid, life is perhaps less than a thousand million years old on earth, though the earth is probably three or four times that age.*

Pringle thinks that 'the coherent organism as we know it must have been preceded by an organization dispersed in a large volume of water.' This water cannot have been turbulent, and was probably, he thinks, at a great depth in the sea, though I think waterlogged soil** a possibility. Oxygen and perhaps relatively oxidized compounds were diffusing down, hydrogen and other reducing substances diffusing up. There was a gradient of reducing potential such as, according to Joyet-Laverque, exists in most cells, the nucleus being more reducing (high *r*H) than the surrounding cytoplasm. In this situation complex molecules could built up.

The most lifelike molecule known to us at present is adenosine-triphosphoric acid (ATP). Two ATP molecules can each give a phosphoric acid residue to a glucose molecule, which then splits up. The products of the split glucose phosphate, which are diphosphoglyceric acid, and later phosphopyruvic acid, will later give back phosphoric acid residues to four molecules of adenosine-diphosphoric acid, regenerating four ATP molecules. These events occur in fermenting yeast and in our muscles. Thus ATP can replace lost parts, or be said to have a metabolism. More surprisingly it has something like a sexual process which comes into operation when a good deal of the labile phosphate (i.e. the third phosphate residues on its molecules) has been lost. Two adenosine-diphosphoric acid molecules can give rise to one of ATP and one of adenylic acid, which is generally quickly broken down by deamination, like a polar body, if we want to press our analogy.

These processes are all catalysed by different enzymes and would go on very slowly without them. Baldwin (1952) gives an account of the 'ecology,' 'instincts,' and so on, of ATP, but its embryology is not yet worked out. I do not, of course, think it is alive in any meaningful sense, but already we can begin to apply biological terms to it with as great propriety as we can apply mechanical terms to higher animals. It is, however, a complicated substance, and could only be formed, except as a great rarity, when suitable catalysts had evolved. But yeast and the mould *Neurospora*, and quite possibly our own cells, contain an inorganic anion which seems to be a hexametaphosphate, and to be performing functions in the cell similar to those of ATP. It is possible that in an environment where suitable oxidations are going on, such a chain molecule could give up bits of itself to some organic molecules, receive more than the same number of phosphoric

* [It is now known that the conclusion of Thode, Macnamara, and Fleming is not valid and that photosynthetic life has existed for at least 1.9 billion years and perhaps more than 3 billion years. —P. C.]

** In deference to a criticism by Pirie, I must admit that I have used the word 'soil' as a layman to include clay, silt, ooze, sand, or perhaps even gravel. Pedologists use this word for the products of various biological actions on such inorganic materials.

acid residues back from their oxidation products, split, and increase its numbers. Such a process would doubtless be slow in the absence of specific enzymes, but it might occur. In twenty years we shall probably know whether it does so.

I suggest, then, that in the pre-Cambrian waters of the earth, whether in the depths of the ocean as Pringle suggests, in layers adsorbed on clay, as Bernal thinks, in soil water, or in layers adsorbed at air-water interfaces (Haldane, 1929), there were enough metastable molecules (of which glucose will serve as an example) and molecules available for growth (of which phosphate ions will serve as an example) to allow catalytically active molecules to grow, split, and increase their number.

Three sorts of long chain polymer are known in biological systems. Nucleic acids have a 'backbone' of phosphoric acid residues, proteins a backbone of glycine residues, polysaccharides and related compounds such as chitin and alginic acid a backbone of pentose residues. The polysaccharide chains are so far 'lifelike' that they will not begin to grow in the presence of their normal 'food,' which is usually glucose-1-phosphate, but in some bacteria maltose, and of a suitable enzyme, until they have reached a minimum length of about six links. Quite possibly all such chains in living cells are 'descended' from other chains which grew and then split.

There is some evidence that amino-acids must be phosphorylated by ATP before they can be incorporated into proteins, though this may be no more obligatory than the phosphorylation of glucose before starch is formed. There is also good evidence that large ribonucleic acid molecules are concerned in protein synthesis, perhaps because the links are of the same length in both types of chain, and proteins are laid down on the nucleic acid chains as templates. We do not yet know how nucleic acid grows. But it may well need a protein chain as a template (cf. Haldane, 1954). However, it is quite possible that these chains could grow without such catalysts, but more slowly and with a less regular pattern.

The conditions for growth and reproduction by splitting of these long chain molecules may have been rather fugitive, and such subvital units, as that brilliant imaginer O. W. Stapledon (1930) called them, may have come into being, reproduced for a while, and 'died out' again on millions of millions of occasions.

I must now bring into my speculations a fact which was quite unexpected in 1929, except by a few far-sighted Frenchmen and Frenchwomen such as the Wollmanns and Hauduroy, who at that time were regarded as somewhat uncritical. Simple organisms such as bacteria and viruses can use and copy parts of other simple organisms, even of different species. So can higher plants, according to Michurin. We, of course, use parts when we eat cabbage or beef, but we first break down the large molecules such as proteins into smaller ones such as amino-acids which are not 'foreign' to us. A bacterium can incorporate into itself one or more large molecules of nucleic acid from another race or probably another species. These are then reproduced in their new environment, and enable the 'synthetic' bacterium to make a new type of polysaccharide or enzyme. What is even more remarkable, Taylor has recently shown that a Pneumococcus may incorporate such 'transforming substances' from two different sources, and make a 'hybrid molecule' presumably by a transphosphorylation analogous to the 'crossing over' of chromosomes. In higher organisms similar processes of course occur in sexual reproduction, but they are hedged round by the elaborate ceremonial which we call meiosis, and the elaborate taboos which we call interspecific sterility.

A nucleic acid molecule is a chain of phosphoric acid residues, each with a sugar residue (ribose or desoxyribose) and a purine or pyrimidine base residue attached. Adenylic acid (adenosine monophosphate) is a component of ribonucleic acid. We have seen that molecules of this type can 'grow' and 'mate' under suitable conditions. I suggest that different catalysts, each adapted to a different 'food' of smaller, mostly metastable molecules, may have united or 'mated' to form catalysts with a wider 'food' range, till a relatively large molecule, still capable of growth and splitting, was formed. The result might be something like a simple molecular virus or a very small chromosome with different catalytically active groups corresponding to different genes.

Such processes may well have occurred in

different environments. It is at least conceivable that Oparin, Bernal, Pirie, Pringle, and Haldane are all correct, as far as they go. Posterity may decide wehther a single molecule of the kind suggested could legitimately be called living, or whether this term would be better reserved for a number of such molecules enclosed in a membrane.

Most later writers have frowned on Haldane's suggestion that the molecular viruses existing today can be regarded as in any way resembling the first living or subvital units. This suggestion may be correct even if in fact the modern viruses are simpler than their immediate ancestors. Until other types of chain molecule have been shown to undergo processes as like metabolism and conjugation as chains with a phosphate 'backbone' can do, the suggestion should not, perhaps, be dismissed.

I suggest then that various kinds of subvital unit molecules were able to reproduce themselves in suitable environments. Any such 'sub-life' may have lasted for minutes, or for thousands of years. Occasionally such sub-lives combined to produce something more complicated. But almost all such 'molecular races' died out for one reason or another. The fortunate combination which gave rise to our ancestors may have involved the meeting together —the marriage if you like—of a number of such molecular races. There may have been several such events. One can imagine a virus-like organism which had just held its own for millions of years in an environment such as that postulated by Pringle, until a fragment of clay with a Bernal 'organism' fell to the depths. Some components of this were incorporated and enabled it to extend its range considerably.

Self-reproducing chain molecules of several types may even have lived in a sort of symbiosis, each using the 'metabolic' products of other types. We should have then something like the parts of von Neumann's machine floating around. If so possibly the decisive step was the formation of the first cell, in which chain molecules of at least two of the three types now represented by nucleic acids, proteins, and polysaccharides were enclosed in a semi-permeable membrane which kept them together but let their food in. Such a system would have had the enormous advantage that symbiosis no longer depended on two molecules of different types being brought together by Brownian movement. But the conditions for self-reproduction of such a cell may have been extremely precise. If hypothesis (4) has any validity, I suspect that it applies to the formation of the first workable cell, rather than to earlier biochemical evolution.

As Boyden (1953) pointed out in a very interesting discussion which, however, concerns the early stages of cellular life rather than its origin, mitosis was probably only very slowly perfected. The first cells may have divided so irregularly that on an average a division produced only a little more than one survivor. But quite often one or both products died. I disagree with Boyden's view that reproduction was exclusively asexual over long periods. On the contrary I think it is quite likely that primitive cells often fused with others or performed exchanges of parts such as are still possible in bacteria. The consequences were perhaps often disastrous, but sometimes gave new possibilities. If the origin of cellular life was the decisive step (and even a bacteriophage seems to be surrounded by some sort of membrane) it may have occurred as a result of a lucky chance. If not it is rather surprising that life did not start earlier. The earth appears to be three or four thousand million years old. . . . If life arose, as Pringle thinks, by a fairly steady evolutionary process, I should have expected it to have got a little further by now.

I shall now try to defend myself against some probable criticisms. I shall be criticized for bringing in 'chance.' All that we mean by chance is partial unpredictability. Some atomic processes may be unpredictable, however great our knowledge. Most large-scale processes are not unpredictable in principle; but it is impracticable to predict anything, except that some critical event has a given probability of occurring in a given time. If I strike a match some small areas on its surface are heated by friction. When a sufficiently large number of neighbouring molecules have been heated up enough to start an oxidation the process will spread and the match will light. The details are unpredictable, but there may be a 99 per cent chance that a good match will light. Just the same is true for the biochemical processes concerned in starting a muscle fibre contracting. The postulation of a rare chance (hypothesis 4) is not even incompatible with that of supernatural creation or guidance. To avoid postulating infinities let us merely postulate a Director of our galaxy. His or her simplest method of producing a variety of forms of life may be to leave a few hundred million planets near suitable suns for three thousand million years, in the confidence that within that time cellular life will have started on 90 per cent of those where the surface temperatures and so on are suitable.

Other critics will say that a self-reproducing machine is still a machine, and that there is an absolute gulf between any possible activity of such a machine and the most elementary feeling or desire, let alone human consciousness. Of such a critic I ask, 'Do you think that your idea or perception of a stone is like the stone?' The answer does not depend on whether my critic is a materialist or an idealist. If he says 'No' he may be an idealist of the Kantian type, like Eddington, who believes that the real nature of the stone is unknowable, and all the qualities which he attributes to it are products of his own mind. Or he may be a materialist who thinks that mind is an epiphenomenon of brain, but that its components, such as ideas, do not truly reflect the external world. If he says 'Yes' he may be a materialist, naïve or dialectical, who thinks that the stone really exists, and his perception resembles it. Or he may be an idealist who thinks with Russell in one of his phases that the stone is the class of all possible perceptions of it, or an idealist of several other types. A materialist must stand such an idealist on his head, as Marx said of Hegel, to follow his argument, and conversely. But a measure of agreement is possible.

I think that my sensations and ideas are events occurring in my brain which are something like events occurring outside it, which they reflect. If A is like B, B is like A; so I agree with those idealists who say that matter is like my sensations and ideas. We disagree about whether A or B was there first. But that is a matter of historical fact to be decided by evidence and argument. In this article I have produced a little evidence and argument for the view that matter was present before mind on our planet, even if they are coeternal in the universe as a whole.

A good deal more evidence on the whole question should be provided by astronautics. One of the earliest parties to land on the moon should be able to look for astroplankton, that is to say spores and the like, in dust from an area of the mooon which is never exposed to sunlight. If any is found, this will support hypothesis (1). If no evidence of present or past life is found on Mars or Venus, though simple terrestrial organisms can live there without an artificial atmosphere, this will be an argument against hypothesis (3). If life is found on Mars with a similar biochemical basis to our own (in which case the explorers may be in danger from Martial bacteria and viruses, and the Martial higher organisms from terrestrial ones) this will tell against hypothesis (1) if, and only if, the Martial organisms are built of 'looking glass' sugars and amino-acids. Jupiter is very possibly covered with an ocean of liquid ammonia containing ice and salts in solution, and resting on rocks of ice. There is a whole system of inorganic and organic chemistry in which liquid ammonia takes the place of water (for example, salts crystallize with ammonia of crystallization). Life in which ammonia replaces water may be possible, though in the absence of free oxygen I doubt if Jovial life can have got beyond the plant stage. Our descendants may even find evidence for another type of life in the interior of our earth with a material basis of partly molten silicates and an energy supply from the oxidation of the metallic core; though I think this unlikely.

Ultimately it should be possible to settle the problem by making synthetic living things, and working out the probability that such a synthesis could have occurred within the time available, on an initially lifeless planet. If such a synthesis is colossally improbable the possibility would remain that our earth was the only abode of life in the known universe. If life were found on Mars this would be ruled out. If it were further found that no spores could survive an interstellar journey the 'supernatural' hypothesis (2) would have to be considered seriously once more, whereas at present it seems to be becoming less plausible. More probably, I suspect, our descendants will have discovered facts about the nature of the universe which will make them laugh at our simplicity in posing such alternatives as these.

Meanwhile, however, it is worth showing that we can at least frame our questions clearly enough to pose problems, whether in biochemistry or mathematical logic, in geology or in astronautics, which we cannot solve at present, but which are not in principle insoluble. The history of science makes it almost certain that the attempt to solve any of these problems will have practical and theoretical consequences in different fields. Thus the biochemistry of molecules which reproduce themselves under special conditions is probably the clue to a full understanding of genetics, and probably also to an understanding of tissue differentiation, one of whose by-products would be the prevention of cancer. Again the self-reproducing machine includes a set of instructions for copying itself, and its design involves research on communication. Conversely research on cancer or communication may throw light on the origin of life.

To sum up, I suggest the following hypotheses. Metastable organic compounds were formed by the action of solar radiation on the atmosphere before it contained much free oxygen. Catalytically active molecules which could increase their own number while breaking down these compounds came into being. No such molecule is certainly known at present, but adenosine-triphosphoric acid comes near to being one. The long-chain polymers found in living organisms have 'back-bones' composed of phosphate, glycine, or pentose residues. The first seem to be the most catalytically active, and may be the most primitive. The critical event which may best be called the origin of life was the enclosure of several different self-reproducing polymers within a semipermeable membrane.

The problem of describing the origin of life is curiously like its actual origin. In each case it seems likely that a number of attempts were made, and almost all of them did not work. Natural selection eliminated them. But those who, like myself, are speculating on this problem, have one great advantage over our 'sub-vital' ancestors. We can learn from the mistakes of others, for example, Virgil and van Helmont, and need not repeat them. The analogy perhaps goes deeper. The final synthesis in each case may consist of parts of several attempted syntheses, each of which worked, up to a point. Perhaps, for example, I have contributed the idea of the coming together of catalysts from different sources, but every other hypothesis in the last paragraph is false. Bernal has contributed the idea of an adsorbed layer, but it was not on clay, Pringle has contributed the idea of a chemical gradient, but it was not in the deep sea, and so on. If any of us has contributed even a molecule of thought to the final synthesis we have not written in vain.

FOR FURTHER READING

Ambarzumian, W. A., 1953, Das Weltall (translated from Russian) *in* Sowjetwissenschaft: Naturwissenschaften Abt., 1953, p. 278–291.

Baldwin, E., 1952, Dynamic aspects of biochemistry: Cambridge University Press.

Bernal, J. D., 1951, The physical basis of life: London, Routledge and Kegan Paul.

Bondi, H., 1952, Cosmology: Cambridge University Press.

Boyden, A. A., 1953, Comparative evolution—with special reference to primative mechanisms: Evolution, v. 7, p. 21–30.

Haldane, J. B. S., 1929, The origin of life: Rationalist Annual, 1929.

———, 1954, The biochemistry of genetics: London, Macmillan.

Neumann, J. von, 1951, Cerebral mechanisms in behavior: New York and London.

Oparin, A. I., 1938, The origin of life (translated by S. Morgulis): New York, Academic Press.

Pringle, J. W. S., 1953, The origin of Life: Soc. Exp. Biol. Symposium, v. 7, p. 1.

Stapledon, O. W., 1930, First and last men: London.

Thode, H. G., J. Macnamara, and H. W. Fleming, 1953, Sulfur fractionation in nature and geological and biological time scales: Geochim. et Cosmochim. Acta, v. 3, p. 235–243.

38

What is Life?

DANIEL MAZIA
1966

The question "What is Life?" begins to acquire newer implications in a time when the exploration of space is beginning. Whatever the probability of life in other worlds, the possibility of an answer turns old philosophical exercises on the definition of life into a concrete observational problem: What criteria are significant, what observations would be practicable, what does this or that kind of measurement or observation tell us about living things, what observations of non-living things could confuse us, what exotic departures from the kind of life we know could go unrecognized? The same questions concern both the advocates of the explorations and their critics.

We begin, then, with the modest affirmation that the world of things in general—the domain of physics—includes a class of things that are highly distinctive—the domain of biology. As we shall see, the question of a blurring of the boundaries between the two is far from damaging in an evolving universe; on the contrary, we think we could recognize the transitional stages and learn much about living things from them. Though we seek the distinctiveness of living things by studying them as things, we do not deny alternative approaches to the distinctiveness of life: through instinct, poetry or religion. The present discussion, however, conforms to the limitations of science and exploration.

A measure of the distinctiveness of the living world is that it confronts us with phenomena, principles and values that are essential to itself but not to the physical world as a whole. If in the end we must investigate living things as things having a special—a very special—material organization, we begin by noting that the values that govern the investigation are also distinctive. Put more plainly, living things are characterized by the kinds of questions we put to them—or more simply, *by what is interesting about them.* It is important that the scientific investigation of rock and of cells gives different answers, but just as important that it asks quite different questions.

What is interesting about living things—

From *Biology and the Exploration of Mars* (NAS-NRC Publication 1296), edited by C. S. Pittendrigh, pp. 25–40. National Academy of Sciences, 1966. Reprinted with permission of the author and the publisher.

and the focus of all questions about them—is contained in the idea of *survival*. Survival contains the idea of an *organism*. The living world thwarts time by survival, all the rest combats time by endurance. An organism lives; its fossil relic endures. Survival contains the idea of an *organism*, an individual that can change and replace its atoms and molecules without loss of identity. Survival contains a special version of the idea of a *species;* in the living world the similarity of members of a species derives from common descent and from no other cause. Survival implies a particular version of *purpose* and *value*, although these philosophical swear-words are usually concealed prudishly in the term *function*. There is no biologist, whether he be a biochemist who discovers some small molecule in a microorganism, or a student of behavior examining the social organization of apes, who does not seek, in his observations, for purpose and value in relation to survival.

Thus we approach living things as things designed for survival. Our observations and measurements concern the things; our judgments of what we seek, observe and measure concern survival. All this would be rather abstract and, perhaps, marginal to the practice of science, if the world we know contained a great variety of things designed for survival, sharing only the characteristic that they *are* designed for survival. But that is not the case. The most important fact of the biology that we know is that living things are profoundly similar, and the most important deduction from this fact is that the similarities represent true relationship by common descent. The wonderful thing about evolution on the Earth is that it can produce such a beauty of variety and variety of beauty among things that are fundamentally the same. It is by virtue of that fundamental sameness that we can surely identify living things on Earth, as well as things that were once alive and (would that we could find them!) things in the process of evolution toward life, if only we are given the means to make a sufficient number of observations. It is the general principles of operation of living things on Earth, as well as the general principles of their material organization, that permit us to make judgments about the biological exploration of other worlds.

Survival of living things on Earth is observed on two scales of time, and the time itself is biological time (the unit of which is a generation), not clock time. The smaller scale contains those attributes that govern the survival of the individual. Otherwise expressed it contains all the attributes of the individual, judged by the values of survival. It includes the form, organization and anatomy, that identify the individual visibly as the thing that survives. It includes his developmental history, for we are interested in eggs as well as chickens. It includes all the flow of matter through the individual, all the self-sustaining transformations of the invariably simple substances of the non-living world into the often-complex substances making up the fabric of living bodies. It includes the flow of energy by which all the improbable operations of living things become possible operations. It includes all the movement, responses and behavior of the organism, for all of these may be interpreted as purposeful, once we recognize purpose as survival. It includes behavior of organisms in relation to other organisms; not only competition, but also social behavior and cooperation for no inference from natural selection is more obsolete than the idea that survival means only tooth-and-claw conflict.

The individual on the smaller scale of time is a self that is self-making and self-sustaining at the expense of the world outside.

The larger time-scale of survival is imposed by the physical fact of death. . . . Any static population of organisms would be destroyed in time or, if aging is an intrinsic property, by time. The means of survival over an indefinite time-span is reproduction: replacement and increase of individuals of a kind by more of the same kind. Most descriptions of life include reproduction as the most important attribute, and correctly so. Other activities that contribute to survival would be futile if organisms could not reproduce; indeed the survival of the individual is often sacrificed to the propagation of the kind. Reproduction itself allows for indefinite survival of a species so long as the external conditions permit survival at all. Species are, however, not absolutely stable, but change in time, for organisms are subject to alterations (mutations) that are propagated by reproduction. The survival and accumulation of inheritable changes are governed by their value for the survival of the reproducing individuals; thus viewed the fruit of Darwin's genius becomes a truism. It has been said that living things are *things that can reproduce, mutate and reproduce mutations*. We are fairly sure that this statement covers all the living things in nature on this planet and that it is free from ambiguity so far as natural objects are concerned. . . .

If an object is most satisfactorily identified as a living thing by showing it to be capable of self-replication, mutation and replication of mutation, that is not necessarily the only or the most practical expedient. It certainly would not be the best means of attributing life to an elephant; it takes much enterprise to observe the reproduction of elephants and excessive patience to demonstrate their mutations. On the other hand, it is easy to demonstrate reproduction of a bacterium (and almost as easy to demonstrate mutation).

In practice, we would seldom be mistaken in assuming that an elephant is alive because he is wagging his tail, but it takes a good microscopist to observe a bacterium waving its tail. In fact, there has been considerable debate as to whether a bacterium moves its flagellum or whether the flagellum moves the bacterium. The admission that we cannot always appeal to the ideal criteria of an organism—reproduction and mutation—is inconvenient, but not very damaging. We are assisted by recognizing that the processes of organisms are so interlocked that the observation of any one of them leads to inferences about the survival of individuals and species. . . .

Organisms are surviving things: self-making, self-sustaining, kind-conserving things. And it is as things in the ordinary sense, as objects defined by their *form,* that we commonly identify them among things in general and classify them among themselves. The forms of organisms are hardly the sole basis for discriminating decisions about living things, as we shall see, but they can be the most immediate and most subtle ones. We may resist them in scientific principle—while never failing to resort to them in practice—because the judgments are inherently subjective and qualitative, difficult to express and impossible to measure. The values and the pitfalls of morphology have the same cause: our total perceptions are far more subtle and discriminating than are readings of meters, but harder to describe and agree upon. . . .

In appealing to morphology as a criterion of living things, we are in that ever-embarrassing position of feeling confident that we could recognize something though we are unable to state with great precision what we are looking for. We want a language, a mathematics of form. What we can say is that the organization of living things is expressed in complex form, in form-within-form. The forms are plastic, topological in spirit, recognizable and functional despite distortion. (When Donald Duck is flattened by a steamroller, he is still Donald Duck.) . . . Most important, because deriving from the survival principles themselves, is the generic character of biological form; identification is not based solely on the finding of one individual with a given complex form but on the fact that there will be many individuals with *similar* form. . . .

The appeal of morphology in the identification of living things rests on the multiplicity of clues rather than the precision of single criteria. A common paradigm of scientific insight —and one of considerable literary appeal—is our ability to deduce from fossil shadows the forms and ways of life of organisms that have long ago surrendered survival to durability. It is a true paradigm. Complex forms are always taken seriously as signs of living things. We can be moved by fossil forms and find a singular beauty in form that is congealed in time.

If seeing is at least a strong invitation to believing, it goes without saying that seeing is not limited to naked vision. The clues of complex form hold good for all levels of "seeing," not only for the smallest organisms, but for the smallest parts of organisms. If biological science admitted its dogmas, "function goes with form" would stand high on the list. We have a rather good historical test in the work of the early microscopists: old Leeuwenhoek, an uneducated man who made crude microscopes in the 17th century, had no hesitation in identifying "animalcules" in the world he found beyond the limits of the unaided eye and he did not make many mistakes.

In our own world, there are few organisms that cannot be seen with the ordinary light microscope, and there is a good reason for this: even simple surviving things require a considerable number of large molecules for their minimum functions and the smallest living thing is bound to be rather large. There are some forms whose dimensions are just beyond the power of the optical microscope—for example the so-called PPLO (pleuromonia-like) organisms. Their existence tells us that the search is not ended at the limits of the light microscope, but no change of principle is called for: such organisms have regular and complex form, not easily confused with that of any known natural non-biological system when viewed with the electron microscope. We do not think that much smaller, still-undiscovered organisms exist in our world.

Viruses are a little aside from the point. They do have complex form but generally are recognized either by chemical criteria (which we shall discuss later) or by the fact that they reproduce in larger organisms. The very idea of a virus implies the existence of larger and more complex organisms; if we were to find something with a virus-like chemistry we would strongly suspect that cellular organisms were also present.

The great generalization of morphology is the cell theory, which states that organisms are either cells or societies of cells. Despite the myriad variations of cells, ranging from relatively large and elaborately equipped protozoa to degenerate forms such as red blood cells, the microscopist can identify cell structure with reliability and certainly will not confuse it with anything belonging to the inorganic world. He has an abundance of criteria and does not need a full-fledged "typical" cell in order to know that he is observing a cell.

The prevalence of morphology does not end there. Cells are composed of sub-units: walls, nuclei, various particles, *all* of which are recognizable as having consistent forms, which is only to say that the principle of survival is a very strict one and that all the finer details of the organization of the living things we know are preserved and propagated.

Thus, as a naturalist exploring a strange world, I think I would recognize a cow as a living thing, but if I were not permitted to see the cow but could examine a sample of hamburger with an ordinary microscope I would have little difficulty in knowing that I was observing the vestiges of an animal and might be able to say something about the animal. If the hamburger were so finely ground that I could not longer see cells, I would see nuclei, mitochondria, membranes, etc., all of them bodies of characteristic form. Even small pieces of these pieces would be identifiable with the electron microscope. . . .

True, there are imaginable simplicities of biological form that might call for some reservations. The simplest imaginable cell would be a membrane-enclosed sphere in which the macromolecules responsible for life-processes would not be organized into formed "organs," but would be dispersed in a liquid internal medium. If one found a population of such limp bags, all very much alike, he would strongly suspect that they had significance for biological evolution, though he could not be so sure he was dealing with an organism as if he had found a cow. Such a discovery would excite us greatly; it would be an ambiguity, but one that could be resolved by appeal to the molecular properties of living things. . . .

The maxim that relates form to function holds at the deepest analytical level. The cell, the fundamental unit, is both the unit of biological form and the atom of survival. Its own form, and the form of its parts, can be understood as a device for maintaining a rather precisely defined population of molecules and maintaining these molecules in proper—for survival—spatial relationships to each other. Conversely, the maintenance of these spatial relations of molecules is the ultimate source of all biological form.

Thus we arrive at the idea of a Molecular Biology: namely that the form of living things and the operations that produce and are produced by that form are reflections of a definite and definable organization of matter. The molecular approach to biology is not the only one, but it needs no justification. We study Life as a molecular operation because it *is* a molecular operation.

It would be unfortunate if this outlook seemed to arouse archaic misgivings about "materialism." The whole point is that molecular biology discovers in organisms potentialities, subtleties, values and purposes in the organization and operation of matter that are not disclosed in the elementary properties that are the domain of physics; we could not know, but had to discover, that matter is not necessarily undignified dirt.

We are allowed to make rather firm general statements about the organization of the living things we know by the *fact* that they are so much alike in so many ways. It is a fact that we can explain on evolutionary grounds. We may even think that they are too much alike for the purposes of a still more general understanding. Natural Selection could tend to eliminate alternatives that would be viable under other conditions; that is one reason why concern about life in other worlds is as relevant to our own biology as it is to a fundamental curiosity about the universe.

Let us consider some of the ways in which all the cells we know are fundamentally alike.

THE CELL AS AN ENCLOSED AQUEOUS SYSTEM

Cells contain water, usually more than 50 per cent by volume, and cease to operate when the water content falls too low. This inability to operate without an ample amount of liquid water is not necessarily fatal; there is the fascinating possibility of dormant life-processes that resume when the liquid water is restored. An ordinary seed is an example of this.

The cell is bounded by a membrane that separates the inside aqueous solution from the outside aqueous medium. The membrane is a lipid-protein complex about 50–100 Å thick and is rather similar in form in every kind of cell. The similarities extend to fine details, which will not be described here.

A living system does not conform even in its simple internal chemistry to the chemistry of its surroundings, but selects and rejects among even the simplest components of its world. The chief constituent of the internal solution is the potassium ion. This ion is relatively scarce in the environment and the internal concentration of potassium is almost invariably higher than that in the medium. Other ions are either concentrated or excluded and it can be said that the composition of the internal solution is invariably different from that of the bathing environment.

ENZYME PRINCIPLE

The entire chemistry of the cell is governed by the principle that all reactions are catalyzed by enzymes and that each reaction is catalyzed by a different enzyme. This principle, exceptions to which are rare, sets biochemistry apart from the natural chemistry of the non-living world and even from chemical technology, which may employ catalysts but does not possess such a variety and specificity of catalysts. (The enzyme principle is seldom named as such in the biological literature, apparently because it developed gradually and is not associated with a single sensational discovery.) In our world, all the enzymes are proteins. In any other world in which the principle applies, they would have to be a class of molecules with the same possibility of variety. The fundamental meaning of the enzyme principle is not merely that life-processes are very rapid, even though they take place at low temperatures, but that their rates are governed and balanced by the nature of the enzymes and are not at the mercy of their spontaneous rates. Sometimes we exaggerate when we say that the life of a cell could be completely described if we knew enough about its enzymes, but it is not an outrageous exaggeration.

FLOW OF MATTER AND ENERGY

The conservation principle of living things is different from, in fact opposite to, the main conservation principles of physics. Survival is a synonym for the "conservation of individual and kind" and it takes place by an expenditure of both matter and energy by the individual and the kind. (Only if we had some quantitative expression for what is conserved in survival would biology cease to be an essentially qualitative science.)

The flow of matter in living systems in our world is ultimately governed by the capture of simple constituents of the Earth and its atmosphere, such as carbon dioxide, nitrogen or its simpler compounds, water and a small number of inorganic elements. These are built into molecules much more complex than any that exist in the non-living world itself and if we find complex molecules outside organisms we always assume that they were put there by organisms. The life-death cycle returns matter to the non-biological world, so that the total flow of matter is describable in terms of cycles. It is, of course, incorrect to say that living things consume matter; what we mean is that their mere survival demands an enormous flow of matter through them.

The source of energy for the transformations of matter in our kind of living things is chemically reduced molecules and the energy is made available by catalyzed oxidation of reduced molecules. The major ultimate source of energy is sunlight, which is used in photosynthesis to reduce carbon compounds. But there are other sources available to specialized organisms, such as reduced inorganic elements. It is also postulated in contemporary discussion that the early history of our planet, and perhaps of others, included the production of reduced organic compounds by processes not requiring organisms, so that a ready source of energy and of prefabricated organic molecules could have been available at primitive stages of evolution.

The fundamental principles of our biological energetics may first be stated in negative form by contrasting organisms with familiar engines: organisms cannot use directly the energy released by oxidation, nor can they exploit temperature differences to perform work. They employ what may be called a principle of chemical energy coupling, a two-step process. Energy is "stored" in so-called *high-energy* compounds and "used" by breaking down these compounds, much as an old-fashioned submarine burned fuel in its engines to charge its batteries on the surface, then used the stored energy to propel it under water. In cells, the energy made available by oxidation of food (reduced compounds) is used to form high-energy compounds. The latter supply energy to the systems of the cell, where it is expended in many ways: synthesis, "pumping" of matter, movement, production of electricity, production of light, communication, etc. All the organisms we know use the same high-energy compound for carrying out most of their work —adenosine triphosphate, familiarly called ATP. Thus living things are quite different kinds of machines from those made for us by our engineers. An automobile is a device for oxidizing reduced compounds by combustion, using the heat to drive pistons. A horse is a cool device in which the muscles oxidize sugar without combustion, storing the chemical energy (originally solar energy) in ATP. The ATP then reacts with a system of molecular fibers in the muscle, causing motion as the ATP is broken down.

We would expect the principle of chemical energy coupling to apply to any form of life; to imagine surviving systems that solve their energetic problems in any other way is to appeal to an extreme of science fiction that is beyond the asymptotes of our knowledge. Still, the details we know about such systems are not so demanding. We cannot say why ATP in particular was chosen during evolution of life on our world, since chemical considerations suggest that many kinds of compounds may be suitable for energy storage.

THE DESIGN FOR SURVIVAL

Survival, both of the individual and of its kind, implies a conservation of *character* in the face of a continuous flux of matter. Stability of the matter itself is secondary to the character by which we acknowledge the individual or species; whether this dog is still the same dog named Igor or whether he is a descendant or an ancestor of dogs, does not depend at all on whether he still has any of the atoms he was born with. . . .

Modern biology has accepted the task of accounting for what is conserved, and for the means of conserving it, in terms of the molecules of which living things are made. It is superfluous to say that living systems *are* molecular systems; the objective of molecular biology is to translate the meanings of survival into molecular terms. The skeleton of the design is now perceived; the cardinal intellectual sin is to think the story complete. The essential points are these:

(1) The unit organism, the biological atom capable of surviving in a non-living environment, is the cell. If we abstract to the essentials, all cells are the same.

(2) The two main domains of action in the

cell are what we may call, loosely, a *genome* and a *cytoplasm*. The *genome* embodies the hereditary material. It is the embodiment of conservation and survival, that part of the organism which remains constant in character and is transmitted from generation to generation. The replication of genomes is the ultimate basis of survival, for so long as exact copies of the genome can be made and exact copies of the copies can be made, survival becomes independent of the flux of matter.

(3) The replication of genomes is an extraordinarily exact process, but mistakes can be made. The mistakes are then replicated indefinitely. These are the hereditary changes or *mutations*, that are thought to be the sources of variation at the disposal of the evolutionary process.

(4) The cytoplasm—all the structure and working-equipment of the cell—forms itself and grows under the government of the genome. Its constancy is a reflection of the constancy of the genome; its ability to vary in a consistent way is a reflection of the versatility of the genome. The genome seems to be programmed to give a consistent pattern of instructions over the life of the organism, yet also is responsible in its commands to "needs" of the organism.

(5) The molecular basis of the genome is deoxyribonucleic acid (DNA); the inherited instructions to the organism are coded by the sequence of subunits (nucleotides) in DNA as letters of a language are coded by their sequence in words and sentences. DNA is the self-replicating molecule, and many of the chemical principles of its replication are known.

(6) The main molecular basis of the form and functions of the cytoplasm—both factory and machinery—is expressed in protein molecules, whose individual character depends on a sequence of small component molecules, the amino acids. This is clearer in the chemical operations of the cell which, as we have seen, are governed by the amounts and kinds of enzymes. All known enzymes are proteins. The genome determines the character of the cell as a machine for capturing and transforming matter by determining the kinds of enzymes, the amounts of enzymes, and the time when each enzyme is made.

(7) The instructions in the genome, which is DNA, are translated into the formation of proteins by a system of molecular transcription, many of whose features are known.

Thus, the minimum design for survival can be expressed in the proposition that the cell is a device for maintaining and propagating a genome. The genome determines the structures and the operations of a cytoplasm which in turn provides the genome with all the goods and services it needs for its maintenance and propagation. The genome makes only two things: copies of itself and copies of commands to the cytoplasm. The cytoplasm makes everything else, structures, enzymes, ATP, etc., carries on the business with the outside world and plays peasantry and proletariat to the autocratic (and parasitic) dynasties of the genome.

These features of the living things we know are common to all of them, and each contains details that are equally common. We may repeat once more that in the life we know it is not only the principles that are shared, but the material embodiments of the principles. Instead of stating principles we could list the corresponding substances: water, potassium and other characteristic elements, the molecules of cell membranes, ATP and lesser high-energy compounds, an immense number of protein catalysts (all of which we would expect to find in every cell), DNA, the chemical constituents involved in the replication of DNA, the substance ribonucleic acid (RNA) into which the messages of the genome are transcribed, the chemical machinery of genome-directed protein synthesis . . . and the list would go on with molecules we have not mentioned. If we think of living things as chemical systems, evolution, which has produced such a vast variety of forms, has been rather conservative in the kinds of molecules it seems to have used from the first. It is not that there has been no molecular evolution, but that molecular evolution leaves its imprint mainly in the finer details of molecules and in those molecules (the pigments of flowers, for example) that are significant to the special problems of survival of special organisms, but are not fundamental to the state-of-being-a-living-thing. Anyone can observe the difference between a man and a chimpanzee, but it takes rather clever chemistry to establish the fact that the molecules of the two are different. On the other hand, it takes only very simple chemistry to decide that both are organisms.

If we contemplate living things over the longest time scale, we will not confine our thoughts to self-maintaining, kind-maintaining organisms. We will acknowledge that something came before them, and find force for that opinion in the very fact that existing organisms have so much in common. For the quintessential point of evolutionary reasoning is that similarity implies common descent and, if that point has sometimes been misleading, we still are inclined to think that the common material features of living things imply common descent beginning with a common supply of molecules out of which the first organisms were made.

Therefore, an evolutionary frame of thought leads to the conclusion that a biological exploration of this world at one time would have been a search for the molecular features of a planet on its evolutionary way to the production of full-fledged organisms. Some of these features are contained in a familiar word that has lost some of its original implications but not all of them: the term *organic chemisty.* Originally implying that certain kinds of molecules could be produced only by the action of living things, it lost its vitalistic meaning when the chemist in his laboratory began to learn how to make similar molecules and so became an organic chemist. In a way, that event which was so portentous in the history of science and technology seems rather insignificant from our immediate standpoint; it merely says that one kind of organism, which we call an organic chemist, is capable of imitating in the laboratory the molecules made by other organisms. But evolution gives it a deeper meaning: that there must have been a time in this world when molecules now made in nature by organisms (which have a sumptuous battery of enzymes at their disposal) were made directly and without the guidance of enzymes by natural processes of the planet itself.

Organic chemistry defines itself as the study of that immense class of compounds that is made possible by the ability of carbon atoms to bond to other carbon atoms in a great variety of linear and cyclic forms. On the planet Earth, the presence of such molecules can be taken as traces of life: signs of living things, the remains of living things that have lost their investment in survival, or products made and cast off by living things. But the chemical traces of life can be much more definite than the mere presence of organic compounds and more compelling as evidence of the presence or transit of organisms. If we limit our consideration of biochemistry only to that chemistry which is characteristic and indispensable to all the organisms we know, we can appeal to distinct classes of carbon compounds, to extraordinarily important linkages of carbon to nitrogen or to phosphorus or to sulfur, can search for those vital complexes of organic molecules with metals, iron or magnesium or others, that play such a part in the energetics of organisms. We need not be more specific here; any elementary text of biochemistry lists dozens of compounds that belong only to the world of organisms in the world we know.

Another general principle of the chemistry of biological systems is that of polymerization. We have seen that the design for survival and reproduction calls for operations of very large molecules; all the naturally occurring molecules at the long end of the chemists' size-spectrum are products of organisms. The crucial classes of such large molecules are the nucleic acids, by which the genetic record is coded, replicated and translated, and the proteins, whose subtle and varied chemical shapes are adapted to recognizing particular molecules, combining with those molecules, and catalyzing their transformations. The nucleic acids are the genes, the regulators of the genes, the messengers of the genes; the proteins are the enzymes. This variety of immense molecules is made by stringing together smaller molecules. In the case of nucleic acids the huge molecules represent merely permutations of the sequence of four kinds of small molecules called nucleotides. In the case of the proteins, the variety and subtlety is achieved by the patterned folding of chains that themselves comprise permutations of the sequence of about 20 types of smaller molecules, the amino acids, molecules of the same kind but different in important ways. Thus, all the variety of living things as we know them is derived essentially from four kinds of nucleotides (or 8 kinds by a different reckoning that is mainly of technical interest), and from 20 kinds of amino acids. The trick lies in how they are lined up, much as all the meanings and operations of all the languages using our alphabet depend on the ordering of 26 or so letters.

The spoor of life is in such chemical traces, and the means for observing them are powerful and objective. It makes sense to think that instruments detecting the constellations of atoms that go with living things could give us news about life, though it might say very little about organisms. The chemical traces would be expected in a world at the early stages of biological evolution, before organisms; according to prevailing ideas, the molecules might be accumulated in even greater abundance than in an evolved biological world, precisely because of the absence of reproducing organisms to "eat them up." The traces might be found in a world in which organisms were now extinct; we do not always think of an oil well as a trace of life, though we know it is.

To think of a universal biology is to test the generality of propositions that apply to our own biological world. A basic example is a question that has often been discussed since it can be approached through theoretical chemistry: must organic chemistry be a chemistry of carbon, or can one think of a comparable variety of biochemical compounds and reactions that is based on some other element? For example, could a comparable chemistry be achieved with the silicon atom? The answer generally has been negative, although such questions will continue to be asked. At an even more fundamental level, it has been asked whether water should be regarded as a unique medium for organic reactions, or whether other solvents (for example, liquid ammonia) might not serve the same purpose in another world. Again, the answer has seemed dubious, yet no one would exclude categorically the possibility of other solvents though we probably would insist that biological systems would have to be liquid systems. As we turn to molecules with a more particular significance for survival, the estimates of their universality are even less certain. In principle, a biological system will require "high-energy compounds" but how similar to ATP would they have to be? Heredity would require a coded replicable polymer (unless governed by a principle not yet imagined); what properties of DNA could be embodied in a polymer that was quite different from DNA—so different that it would not give any of the chemical tests for a DNA-like molecule? What kinds of large molecules that did not test as proteins could have the same versatility of catalytic powers? Perhaps theory can expose possibilities and probabilities; the explorer will make the tests.

We ask "What is Life?" but find that we can define only the attributes and material traces of living things. The definition is not succinct, for it comprehends all the principles and material facts that distinguish the life we know, and gains precision from the specification of additional detail. Nevertheless, the distinction between the living and the non-living is no less real because the boundary seems blurred. Indeed, the evolutionary approach to biology implies that we should expect the boundary to be diffuse (in the past, if not now), though the domains on either side are quite different. The problem is not that our conception of a living thing is vague; on the contrary, our concern is that it is too definite because it is too provincial.

39

Chemical Evolution

MELVIN CALVIN
1965

The term Chemical Evolution is here used in a very specific sense to refer to that period of the evolutionary history of the Earth during which the chemical components on its surface were changed from their primeval form into chemicals upon which living organisms, or from which living organisms, could develop. The idea that living organisms arose as a natural development in the course of the chemical transformation of the surface of the Earth is not new. In fact, it was recognized by Darwin himself that the basic notions of evolution which he formulated were in fact continuous, not only throughout the appearance of living organisms and their varieties but continuing back through that stage of history into the period which preceded the existence of living organisms on the surface of this Earth. This was recognized by him in a very famous remark which I thought it might be worth repeating now to make you more familiar with some of Darwin's chemical concepts held as early as 1874. He says (de Beer, 1959):

> You expressed quite correctly my views where you said that I had intentionally left the question of the Origin of Life uncanvassed as being altogether *ultra vires* in the present state of our knowledge, and that I dealt only with the manner of succession. I have met with no evidence that seems in the least trustworthy in favour of so-called spontaneous generation. I believe that I have somewhere said (but cannot find the passage) that the principle of continuity renders it probable that the principle of life will hereafter be shown to be a part, or consequence, of some general laws.

The statement to which Darwin refers, and which he had forgotten, was written earlier, before 1871:

> It is often said that all the conditions for the first production of a living organism are now present, which could ever have been present. But if (and oh! what a big if!) we could conceive in some warm little pond,

From *Proceedings of The Royal Society*, ser. A, vol. 288, pp. 441–466, 1965. Reprinted with permission of the author and The Royal Society.

with all sorts of ammonia and phosphoric acid salts, light, heat, electricity, etc. present, that a proteine compound was chemically formed ready to undergo still more complex changes, at the present day such matter would be instantly devoured or absorbed, which would not have been the case before living creatures were formed.

Darwin there exhibited two qualities: First, a remarkable perspicacity about the nature of chemistry, and, secondly, an altogether characteristic conservatism about how much he knew, and how much chemists knew, at that time, about the nature of molecules. And he was quite right. In those days so little was known about the nature of molecules and their interactions and behaviour that it was fruitless for him, and others like him, even to try to reconstruct the chemical evolutionary history of prebiotic times.

Today there are possible two approaches to gaining a concept, at least, if not direct unequivocal knowledge, of what this sequence of events might have been. One of these is to continue the Darwinian approach itself, namely, the examination of the record as it may exist in the rocks and surface formations of the Earth. Darwin used only that part of the record—the fossil record—in which recognizable life forms existed; in which morphologically recognizable entities could be examined and described. Today, however, it is possible for us to go beyond this level of examination because of our biochemical knowledge and because of the evolution of analytical devices which permit us to not only determine that there are organic materials of various sorts present in ancient rocks which contain few or no morphological features which are recognizable, but to describe in significant detail the intimate molecular architecture of these substances. This is a kind of 'fossil' examination and correlation exactly analogous to that used by the palaeontologists, but it is in the hands of the organic and biological chemists.

The other approach is that of trying to reconstruct the possible sequence of chemical events that could have occurred before the existence of living things on the face of the Earth, the effort that Darwin referred to as being conceptually possible but as yet not fruitful because, at that time, not enough information was available about the behaviour of atoms and molecules under the influence of various physico-chemical forces. Today, however, this has become a significantly possible effort.

I want to describe some of the things we have done along both of these approaches: (1) to examine the historical record beyond that of the morphologically recognizable forms—'chemical fossils,' if you like—and (2) quite independently to see if we can find and reconstruct some of the chemical reactions which might have occurred among the primeval molecules on the surface of the Earth which could give rise to biologically important substrates, leading ultimately (if we can trace it) to the structures and reactions which we know now are an essential component for the functioning of living organisms (Calvin, 1961a, 1961b, 1962b, 1964; Ehrensvard, 1963; Fox, 1960, 1965a, 1965b; Gaffron, 1960; Horowitz and Miller, 1962; Keosian, 1964; *New Biology*, 1954; Oparin, 1957, 1959, 1961, 1964; Wald, 1964).

This kind of effort is more than just an exercise in detective work, because the possibility is now with us, within most of our lifetimes, of exploring other sites then the surface of the Earth for a possible corroboration, or denial, of the kind of sequence with which we might come up, as a result of this study. . . .

ORGANIC GEOCHEMISTRY

We shall now undertake the two exercises which I have described earlier, namely, looking at the 'molecular fossils' on the Earth's surface and seeing what we can find and then, after that, examining the possible chemical reactions that might give rise to important systems today.

Figure 39.1 gives us some clue to the geological history with which we have to deal. The age of the Earth is approximately 5000 m.y. [million years], and this figure has not changed much since this picture was first drawn. . . . The period of chemical evolution presumably begins with the formation of the Earth in its present form and gave rise to more and more complex chemicals, and at some point in time organic evolution, that is, evolution based upon living systems as we know them today, began. I suspect that the asymptote as here drawn will probably have to be modified somewhat: with new knowledge we are pushing the beginning of organic evolution further and further back in time.

We are going to spend much of our time tracing organic evolution back in so far as we can trace it back in terms of 'molecular fossils' from the earliest well recognized [metazoan] fossils of morphological form, approximately 600 m.y. ago, and we are going to talk about chemicals which we can find in rocks which are older than 600 m.y., some as old as 2700 m.y.

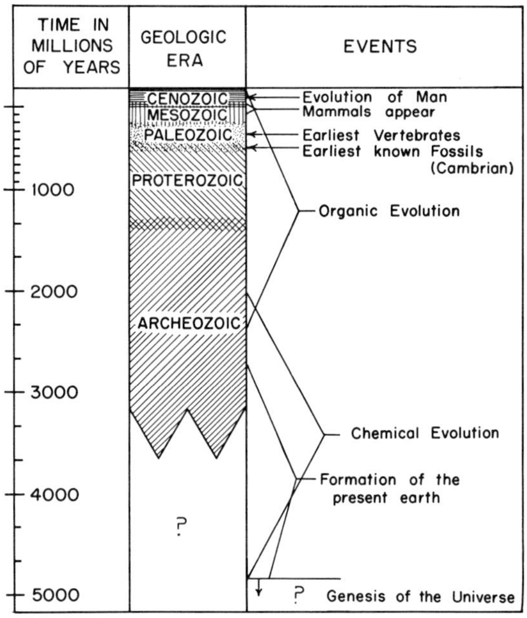

FIGURE 39.1
Time scale for total evolution

While many rocks in which known fossils have been seen have been analysed and the methods of analysis which were used for these rocks were just adequate, the determination of the detailed molecular structures which are present in the younger rock in correlation with the recognizable fossil elements is only just beginning. This is partly because the analytical tools have only recently been refined to the point in which we can describe the intimate details of the molecular architecture that is present. The various kinds of molecules that one can look for are obvious ones. One would look for amino acids and heterocyclic bases as representative of fossils of the proteins and nucleic acids. This latter has not been done to the same extent as the amino acid search because the analytical tools available to identify amino acids in trace amounts in the rocks were much better than for the nucleic acid bases. The third group of molecules which has been known for a long time as organic fossil material but whose intimate structures have not been analysed with this in mind are the hydrocarbons themselves, that is, molecules made up only of carbon and hydrogen in special architectural arrangements as represented by petroleum and the materials found in it.

We have chosen to examine the hydrocarbon composition of the ancient rocks to see if we could not find characteristic features of the hydrocarbons which could be correlated in some way with the organisms which might have given rise to them. In order to get a date line for our work, we elected to examine some young rocks of recent origin whose biological precursors, at least, were well established. Using the modern analytical tools we undertook the examination of the Green River Shale which underlies a large part of the western North American continent. The Green River Shale is only 60 m.y. old and it has in it a high proportion of hydrocarbons; in fact, it is presumed to be one of the rich oil shales of the world. It was relatively easy to obtain samples and to undertake this analysis.

The Green River Shale was analysed by suitable extractions and fractionations (Eglinton et al., 1965) and Figure 39.2 shows the vapour phase chromatogram of the alkanes from the Green River Shale. The upper chromatogram shows the total hydrocarbon extract after the removal of any non-hydrocarbon and aromatic components. This is clearly a complex mixture. It was possible to separate the hydrocarbon extract into two quite distinct components by means of molecular sieves (5 Å). These sieves allowed the straight chain hydrocarbons to wend their way through the 5 Å holes, and to prevent the passage of any material with a branch or cyclic component. We were thus able to separate the straight-chain hydrocarbons from the rest of the materials which were present. None of the branched and cyclic hydrocarbons, which

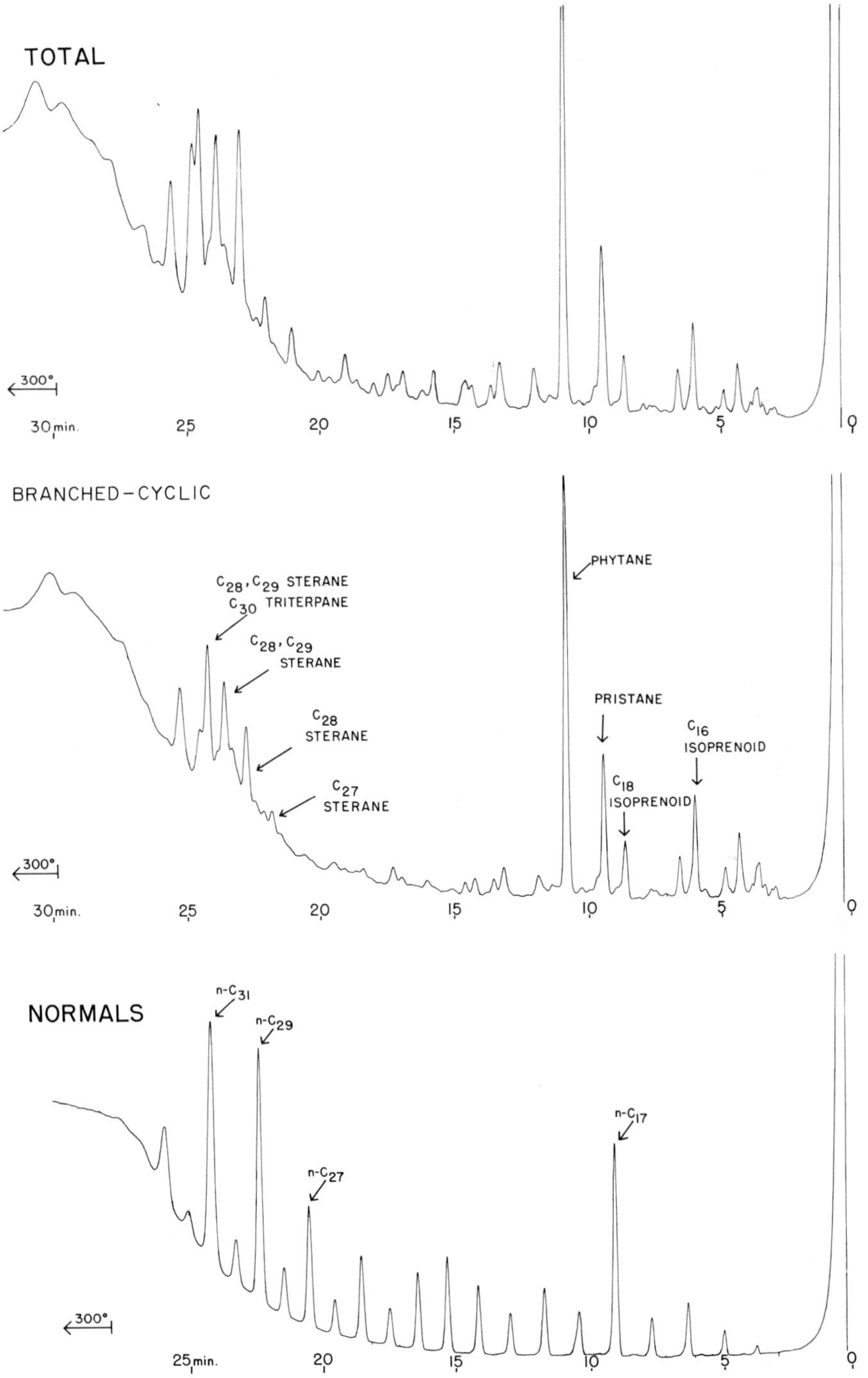

FIGURE 39.2
Vapour phase chromatogram of alkanes from Green River Shale. (Attn. 10×8.)

are shown by the centre portion of Figure 39.2, pass into the molecular sieve. In the bottom part of this figure is shown the fraction that entered the sieve. At least in the Green River Shale this fraction represents a nice, clean sequence of a normal saturated hydrocarbon homology.

We have since learned that these 5 Å sieves will also absorb straight-chain hydrocarbons with at least a terminal olefin in them. Whether they will absorb straight-chain hydrocarbons with an internal olefin or not remains to be determined. From an examination of models it seems as though the cis internal olefin should not enter the 5 Å hole while the trans might.

The branched cyclic components can thus be separated from the straight-chain hydrocarbons, and the non-thermodynamic distribution of the normal hydrocarbons can be seen—the general dominance of the odd-numbered hydrocarbons represented here by the C_{17} and C_{19}, etc. There is no question about the biological origin of these straight-chain hydrocarbons; most of them come by the decarboxylation of the even-number saturated carboxylic acids.

Few compounds have been labelled in the branched cyclic series. Among them are the C_{16}, C_{18}, C_{19} and C_{20} polyisoprenes; these were determined by cochromatography and by mass spectrometry, and there is no ambiguity about them. Phytane, of course, is the dominant one and pristane (one carbon atom less than phytane) next, and you will see the relation between these in a moment. The absence of the C_{17} isoprenoid is also something to note, because I think it may give us some clue as to how these polyisoprenoids originated and how they may have been transformed. In addition, a number of cyclic polyisoprenes are present (see Figure 39.2, branched-cyclic fraction); among these are the C_{27} sterane, cholestane, and probably coprastane, and the C_{28} and C_{29} saturated steroids, ergostane and sitostane. The presence of terpane, that is, C_{30} pentacyclic hydrocarbons, is also indicated (Burlingame, Haug, Belsky, and Calvin, 1965). These are not simple peaks—they are multicomponent peaks as the mass spectrometer has told us. At least two of them contain both the C_{28} and C_{29} steranes. The origin of these materials is probably the reduction of the corresponding unsaturated, or oxygenated, sterols. Here are shown the carbon skeleton of coprastane and cholestane:

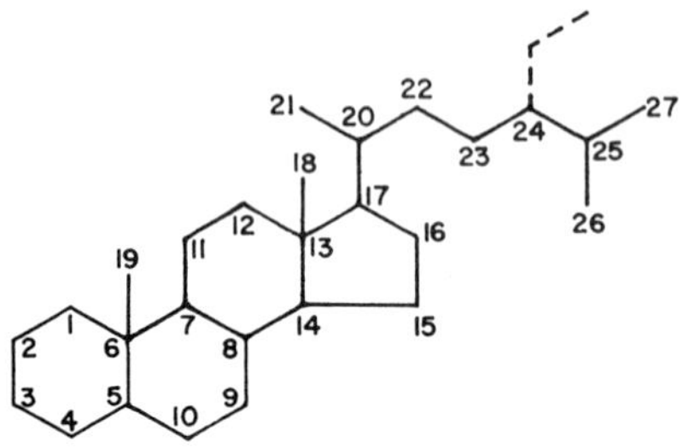

C_{27} sterane (cholestane, coprostane).
C_{28} sterane (24-methyl C_{27} sterane, ergostane and isomers).
C_{29} sterane (24-ethyl C_{27} sterane, sitostane and isomers).

The ergostane has a C_{24} methyl and the sitostane a C_{24} ethyl group. In addition to that, the possibility exists in ergostane of four isomers because there can be *cis-trans* junction of various rings. The possibility that there are four isomers of ergostane probably accounts in part for the multiple distribution of the ergostane mass-spectrometry pattern in those four peaks, although this yet remains to be determined. The mass spectra of the three steranes and the pentacyclic triterpane which permitted their unambiguous identification in the five g.l.c. [gas liquid chromatography] peaks (Figure 39.2) between 22 and 26 min are shown in Figure 39.3.

Here are relatively stable hydrocarbon markers whose biological origin is pretty much unambiguous, and the probable origin of the phytane and polyisoprenoids is shown in Figure 39.4. Phytane very likely comes from chlorophyll which has the phytol alcohol as an ester on one of the carboxyl groups. It is a tetraisoprenoid and has one double bond and one terminal hydroxyl group which, upon hydrogenation and hydrogenolysis, will give the C_{20} phytane. By hydrogenation and then oxidation of the terminal alcohol, followed by decarboxylation, the C_{19} polyisoprene pristane is obtained. The fact that the phytane is the dominant peak in the Green River Shale with

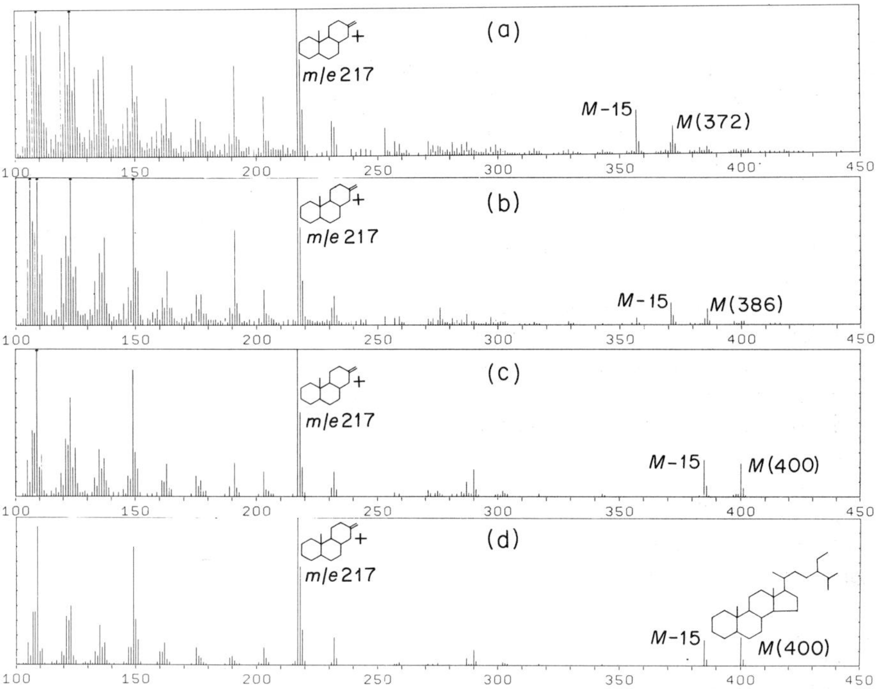

FIGURE 39.3
Mass-spectrometric analysis of g.l.c. peaks (22 to 26 min) of Green River Shale. *a*, C_{27} sterane; *b*, C_{28} sterane; *c*, C_{29} sterane; *d*, C_{30} pentacyclic triterpane.

pristane as the next one seems to be significant, probably of the presence of chlorophyll in the biological material from which the Green River hydrocarbons arose. The presence of C_{16}, C_{18}, C_{19} and C_{20} polyisoprenes together with the unequivocal absence of the C_{17} compound would require two carbon-carbon bond cleavages and would, therefore, be highly improbable.

This work on the Green River Shale is, of course, only a preliminary exercise in learning how to perform the analysis and to read and understand the data which the analysis provides. What we are really trying to do is to go to much older rock formations in which the hydrocarbon content is the only evidence that we may have upon which to base our conclusions. We have done this, and have gone to several older rocks. We reported last year on the presence of the same two isoprenoids (phytane and pristane) in a rock of about 1000 m.y., the Nonesuch Shale of Northern Michigan (Eglinton, Scott, Belsky, Burlingame, and Calvin, 1964; Barghoorn, Meinschein, and Schopf, 1965). The presence of both phytane and pristane in the Nonesuch Shale we took to mean that chlorophyll, or chlorophyllous materials, were already in existence as early as 1000 m.y. ago. That is to say, that the whole photosynthetic apparatus was functioning as early as 1000 m.y. ago (Calvin, 1962a).

Since that was reported roughly a year ago, we have gone still further back. We have obtained a piece of the Soudan Iron Formation of Minnesota which is dated at 2700 m.y. (Cloud, Gruner, and Hagen, 1965). If you remember the time scale, that is more than half-way back toward the origin of the present Earth. The Earth is 4700 m.y. and the Soudan is dated at > 2700 m.y. The analysis of the Soudan Shale alkane fractions is shown in Figure 39.5. This is the same kind of analysis which I described for the Green River Shale. However, as you can see, the Soudan which is 2700 m.y. old gives a different distribution of hydrocarbons: note that the straight-chain series is very much contracted and no longer has the sharp odd-even behaviour that the normal hydrocarbon series had which we found in the very young oils. First of all, the Soudan has a very much narrower distribution over a very much narrower range, dominated by C_{17}. You can see that the C_{18} is really higher than it ought to be if we are going to have a C_{17}-C_{19} dominant series. However, the distribution is still far from anything that might be called thermodynamic in character. The presence in the 2700 m.y. old Soudan of the isoprenoid series, again (C_{18}, C_{19}, C_{20} and even the C_{21} isoprenoid) attests to the existence of the isoprene system even as early as 2700 m.y. ago (Belsky, Johns, McCarthy, Burlingame, Richter, and Calvin, 1965). What may be even more significant is the presence of the C_{27}, C_{28} and C_{29} steranes in the branched-cyclic fraction from this very ancient rock as well (Burlingame, Haug, Belsky, and Calvin, 1965).

Figure 39.6 gives a comparison of a straight-chain set as a function of age (Antrim, Nonesuch, and Soudan Shales). I hesitate to draw any very significant conclusions from these relative distributions, because not only do the ages of the rocks differ but the nature of the deposits from which they come are different. . . .

I neglected to mention that there were really four different homologies present in the ancient rocks: the normal homology of the straight chain, the isoprene homology, the anteiso series and the iso series. Figure 39.7 gives the structural relationships between the homologies. The ones with the numbers under certain atoms are the ones, except for the C_{17} isoprenoid, which represent the dominant compounds in each of these series. Among the isoprenoids formed from phytane, the C_{19} is undoubtedly made by stripping off the terminal hydrocarbon atoms (C_{20}), the C_{18} by breaking the bond between the C_{17} and C_{19} atoms. I think you can see that the next one can be formed by splitting off between C_{16} and C_{17}. In order to get the C_{17} isoprenoid we would have to make two breaks—the one between C_{17} and C_{19} and the one between C_{17} and C_{18}. As we have previously suggested, that is probably the reason why the C_{17} isoprenoid is not present in the ancient rocks, but the others are.

What are the structures of the polyisoprenes and how do we believe they came into being? What does it mean that the presumed biological apparatus for their synthesis was already fully developed, or well developed, as early as 2700 m.y. ago? How are these homologies formed in the first place? Figure 39.8 gives a brief summary of the potential isoprenoid reactions. First of all, we get Δ^3-isopentenyl pyrophosphate by a series of reactions through mevalonic acid from acetyl coenzyme A. The pyrophosphate can then react with more acetyl *CoA* to give rise to the anteiso series. The condensations (with isopentenyl pyrophosphate) initiated by the incipent carbon ions arising from the dimethallyl pyrophosphate give rise, of course, to the polyisoprenoids. The condensation of this same incipient carbonium ion with the acetyl *CoA*, and followed by further acetyl *CoA* condensation, will give rise to the iso

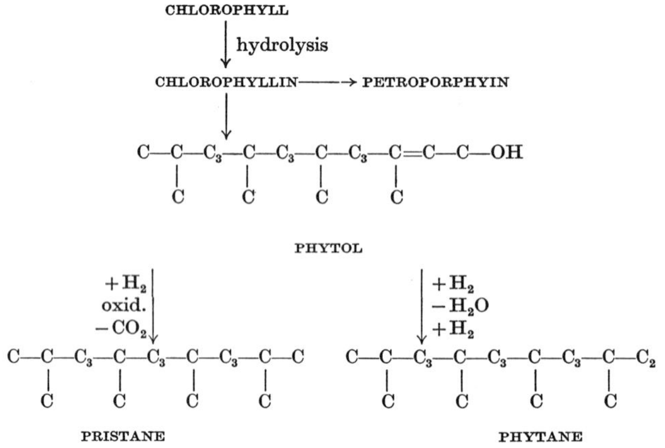

FIGURE 39.4
A possible source of pristane and phytane. (Bendoraitis et al., 1963.)

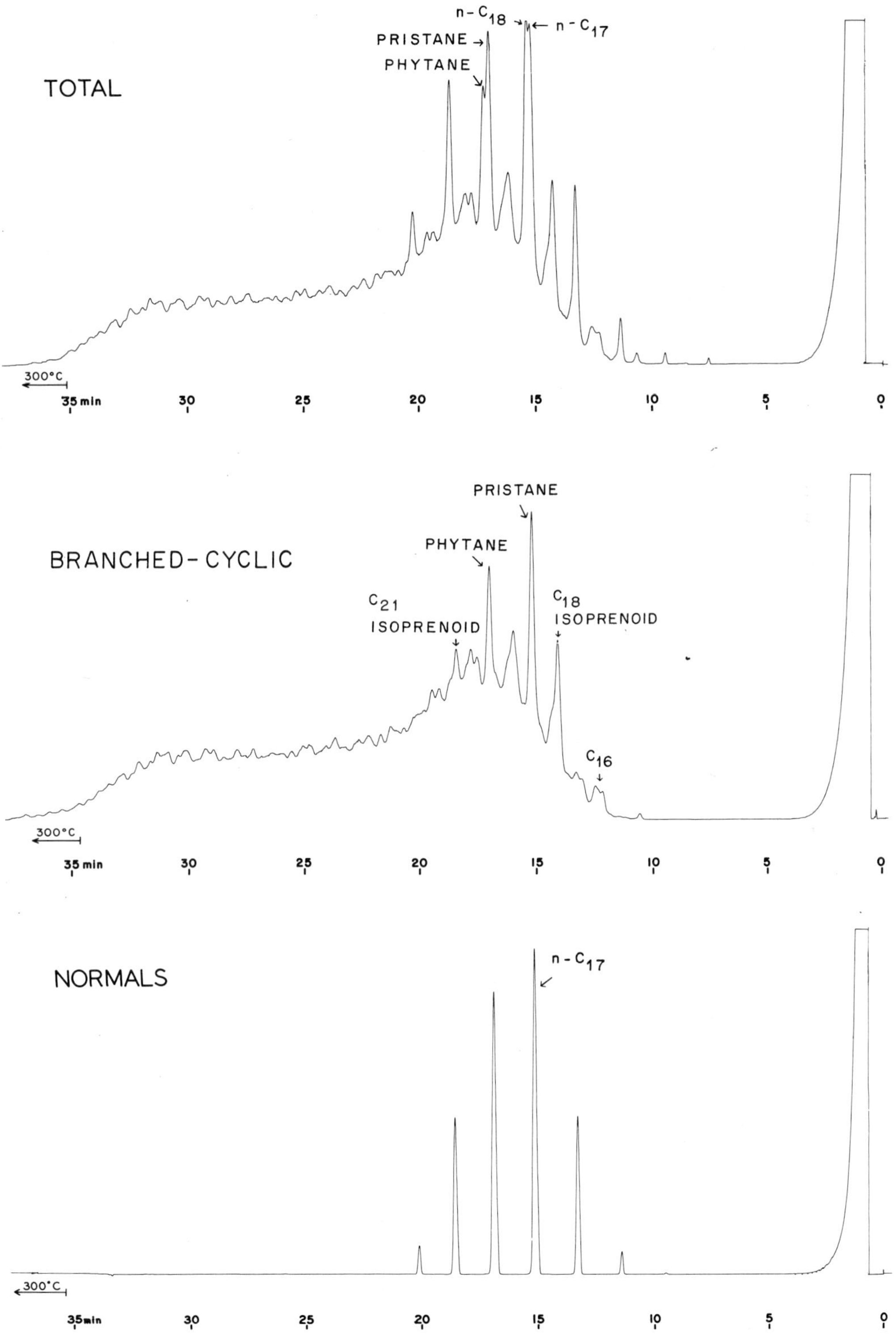

FIGURE 39.5
Vapor phase chromatogram of alkanes from Soudan Iron Formation. (Attn. 100 × 1.)

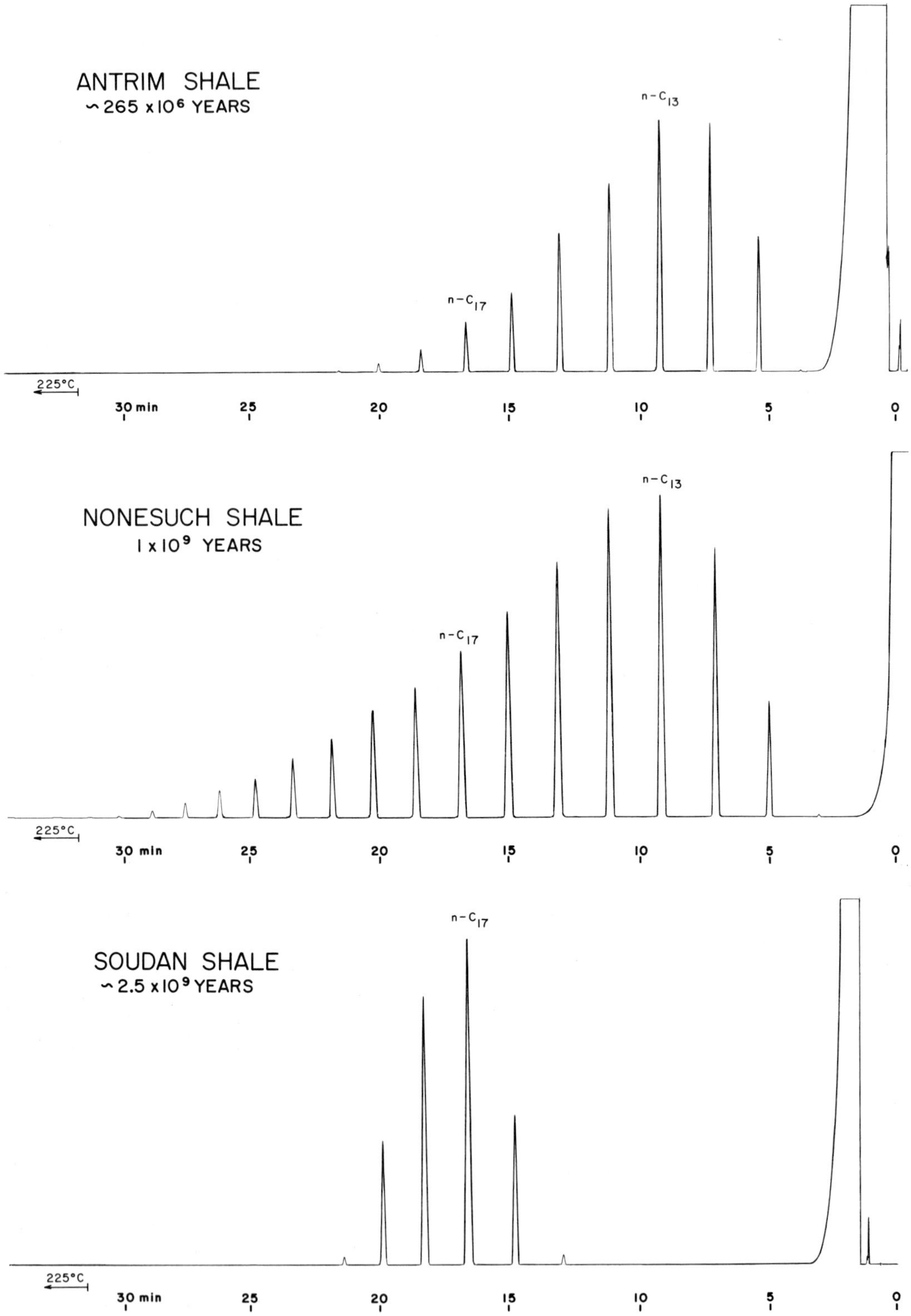

FIGURE 39.6
Vapour phase chromatogram of straight-chain hydrocarbons in three shales of different geological ages. *Top,* Antrim (ca. 265 m.y., attn. 100 × 1); *middle,* Nonesuch (1000 m.y., attn. 100 × 2); *bottom,* Soudan (ca. 2500 m.y., attn. 100 × 1).

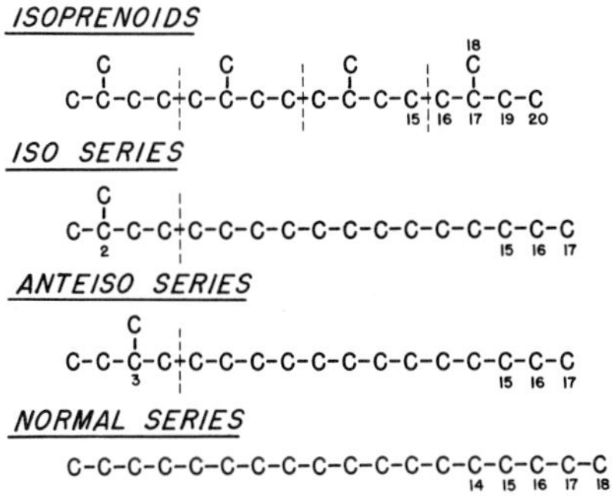

FIGURE 39.7
Structural relation between homologies in ancient rocks

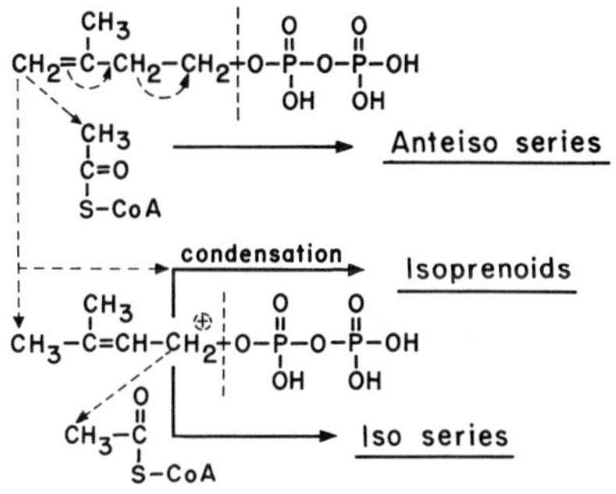

FIGURE 39.8
Summary of potential isoprenoid reactions

series. The acetyl *CoA* would itself give rise to the normal series. We have here a rather complex sequence of chemical reactions which are required to produce the unsaturated pyrophosphate (isopentenyl and its isomer, dimethallyl) which is the common precursor to all of them with branches and also to produce the acetyl *CoA*. These are to be followed by all of the reactions which are required to make these four homologies. The number of reactions is considerable, and the specificity is high.

The interpretation which I want to make of this is that as early as 2700 m.y. ago the whole biosynthetic apparatus for producing these intermediates had evolved, thus giving rise to the very specific isoprenoids as well as the peculiar distribution of the straight-chain homologies which we now find as the molecular fossil evidence of the early existence of this apparatus.

If we now have to produce these complex molecules and the whole apparatus for making them in such a short evolutionary period of something less than 2000 m.y., the whole sequence of evolutionary events must be much faster than most of us had originally supposed (Calvin, 1965). I am afraid that this time will become still shorter as we finish our present series of observations. As we go back in our examination of these ancient rocks it would seem reasonable to find a period in time at which these hydrocarbons in the rocks begin to get simpler; in which, for example, the entire isopentenyl pyrophosphate sequence is no longer present but something more elementary in the way of biosynthetic reactions would have been occurring. I would like to find that point in time, and I suspect that it will bring us so close to what is now believed to be the age of the formation of the Earth that we are going to face some kind of a revolution in our thinking about this early evolutionary history (Cloud, 1965). The possibility that many of the organic compounds now believed to be the proximate substrate for organic evolution might have been present in the original cosmic dust which gave rise to the Earth itself has recently received added support (Studier, Hayatsu, and Anders, 1965).

We are searching for still older rocks, rocks which have ages beyond 3000 m.y. and which contain carbon. The amounts of carbon we need are, of course, getting smaller as our analytical tools are becoming more sophisticated, and I believe that we will be able to determine the nature of the carbon-containing molecules present in even the oldest rocks.

There is at least one ambiguity in this whole question, and that is whether the rocks and the hydrocarbons in them are of the same age. It is conceivable that some of the hydrocarbons may have settled into the rocks long after the rocks were formed. . . .

PREBIOTIC CHEMISTRY

Let us now take the other approach to the problem of chemical evolution, namely, that of starting with the primitive Earth, at the other end of the evolutionary sequence. Let us begin with what the astronomers tell us was the nature of the primitive Earth. They tell us that the primitive Earth was formed by a cold aggregation of dust and gases, and that it was originally dominated by hydrogen. Therefore, the primitive Earth's atmosphere was dominantly populated by reduced molecular species shown in the first row of Figure 39.9, where the carbon, nitrogen and oxygen are all attached primarily to hydrogen to give methane, ammonia and water. This is presumed to be the population of the primeval atmosphere of the Earth's surface.

The question is: Can we, by introducing energy into such an aggregation of molecules, achieve any kind of evolutionary development of molecular structures of any significance? The answer lies in the fact that such a question is subject to experimental test. We can set up such molecular compositions and subject them to a variety of energy sources, such as ionizing radiation in the form of either particulate or gamma radiation; or we can introduce energy in the form of ultraviolet radiation or in the form of electrical discharge (such as lightning might produce). All of these have been done (Garrison et al., 1951; Calvin, 1956; Miller, 1955; Miller and Urey, 1959; Oro and Kimball, 1961, 1962; Palm and Calvin, 1962; Ponnamperuma et al., 1963a, 1963b, 1963c, 1964, 1965a, 1965b; Steinman et al., 1964, 1965a, 1965b). Indeed when such high energy sources are brought to bear on such molecular aggregates, the molecules do indeed break—the carbon-hydrogen, hydrogen-hydrogen, nitrogen-hydrogen and oxygen-hydrogen bonds break—and the radicals, or ionic fragments, which result from such breakage recombine not necessarily in their original forms but in other metastable forms. We have been able to demonstrate the formation of all the compounds in the second and third rows of Figure 39.9 as formed from the primeval molecules in the top row. Note that these primitive secondary molecules are the very same small molecules upon which present day living organisms are based, both as metabolites and as structural elements.

The experiments have been carried much further than this would seem to indicate. Sugars have been formed (Miller, 1955; Miller and Urey, 1959); heterocycles have been formed (Oro and Kimball, 1961, 1962; Ponnamperuma et al., 1963a, 1963b, 1963c, 1964, 1965a, 1965b); and other compounds are formed from the HCN first produced and the ammonia present (Schimpl, Lemmon, and Calvin, 1965). This is an important comment which at the time Figure 39.9 was initially prepared we did not appreciate. We have since looked for compounds which can be formed from ammonia and HCN, namely, cyanamide (Schimpl et al., 1965) and its various relatives,

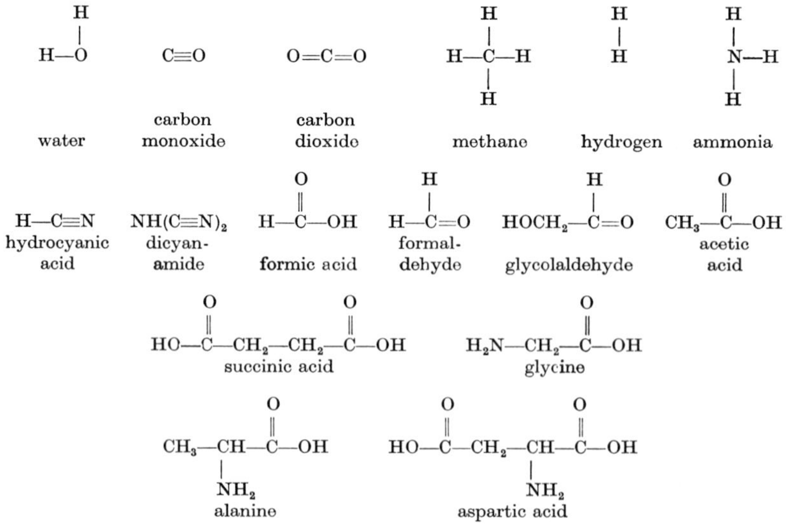

FIGURE 39.9
Primeval and primitive organic molecules

such as the dimer of cyanamide, dicyandiamide (Schimpl et al.), melamine (Hayatsu, 1964), and, of course, dicyanamide.* All of these molecules which have been sought have been found after we specifically sought them, and the reason for this search will become apparent.

The important result of these experiments is that the introduction of energy into the primeval reduced molecular system does indeed convert the system into a more complex one, and the direction of that conversion seems to be toward the molecules which are today the real substrates of living organisms, both in structure and in function. Note that the amino acids, the hydroxy acids, the dicarboxylic acids, the sugars und related substances are the common materials upon which the present day living organisms can operate.

How does a living organism operate on these materials? As you well know, this is accomplished by virtue of its structural features. Many of these features, as well as the enzymes which are required for modern living organisms, are made up of polypeptides and protein molecules. The energy conversion apparatus is very sharply dependent upon highly structured features of the specific catalytic systems which the linear array of polypeptides contain, or can develop; the informational transfer aspect of living organisms is contained in another kind of linear array, the polynucleotides, and there is a complex interrelation between these various types of substances. All of these properties and behaviours are dependent upon structural features which are built into the molecules and which show in the next stage of their evolution.

DEHYDRATION CONDENSATION REACTIONS

In order to achieve the next stage of the evolution of the biologically important molecules, the necessity for hooking the small molecules together must be established. When you examine the biological micromolecules which constitute the structural and much of the catalytic basis for living organisms, you can see that they are derived by a reaction common to all of them. They are made from the primitive molecules (amino acids, sugars, phosphoric acid, hydroxy acids and the like) by a single kind of reaction, namely, a dehydration condensation. Figures 39.10 and 39.11 show the dehydration condensation reactions in principle, at least. Figure 39.10 shows the dehydration condensation of the amino acids; the carboxylic acid and the amino group interact to give the peptide linkage and then, of course, the molecule can grow from either end (the amino end or the carboxyl end) to make the polypeptides, which ultimately become large enough to have catalytic and structural properties which we now recognize as characteristic of proteins. The formation of polysaccharides is also a dehydration polymerization. (It is drawn in Figure 39.10 as a glucosidic linkage between the semiacetyl structure of one glucose molecule and the 4-hydroxyl group of another, but there are other types of dehydration reactions which would give rise to polysaccharides.) The lipids also are the result of dehydration condensation reactions, the alcohol and the carboxylic acid giving rise to ester linkage, and this occurring on several of the hydroxyl groups of the glycerine will, of course, give rise to the ordinary lipid type of structure.

The fourth of the biological macromolecules of great importance is the group of nucleic acids, and Figure 39.11 shows how nucleic acids may be formed as the result of several different kinds of dehydration condensation. First is the dehydration condensation which gives rise to the glycosidic linkage between the heterocyclic NH group and the glycosidic hydroxyl of the sugar; second, the ester linkage between the primary hydroxyl (5′) of the sugar and the phosphoric acid, and, finally, a second esterification between the second hydroxyl of the phosphoric acid and another hydroxyl group (3′) of another sugar molecule on a second mononucleotide. This, of course, can go on to another sugar, etc., giving rise, finally, to a polynucleotide.

All of these, as you can see, are reactions of the same kind—dehydration condensations—and various methods have been conceived as routes to achieving these dehydration condensations in an abiological system. The first one which the chemists would immediately consider is to put the monomeric material into an

* Dicyanamide is formed in greater than 1% yield upon ultraviolet irradiation for a few hours of *ca.* 0.01M solution of NH_4CN, as observed in our laboratory by Steinman, Kenyon, and Calvin (1965b).

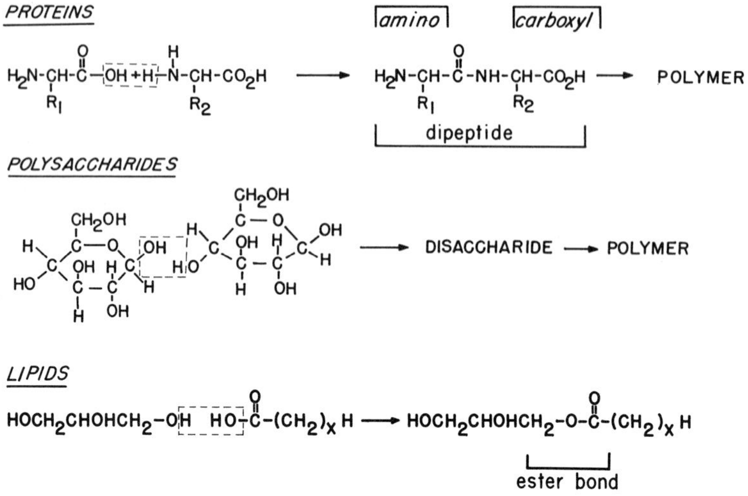

FIGURE 39.10
Dehydration condensation of amino acids

anhydrous situation—into a medium in which the activity (thermodynamic) of the water is somehow depressed—such that the dehydration will proceed spontaneously. This has been done. One can, as you know, simply dissolve amino acids in a suitable non-aqueous medium and get dehydration condensation reactions which can be carried to such an extent as to give polypeptides of high molecular weights. Fox (Harada and Fox, 1964) has been the principal protagonist of this approach.

There are other ways, and one could imagine that the hydroxylic and amino containing compounds could be absorbed on a specific type of clay or mineral surface in which the activity of the water is in some specific way reduced. Thus the dehydration condensation would be made to take place on the dehydrating surface of a particular kind of mineral. The chief protagonist of this approach to the formation of these polymeric materials has been Bernal (1959), and very early he proposed the clay mineral surface as the principal site for the formation of these polymeric materials; however, the experiments which might demonstrate this on any significant scale have not yet been carried to the point where we can presume all of the kinds of the dehydration reac-

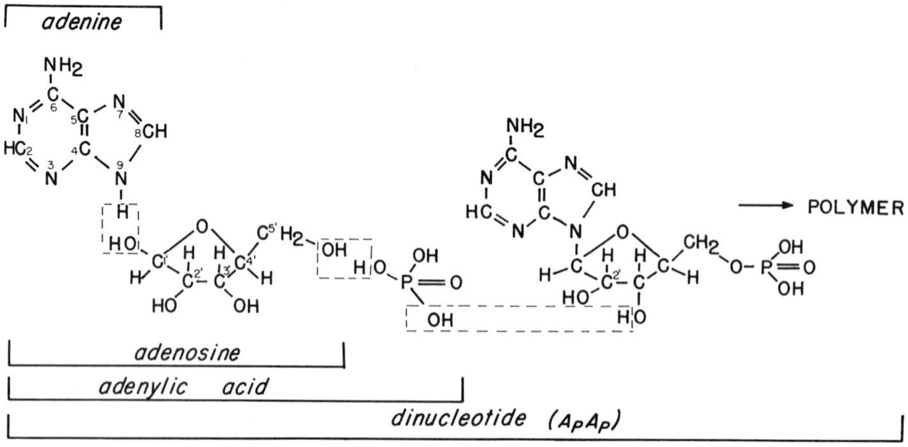

FIGURE 39.11
Dehydration condensation of nucleic acids. RNA shown; DNA lacks OH on 2′ position.

tions under these circumstances (Miller and Parris, 1964).

We have taken a still different approach. We felt that since these monomeric units are formed primarily in dilute aqueous media, we should try to find ways of inducing the dehydration condensation in such dilute aqueous media. To chemists this might seem like something that is a foolish thing to try, i.e. to try to induce a dehydration in water solution, but it turns out that this can be done.

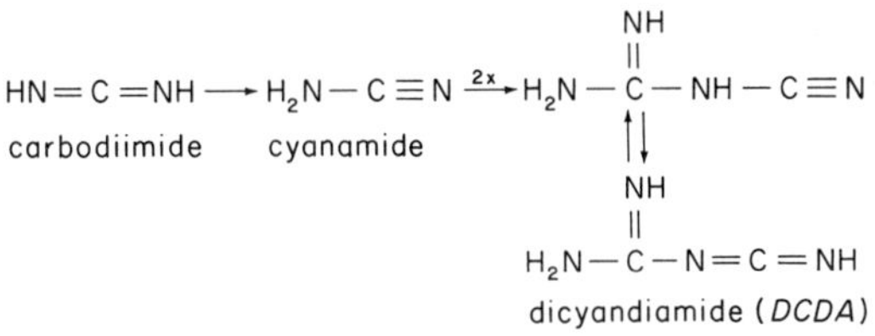

FIGURE 39.12
Cyanamide dimerizes to form dicyandiamide

We took our cue from the presence of HCN in the reaction mixture in the first instance (Miller, 1957), recognizing that even though HCN has in it the capacity for absorbing the elements of a water molecule to form formamide, it does not do it very readily in water itself. Then, coupling this idea with the knowledge of the use of a multiple carbon-nitrogen bond in a specific dehydration condensation which exists in the use of the carbodiimides in the accomplishment of these dehydration condensation reactions (Khorana, 1961), we took the next step and asked, 'why can't we use the parent carbodiimide?' The tautomer of carbodiimide is, of course, cyanamide. Cyanamide in aqueous solution does not remain as cyanamide very long but dimerizes to form dicyandiamide (Figure 39.12).

Although we started with cyanamide we very quickly moved our efforts to dicyandiamide (DCDA) because of its greater stability in aqueous media. It turns out that dicyandiamide can indeed achieve these dehydration condensations, all of them, in dilute aqueous solution (Steinman et al., 1964, 1965a, 1965b). By dilute I mean 0.01M in dicyandiamide, 0.01M or 0.001M in amino acids, phosphates, sugars and ribosides. All of these reactions have been accomplished with dicyandiamide, with varying degrees of efficiency.

Table 39.1 shows the types of dehydration condensation reactions promoted by dicyandiamide—peptides, phosphate ester, pyrophosphate and acetate ester; all of these have been done with DCDA. Figure 39.13 shows a likely mechanism by which the DCDA makes the dipeptide, and you can see that we use it in the form of the carbodiimide. The carbodiimide amidinium form will add the carboxylic acid to form the intermediate, which has not yet been isolated and which would undergo a nucleophilic substitution of the incipient carbonium ion to form the peptide and guanylurea. I might add that this quantitative relation

TABLE 39.1
Types of chemical bonds promoted by dicyandiamide

Peptide:
alanylalanine (from alanine)
alanylalanylalanine (from alanine)
Phosphate ester of a primary alcohol:
glucose-6-phosphate (from glucose)
ribose-5-phosphate (from ribose)
adenosine-5′-phosphate (from adenosine)
o-phosphoserine (from serine)
glycerol-1-phosphate (from glycerol)
Pyrophosphate (acid anhydride):
adenosine diphosphate (from AMP)
adenosine triphosphate (from ADP)
pyrophosphorci acid (fr. orthophosphoric acid)
Acetate ester of a primary alcohol:
glycerol-1-acetate (from glycerol)

between peptide formation and guanylurea formed has been established, at least as far as dicyandiamide is concerned. We took this step about six months ago, and although there was a quantitative relation between the amount of peptide formed and the amount of guanylurea formed (and a similar relationship of guanylurea to phosphate anhydride, or ester formed), this was not very satisfactory because the yields were most often less than 10% and frequently less than 1%. It should be kept in mind that we have not yet studied the mechanism of this reaction in detail.

However, it occurred to one of the students that if cyanamide is good for dehydration in aqueous solutions, dicyanamide might be better. (I don't know whether that is a very logical argument, but that is not always the way science progresses anyhow.) It turned out that dicyanamide (DCA) is indeed better (Steinman et al., 1965b). In fact, one of the reasons we had originally been disappointed with cyanamide was that we could not build the polypeptide very large. We had to run the concentration of amino acids up very high before we could get the polymerization to go very far, and this was another reason for seeking better agents. It turns out that dicyanamide is remarkable. Not only does it make the dipeptide but its reactivity with a dipeptide appears to be greater than it is with the amino acids. When you start with an amino acid you will not get much dipeptide; the second reaction is faster than the first. For example, we can get 6% yield of tetraglycine with only 2.5% yield of diglycine, and this is a very short reaction time. A whole sequence of investigations now is opening up. The examination of this reaction in terms of mechanism, in terms of its significance for dehydration polymerization in general, the conditions that are required for surface catalysis and *p*H are just now being explored.

GENERATION OF ORDER AND NEW INFORMATION

The next step in the generation of structure is to recognize that once having obtained these biopolymers they contain within their linear sequence structural instructions, in fact, thermodynamically stable structural possibilities. There follows now a series of four illustrations which show something with which most of you are familiar: that the linear array of polypeptides has in it structural information giving rise to this second-order structure (alpha helical structure) by virtue of the hydrogen bonding between every third or fourth amino acid carbonyl group (Figure 39.14). The interaction of the side chains (indicated here by the stars) also plays an important role not only in the stabilization of that structure but also, of course, in its catalytic and other properties. The evidence for the fact that this is a thermodynamically stable structure, one that is the result of the polypeptide sequence itself, is shown by the fact that after we have destroyed that structure by suitable means (either temperature or *p*H adjustment) we can, by reversing either the temperature or the *p*H change, recover that structure. It is thermodynamically built in and is part of the atomic arrangement and amino acid sequence. The evidence for that reversibility is a spectroscopic one, as shown in Figure 39.15. This is for polyglutamic acid, a synthetic polypeptide. When the terminal carboxyl group is ionized by raising the *p*H, the charge repulsion between the negative carboxyl groups is sufficiently great to break down the helical structure, and you get a random coil; when the terminal carboxyl groups are neutralized, which they would be at *p*H 4.9, the α-helix structure returned, as is evidenced by this reversible absorption spectrum.

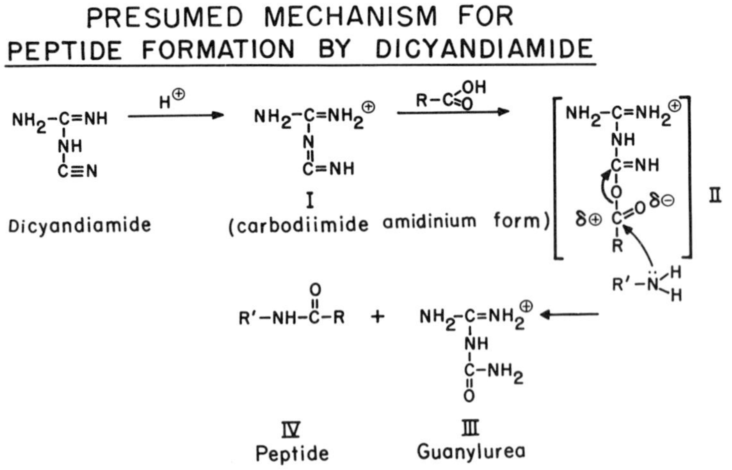

FIGURE 39.13
Presumed mechanism for peptide formation by dicyandiamide

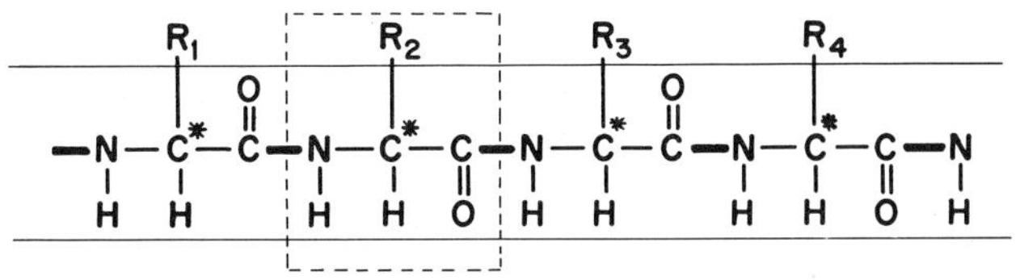

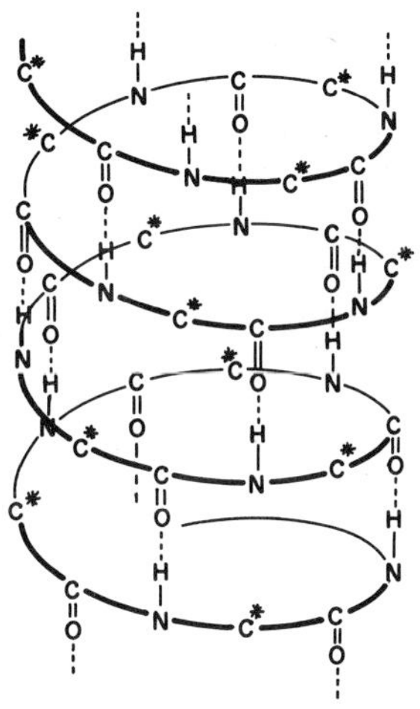

FIGURE 39.14
Protein structure

The same kind of evidence is available for the double helix structure of the sequence of bases which is a result of base pairing and hydrogen bonding of the polynucleotides (DNA). The structure of the molecular components of DNA) is shown in Figure 39.16. Here are shown the sugar phosphate chains as a pair of ribbons from which is hung a series of bases (guanine, adenine, cytosine, thymine). Two such chains are paired in this particular manner to give rise to a helical structure which one can visualize as resulting from the two strips being twisted, thus turning the base pairs flat-on to each other in an aromatic type of stacking. The aromatic type of stacking, in addition to the hydrogen bonding, holds the

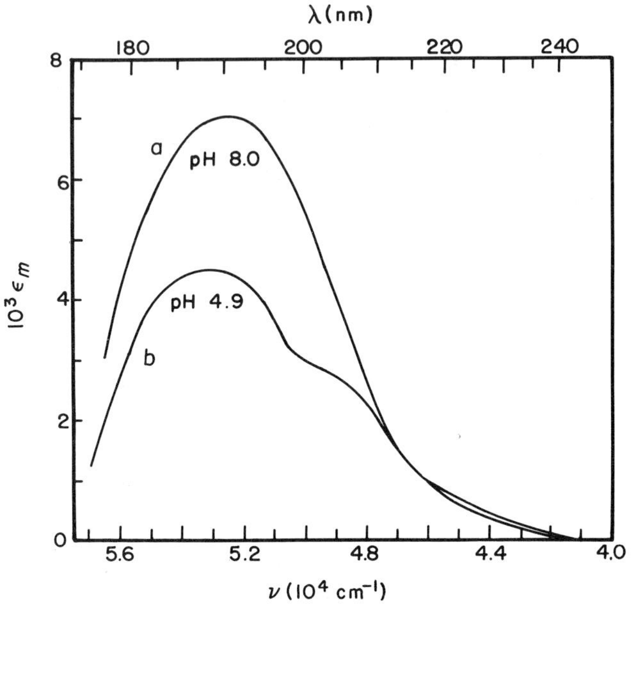

FIGURE 39.15
Absorption spectrum of polyglutamic acid: *a*, random coil form; *b*, helical form. (Tinoco et al., 1962.)

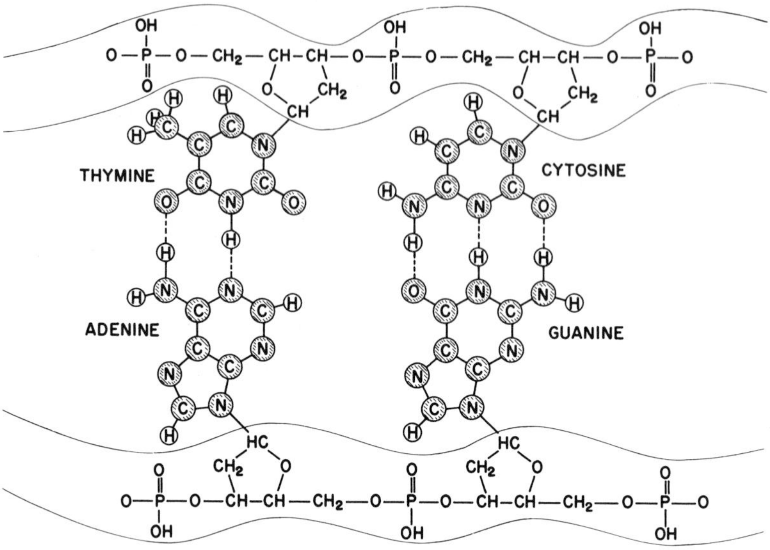

FIGURE 39.16
Molecular drawing of components of DNA

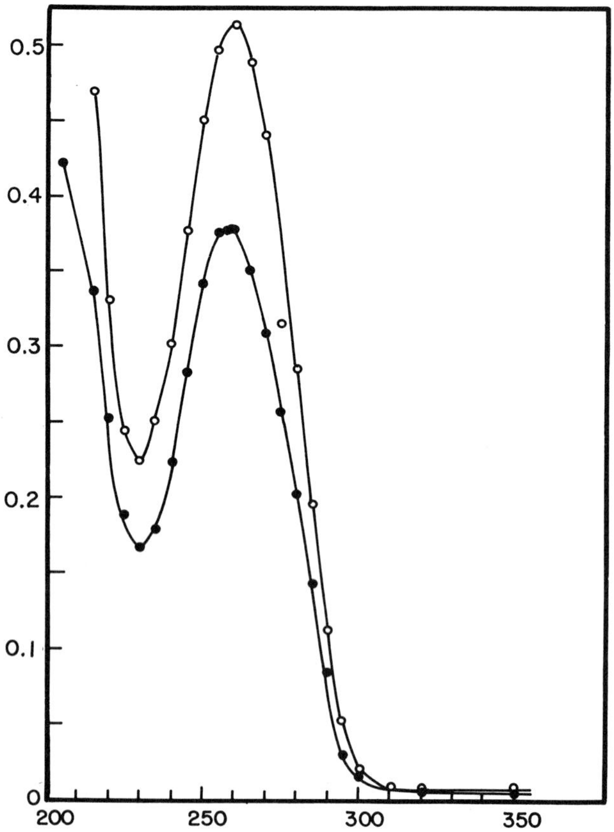

FIGURE 39.17
Hyperchroism on nucleic acid. *Solid dots,* native calf thymus DNA (helical, 228° C); *open dots,* denatured calf thymus DNA (random coil, 99.4° C).

chains together; the aromatic stacking helps to stabilize the helical structure. The helical structure makes itself apparent in many ways, among which is a change in the ultraviolet absorption of the base pairs. In Figure 39.17 is shown the spectrum of the helical structure, as well as that of the random coil. The reversible transition between them is also demonstrated as a sort of melting and crystallization phenomenon. As the temperature is raised, the helix is melted into the coil, and upon slowly lowering the temperature the helix comes back again. All that is shown here is that the secondary helical structure of the polymers is built right into the linear array of the units of which they are made.

Beyond this, there is a third degree of order which is again thermodynamically controlled. If we now take some of the helices, for example, the helix of protein or polypeptide, and put them into a solution of suitable ionic strength and *p*H, the helices themselves can begin to aggregate in a thermodynamically controlled fashion, and we will find that certain kinds of polypeptides will aggregate to

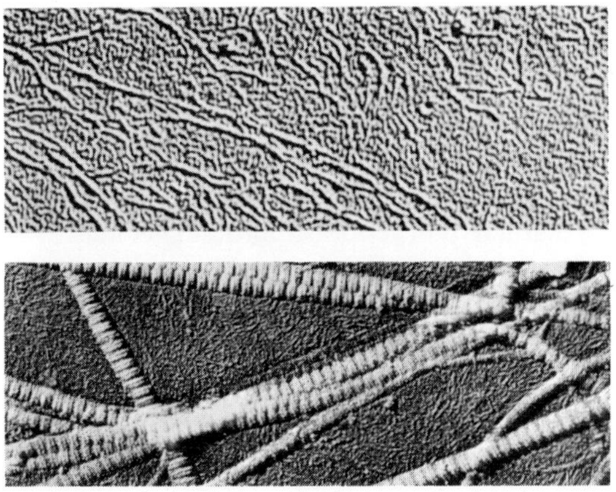

FIGURE 39.18
Electron micrograph of collagen filaments. *Top*, filaments of collagen, a protein which is usually found in long fibrils, were dispersed by placing them in dilute acetic acid. (This electron micrograph was made by Jerome Gross of the Harvard Medical School.) *Bottom*, fibrils of collagen formed spontaneously out of filaments such as those shown above when 1% of sodium chloride was added to the dilute acetic acid. These long fibrils are identical in appearance with those of collagen before dispersion.

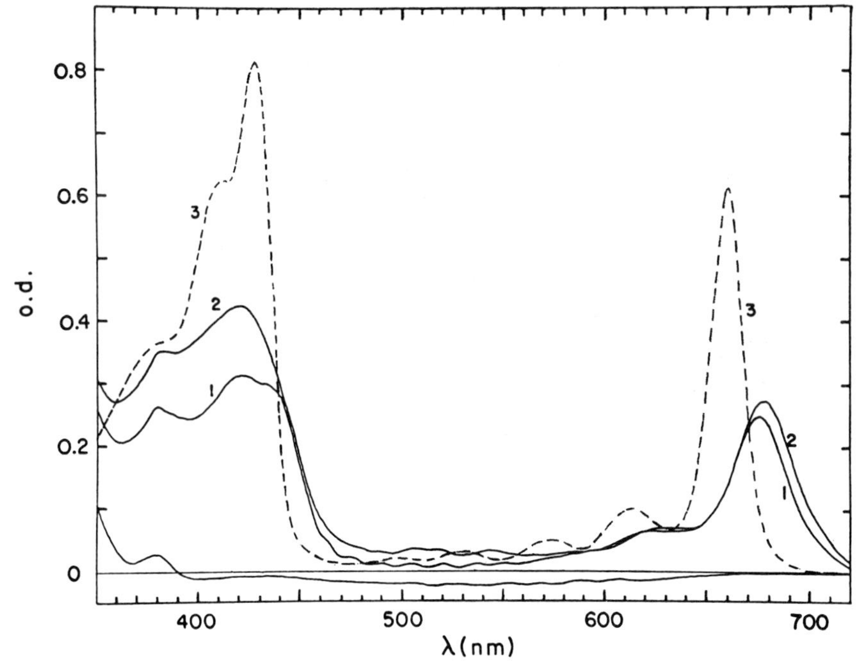

FIGURE 39.19
Film spectra of chlorophyll at water/air interface (*1*, *2*), and spectrum of chlorophyll in ether (*3*).

give certain types of structure, and only certain types of structure. The evidence for this is again manifold. I have picked only one case because it is a rather well known one and a rather spectacular phenomenon. This is the case in which one takes apart a collagen fibril (a natural polypeptide) into single helices—single protein molecules—and then, by suitably adjusting the salt concentration and *p*H, allows them to reaggregate and to get back the original microscopically visible biological structure, as shown in Figure 39.18. In the upper half we can see the single collagen molecules, and in the lower half they are reaggregated from the single collagen molecules. The collagen fibrils shown here appear to be identical with the naturally isolated original collagen fibrils. This is a higher degree of order than the previous one (which was the second degree of order) which is built right into the linear array of polypeptides. Here, in the collagen, is exhibited a third degree of order which is again the result of the helical structure of the polypeptides which we have already seen is built into the linear array of the amino acids. We have now reached something which is visible

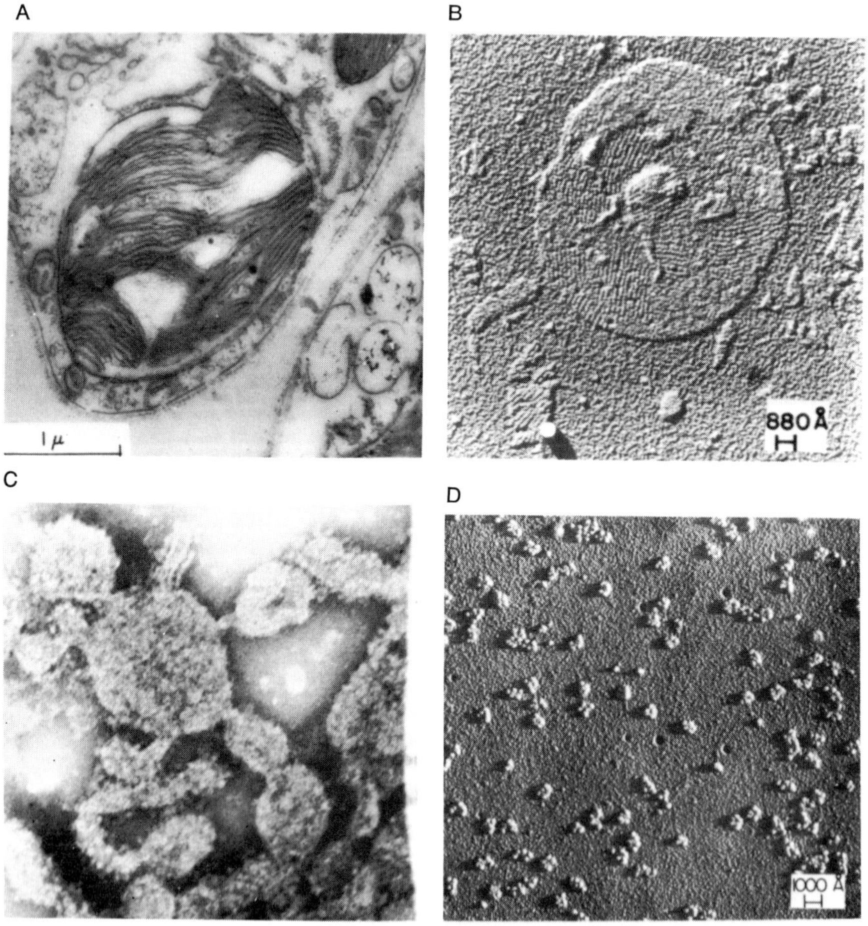

FIGURE 39.20
Electron micrograph showing the "fundamental particles" of biology: ribosomes, electron transport particles of the mitochondria, quantasomes of the chloroplasts and unit lipoprotein membrane. *a,* chloroplast with mitochondria of *Chlamydomonas* (Sager); *b,* quantasomes from spinach (Park and Healey, unpublished); *c,* negative-stained mitochondria (Park and Packer, unpublished); *d,* polysomes making haemoglobin (Warner, Rich and Hall, 1962).

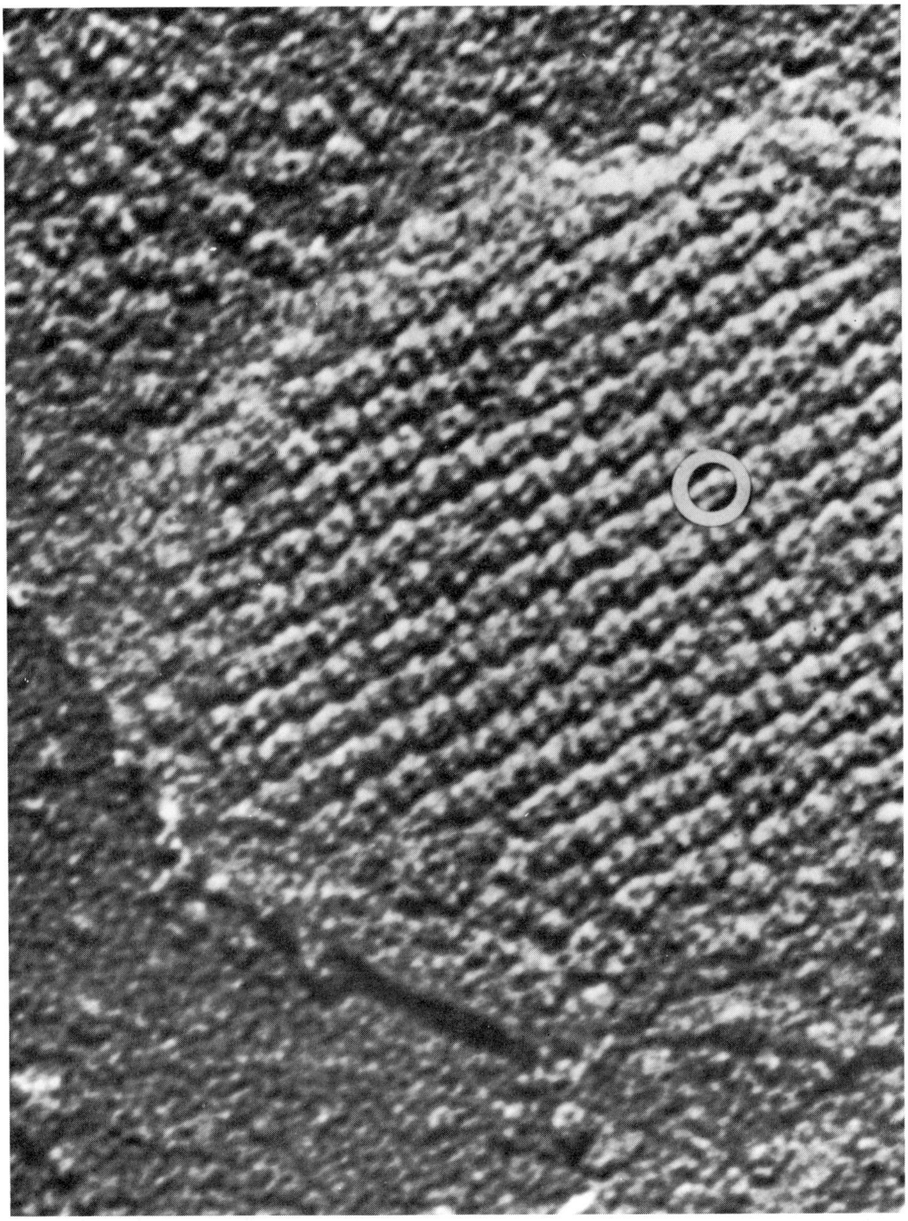

FIGURE 39.21
Quantasomes from spinach chloroplast lamellae. Shadowed paracrystalline quantasome array (magn. × 300,000); quantasome with contained subunits is circled.

—a visible structure built into the molecules as a result of the atoms of which they are made.

We can go one step further and say that similar kinds of structural features in two dimensions can be built in, and have been observed with lipid type molecules, giving rise to the two-dimensional structure of surface films. This is a much less developed field of work, in these terms at least, and is only just beginning to explode as a possible area for organic, physical and biological investigation; it is one of the areas which I think will develop very quickly in the next few years (Luzzati and Husson, 1962). Figure 39.19 shows, using chlorophyll as the lipid, the spontaneous aggregation of chlorophyll in monolayers at a water/air interface, to show that the two-dimensional array is a thermodynamically controlled phenomenon (Trurnit and Colmano, 1959).

Finally, I want to pass on from that to the next higher level of biological structure shown in Figure 39.20, which is a collection of microscopically visible things which we know play an important role in biological phenomena—in energy transfer and information transfer, the two major kinds of things which a living organism has to be able to do. The chloroplasts here (upper left) show the lamellar array, and upper right shows the structure of one of these lamella looking flat-on. You can see that it is made up of particles roughly 100 to 200 Å in diameter, shown in greater detail in Figure 39.21 (Park, 1965). It is beginning to be evident that even the quantasomes can be resolved into what appear to be subunits (perhaps four) with an approximate dimension of 60 Å. Since the major dimension of the porphyrin head of the chlorophyll molecule is of the order of 15 to 20 Å it is evident that there cannot be many in each of these subunits and that they are not likely to be randomly arranged therein.

We are now coming down from the biological level to the molecular level, and within the not too distant future I believe we will be able to reconstruct this chlorophyll-containing structure (quantasomes of Figure 39.21) from its component molecular parts. When we can do that we will have carried out the whole structural evolution from the atoms of which the molecules are made up, to the visible, biological functioning structure.

CONCLUSION

We have, I believe, reached a level of understanding of the nature of biological structure and function in molecular terms which allows us to suggest a reasonable sequence of events from the primeval molecules of the Earth's surface to the structural units which constitute the functioning living organism. Because we have been able to do this in terms of a chemistry we think we understand, we are prone to take the next step. It seems like an obvious one, but it could be quite wrong. That is to suggest that, given a starting environment anywhere which resembles what we think was the primeval environment of the Earth's surface, the same kind of sequence of events is likely to have occurred—in fact, it would have been inevitable. The exciting thing about this point in time, especially for students who have the future ahead of them, is that we (they) will be able to find out whether this notion, which is really a fundamental notion in all human thinking, is so or is not so.

REFERENCES

Barghoorn, E. S., W. G. Meinschein, and J. W. Schopf, 1965, Paleobiology of a Precambiran shale: Science, v. 148, p. 461–472.

Bolsky, T., R. B. Johns, E. D. McCarthy, A. L. Burlingame, W. Richter, and M. Calvin, 1965, Evidence for life processes in a sediment two and a half billion years old: Nature, v. 206, p. 466–467.

Bendoraitis, J. G., B. L. Brown, and L. S. Hepner, 1963, Isolation and identification of isoprenoids in petroleum: World Petroleum Cong. 6th Sess. Rept., sec. V, paper 15.

Bernal, J. D., 1959, The problem of stages of biopoesis, *in* D. I. Oparin et al., eds., The origin of life on earth: London, Pergamon Press, p. 38–53.

Burlingame, A. L., P. Haug, T. Belsky, and M. Calvin, 1965, Occurance of biogenic steranes and pentacyclic triterpanes in an Eocene shale (52 million years old) and in an early Precambrian shale (2.7 billion years)—a preliminary report: [U.S.] Natl. Acad. Sci. Proc., v. 54, p. 1406–1412.

Calvin, M., 1956, Chemical evolution and the origin of life: Am. Scientist, v. 44, p. 248–263.

———, 1961a, Origin of life on earth and elsewhere: Ann. Int. Medicine, v. 54, p. 954–976.

———, 1961b, Chemical evolution: Eugene, University of Oregon Press.

———, 1962a, Evolution of photosynthetic mechanisms: Perspectives in Biology and Medicine, v. 5, p. 147–172.

———, 1962b, Communications—from molecules to Mars: Am. Inst. Biol. Sci. Bull., v. 12, no. 5, p. 29–44.

———, 1965, Chemical evolution: Internat. Bot. Cong. 10th Sess. Proc., p. 41–56.

Calvin, M., and G. J. Calvin, 1964, Atom to Adam: Am. Scientist, v. 52, p. 163–186.

Cloud, P. E., Jr., 1965, Significance of the Gunflint (Precambrian) microflora: Science, v. 148, p. 27–35.

Cloud, P. E., Jr., J. W. Gruner, and H. Hagen, 1965, Carbonaceous rocks of the Soudan iron

formation (early Precambrian): Science, v. 148, p. 1713–1716.
de Beer, Sir Gavin, ed., 1959, Some unpublished letters of Charles Darwin: Royal Soc. [London] Notes and Records, v. 14, p. 59.
Eglinton, G., P. M. Scott, T. Belsky, A. L. Burlingame, W. Richter, and M. Calvin, 1965, Occurrence of isoprenoid alkanes in a Precambrian sediment, *in* G. D. Hobson and M. C. Louis, eds., Advances in organic geochemistry (v. 2): London, Pergamon Press.
Ehrensvaard, G., 1963, Life—origin and development: Chicago, University of Chicago Press.
Fox, S. W., 1960, How did life begin? Science, v. 132, p. 200–208.
———, ed., 1965a, The origins of prebiological systems and of their molecular matrices: New York, Academic Press.
———, 1965b, A theory of macromolecular and cellular origins: Nature, v. 205, p. 328–340.
Gaffron, H., 1960, The origin of life: Perspectives in Biology and Medicine, v. 3, p. 163–212.
Eglinton, G., P. M. Scott, T. Belsky, A. L. Burlingame, and M. Calvin, 1964, Hydrocarbons of biological origin from a one-billion year old sediment: Science, v. 145, p. 263–264.
Garrison, W. M., D. C. Morrison, J. G. Hamilton, A. A. Benson, and M. Calvin, 1951, Reduction of carbon dioxide in aqueous solution by ionizing radiation: Science, v. 114, p. 416–418.
Harada, K., and S. W. Fox, 1964, Thermal synthesis of natural amino acids from a postulated primitive terrestrial atmosphere: Nature, v. 201, p. 335–337.
Hayatsu, R., 1964, Orgueil meteorite—organic nitrogen content: Science, v. 146, p. 1291–1293.
Horowitz, N. H., and S. L. Miller, 1962, Current theories on the origin of life: Fortschr. Chem. Org. Naturstoffe, v. 20, p. 423–459.
Keosian, J., 1964, The origin of life: New York, Reinhold.
Khorana, H. G., 1961, Some recent developments in the chemistry of phosphate esters of biological interest: New York, John Wiley and Sons. (See p. 33.)
Luzzati, V., and F. Husson, 1962, The structure of the liquid-crystalline phases of lipid-water systems: Jour. Cell Biology, v. 12, p. 207–219.
Miller, S. L., 1955, Production of some organic compounds under possible primitive earth conditions: Am. Chem. Soc. Jour. v. 77, p. 2351–2361.
———, 1957, The mechanism of synthesis of amino acids by electric discharges: Biochim. et Biophys. Acta, v. 23, p. 480–489.
Miller, S. L., and M. Parris, 1964, Synthesis of pyrophosphate under primitive earth conditions: Nature, v. 204, p. 1248–1250.
Miller, S. L., and H. C. Urey, 1959, Organic compound synthesis on the primitive earth: Science, v. 130, p. 245–251.
New Biology, no. 16, 1954, The origin of life: London, Penguin Books, Ltd.
Oparin, A. I., 1957, The origin of life (3rd ed., trans. Ann Synge): London, Oliver and Boyd. [See also earlier edition, 1936 (trans. S. Margulis): New York, Macmillan.]
———, 1961, Life—its nature, origin and development (trans. Ann Synge): New York, Academic Press.
———, 1964, The chemical origin of life (trans. Ann Synge): Springfield, Ill., Charles C. Thomas.
Oparin, D. I., 1959, The origin of life on the Earth: London, Pergamon Press.
Oro, J., and A. P. Kimball, 1961, Synthesis of purines under possible primitive earth conditions. I. Adenine from hydrogen cyanide: Arch. Biochem. Biophys., v. 94, p. 217–227.
———, 1962, Synthesis of purines under possible primitive earth conditions. II. Purine intermediates from hydrogen cyanide: Arch. Biochem. Biophys., v. 96, p. 293–313.
Palm, C., and M. Calvin, 1962, Primordial organic chemistry. I. Compounds resulting from electron irradiation of $C^{14}H_4$: Am. Chem. Soc. Jour., v. 84, p. 2115–2121.
Park, R. B., 1965, Substructures of the chloroplast lamellae: Jour. Cell Biology, v. 27, p. 151–161.
Park, R. B., and W. Healey, unpublished results.
Park, R. B., and L. Packer, unpublished results.
Ponnamperuma, C., R. Mariner, R. M. Lemmon, and M. Calvin, 1963a, Formation of adenine by electron irradiation of methane, ammonia and water: [U.S.] Natl. Acad. Sci. Proc., v. 49, p. 735–740.
Ponnamperuma, C., R. Mariner, C. Sagan, 1963b, Formation of adenosine by ultraviolet irradiation of a solution of adenine and ribose: Nature, v. 198, p. 1199–1200.
Ponnamperuma, C., C. Sagan and R. Mariner, 1963c, Synthesis of ATP under possible primitive earth conditions: Nature, v. 199, p. 222–226.
Ponnamperuma, C. and P. Kirk, 1964, Synthesis of deoxyadenosine under simulated primitive earth conditions: Nature, v. 203, p. 400–401.
Ponnamperuma, C., and E. Peterson, 1965a, Peptide synthesis from amino acids in aqueous solution: Science, v. 147, 1221–1223.
Ponnamperuma, C., and R. Mack, 1965b, Nucleotide synthesis under possible primitive earth conditions: Science, v. 147, p. 1221–1223.
Schimpl, A., R. M. Lemmon, and M. Calvin, 1965, Formation of cyanamide under 'primitive earth' conditions: Science, v. 147, p. 149–150.
Steinman, G., R. M. Lemmon, and M. Calvin, 1964, Cyanamide—a possible key compound in chemical evolution: [U.S.] Natl. Acad. Sci. Proc., v. 52, p. 27–30.
———, 1965a, Dicyandiamide—possible role in peptide synthesis during chemical evolution: Science, v. 147, p. 1574–1575.
Steinman, G., D. H. Kenyon, and M. Calvin, 1965b, Dehydration condensation in aqueous solution: Nature, v. 206, p. 707–708.

Studier, M. H., R. Hayatsu, and E. Anders, 1965, Organic compounds in carbonaceous chondrites: Science, v. 149, p. 1455–1459.

Tinoco, I., Jr., A. Halpern, and W. T. Simpson, 1962, The relation between conformation and light absorption in polypeptides and proteins, *in* Mark A. Stahman, ed., Polyamino acids, polypeptides and proteins: Madison, University of Wisconsin Press, p. 147–157.

Trurnit, H. J., and G. Colmano, 1959, Chloroplast studies. I. Absorption spectra of chlorophyll monolayers at liquid interfaces: Biochim. et Biophys. Acta. v. 30, p. 434–447.

Wald, G., 1964, The origins of life: [U.S.] Natl. Acad. Sci. Proc., v. 52, p. 595–611.

Warner, J. R., A. Rich, and C. E. Hall, 1962, Electron microscope studies of ribosomal clusters synthesizing hemoglobin: Science, v. 138, p. 1399–1403.

40

The Origins of Life

GEORGE WALD

1964

From *Proceedings of the National Academy of Sciences*, vol. 52, pp. 595–611, 1964. Reprinted with permission of the author and the National Academy of Sciences.

We have had a century in which to assimilate the concept of organic evolution, but only recently have we begun to understand that this is only part, perhaps the culminating part, of cosmic evolution. We live in a historical universe, one in which stars and galaxies as well as living creatures are born, mature, grow old, and die. That may indeed be true of the universe as a whole; if so, it appears by some recent estimates to be about 20 billion (twenty thousand million) years old. But whatever doubt is held of the transitory nature of the universe, such a galaxy as ours surely had a beginning, and pursues its course toward an eventual end; and this, the Milky Way—perhaps 15 billion years old [1], about 100,000 light years across, and containing about 100 billion stars—provides a quite adequate stage on which to explore the enterprise of life [2–6]. . . .

How had it begun? We assume that during the early history of the Earth, in an atmosphere almost wholly lacking free oxygen, such simple gases as methane, water vapor, ammonia, and hydrogen, later probably also carbon monoxide and dioxide and nitrogen, reacted slowly but continuously with one another to form the smaller organic molecules. Most of this chemistry probably took place in the upper reaches of the atmosphere, activated mainly by ultraviolet radiation from the Sun and by electric discharges. Leeched out of the atmosphere over long ages into the waters of the Earth, organic molecules accumulated in the seas and there interacted with one another so that the seas gradually acquired an increasing concentration and variety of such molecules.

Model experiments have shown how such processes can yield amino acids [7–9], nucleotide bases [10], and other molecules that enter into the composition of living organisms. One of the most difficult problems is to attempt to understand how such unit structures combined with one another and polymerized against thermodynamic gradients that tended rather toward hydrolysis—how amino acids could have combined to form polypeptides and proteins, and nucleotides to form nucleic acids, apart from the precise activating mechanisms that guide and provide the energy for such syntheses in cells. Several interesting models for amino acid polymerization have been described, yet involving circumstances that seem to differ significantly from those that could have worked on an adequate scale in nature [11].

It is thought that over long ages such molecules, large and small, collected in the oceans and there came together eventually to form aggregates which in turn grew more numerous and complex. These competed with one another, so that some aggregates, by virtue of particularly favorable constitution or organization, proved more efficient than others at sweeping organic molecules out of their surroundings, and so grew at the expense of the others—a primitive beginning of natural selection [3]. It is supposed that sometime, somewhere, or perhaps several times in several places, such an aggregate reached a state that an experienced biologist, had one been present, would have been willing to call alive.

A great question concerns the composition of the primitive atmosphere and hence the gases which were available for the synthesis of the unit organic molecules. Urey [12, 13] has defended strongly the thesis that this was a reducing atmosphere, containing large amounts of methane, hydrogen, ammonia, and water vapor. This is the mixture of gases with which Miller first demonstrated the synthesis of amino acids and other organic molecules [7]. Later, Abelson [8] observed amino acid formation in similar experiments with gas mixtures that included carbon monoxide and dioxide, and nitrogen, always in combinations that involved at least one reducing gas. Heyns et al. [9] found that adding hydrogen sulfide to similar mixtures led to the synthesis of a variety of organic sulfur compounds.

A central point is that the primitive atmosphere was anaerobic, and all such model experiments are performed in the absence of oxygen. Under those circumstances they lead to the synthesis of organic molecules; were oxygen present, they would end simply in combustions.

The maintenance of a reducing atmosphere depends upon the presence of reasonably high pressures of hydrogen. The lightest of gases, this escapes from the Earth's atmosphere so rapidly that it would have maintained a sufficiently high concentration only throughout the planet's early history. Urey has calculated that a hydrogen pressure of 1.5×10^{-3} atm should suffice to maintain a reducing atmosphere, and that this may have declined to the present level of about 10^{-6} atm at the Earth's surface some two billion years ago [13]. Ammonia and methane, which are unstable in the absence of hydrogen, may shortly afterward have left the atmosphere, to be replaced mainly by nitrogen and carbon dioxide. By that time the organic syntheses we have discussed were presumably already well completed.

It should be noted, however, that this type of discussion rests entirely upon thermodynamic considerations, and takes no account of the kinetics of the reactions concerned. It assumes that the great expanses of geological time are sufficient to complete all spontaneous chemical reactions and to bring all chemical systems into equilibrium. In fact that is by no means true. Abelson [14], for example, has shown that the spontaneous decarboxylation of alanine requires more than 10 billion years at 20°C to be half completed; and the same is likely to be true of any first-order reaction with an Arrhenius energy of activation of more than 40,000 cal per mole. Second-order reactions, the rates of which depend of course upon concentration as well as activation energy, must in given instances take equally long. Not all possible reactions therefore need to be completed even within geological times; and obviously this must be an important consideration in dealing with the evolution of the atmosphere. It may well be that simple inertia of reaction permitted much more varied mixtures of gases to persist over long periods than could have occurred under equilibrium conditions.

The existence of molecular oxygen in the atmosphere is a separate issue, and so crucial for our argument that however plausible the geochemical reasons for believing that oxygen was absent initially, some further reassurance would not be amiss [cf. ref. 15].

I think that the present organization of cellular metabolism, together with what we can

TABLE 40.1
Evolution of energy metabolism

Anaerobic Phase

(1) Fermentation: a chemical source of energy; by-product CO_2
e.g., $C_6H_{12}O_6 \rightarrow 2C_2H_5OH + 2CO_2 + 2 \sim P$

(2) Hexosemonophosphate cycle: metabolic hydrogen for reductions
$6C_6H_{12}O_6 + 6H_2O + 12 \sim P \rightarrow 12H_2 + 5C_6H_{12}O_6 + 6CO_2$

(3) Photophosphorylation: light into high-energy phosphates
$\xrightarrow[\text{chlorophylls, cytochromes}]{\text{light}} \sim P$

(4) Photosynthesis: light into new organic molecules; by-product O_2
Bacteria: $6CO_2 + 12H_2A \xrightarrow[\text{chlorophyll}]{\text{light}} C_6H_{12}O_6 + 6H_2O + 12A$
Algae, higher plants: $6CO_2 + 12H_2O \xrightarrow[\text{chlorophyll}]{\text{light}} C_6H_{12}O_6 + 6H_2O + 6O_2$

Aerobic Phase

(5) Respiration: metabolic energy from combustions
$C_6H_{12}O_6 + 6H_2O + 6O_2 \rightarrow 6CO_2 + 12H_2O + 30 - 40 \sim P$

surmise to have been the course of its evolution, provides internal evidence that organisms went through much of their early development on this planet in the absence of oxygen. It would otherwise be difficult to understand the ingenuity they have displayed in developing anaerobic pathways of metabolism. The whole basic structure of cellular metabolism is anaerobic. Reactions with molecular oxygen appear as a late epiphenomenon, added to an already complete and, within its bounds, adequate substructure. The nub of the argument is outlined in Tables 40.1 and 40.2.

If, as we suppose, life first appeared in an organic medium in the absence of oxygen, it must first have been supported by fermentations [3]—Pasteur's "life without air." Insofar we beg the question. But fermentation remains in a sense the basic way of life. Fermentative processes underlie all other forms of metabolism; and virtually all types of cell can survive for periods on fermentation if deprived of oxygen. Fermentation degrades organic molecules anaerobically, making the free energy so released available to the cell in the form of high-energy phosphates (e.g., adenosine triphosphate, ATP, represented here by the symbol $\sim$P). Certain familiar forms of fermentation, e.g., the alcohol fermentation shown in Table 40.1, produce as by-product carbon dioxide. This gas, like oxygen, was probably in very low concentration in the primitive atmosphere, and its production by fermentation probably played a great role in the further evolution of metabolism.

There is good reason to believe that the next type of metabolism to develop was the hexosemonophosphate (HMP) cycle. Since this has been worked out relatively recently, it still tends to be thought of as rather esoteric; in fact it is basic. It is often characterized as an alternative ("shunt") pathway of respiration; but it is that only when frustrated. In fact it is essentially an anaerobic process, more closely related therefore to fermentation. This process develops hydrogen for organic reductions and reductive syntheses anaerobically, from sugar with the aid of energy derived from ATP. Incidentally it yields carbon dioxide as by-product [16]. It presents us also with a first example of a reaction of fundamental importance, the metabolic splitting of water, for half the hydrogen produced by the HMP cycle is derived ultimately from water.

If the primitive atmosphere contained much hydrogen, it may be asked why cells could not have used this directly, rather than having to produce hydrogen metabolically. The answer is probably, as already indicated, that by the time living cells had developed to this point, all but the last remnants of hydrogen had already escaped from the atmosphere.

The next process to develop was probably

photophosphorylation—the direct utilization of sunlight to produce ATP [17]. This involves also the first appearance in metabolism of the metalloporphyrins: the pigment, chlorophyll, a magnesium porphyrin to absorb the light; and cytochromes, iron porphyrin proteins, to aid in the transduction of the absorbed energy to ATP.

With that, the way was open to a fourth development, photosynthesis, largely an integration of developments already achieved in steps (2) and (3). In photosynthesis the energy of sunlight, transduced through chlorophylls and then in part through ATP, is used to synthesize glucose on the basis of a modified HMP cycle, running in reverse [16, 17]. The over-all process involves the splitting of hydrogen from a donor molecule, and its use to reduce carbon dioxide to carbohydrate. A variety of organic and inorganic molecules serve as hydrogen donors in photosynthetic bacteria; but in algae and higher green plants water itself donates the hydrogen, and molecular oxygen is released as by-product.

This is the means by which molecular oxygen entered our atmosphere. When it had reached a sufficient concentration—about 10^{-3} to 10^{-2} atmospheres at sea level—that at last made possible the first aerobic form of metabolism, cellular respiration. In its over-all effects, and even to a large extent in its mechanisms, respiration is the reverse of algal and higher plant photosynthesis. Chemical energy obtained by the combustion of glucose and other organic molecules is made available in the form of ATP, with carbon dioxide and water as principal end products.

Since its advent, respiration and the reverse process of photosynthesis have been pitted against each other. Presumably they came into balance ages ago. Yet there must have been a great interval in which organisms were slowly turning an anaerobic into an aerobic world; and the increase of oxygen in our atmosphere from negligible beginnings to its present content of 21 per cent testifies to the long period in which photosynthesis overbalanced respiration.

It is usual to think of the physical environment as given, as the absolute setting to which organisms must at all times adapt if they are to survive. It is becoming plain, however, that some of the salient features of our physical environment are themselves the work of living organisms. They not only put molecular oxygen into the atmosphere. By now also organisms have spread upon the Earth on such a scale that the atmosphere and hydrosphere have become components in their metabolism. It is estimated that at present all the oxygen in the atmosphere passes through organisms—in by respiration and out by photosynthesis—every 2000 years; that all the carbon dioxide in both the atmosphere and hydrosphere cycles through organisms in the reverse direction every 300 years; and that all the waters of the Earth are decomposed and recomposed by photosynthesis and respiration every 2,000,000 years [18].

The combustion of organic molecules is an over-all effect of respiration, but not its mechanism. The actual mechanism is peculiarly significant for our problem. Biological oxidations, with rare exceptions, are performed, not by

TABLE 40.2
Alternative ways of burning carbon

Aerobic:

$C + O_2 \rightarrow CO_2$ (combustion of coal)

Anaerobic—Aerobic:

$C + H_2O \rightarrow CO + H_2$ (water gas)
$CO + H_2O \rightarrow CO_2 + H_2$ (industrial production of hydrogen)
$2H_2 + O_2 \rightarrow 2H_2O$ (combustion of hydrogen)

Metabolism of Living Organisms:

$(CH_2O)_n$ = carbohydrate (*n* equivalents of water gas)
$(CH_2O) + H_2O \rightarrow CO_2 + H_2$ (glycolysis)
$2H_2 + O_2 \rightarrow 2H_2O$ (respiration)

adding oxygen, but by removing hydrogen. Even when the oxygen content of some molecule in the organism is increased, this is almost always done by adding water and removing hydrogen. Organisms are remarkably adept at performing their oxidations anaerobically. Their only direct combustion is the burning of hydrogen; and the incorporation of part of the energy of this process into ATP is the principal contribution of cellular respiration. But this is still, with relatively few exceptions, the only use that organisms make of molecular oxygen.

The point can perhaps be made clearer with a simple industrial analogy (Table 40.2). Coal can be burned in either of two ways: directly with oxygen to carbon dioxide, as in a furnace; or it can be used to draw an atom of oxygen out of water, yielding as products the inflammable mixture of carbon monoxide and hydrogen called water gas. Water gas in turn might simply be burned with oxygen to carbon dioxide and water; but instead the carbon monoxide can be used to draw another atom of oxygen out of water, yielding another hydrogen molecule, as in the process for the industrial production of hydrogen. Finally, the hydrogen can be burned with oxygen to water [19].

Glucose, the principal metabolite for energy production in living organisms, is a form of carbohydrate, the unit structure of which is CH_2O (taken 6 times over in glucose and other hexoses, $C_6H_{12}O_6$). This has the same composition as water gas. Like water gas, a unit of carbohydrate could be burned with one molecule of oxygen to CO_2 and H_2O; but that is not the organism's way. Instead, the carbohydrate is used to split water according to the fundamental equation, $CH_2O + H_2O \rightarrow CO_2 + 2H_2$, a somewhat disguised equation of preparatory glycolysis, exactly analogous to the industrial production of hydrogen. This is then followed by the combustion of hydrogen, $2H_2 + O_2 \rightarrow 2\ H_2O$, the fundamental equation of cellular respiration.

Horowitz [20] has proposed a plausible mechanism by which biosynthetic pathways may have evolved during the period when organic metabolites were still plentiful in the environment. He suggests that biosynthetic sequences developed in reverse, starting at the end of the chain, and working backward by adding one enzyme at a time. An organism dependent upon some available metabolite, as that became depleted, might develop an enzyme for performing the last step in its synthesis, so that the organism's needs were now transferred to the immediate precursor. As that in turn became depleted, the organism might evolve an enzyme for the previous step in synthesis. So it would work its way step by step backward through the sequence until the entire synthesis could be performed from simple and readily obtainable precursors.

This seems then to have been the history of life upon this planet: the slow combination of the gases of the primitive atmosphere to form simple unit organic molecules which accumulated in the sea; the polymerization of some of those molecules to form the first macromolecules comparable with our present proteins and nucleic acids; the aggregation of such large and small molecules in the sea to form micelles of various sizes and grades of complexity, with the final achievement of the living state. Then the gradual mastery of the fundamental problems of deriving energy and preparing new organic molecules with which life could eventually spread upon a cosmic scale, in the process transforming radically the atmosphere of the planet.

I think that some such account as this would now be widely accepted as describing the origin of life on the Earth. What is perhaps more interesting is the dawning realization that this problem involves universal elements, that life in fact is probably a universal phenomenon, bound to occur wherever in the universe conditions permit and sufficient time has elapsed.

Those conditions almost surely involve a planet somewhat resembling the Earth, of about this size and temperature, and receiving about this quality and amount of radiation from its sun. To mention a few points of the argument: a much smaller planet could not hold an adequate atmosphere, a much larger one might hold too dense an atmosphere to permit radiation to penetrate to its surface. Too cold a planet would slow down too greatly the chemical reactions by which life arises; too warm a planet would be incompatible with the orderly existence of macromolecules. The limits of temperature are probably close to those at which water remains liquid, itself almost surely a necessary condition for life. Life can arise without continuously absorbing radiation, though, as we have noted, radiation prepares the way by activating organic syntheses in the atmosphere; but it is difficult to see how life can go far, or even persist indefinitely without an external source of energy. By now all life upon the Earth runs on sunlight, with the exception of a few chemosynthetic bacteria. Not all radiations are adequate; a range of wavelengths, *ca.* 300–1100 mμ, is needed. Shorter wavelengths than 300 mμ destroy macromolecules; on the Earth they denature proteins and depolymerize nucleic acids. Longer wavelengths than about 1100 mμ involve quanta too small to excite molecules electronically, and hence to activate photochemical reactions.

TABLE 40.3
An alphabet of organisms

Elementary particles (4)	
Protons	
Electrons	
Neutrons	
Photons	
Bioelements (16–21)	
Water:	H, O
Organic:	H, C, N, O; P, S
Ions:	Na^+, K^+, Mg^{++}, Ca^{++}, Cl^-
Trace elements:	Mn, Fe, Co, Cu, Zn (B, Al, V, Mo, I)*
Unit molecules (29)	
Glucose	
Ribose	
Fat	
Phosphatide	
Amino acids (20)	
Nucleotide bases (5)	

* The elements within parentheses are restricted to special groups of organisms; the others are very generally distributed.

How many such planets exist? By present estimates about 1–5 per cent of the stars in our galaxy might possess planets capable of supporting life [22]. That would mean at least one billion such planets in our galaxy alone; and since there are about 100 million galaxies now within range of the most powerful telescopes, the number of planets suitable for life in the already observed universe may be of the order of 10^{17}. This number is so vast—even if it were reduced a million times—as to make it difficult to avoid the conclusion that life is widespread in the universe.

On this planet, living organisms are composed almost entirely of 16–21 elements—16 found in almost all organisms, 5 more restricted to particular groups (Table 40.3). A first striking regularity is that these tend to be light elements. All the bioelements except molybdenum and iodine occur within the lightest 30 of the 92 natural elements. That in itself does not seem strange, for the lightest elements tend also to be the most abundant, on the Earth as elsewhere in the cosmos.

The bioelements fall into three natural groups, according to the uses organisms make of them: those that form water and the bulk of the organic molecules; the monatomic ions; and the trace elements.

The group of monatomic ions may have been chosen mainly on the basis of their relative abundance, though I do not think that is the whole story even with them. They are the ions most prevalent in the sea; and that may account largely not only for their appearance in cells, but for the fact that animal blood tends to resemble sea water so closely. Most marine invertebrates circulate a solution of ions in their bloods that is essentially sea water. The ionic composition of vertebrate blood so closely resembles sea water diluted 3–4 times as to have prompted the suggestion that it represents sea water of the remote period in which the ancestors of the vertebrates closed off their circulations [23].

An argument from abundance, however, cannot be consistently maintained for the other two groups of bioelements. Some of them are abundant; others of equal importance are relatively rare, and organisms concentrate them many times over out of very dilute environments. These elements were selected on the basis of their essential properties rather than their availability; and that is true to a degree even of the monatomic ions. One has a strong indication of this in the fact that the three groups into which the bioelements are divided functionally are reflected in their positions in the Periodic System, where, except for the halogens Cl and I, they form three clusters: the organic elements at the right in the first three periods, the monatomic cations at the left of the third and fourth periods, the major trace elements toward the middle of the fourth (the first long) period, all of them but zinc being so-called transition elements. Being transition elements, these last readily form complexes, as does also zinc; and—being atoms of variable valence—they readily exchange electrons, properties that fit them admirably for the roles we find them principally playing in organisms, as the nuclei of metallo-organic complexes and oxido-reduction enzymes.

The most important such argument, however, involves the four elements hydrogen, oxygen, nitrogen, and carbon, which together make up about 99 per cent of the living parts of living organisms. I think that a responsible examination of the possibilities leads inevitably to the conclusion that life everywhere in the universe must be constructed primarily of these four elements.

Hydrogen, of course, is the most abundant element in the universe, and hydrogen and oxygen constitute large fractions (15.40 and 55.19%) of the atoms in those portions of the Earth accessible to living organisms (the whole hydrosphere and atmosphere, and the crust to a depth of 10 miles) [24]. On the other hand, carbon must be extracted from the last 0.44 per cent of the accessible atoms, and nitrogen from the last 0.16 per cent (one may add that phosphorus must be found in the last 0.23% and sulfur in the last 0.12% of the accessible atoms). These are therefore not consistently the most plentiful elements. They owe their status rather to their essential "fitness": they alone among the natural elements possess the critical properties upon which the existence of life everywhere in the universe must depend.

(I have been asked sometimes how one can be sure that elsewhere in the universe there may not be further elements, other than those in the Periodic System. I have tried to answer by saying that it is like asking how one knows that elsewhere in the universe there may not be another whole number between 4 and 5. Unfortunately, some persons think that is a good question, too.)

We are, understandably, so greatly impressed with the regularities in the Periodic System that we sometimes exaggerate them. The lightest elements, specifically those in the first two periods, in fact exhibit quite distinctive properties, not repeated in the lower periods. It hardly needs urging that silicon has quite different properties from carbon, phosphorus from nitrogen, and sulfur from oxygen. Hydrogen, of course, has wholly unique properties.

The special distinction of hydrogen, oxygen, nitrogen, and carbon is that they are the four smallest elements in the Periodic System that achieve stable electronic configurations by gaining, respectively, 1, 2, 3, and 4 electrons. Gaining electrons, in the form of sharing them with other atoms, is the means of making chemical bonds, and so of making molecules. The special point of smallness is that these smallest elements make the tightest bonds and so the most stable molecules; and that carbon, nitrogen, and oxygen are the only elements that regularly form double and triple bonds. Both properties are critically important.

It is frequently suggested that elsewhere in the universe silicon may substitute for carbon in living organisms. The reasons for considering silicon are that it falls just below carbon in the Periodic System; like carbon it can combine with itself to form long chains, and hence very complex molecules; and here on Earth there is about 135 times as much silicon as carbon in the areas accessible to life.

Silicon, however, cannot replace carbon in living organisms [25]. For one thing, it forms looser, less stable compounds, but that, though a disadvantage, might be tolerated (Table 40.4). Silicon chains, however, are susceptible to attack by molecules possessing lone pairs of electrons, in part because of their open structure, but still more because silicon, a third-period element, possesses 3*d* orbitals available for further combination. For this reason silicon

TABLE 40.4
Carbon and silicon chains

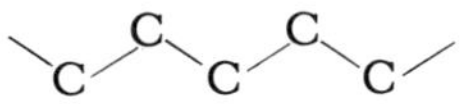

C–C distance, 1.54 Å (bond energy, 83.1 kcal per mole)

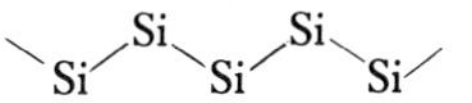

Si–Si distance, 2.34 Å (bond energy, 42.5 kcal per mole)*

* Such silicon chains are unstable to O_2, NH_3, and H_2O, one electron pair of each of which can attack by occupying 3*d* orbitals of Si.

chains cannot exist for long in the presence of oxygen, ammonia, or water. I think that in itself must eliminate silicon as a possible basis for life.

Silicon, however, has another fatal disability, its failure to form multiple bonds. The importance of this factor can be understood if one compares carbon dioxide with silicon dioxide (Table 40.5). In carbon dioxide, double bonds between the carbon and oxygen atoms completely saturate their combining capacities. The molecule goes off freely as a gas, and dissolves in and combines with water, the forms in which organisms obtain it. In silicon dioxide, however, silicon remains singly bonded to oxygen, leaving four unpaired electrons on the molecule. These promptly form bonds with adjacent silicon dioxide molecules, and they in turn with others. The result is a huge polymer, a supermolecule such as quartz, so hard because it can be broken only by breaking covalent bonds. That is why silicon is fit for making quartz, but living organisms must be made of carbon.

Somewhat less compelling arguments of special fitness involve phosphorus and sulfur [25], which among the other functions they perform in organisms have the special role of forming high-energy compounds (e.g., ATP, acetyl coenzyme A) which transfer energy and organic groups within the cell. The very factors that constitute a disability in silicon become an advantage in phosphorus and sulfur (Table 40.6). The openness of their bonds and their possession of 3*d* orbitals capable of receiving further electrons make their compounds susceptible to attack by molecules that can offer lone pairs of electrons; and this provides a mechanism for the participation of phosphorus and sulfur compounds in the energy- and group-transfer reactions that constitute their principal contribution to cellular metabolism.

The major bioelements therefore present unique properties indispensable for the formation and function of living organisms. They—particularly carbon, hydrogen, nitrogen, and oxygen—form also a number of unique molecules, indispensable or of quite singular importance for organisms. Of these the chief is water, which I believe to be altogether indispensable. Carbon dioxide must be hardly less important, a gas highly soluble in water, which therefore permeates the atmosphere and hydrosphere, and so is uniquely suitable for circulating carbon among organisms. Carbon dioxide possesses many other fortunate properties—great stability, high density, the capacity rapidly to achieve complex equilibria involving the gas, carbonic acid, and solid carbonates and bicarbonates—all potentially of the highest importance for the formation and maintenance of life [26].

As already noted, organisms seem to have arisen on Earth, and might conceivably have persisted indefinitely in the absence of molecular oxygen. Yet oxygen, in permitting the development of cellular respiration, provides by far the most efficient chemical source of energy

TABLE 40.5
Carbon dioxide and silicon dioxide

Carbon dioxide: CO_2

Silicon dioxide: $(SiO_2)_n$

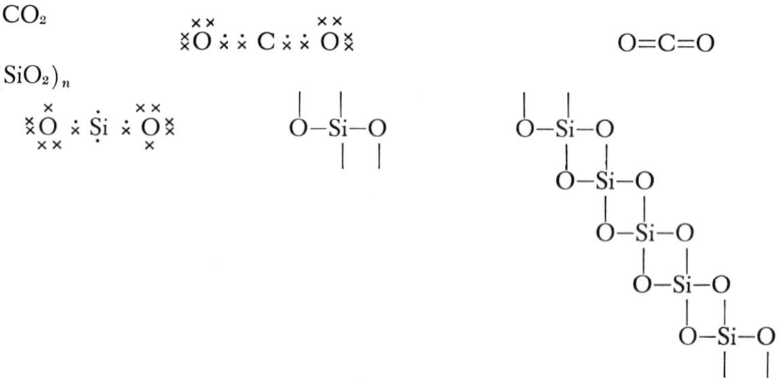

Note: the diagram of the silicon dioxide polymer is intended only to represent the mutual saturation of valences, not at all the spatial relationships in the crystal.

available to organisms, based upon the most energetic of combustions, that of hydrogen. On this planet, organisms, when not living directly upon the energy of sunlight, live for the most part on respiration. Living organisms everywhere should have to solve sooner or later the problem of obtaining energy economically by chemical means, in order to survive periods of darkness, even if only cycles of day and night. It is doubtful that such needs can be met more effectively than by combustions.

TABLE 40.6
High-energy bonds of P and S

Bond	Bond lengths
C—O—P	1.431, 1.76
P—O—P	1.76, 1.76
N—P	1.80
C—S	1.81

Note: the valence electrons of P and S are in the third shell, which, beyond holding 8 electrons in its *s* and *p* orbitals, can accept further electrons in its *d* orbitals. This, in addition to the large bond radii of P and S, opens the compounds of these elements to attack by molecules possessing lone pairs of electrons, such as H_2O.

Oxygen makes another kind of contribution to the evolution of life. As it accumulates, a layer of ozone, formed from it by high-energy radiation in the upper atmosphere, screens out the far ultraviolet that would otherwise destroy all exposed organisms. Not much ozone is needed for this. The amount in the Earth's atmosphere, isolated and brought to 0°C and 1 atm pressure, would form a layer only 3 mm thick. Water also screens out the hard ultraviolet; and until such a layer of ozone had developed in our atmosphere, life presumably remained aquatic. The entry of oxygen into the atmosphere not only permitted the development of respiration, but allowed life to emerge from the water onto land. For both reasons, oxygen, though not indispensable for life, must be reckoned among the special molecules needed for its fullest development [27].

It has often been suggested that elsewhere in the universe liquid ammonia may take the place of water as a substrate for life. In most important regards, however, liquid ammonia is inferior to water in the properties upon which organisms most depend [26]. An obvious disadvantage is that ammonia remains liquid over a much narrower temperature range than water (Table 40.7); keeping ammonia liquid therefore demands a greater stability of temperature over long periods than many planets afford. But to keep it liquid demands also temperatures that would never rise above perhaps −40°C, that is, at least 60° below prevailing temperatures upon the Earth. (Raising the atmospheric pressure considerably would, of course, permit ammonia to stay liquid at higher temperatures, but would introduce other equally serious difficulties.) If we assume the modest temperature coefficient (Q_{100}) of 2, chemical processes in general would take about 2^6 as long to complete at −40°C as upon the Earth. The processes that led to the origin of life within perhaps a billion years upon this planet might then take some 64 billion years in an environment of liquid ammonia. That is far greater than any present estimates of the age of our galaxy, and much longer than a star like the Sun could remain on the main sequence, i.e., remain adequately supplied with hydrogen to maintain conditions that would make life possible on one of its planets.

TABLE 40.7
Properties of ammonia

Boiling point:	−33.35°C (at 1 atm pressure)
Freezing point:	−77.7° (at 1 atm pressure)
Density at −79°C:	
Liquid:	0.7354 gm per cm³*
Solid:	0.817 gm per cm³†

* *Source:* Cragoe, C. S., and D. R. Harper, III, *U. S. Bur. Standards Sci. Papers,* v. 17, p. 287 (1921).
† *Source:* McKelvy, E. C., and C. S. Taylor, *U. S. Bur. Standards Sci. Papers,* v. 18, p. 655 (1922–23).

L. J. Henderson [26], in his classic exposition of the many extraordinary properties which make water critically important for living organisms, made much of one of its most peculiar properties—that ice floats. If ice did not float, the waters of the Earth would long ago have frozen solid. Even relatively long periods of warm weather could not have thawed them; and life arising or persisting under such conditions would be well-nigh impossible.

Water owes this strange property to the fact

that though on cooling it contracts, as do other well-behaved substances, below 4°C it expands, so that at its freezing point (0°) it has a lower density than liquid water. The reason for this is that below 4°C water molecules become increasingly hydrogen-bonded to one another. By the freezing point every hydrogen atom is engaged in both covalent and hydrogen bonding to adjacent oxygen atoms, holding all the water molecules rigidly in an open structure in which they are less densely packed than in liquid water.

Some years ago I began to wonder whether ammonia ice floats. Unable to find this information in the literature, I was glad to have the question answered for me experimentally [28]. Later, wanting to be doubly sure, I repeated the experiment myself; and just afterward found that the information had been published 20 years before (Table 40.7). Ammonia ice sinks in liquid ammonia, rapidly and unequivocally, hitting the bottom of the vessel with a distinct thud. That can be added to the disabilities of ammonia as a medium for life.

The splitting of water in higher plant photosynthesis yields as a by-product molecular oxygen, permitting eventually the development of cellular respiration. A comparable process performed with ammonia might instead yield nitrogen, a depressingly inert gas. An English astronomer was reported recently to have said that there may be places in the universe where life is based on ammonia rather than water, and where living creatures respire nitrogen instead of oxygen. One can of course *breathe* nitrogen, as we do all the time; but respiration is in essence a combustion, and nitrogen cannot support combustions here or anywhere. For that oxygen is needed, the most electron-avid element after fluorine, so facile at removing electrons from other atoms that that process (oxidation) has been named for it.

For these and similar reasons I have become convinced that life everywhere must be based primarily upon carbon, hydrogen, nitrogen, and oxygen, upon an organic chemistry therefore much as on the Earth; and that it can arise only in an environment rich in water. Though the preparatory geochemical syntheses of organic molecules seem to demand an anaerobic environment, and are probably fostered by a generally reducing atmosphere, the later history of these developments must be greatly furthered by the more or less automatic appearance of carbon dioxide as the atmosphere loses hydrogen; and living organisms having arisen would in time almost surely find their way to the production and utilization of molecular oxygen.

How formidable a condition is the geochemical accumulation of unit organic molecules—the building blocks of which macromolecules and eventually the first primitive organisms are to be composed? How many such units are needed, at a minimum? I think perhaps fewer than is generally supposed.

I have had the experience lately of introducing young students, many of whom had not studied chemistry before, to some of the basic essentials of biochemistry. I build the subject up from the elementary particles, then the atoms we have been discussing, to end with what I call an alphabet of biochemistry (Table 40.3). It turns out that about 29 organic molecules are enough to introduce the bare essentials. They include glucose, the major product of photosynthesis and major source of metabolic energy and hydrogen; fats as a principal storage form of metabolic energy; phosphatides as a means of circulating lipids in aqueous media and for their remarkable structure-forming proclivities; then the 20 amino acids from which all proteins, including all enzymes, are derived. Five nitrogeneous bases (adenine, guanine, cytosine, uracil, thymine), together with ribose or its simple derivative deoxyribose and phosphoric acid, form all the nucleic acids, both RNA and DNA. These 29 molecules give students a first entry into the structures of proteins and nucleic acids, the coding of genetic information, the structures of enzymes, the composition and general properties of cell structures, and bring them to a point from which they can begin to explore the complexities of energy metabolism. That this is not the whole of biochemistry goes without saying; the extraordinary thing is that it makes so good a start. Yet this alphabet of biochemistry is hardly longer than our verbal alphabet. That seems to me to imply that the provision of unit molecules preparatory to the rise of living organisms is a reasonably limited enterprise. I cannot help but feel that this situation, that makes it relatively easy to give young students a first taste of biochemistry, must have made it easier also for the first primitive cells to obtain the molecules they needed.

Many of these molecules display in solution the property of optical activity, the capacity to rotate the plane of polarized light to the right or left. This property is almost uniquely associated with the components and products of living organisms; it is as characteristic of life as any property we know. It has its source in so-called asymmetric carbon atoms, carbon atoms bonded to four different groups. All molecules possessing such asymmetric atoms can exist in right- and left-handed forms (dextro- and levo-, D- and L-). When synthesized artificially, such molecules always emerge as equal mixtures of the D- and L-forms, hence optically inactive. Living organisms, however, invariably incorporate one form or the other. Thus, virtually all natural amino acids are L-, all natural sugars D-, α-phosphatides L-, and so on [29].

The point is not that L-amino acids are intrinsically better suited for living organisms than D-, or D-sugars than L-, but that organisms derive important advantages individually and collectively from working consistently with one configuration or the other [30]. Large portions of native proteins exist in the form of the α-helix. They assume that configuration spontaneously, but could do so only with great difficulty, if at all, were they made of mixtures of both D- and L-amino acids. This is an important consideration, since most of the specific properties of proteins depend in part upon this feature of their geometry. Similarly, the two-stranded helical structure characteristic of DNA and long sections of RNA demands specific choices in the configurations of three asymmetric carbon atoms in deoxyribose or ribose—carbon atoms 1, 3, and 4. Enzymes, being proteins, are themselves optically active, and in many cases react only with L- or D-substrates, not with both. For these and other reasons organisms consistently choose one configuration or the other, though in each category of molecule either choice would do equally well. Since also the molecules of organisms are in constant flux and interchange, and are passed about widely from one organism to another in complex food chains, there is enormous advantage in staying with consistent series of configurations throughout the whole metabolism, and indeed throughout the population of the planet. For this reason I would suppose that biota that may incorporate amino acids on other planets divide about equally between the L- and D-configurations, keeping their other choices consistent with this one.

To go a step further, I think that when confronted with the necessity to develop a molecule to perform some basic cellular function, organisms are highly limited in their choices, though not as limited in their first choices as in their last. Such molecules as the chlorophylls for photosynthesis, the heme pigments for cellular respiration, the carotenoids and vitamins A for photoreception, all represent the outcome on this planet of long and rigorous selective processes that tended constantly toward achieving optimal solutions. All these molecules possess properties that fit them particularly to perform their functions in organisms; and I have no doubt that the better we come in each case to understand the nature of the problem, the clearer it will be why those molecules and not others were selected. Sometimes these molecules present strange mixtures of fortunate and disadvantageous properties; the chlorophylls, for example, all have the strange property of absorbing light most poorly at those wavelengths at which sunlight at the surface of the Earth or under water is most intense. Obviously the chlorophylls must possess other advantages for photosynthesis that far outweigh this disability; and those advantages, since they have given the chlorophylls a unique status in photosynthesis on the Earth, might be equally effective in promoting their selection elsewhere [21].

Again, three animal phyla on the Earth, having developed three very different kinds of eye in complete independence from one another, have all arrived at the same molecule, 11-*cis* retinene (11-*cis* vitamin A aldehyde), as the chromophore of their visual pigments. Yet the 11-*cis* isomer is an improbable, intrinsically unstable variant of retinene. Why then choose it repeatedly for this function? It has turned out that the only action of light in vision is to change the *shape* of a molecule; and 11-*cis* retinene fills that role in an exemplary way, light isomerizing it from the bent and twisted

11-*cis* configuration to the relatively straight all-*trans* with high efficiency. The same forces that guided the selection of this improbable molecule three times independently on this planet might well arrive at the same or similar solutions elsewhere [21, 31].

To sum up, faced with well-nigh universal problems, organisms everywhere may tend to gravitate toward common solutions, types of molecule that within the bounds of organic structure may represent optimal or near-optimal solutions. I say types rather than individual molecules, since in each of the cases mentioned we find here upon the Earth not one molecule but a category of them at work: at least five different chlorophylls, a variety of hemes, several active carotenoids, two vitamins A.

Such choices must be governed everywhere by natural selection, the process described a century ago by Darwin and Wallace. This is at once the formative and conservative principle in the evolution of living things. It involves three components: a mechanism of inheritance, without which life could not continue to exist anywhere; a continuous intrusion of "noise" into the genetic message, appearing in the offspring as random inherited variations (mutations); and the struggle for existence, the competition for the necessities of life, any temporary alleviation of which is met with a leap in population that brings it back into force. These are universal elements, hardly to be avoided in any population of living things. Their outcome is the survival of the fittest—the continuous trend toward optimization, the effects of which on molecular design were invoked above.

It has sometimes been argued that natural selection is "not enough"—not enough to account for the evolution of an eye, or a wing, or the near-perfection of embryonic development, or the mating behavior of gulls. But one cannot dismiss natural selection just because it works better than one thinks it should. A hypothesis should be damned for its failures, not its successes—cases in which evolution has appeared to work to the net disadvantage of organisms. That is, of course, just the problem raised by some instances of the extinction of species in the course of evolution; and some cases of extinction do represent a failure of natural selection, owing, we believe, to the inertia of the selective process, which on occasion operates too slowly to cope with abrupt changes in the conditions of existence.

Wigner [32] has recently remarked upon "what appears to be a miracle from the point of view of the physicist: that there are (living) structures which produce further identical structures." Fortunately, no such miracle occurs. If it did, heredity might seem to work better, but natural selection would not work at all. Wigner offers a calculation to show the quantum-mechanical impossibility of keeping the information coded in the genes from growing increasingly disordered as it is transmitted. The point is that the genetic message is continuously disordered by mutation; but that the selective process as continuously prunes it back to orderly, and indeed toward optimal, sequences. Wigner's calculation can be turned to positive account; it provides some assurance that any molecular genetic code must continually produce such random variations as natural selection demands. Order in living organisms is introduced not beforehand, by preconceived design, but after the fact—the fact of random mutation—by a process akin to editing. We are the products of editing rather than of authorship. . . .

I have tried in this paper to consider all too briefly some of the conditions that have molded life here, and some of the reasons for believing that they would mold life anywhere. The nub of such an argument is to bring life within the order of nature, to see its development as an orderly process, everywhere affording full play to chance, but not in any important degree accidental.

We living things are a late outgrowth of the metabolism of our galaxy. The carbon that enters so importantly into our composition was cooked in the remote past in a dying star. From it at lower temperatures nitrogen and oxygen were formed. These, our indispensable elements, were spewed out into space in the exhalations of red giants and such stellar catastrophes as supernovae, there to be mixed with hydrogen, to form eventually the substance of the sun and planets, and ourselves. The waters of ancient seas set the pattern of ions in our blood. The ancient atmospheres molded our metabolism.

We have been told so often and on such tremendous authority as to seem to put it beyond question, that the essence of things must remain forever hidden from us; that we must stand forever outside nature, like children with their noses pressed against the glass, able to look in, but unable to enter. This concept of our origins encourages another view of the matter. We are not looking into the universe from outside. We are looking at it from inside. Its history is our history; its stuff, our stuff. From that realization we can take some assurance that what we see is real.

Judging from our experience upon this planet, such a history, that begins with elementary particles, leads perhaps inevitably toward a strange and moving end: a creature that knows, a science-making animal, that turns back upon the process that generated him and attempts to understand it. Without his like, the universe could be, but not be known, and that is a poor thing.

Surely this is a great part of our dignity as men, that we can know, and that through us matter can know itself; that beginning with protons and electrons, out of the womb of time and the vastness of space, we can begin to understand; that organized as in us, the hydrogen, the carbon, the nitrogen, the oxygen, those 16 to 21 elements, the water, the sunlight—all, having become us, can begin to understand what they are, and how they came to be.

REFERENCES

1. F. Hoyle, *Am. Scientist*, v. 49, p. 188 (1961).
2. J. B. S. Haldane, in *The Inequality of Man* (Penguin Books, 1937).
3. A. I. Oparin, *The Origin of Life* (New York: Macmillan, 1938); (New York: Academic Press, 1957), 3rd ed.
4. Recent general articles and book on this subject include: *Origin of Life on the Earth*, ed. D. I. Oparin (London: Pergamon Press, 1959); P. Moore, and F. Jackson, *Life in the Universe* (London: Routledge and Kegan Paul, 1962); S. L. Miller and H. S. Urey, *Science*, v. 130, p. 245 (1959); J. Keosian, *Science*, v. 131, p. 479 (1960); J. Lederberg, *Science*, v. 132, p. 393 (1960).
5. P. M. Hurley, *How Old is the Earth?* (Anchor Books, 1959).
6. S. A. Tyler, and E. S. Barghoorn, *Science*, v. 119, p. 606 (1954). See also J. S. Harrington and P. D. Toens, *Nature*, v. 200, p. 947 (1963).
7. S. L. Miller, *Science*, v. 117, p. 528 (1953); *Am. Chem. Soc. Jour.*, v. 77, p. 2351 (1955); *Biochim. et Biophys. Acta*, v. 23, p. 480 (1957).
8. P. H. Abelson, *Science*, v. 124, p. 935 (1956).
9. K. W. Heyns, W. Walter, and E. Meyer, *Naturwissenschaften*, v. 44, p. 385 (1957).
10. J. Oro, *Biochem, Biophys. Research Commun.*, v. 2, p. 407 (1960); S. W. Fox and K. Harada, *Science*, v. 133, p. 1923, (1961).
11. S. W. Fox and K. Harada, *Science*, v. 128, p. 1214 (1958); J. Oro, and C. L. Guidry, *Nature*, v. 186, p. 156 (1960).
12. H. C. Urey, [*U.S.*] *Natl. Acad. Sci. Proc.*, v. 38, p. 351 (1952); *The Planets* (New Haven: Yale University Press, 1952).
13. S. L. Miller and H. C. Urey, *Science*, v. 130, p. 245 (1959).
14. P. H. Abelson, *New York Acad. Sci. Annals*, v. 69, p. 276 (1957); also in *Researches in Geochemistry*, P. H. Abelson, ed. (New York: Wiley and Sons, 1959).
15. W. W. Rubey, *Geol. Soc. America Spec. Paper* 62, p. 631 (1955).
16. J. A. Bassham and M. Calvin, *The Path of Carbon in Photosynthesis* (New Jersey: Prentice Hall, 1957); E. Racker, *Nature*, v. 175, p. 249 (1955); *Harvey Lectures*, v. 51, p. 143 (1955–56).
17. D. I. Arnon, *Nature*, v. 184, p. 10 (1959).
18. E. I. Rabinowitch, *Photosynthesis* (New York: Interscience, 1945), v. 1, p. 7–10.
19. G. Wald, in *Abstracts of Papers*, 135th National Meeting, American Chemical Society, Boston, Massachusetts, April 1959, p. 22C.
20. N. H. Horowitz, [*U.S.*] *Natl. Acad. Sci. Proc.*, v. 31, p. 153 (1945).
21. G. Wald, *Scientific American*, v. 201, p. 92 (1959).
22. B. Lovell, *The Exploration of Outer Space* (London: Oxford University Press, 1962), p. 70–72.
23. A. B. Macallum, *Physiol. Rev.*, v. 6, p. 316 (1926). For a quite different view of this situation, however, see E. J. Conway, *Royal Irish Acad. Proc.*, sec. B., v. 48, p. 161 (1943).
24. G. Berg, *Das Vorkommen der chemischen Elemente auf der Erde* (Leipzig: J. A. Barth, 1932), p. 113.
25. G. Wald, in *Horizons in Biochemistry*, ed. M. Kasha and B. Pullman (New York: Academic Press, 1962), p. 127.
26. L. J. Henderson, *Fitness of the Environment*

(New York: Macmillan, 1913); (Boston: Beacon Press, 1958), reprint ed.
27. G. Wald, *Scientific American,* v. 191, p. 44 (1954).
28. This experiment was first done for me by R. C. Bray and H. W. Dougherty, then graduate students in the Biochemistry Department at the Columbia University College of Physicians and Surgeons.
29. Small fractions of D-amino acids appear in a few strange places: several antibiotics and the capsular substance of the pathogenic bacterium *Bacillus anthracis.*
30. G. Wald, *New York Acad. Sci. Annals,* v. 69, p. 352 (1957).
31. G. Wald, in *Comparative Biochemistry,* ed. M. Florkin and H. S. Mason (New York: Academic Press, 1960), v. 1, p. 311.
32. E. P. Wigner, in *The Logic of Personal Knowledge* (Festschrift for Michael Polanyi) (London: Routledge and Kegan Paul, 1961), chap. 19.

The Barberton Mountain Land

Clues to the Differentiation of the Earth

A. E. J. ENGEL

1966

The Barberton Mountain Land offers the geologist a unique opportunity to study early stages in the evolution of the earth. There, in southeast Africa, remnants of the oldest upper mantle, oceanic crust, and an overlying island-arc-like rock complex are fossilized in a sea of granite and granitic gneiss some 2.9–3.3 aeons (10^9 years) old. Studies of these rocks offer deep insight into many aspects of terrestrial differentiation, especially the early evolution of oceanic and continental crusts, the seas, and the atmosphere.

A knowledge of the geological features of the Barberton Mountain Land is essential to this discussion. The geology of this region was first studied by Hall (1918). Recent contributions include the Barberton Memoir of the Geological Survey of South Africa (Visser et al., 1956) and the work of local mine geologists (Cooke, 1965; Steyn, 1965), of the Swaziland Geological Survey (Hunter, 1957; Hunter, 1965; Urie and Jones, 1965), of the Bernard Price Institute for Geophysical Research (Allsopp et al., 1962; Nicolaysen, 1962; Nicolaysen et al., 1965), and of the Economic Geology Research Unit (Ramsay, 1963; Anhaeusser and Viljoen, 1965; Roering, 1965).

The continuing studies of the Onverwacht Series by M. J. and R. P. Viljoen, as part of South Africa's contribution to the International Upper Mantle Project, are, however, the most invaluable contribution to our understanding of this region. (See Anhaeusser et al., 1969.)

SWAZILAND SYSTEM

The Swaziland System and the associated granites are the two dominant Barberton rock complexes. The Swaziland System is almost unique in variety of igneous and sedimentary rock types, their age, and degree of preservation. Pillowed flows and sills of peridotite and basalt form the base of the System. Thick orthoquartzites cut by granodiorite occur at the top.

Revised in 1969 from *EGRU Information Circular No. 27,* 1966. Reprinted with permission of the author, the Economic Geology Research Unit of the University of the Witwatersrand, and the Geological Society of South Africa.

Intermediate igneous and sedimentary series range from the more "primitive" types upward into more highly differentiated rocks. A traverse from base to top of the Swaziland Series reveals the remarkable complementarity of its component igneous-sedimentary rock series. Above the basal peridotite and tholeiitic basalts—which form a sort of primordial Moho and oceanic crust—is a typically calcalkaline igneous series of lavas, especially andesitic, dacitic flows, and tuffs, and consanguineous quartz-dioritic to quartz-monzonitic intrusive plutons.

The volcanic rocks appear as several repeated rock series, or "cycles." The intimately interlayered sedimentary rock series range from mafic debris flows at the base, through cherts, minor carbonate, thence upward into progressively more chert and clastic sediments. Dacitic agglomerates and graywackes are overlain by argillites, subgraywacke, argillaceous sandstones, and capped by the abundant Moodies quartzite. The whole sequence is cut by the most felsic of the plutons, epizonal quartz-monzonites.

The relations permit the Swaziland System to be bracketed in age and subdivided into three rock series. In order of decreasing geologic age these are: (1) Onverwacht Series, (2) Fig Tree Series; (3) Moodies Series (Anheusser et al., 1969; Visser et al., 1956).

The Onverwacht Series is well-exposed and preserved in and near the Komati River Valley, 15 to 30 km east of Badplaace. It includes the Moho-oceanic crust complex at its base, and in this respect is somewhat more completely developed, and preserved, than the base of most analogous "greenstone" belts of continental shield areas. Most of the initial volcanic structures and textures, including pillowed peridotite flows are readily recognizable in the basal and median successions of ultramafic and mafic lavas of the Onverwacht. Each of the older volcanic successions or series is capped with quite subordinate layers of dacitic agglomerate, tuff, chert, and clastic sediments.

The lowermost preserved sedimentary zone, in the lower Onverwacht, overlies a major sequence of mafic and ultramafic flows and is largely lithic tuff, with thin lenses of laminated, carbonaceous and white chert. Alga-like forms, perhaps the oldest life preserved on earth, occur in these beds (Engel et al., 1968). These sedimentary beds and the lavas were deposited in water. This is clearly indicated by graded- and cross-bedding, detailed and uniform laminations, and scour and fill structures in the sediments, and by numerous and widespread pillows in the associated lavas. The ratio of mafic and ultramafic lavas to sediment in the lower and middle Onverwacht rock series is about 50:1. This ratio is abruptly reduced in the upper Onverwacht where the lava types change from peridotite and basalt, to basalt, andesite, and dacite. Associated tuffs, cherts with carbonate interlayers, agglomerates, and volcanic graywacke dominate the section. The thickness of the Onverwacht at and near the type locality varies up to about 11,000 m.

The Fig Tree Series overlies the Onverwacht Series, in part unconformably, and varies in thickness up to approximately 3600 m. It consists largely of graywackes, carbonaceous argillites, arkoses, and argillaceous sandstones, with subordinate amounts of banded, iron-bearing and carbonaceous cherts, tuffs, and conglomerates. Lavas and pyroclastic rocks are rare in the Fig Tree, except for the tuff components in the finer-grained clastic sediments. Associated igneous plutons of quartz-diorite and granodiorite are common.

The Moodies Series lies unconformably upon the Fig Tree and consists mostly of arkosic sandstones, shales, and thick ortho-quartzites which are in part recycled. These rocks are intruded by more felsic plutons, granodioritic to quartz-monzonitic in composition. The thickness of the Moodies varies up to approximately 3600 m.

The Swaziland System is accordingly a case history in the emplacement and deposition of progressively more felsic igneous rocks and more highly differentiated, residuate-type sedimentary rocks, as successive series, built upon a primitive Moho-oceanic rock substructure over a period of some 300 to 400 million years, prior to 3 aeons ago. The entire System now appears as a faulted synclinorium, engulfed and cut by the granitic intrusives emplaced during and after it evolved. The rate of construction was rapid relative to geologic time —largely between 3.4 and 3 aeons ago (Nicolaysen, 1962; Allsopp et al., 1962). Today the region forms a part of the nucleus of the South

African Shield, a very old, stable, thick, "granitic" segment of the continental crust. Most of the ancient "greenstone" belts of other continental shield areas are crudely analogous in their first order features, but most are variously aborted, less obviously differentiated, and more pervasively metamorphosed; hence less clearly indicative of the several sequential evolutionary stages in their evolution. Few exhibit the upper mantle-oceanic crust stage characterized by the lower and middle Onverwacht lavas.

DIFFERENTIATION OF THE EARTH

DIFFERENTIATIVE EPISODES

The fact that the Swaziland System, and many of the enveloping granites, exceed 3 aeons in age raises many questions. On other continents, most of the oldest granites and migmatites surrounding greenstone belts appear to be some 300 to perhaps 600 million years younger (Lowden, 1961; Lowden et al., 1963; Giletti and Gast, 1961; Goldich et al., 1961; Wilson et al., 1961). And as noted above, few of these old crustal fragments are as well-exposed as the Barberton belt, or as free of dynamic metamorphic overprint. This conjunction of extreme age and preservation in the Barberton area raises the question whether this entire fragment of continental crust was formed earlier than most, if not all, of the other greenstone-granite belts of the world; or whether it is a remnant that survived, while its contemporary analogues in Australia, North America, and other continents were largely obliterated by more recent granite-forming orogenic episodes. Ghost-like remnants of other Swaziland-like series are now largely amphibolized streaks in the seas of granitic gneiss. We are left to speculate whether these were formed along with, or as predecessors to, the Swaziland System. The data to resolve this problem appear almost unobtainable with existing geochronological methods.

Available geologic data suggest that, in any given terrain, the oldest greenstone belts, as well as the enveloping granites, vary in age. Reasoning from this, via uniformitarianism, one might conceive of all the old greenstone-granite belts as a second, or subsequent, generation of volcanic-greywacke complexes, the predecessors of which are now the mafic screens and ghost-like streaks within the oldest granite gneiss. Via this actualistic approach, the onset of continental evolution also might be envisaged with the birth of the first rift volcanoes, or island arc-like welts in much earlier, primeval seas (Macgregor, 1951). These initial volcanic edifices may have evolved upon, and from, a protocrust even more primitive in its chemical characteristics than the modern ocean basins (Engel et al., 1965; Tatsumoto et al., 1965). In South Africa, the oldest Barberton granites and migmatites may thus be regarded as extracts from, at least, several preceding cycles, each involving volcanism, weathering, sedimentation, and orogeny. Each cycle could have added, in turn, some ultimate differentiate, granite, and migmatite, to the spreading and thickening sial. This hypothesis predicates the evolution of the greenstone-granite terrain as crudely linear with time, or, at least, the by-product of many granite-forming, orogenic episodes, similar in kind and not too dissimilar in degree. Although this interprètation has the merits of uniformitarianism philosophy, it will be seen that it encounters serious difficulties in explaining features of the Barberton Mountain Land.

The accumulating mass of age and field data certainly suggests that the major granite-forming and orogenic cycles are episodic. The major episodes appear to have occured at intervals of several hundred million years. Reading backward from the present, major granite-forming orogenic events in the crust are dated at about (in millions of years): 100, 400, 1000, 1500, 1900, 2600, and 3200 (Gastil, 1960; Engel and Engel, 1964). The granite-forming episode at about 2600 million years is defined by the ages of many of the granites in the oldest greenstone-granite belts of Western Australia (Wilson et al., 1961; Leggo et al., 1965) and of the Canadian shield of North America (Goldich et al., 1961; Lowden, 1961; Engel and Engel, 1964). The oldest clearly recognizable granite-forming episode on the Earth, at about 3200–3400 million years, has, as its most decipherable rocks, the granites of the Barberton Mountain Land.

Crustal regions that are stabilized and

welded to pre-existing shield areas of each continent by the succession of granite-forming orogenic events may be designated provinces. In North America, the provinces, as thus defined, form a striking, accretionary pattern, the younger enveloping the older (Engel and Engel, 1964; Figure 41.1). In Australia, the provinces decrease in age from west to east (Wilson et al., 1961). In South Africa, the provinces tend to decrease in age towards the Cape (Nicolaysen, 1962). A plot of the area of each of the provinces of North America, including in these "areas" the known initial overlap of each province into adjoining younger provinces, is given in Figure 41.2. This plot suggests that each of the provinces is of approximately equivalent area, and that the growth of the stable shield areas of the North American continent is crudely linear with time.

But the question of continental differentiation also involves the *volumes* of sialic constituents that have been contributed directly from the mantle, and the rates at which this took

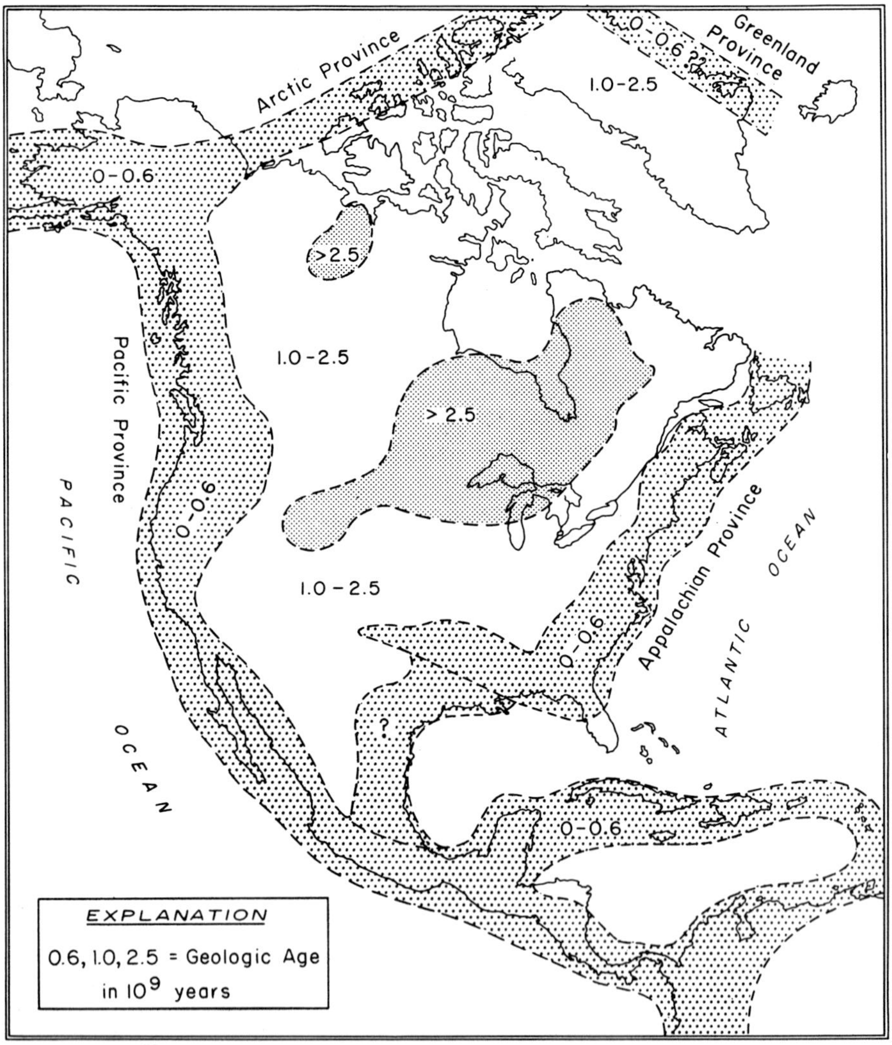

FIGURE 41.1
Gross patterns and ages of geologic provinces in North America. Defined by major granite-forming, mountain-building events. Numbers refer to ages of emplacement of major granites, in thousands of millions of years.

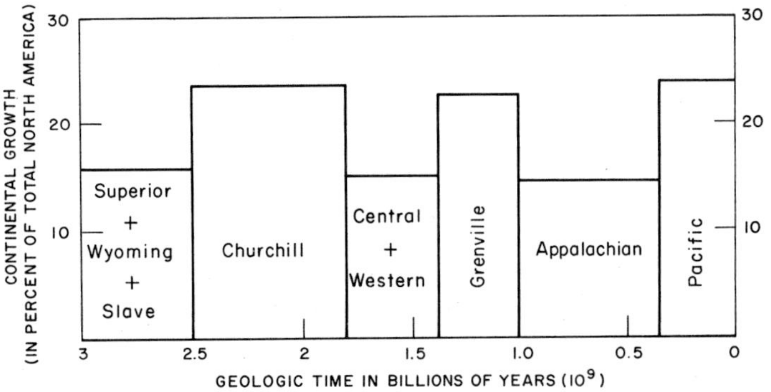

FIGURE 41.2
Graphic representation of the crudely linear rate of continental evolution in North America. Indicated by ages of emplacement of most granites in each geologic province. The area of each block reflects the known extent, and overlap, of the several geologic provinces.

place, not only during the successive stabilizing granite-forming orogenies, but also during anorogenic periods. Was this direct contribution from the mantle fairly uniform with time, or was there a major early effusion of sialic materials, followed by quite subordinate more recent additions?

The migration of sialic materials from the mantle into the crust is but a part of the broader differentiative history of the Earth into core, mantle, and crust, for it is inevitable that the differentiation of the Earth's core and mantle are reflected in important geologic events and processes in the crust.

RATES OF DIFFERENTIATION

At present, there exist widely divergent concepts of the rate, magnitude, and nature of the successive episodes of differentiation of the Earth. Examples of two extreme interpretations are the hypotheses of Runcorn (1965) on one hand, and Patterson and Tatsumoto (1964) on the other.

Runcorn (1965) has suggested that the differentiation of the Earth from a cold, essentially homogeneous agglomerate began about 3000 million years ago, that is, at the onset of the first clearly recognizable granite-forming episodes in continental crusts. His plot of the growth of the Earth's core, or, more precisely, of the ratio (n) of the radius of the core to the radius of the Earth is shown in Figure 41.3. Runcorn (1965) has attempted to relate a spherical harmonic analysis to certain of the major granite-forming episodes, which he infers are crustal manifestations of core growth and mantle convection. It can be seen in Figure 41.3 that Runcorn's Curve (R) involves the series of granite-forming episodes from about 2700 million years, and that the earth is almost completely differentiated at present. However, a more critical aspect of Runcorn's

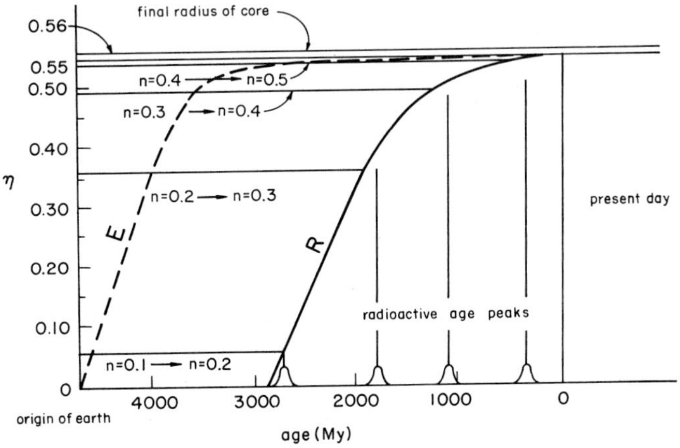

FIGURE 41.3
Diagram indicating two alternative rates of growth of the earth's core. (Modified from Runcorn, 1965.) n is the radius of the earth's core to the radius of the earth. The curve R is based upon a hypothesis of convection, correlated with specific spherical harmonics (Runcorn, 1965). The curve E appears to be more consistent with the geological features of the oldest granite-greenstone terrains.

scheme is that, in Onverwacht time, the Earth was essentially undifferentiated! This clearly is not so.

In contrast, Patterson and Tatsumoto (1964) have interpreted a continent-wide array of lead, uranium, and thorium isotope data, derived from potassium felspars of North America, to mean that there was an early major migration of Pb, U, and Th from the Earth's interior to the crust. This initial differentiative pulse appears to have been followed by a sharp decrease in the rates of transport of these elements during, or near the end of, the first thousand million years after the Earth was formed. The strong coherence of potassium with lead, uranium, and thorium is well demonstrated. Implicit in these studies, therefore, is the conclusion that the rate of migration of the critical sialic constituents K, Pb, U, and Th, from the interior of the Earth is more nearly as shown by Curve E in Figure 41.3 or by Curve P in Figure 41.4.

The accumulating data from the Barberton Mountain Land, and other greenstone-granite terrains seem to support a differentiative history more like that suggested by Patterson and Tatsumoto (1964), and to invalidate the proposal of Runcorn (1965). The data also suggest that the first-order differentiation of the Earth into core, mantle, and sialic crust involved a major thermal event in the mantle. The resultant activation and migration of K, U, Th, and Pb from the Earth's interior to the surface is an intrinsic part of the evolution of the enveloping sea of granites. Comparison of the Onverwacht Series of the Swaziland System in South Africa with more recent volcanic suites also indicates that, since some 3000 million years ago, the upper mantle has not changed appreciably in its chemical composition, although the interior of the Earth has continued to degas and supply amounts of sialic constituents to the crust at lower rates (Figure 41.4, Curve P).

The oldest greenstone-granite analogues of the Barberton Mountain Land in North America form the Superior-Wyoming and Slave Provinces—an area exceeding half-a-million square miles. These are described in numerous reports, especially those of the Canadian Geological Survey, the Ontario Geological Survey, and the Bulletin of the Geological Society of

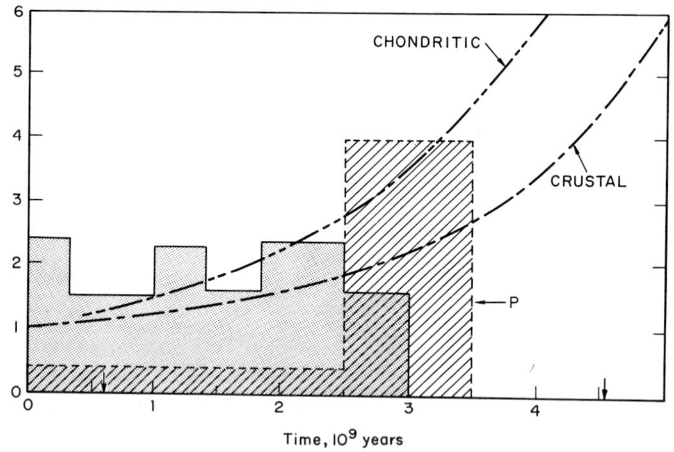

FIGURE 41.4
Curves indicating two possible rates of radioactive heat generation in the earth related to relative rates of continental growth. The curve marked *chondritic* is derived from concentrations of radioactive elements in chondrites. The curve designated *crustal* is derived from the terrestrial concentrations of K, U, Th, and Pb, inferred by Wasserburg et al. (1964). The *solid line* encloses the areas of continent shown in Figure 41.2, which imply a linear rate of continental growth. The *dashed line* enclosing the ruled area indicates the addition of sialic constituents to the crust, as proposed by Patterson and Tatsumoto (1964) and suggested by the studies of old granites (diagram from Birch, 1965; Engel and Engel, 1964; Patterson and Tatsumoto, 1964).

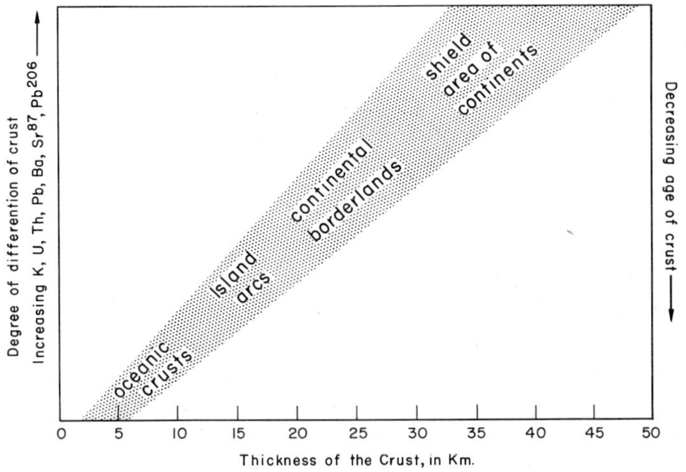

FIGURE 41.5
Graph of the interrelations between the degree of differentiation of the earth's crust, its thickness, and known age

America. Brief summaries appear in (Engel and Engel, 1964; Lowden, 1961; Lowden et al., 1963; Stockwell, 1962; Wilson, 1956).

The oldest greenstone-granite provinces of Australia constitute roughly half-a-million square miles of Western Australia (Low and Connelly, 1957). This region is the subject of considerable investigation at present. Constituent areas are described in publications of the Geological Survey of Western Australia. A brief summary appears in Wilson (1958). Knowledge of the oldest greenstone-granite regions of South America and Asia is less complete. Obviously no extended synthesis is possible until these areas are described in detail.

It is clear, however, that, in each of the continents, the greenstone-granite regions now form the oldest, thickest, stablest, and coolest crustal fragments (Clark and Ringwood, 1964). Therein, the sial, plus subjacent sima, is from 30 to 45 km thick (Press, 1961). Half of this appears to be "granitic," with the bulk chemistry of a granodiorite (Poldervaart, 1955). Heat flow is invariably low, of the order of 0.8×10^{-6} cal/cm^2/sec (Clark and Ringwood, 1964). Hence, temperatures at the base of these old crustal fragments may be inferred to be about 350°C, with some 60 to 80 per cent of the important heat-producing, long-lived, radio-active nucleides now concentrated from the mantle into this composite crust (MacDonald, 1959, p. 1982). This implies that the mantle under these areas is largely depleted in the elements K, U, Th, and Pb (MacDonald, 1963; Clark and Ringwood, 1964). The present quest is for the rate of, and the major episodes involved in, this migration of the heat-producing large cations K, U, and Th, and their chemical cogeners, from the interior of the original homogeneous Earth and their concentration in its continental crust.

CRUSTAL THICKENING

A start will be made, as near the beginning as possible, with the Onverwacht Series at the base of the Swaziland System. Many features of the Onverwacht, and analogous basalt units in other old greenstone belts, imply an origin on a relatively thin crust. Specifically, the closest analogies to these old volcanic series are the recently-evolved island arcs of the circum-Pacific (Adams, 1962; Australasian Petroleum Company, 1961; Byers, 1959; Coats, 1959; Goryatchev, 1962; Liechti et al., 1960; Pergament, 1958; Raitt et al., 1955; Routhier, 1953; Schmidt, 1957; Shor, 1962; Yerokhov, 1960), and of the Caribbean (Dengo, 1962; Ewing and Ewing, 1959; Maxwell, 1948; Officer et al., 1957; Talwani et al., 1959). Recent detailed studies of these arcs suggest that their thickness is a function of their degree of differentiation and age. The Onverwacht-type assemblage of rocks, if considered separately, has analogies in parts of the Kuriles and Aleutians, where crustal thicknesses are about 12 to 15 km (Coats, 1959; Goryatchev, 1962; Shor, 1962). The Swaziland System, taken as a whole, has its closest recent analogies in parts of the Philippines (Durke and Pederson,

1961), New Caledonia (Routhier, 1953), Kamchatka, and some islands in the Carribbean (Burk et al., 1964; Dengo, 1962; Maxwell, 1948). These regions have crustal thicknesses ranging from 15 to 25 km (Officer et al., 1957; Talwani et al., 1959).

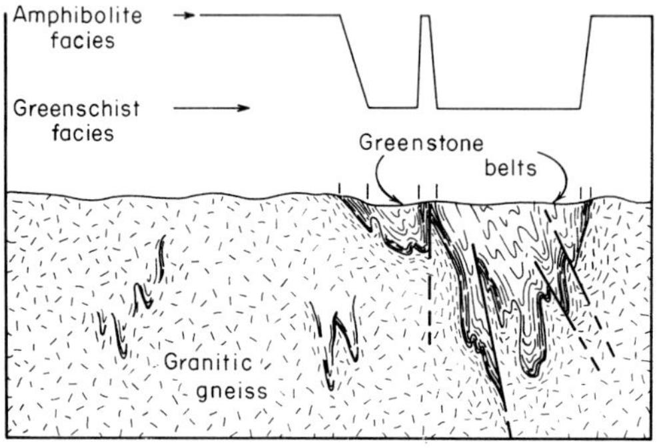

FIGURE 41.6
Diagrammatic cross section of an old greenstone-granite terrain. Illustrates the strongly bimodal metamorphic facies and the telescoped nature of the metamorphic aureoles that are formed in the greenstone by the invading granite.

In effect, the degree of differentiation of the crust, or its age, may be plotted as a function of its thickness, as in Figure 41.5. The thinnest, youngest (?), most primitive crusts are under the oceans (Engel et al., 1965; Press, 1961). The thickest, oldest, and most granitic crusts are now the ancient greenstone-granite shields of the continents.

The basal and median parts of the Onverwacht Series, considered as an isolated crustal complex, would plot in the area of the oceanic crust assemblage (Figure 41.5). The upper Onverwacht, with its volcanic agglomerates, graywackes, and tuffs, is analogous to rocks of incipient island arcs of the Pacific; but, if the entire Swaziland System is considered, this complex falls much farther up the slope of the plot, in the area between the island arcs and continental borderlands. Hence, the data that are synthesized in Figure 41.6 imply that, as the Swaziland System evolved from the basal Onverwacht Series to the topmost Moodies Series, this area of crust, and adjacent source regions of detritus, also thickened, stabilized, and became more granitic. Certainly, this is what the lithologic features of the succession Onverwacht–Fig Tree–Moodies reveals: an upward progression from primitive mafic and ultramafic lavas and volcanic debris through more differentiated and highly weathered sediments, which show an increase in the ratios of potassium felspar to plagioclase, clay minerals to chlorites and micas, potassium to sodium, and silica to magnesium. These upward-changing sedimentary attributes are accompanied by a marked decrease in the ratio of volcanics and tuffs to residuate sediments, and by abrupt decreases in landslides, debris flows, and other evidence of crustal instability. The ultimate rock-types are the essentially clean quartzites of the upper portion of the Moodies Series (Steyn, 1965; Visser et al., 1956).

These general characteristics of the Swaziland System are repeated with striking similarities in the more mature island arcs, and in all the older greenstone belts of the world. Yet, the extreme stability of the oldest of these

FIGURE 41.7
Plot of the variation of temperature in the earth as a function of time and depth. Data used was that employed in deriving the *crustal* curve in Figure 41.4. The cross-hatched zone may have become partially or entirely molten due to heat from the earth's radioactivity. (Adapted from Reynolds et al., 1966.)

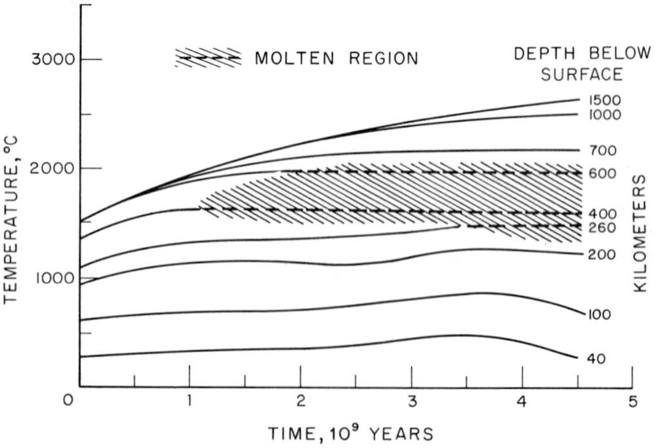

greenstone-granite terrains during the past 2500 to 3000 million years also indicates that the associated crust must have grown sufficiently strong (thick ?), and the underlying mantle sufficiently quiescent (depleted in K, U, Th, Pb ?) to prevent the onset of orogenic episodes.

Other characteristics of the Barberton rocks suggest their emplacement on a crust much thinner than the present. An example is the telescoped nature of the metamorphic aureoles at contacts with the younger granites, and the bimodal nature of the mineral facies (Figure 41.6). In many of the greenstone-granite contacts, the zones of obvious contact metamorphism are no more than a few thousand feet wide (Urie and Jones, 1965; Anhaeusser and Viljoen, 1965). At the granite, the greenstones are reconstituted to amphibolite-facies rocks; yet, in the greenstone away from the granite, the grade of metamorphism drops abruptly to the greenschist facies, as illustrated in Figure 41.6. Telescoped metamorphic aureoles of this kind are known, from studies of much more recent geological environments, to be products of granite invading and enveloping near-surface parts of the crust. Buddington (1959) has characterized the nature of these epizonal granites and their host-rocks in North America. Some of the most illuminating examples are found in the Great Basin of North America, where it is sometimes possible to reconstruct the amount of rock that covered the rising granite, as Hunt (1953) has done in the Henry Mountains, Utah. From studies of this sort, it may be inferred that the "younger" granites which envelop, cut, and reconstitute the Onverwacht–Fig Tree, and most old volcanic-graywacke (greenstone) belts were emplaced at depths of 5 miles or less; and that the heat of these intrusions was dissipated very rapidly upward to the surface by convective streaming along faults and other fractures in the thin overlying crust.

There are also only greenschists, and no *blueschists*, in these sequences, although the chemistry of the graywackes and related volcanic rocks would seem favorable to blueschist formation if pressures (depth of burial) were great enough.

These observations also imply a steeper thermal gradient in the crust and upper mantle 3000 million years ago than now, and this suggestion seems documented by the widespread eruptions of peridotitic lavas on the sea floor, a process probably unique to the second aeon of the earth's history. All of these observations are consistent with other evidence of a major thermal event in the upper mantle preceding and during Onverwacht times (Figures 41.4 and 41.7).

GRANITES AND THE DIFFERENTIATION OF THE SIAL

ORIGIN AND EMPLACEMENT OF GRANITES

Another source of information about the early earth's crust is the enveloping granites. The thoughtful, detailed work of Hunter (1957 and 1965), Roering (1965), and Anhaeusser and Viljoen (1965) indicates the oldest "granites" and granitic gneisses are either pre-Onverwacht or were emplaced during, and immediately after, its development. Some of the quartz-porphyries of Hall (1918) are felsic tuffs and thus integral parts of the Onverwacht Series, whereas some are intrusives in the Onverwacht (Steyn, 1965). There are also major pulses of granite emplaced during, and immediately after, the deformation of the Swaziland System (Hunter, 1957).

This means that an enormous flood of granite, several times the volume of the existing greenstone belts, was emplaced, in part, orogenically, and, in part, anorogenically (Roering, 1965). The anorogenic granites may be merely the surface manifestations of a widespread sialic accretion from below—a passive sialic underplating and thickening of the crust, accomplished by convective streaming of granite-forming constituents from the mantle. The earlier synorogenic granites, and the very old granitic gneisses certainly appear to mark a major flood of granitic fluids from the mantle. They clearly are not products of partial melting of sedimentary piles, or pre-existing sial, for these simply did not exist in or below the basal Onverwacht. Before evaluating this major episode, it should be noted that evidence for the active, and passive, sialic underplating of continental blocks is by no means confined to the Barberton Mountain Land. Both orogenic and relatively young anorogenic granites appear in all the old greenstone-granite regions. The similarities are worldwide. The greenstone belts have the geological characteristics of rocks known to be emplaced on thin, relatively primitive oceanic crusts; yet, they float in a sea of granite, and now, with the granite, constitute the thickest, most stable parts of continental blocks.

More indirect, but important, arguments for secular, sialic underplating also are implicit in the studies of Rubey (1951), Holland (1962), Patterson and Tatsumoto (1964), and many others. These investigators have marshalled a vast array of data that suggests that differentiation and degassing of the Earth has continued up to the present. All of these data seem to require a secular thickening of continental crusts, complementary to a deepening of the oceans. The concept of isostatic equilibrium dictates that, if a secular increase in the depth of the oceans has occurred, the sialic continents have thickened to maintain "freeboard" above sea-level.

VOLUME OF OLD GRANITES

The rise of plateaus, and the appearance of intracratonic basins suggest that a passive sialic underplating at one site may be preceded or accompanied, by subcrustal erosion or thinning of other areas. In general, however, the amount of anorogenic granite, and the amount of sialic underplating seem to have decreased from Onverwacht time to the present. Most granite emplaced during the last thousand million years of the Earth's history seems to be of the classical, orogenic variety—an anatectic melt in the roots of evolving geosynclines. It is the older granites that require the most explanation, as Roering (1965) has pointed out. There are too many of them, and this volume relationship, as well as the anorogenic granites, cannot be explained as a product of the conventional geosynclinal-orogenic cycle (Roering, 1965).

For example, in the Barberton region it appears that a near-surface zone of granitic rock, at least one mile thick, perhaps 10 miles thick, was emplaced by about 3000 million years ago. The existing ratio of granite to greenstone is more than 4:1. Let it be assumed that, at Onverwacht time, the ancient sial of South Africa was about 5 miles thick, more than 80 per cent granitic rock, and less than 20 per cent Onverwacht and other greenstones. The average amounts of the critical sialic elements K, U, Th, and Pb in this old granitic crust may be readily inferred from the potassium content. The analytical data of Hunter (1957) and van Eeden and Marshall (1965) suggest that this ancient sialic crust contained about (in ppm): K, 30,000, and, hence, also about Th, 15; U, 4; and Pb, 20.

Very similar ratios of granite to greenstone, and equivalent, or larger, amounts of K, U, Th, and Pb exist in the old granite-greenstone regions of other continents. In South Africa, the area of this ancient granitic crust probably exceeded half-a-million square miles. In general, in all the continents, this oldest granite-greenstone terrain appears to have covered at least one-fifth of the area of present-day continents, and, perhaps, even much more of a crust now reconstituted into, and obliterated by, succeeding orogenic episodes in the adjoining, younger provinces. These data on area and volume are minimal, and may be low by a factor of two or more.

The choice of a widespread thermal, differentiative event in the Earth to explain this old granitic crust also is dictated by the conception of the composition of the upper mantle from Onverwacht time to the present. The limiting, and critical, conditions appear to be imposed by the composition of the basalts and peridotites in the Onverwacht and younger volcanic series.

BASALTS AND THE DIFFERENTIATION OF THE SIAL

PARENTAL BASALTS

It is generally agreed that basalt is the one magma erupted from the mantle in great volumes, essentially ubiquitous in time and in geologic environment. At least two primary basaltic magmas have been postulated—one of tholeiitic basalt, and the other alkali-rich (Kushiro and Kuno, 1963; Yoder and Tilley, 1962; Engel and Engel, 1969). Recent studies on both continents and oceans suggest, however, that tholeiitic basalts are the predominant, if not the only, mantle-derived basalt (Engel et al., 1965). In fact, alkali-rich basalts constitute less than one per cent of the total volcanic sequence in the oceans, and appear to be limited largely to the surficial carapaces of the larger volcanoes. In the continents, the volume and structural relations are much the same. There are essentially no alkali-rich basalts in the Precambrian, which constitutes some four-fifths of geologic time (Engel et al., 1965).

The dominant tholeiitic basalts show only moderate, but apparently significant, variations in composition. The variations of interest at present are the amounts of K, U, Th, and Pb. These, with silica, vary systematically with the crustal environment in which the tholeiitic basalts are emplaced. In the oceans, where the great floods of tholeiitic basalt are extruded through a thin, basaltic crust, the average values are (in ppm): K, 1,000; U, 0.1; Th, 0.2; and Pb, 0.8 (Tatsumoto et al., 1965).

In the island arcs and old greenstone environments, the values for K, U, Th, and Pb rise to double or triple these amounts. In the stable continental regions, the flood basalts and swarms of diabase and dolerite have an average potassium value of about 7000 parts per million (Walker and Poldervaart, 1949) with proportional increases in U, Th, and Pb. There is, accordingly, an increase in these elements in flood basalts that is closely correlative with the increasing thickness, age, and degree of differentiation of the crust which they intrude (Figure 41.5).

One interpretation of these data is that the upper mantle source of all flood basalts had initially about the same low amounts of K, U, Th, and Pb. If this is true, the systematic environmental increase is due to an increasing contamination of the rising basalt melt by K, U, Th, Pb and Si from the progressively thicker, more sialic crust. An alternative possibility is that the primary basaltic melt under the continents is blended with the continent-thickening, sialic constituents that are rising from the interior of the Earth.

The point of immediate interest is that the compositions of these tholeiitic basalts seem to place limiting conditions on the amounts of K, U, Th, and Pb in their mantle source-regions under the relatively thin, primitive oceanic, island-arc, and greenstone crusts (Engel et al., 1965). Moreover, for these specific crustal environments, the conditions in the subjacent mantle do not appear to have varied much with time. The present analytical studies of Onverwacht rocks are far from complete, but it is clear that the constituent pillow basalts average about (in ppm): K, 1500; U, 0.15; Th, 0.3; and Pb, 1.0. Similar concentrations of K, U, Th, and Pb exist in the basalts of both of the old greenstone belts of North America, and in the tholeiitic basalts of young island arcs in analogous, incipient stages of development.

Because seismic data imply that the composition of the upper mantle is peridotitic, the tholeiitic flood basalts are probably partial melts, originally blended with peridotite, in ratios of perhaps 3:1 or 4:1 (Clark and Ringwood, 1964). If this is correct, the concentrations of K, U, Th, and Pb in the mantle under the oceans, evolving island arcs, and greenstone belts, throughout the last 3000 million years has, been about (in ppm): K, 400; U, 0.04; Th, 0.08; and Pb, 0.3.

A test of this inference is possible through studies of the K, U, Th, and Pb in peridotites of the Onverwacht and younger greenstone and island arc environments. The agreement is good. These peridotites contain on the average about 50 to 250 ppm K, and appropriate very low concentrations of U, Th, and Pb, often so low, in fact, as to defy accurate analysis by contemporary techniques.

Almost surely, both the pillow basalts and ultrabasics of these sequences offer the upper and, probably, the lower limits of K, U, Th, and Pb in the upper mantle from which they have been derived; the basalts are partial melts, the peridotites are total melts, or residuates from which some basalt already has been extruded.

Summarizing these conjectures: (1) the composition of the upper mantle from which the basalts and peridotites of specific crustal environments have been derived has not varied significantly in composition for at least 3000 million years, and (2) during this time the concentrations of the elements K, U, Th, and

Pb in the upper mantle under oceanic, island-arc, and greenstone belts have been low, of the order of K, 400; U, 0.04; Th, 0.08; and Pb, 0.3 (in ppm).

DIFFERENTIATION OF THE SIAL

Because numerous lines of evidence point to a primordial Earth composed of far more primitive material, perhaps a mix of stony and iron meteorites in ratios of 4:1 to 7:1 (Birch, 1964), it may be readily inferred that the differentiation of this primordial mix into iron-rich core and silicate-rich mantle and crust preceded Onverwacht time. If the mantle source of the Onverwacht volcanics was much more primitive than at present, the partial and total melts extruded therefrom would clearly indicate this primordial legacy.

The second conclusion, that the amounts of K, U, Th, and Pb in the mantle below greenstone belts were low in Onverwacht and succeeding times, follows from the first. If these elements were abundant in the upper mantle, they would be abundant in its partial and total melts extruded as island-arc and greenstone volcanics.

The implications of this fact are crucial to the problem of the old granites. The derivation of the old granitic crust, some 5 miles thick, that has been inferred for the Barberton Mountain Land, and for other old greenstone-granite terrains, would require almost complete extraction of the K, U, Th, and Pb from an underlying zone of the mantle some 100 to 200 miles thick. If the thickness of the old South Africa granites has been appreciably underestimated, then their total K, U, Th, and Pb, would have to come from the nearly complete extraction of these elements from much of the upper mantle. Hence, there is a prejudice in favour of a major, early differentiation of the Earth, accompanied by a major, large-scale, thermal event in the mantle in the period preceding Onverwacht time.

The similar requirements of the lead-uranium isotope data from North America have been emphasized. Further support for this differentiative event is derived from recently analyzed thermal models of the Earth (Reynolds et al., 1966). The conclusions are summarized in Figure 41.7. Conditions suggested by the "uniform terrestrial model" of the Earth's composition seem to require partial, or total melting of a large zone in the upper mantle, during the early history of the Earth. Reynolds and his colleagues suggest that a zone of the mantle some 400 km thick, reaching to within 200 to 250 km of the surface, was molten during the period of generation of the older granites, some 2500–4000 million years ago.

It appears that independently derived geochemical and geophysical data point to a partial or complete melting of the outer Earth early in its history. This process would greatly accelerate the differentiation of core, mantle, and crust by permitting the iron to settle into the Earth's core, and the more volatile constituents, together with K, U, Th, Pb, and other granite-forming elements to rise towards the surface.

Elsasser (1963) in a discussion of the Earth's differentiation attempts to explain why this upward streaming of sialic constituents was concentrated on one side of the Earth and retarded in oceanic areas. If this protocontinent was Gondwanaland, the Barberton Mountain Land was near its centre. It may be speculated that upward convective streaming of sialic material began here, and that the sial grew laterally with time, thus accounting for the great age of the South African crust relative to that of Australia and North America.

But these are more speculative aspects of the Earth's history that cannot now be tested. It is possible, however, to evaluate, at this time, the concept of passive sialic underplating, and to further quantify the scale of the several, early granite-forming events in the Barberton Mountain Land. Deep drill-holes into the Nelspruit, Kaap Valley, and old Swaziland granites would produce cores from which more exact volumes and ages of the several granites could be determined as a function of depth. Such deep sial-holes may prove as fruitful a source of the Earth's history as oceanic moholes. South Africa is, indeed, a critical region.

SUMMARY

The Swaziland System of the Barberton region may be considered an archetype of most ancient "greenstone" belts within the continental nucleii. Basal parts of the Swaziland System (Onverwacht-type) are strikingly like contemporary oceanic crust. Locally, segments of ultramafic "upper mantle-like" flows and thick, differentiated sills are interleaved with basalts in relations and proportions suggestive of a fossil oceanic Moho, and an uppermost mantle of the earth preserved for some 3.4 aeons (10^9 years). Superposed upon this oceanic-mantle complex is an emergent island arc-like series of predominantly volcanics, tuffs, wackes, and cherts (upper Onverwacht). The succeeding (overlying) parts of the Swaziland System (Fig Tree and Moodies types) obviously have been derived from, and deposited upon, a progressively more stable, thickened and increasingly felsic crust. The rocks are predominantly sedimentary. The ratio of residuate type clastics to wackes and tuffs increases upward. The top of the section includes a thick, possibly recycled ortho-quartzite, cut by syn-tectonic and post-tectonic granodiorites and quartz-monzonite plutons.

The net result is a faulted synclinorium of ordered volcanics and sediments, immersed in a sea of granitic gneiss and granite, which, with adjoining segments, forms one of the oldest, thickest, coolest, and most stable shield areas of the world.

Although most other least metamorphosed parts of the South African Shield, and ancient nuclei of other continents, contain variously aborted or exaggerated analogues of the Swaziland System and its enveloping sea of granitic gneiss, few if any are as old, well-developed, preserved, exposed, and sequentially ordered.

In the Barberton region—as in the other old granite-greenstone regions of the continents—the granitic gneiss appears to exceed in volume the greenstones by perhaps an order of magnitude. The surficial ratio is about 4:1. The actual ratio is much larger, a function of the thickness of the ancient granites—a presently unknown quantity.

Many of the surficial granitic gneisses are over 3.2 aeons old and most exposed granite is more than 2.5 aeons in age.

The "granite" clearly has been added, from the mantle, to the greenstone-granite terrains as they were built, during both orogenic and anorogenic periods. Much of it may have been passively accreted from below, but meso- and epizonal plutons were emplaced during and in the waning stages of the major crust-building episode, 2.5–3.5 aeons ago.

The basalts and peridotites of the basal Onverwacht-type are depleted in the radiogenic nucleides K, U, and Th. Lavas of this composition, as well as overlying andesites and dacites, have been erupted from the mantle in island-arc environments for over 3 aeons. Some of the peridotites and most of the basalts probably are the most "primary" magma-types erupted at the surface. Many are pillowed; most were erupted underwater. Their constancy in composition throughout decipherable geologic time suggests that their source or sources in the mantle also has been of nearly uniform composition, or of nearly uniform P-T conditions, or both. These and related data indicate that the first-order differentiation of the mantle and protocore preceded the emplacement of the Onverwacht lavas, that is, prior to 3.4 aeons ago. The small amounts of K, U, and Th in the floods of basalt and ultramafic indicate that neither sedimentary prisms nor localized source-regions of the mantle have been the source of the associated oldest granites. The widespread granite and related members of the calc-alkaline series in the ancient continental nucleii appear to be derived from, and the result of, large-scale melting and differentiation of large magma chambers in the mantle prior to, during, and in the several hundred million years after Onverwacht times.

LIST OF REFERENCES CITED

Adams, R. D., 1962, Thickness of the earth's crust beneath the Campbell Plateau: New Zealand Jour. Geology and Geophysics, v. 5, p. 74.

Allsopp, H. L., H. R. Roberts, G. D. L. Schreiner, and D. R. Hunter, 1962, Rb-Sr age measurements on various Swaziland granites: Jour. Geophys. Research, v. 67, no. 13, p. 5307–5313.

Anhaeusser, C. R., and M. J. Viljoen, 1965, The base of the Swaziland System in the Barberton-Noordkaap-Louw's Creek area, Barberton Mountain Land: Geol. Soc. South Africa Trans., v. 68, annexure.

Anhaeusser, C. R., C. Roering, M. Viljoen, and R. Viljoen, 1969, The Barberton Mountain Land, *in* C. Gibson, ed., The Rhodesian Shield (a symposium volume): Johannesburg, Geological Society of South Africa.

Australasian Petroleum Company Proprietary, 1961, Geological results of petroleum exploration in western Papua: Geol. Soc. Australia Jour., v. 8, pt. 2, 113 p.

Birch, F., 1964, Density and composition of mantle and core: Jour. Geophys. Research, v. 69, p. 4377–4388.

———, 1965, Speculations on the earth's thermal history: Geol. Soc. America Bull., v. 76, p. 133–154.

Buddington, A. F. 1959, Granite emplacement with special reference to North America: Geol. Soc. America Bull., v. 70, p. 671–747.

Burk, C. A., et al., 1964, A study of serpentinite —the AMSOC core hole near Mayaguez, Puerto Rico: Natl. Acad. Sci.-Natl. Research Council Pub. 1188, 175 p.

Byers, F. M., 1959, Geology of Umnak and Bogoslof Islands, Aleutian Island, Alaska: U.S. Geol. Survey Bull. 1028-L, p. 267–369.

Clark, S. P., Jr., and A. E. Ringwood, 1964, Density distribution and constitution of the upper mantle: Rev. Geophysics, v. 2, p. 35–88.

Coats, R. R., 1959, Magma type and crustal structure in the Aleutian Arc, *in* The crust of the Pacific Basin: Am. Geophys. Union Mon. 6, p. 92–109.

Cooke, R., 1965, The pre–Fig Tree rocks in and around the Moodies Hills, Barberton Mountain Land: Geol. Soc. South Africa Trans., v. 68, annexure.

Dengo, G., 1962, Tectonic-igneous sequence in Costa Rica, *in* A. E. J. Engel, H. L. James and B. F. Leonard, eds., Petrologic studies—a volume in honor of A. F. Buddington: Boulder, Colo., Geological Society of America, p. 133–161.

Durke, E. F., and S. L. Pederson, 1961, Geology of Northern Luzon, Philippines: Am. Assoc. Petroleum Geologists Bull., v. 45, p. 137–168.

Elsasser, W. M., 1963, Early history of the earth, *in* J. Geiss and E. D. Goldberg, eds., Earth science and meteorites: New York, John Wiley and Sons, Interscience, p. 1–30.

Engel, A. E. J., and C. G. Engel, 1964, Continental accretion and the evolution of North America, *in* A. P. Subramaniam and S. Balakrishna, eds., Advancing frontiers in geology and geophysics—a volume in honour of M. S. Krishnan: Hyderabad, Indian Geophysical Union, p. 17–37.

———, 1969, Mafic and ultramafic rocks of the oceans, *in* A. Maxwell, ed., The Sea (v. IV): New York, John Wiley and Sons, Interscience.

Engel, A. E. J., C. G. Engel, and R. G. Havens, 1965, Chemical characteristics of oceanic basalts and the upper mantle: Geol. Soc. America Bull., v. 76, p. 719–734.

Engel, A. E. J., B. Nagy, L. A. Nagy, C. G. Engel, G. D. W. Kremp, and C. M. Drew, 1968, Alga-like forms in Onverwacht Series, South Africa—oldest recognized lifelike forms on earth: Science, v. 161, p. 1005–1008.

Ewing, J. T., and W. M. Ewing, 1959, Seismic refraction measurements in the Atlantic Ocean basins, in the Mediterranean Sea, on the Mid-Atlantic Ridge, and in the Norwegian Sea: Geol. Soc. America Bull., v. 70, p. 291–317.

Gastil, G., 1960, The distribution of mineral dates in time and space: Am. Jour. Sci., v. 258, p. 1–35.

Giletti, B. J., and P. W. Gast, 1961, Absolute age of Precambrian rocks in Wyoming and Montana: New York Acad. Sci. Annals, v. 91, p. 454–458.

Goldich, S. S., A. O. Nier, H. Baadsgaard, J. H. Hoffman, and H. W. Krueger, 1961, The Precambrian geology and geochronology of Minnesota: Minnesota Geol. Survey Bull., v. 41, 193 p.

Goryatchev, A. V., 1962, On the relationship between geotectonic and geophysical phenomena of the Kuril-Kamchatka folding zone at the junction zone of the Asiatic Continent with the Pacific Basin, *in* The crust of the Pacific Basin: Am. Geophys. Union Mon. 6, p. 41–49.

Hall, A. L., 1918, The geology of the Barberton gold mining district: Geol. Survey South Africa Mem. 9.

Holland, H. D., 1962, Model for the evolution of the earth's atmosphere, *in* A. E. J. Engel, H. L. James, and B. F. Leonard, eds., Petrologic studies—a volume in honor of A. F. Buddington: Boulder, Colo., Geological Society of America, p. 447–477.

Hunt, C. B., 1953, Geology and geography of the Henry Mountain region, Utah: U.S. Geol. Survey Prof. Paper 228, 234 p.

Hunter, D. R., 1957, The Precambrian granitic terrain in Swaziland: Geol. Soc. South Africa Trans., v. 68, annexure.

Kushiro, I., and H. Kuno, 1963, Origin of primary basalt magmas and classification of basaltic rocks: Jour. Petrology, v. 4, p. 75–89.

Leggo, P. J., W. Compston, and A. F. Trendall, 1965, Radiometric ages of some Precambrian rocks from the northwest division of Western Australia: Geol. Soc. Australia Jour., v. 12, pt. 2.

Liechti, P., F. W. Roe, and N. S. Haile, 1960, The geology of Sarawak, Brunei, and the western part of North Borneo: Borneo Geol. Survey Bull., v. 3, 360 p.

Low, G. H., and R. R. Connelly, 1957, Geological sketch map of Western Australia: Perth, Geol. Survey of Western Australia.

Lowden, J. A., 1961, Age determinations by the Geological Survey of Canada: Geol. Survey Canada Paper 61-17, 127 p.

Lowden, J. A., C. H. Stockwell, H. W. Tipper, and R. K. Wanless, 1963, Age determinations and geological studies: Geol. Survey Canada Paper 62-17, 140 p.

MacDonald, G. J. F., 1959, Calculations on the thermal history of the earth: Jour. Geophys. Research, v. 64, p. 1967–2000.
———, 1963, The deep structure of continents: Rev. Geophysics, v. 1, p. 587–665.
Macgregor, A. M., 1951, Some milestones in the Precambrian of Southern Rhodesia: Geol. Soc. South Africa Trans., v. 54, p. 27–71.
Maxwell, J. C., 1948, Geology of Tobago, B. W. I.: Geol. Soc. America Bull., v. 59, p. 801–854.
Nicolaysen, L. O., 1962, Stratigraphic interpretation of age measurements in southern Africa, *in* A. E. J. Engel, H. L. James, and B. F. Leonard, eds., Petrologic studies—a volume in honor of A. F. Buddington: Boulder, Colo., Geological Society of America, p. 569–598.
Nicolaysen, L. O., et al., 1965, Age measurements on rocks from Swaziland and the area around Barberton: Geol. Soc. South Africa Trans., v. 68, annexure.
Officer, C. B., J. I. Ewing, R. S. Edwards, and H. R. Johnson, 1957, Geophysical investigations in the Eastern Caribbean–Venezuelan Basin, Antilles Island Arc, and Puerto Rico Trench: Geol. Soc. America Bull., v. 68, p. 359–378.
Patterson, C., and M. Tatsumoto, 1964, The significance of lead isotopes in detrital feldspar with respect to chemical differentation within the earth's mantle: Geochim. et. Cosmochim. Acta, v. 28, p. 1–22.
Pergament, M. A., 1958, Upper Cretaceous rocks of northwestern Kamchatka: Acad. Sci. U.S.S.R. Proc. Geochemistry Sec. (English Transl.), v. 120.
Poldervaart, A., 1955, Chemistry of the earth's crust, *in* A. Poldervaart, ed., Crust of the earth: Geo. Soc. America Spec. Paper 62, p. 119–144.
Press, F., 1961, The earth's crust and upper mantle: Science, v. 133, p. 1455–1463.
Raitt, R., R. L. Fisher, and R. G. Mason, 1955, Tonga Trench, *in* A. Poldervaart, ed., Crust of the earth: Geol. Soc. America Spec. Paper 62, p. 237–254.
Ramsay, J. G., 1963, Structural investigations in the Barberton Mountain Land, Eastern Transvaal: Geol. Soc. South Africa Trans., v. 66.
Reynolds, R. T., P. E. Fricker, and A. L. Summers, 1966, Effects of melting upon thermal models of the earth: Jour. Geophys. Research, v. 71, p. 573–582.
Roering, C., 1965, The tectonics of the main gold producing area of the Barberton Mountain Land: Geol. Soc. South Africa Trans., v. 68, annexure.
Routhier, P. P., 1953, Nouvelles donnees sur l'histoire geologique de la cote ouest de Nouvelle Caledonie: Pacific Science Assoc. 7th Cong. Proc., v. II (Geology), p. 47–61.
Rubey, W. H., 1951, Geologic History of Seawater: Geo. Soc. America Bull., v. 62, p. 1111–1147.
Runcorn, S. K., 1965, Changes in the convection pattern in the earth's mantle and continental drift—evidence for a cold origin of the earth: Royal Soc. [London] Philos. Trans., ser. A, v. 258, p. 228–251.
Schmidt, R. G. 1957, Geology of Saipan, Mariana Islands—petrology of the volcanic rocks: U.S. Geol. Survey Prof. Paper 280B, p. 127–174.
Shor, G. G., Jr., 1962, Seismic refraction studies of the coast of Alaska—1956–57: Geol. Soc. America Bull., v. 72, p. 721–730.
Steyn, M. v. R., 1965, Basal rocks of the Swaziland System in the Steynsdorp Valley and Fairview areas of the Barberton Mountain Land: Geol. Soc. South Africa Trans., v. 68, annexure.
Stockwell, C. H., 1962, A tectonic map of the Canadian Shield, *in* The tectonics of the Canadian Shield: Royal Soc. Canada Spec. Pub. 4, p. 6–15.
Talwani, M., G. Sutton, and J. Worzel, 1959, A crustal section across the Puerto Rico Trench: Jour. Geophys. Research, v. 64, p. 1545–1555.
Tatsumoto, M., C. E. Hedge, and A. E. J. Engel, 1965, Potassium, rubidium, strontium, thorium, uranium, and the ratio of strontium-87 to strontium-86 in oceanic tholeiitic basalt: Science, v. 150, no. 3698, p. 886–888.
Urie, J. G., and D. H. Jones, 1965, Metamorphic zones of the Archean Fold belt in northwestern Swaziland: Geol. Soc. South Africa Trans., v. 68, annexure.
Van Eeden, O. R., and C. G. Marshall, 1965, The granitic rocks of the Barberton Mountain Land in the Transvaal: Geol. Soc. South Africa Trans., v. 68, annexure.
Visser, D. J. L., et al., 1956, The geology of the Barberton area: Geol. Survey South Africa Spec. Pub. 15.
Walker, F., and A. Poldervaart, 1949, Karroo Dolerites of the Union of South Africa: Geol. Soc. America Bull., v. 60, p. 591–706.
Wasserburg, G. J., G. J. F. MacDonald, F. Hoyle, and W. A. Fowler, 1964, Relative contributions of uranium, thorium, and potassium to heat production in the earth: Science, v. 143, p. 465–467.
Wilson, A. F., 1958, Advances in the knowledge of the structure and petrology of the Precambrian rocks of southwestern Australia: Royal Soc. Western Australia Proc., v. 41, p. 57–83.
Wilson, A. F., W. Compston, and P. M. Jeffery, 1961, Radioactive ages from the Precambrian rocks of Australia: New York Acad. Sci. Annals, v. 91, p. 514–520.
Wilson, M. E., 1956, Early Precambrian rocks of the Timiskaming region, Quebec and Ontario, Canada: Geol. Soc. America Bull., v. 67, p. 1397–1430.
Yerokhov, V. F., 1960, New data on the age of the Neogene formations of the northeastern part of Iturup Island (Kuriles): Doklady Acad. Sci. U.S.S.R. Earth Sci. Sec., v. 130, p. 1–15.
Yoder, H. S., and C. E. Tilley, 1962, Origin of basalt magmas—an experimental study of natural and synthetic rock systems: Jour. Petrology, v. 3, p. 342–532.

42

Atmospheric and Hydrospheric Evolution on the Primitive Earth

PRESTON CLOUD
1968

From *Science*, vol. 160, pp. 729–736, 1968. Reprinted with permission of the American Association for the Advancement of Science.

This discussion focuses on the interactions that necessarily took place between biospheric, atmospheric, lithospheric, and hydrospheric evolution on the primitive earth and perhaps the moon. How can evidence and conjecture about each of these different kinds of evolution limit or illuminate hypotheses about the others, and how can all such lines of thought be integrated to bring us closer to a consistent and plausible model of early terrestrial events?

A salient and long-appreciated aspect of the terrestrial atmosphere is its great depletion in the noble gases, relative to their cosmic abundances [1]. This seems to require the conclusion that the atmosphere as we know it is of secondary origin. Either the earth originated without a primary atmosphere, or such an atmosphere was mainly lost in a subsequent thermal episode.

Actually, an internal source for our atmosphere as a result of gradual, episodic, or rapid volcanic outgassing and weathering was proposed long before the depletion in noble gases was recognized. The Swedish geologist Högbom [2] suggested this in 1894, and his countryman Arrhenius [3], in 1896. Later Chamberlin [4] recognized a post-accumulational generation of the atmosphere from occluded gases as a necessary consequence of his and Moulton's planetesimal hypothesis for the origin of the earth. Rubey's critical and comprehensive assessment [5] of possible sources for the volatiles that comprise the atmosphere and hydrosphere has led to wide acceptance of the concept of accumulation of both from juvenile sources.

As far as the atmosphere is concerned, dispute focuses on the composition and time of origin of the primitive atmosphere and the original proportions and changes in the proportions of O_2, N_2, CO_2, and H in it.

The atmosphere cannot be older than the earth. Hence an outside limit on its time of origin is the time of origin of the earth. Much evidence has been adduced in recent years, based on the ages of meteorites [6, 7] and on isotopic composition of terrestrial leads [7, 8], to suggest that both meteorites and leads were involved in some kind of homogenization event about 4.6×10^9 years ago (10^9 years is hereafter referred to as an aeon). Small excesses of xenon-129 in some meteorites [9] support the inference that this event closely approximates the time of origin of the solar system and hence the approximate time of formation of the earth. Such an interpretation, however attractive and highly probable as it seems, is not the only possible one. On the one hand, available evidence does not completely eliminate the possibility that the earth as a solid body in the general form we know it might be as much as an aeon younger than the parts from which it accumulated [10]. On the other hand, Baranov [11] suggests ways of looking at the lead isotope data which *might* require as much as 7.5 aeons for the radiogenic lead isotopes to reach current crustal ratios.

A minimal age for the earth is, of course, given by the most ancient minerals dated. This age appears to be around 3.5 to 3.6 aeons. Zircons from gneisses in Minnesota show uranium-lead isotope ratios which, on a concordia curve, indicate an age of 3.5 aeons [12]. Amphibolites from the central Ukraine are said to give potassium-argon ages exceeding 3.5 aeons [13]. Granites which are apparently not the oldest in South Africa [14] yield rubidium-strontium ages of 3.2 aeons or more, and some pegmatites give whole-rock ages as great as 3.4 aeons [15], although the larger figures are very uncertain. The basement complex of the Congo is said to yield lead-isotope ages approaching 3.3 to 3.4 aeons [16]. And in Western Australia, rubidium-strontium ages indicate that granites and greenstones were metamorphosed 2.7 aeons ago [17] and probably originated 3 aeons or more ago [17, 18]. Thus the earliest dates so far obtained in the rather intensively studied older parts of North America and Europe are remarkably close to each other and are approached by the ages of the oldest dated rocks in the Southern Hemisphere. Although the record is distressingly sparse, it underscores the question: What was happening for the first aeon or so of the earth's history, if accumulation of the earth was completed not long after the homogenization event that took place approximately 4.6 aeons ago? We will return to that question, and to the fact that a later marked uranium-lead segregation, presumably denoting a significant episode in crustal evolution, is dated at about 3.5 aeons [7, 19]—coincidentally, about the same age as that suggested by the regrettably sparse record of dated minerals in the most ancient rocks.

The immediate point is that, inasmuch as we do not have rocks known to be older than about 3.5 aeons, geology can as yet do little to place limitations on conjecture about the nature and time of origin of an atmosphere or hydrosphere that might have existed before that time. Indeed, these oldest dated rocks have only an indirect bearing on the questions before us, and the ages obtained for them probably date only an early episode of metamorphism and not their time of primary origin.

SOME LIMITATIONS ON CONJECTURE

What are the oldest rocks that tell us something reasonably unequivocal about the existence and nature of the contemporaneous hydrosphere and atmosphere? They are sedimentary rocks, considered from several lines of converging evidence to have a minimum age of about 3 aeons in South Africa and Swaziland [15], to be more than 2.7 aeons old in Minnesota [20], and mainly younger than 2.5 to 2.7 aeons at other places. These rocks consist of water-laid detrital and chemical sediments that clearly could not have originated without the prior existence of atmospheric weathering and a substantial hydrosphere (see ref. 21 for questionable older records).

As Holland [22], Abelson [23], Cloud [24], and others cited by them have pointed out, these rocks and associated minerals also place limitations on conjecture about the composition of the atmosphere beneath which they were deposited. Apparently detrital uraninite and pyrite at various localities combine with more esoteric geochemical evidence to indicate that the atmosphere before 1.8 to 2 aeons ago could have contained little or no free oxygen. The abundance of bedded chemical silicates, representing the chert component of the banded iron formation, and the relative rarity of limestone and dolomite among the oldest sedimentary rocks also imply that there could have been little ammonia in the atmosphere of those times. For ammonia would raise the *p*H of the hydrosphere and favor an abundance of carbonate rocks and a rarity of bedded chert. Abelson [23], moreover, has shown that, in an atmosphere devoid or nearly devoid of free oxygen, the dissociation of methane, had it been abundant, should have given rise to a rain of carbon of nonvital origin; yet carbon, although not uncommon, is not a conspicuous component of the oldest sediments. Thus it may be concluded that the atmosphere, from about 3 aeons onward at least, was not, as some have suggested, rich in methane or ammonia. The sedimentary record, rather, supports Rubey's conjecture [5] that the early atmospheric gases would be those which are occluded in igneous rocks, or which on other grounds are recognized as juvenile components of volcanic and hot-spring gases. These are H_2O, CO_2, CO, N_2, SO_2, HCl, and a few other trace gases.

POSSIBLE TIMING AND SIGNIFICANCE OF POSTACCUMULATIONAL MELTING

How far back might such an atmosphere go? How would its accretion have become initiated? And what can we postulate about its evolution from the known records of biospheric and lithospheric evolution? Here we will become involved with some paleontologic and geologic evidence bearing on the appearance of the moon in orbit around the earth, not because the evidence for a postaccumulational melting episode depends on this, but because there could be a relation between these phenomena and it is interesting to examine that possibility.

In order for an atmosphere and hydrosphere to begin to accrete on an earth which, during accumulation, probably had an outer temperature of no more than a few hundred degrees Kelvin, some significant part of the outer shell or mantle of that earth would have had to undergo melting sufficient to start release of its volatiles to the surface. Such melting might have resulted from either or both of two postulated thermal episodes. One is the combined effect, early in the earth's history, of the normal evolution of radiogenic energy and the conversion of gravitational energy to heat. The other is the generation of heat from tidal friction incident to lunar capture [25–28], abetted by the two other factors.

Direct geologic evidence, we have seen, as yet tells us little about the nature of the earth and its enveloping hydrosphere and atmosphere before about 3 aeons ago. However, if we could find among the older rocks or fossils some that provided clues as to tidal amplitudes, this information would have a bearing on whether or not the moon might have been in orbit at any particular time. Such data, then, would constitute a test as to whether it would be consistent with the geologic record to hypothesize that lunar capture might have stimulated an early pulse of melting and outgassing, as Singer [27] has suggested.

Such fossils and rocks do, in fact, exist. They include the variously shaped but often

TABLE 42.1
Stromatolites of large amplitude

Approximate amplitude (meters)	Approximate age (10^9 years)	Geologic unit	Locality
6	0.63	Otavi "Series," Tsumeb Formation	Kombat Mine, S.W. Africa
> 5	> 1.1	Belt Supergroup, Helena Limestone	Helena, Montana
2.5–3	> 2	Dolomite "Series"	Boetsap, S. Africa
2.5–3	1.6	Paradise Creek Formation	N.W. Queensland

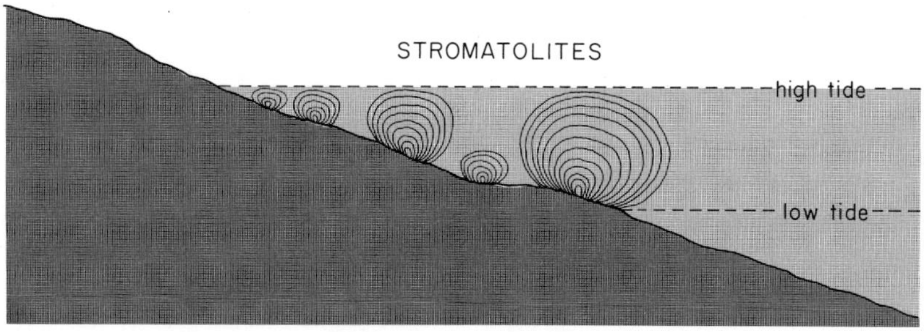

FIGURE 42.1
Schematic profile showing relation of domal stromatolites to intertidal zone

domal sedimentary structures of algal origin known as stromatolites, plus various cross-bedded and desiccation-cracked sediments indicative of extensive tidal-flat deposition. The stromatolites are the most impressive evidence bearing on tidal amplitude for rocks up to somewhat more than 2 aeons old.

Stromatolites in process of formation are known from recent intertidal and shallow subtidal environments of Western Australia [29, 30], the Bahama Islands [30, 31], and Bermuda [32]. From the few records known in modern seas, it seems that subtidal stromatolites characteristically take the form of undulating crusts and small nodules. Stromatolites that rise conspicuously above the surface on which they grow have so far been found only in the intertidal environment, where they reach a maximum known relief among recent forms of 0.7 meter in Western Australia. Logan [29] found that the height at maturity was "determined by the tidal range and the position of the structure in the intertidal zone." If this is true generally it would give us important clues to tidal ranges in the geologic past.

We are not entirely limited to analogy with present structures. Stromatolites in the geologic past are commonly associated with interstitial breccias and oölites suggesting turbulent waters, and with contraction-cracked sediments and truncated flat-topped ripple marks implying exposure to the atmosphere. Indeed some stromatolitic domes from 2-aeon-old rocks in South Africa (Schmidts Drift, northeastern Cape Province) show polygonal patterns of desiccation cracking on their own planed-off upper surfaces. The geologic record is thus consistent with their characteristic habitat being an intertidal one [at least for domal forms—there now being evidence of subtidal habitat for some or many purely branching forms]. It is also a feature of the geologic record that [domal] stromatolites of pre-Paleozoic and even early Paleozoic age often have far greater heights than do younger ones, and over areas far too extensive to represent abnormal local tidal ranges. If stromatolites, however, are to give us useful clues to ancient tidal amplitudes, we must be careful about what we measure. Some stromatolitic domes build up through the rock section. We should measure only the demonstrable height of a particular unit structure above a related bedding surface, or, better yet, the amplitude of a particular upwardly convex and complete stromatolitic lamina above the surrounding contemporary sea floor. If the characteristic habitat and manner of growth are correctly understood, this then implies, for such stromatolites, that tidal amplitude at a given time and place was at least as great as the amplitude of individual stromatolitic laminae.

What are some of these stromatolite amplitudes? I had observed that stromatolites of large amplitude were widely distributed in the pre-Paleozoic long before it occurred to me that it might be significant to keep a careful record of such measurements. A great many pre-Paleozoic stromatolites, however, have amplitudes, above the growing surface, of a meter or more. Four occurrences that show amplitudes from 2.5 to 6 meters or more and have stratigraphic associations that convey little likelihood of locally exceptional tidal ranges are listed in Table 42.1. These stromatolites are found in dolomites and limestones ranging in age from about 1 to more than 2 aeons, and it seems likely, from my own field reconnaissance and scanning of published accounts, that concerted effort would reveal other, similar records in this age range on all continents where such rocks occur. [Stromatolitic domes of large amplitude are common in the older Riphean strata of the U.S.S.R., according to M. A. Semikhatov (oral communication, Nov. 1969). In addition, extensive deposits of muddy siltstone and shale of the same general age show polygonal patterns of desiccation cracking and truncated ripple marks indicative of equally extensive tidal-flat deposits (the Belt and Grand Canyon Series, for example). The giant individual stromatolite domes in the Belt Series near Helena, Montana, are illustrated by Knopf [33, p. 85], who describes them as "up to 15 feet thick [that is, in amplitude] and traceable for thousands of feet along the strike . . . from the bottom to the top of the Helena dolomite," a unit more than 1200 meters thick.

The implication I draw from this and other records is that tidal amplitudes too great to be accounted for by the solar component alone existed at least 2 aeons ago, that tides generally were probably greater then than they are now, and that the moon was, therefore, at that time already in orbit and presumably somewhat closer to the earth than it is now. This timing, of course, is contrary to some theoretical expectations . . . [and inconsistent with recent reports, such as that of Olson [34], calling for very large tidal amplitudes in latest pre-Paleozoic time].

Stromatolites of large amplitude (about 2 meters) in ankeritic dolomite at Steeprock Lake, Ontario, may give a record of large tides of even greater age. Although not radiometrically established, geologic relations suggest that the age of these rocks may approach 2.5 aeons. The evidence of the approximately 3-aeon-old [15] rocks of the Swaziland System is even more tenuous, but also consistent with the moon's then being already in orbit around the earth. This succession of rocks, beginning with a typical, and the oldest known, marine ophio-

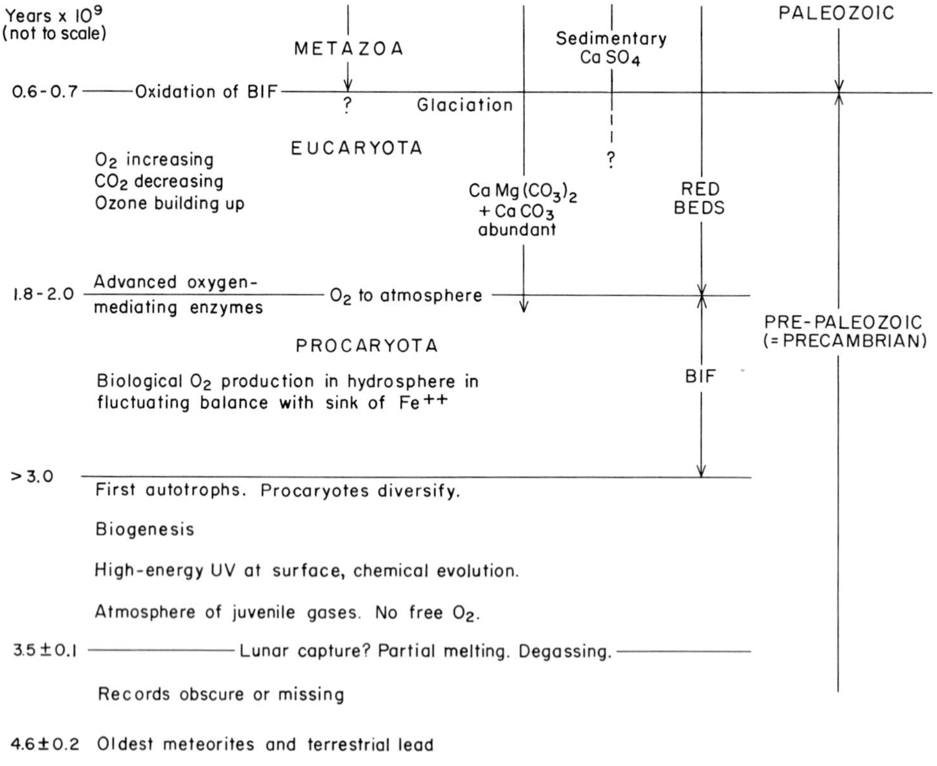

FIGURE 42.2
Biospheric, lithospheric, and atmospheric evolution on the primitive earth

litic and eugeosynclinal succession, is terminated by the Moodies Series of characteristic molasse facies [35]. This includes an abundance of markedly cross-bedded and ripple-marked sandstone and conglomerate sheets, and desiccation-cracked shales. The association implies extensive intertidal deposits and again points to tidal amplitudes too great to be explained by the solar component alone (although, like most of these older pre-Paleozoic records, it needs more study from this aspect).

If the moon was in orbit 3 aeons or more ago, and if it did not originate concurrently with the accumulation of the earth, perhaps its origin had something to do with the thermal event of 3.5 to 3.6 aeons ago suggested by the oldest known metamorphic and granitic rocks and the lead isotope composition of various minerals (Figure 42.2).

If our moon was captured . . . tidal friction sufficient to induce subcrustal melting would have been likely (see ref. 26, pp. 772–780, for a review of the theories; refs. 36–38 for general background). Indeed, the theoretical problem is how to avoid vaporization of the earth and concomitant disintegration of the moon. Singer [27, 28] has suggested how such events might be circumvented, by postulating capture in a prograde rather than a retrograde orbit. This would extend the initial spin period of the earth to about 5 hours (rather than less than 1 hour) but still produce enough melting to generate a considerable concurrent accretion of atmosphere and hydrosphere. Likely related consequences for lithospheric evolution would include large-scale volcanism, plutonism, and metamorphism of preexisting cosmic debris (and of any preexisting volcanic and sedimentary rocks) as well as the general resetting of nuclear decay series.

Thus the limited chronology of the oldest rocks, and the hints from lead isotope data of the concomitant beginning or peaking of internal differentiation of the earth, can be seen as consistent with a near approach of the moon to the earth about 3.5 to 3.6 aeons ago. What little is known about lunar evolution also seems to be consistent with such an interpretation (although by no means proof of it). Just as the oldest terrestrial rocks, and conceivably the initiation or climaxing of core and mantle formation, may be related to processes incident to lunar capture, so also may the surfaces of the lunar maria, indicating as they do, from observations by Shoemaker [38], a welling-up from beneath to a "nearly common level." What would account for such a widespread welling-up to fill the presumably collisional maria and some smaller preexisting impact craters (for example, Archimedes) to "an approximately hydrostatic level" [38]? This would seem to require both a major episode, or a sequence of related episodes, of partial internal melting and a widely interconnected series of conduits along which molten or fluidized particulate matter could travel to such a nearly general level. In the absence of a core or other evidence of major internal differentiation of the moon, tidal friction provides a source of heat for fluidization otherwise difficult to visualize. In addition, stresses incident to capture might well account for an extensive interconnected lunar fracture system, along which lava, ash, or both, could ascend (as well as the impacting masses that produced the maria) [27, 28]. Difficulties arise in trying to explain the preservation of large-scale relief in the lunar highlands, the absence of large surface offsets due to faulting, and the lesser relief within the maria themselves. If a major melting episode did occur as postulated, it could not have been a general liquefaction of the interior of the moon nor could it have been narrowly synchronous at all places. Something more like a pervasive partial melting is called for. Interconnecting fractures along which effusive matter would have traveled outward cannot have had large offsets. And results of statistical treatments suggesting high relief within the maria [39] would require some other explanation. These difficulties circumscribe the model envisaged. Like it, they must undergo further critical examination, hopefully with more abundant and better evidence. [Evidence from the landings of Apollo 11 and Apollo 12 is not inconsistent with this model, but it does suggest alternatives.]

The rocks we now know cannot of themselves tell us *how* the moon originated. Among hypotheses available to choose from, however, the testimony that can be wrung from the rocks is consistent with Singer's suggested prograde lunar capture and not consistent with an origin of the moon in relatively late pre-Paleozoic time. This testimony can also be interpreted as suggesting that, however the moon originated, a near approach of moon to earth may have taken place closer to 3.5 to 3.6 aeons ago than to the 4 to 4.5 aeons suggested by Singer from tenuous geochronological inferences. And, after all, a considerable pre-mare (or pre-Imbrian) lunar history would be in order to account for the extensive lunar highlands whose infrapositional relations to debris seemingly splashed from the maria imply a significantly greater age for these highlands [38].

A special problem that arises in connection with a date as late as 3.5 to 3.6 aeons ago for lunar capture is that of where the moon could have been stored for a whole aeon if the earth [and the moon] is about 4.6 aeons old. . . . at least one piece of evidence points to . . . [an asteroidal] source for the moon. This unique planetary body, with density intermediate between that of the inner and outer planets, is the most inconsistent item in the distribution of planetary densities [36, p. 143] unless it did originate in the asteroid belt. If it did, and if it could be transferred from the asteroid belt to the vicinity of the earth, the storage problem would vanish. [But see Öpik, 1970, in the Supplemental Reading for Section VI.]

If these conjectures should happen to be correct (and they certainly have their shaky aspects), then, when samples of the mare fillings are obtained from beneath any superficial covering debris of cosmic or local origin, such samples should give radiometric ages of about 3.5 to 3.6 aeons. Another likely corollary is that any preexisting terrestrial atmosphere and hydrosphere [21] would have been largely lost at that time and a new or first atmosphere and hydrosphere started, with a sizable input of volatiles. At the beginning this would probably have been no more than about 10 per cent of the present mass of the atmosphere and hydrosphere, however, on the basis of Rubey's calculations showing that no more than about 10 per cent of the present hydrosphere can be retained as gaseous H_2O in equilibrium with even a generally molten earth. Nevertheless, a prolonged episode of accelerated degassing could have led to fairly rapid growth of terrestrial atmosphere and hydrosphere in the following few tens or hundreds of millions of years. . . .

INFERENCES FROM BIOSPHERIC AND LITHOSPHERIC EVOLUTION

Such reflections suggest that the present terrestrial atmosphere and hydrosphere may have evolved, with additions, from one that began or underwent great increase as a result of a major thermal episode about 3.5 to 3.6 aeons ago (Figure 42.2). Life as we know it, then, would have had to originate within the next few hundred million years, if we accept as evidence of once-living things the structures described by Pflug [40] and by Barghoorn and Schopf [41] from the Swaziland System. (In Figure 42.2, *biogenesis* denotes simply the origin of life in the strict etymological sense of the word and not any particular theory of origin. Pirie has used the term *biopoesis* for this, to avoid the connotation that *biogenesis* once held—of life only from preexisting life. It no longer seems helpful, however, to give up a good term like *biogenesis* merely because of historical precedent, and there is now no other reason to do so.)

In any case, first life would presumably have been anaerobic in the absence of oxygen and heterotrophic (that is, dependent on external food sources) short of a highly improbable coincidence. But it could not have continued, to give rise to the observed evolutionary record, without the emergence of an organism that could manufacture its own substance—an autotroph. However many unsuccessful starts there may have been, it is clear that one start eventually did give rise to an autotroph. But what kind? Since the biochemical complexity of the chemoautotrophs suggests a late origin for them, it was probably a photoautotroph—an organism that manufactures its food by photosynthesis. And photosynthesis is the likely process whereby oxygen might eventually appear and be generated fast enough to oxidize most of the reduced substances of the hydrosphere, atmosphere, and surface of the earth and begin to accumulate as a free gas.

Only one of the three known types of photosynthesis, however, releases free oxygen, and it is unlikely that *it* was primitive. Nevertheless, oxygen-releasing photosynthesizers did arise, and when they did they would have faced the problem of disposing of oxygen in such a way as not to burn themselves up.

Unless advanced oxygen- and peroxide-mediating enzymes, therefore, arose simultaneously with, or preceded, the origin of oxygen-releasing green-plant photosynthesizers, such organisms would probably have been dependent on an associated oxygen acceptor in the physical environment.

The abundance of hematitic banded iron formation (BIF in Figure 42.2) among sediments deposited between about 3 and 1.8 to 2 aeons ago suggests that the available oxygen acceptor may have been the ferrous ion. Banded iron formation is a rhythmically banded chemical sediment of large, open water bodies that takes different aspects but most characteristically consists of alternating layers of iron-rich and iron-poor silica. Nothing like it of any thickness or regional extent is found in younger rocks; and younger (but not time-restricted) types of sedimentary iron deposits appear to be mainly replacement bodies of a quite different sort. The geochemical problem of the banded iron formation has been that of explaining transport of the iron in solution under oxidizing conditions, or precipitation of the iron under anoxidizing conditions. This problem, as well as that of an oxygen acceptor for the primitive green-plant photosynthesizers, is largely resolved by the concept of a balanced relationship between organisms and banded iron formation. The iron could be transported in solution in the ferrous state and precipitated as ferric or ferro-ferric oxides upon combining with biological oxygen. The rhythmic banding could result from a fluctuating balance between oxygen-producing biotas and supply of ferrous ion. The facies of iron formation can be visualized as incidental products of this regime. The oxygen presumably became locked in chemical sediments precipitated from the hydrosphere and did not appear in the atmosphere except for small quantities from photolytic dissociation of H_2O and CO_2, rapidly scavenged by reduced substances then abundant in the atmosphere and at the surface of the lithosphere.

Eventually, however, efficient oxygen- and peroxide-mediating enzymes did arise, and when that happened the postulated balance would have collapsed. Green-plant photosynthesizers, equipped with such enzymes, could then spread as widely through the hydrosphere as light penetration and high-energy ultraviolet (UV in Figure 42.2) shielding mechanisms would permit. The hydrosphere would be swept free of ferrous ion in a last great episode of banded iron formation. And O_2 would accumulate in excess in the hydrosphere and begin to evade to the atmosphere. The last great episode of banded iron formation, about 1.8 to 2 aeons ago, may mark such an event, and blue-green algae are known to have been associated with it.

What would happen when O_2 began to evade to the atmosphere? At that time, in the absence of an ozone screen, ultraviolet light in the range of 2000 to 2900 angstroms would impinge on the surface of the earth, some of the molecular oxygen (O_2) would be converted to atomic oxygen (O) and ozone (O_3), and iron would be retained in the weathering profile of the earth in the ferric state. Because of the high chemical activity of O and O_3, even a low rate of evasion of O_2 to the atmosphere should give rise to a high rate of oxidation of surface materials. Red beds—detrital continental or marginal marine sediments in which the individual grains are coated with ferric oxides—should appear in abundance in the geological column at that time.

Available records indicate that the oldest thick and extensive red beds are about 1.8 to 2 aeons old—a little younger than, or overlapping slightly with, the youngest banded iron formation. The evidence of lithospheric evolution suggests that this may mark the time in atmospheric evolution when free O_2 began to accumulate, perhaps following the appearance of advanced oxygen- and peroxide-mediating enzymes in biospheric evolution.

This would also set the stage for the appearance of a new type of cell and organism. Paleontological evidence [24] implies that until then all organisms were procaryotes, having no nuclear wall or clearly structured chromosomes, and being incapable, therefore, of mitotic cell division and sexual reproduction in the usual sense. The presence of free oxygen, even in small quantities, was presumably followed by the evolution of the eucaryotic cell, with nuclear wall, well-defined chromosomes, mitotic cell division, and the capacity for sexual reproduction. (The oxygen requirements of a single eucaryotic cell, to be sure, are much more easily satisfied than those of a differentiated multicellular animal.)

How fast did O_2 accumulate in the atmosphere once it began? Probably slowly at first. The green-plant photosynthesizers would still be restricted by high-energy ultraviolet radiation to protected sites in stromatolite-forming sedimentary mats, or at locations where they would not be circulated into surface waters, until such time as ozone built up to a sufficient density to exclude DNA-inactivating radiation in the neighborhood of 2600 angstroms. Berkner and Marshall [42] found that this happens when the atmospheric level of oxygen reaches about 1 per cent of the present level. In addition, both they and, earlier, the Canadian biologist Nursall [43] suggested that the appearance of the Metazoa (differentiated multicelled animal life) was a consequence of the reaching of atmospheric oxygen concentrations sufficient to support a metazoan level of oxidative metabolism.

Certainly the appearance of the Metazoa in the geologic record does signify the previous fulfillment of two necessary if not sufficient preconditions. One is the origin of the eucaryotic cell, of which all metazoans are constituted. The other is a sufficient level of free oxygen—although perhaps closer to 3 per cent of the present atmospheric level than to 1 per cent (better data on this are needed). Now the oldest rocks in which eucaryotic fossils are known are probably more than 0.7 aeon old [44], although the minimal conditions necessary for primitive eucaryotes may have appeared much earlier [24]. [Eucaryotes are now known from the Beck Spring Formation of eastern California, believed to be about 1.3 aeons old.] At least the precondition of the eucaryotic cell, therefore, was satisfied well before the dawn of the Paleozoic; and I have elsewhere [24] provided documentation for the conclusion that there are as yet no records of unequivocal Metazoa in rocks of undoubted pre-Paleozoic age.

This, then, can be interpreted as suggesting that the precondition of sufficient free oxygen may have been the triggering event. The necessary compression of early metazoan evolution may be partially explained by postulating a polyphyletic origin. This can be visualized as a wave of multicellularization affecting different pre-metazoan ancestors almost simultaneously in the geological sense. Since, moreover, all ecologic niches that could ever be occupied by Metazoa were unoccupied when the Metazoa first arose, adaptive radiation probably contributed to a geologically rapid diversification of the metazoan root stocks. This may have taken place over an interval of, say, 100 million years, more or less—perhaps somewhat less than the time required for chemical evolution leading to the origin of life itself, and somewhat more than that required for the Cenozoic diversification of the mammals following extinction of the dinosaurs.

Is there evidence other than the geologically rapid evolution of the earliest Metazoa at this time to suggest that the dawn of the Paleozoic might indeed have closely followed the appearance of a level of free O_2 adequate for metazoan metabolism? First consider what might happen when ozone reached a level sufficient to exclude the DNA-inactivating ultraviolet radiation at about 1 per cent of the present atmospheric level of O_2. As Berkner and Marshall recognized [42], this would open up the surface waters of the entire hydrosphere to occupation by photosynthesizing phytoplankton, and such occupation, in turn, could lead to rapid and large increase in the amount of O_2 in the atmosphere. Such a step-increase in atmospheric O_2 might be related to three features in lithospheric evolution—late pre-Paleozoic glaciation, oxidative enrichment of the banded iron formation to produce high-grade ores, and the appearance of thick and extensive deposits of sedimentary calcium sulfate in the geologic record.

Inasmuch as the increase in O_2 would presumably have been paralleled by a decrease in long-radiation-reflecting CO_2, this could have led to a temperature decrease that might have triggered the widespread late pre-Paleozoic glaciation often suggested to account for certain rocks of that age having resemblance to deposits of modern and Pleistocene glaciers (another matter needing more study).

Enrichment of the emerged banded iron formation by surface oxidation during late pre-Paleozoic or earliest Paleozoic time converted the lean primary deposits into the bonanza ores that were first mined in the Lake Superior region. This event also would be consistent with a substantial contemporaneous increase in the amount of oxygen in the atmosphere, and it may have coincided with similar oxidative enrichments in other regions to denote a broadly contemporaneous episode of surface oxidation and laterization in late pre-Paleozoic or earliest Paleozoic time.

The record of sedimentary calcium sulfate may also be consistent with the postulated late pre-Paleozoic increase in O_2. Thick and extensive deposits of gypsum and anhydrite require large amounts of sulfate ion, and the only likely adequate sources are from the oxidation of sulfides and sulfurous volcanic gases (SO_2, SO_3, H_2S). Sedimentary calcium sulfate is abundant from the base of the Paleozoic onward, yet occurrences of appreciable volume appear to be rare in, or absent from, all but perhaps the uppermost part of the pre-Paleozoic [24]. Anhydrite in the Grenville, for instance, could be a later replacement of a tabular marble body [45]. The most likely candidates yet proposed for thick and extensive pre-Paleozoic sedimentary sulfates are deposits in the Shaler Group of arctic Canada [46], although they appear to be very late pre-Paleozoic indeed [47, p. 55]. On balance it seems that the appearance of abundant sedimentary sulfates in the geologic record may precede by only a little the origin of the Metazoa, and that both, together with oxidative enrichment of the iron protores and a reputed episode of glaciation, could be partial consequences of a relatively large-scale increase of free O_2.

The relative abundance of limestone and dolomite among the younger pre-Paleozoic rocks, as contrasted to their near absence from sequences older than about 2 aeons, may, in turn, reflect a gradual diminution of CO_2 and increased *p*H of the hydrosphere, accompanying the relatively slow buildup of O_2 in the atmosphere after it began to accumulate but before ozone reached effective ultraviolet-screening levels.

These are the kinds of things we can postulate about the composition and evolution of the primitive atmosphere by calling on the combined evidence of biospheric and lithospheric evolution.

THE HYDROSPHERE

As for the hydrosphere, there is little to add to what Rubey [5] has already so brilliantly developed. On grounds of the occasional occurrence of glauconite in rocks as old as 1.2 to 1.5 aeons [48]—glauconite being a mineral characteristic of the diagenesis of various siliceous and clay-like parent materials in contact with potassium-rich solutions—the hydrosphere is presumed to have had saline components at least that long ago. The prevalence of dolomite among rocks as old as 2 aeons also implies normal marine to hypersaline environments at least that far back. The evidence of the older rocks is less clear; but the occurrence of sedimentary siderite, sulfide-rich sediments, bedded chert, and so on, is consistent with the presence of a hydrosphere not drastically different in its *p*H and mix of dissolved salts from the present one. The *Eh*, at least before about 2 aeons ago, was probably negative or neutral, however, and the *p*H may have been slightly lower than now. Sulfate ion was apparently present in solution only in quantities too small to account for much $CaSO_4$ until the latest pre-Paleozoic.

Evidence that might suggest nonsaline seas includes the interesting fact that, among the commoner elements of the microbiotas now being found in rocks of various ages in the pre-Paleozoic, many are morphologically close to living freshwater forms. Such organisms, however, are characterized by a combination of morphological conservatism and ecological plasticity. Similar living forms tolerate a wide range of salinity. Their pre-Paleozoic ancestors probably lived in salt water. The iron formation itself, however, has been taken as evidence of a freshwater environment. That is because iron in modern marine waters occurs only in vanishingly small quantities. Under anoxygenous conditions, though, dissolved ferrous ion could have been, and evidently was, relatively common in older pre-Paleozoic seas of approximately normal salinity, and probably of a range of *p*H and temperature not greatly different from the range for younger seas.

There remains the question of the configuration of the pre-Paleozoic hydrosphere. If, as suggested, it accumulated gradually, while the continents and ocean basins were still differentiating, the main part of it may in early times have occupied isolated basins of intermediate depth rather than deep interconnected ones, such as comprise the present world ocean. If this was the case, the sequence and timing of events postulated might have varied from one basin to another. The record as now understood does not support such a variation, but differences in the range of tens of millions of years are not yet resolvable in pre-Paleozoic time. Among the many unfinished jobs ahead for geologists, one of the most important is to map and date the shorelines and to estimate the physical structure and environments of the pre-Paleozoic sedimentary basins. When such information is available over very large regions we should be able to make better informed guesses as to the configurations, volumes, tidal range, and history of the evolving early hydrosphere and its relation to other parts of the primitive earth.

REFERENCES AND NOTES

1. N. Russell and H. Menzel, [U.S.] *Natl. Acad. Sci. Proc.*, v. 19, p. 997 (1933); H. Brown, in *The Atmospheres of the Earth and Planets*, ed. G. P. Kuiper (University of Chicago Press, 2nd ed., 1952), p. 258–266.
2. A. G. Högbom, *Svensk Kemisk Tidskr.*, v. 6, p. 169 (1894), [See Arrhenius (3), p. 269–273, for summary].
3. S. Arrhenius, *Philos. Mag.* v. 41, p. 237 (1896).
4. T. C. Chamberlin, *Jour. Geology*, v. 5, p. 653 (1897).
5. W. W. Rubey, *Geol. Soc. America Bull.*, v. 62, p. 111 (1951).
6. E. Anders, in *The Moon, Meteorites, and Comets* (v. 4, *The Solar System*) ed. B. M. Middlehurst and G. P. Kuiper (Chicago: University of Chicago Press, 1963), p. 402–495.
7. C. Patterson, *Geochim. et Cosmochim. Acta*, v. 10, p. 230 (1956); C. Patterson, in *Isotopic and Cosmic Chemistry*, ed. H. Craig, S. L. Miller, G. J. Wasserburg (Amsterdam: North-Holland, 1963), p. 244–268.
8. G. R. Tilton and R. H. Steiger, *Science*, v. 150, p. 1805 (1965).
9. J. H. Reynolds, *Scientific American*, v. 203, p. 171 (1960).
10. L. T. Silver, oral communication, December 1967.
11. V. J. Baranov, *Soviet Astron.—AJ (English Transl.)*, v. 10, no. 5, p. 860 (1967).
12. E. J. Catanzaro, *Jour. Geophys. Research*, v. 68, p. 2045 (1963); S. S. Goldich, E. G. Lidiak, C. E. Hedge, F. G. Walthall, *Jour. Geophys. Research*, v. 71, p. 5389 (1966).
13. N. P. Semenenko, *UNESCO Bull. Internat. Hydrol. Decade*, v. 3, no. 3, p. 23 (1967); A. J. Tugarinov, oral communication, 9 April 1965.
14. A. E. J. Engel, "The Barberton Mountain Land—Clues to the Differentiation of the Earth," *Univ. Witwatersrand Econ. Geology Research Unit Inf. Circ.* 27 (1966).
15. L. O. Nicolaysen, in *Petrologic Studies—A Volume in Honor of A. F. Buddington*, ed. A. E. J. Engel, H. L. James, B. F. Leonard (Boulder, Colo.: Geological Society of America, 1962), p. 569–598; H. L. Allsopp, T. J. Ulrych, L. O. Nicolaysen, paper presented at the University of Alberta in 1967 at a conference of the International Union of Geological Sciences, Geochronology Commission.
16. W. L. Donn, B. D. Donn, W. G. Valentine, *Geol. Soc. America Bull.*, v. 76, p. 287 (1965); R. Furon, *Geology of Africa* (Edinburgh: Oliver and Boyd, 1963), p. 5.
17. A. F. Wilson, W. H. Compston, P. M. Jeffery, G. H. Riley, *Geol. Soc. Australia Jour.*, v. 6, p. 179 (1960). Some refinements of these numbers are reported by W. Compston and P. A. Arriens in a paper presented at the University of Alberta in 1967 at a conference of the International Union of Geological Sciences, Geochronology Commission.
18. R. P. Dunn, K. A. Plumb, H. G. Roberts, *Geol. Soc. Australia Jour.*, v. 13, p. 593 (1966).
19. M. Tatsumoto and C. Patterson, *Jour. Geology*, v. 72, p. 232 (1964).
20. P. E. Cloud, Jr., J W. Gruner, H. Hagen, *Science*, v. 148, p. 1713 (1965).
21. A. O. Woodford [*Historical Geology* (San Francisco: W. H. Freeman and Company, 1965), p. 204–205] and Donn, Donn, and Valentine (see 16, p. 292–293) have summarized available data on reportedly 3.4 to 3.5×10^9-year-old associated "sedimentary" and plutonic rocks in the Kola Penninsula, U.S.S.R. The validity of the older dates from the Kola Penninsula, however, is much disputed, both in the U.S.S.R. and the United States, and the nature of the "sedimentary" rocks and their relations to the dated rocks is not, clear from descriptions available. Similarly, Semenenko (13) refers to the most ancient Ukranian (amphibolite) schists as "normal geosynsynclinal complexes of sedimentary volcanogenic formations." And Donn, Donn, and Valentine (16, p. 291–292 report that the undoubtedly sedimentary Sebakwian Series of Rhodesia is older than an unconfirmed date of 3.44 aeons obtained by the potassium-argon technique on micas from an associated pegmatite. Should it turn out that one or more of

these interpretations (and the associated ages) is correct, and that there exist sedimentary or truly metasedimentary rocks that predate, or were metamorphosed by, the postulated thermal event of 3.5 to 3.6 aeons ago, the prior existence of an atmosphere or hydrosphere will be demonstrated. Such an atmosphere and hydrosphere, however, could probably not have been more than a small fraction of the present one and might well have been lost as a result of the thermal event. There is much need for further study and supplementation of the relevant data.

22. H. D. Holland, in *Petrologic Studies—A Volume in Honor of A. F. Buddington*, ed. A. E. J. Engel, H. L. James, B. F. Leonard (Boulder, Colo.: Geological Society of America, 1962), p. 447–477.
23. P. H. Abelson [*U.S.*] *Natl. Acad. Sci. Proc.*, v. 55, p. 1365 (1966).
24. P. E. Cloud, Jr., in *Evolution and Environment*, ed. E. T. Drake (New Haven, Conn.: Yale University Press, 1968), p. 1–72.
25. G. J. F. MacDonald, *Science*, v. 145, p. 881 (1964).
26. G. J. F. MacDonald, *New York Acad. Sci. Annals*, v. 118, p. 739 (1965).
27. S. F. Singer, "The Origin and Dynamical Evolution of the Moon," *Am. Astronautical Soc. Pub.* AAS96–192 (1966).
28. S. F. Singer, *Sci. Research*, v. 1967, p. 69 (Nov. 1967).
29. B. W. Logan, *Jour. Geology*, v. 69, p. 517 (1961).
30. B. W. Logan, R. Rezak, R. N. Ginsburg, *Jour. Geology*, v. 72, p. 68 (1964).
31. C. Monty, *Ann. soc. géol. Belgique Bull.*, v. 88, p. 269 (1965).
32. C. D. Gebelein, paper presented at the annual meeting of the Geological Society of America, 1967.
33. A. Knopf, *Am. Jour. Sci.*, v. 255, p. 81 (1957).
34. W. S. Olson, *Am. Scientist*, v. 54, p. 454 (1966).
35. C. R. Anhaeusser, C. Roering, M. J. Viljoen, R. P. Viljoen, "The Barberton Mountain Land—A Model of the Elements and Evolution of an Archean Fold Belt," *Univ. Witwatersrand Econ. Geology Research Unit Inf. Circ.* 38 (1967).
36. H. D. Urey, in *Space Science*, ed. D. P. Le-Galley (New York: John Wiley and Sons, 1963), p. 123–168.
37. G. P. Kuiper, in *Advances in Earth Science*, ed. P. M. Hurley (Cambridge, Mass.: M.I.T. Press, 1966), p. 21–70.
38. E. Shoemaker, *Scientific American*, v. 211, p. 38 (Dec. 1964).
39. E. R. DeFresne, *Astrophys. Jour.*, v. 124, p. 638 (1956).
40. H. D. Pflug, "Structured Organic Remains from the Fig Tree Series of the Barberton Mountain Land," *Univ. Witwatersrand Econ. Geology Research Unit Inf. Circ.* 28 (1966).
41. E. S. Barghoorn and J. W. Schopf, *Science*, v. 152, p. 758 (1966).
42. L. V. Berkner and L. C. Marshall, *Farady Soc. Discussions*, v. 37, p. 122 (1964); [*U.S.*] *Natl. Acad. Sci. Proc.*, v. 53, p. 1215 (1965).
43. J. R. Nursall, *Nature*, v. 183, p. 1170 (1959).
44. E. S. Barghoorn and J. W. Schopf, *Science*, v. 150, p. 337 (1965); P. E. Cloud, Jr., G. R. Licari, L. A. Wright, and B. W. Troxell, [*U.S.*] *Natl. Acad. Sci. Proc.* v. 62, p. 623.
45. A. E. J. Engel, letter of 5 October 1966.
46. R. Thorsteinsson and E. L. Tozer, "Banks, Victoria, and Stefansson Islands, Arctic Archipelago," *Geol. Survey Canada Mem.* 330 (1962).
47. G. B. Leech, J. A. Lowdon, C. H. Stockwell, R. K. Wanless, "Age Determinations and Geologic Studies," *Geol. Survey Canada Paper* 63-17 (1963).
48. R. A. Gulbrandsen, S. S. Goldich, H. H. Thomas, *Science*, v. 140, p. 390 (1963).

43

Precambrian Marine Environment and the Development of Life

PETER K. WEYL
1968

From *Science,* vol. 161, pp. 158–160, 1968. Reprinted with permission of the author and the American Association for the Advancement of Science.

In order to investigate the origin and early evolution of life on Earth one must consider the Precambrian environment. Our knowledge of Precambrian paleooceanography is extremely limited, and so the Precambrian ocean has usually been characterized by a single value for its parameters as if it had been a well-mixed system. A more realistic reconstruction of the Precambrian ocean may lead to new insights into the early development of life on Earth.

The distribution of noble gases on Earth and in stars indicates that Earth initially lost its fluid envelope, and that the present ocean and atmosphere must have accumulated from outgassing of Earth's interior [1]. Thus the volume of the oceans has increased with time during the last 4×10^9 years. If the ratio of outgassing of chlorine and water remained relatively constant, the salinity of sea water did not vary greatly; thus its density has probably always been a function of salinity as well as temperature.

The volume of the oceans increased significantly during Precambrian times and approached its present value at the beginning of the Cambrian. This increase in volume does not necessarily imply an increase in the fractional area of Earth covered by the oceans. If, as is probable, the evolution of continental crust paralleled the outgassing of the mantle, the ocean became deeper with time, while covering approximately the same area.

As a first approximation we can consider the ocean to consist of three superimposed layers: a seasonally variable mixed surface layer, a layer in which the density increases rapidly with depth, and a more uniform deep layer. In low latitudes the density gradient in the intermediate layer results primarily from a decrease in temperature (thermocline), while in high latitudes the density gradient results from increase in salinity with depth (halocline). The two upper layers extend to a depth of only about 200 m, while the third layer comprises most of the ocean.

The density-gradient layer results from the

latitudinal variation of the insolation at the top of the atmosphere, which in turn results from the spherical shape of Earth and the inclination of its axis to the plane of its orbit. The latitudinal variation of the heat received results in a poleward transport of heat by winds, as latent heat of vaporization, and by ocean surface; thus the temperature difference across the thermocline has varied significantly over geologic time. When the temperature gradient was great, the salinity gradient also was great; during times of low temperature gradient the more rapid circulation resulted in a lesser salinity gradient. Since heat and salt affect the density oppositely, the density gradient across the thermocline has varied relatively little.

During the Precambrian the gross density structure of the two upper layers probably differed little from the present configuration. As soon as the ocean became deeper than 300 m, the vertical layering must have been similar to that of today's ocean. The Precambrian density-gradient layer, particularly the thermocline between 30°N and 30°S, may have played an important role in the origin and Precambrian evolution of life.

The initial surface environment being devoid of oxygen [2], ultraviolet light from Sun penetrated the upper 10 m of the ocean [3]. The ultraviolet irradiation of the reducing atmosphere and ocean led to abiotic photosynthesis of organic molecules [4]. Bernal [5] has suggested that this organic matter became concentrated by absorption on mineral grains on the seashore where it was polymerized into coacervate drops. An alternative mechanism for concentration is provided within the ocean. In today's ocean, surface-active dissolved organic matter is swept to the surface by rising bubbles and compressed into lines of convergence by the Langmuir circulation, where it is polymerized into particulate organic matter [6].

In the present ocean, the dissolved organic matter is derived from organisms, and the particulate organic matter produced sinks in the zones of convergence, where it is consumed by zooplankton. In the early ocean, the organic molecules would have been produced by abiotic processes, and the aggregates would not have been consumed. Depending on their bulk densities, the aggregates would have been concentrated in the density-gradient layer and on the ocean bottom. The steepest density gradients, and hence the largest concentrations, would have accumulated in low latitudes on both sides of the equator, where the present density increases from 1.023 to 1.026 between 50 and 100 m. Once removed from the sea surface, the organic aggregates would have been shielded from ultraviolet radiation. Prokaryotic heterotrophs could have evolved either at the ocean bottom or within the density-gradient layer where there was a concentration of organic aggregates and where they were shielded from ultraviolet radiation.

Conditions for the evolution of photosynthetic prokaryotic autotrophs would have been optimum in the tropical thermocline which was shielded from ultraviolet radiation while visible sunlight penetrated this layer. Evolution would have proceeded at constant density, since cells that became too heavy would have sunk below the illuminated region, while a reduction in density would have carried the cells into the mixed surface layer where they would have become exposed to ultraviolet radiation. The thermocline is a more extensive and more stable environment than the bottom of the shallow seas.

Vertical convection across the density-gradient layer is very slow, so that significant oxygen concentrations would have accumulated in the thermocline once oxygen was evolved by the blue-green algae. By use of data from the low-productivity regions of the present tropical oceans, an oxygen production rate of 1 mole m^{-2} $year^{-1}$ would have led to an oxygen partial pressure in the themocline equivalent to about 3 per cent of the present atmospheric level.

Oxygen that diffused from the thermocline would have been mixed rapidly into the atmosphere and the underlying sediment—where it would have been used for oxidation of reduced minerals. If the algae were primarily restricted to the density-gradient layer, that layer would have had a significant concentration of oxygen while the concentration in the rest of the ocean and the atmosphere would have been very low until the products of weathering were oxidized. Thus the thermocline probably was an extensive, stable, oxygenated environment for the evolution of eukaryotic cells. This environment was more extensive in time and space than the microenvironments postulated by Fischer [8].

Where the thermocline intersected the sea floor, mixing would have been enhanced by the breaking of internal waves and by upwelling. As a result of rapid diffusion, the oxygen content of the water over the continental shelf would not have been significantly greater than that of the atmosphere. Therefore the early animals probably were planktonic and restricted to the density-gradient layer over the deeper parts of the oceans. The evolution of a skeleton would have been strongly inhibited since such organisms would have sunk out of the oxygen-containing layer unless their bulk densities were maintained constant by the simultaneous evolution of flotation mechanisms.

Blue-green algae were able to carpet the bottoms of the continental shelves, where development of a shallow seasonal thermocline would have provided temporary concentrations of oxygen. Thus organisms that evolved active swimming mechanisms could have seasonally exploited the food resources on the continental shelves. As winter mixing reduced the oxygen concentration on the shelves, these organisms had to return to the deep-water thermocline region to survive. Only after the atmospheric concentration of oxygen became sufficiently high could the continental shelves have been permanently inhabited by animals. At that time the organisms could have adapted to a benthic habit and increased their bulk density by skeletogenesis. This transition supposedly occurred at the beginning of the Cambrian.

If the blue-green algae in the open ocean were concentrated in the tropical thermocline as I have suggested, an environment containing sufficient oxygen for the evolution of Metazoa existed earlier than 10^9 years before the Cambrian. The early animals could not permanently populate the continental shelves and could not readily evolve a skeleton; thus the probability of their preservation in the fossil record would have been small. Without a Precambrian thermocline, one is forced to assume a very rapid rate of evolution for the Metazoa once the concentration of oxygen in the atmosphere was adequate for respiration [9]. The thermocline, however, provided an extensive offshore environment between about 50 and 150 m that probably was oxygenated and within which floating and (later) swimming animals were able to evolve. The existence of a seasonally oxygenated continental-shelf environment, carpeted by algae, would have offered an adaptive advantage to organisms that evolved swimming mechanisms. Once the atmospheric concentration of oxygen became sufficient, these swimming organisms could have adapted to a benthic habit on the shelves. At this stage, density would no longer have been a problem, and the organisms could have evolved skeletons. In the early stages these exoskeletons would have provided an adaptive advantage as ultraviolet shields and would have permitted the organisms to seal themselves from the environment to survive temporary anoxia. According to my hypothesis the beginning of the Cambrian marks the first time Metazoa could permanently occupy the floors of the continental shelves.

REFERENCES

1. W. W. Rubey, *Geol. Soc. America Bull.*, v. 62, p. 1111 (1951).
2. H. D. Holland, [*U.S.*] *Natl. Acad. Sci. Proc.*, v. 53(6), p. 1173 (1965).
3. L. V. Berkner and L. C. Marshall, *Jour. Atmos. Sci.*, v. 22, p. 225 (1965); v. 23(2), p. 133 (1966).
4. S. L. Miller, "Formation of organic compounds on the primitive earth," in *The Origin of Life on the Earth* (v. 1) ed. F. Clark and R. L. M. Synge (New York: Pergamon, 1959).
5. J. D. Bernal, in *Oceanography*, ed. M. Sears (Washington, D. C.: American Association for the Advancement of Science, p. 95–118.
6. W. H. Sutcliffe, Jr., E. R. Baylor, D. W. Menzel, *Deep-Sea Research*, v. 10, p. 233 (1963).
7. W. J. Schopf, "Antiquity and evolution of Precambrian life," in *McGraw-Hill Yearbook of Science and Technology* (New York: McGraw-Hill, 1967).
8. A. G. Fischer, "Fossils, and early life, and atmospheric history," [*U.S.*] *Natl. Acad. Sci. Proc.*, v. 53 (15 June 1965).
9. P. E. Cloud, Jr., "Premetazoan evolution and the origins of the Metazoa," in *Evolution and Ecology*, ed. E. Drake (New Haven, Conn.: Yale University Press, 1968).

44

Problems of Stratigraphy and Correlation of Precambrian Rocks

with Particular Reference to the Lake Superior Region

HAROLD L. JAMES

1960

From *American Journal of Science*, vol. 258A, pp. 104–114, 1960. Reprinted with permission of the author and the *American Journal of Science*.

The history of attempts at correlation (of Precambrian rocks) has been one of early simple generalization, followed by the recognition of many qualifications and increasing complexity to a point where the initial simple assumptions become almost unrecognizable or are abandoned entirely. Looking back on most of the sweeping generalizations which were made in the past, it is easy to recognize the influence of the Wernerian hypothesis of sedimentation, the assumption of uniform marine conditions, the assumption of uniform orogenic and epeirogenic disturbances over wide areas, belief in the wide extent and uniformity of unconformities and metamorphic conditions, and, finally, a lingering faith in the existence of an igneous basement complex, possibly a remnant of the primordial shell, affording a world-wide base for beginning pre-Cambrian sedimentation. (Leith, 1934), p. 167.)

This statement, made by Leith in his presidential address to the Geological Society of America a quarter century ago, is as pertinent today as it was then. The retreat from the broad generalizations and correlations of the past still continues. By now, most of our familiar time and time-stratigraphic terms—such as Archean, Proterozoic, Algonkian, Laurentian, Keewatin, Algoman, and Huronian—have been abandoned or are under attack except in their type areas; in their place we see a chaotic proliferation of local names that do not lend themselves to regional synthesis. In view of the unquestioned need, both economic and scientific, for syntheses broader than those of small districts, it is worthwhile to look into the basic causes of the apparent degeneration of stratigraphic concepts for the Precambrian, then to consider what can be done and, for one small region, what is being done.

DURATION OF PRECAMBRIAN TIME

The first great factor affecting the status of Precambrian stratigraphy is the immense change that has taken place in the concept of duration of Precambrian time. Walcott (1893, p. 675), using rate and volume of sedimentation as a guide, held that the span of Earth's history was about 55 million years, and Sollas (1909, p. cxii), following Joly, recomputed the salt content of the oceans to arrive at an estimate of "between 80 and 150 millions of years." In 1917, the classic paper by Barrell was published in which full account was taken of radiometric age determinations (Barrell, 1917), but even as late as 1924, Clarke, author of the authoritative Data of Geochemistry, doubted the validity of the radiometric method and stated (Clarke, 1924, p. 323):

> From chemical denudation, from paleontological evidence, and from astronomical data the age has been fixed with a noteworthy degree of concordance at something between 50 and 150 millions of years. The high values found by radioactive measurements are therefore to be suspected until the discrepancies shall have been explained.

Barrell's assignments of time for the Paleozoic, Mesozoic and Cenozoic are not greatly different from those now accepted, but Precambrian time was assumed to be "perhaps a billion years" (Barrell, 1917, p. 895). In 1947, Holmes published his "A" and "B" scales, the latter of which has received wide acceptance. Holmes' estimate (p. 147) at that time for the age of the earth was "about 3,000 m.y." Recent work has suggested some appreciable modification of the "B" scale for Paleozoic and younger time units, and most present estimates for the age of the earth are 4,500 m.y. or greater (Patterson, Tilton, and Inghram, 1955). These changes in age concepts are shown graphically in Figure 44.1. The oldest rocks dated by radiometric methods are older than 3,000 m.y. (see Aldrich and Wetherill, 1958, for a recent comprehensive review of radiometric dating).

Of more critical importance to the problems of Precambrian correlations than absolute age assignments, however, are the early underestimates of the *relative* length of Precambrian time as compared to that of younger eras. When much of the major nomenclature of the Precambrian was set up 50 or 60 years ago, the duration of Precambrian time was assumed to be roughly equal to or less than that of the Paleozoic, Mesozoic, and Cenozoic combined. Correlations, under this concept, had a far greater *a priori* chance of being correct than in the light of present knowledge—if separated areas, for example, each contained three well-defined rock sequences separated by profound unconformities, it would not seem unreasonable to conclude that they were correlative. But now that it is known that at least 2,500 m.y. of Precambrian history is represented by rocks—a period at least five times as long as all succeeding time—it is quite evident that the probability of *any* correlation being correct is greatly reduced. To put this in another way: if a Precambrian system equivalent in time duration to the Cretaceous is given a length of 3 inches, 50 years ago it had to be placed in a scale 20 inches long; now this 3 inches has to be given a position in a scale with a minimum length of 9 feet and a possible length of 15 feet.

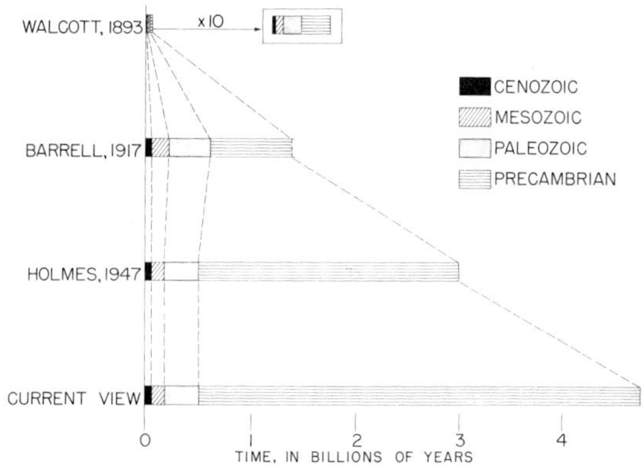

FIGURE 44.1
Graphic illustration of changes in concepts of geologic time

The significance of the great expansion of the time scale for the Precambrian is still not fully appreciated—probably not even by those of us working actively in the field—and the impact is not restricted to stratigraphy alone. Gilluly (1949, 1950) has effectively pointed out that if correlated sequences in separated areas are not truly equivalent in age, if doubt is placed on equivalence of their bounding unconformities (which represent orogenic intervals), and if proper account is taken of greater opportunity for observation for younger rocks, then some common generalizations, such as those dealing with "increasing tempo of orogenies with time" and progressively greater rate of sedimentation with time, rest on very shaky foundations. In the Precambrian, as for younger rocks, each rejected correlation may add significantly to the cumulative total of stratigraphic thicknesses (and therefore increase the apparent rate—though not necessarily the volume—of sedimentation per unit of time), and it may add one or more orogenies to the record. The ultimate dependence of concepts of this sort upon correlation is perhaps more evident for younger rocks, but it is no less true for the Precambrian. And it is within the Precambrian that correlations are most uncertain and for which unrealistic correlations are clung to most tenaciously. Stille (1955, pp. 188–189), for example, writes:

> Between Huronian and Algonkian* occurred one of the mightiest folding deformations of the earth, known as the Algoman revolution in American usage or the Karelian revolution elsewhere. One can say that this event produced an essentially complete consolidation of the earth's crust in the sense that there were no regions of appreciable size capable of sustaining Alpine-type folding. *This is borne out by the fact that not a single instance of unquestionable orthogeosynclinal continuity between the Huronian and the Algonkian has been discovered.* (My italics.)

Similarly, Bucher (1933, p. 418) states:

> So far as the writer knows, the Archeozoic rocks were strongly deformed everywhere on the face of the earth before the Proterozoic era began.

But the argument is completely circular: it is precisely *because* of great structural discordance that rocks in individual regions have been designated Archeozoic and Proterozoic (or "Huronian and Algonkian"). Until the advent of radiometric dating, there was no independent evidence to show, for example, that the Proterozoic of one area is equivalent to that of another, or that their bounding unconformities are the same. Gilluly's trenchant analysis (Gilluly, 1949) shows that even for thoroughly studied fossiliferous strata, the minimum unit of time that can be distinguished is rarely less than several million years, and that events that take place intermittently or continuously during this period are commonly grouped to give an erroneous impression of widespread simultaneity. For the Precambrian, the minimum unit of time that can be discriminated by radiometric methods surely is at least tens of millions of years; as a result, for rocks in excess of a billion years old it is quite unlikely that successive deformations comparable to the Nevadan and Laramide orogenies could be separately defined. It is small wonder that the classic Precambrian deformations appear to have been events of vast significance; each named orogeny, such as Algoman and Laurentian, probably is a composite of many diastrophisms that took place in different places at different times.

The great increase in time assigned to the Precambrian has impact on other facets of the analysis of earth history. The limitation of the cherty iron-formations to the Precambrian, for example, often has been cited as potent evidence in favor of the view that the Precambrian atmosphere and environment must have been substantially different from those of younger eras. Differences may have in fact existed, but the lack of iron-formation in post-Precambrian rocks is now far from a compelling argument. Iron-formations of many different ages occur in the Lake Superior region. Radiometric dating of rocks in Minnesota (Goldich, Baadsgaard, and Nier, 1957b) indicates that the Biwabik iron-formation of the Mesabi district is 700 m.y. or more younger than the Soudan iron-formation of the Vermilion district. Unless it can be shown that iron formations of intermediate age exist, this could mean that there were intervals within the Precambrian as long as or longer than all of post-Precambrian time during which the specific combination of environmental factors necessary for deposition of iron-formation did not exist.

* Stille's use of Huronian, Algonkian, and Algoman is, of course, completely at variance with "classic" terminology in the type areas from which these names are derived. As that terminology is summarized by Leith (1935, table opp. p. 10), Huronian is a subdivision of Algonkian and rocks assigned to it rest unconformably on Algoman granite.

NEWER CONCEPTS OF SEDIMENTATION AND OROGENESIS

The second great factor in the apparent degeneration of stratigraphic generalizations for Precambrian rocks is the advance in knowledge of spatial and temporal aspects of sedimentation and of orogenesis.

Some part of older views on deposition of sediments is expressed in the term "layer-cake stratigraphy"—the assumption that similar or identical conditions existed over great areas and that the interruptions or changes in conditions of sedimentation were similarly widespread. As a result correlations were accepted because, and often only because, of similarities in lithology; correlations were rejected because of dissimilarities. In the absence of any means of establishing age equivalence or the lack of it, both acceptances and rejections must be reviewed critically. It is more difficult to establish the existence and nature of lateral changes in unfossiliferous rocks than in fossiliferous rocks, but that these changes must exist is not open to question. The fine study by White of the iron-formation of the Mesabi district (White, 1954) demonstrates that facies analysis of Precambrian stratigraphic units is possible if sufficient data can be acquired.

The development of major terminology for Precambrian strata was also greatly influenced by a concept, largely abandoned by 1900 but still exerting subtle influence, that Precambrian rocks are the products of truly world-wide processes that took place during the transition from a primordial crust to what would be considered normal geologic conditions (for review and criticism, see Irving, 1888). These processes were conceived to be essentially chemical, and they demanded a universal and certain succession; gaps in the record might exist, but the order is invariable. Names such as Laurentian and Huronian were applied to subdivisions and doubtless this accounts in part for the use of these terms in many parts of the world. A curious sidelight of this classification is afforded by the evolution of the word "taconite," now a well-known term for low-grade iron ores of the Lake Superior region. The term stems from "Taconic," one of the major subdivisions of this older classification of the Precambrian, which in turn is derived from the Taconic Mountains of New York, the strata of which are now known to be Paleozoic in age; "taconite" is the only relic of this nomenclature remaining in the Lake Superior region.

Many other correlations were made and names assigned on the basis of similarity in degree of deformation and metamorphism—in fact, the early definitions of "Archean" were in terms of such criteria—and on the assumption that orogenic revolutions were of great extent, perhaps even world wide. The temporal aspects of orogeny are discussed earlier in this essay; the spatial aspects also have significance to the problems of correlation. The concept of orogeny affecting broad areas has long since given way to that of deformations confined to narrow belts, with rapid cross-strike transition from orogenic to non-orogenic environments. Age equivalence between rocks strikingly different in structural and metamorphic characters must not only be accepted, it must be expected. The attempts to define Precambrian orogenic belts for the Canadian Shield (Wilson, 1949) is recognition of the predominantly linear aspect of zones of orogenic deformation. If such belts could be located accurately by geologic mapping, perhaps some headway could be made toward proper correlation of dissimilar rocks.

METHODS OF ATTACK ON CORRELATION PROBLEMS OF THE PRECAMBRIAN

Abundant reasons have been given in the preceding pages for viewing with great skepticism most of the classic generalizations regarding Precambrian stratigraphy and history. How then do we cope with the problems of analyzing and synthesizing the more than three-fourths of all geologic history represented by the non-fossiliferous Precambrian rocks? And cope we must, because no matter what the difficulties, the questions are far too important, for both scientific and economic reasons, to be ignored. Even though we must acknowledge that in some places intense deformation and metamorphism have virtually destroyed original characteristics of the rocks, in many areas and probably in parts of all areas, stratigraphic geology is possible. It is my purpose now to show that in the attack on such areas we are not wholly without weapons, nor are we wholly without success in using them.

The weapons are the physical criteria of correlation and radiometric age determinations.

The most basic geologic law is that of superposition. Though the principle itself can be called obvious, its application to highly deformed rocks is rarely easy. In many Precambrian terranes, the dip of a bed is without significance as to which rocks are younger or older. Determination of the original "top direction" of a bed may not be possible from internal evidence, as it depends first upon whether diagnostic features ever existed and second upon whether they have been preserved. Even where there is preservation, recognition may be difficult, but in rocks of sedimentary origin features such as crossbedding, ripple mark, cut-and-fill, graded bedding, and algal structures commonly are retained to some degree in all but the most intensely sheared and altered terranes. The recognition does of course require knowledge both of the nature of the original feature and the effects of later processes on that feature, as in the familiar example of grain-size reversal in an original graded bed because of metamorphism. In rocks of volcanic origin, one uses relict pillow structures in greenstone and vesicular and breccia tops in subaerial flows. In igneous rocks it may be a pattern of differentiation—granophyre near the top of a gabbroic sill and ultramafic rock near the base, or their metamorphic equivalents. The determination of top direction in areas of low to moderate metamorphism may be based on secondary structural features, particularly drag folds and cleavage, by means of which a particular bed can be located with respect to synclinal or anticlinal fold axes, and by the mapping out of major folds. These procedures are time consuming, and rarely do they yield results that are beyond question, but it is by such means that the stratigraphic order within sequences, and the relationships between sequences, are established for individual districts.

In correlating from one area to another, we must rely on a combination of clues, none of which individually is above suspicion. In districts such as Lake Superior, formations cannot be "walked out" between areas because of lack of exposure or because of structural discontinuities. More often, the gross position of a sequence must be fixed by broader relations to igneous activity, deformation, and metamorphism. This must, of course, be done with full awareness of the dangers involved, but the errors are perhaps more likely to be those of failure to correlate strata that are actually time equivalent than those of incorrect correlation.

Within the shaky framework set by major unconformities, use is then made of distinctive aspects of the succession. This might be a single unit, such as a thick dolomite that might reasonably be inferred to have had wide original extent, but more reliable are distinctive combinations of clastic sediments, chemical sediments, and volcanic rocks. The point can be illustrated by reference to rocks of the Lake Superior region (Figure 44.2). The Animikie group of Minnesota, for example, consists of the basal Pokegama quartzite, the Biwabik iron-formation, and the overlying Virginia slate* (Grout, Gruner, Schwartz, and Thiel, 1951). On the south shore of Lake Superior, in the Gogebic district of Wisconsin and Michigan, a sequence occupying a similar structural position consists of the basal Palms quartzite, the Ironwood iron-formation, and the Tyler slate, which like the Virginia slate is a thick formation of graywacke and argillite. In the Gogebic district, however, remnants of quartzite and dolomite locally separate this sequence from the underlying crystalline rocks. Farther east, in the Marquette and Menominee district of Michigan, the quartzite and dolomite are thick formations that conformably or disconformably underlie the iron-bearing sequence, and the overlying rocks attain great thickness and complexity. The entire succession, despite the presence of minor unconformities, has unity in character in that the rocks provide a record of progressive change in depositional environment from that of a stable shelf, characterized by deposition of quartzite

* These individual formations, and others mentioned, are indicated only by lithologic pattern on Figure 44.2.

and dolomite, to that of a eugeosyncline characterized by deposition of graywacke and submarine volcanic rocks. It has therefore been designated as the Animikie series (James, 1958). Aside from correlated equivalents and subdivisions of individual formations, it contains about 20 established stratigraphic units that are placed in four groups; the aggregate thickness is at least 50,000 feet.*

Below the Animikie group in Minnesota and Ontario are two more groups, the Knife Lake with between 10 and 20 formational units, and the Ely greenstone with the interbedded Soudan iron-formation. Similarly, in Michigan, the Animikie series is underlain by relics of two older groups. But correlation between these older groups is not possible, at least with the means at hand. Overlying the Animikie is the Keweenawan series, which has several major subdivisions and a total thickness of 40,000 to 50,000 feet. In all, at least 100 noncorrelative Precambrian formations, with an aggregate thickness of more than 150,000 feet, can be placed in sequential position within the Lake Superior region. Correlations within this immense pile of rock are of varying degrees of reliability, but still they are adequate for reconstruction of large chapters of geologic history—a history that spans more than 2,000 million years. I might add that there is evidence of life throughout: graphitic rocks in the Soudan iron-formation, algal forms and structures in the Kona dolomite and the Biwabik iron-formation, coal in strata of the Paint River group, and oil in the Keweenawan.

In order to place these sequences in a time scale—and to provide a basis for correlation between separated regions—it is necessary to turn to radiometric dating. While this is the shining hope for ultimate subdivision of the Precambrian, it must not be thought that it requires merely more measurements, or even that ultimate success is assured. In the first place, only in rare cases will it be possible to obtain suitable material of primary or diagenetic origin by means of which the actual age of a stratigraphic unit can be determined; in general, most of the age determinations will be made on minerals of igneous or metamorphic origin. The values obtained for the minerals from a metamorphic rock provide only the age of recrystallization, which may be far removed from the original age of the rock unit. In the second place, metamorphic and igneous rocks alike may be remetamorphosed, with varying degrees of response by individual minerals in the rocks, so that the age values obtained may be discordant or lacking in agreement with geologically determined relationships.

The kinds of complexity that must be dealt with are illustrated by the geochronologic data now available for Dickinson County, in northern Michigan. The Felch trough in this area is a complex infold of strata of the Animikie series. These strata rest with profound unconformity on an older granite, which is later than the metasedimentary and metavolcanic rocks of the Dickinson group. Pegmatite dikes cut the granite and older metamorphic rocks, and granite dikes cut the Animikie strata. The relations are shown diagrammatically in Figure 44.3. Age determinations from localities 1–8 were made by L. T. Aldrich of the Carnegie Institution, using the Rb/Sr and K/A methods, and the data are reproduced here with his permission. Data for localities 1a and 6a are reported by Wasserburg, Hayden, and Jensen (1956, p. 159); these were obtained by the K/A method, with an empirical factor used to correct for assumed argon loss in the microcline and whole-rock samples. The value for the muscovite from locality 1a has been recalculated from the basic data given, using the same constants used by Aldrich. The disagreement between the radiometric age determinations and the geologic history deduced from field studies is profound, and significant differences exist between ages obtained by different methods or from different minerals in the given rock. This lack of agreements does not necessarily mean that some of the data or geological interpretation must be incorrect, though this possibility must be continually appraised. In actual fact, all may be valid, and each "disagreement" may furnish important evidence leading to a more complete geologic history.

This is not the place to attempt interpretation of the discordant data given in Figure

* For nearly 60 years this sequence was called Huronian and correlated with the rocks of the type area 300 miles to the east. The abandonment of that designation is part of the general retreat from older and now uncertain correlations.

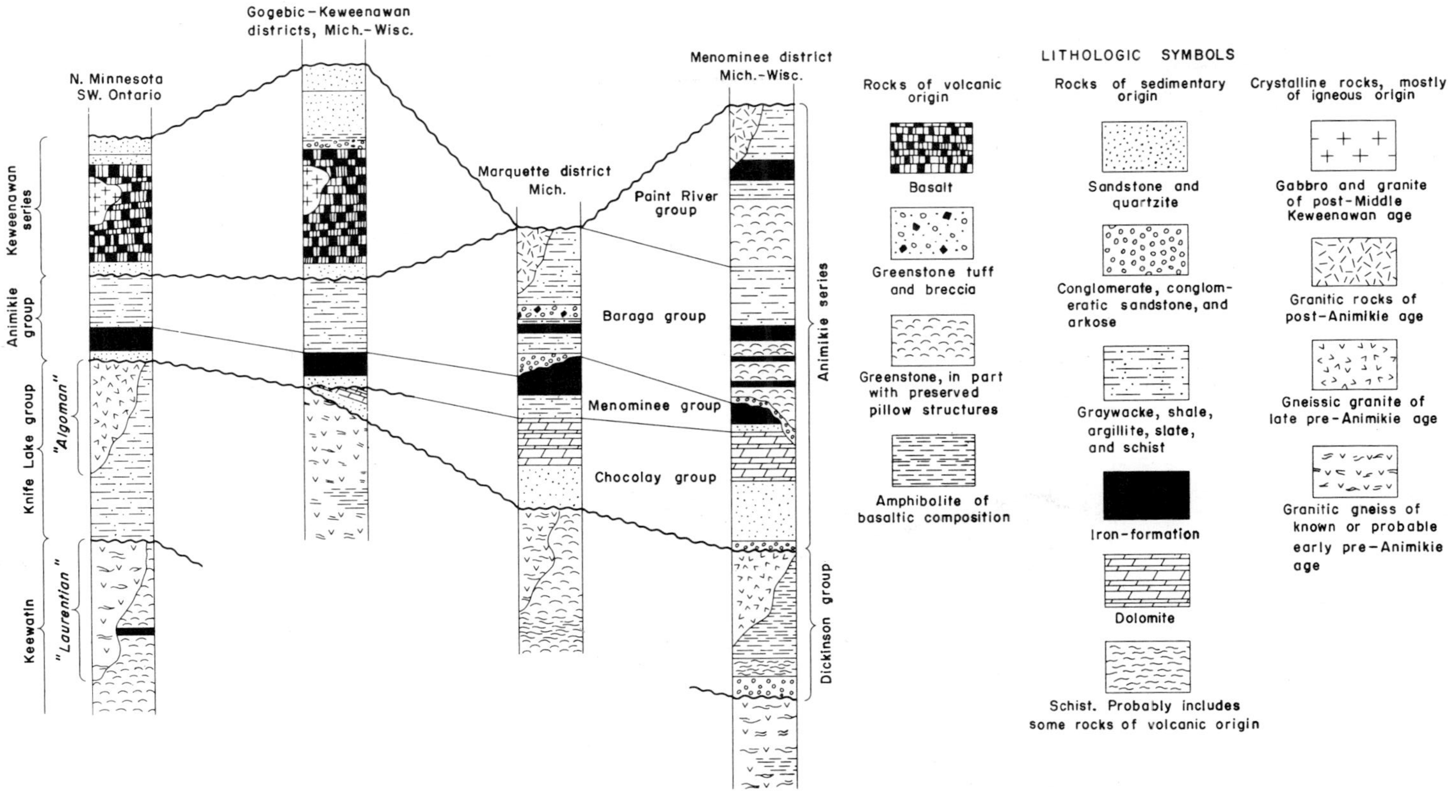

FIGURE 44.2
Generalized stratigraphic successions in Precambrian rocks of the Lake Superior region

44.3. A more complete statement of the problem, together with further data and possible solutions, will be made in a forthcoming paper by Aldrich and his associates. But it is clear that any interpretation will call for some of the rocks to have undergone more than one metamorphism.

Two possibilities remain for obtaining an age closer to the real value for remetamorphosed rocks. First, by correlation, a given rock unit may be traced into areas of negligible metamorphism. In Minnesota, for example, where much of the Animikie is very weakly metamorphosed, ages of 2,500–2,700 m.y. have been obtained for minerals in the pre-Animikie rocks (Goldich, Nier, and Baadsgaard, 1957a), and although no correlations can be made with the Michigan rocks at the present time, the possibility does exist. Second, the work of Tilton, Wetherill, Davis, and Hopson (1958) on the Baltimore gneiss has shown that isotopic measurements of uranium-lead in zircon may yield an "original" age whereas K/A and Rb/Sr measurements on micas give an age of a later metamorphism; the "primary" age for the Baltimore gneiss is about 1,100 m.y. and the superimposed metamorphism is about 300 m.y. These methods give hope that most major sequences can eventually be bracketed so that at least crude correlation from region to region or even continent to continent can be eventually made.

In conclusion, I want to make it clear that although the immense duration of time and the lack of diagnostic fossils are formidable obstacles to overcome, the problems of stratigraphy and correlation in the Precambrian can and must be solved. Despite the difficulties, the Precambrian is not a world apart: It contains the same kinds of rocks and reveals the same kinds of geologic processes known from the record of younger eras; the same principles apply and the same rules must be used. And as with rocks of the younger eras, stratigraphy and correlation are the very essence of understanding the geologic record.

SUMMARY

Two great advances in geologic knowledge—the gradually accruing evidence of the immense duration of Precambrian time, which is now believed to represent about 8 times that

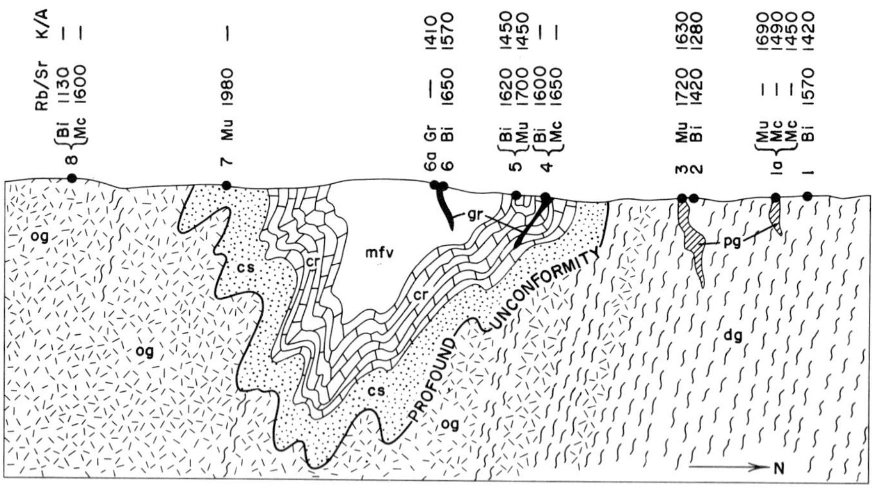

FIGURE 44.3
Schematic cross section of the Felch trough, Dickinson County, Michigan. Rock units as follows: *dg*, gneiss and schist; *og*, pre-Animikie granite; *cs*, Sturgeon quartzite (basal member of Animikie series); *cr*, Randville dolomite; *mfv*, Felch formation and Vulcan iron-formation. Pre-Animikie rocks cut by pegmatite (*pg*); strata of Animikie series cut by granite (*gr*). Age determinations on biotite (*Bi*), muscovite (*Mu*), microcline (*Mc*), and mica-free granite (*Gr*), in millions of years; sample localities (*solid circles*) projected as much as 10 miles into plane of section. Length of cross section about 5 miles, but units are not drawn to scale.

of the Paleozoic, Mesozoic, and Cenozoic combined, and development of the facies concept, with concomitant destruction of "layer cake" stratigraphy—have forced thorough reappraisal of stratigraphic correlations of Precambrian rocks. This reappraisal, which is being made by many students of the Precambrian, has thrown doubt on heretofore accepted correlations and has led to greater caution in regional syntheses. Most of the familiar time and time-stratigraphic terms have been virtually abandoned except in type areas, but despite this apparent retrogression, Precambrian stratigraphy probably is on a sounder basis than ever before.

Within individual areas, even areas of highly deformed and metamorphosed rocks, problems of stratigraphy and of correlation are being solved by detailed mapping and application of the physical criteria of correlation. In the Lake Superior region, for example, about 100 formations, plus named stratigraphic equivalents, can be placed in sequential position; these formations represent a probable time span of more than two billion years. District-to-district correlations are made on the basis of structural position, highly distinctive sequences and "carry-over" units, and bracketing by isotope age determinations on older and younger crystalline rocks. The resultant stratigraphic classifications and correlations cannot attain the refinement possible in fossiliferous strata, but they provide useful approximations for reconstruction of regional geologic history.

REFERENCES CITED

Aldrich, L. T., and G. W. Wetherill, 1958, Geochronology by radioactive decay: Ann. Rev. Nuclear Sci., v. 8, p. 257–298.

Barrell, J., 1917, Rhythms and the measurement of geologic time: Geol. Soc. America Bull., v. 28, p. 745–904.

Bucher, W. H., 1933, The deformation of the earth's crust: Princeton, N. J., Princeton University Press, 518 p.

Clarke, F. W., 1924, Data of geochemistry: U. S. Geol. Survey Bull. 770, 841 p.

Gilluly, James, 1949, Distribution of mountain building in geologic time: Geol. Soc. America Bull., v. 60, p. 561–590.

———, 1950, Reply to discussion by Hans Stille: Geol. Rundschau, v. 38, no. 2, p. 103–107.

Goldich, S. S., A. O. Nier, and H. Baadsgaard, 1957a, A^{40}/K^{40} dating of rocks of the Lake Superior region (abstract): Am. Geophys. Union Trans., v. 38, p. 392.

Goldich, S. S., H. Baadsgaard, and A. O. Nier, 1957b, Investigations in A^{40}/K^{40} dating: Am. Geophys. Union Trans., v. 38, p. 547–551.

Grout, F. F., J. W. Gruner, G. M. Schwartz, and G. A. Thiel, 1951, Precambrian stratigraphy of Minnesota: Geol. Soc. America Bull., v. 62, p. 1017–1078.

Holmes, A., 1947, The construction of a geological time scale: Geol. Soc. Glasgow Trans., v. 21, p. 117–152.

Irving, R. D., 1888, On the classification of early Cambrian and pre-Cambrian formations: U.S. Geol. Survey Seventh Ann. Rept., p. 371–454.

James, H. L., 1958, Stratigraphy of pre-Keweenawan rocks in parts of northern Michigan: U.S. Geol. Survey Prof. Paper 314-C, 44 p.

Leith, C. K., 1934, The pre-Cambrian: Geol. Soc. America Proc. for 1933, p. 151–180.

———, 1935, Pre-Cambrian rocks of the Lake Superior region: U. S. Geol. Survey Prof. Paper 184, 34 p.

Patterson, C., G. Tilton, and M. Inghram, 1955, Age of the Earth: Science, v. 121, p. 69–75.

Sollas, W. J., 1909, The anniversary address of the President: Geol. Soc. London Quart. Jour., v. 65, p. l–cxxii.

Stille, H., 1955, Recent deformations of the Earth's crust in the light of those of earlier epochs, *in* A. Poldervaart, ed. Crust of the earth: Geol. Soc. America Spec. Paper 62, p. 171–192.

Tilton, G. R., G. W. Wetherill, G. L. Davis, and C. A. Hopson, 1958, Ages of minerals from the Baltimore gneiss near Baltimore, Maryland: Geol. Soc. America Bull., v. 69, p. 1469–1474.

Walcott, C. D., 1893, Geologic time, as indicated by the sedimentary rocks of North America: Jour. Geology, v. 1, p. 639–676.

Wasserburg, G. J., R. J. Hayden, and K. J. Jensen, 1956, A^{40}-K^{40} dating of igneous rocks and sediments: Geochim. et Cosmochim. Acta, v. 10, p. 153–165.

White, D. A., 1954, The stratigraphy and structure of the Mesabi range, Minnesota: Minnesota Geol. Survey Bull. 38, 92 p.

Wilson, J. T., 1949, The origin of continents and Precambrian history: Royal Soc. Canada Trans., sec. IV, v. 43, p. 157–184.

Wilson, M. E., 1958, Precambrian classification and correlation in the Canadian Shield: Geol. Soc. America Bull., v. 69, p. 757–774.

45

Biological Events and the Precambrian Time Scale

M. F. GLAESSNER
1968

From *Canadian Journal of Earth Sciences,* vol. 5, pp. 585–590, 1968. Reprinted with permission of the author and the National Research Council of Canada.

Time scales for stratigraphic purposes can be based either on geophysical and geochemical or on biological data. Radioactive processes in the rocks are the basis of measurement of the age of rocks in years. Chronological scales are, however, useful if they give a sequential ordering of events in time, rather than a measure of the time elapsed since the event. Such events may be geophysical, such as changes in solar or cosmic radiation or in the composition of the atmosphere, or climatic changes such as ice ages with their more or less distinctive record of rocks, or magnetic reversals. They may be geochemical if the composition of sediments has changed in the course of time, or they may be biological, reflecting evolutionary changes in the nature of the organisms existing at different times. Although evolution does not proceed at a constant rate and therefore cannot be used for the measurement of time, the ordering of Phanerozoic rocks in a time scale of Eras and Periods is largely based on evolutionary events, which produced new faunas and floras in rapid succession. Many of the terms proposed for divisions of Precambrian time reflect the desire for uniform extension of the successful scheme of Cenozoic–Mesozoic–Paleozoic Eras farther back in time, despite the apparent absence of significant earlier fossils. Hence terms like Proterozoic (early life), Archeozoic (archaic life), Agnotozoic (unknown life), Azoic (no life), Eozoic (dawn of life), Cryptozoic (hidden life) were proposed and used in different ways, together with other similar terms, which were proposed but subsequently never used (Gregory and Barrett, 1927). The literal meaning of these terms is irrelevant and their definition and usefulness is disputed. The only "-zoic" terms still in more or less frequent use are Cryptozoic (=Precambrian, opposed to Phanerozoic) and Proterozoic (for Middle and Late Precambrian, opposed to Archean and commonly defined as beginning at 2500 ±100 million years). It so happens that the literal meaning of these two terms is unobjectionable. The continued use of the term Proterozoic in this sense, divided into

Early, Middle, and Late Proterozoic, corresponding approximately to Stockwell's (1968) Aphebian, Helikian, and Hadrynian, respectively, is useful at least for the following discussion. Intensive studies of the Precambrian record of life have led to two important conclusions: (1) the main diversification of life occurred not earlier than in Late Proterozoic time; (2) only primitive plants (and bacteria) are recorded definitely from many sediments of Middle and Early Proterozoic age and also from a few Archean rocks. The origin of life early in the history of the earth is a fact of great theoretical but of limited practical importance as far as the use of biological events for the dating of rocks is concerned. The presence of fossils in sediments representing 2000 million years of Proterozoic time requires careful assessment of their stratigraphic potential. Not their absence but the slowness of evolutionary progress during this long span of time, the lack of differentiation of the organic world until late in the Precambrian, constitutes the main problem.

PROBLEMS OF FOSSILIZATION AND CLASSIFICATION

The evidence of Precambrian life should be assessed not only with skepticism because its remains are not easily recognizable as such (Cloud, 1965), but also on the basis of new approaches to the study of fossilization and of classification of these remains. Precambrian fossils are not hard skeletal parts, mineralized during the life of the organism, as most Phanerozoic fossils are. They are either organic substances more or less altered by carbonization or mineral replacement, or gelatinous and other soft bodies either silicified or preserved as casts and impressions, or they are sedimentary structures formed by life activities of the organisms. These processes of fossilization are less well known than the processes involved in the preservation of hard skeletons and shells and it is more difficult to achieve the main aim of paleontological studies—the reconstruction and complete understanding of functional morphology of the living organism—on this basis. The classification of Precambrian fossils is difficult not only for this reason but also because even major groups of organisms may have become extinct during the long time spans involved. Even in Lower Cambrian strata there are Echinoderms and Mollusca that do not belong to any existing classes within these phyla, and there are well-known skeletal Invertebrata, such as the Archaeocyatha and the Hyolithida, which do not fit into any of the existing phyla. Similar difficulties in classifying primitive plants have been noted. There is a strong probability that evolutionary diversification at all levels, particularly in early stages, produced many phyletic side branches, which did not survive beyond Precambrian or early Paleozoic time, when the sucessful and therefore surviving existing major groups of organisms became fully established. Hence, paleontologists will be unable to relate such early fossils to known major systematic categories.

PLANT MICROFOSSILS

Fortunately, as in Phanerozoic paleontology, there are examples of unusually good preservation of fossils showing more detail than can be expected in normal circumstances. The best known example is the algal flora of the Gunflint chert (Barghoorn and Tyler, 1965; Cloud, 1965) of Early Proterozoic age. A recent study by LaBerge (1967) has shown that such microscopic remains may well be widespread in cherts of banded iron-formations, but that they are generally so much altered that most of their distinguishing features are lost and therefore their uses for correlation and relative age determination are limited. [See also studies by Pflug (1965, 1966) on the Beltian rocks.]

Alteration during fossilization as well as the low level of morphological differentiation affects the stratigraphic value of Precambrian plant microplankton. The evidence was reviewed recently by Downie (1967) and Timofeev (1966). These minute spherical or ellipsoidal bodies are known from rocks more than 3000 million years old and are widespread in Proterozoic formations. In his monograph, Timofeev (1966) added much new information, which was not available to Downie, but it does not appear to affect Downie's conclusion (Downie, 1967, p. 272) that: "The evidence points to the presence of a marine plankton in the Precambrian represented in the fossil record by cysts of unicellular algae and possibly by spores of multicellular algae." Such microfossils are now classified as Acritarcha (Evitt, (1963) and placed in the Subgroup Sphaeromorphitae ("Group Sphaeromorphida," Timofeev 1966). A microflora containing Acritarchs was described recently from the Muhos Formation of Finland, 1300 million years old, by Tynni and Siivola (1966). The microflora becomes more varied in the Late Precambrian, particularly the Riphean and Vendian. Timofeev (1966, p. 101) claimed that these fossils form a surprisingly constant association (particularly in strata 1100–700 million years old) from the European part of the U.S.S.R. to eastern Siberia and that that they can be used for stratigraphic correlation throughout this region. Similar previous claims have not been accepted unanimously by other investigators. In the Vendian (from about 700 million years to the base of the Cambrian) the Acritarchs are still more varied and some are larger. They have also been recognized in strata of the same age in Scandinavia and northern France.

STROMATOLITES

The most abundant Precambrian fossils are the stromatolites (Figure 45.1), which are now generally recognized as biogenic sedimen-

FIGURE 45.1
Stromatolites. Irregully Formation, Bangemall Group, East Branch of Henry River, Capricorn Ranges, Western Australia. The Bangemall Group is currently placed in the lower part of the Upper Proterozoic, but it could be between 1100 and 1400 million years old. (Photo by M. R. Walter, University of Adelaide. × 0.15.)

tary structures. Many of them are large and easily recognizable in the field. Russian workers have proved that they can be used in stratigraphic correlation of Upper Precambrian strata. Investigation of Middle and Upper Precambrian material is in progress in Australia and elsewhere.

Stromatolites are notoriously variable. Modern studies of Recent stromatolites, particularly by Logan et al. (1964), have shown the dependence of variability on environmental conditions. Earlier descriptions of Precambrian and Paleozoic stromatolites had indicated a similar variablity of form, but in these limited studies a multitude of names was given to different observed shapes and structures. It was rightly pointed out, by Cloud (1942) and others, that these genera and species had neither precise morphological meaning nor stratigraphic value, beyond strictly local application. From this correct observation, however, the incorrect generalization was made that stromatolites could not be grouped into taxonomically valid form genera and species, and that they never changed in a recognizable manner in the course of geological time. Conversely, all observable differences were ascribed to different local conditions. The theoretical basis of these views was the undisputed fact that the stromatolites were not the fossilized remains of specific organisms but merely sedimentary structures modified by the life activities of a variety of blue-green algae and possibly other plants and bacteria. The question of the stratigraphic use of stromatolites, like any other question of stratigraphic evidence for correlation, cannot be decided by theory alone but by the weight of empirical data. When specimens were collected from long and continuous stratigraphic sequences representing deposits of Late Precambrian age from a large territory, it was found that the organisms which produced these structures had changed sufficiently in the course of time to make them usable as time markers. Efforts are now being made to prove the validity of this conclusion over still larger areas and possibly on a world-wide scale. The positive conclusions were not reached quickly and easily. There are problems of sampling of these often unwieldy objects. There are other and more important problems of recognition of significant characters for classification and recognition of identity. After considerable arguments among Russian workers as to the most important character in stromatolites, the latest summaries (Krylov, 1963; Komar et al., 1965; Komar, 1966) mentioned for the most important group, the columnar stromatolites, the following four groups of diagnostic characters: branching, shape of the columns, presence or absence of a marginal layer, and particularly the microstructure of the layers of which the stromatolites consist. This is the microstructure of a biogenic sediment, not the cellular structure of algae. On this basis, many new genera and species were established, but the nomenclature of stromatolites is still unsatisfactory. Having established recognizable categories of stromatolites, the Russian workers were able to demonstrate the successive occurrence of four different assemblages. When the isotopic dating of the rock sequences in which they occur was considered, it was found that they range from about 1600–1350, 1350–1100, 1100–700, and 700–570 million years (Figure 45.2).

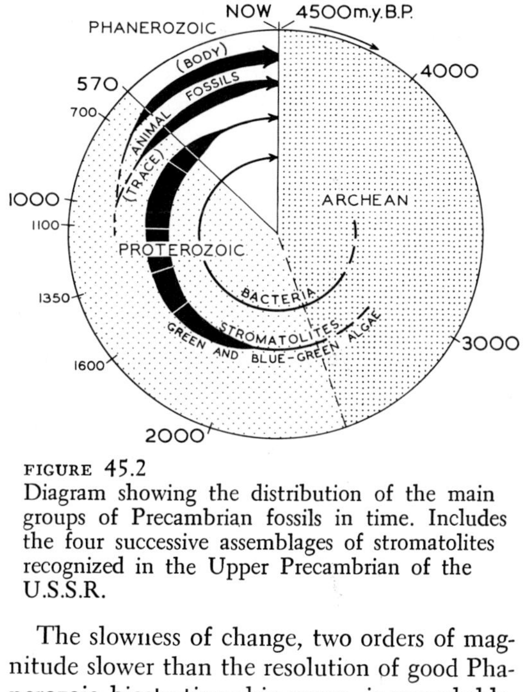

FIGURE 45.2
Diagram showing the distribution of the main groups of Precambrian fossils in time. Includes the four successive assemblages of stromatolites recognized in the Upper Precambrian of the U.S.S.R.

The slowness of change, two orders of magnitude slower than the resolution of good Phanerozoic biostratigraphic zones, is remarkable. It is not surprising that early investigators, studying much more limited ranges of stromatolite occurrence, were inclined to deny any change. It is not necessarily the finest division attainable, but there is at present no proof of regional significance of any finer divisions. There are, however, indications that Lower Proterozoic stromatolites from Australia and Africa, which have not yet been studied with modern methods, may prove significantly different from the four Middle and Upper Proterozoic "phytems." Phytem is the name recently applied by Keller (1966) for these units of long duration based on changes in aquatic plant activities.

We are beginning to see also possibilities of biostratigraphic use of other algal structures. Russian workers have claimed success in correlation on the basis of onkolites, which are a nodular form of stromatolite, and catagraphia, a diverse group of oolite-like structures in carbonates with distinctive microscopic structures unlike typical chemically precipitated ooids. These, too, are claimed to change during Late Precambrian and Cambrian times, with somewhat more widely spaced horizons of change than the stromatolites. Similar problematic fossils have been described from the Precambrian II of the Anti-Atlas (Choubert and Termier, 1951), and I have observed others in a sample from the Ocoee Series of Tennessee. There are also macroscopic disc or ring-shaped structures in clastic sediments, which are still unexplained, but which are possibly of algal origin and potentially time-significant.

METAZOA

It has been suggested that, at least theoretically, the first appearance of multicellular animals or Metazoa should be a time-marking event in earth history. According to Cloud (1965, p. 34) "Evidence currently available indicates that such conditions (i.e. atmospheric conditions suitable for metazoan metabolism) arose between about 1.2 and 0.6 billion years ago, and that the Metazoa made their debut about 0.6 billion years ago. The beginning of the Paleozoic might, then, be defined operationally as the base of the range-zone of Metazoa (or Eumetazoa if we exclude sponges). But a boundary (or a transition) should be limited from both sides, so I have added to this working definition the further limitation that the top of the Precambrian paleontologically approximates the top of the range-zone of the distinctive conical stromatolite conophyton." The disappearance of *Conophyton* at the end of the Vendian was confirmed by Komar et al. (1965), but the age of the Vendian is about 700–550 million years (Keller, 1966) and there are undisputed metazoan remains in the Vendian and in other strata of the same age. The Vendian is the transitional interval of the stratigraphic scale between the typical Riphean and the Baltic Cambrian. It has been added to the Cambrian by some and considered as pre-Cambrian Paleozoic by others, but there is a considerable body of opinion in favor of leaving the base of the Cambrian and of the Paleozoic in its traditional place. This question will be further discussed at the 23rd International Geological Congress.

For the stratigrapher, a time-marker is not the beginning of a postulated stage in history but an event that has left evidence in the rock record. The first appearance of animals of the lowest Metazoan grade is unrecorded because they were small and soft-bodied, and even their living representatives cannot be preserved as fossils. There are, for example, no fossil flatworms. Naked coelenterates and annelid worms must have been common throughout Phanerozoic time at least, but they are very uncommon as fossils. The earliest animals, like some of the earliest plants, will probably be recognized not by their structural preservation in the rocks but by traces of their life activities. It is still common practice to record "worm trails" on or in sedimentary rocks in the field and to leave them there. This disregards the considerable progress made during the last 20 years in their paleontological and stratigraphic evaluation and makes it impossible to date at present the first appearance of animals as trace fossils in the geological record. The problem is further complicated by the occurrence of peculiar structures, which have been variously interpreted as infillings of drying cracks, possibly caused by syneresis within the sediment, or as sinuous worm trail castings. The structures from the Huronian, Willouran, and Sinian rocks, which I included in a distribution chart of Precambrian fossils (Glaessner, 1966a, Fig. 2; see also Glaessner, 1966b, Fig. 2), belong to

FIGURE 45.3
Worm track on the upper surface of a dark siltstone. Brachina Formation, Bunyeroo Gorge, Western Flinders Ranges, South Australia. This formation is in the lower part of the Wilpena Group of the Adelaide System, separated from the "Upper Glacials" (Elatina Formation) only by a thin dolomite. (Natural size.)

this problematic category. This complex problem will be reviewed elsewhere. It was further complicated by the remarkable recent discovery (Hofmann 1967) of similar structures in the Huronian, which are unique in showing curious surface corrugations. Their presence, unexplained thus far by mechanical processes, seems to favor an organic origin, while their directional relation to the curvature of the bodies does not support it. The "worm trails" figured by Fenton and Fenton (1937) from the Beltian could be of non-biogenic origin.

Clearly, the problem of the first appearance of Metazoan animal remains in the geological record is unsolved. The earliest record of an unquestionable worm-like animal trail known to me is from the Brachina Formation, an estimated 5000–6000 ft below the base of the Cambrian and less than 1000 ft above the upper glacial beds (Elatina Formation) of the Adelaide System in the Flinders Ranges of South Australia (Figure 45.3).

The Late Precambrian glaciation and the first appearance of Metazoa should continue to be part of the Precambrian record. We know an assemblage of essentially soft-bodied Meta zoa, bodily preserved in rocks of Late Precambrian age, below Lower Cambrian fossiliferous strata. Elements of this fauna, which has been fully described from Ediacara in South Australia (Glaessner and Wade, 1966) are now known from southern and central Australia, from southwest Africa, England, Northern Siberia, and western Russia. In various places these occurrences are in rocks dated at about 680 million years, and they fall generally within the last 100–150 million years of Precambrian time if we accept 570 years as the most appropriate dating of the base of the Cambrian. This fauna is not associated with any Cambrian fossils. The fossil provisionally recorded as *Pteridinium* by Cloud and Nelson (1967, Fig. B) is a Lower Cambrian trace fossil similar to *Plagiogmus* Roedel and has no bearing on the age of the Ediacara fauna.*

CONCLUSIONS

(1) Primitive plants, filamentous algae and microplankton consisting of minute organic bodies of uncertain affinities, are widespread throughout the Precambrian. Their use for stratigraphic correlation of Middle and Upper Precambrian rocks has been claimed and seems to offer possibilities of further development.

(2) Stromatolites are the most abundant and conspicuous fossils throughout the Middle and Upper Precambrian rocks. Earlier naming and classification based on general shape of these biogenic sedimentary structures have been misconceived, as general characters mostly reflect environmental conditions. More detailed investigations by Russian workers have shown a succession of four different structural groups, which appear to represent evolutionary changes in the organisms responsible for stromatolite structures. The first three assemblages remained substantially unchanged for time spans of more than 200 million years. Firm recognition of even such long time spans (compared with Phanerozoic biostratigraphic zones of 1–2 million years duration) should prove most useful in Precambrian stratigraphy and current investigations are directed towards tests of this possibility in other continents. Other sedimentary structures of algal origin, known as onkolites and catagraphia, are also being tested for changes in the course of Precambrian time.

(3) The first known animal remains appear late in the Precambrian record. A distinctive assemblage of soft-bodied animals post-dates the widespread Late Precambrian glaciation, which has been dated in some areas as 700–800 million years. It pre-dates the first occurrence of other fossils such as Archaeocyatha and trilobites, which can be correlated with the Lower Cambrian of Great Britain and the Scandinavian-Baltic region. This assemblage is considered as a Late Precambrian (Eocambrian, Varegian, Vendian) time marker. Earlier occurrences of trace fossils representing activities of soft-bodied animals and instances of preservation of their bodies have yet to be definitely proved. On present evidence they are not likely to be stratigraphically significant.

* [This charmingly flat contradiction invites inspection of published illustrations. If the reader is interested, an illustration of *Plagiogmus* may be found in R. C. Moore, ed., 1962, Treatise on invertebrate paleontology (pt. W): Boulder, Colo., Geological Society of America, fig. 128–6, p. W206.—P. C.]

REFERENCES

Barghoorn, E. S., and S. A. Tyler, 1965. Microorganisms from the Gunflint Chert: Science, v. 147, p. 563–577.

Choubert, G., H. Termier, and G. Termier, 1951, Les calcaires précambriens de Tahgdout et leurs organismes problématiques: Service Géol. du Maroc Notes et Mém. 85, p. 9–34.

Cloud, P. E., Jr., 1942, Notes on stromatolites: Am. Jour. Sci., v. 240, p. 363–379.

———, 1965, Significance of the Gunflint (Precambrian) microflora: Science, v. 148, p. 27–35.

Downie, C., 1967, The geological history of the microplankton: Rev. Paleobotany and Palynology, v. 1, p. 269–281.

Evitt, W. R., 1963, A discussion and proposals concerning fossil dinoflagellates, hystrichospheres, and acritarchs, I: [U.S.] Natl. Acad. Sci. Proc. v. 49, p. 158–164.

Fenton, C. L., and M. A. Fenton, 1937, Belt series of the north; stratigraphy, sedimentation, paleontology: Geol. Soc. America Bull., v. 48, p. 1873–1969.

Glaessner, M. F., 1966a, Precambrian palaeontology: Earth-Science Rev., v. 1, p. 29–50.

———, 1966b, The first three billion years of life on earth: Jour. Geography (Chigaku Zasshi), v. 75, p. 307–315.

Glaessner, M. F., and M. Wade, 1966, The Late Precambrian fossils from Ediacara, South Australia: Paleontology, v. 9, p. 599–628.

Gregory, J. W., and B. H. Barrett, 1927, The major terms of the pre-Paleozoic: Jour. Geology, v. 25, p. 734–742.

Hofmann, J. J., 1967, Precambrian fossils (?) near Elliot Lake, Ontario: Science, v. 156, p. 500–504.

Keller, B. M., 1966, Podrazdeleniya edinoy stratigraficheskoy shkaly dokembryia (Subdivisions of the Unified Stratigraphic Scale of the Precambrian): Akad. Nauk SSSR Doklady, v. 171, p. 1405–1408.

Komar, V. A., 1966, Upper Precambrian stromatolites in the north of Siberian Platform and their stratigraphic significance: Acad. Sci. USSR Geol. Inst. Trans., v. 154, p. 5–120.

Komar, V. A., M. E. Raaben, and M. A. Semihatov, 1965, Conophytons in the Riphean of the USSR and their stratigraphic importance: Acad. Sci. USSR Geol. Inst. Trans., v. 131, p. 5–72.

Krylov, I. N., 1963, Stolb'chatye vetvyashchiesya stromatolity Rifeyskikh otlozheniy yuzhnogo Urala i ikh znachenie dlya stratigrafii verkhnego dokembriya (Columnar branching stromatolites from the Riphean deposits of the Southern Ural and their significance for the stratigraphy of the Upper Precambrian): Akad. Nauk SSSR Geol. Inst. Trudy, no. 69, p. 3–133.

LaBerge, G. L., 1967, Microfossils and Precambrian iron-formations: Geol. Soc. America Bull., v. 78, p. 331–342.

Logan, B. W., R. Rezak, and R. N. Ginsburg, 1964, Classification and environmental significance of algal stromatolites: Jour. Geology, v. 72, p. 68–83.

Pflug, H. D., 1965, Organische Reste aus der Belt-Serie (Algonkium) von Nordamerika: Paläont. Zeitschr., v. 39, p. 10–25.

———, 1966, Einige Reste niederer Pflanzen aus dem Algonkium: Palaeontographica, ser. B, v. 117, p. 59–74.

Stockwell, C. H., 1968, Geochronology of stratified rocks of the Precambrian Shield: Canadian Jour. Earth Sci., v. 6, p. 693–698.

Timofeev, B. V., 1966, Mikropaleofitologicheskoe issledovanie drevnikh svit (Micropaleophytological study of ancient rock sequences): Leningrad, Laboratory of Pre-Cambrian Geology, Academy of Sciences of the USSR, 147 p.

Tynni, R., and J. Siivola, 1966, On the Precambrian microfossil flora in the siltstone of Muhos, Finland: Soc. géol. Finlande Comptes rendus, v. 38, p. 127–133.

SECTION VII

SELECTIONS FROM PHANEROZOIC HISTORY

There is a wide country before us, though the horizon is mist and shadow.

Sir John Buchan

That part of earth history for which there is a record of Metazoa (differentiated multicellular animal life) is called the Phanerozoic. It is divided into three eras—the Paleozoic, Mesozoic, and Cenozoic—which are, in turn, divided into periods of time and systems of rocks, as shown on the front endpapers of this book. Although the Phanerozoic represents only the last seventh of earth history, the presence in Phanerozoic rocks of a good metazoan fossil record in extensive and little-deformed exposures has given rise to a detailed sequential geochronology, and has permitted biologic correlation of rocks from one part of the world to another. The concepts of historical geology originated in parts of the earth with a well-developed and richly fossiliferous Phanerozoic succession and they have been most generally applied in such places. Thus it happens that Phanerozoic history is known in considerable detail and is the subject of the great bulk of historical geological publication. To select a few relatively brief and literate samples to illustrate problems in Phanerozoic history was an unenviable task. Those chosen for Section VII are arranged to give a sense of sequence, despite large gaps, and to lead naturally into the succeeding three sections, which deal with more specific aspects of Phanerozoic history. For world-wide summaries of Phanerozoic stratigraphy, see the books by Gignoux (1950), Woodford (1965), and Kummel (1961) in the Supplemental Reading.

The first paper in this section (Reading Selection 46) is by geologist John Rodgers of Yale University. It deals with the problem of locating the base of the Cambrian, widely considered as the lowest of the Phanerozoic systems. Rodgers's locale is the central and southern Appalachian Mountains, near the eastern margin of North America, where a thick sequence of detrital rocks, unfossiliferous in the lower part, extends upward into fossiliferous beds definitely attributable to the Lower Cambrian. Similar situations, involving a transitional (and, commonly, time transgressive) clastic sequence at or near the "boundary" between pre-Paleozoic and Paleozoic, give rise to similar problems of boundary definition in other regions. Nowhere, however, has the problem generated more interest than in the Appalachians. Rodgers examines the evidence but finds no grounds for the clear-out placement of a boundary. His commendable but not sufficiently heeded solution: a liberal use of question marks.

Though written in 1882, Reading Selection 47, by Captain Clarence Dutton, is still a broadly valid summary of the classical Phanerozoic history of the Grand Canyon from the pre-Paleozoic to the present (although different stratigraphic names and age designations are now in use, as partly indicated in Figure 47.1; and some different interpretations are now made of the stratigraphy). Dutton discusses the great unconformity there to be seen at the base of the Paleozoic (his basal Carboniferous); the general flux of earth history through much of the Phanerozoic; and uplift, with two-stage down-cutting of the Canyon—the first stage beginning in Pliocene time and cutting to a temporary base level, and the second beginning at the end of the Pliocene. He also introduces, or elaborates, a number of concepts and interpretations that were new at the time he wrote: (1) that thick accumulation of shallow water sediments means continuing subsidence; (2) that the base level of erosion is an end level beyond which only lateral erosion takes place; (3) that the Mesozoic and Cretaceous ended with broad, regional ("Laramide") tectonism; (4) that extensive Tertiary lacustrine deposits formed in the Plateau area; and others. Perhaps the most interesting feature of Dutton's work, however, is his use of geomorphic detail in deducing structural, erosional, and climatic history. The paper is but a summary chapter from Dutton's *The Tertiary History of The Grand Cañon District*, one of the early classics of historical geology—a book that deserves reading in its entirety as an illustration of the stirring descriptions that the early geological explorers brought out of the then undeveloped American West. (A modern account is given in Chapter 5 of A. O. Woodford's *Historical Geology*; see Supplemental Reading.)

Following Dutton's introduction to the Phanerozoic, we turn to a well-documented modern classic that compresses the physical history of the western United States into remarkably short compass: "The Tectonic Evolution of the Western United States," by James Gilluly, his William Smith Lecture to the Geological Society of London (Reading Selection 48). As yet, little can be made of the fragmentary pre-Paleozoic history of the western United States, but it has a rich Phanerozoic record, including an eventful tectonic and plutonic history. Gilluly treats the tectonic history in the broadest terms, in sequence, and by geologic provinces. The sedimentary, physiographic, volcanic, and plutonic records are interwoven with the evidence of physical deformation to give a coherent view of essentially continuous crustal mobility, punctuated by episodes of plutonism at the sites of previously persistent geosynclinal depression. Then he considers six special topics: the Colorado Plateau, the Basin Ranges, transcurrent faulting, volcanic history, Phanerozoic plutonism, and the Pacific continental margin. This analysis repeatedly leads to certain broad conclusions: that, in order to satisfy isostasy, the observed topographic evolution required the lateral transfer of subcrustal and basal crustal material involving upper mantle motions; that the foundering and assimilation of large volumes of continental material is required to explain Pacific Coast disjunctions and the generation of extensive early Late Cretaceous granitic batholiths at formerly eugeosynclinal sites; and that there is no systematic connection between plutonism, volcanism, and tectonism. The abrupt boundary between continental and oceanic structure at the Pacific margin, in particular, demands an explanation, Gilluly contends. "Either the continent is drifting westward over the ocean floor, or the ocean floor . . . is moving eastward under the continent."

An earlier paper by Gilluly (1949, see Supplemental Reading), in which he argues the essential continuity (as opposed to periodicity) of orogenesis, is worth reading at this point. It is important to recognize that, although he sees no periodicity in orogenesis in the usual sense, he does see periodicity of plutonism, and at the sites where mountains are built. His challenge to demonstrate undeniable Paleozoic plutonism in the western states, moreover, has now been met. We may note, among several such records, that extensive quartz syenites and quartz diorites in the San Gabriel Mountains of southern California have been found by L. T. Silver to have an age of 245 ± 10 million years, and thus to be roughly Upper Permian in the sequential time scale.

In contrast to the crustal mobility described by Dutton and Gilluly, large areas of the continents were essentially stable for long intervals during the Phanerozoic, undergoing only broad migrations of the strand line that probably represent global fluctuations of sea level. Such migrations may show a remarkable cyclicity at some times and places, as recorded by essentially contemporaneous and usually thin but extensive sedimentary deposits. Among the more striking cyclic sequences is that of the Upper Carboniferous and Lower Permian deposits of the central United States, whose several types of cyclothems (and megacyclothems) are described in Reading Selection 49 by a leading student of that region and problem, R. C. Moore, professor emeritus of geology at the University of Kansas. The sequence—from nonmarine sandstones or red shales through coals or coal-bearing beds to marine shales and limestones and back to nonmarine again (a "cyclothem")—is repeated nearly 100 times in beds of this age throughout an area of over 100,000 square miles in the mid-continent region. Such cyclicity is not unique, however, nor does it always involve marine-nonmarine successions. Wholly marine cyclothems have been described from Alpine Mesozoic strata by A. G. Fischer (1964) and by Rudolf Trümpy (1960), for instance (see Supplemental Reading). Cyclic sequences lead to provocative questions and conclusions about paleoclimatic evolution, crustal history, land-sea relations, and the shifting locations of seaways and oceans, which are, in part, discussed in the two papers referred to above.

Another distinctive aspect of Phanerozoic history involves the episodic local growth of biogenic reefs that rise to sea level, interfere with the circulation of sea water, affect climate and sedimentation, and lead to drastic lateral changes in sedimentary facies. The best known and most extensively studied and described of these reef suites is the Capitan reef and its associated deposits of Permian age in west Texas and New Mexico. Extended discussions of the Capitan reef suite may be found under Supplemental Reading in papers by Adams and Frenzel (1950), King (1950), Newell (*in* Ladd, 1957), and Newell and others (1953). At this point, however, it seems preferable to consider the brief but interesting comparison that paleontologist John W. Wells of Cornell University makes between the Capitan reef suite and a reef suite of the Lower Carboniferous of northeastern England. In Reading Selection 50, Wells draws on, and greatly condenses, the descriptions of others to focus on the point of primary interest: that essentially similar reef suites, having similar historical effects, occur on a grand scale in different regions and in different parts of the geologic column. (Passing discussion of the Capitan reef suite is also given in the following article by Dunbar.)

Lateral variation in lithofacies and biofacies is perplexingly evident when one examines reef suites such as those above; yet awareness of the significance of these variations grew slowly. Now it is recognized by all geologists that the boundaries of rock units almost everywhere transgress time, either abruptly or imperceptibly. The study of such transitions reveals much about the biological and sedimentary history of the earth, but one good example will suffice. In his presidential address to the Paleontological Society of America (Reading Selection 51), C. O. Dunbar, professor emeritus at Yale University, draws on a background of many years of research to identify the central problems of Permian biostratigraphy as a function of change in lithofacies and biofacies. The type locality for the Permian is a region of striking facies change, and much of the upper half of the sequence lacks marine fossils. Nevertheless, by drawing on the biologic successions of other regions that could be identified as Permian on other grounds, Permian biologic zones have been established, correlations have been made to distant regions, and biologic history has been interpreted. Dunbar discusses the paleoecological and stratigraphic problems involved in several classic regions in the United States, East Greenland, and Eurasia and compares ancient with existing environments.

The Permian is the youngest of the Paleozoic systems and the focus of much geologic history in terms of biologic and paleogeographic change. The final movement of the Appalachian orogeny occurred in the Permian; but the earth is never free of orogenic movement for long, and the next succeeding major North American tectonism involved movements that began in the Mesozoic and extended into the Cenozoic. In the Rocky Mountain region that tectonism is known as the Rocky Mountain or (loosely) Laramide orogeny (strictly speaking Laramide implies post-Cretaceous, i.e., post-Laramie). Events related to it, as well as an important and well-described Mesozoic sequence, are the subjects of the next paper (Reading Selection 52), by E. M. Spieker of Ohio State University. An outstanding field geologist, Spieker reconstructs the relations between "Sedimentary Facies and Associated Diastrophism in the Upper Cretaceous of Central and Eastern Utah." The rocks involved reach westward from the western Colorado Basin to beyond the Wasatch Plateau. The Upper Cretaceous section there is thick, complete, and diversified. Unlike the cyclothemic Upper Paleozoic beds of the mid-continent described by Moore, it shows striking lateral changes in facies and thickness from east to west—especially among the lower beds, which grade from relatively thin offshore marine shales at the east through nearshore sands at intermediate locations into thick orogenic rubble in the deeply subsiding mobile zone at the west. The different sedimentary facies intertongue and vary systematically in both vertical and lateral sequence, revealing strikingly cyclic and regular interrelations between disastrophism, physical environment, and sedimentation—both vertically and laterally. All facies become thin, and time lines converge, toward the east. Throughout his discussion Spieker uses rocks to illustrate principles of stratigraphy, sedimentation, tectonic reconstruction, nomenclature, and time transgression. An interesting generalization is Spieker's observation that the abrupt tops and gradational bases of the sandstone tongues in his sequence indicate their deposition during standstills of the sea, and that the smooth tops of these sandstone wedges are tractionally smoothed contemporaneous surfaces—an interesting contrast with turbidity current sediments, where the tops are gradational, the bottoms are sharp, and deposition is essentially an instantaneous episode. The complexity of Spieker's paper may make it somewhat difficult to read, but the attentive reader will be amply rewarded, both by the insights into Mesozoic history, and with an understanding of principles that can be applied to rocks of any age.

The orogenic and epeiorogenic movements that marked the transition from the Mesozoic to the Cenozoic apparently resulted in a major uplifting of the continents, or a deepening of the ocean basins, or both, so that the seas never again invaded the continental areas as extensively as before. The records of later Phanerozoic history, therefore, take the form of continental deposits, lake beds, eroded surfaces, and marginally overlapping marine sediments. One of the finest essays on Cenozoic and Tertiary history and paleolimnology is W. H. Bradley's "Limnology and the Eocene Lakes of the Rocky Mountain Region" (Reading Selection 53). Starting from a brief outline of lake theory and comparative limnology, Bradley, former Chief Geologist of the U.S. Geological Survey, takes us on a far-ranging excursion through the 500 to 700 meters of oil shale, carbonate rocks, and sandstone that now fill the basins of three Middle Eocene lakes. He gives special attention to the second largest of the three, Gosiute Lake, which at its greatest extent inundated an area of about 31,000 square kilometers (12,000 square miles) in southwestern Wyoming. His reconstruction reveals that the region had an annual rainfall of perhaps 75 to 100 centimeters (30 to 40 inches) and a mean annual temperature of 16–21°C (60–70°F). Thus, the climate was warm and relatively moist; but evaporation was high, and for long intervals the lakes had no outlets. Dissolved salts accumulated in the lake waters, and a chemical, and later a thermal, stratification developed. Carbonates of sodium, calcium, and calcium-magnesium were precipitated, and below the stagnant anaerobic hypolimnion at the center of the lakes, there formed the thick accumulations of annually layered calcareous muds rich in organic matter that now constitute our greatest deposit of oil shale. Biological productivity was high: many well-preserved fossils are found among the lake sediments, including fish that died in great numbers when anaerobic bottom waters were brought to the surface, as a result, perhaps, of sudden turnover due to surface chilling, or of upwelling to replace surface waters blown away from coastal areas by persistent strong winds. Bradley concludes with a discussion of annual layering in the lake sediments, and a lively reconstruction of the paleolimnology of the smaller of the three lakes (in Fossil Syncline in western Wyoming).

For a final illustration of the bearing of classical stratigraphy on historical geology—with an emphasis on tectonic history and paleogeography—we turn to a paper by W. P. Woodring, "Caribbean Land and Sea Through the Ages" (Reading Selection 54), Woodring's presidential address to the Geological Society of America. Woodring reveals this mobile intercontinental region as one where Late Jurassic and Cretaceous geosynclinal sediments and thick (and mainly pyroclastic) Cretaceous volcanics rest on deformed and metamorphosed Paleozoic rocks, are themselves deformed and intruded by dioritic plutons, and are succeeded upward by a variety of Cenozoic deposits. Some of the Cenozoic deposits are thin and limited in areal extent; others are extensive, transgressive, and in places thick. He shows, by elimination, that the only possible source for the great mass of Cretaceous volcanics observed along the northern, western, and southern borders of the region is beneath the Caribbean Sea. Contrary to premises widely held in 1954, therefore, much of what is now beneath the Caribbean Sea was land during the Cretaceous and even into the Eocene. Renewed deformation at the end of the Oligocene and in the early Miocene tapered off in the later Miocene and then reached a climax during the Pliocene and early Pleistocene. This established the present structural pattern of the region, including, finally, the Panamanian bridge between North and South America (see Woodring, 1966, in the Supplemental Reading). Of the large transcurrent faults that have been hypothesized for the region, the likelyhood of the existence of the one south of Cuba is supported; but that of the one held to have moved Jamaica and southern Haiti more than 800 km eastward to their present locations is not, because of similarities in the Cretaceons and Tertiary geology of Jamaica and northern Haiti. Big questions remain, however, about the precise geochronologic relations of the five recognized episodes of late Paleozoic to early Miocene granitic and dioritic intrusion with the sedimentary, volcanic, and metamorphic record—as well as about the anomalous combination of positive gravity anomalies and deep water in the Caribbean Sea and the Gulf of Mexico, and about the peculiar tectonic morphology of Central America. The unraveling of the geologic history of the Caribbean is only beginning, Woodring maintains. Many unsolved problems await cooperative studies by geologists and geophysicists, in the framework of new concepts of tectonic history.

No one can have read this far without realizing that orogeny and other aspects of diastrophism are important factors in earth history. Diastrophism, indeed, has important effects on, or is in some way related to, nearly all aspects of earth history. Early efforts to subdivide geologic time depended heavily on the identification of gaps in the record related to depression of sea level or uplift followed by nondeposition or erosion. Present concepts are less simplistic, but it is appropriate, nevertheless, to conclude Section VII with a paper on Phanerozoic diastrophism and tectonics by the late E. B. Bailey, master tectonician and former director of the Geological Survey of Great Britain (Reading Selection 55). Bailey's contribution, here titled "Switzerland and the Prealps," comprises Chapters 3 and 6 of his book *Tectonic Essays—Mainly Alpine*. Bailey paints a clear and exuberant word picture of the Alpine tectonic terrane and history, starting with the Jura mountains and then moving south across the Swiss Plain to the Prealps. The Juras are the type region of the Jurassic System, magnificently displayed in the open folds of this great, detached overthrust, or, more likely, gravity-slid mass. The Triassic beneath never appears in the Jura folds. Thus it is believed to constitute the unfolded sliding surface over which the Jurassic rocks crumpled up during Tertiary time, like a wrinkled carpet slipping northward over a smooth floor. The Prealps lie on the border between France and Switzerland, overlooking Lake Geneva. They are of ages similar to the rocks that surround them, but of totally different rock types. The Prealps epitomize Alpine structure and lithology: The contrasting sedimentary facies show that the Prealpine mass is "an erratic 120 km long and 40 broad," consisting of a piled-up succession of detached tectonic sheets, or nappes, that have moved to their present positions from successively greater distances to the south. Bailey's vivid prose brings life to the concepts of flysch, molasse, klippen, and nappes. What is more important, however, is the sweeping picture Bailey presents of the successively detached, piled-up, and isolated sheets of rock (of similar ages but of contrasting facies) stacked during Tertiary Alpine folding. The detail of place names will help the interested reader to follow the discussion on the accompanying or other maps and sections, but is not essential to an understanding of the central points.

Had there been room for one more discussion to round out this sampling of Phanerozoic history, I would have chosen one on the subject of turbidity currents, whose transporting powers explain the presence, throughout the geologic record, not only of coarse clastics interbedded with pelagic sediments, but also of the surface markings and internal structures of flysch-facies sediments. The classic paper on turbidity currents by Kuenen and Migliorini (1950), which established that liberating concept as a valid mechanism, is listed under Supplemental Reading. The compendium edited by R. D. Russell (1951), also listed, contains a number of important papers on the subject—including, notably, a useful study by H. W. Menard and J. C. Ludwick that considers the suspension mechanism, transporting capacity, and origin of several different types of density currents, and their possible significance in interpreting the geologic record. The subject of turbidity currents leads into the wide realm of flysch-facies sedimentation and the interpretation of sole-markings and internal structures among the flysch clastics—a subject of publication so extensive as to warrant a separate course of study (see Dzulynski and Walton, 1965, in the Supplemental Reading). Here, however, it must suffice to draw attention to the value of turbidity current mechanics in interpreting many of the thick and monotonous geosynclinal sequences that account for so much of the sedimentary record.

Supplemental Reading

In addition to the papers listed below and in the bibliographies of the preceding papers, certain general references will be useful to the student in locating further reading along any line of interest and in developing research exercises. They include the well-known bibliographies and lexicons of stratigraphic names published by the U.S. Geological Survey for North America, and by the Geological Society of America and the Centre Nationale de Récherches Scientifique for the rest of the world. Of special value are the various correlation charts for North American stratigraphy published in the Bulletin of the Geological Society of America between 1944 and 1960, and available for purchase individually from GSA headquarters in Boulder, Colorado. Publications of the U.S. Geological Survey may be ordered from the U.S. Government Printing Office in Washington, D.C., or from one of its branch offices.

Adams, J. E., and H. N. Frenzel, 1950, Capitan barrier reef, Texas and New Mexico: Jour. Geology, v. 58, p. 289–312.

Axelrod, D. J., 1957, Late Tertiary floras and the Sierra Nevada uplift: Geol. Soc. America Bull., v. 68, p. 19–46.

Billings, M. P., 1950, Stratigraphy and the study of metamorphic rocks: Geol. Soc. America Bull., v. 61, p. 435–448.

———, 1960, Diastrophism and mountain building: Geol. Soc. America Bull., v. 71, p. 363–398.

Bradley, W. H., 1929, The varves and climate of the Green River epoch: U.S. Geol. Survey Prof. Paper 158-E, p. 87–110.

Briggs, Garrett, and L. M. Cline, 1967, Paleocurrents and source areas of late Paleozoic sediments of the Ouachita Mountains, southeastern Oklahoma: Jour. Sed. Petrology, v. 37, p. 985–1000.

Buddington, A. F., 1959, Granite emplacement with special reference to North America: Geol. Soc. America Bull., v. 70, p. 671–748.

Cline, L. M., 1960, Late Paleozoic rocks of the Ouachita Mountains: Oklahoma Geol. Survey Bull. 85, 113 p.

Cloud, P. E., Jr., and V. E. Barnes, 1948, The Ellenburger group of central Texas: Univ. Texas Pub. 4621, 473 p.

Cooper, G. A., 1930, Stratigraphy of the Hamilton group of New York, pts. 1, 2: Am. Jour. Sci., v. 19, p. 116–134, 214–236.

Dunbar, C. O., 1940, The type Permian—its classification and correlation: Am. Assoc. Petroleum Geologists Bull., v. 24, p. 237–281.

Dzulynski, Stanislaw, and E. K. Walton, 1965 Sedimentary features of flysch and greywackes: New York, American Elsevier, 274 p.

Fischer, A. G., 1964, The Lofer cyclothems of the Alpine Triassic: Kansas Geol. Survey Bull. 169, p. 107–149.

Frye, J. C., and A. B. Leonard, 1967, Buried soils, fossil mollusks, and late Cenozoic environments: Univ. Kansas Dept. Geology Spec. Pub. 2, p. 429–444.

Gignoux, Maurice, 1955, Stratigraphic geology (translated by G. G. Woodford): San Francisco, W. H. Freeman and Company, 682p. [From Maurice Gignoux, 1950, Géologie stratigraphique (4th ed.): Paris, Masson et Cie, 735 p.]

Gill, J. R., and W. A. Cobban, 1966, The Red Bird section of the upper Cretaceous Pierre shale in Wyoming: U.S. Geol. Survey Prof. Paper 393-A, 73 p.

Gilluly, James, 1949, Distribution of mountain building in geologic time: Geol. Soc. America Bull., v. 60, p. 561–590.

Harshbarger, J. W., C. A. Repenning, and J. H. Irwin, 1957, Stratigraphy of the uppermost Triassic and Jurassic rocks of the Navajo country: U.S. Geol. Survey Prof. Paper 291, 74 p.

Hunt, C. B., Paul Averitt, and R. L. Miller, 1953, Geology of the Henry Mountains region, Utah: U.S. Geol. Survey Prof. Paper 228, 234 p.

Huxley, T. H., 1967, On a piece of chalk (ed. by Loren Eiseley): New York, Charles Scribner's Sons, 90 p. (Reprint of 1868 essay, with an introduction and annotations by the editor, and illustrations by Rudolf Freund.)

King, P. B., 1950, Tectonic framework of southeastern United States: Am. Assoc. Petroleum Geologists Bull., v. 34, p. 635–671.

Knopf, Adolph, 1957, The Boulder bathylith of Montana: Am. Jour. Sci., v. 255, p. 81–103.

———, 1960, Analysis of some recent geosynclinal theory: Am. Jour. Sci., v. 258-A, p. 126–136.

Krynine, P. D., 1950, Petrology, stratigraphy, and origin of the Triassic sedimentary rocks of Connecticut: Connecticut Geol. Nat. History Survey Bull. 73, 247 p.

Kuenen, P. H., and C. J. Migliorini, 1950, Turbidity currents as a cause of graded bedding: Jour. Geology, v. 58, p. 91–127.

Kuenen, P. H., and J. E. Sanders, 1956, Sedimentation phenomena in Kulm and Flozleeres graywackes, Sauerland and Oberharz, Germany: Am. Jour. Sci., v. 254, p. 649–671.

Kummel, Bernhard, 1961, History of the earth: San Francisco, W. H. Freeman and Company, 610 p.

Ladd, H. S., ed., 1957, Paleoecology (v. 2, Treatise on marine ecology and paleoecology): Geol. Soc. America Memoir 67, 1077 p.

Landes, K. K., G. M. Ehlers, and G. M. Stanley, 1945, Geology of the Mackinac Straits region: Michigan Geol. Survey Publ. 44, 204 p.

Lapworth, Charles, 1879, On the tripartite classification of the lower Paleozoic rocks: Geol. Mag. [Great Britain], n. s., v. 6, no. 1, p. 1–15.

Lecompte, Marius, 1957, Les récifs Dévoniens de la Belgique: Soc. geol. France Bull., 6 ser., v. 7, p. 1045–1068.

Lowenstam, H. A., 1950, Niagaran reefs in the Great Lakes area: Jour. Geology, v. 58, p. 430–487.

McKee, E. D., and others, 1956, Paleotectonic maps of the Jurassic System: U.S. Geol. Survey Misc. Geol. Inv. Map I-175, a folio of 9 map sheets with text.

———, 1959, Paleotectonic maps of the Triassic System: U.S. Geol. Survey Misc. Geol. Inv. Map I-300, a folio of 8 map sheets with text.

———, 1967a, Paleotectonic investigations of the Permian System in the United States: U.S. Geol. Survey Prof. Paper 515, 271 p.

———, 1967b, Paleotectonic maps of the Permian System: U.S. Geol. Survey Misc. Geol. Inv. Map I-450, a folio of 20 map sheets with text.

Newell, N. D., J. K. Rigby, A. G. Fischer, A. J. Whiteman, J. E. Hickox, and J. S. Bradley, 1953, The Permian reef complex of the Guadalupe Mountains region, Texas and New Mexico: San Francisco, W. H. Freeman and Company, 236 p.

Pepper, J. R., Wallace de Witt, Jr., and D. F. Desmarest, 1954, Geology of the Bedford shale and Beria sandstone in the Appalachian basin: U.S. Geol. Survey Prof. Paper 259, 111 p.

Pettijohn, F. J., and P. E. Potter, 1964, Atlas and glossary of primary sedimentary structures: New York, Springer-Verlag New York, 370 p.

Potter, P. E., and F. J. Pettijohn, 1963, Paleocurrents and basin analysis: New York, Springer-Verlag New York, 296 p.

Robinson, G. D., and others, 1964, Philmont country—the rocks and landscape of a famous New Mexico ranch: U.S. Geol. Survey Prof. Paper 505, 152 p.

Rodgers, John, 1949, Evolution of thought on structure of middle and southern Appalachians: Am. Assoc. Petroleum Geologists Bull., v. 33, p. 1643–1654.

Ross, R. J., Jr., 1964, Relations of Middle Ordovician time and rock units in Basin Ranges, western United States: Am. Assoc. Petroleum Geologists Bull., v. 48, p. 1526–1554.

Russell, R. D., ed., 1951, Turbidity currents and the transportation of coarse sediments to deep water—a symposium: Soc. Econ. Paleontologists and Mineralogists Spec. Pub. 2, 107 p.

Stegner, Wallace, 1962, Beyond the hundredth meridian: Boston, Houghton Mifflin, 438 p.

Størmer, Leif, 1967, Some aspects of the Caledonian geosyncline and foreland west of the Baltic Sheld: Geol. Soc. London Quart. Jour., v. 123, p. 183–214.

Trümpy, Rudolf, 1960, Paleotectonic evolution of the central and western Alps: Geol. Soc. America Bull., v. 71, p. 843–908.

Williams, Howel, 1941, Crater Lake, the story of its origin: Berkeley, Calif., University of California Press, 97 p.

Woodford, A. O., 1965, Historical geology: San Francisco, W. H. Freeman and Company, 512 p.

Woodring, W. P., 1966, The Panama land bridge as a sea barrier: Am. Philos. Soc. Proc., v. 110, no. 6, p. 425–433.

Woodring, W. P., M. N. Bramlette, and W. S. W. Kew, 1946, Geology and paleontology of Palos Verdes Hills, California: U.S. Geol. Survey Prof. Paper 207, 145 p.

46

The Clastic Sequence Basal to the Cambrian System

in the Central and Southern Appalachians

JOHN RODGERS
1956

From *El sistema cámbrico: su paleogeographía y el problema de su base,* vol. II, pp. 385–386, 403–413. 20th International Geological Congress (Mexico, 1956), 1956. [Stratigraphic sections deleted.] Reprinted with permission of the author.

The known Cambrian rocks of the Valley and Ridge province in the Central and Southern Appalachians (Figure 46.1) are underlain along the western front of the Blue Ridge province, wherever the section is not interrupted by faults, by a sequence of clastic rocks —quartzite, siltstone, shale, arkose, conglomerate, and greywacke (also in places volcanic rocks), or their metamorphosed equivalents—ranging in thickness from a few hundred feet to several miles. The top layers of this clastic sequence contain Lower Cambrian fossils (olenellids, inarticulate brachiopods) in many places, but the rest is almost entirely barren; thus their age is in doubt. The top of the clastic sequence is remarkably sharp and therefore serves as a very convenient boundary between the largely carbonate deposits [above] and the clastic sequence [below], but it is *not* the base of the Cambrian System, for at least some beds below it are certainly Cambrian and a great but quite indeterminate thickness may well be.

In many places along the Appalachian chain from New Jersey to Tennessee, and indeed probably everywhere that structure permits us to observe its base, the clastic sequence here discussed rests with profound unconformity on highly metamorphosed, commonly granitoid, gneisses. These rocks are cut by pegmatites containing radioactive minerals that have yielded several absolute age determinations, some as high as 800 million years (Rodgers, 1952, p. 421), and they are certainly Precambrian. Recognizing this unconformity has proved difficult in many areas, however, especially where the rocks above are also metamorphosed; in the Blue Ridge of Maryland and northern Virginia, for example, these gneisses were interpreted as intrusive until comparatively recently (the unconformity is now accepted by all who have done detailed work in the area—Jonas and Stose, 1939; King, 1950; Cloos, and others, 1951; Reed, 1955).

Using lithologic criteria of correlation (since paleontologic criteria are lacking), we can attempt to trace the rock units in this clastic sequences across the Blue Ridge province and, at least from Pennsylvania to Virginia, into the Piedmont province. The farther east we penetrate, however—what with the greater distance from established sections, the increased likelihood of facies changes, the more complicated structure, and especially the greater metamorphism—the less certain and the more controversial the correlations become. Finally we are left with no more than vague suggestions of correlations, which to one geologist hint that a large part of the crystalline schists in the Piedmont are Cambrian or even younger, and to another seem quite irrelevant. . . .

CHILHOWEE GROUP AND PRESUMED EQUIVALENTS

In most areas [of the middle and southern Appalachians, the upper division of the basal clastics], the Chilhowee group, falls fairly naturally into three divisions; as a gross generalization, these divisions (counting from the top down) are characterized respectively by quartzite, shale, and conglomerate. Each of these rock types can be found, however, in each of the three divisions, and the generalization is only schematic.

The upper division, characterized by the presence of clean vitreous quartzite, generally light-colored and thick-bedded and containing *Scolithus*, averages perhaps 800 feet thick; it is thicker in East Tennessee and thinner in Pennsylvania (Hardyston, Antietam, Erwin, Hesse-Nebo, and Weisner quartzites). In some areas most of the division is quartzite, but elsewhere, particularly where the whole clastic sequence is especially thick, such quartzite though prominent is subordinate in amount to darker silty and shaly rocks or their metamorphosed equivalents. In southeast Pennsylvania and northeast Tennessee, the evidence suggests that the proportion of clean white quartzite increases northwestward across the original basin of deposition (the position of sections in Tennessee has been altered by the large-scale thrust faulting), though the thickness of the whole sequence generally decreases in that direction. The uppermost 100 feet or so of the division in virtually every section is less quartzitic—either silty and shaly or calcareous or both—and contains at least a few olenellid trilobites and inarticulate brachiopods; this part is called the Helenmode member of the Erwin and Hesse formations in Tennessee, and could probably be separated elsewhere if exposures permitted. The same kinds of fossils have also been found deeper in the sequence at a few places, but so far only within the quartzitic division of the Chilhowee group.

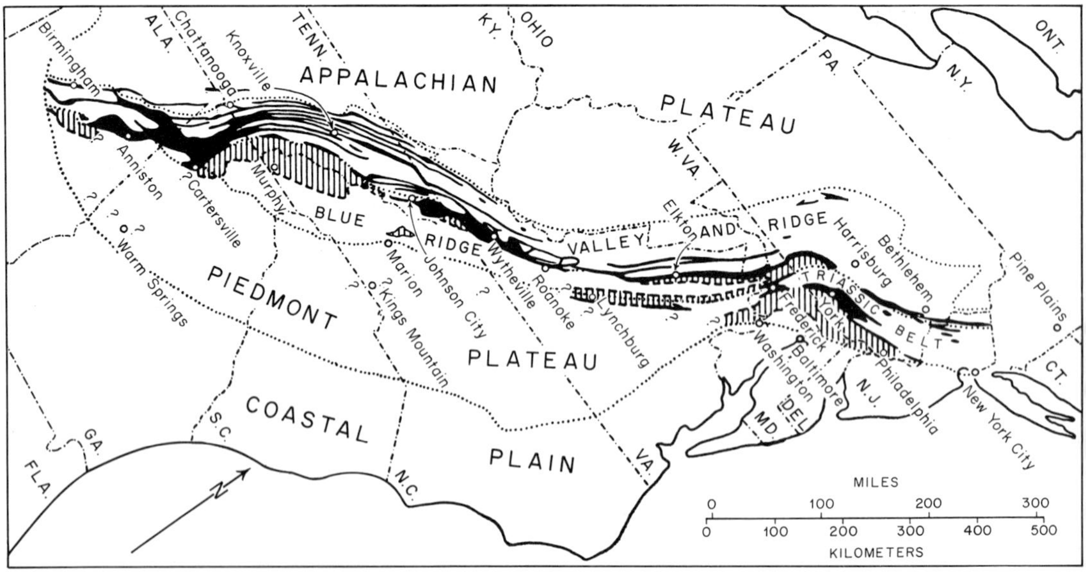

FIGURE 46.1
Index map of the Central and Southern Appalachians. Shows outcrop areas of Cambrian rocks (*solid*) and of the larger bodies of doubtfully Cambrian rocks (*vertical ruling*).

Beneath the quartzitic division in most sections comes a more shaly division (Harpers, Hampton and Nichols formations). It is nowhere pure shale, however; clay shale is generally rare, and most of the rock is silty shale and siltstone, with some quartzite as well in most areas. Commonly the quartzite forms distinct groups of layers in the middle of the division, which locally rank as members. In the Montalto member of the Harpers in the Blue Ridge of southern Pennsylvania and Maryland, the quartzite is as pure and well sorted as in the overlying Antietam, but elsewhere the quartzite is either dark with magnetite or hematite or else distinctly feldspathic. *Scolithus* is not uncommon in these quartzite layers, whether feldspathic or not.

The top of the shaly division is probably not exactly the same age everywhere (it probably becomes older northwestward as more quartzite appears), and the bottom is almost certainly not. The thickness of the division ranges from 500 to 3000 feet; it is generally thickest where the clastic sequence as a whole is thickest. Some of this great variation in thickness may indicate different rates of deposition in different areas, but much of it is probably simply the result of lateral facies change from the shaly rocks into the coarser rocks assigned to the underlying division, along the margins of the subsiding basin.

Under the shaly division the rocks are generally coarser again, and in most areas they include prominent conglomerate layers, though other rock types generally predominate (Chickies, Weverton, Unicoi, and Cochran formations). In general, also, this division is much more variable, both from one area to another and within any one area or section. In several areas quartzite (generally somewhat feldspathic) is prominent in the upper part, whereas the lower part contains a mixture of poorly sorted rocks—conglomerate, arkose, feldspathic siltstone and shale. Thin layers of volcanic rocks are also present in several areas from Maryland to northeasternmost Tennessee. The beds range in thickness from a few hundred to a few thousand feet, and there is little doubt that they represent not a contemporaneous unit but a transgressive facies, thickest and oldest where the whole clastic sequence is thickest, and becoming thinner and younger toward the margins of the subsiding basin. In southeastern Pennsylvania, where the whole sequence is relatively thin, this division is especially quartzitic (and contains *Scolithus*); near the east edge of Pennsylvania and in New Jersey, the three-fold division elsewhere apparent disappears, and the clastic sequence is represented by only a few hundred feet of nearly pure quartzite, slightly feldspathic and conglomeratic at the base. Thus the Hardyston quartzite of New Jersey and the "Chickies" quartzite near Philadelphia are probably equivalent mainly to the Antietam and part of the Harpers farther west; the Chickies of the type area beneath these units is probably equivalent to the lower Harpers and perhaps part of the Weverton in the Blue Ridge; and the Weverton of the Blue Ridge is probably equivalent to the lower Hampton and only the uppermost Unicoi of northeast Tennessee.

ROCKS BENEATH THE CHILHOWEE GROUP

In New Jersey and the eastern part of Pennsylvania, the rocks just discussed rest directly on the gneissic basement, but from York County, Penna., well into Virginia, they are separated from the basement by a group of volcanic rocks. In most of this area the bulk of the volcanic mass is the Catoctin greenstone evidently formed mainly from a thick pile of andesitic or basaltic flows, but associated with it are altered basic tuffs, acid tuffs, and rhyolite flows. In Virginia, an upper layer (Loudoun formation) and a basal layer (Swift Run formation) consist almost entirely of the acid tuffs (now largely purplish, varicolored, or spotted sericite slate or phyllite) mixed with arkosic materials; in Pennsylvania, acid flows and tuffs form a large part of the main mass as well.

The volcanic group as a separate unit disappears southward between Elkton and Lynchburg; on the west side of the Blue Ridge the Chilhowee group rests on the basement again, but on the east side the thick metasedimentary Lynchburg gneiss is intercalated. Finally, in southwest Virginia and extending a few miles into the adjacent corners of North Carolina and Tennessee, a pile of acid volcanics with a few sedimentary layers (Mt. Rogers volcanic group) holds the same position.

The fairly abrupt thinning to disappearance of these volcanic groups at the ends of their outcrop belts has led to the suggestion that they are unconformably truncated by the overlying Chilhowee group. The thinning may merely record the original edges of the volcanic piles, however, and the similarity of the sedimentary rocks in the volcanic groups to those in the Chilhowee group and the presence of volcanic rocks in the lower part of the Chilhowee group through this same area imply that there was no significant hiatus.

Southwest of Johnson City, sedimentary rocks appear again beneath the Chilhowee group, and these thicken rapidly southwestward to the Great Smoky Mountains area southeast of Knoxville, where not less than 3 miles of pre-Chilhowee rocks are present in each of several thrust sheets. Collectively these rocks are called the Ocoee group, but the interrelations of the various sequences in the different thrust sheets are still not clear; it is even possible that the upper beds in some are as young as the Chilhowee group. Certain parts of the group (notably the Great Smoky formation) include vast thicknesses of graded beds composed of graywacke, graywacke conglomerate, siltstone, and silty shale, or their metamorphosed equivalents; other parts (Pigeon, Wilhite, and Sandsuck formations, and upper part of Snowbird formation) are mostly fine-grained or with only local bodies of arkose or coarse conglomerate; in still other parts (some of Snowbird formation) better sorted rocks appear, including feldspathic siltstone, arkose, and feldspathic or calcareous sandstone. Taken as a whole, however, the Ocoee rocks show every sign of very rapid deposition with a minimum of sorting.

POSSIBLY EQUIVALENT SEQUENCES IN THE PIEDMONT

The stratigraphic position of the Chilhowee group, the volcanic group, and even the Ocoee group is fairly clear; they lie between the Cambrian carbonate rocks of the Valley and Ridge province and a Precambrian basement of gneiss and granitoid rocks. But there are several possibly related sequences in the western Piedmont whose position is less clear. In Maryland the Glenarm group lies beneath the possibly Upper Ordovician Peach Bottom slate and above a basal Baltimore gneiss; the Wissahickon may be roughly equivalent to the Antietam-Harpers-Chickies sequence to the north, but the correlation is certainly not secure. In Virginia, the Lynchburg gneiss appears to include at its top an equivalent of the Catoctin greenstone, and it underlies the Evington group, whose age is also uncertain, though the Candler phyllite may be roughly equivalent to the Chilhowee group and the higher Archer Creek formation includes limestone that may be equivalent to the Upper Cambrian Frederick limestone. In Alabama, the lower part of the Talladega series underlies middle Paleozoic beds, and at least its lowest part underlies the Weisner quartzite, which is presumably equivalent to the upper part of the Chilhowee group. All these sequences are now metamorphosed to phyllite, schist, or gneiss, and are of great but largely indeterminate thickness, on the order perhaps of ten to twenty thousand feet. The only sequence of known stratigraphic position whose thickness approaches this figure is the Ocoee group, which also merges southeastward into schists; it is tempting therefore to see all these thick sequences as roughly correlative, vastly thickened southeastern representatives of the basal clastic sequence beneath the Cambrian carbonate rocks, It is also possible, however, that the upper parts of some of these sequences (Peters Creek schist; upper part of Evington group; sequence around Murphy, N.C.; Wash Creek slate) are equivalent to part of the carbonate sequence.

If these sequences in the western Piedmont are actually equivalent to the basal clastic sequence, then much of the schist and gneiss deeper in the Piedmont might be also, but here we have no evidence to bring to bear one way or the other.

POSSIBLE RECONSTRUCTION OF PALEOGEOGRAPHY

About all that can be said for certain about the paleogeography of the central and southern Appalachians before the beginning of the main period of Cambrian carbonate deposition is that the basement subsided unevenly to accommodate a thick mass of clastic sediments, with some volcanics in the middle part of the area. We may surmise however that subsidence at first took the form of a deep trough, in the present western Piedmont from southeastern Pennyslvania to central Alabama; in this trough great quantities of clastic sediment were deposited pell-mell, now coarse and now fine. The sediment was presumably eroded from rapidly rising highlands; unfortunately we have little direct evidence as to the location of the highlands, but it is easier to imagine them along the southeast side of the trough (where we know nothing) than along the northwest side where the Chilhowee group or younger Cambrian rocks transgressed a little later across the apparently stable platform of the center of the continent. The prevailingly dark color of the rocks and the presence of lenticular bodies of carbonate rock in the finer-grained units suggest marine deposition, and the graded bedding in the Great Smoky conglomerate indicates that turbidity currents helped to distribute the sediments part of the time in part of the area. Other parts of the Ocoee sequence were deposited by more "ordinary" bottom currents, however. The eastern border of the trough is completely indefinite; the western border lay at first within the present Blue Ridge province or in the extreme western Piedmont except in East Tennessee (and perhaps locally farther south) where it pushed out toward the edge of the Valley and Ridge province. Along the western margin of the trough, two thick piles of volcanics accumulated, a widespread largely andesitic or basaltic pile in Maryland and adjacent Virginia and Pennsylvania, and a more restricted rhyolitic pile in southwest Virginia and adjacent North Carolina and Tennessee; these piles pinched out westward on the basement and eastward into the mass of accumulating sediments.

About this time, however, the original trough became fairly well filled up, and sediments lapped northwestward out of it onto the basement in the southeastern part of the present Valley and Ridge (and perhaps all across it); apparently the rate of deposition also slowed down, for sorting became slowly better, fragments were rounded somewhat, and cross-bedding was produced. The first sediments were everywhere partly conglomeratic; thereafter finer material spread over the area, perhaps because the supply of sediment also was decreasing. Finally as conditions became more and more stabilized, really thorough reworking of the material began, first at the northwest and then working its way southeastward, producing clean quartz sand. The sand was not only well sorted but well rounded; in some of it cross-bedding was produced, in some worms lived in profusion, riddling it with myriads of tubes. Certainly it was deposited in shallow water with fairly strong currents; perhaps much of it was reworked on beaches. In any case animals (trilobites and brachiopods) now found it possible to colonize the bottom. Shortly thereafter terrigenous sediment ceased to enter the area at all, or at least to be deposited there; the change may have been rather sudden for lime-mud appears to have replaced sand abruptly throughout the entire region.

AGE ASSIGNMENT OF THE BASAL CLASTIC SEQUENCE

The topmost beds of the basal clastic sequence here discussed are certainly Cambrian, and the main problem in age assignment is to determine how to classify the underlying beds and where to draw the base of the Cambrian System. If we analyze what is meant by calling certain rocks in North America Cambrian, however, we find that we can only mean that they are of the same age as rocks called Cambrian in some standard sequence—in Wales or, as the basal part of the system is evidently poorly represented there, some other standard area. But we can judge of this equivalence from Wales, or elsewhere, to North America only by means of fossils; practically therefore Cambrian rocks are those of the same age as rocks that contain organized fossils such as *Olenellus, Archeocyathus, Hyolithes, Salterella, Obolella,* or their relatives or descendents (such imprint fossils as *Scolithus* and cryptozoon are deliberately ignored).

Now organized fossils appear in the Central and Southern Appalachians only as low as the quartzitic division at the top of the Chilhowee group, in the Hardyston, Antietam, Erwin, Hesse, Murray, and Weisner formations; hence only these rocks are certainly Cambrian. But we do not know that similar animals were not living elsewhere at an earlier time, while the underlying layers of the basal clastic sequence were being deposited; indeed it is highly probable that they were. The Lower Cambrian fossils in the Appalachians show little variety, except in certain privileged beds close to the top of the series (the Parker slate of Vermont, the Kinzers formation of Pennsylvania, and the fossiliferous beds near Austinville, Virginia), and it seems likely that they represent only the later stages in the development of Lower Cambrian life, to judge from the long and complex record known in some other areas, notably the Anti-Atlas Mountains of Morocco (Hupé, 1952). In the Appalachians conditions of deposition prior to the deposition of the quartzitic division were probably inhospitable to bottom life so that the animals were excluded. At least the upper part of the basal clastic sequence, therefore, though not certainly Cambrian, is probably Cambrian.

The base of the Chilhowee group and its equivalents is probably not the same age everywhere, even where it rests on older sediments or volcanics; nevertheless it appears to record a change from the deposition of volcanics or largely unsorted sediments to the deposition of somewhat better sorted sediments. King (1949) has emphasized this change, which he considers should mark the base of the Cambrian System in the Appalachians; he thinks it was fairly abrupt and cites evidence of disconformity in certain areas (see also the evidence cited by Rodgers, 1953, p. 27, 29). Other workers in the same areas minimize these breaks, however, in view of the close similarities between some of the rock types, both volcanic and sedimentary, above and below.

The writer agrees with King that a change in the rocks takes place at or near this boundary, which may represent a change in the shape of the basin of deposition, but he believes that the change was a gradual one. In any case it is highly unlikely that this change was produced at the same time that hard-shelled organisms capable of leaving organized fossils first appeared in Morocco or wherever the oldest such fossils may be, the only meaning the writer can attach to the statement that this boundary marks the base of the Cambrian. On the other hand, the existence of the change does make a difference in the degree of probability with which we can speak of the age of the beds above and below. The beds above are intimately associated with the overlying beds known to be Cambrian, and hence they are probably Cambrian; the beds below are less intimately associated, and hence they are only dubiously Cambrian and may instead be Precambrian. We cannot know, of course, or even infer with any certainty, but we can surmise, and our terminology should be chosen if possible to express both our degree of knowledge and acceptable inference and our best guess. Accordingly, the writer proposes the following scheme of age designations for the clastic sequence basal to the Cambrian System in the Appalachians:

Cambrian The upper beds of the Chilhowee group and equivalent units, down to the lowest beds containing fossils; i.e. much of the Antietam, Erwin, and Weisner formations, the Hardyston and Hesse quartzites, and at least part of the Murray shale.

Cambrian (?) The rest of the Chilhowee group, the Evington group, and the sequence around Murphy.

Cambrian or Precambrian The Catoctin greenstone with the Loudoun and Swift Run formations, the Mt. Rogers volcanic group, and the Ocoee group. Also the Glenarm group, the Lynchburg gneiss, and the lower part of the Talladega group, and the bulk of the crystalline schists of the Piedmont province, especially the metasedimentary rocks of the Kings Mountain and Warm Springs belts.

Precambrian The gneisses and granitoid rocks beneath the basal clastic sequence, including the Baltimore gneiss, especially those dated by radioactivity at more than 550 million years.

REFERENCES

Adams, G. I., 1926, The crystalline rocks: Alabama Geol. Survey Spec. Rept. 14, p. 25–40.

Bascom, Florence, W. B. Clark, and others, 1909, Description of the Philadelphia district: U.S. Geol. Survey Geol. Atlas, Folio 162.

Bascom, Florence, and G. W. Stose, 1938, Geology and mineral resources of the Honeybrook and Phoenixville quadrangles, Pennsylvania: U.S. Geol. Survey Bull. 891.

Bascom, Florence, E. T. Wherry, G. W. Stose, and A. I. Jones, 1931, Geology and mineral resources of the Quakertown-Doylestown district, Pennsylvania and New Jersey: U.S. Geol. Survey Bull. 828.

Bloomer, R. O., and R. R. Bloomer, 1947, The Catoctin formation in central Virginia: Jour. Geology, v. 55, p. 94–106.

Bloomer, R. O., and H. J. Werner, 1955, Geology of the Blue Ridge region in central Virginia: Geol. Soc. America Bull., v. 66, p. 579–606.

Brown, W. R., 1953, Structural framework and mineral resources of the Virginia Piedmont: Kentucky Geol. Survey Spec. Pub. 1, p. 38–111.

Butts, Charles, 1926, The Paleozoic rocks: Alabama Geol. Survey Spec. Rept. 14, p. 41–230.

———, 1940, Description of the Montevallo and Columbiana quadrangles: U.S. Geol. Survey Geol. Atlas, Folio 226.

Clarke, J. W., 1952, Geology and mineral resources of the Thomaston quadrangle, Georgia: Georgia Geol. Survey Bull. 59.

Cloos, Ernst, and Anna Hietanen, 1941, Geology of the "Martic overthrust" and the Glenarm series in Pennsylvania and Maryland: Geol. Soc. America Spec. Paper 35.

Cloos, Ernst, and others, 1951, Washington County: Maryland Department of Geology, Mines, and Water Resources.

Crickmay, G. W., 1952, Geology of the crystalline rocks of Georgia: Georgia Geol. Survey Bull. 58.

Espenshade, G. H., 1954, Geology and mineral deposits of the James River–Roanoke River manganese district, Virginia: U.S. Geol. Survey Bull. 1008.

Ferguson, H. W., and Jewell, W. B., 1951, Geology und barite deposits of the Del Rio district, Cocke County, Tennessee: Tennessee Div. Geology Bull. 57.

Furcron, A. S., 1953, Comments on the geology of the Ellijay quadrangle, Georgia–North Carolina–Tennessee: Georgia Geol. Survey Bull. 60, p. 32–40.

Furcron, A. S., and K. H. Teague, 1945, Sillimanite and massive kyanite in Georgia: Georgia Geol. Survey Bull. 51.

Griffin, R. H., 1951, Structure and petrography of the Hillabee sill and associated metamorphic rocks of Alabama: Alabama Geol. Survey Bull. 63.

Hadley, J. B., P. B. King, R. B. Neuman, and Richard Goldsmith, 1955, Outline of the geology of the Great Smoky Mountains area, Tennessee and North Carolina: Guides to southeastern geology, p. 390–427 (Geol. Soc. America, field trip guide, 1955).

Hewett, D. F., and G. W. Crickmay, 1937, The Warm Springs of Georgia, their geologic relations and origin—a summary report: U.S. Geol. Survey Water-Supply Paper 819.

Hupé, Pierre, 1952, Contribution a l'étude du Cambrien inférieur et du Précambrien III de l'Anti-Atlas marocain: Service géol. du Maroc Notes et Mém. 103.

Hurst, V. J., 1955, Stratigraphy, structure, and mineral resources of the Mineral Bluff quadrangle, Georgia: Georgia Geol. Survey Bull. 63.

Jonas, A. I., and G. W. Stose, 1926, Geology and mineral resources of the New Holland quadrangle, Pennsylvania: Pennsylvania Geol. Survey Geol. Atlas, ser. 4, no. 178.

———, 1930, Geology and mineral resources of the Lancaster quadrangle, Pennsylvania: Pennsylvania Geol. Survey Geol. Atlas, ser. 4, no. 168.

———, 1939, Age relations of the pre-Cambrian rocks in the Catoctin Mountain–Blue Ridge and Mount Rogers anticlinoria in Virginia: Am. Jour. Sci., v. 239, p. 575–593.

Kesler, T. L., 1950, Geology and mineral deposits of the Cartersville district, Georgia: U.S. Geol. Survey Prof. Paper 224.

King, P. B., 1949, The base of the Cambrian in the southern Appalachians: Am. Jour. Sci., v. 247, p. 513–530, 622–645.

———, 1950, Geology of the Elkton area, Virginia: U.S. Geol. Survey Prof. Paper 230.

———, 1955, A geologic section across the southern Appalachians—an outline of the geology in the segment in Tennessee, North Carolina, and South Carolina: Guides to southeastern geology, p. 332–373 (Geol. Soc. America, field trip guide, 1955).

King, P. B., H. W. Ferguson, L. C. Craig, and John Rodgers, 1944, Geology and manganese deposits of northeastern Tennessee: Tennessee Div. Geology Bull. 52.

Knopf, E. B., and A. I. Jonas, 1929a, Geology of the McCalls Ferry–Quarryville district, Pennsylvania: U.S. Geol. Survey Bull. 799.

———, 1929b, The geology of the crystalline rocks of Baltimore County: Maryland Department of Geology, Mines, and Water Resources, p. 97–199.

Lewis, J. V., and H. B. Kümmel, 1940, The geology of New Jersey: New Jersey Dept. Conserv. Devel. Geology Ser. Bull. 50.

Ludlum, J. C., 1940, Continuity of the Hardyston formation in the vicinity of Philipsburg, New Jersey: New Jersey Dept. Conserv. Devel. Geology Ser. Bull. 47.

Miller, B. L., 1935, Age of the schists of the South Valley Hills, Pennsylvania: Geol. Soc. America Bull., v. 46, p. 715–756.

———, 1939, Northampton County, Pennsylvania: Pennsylvania Geol. Survey Bull., ser. 4, no. C 48.

———, 1941, Lehigh County, Pennsylvania: Pennsylvania Geol. Survey Bull., ser. 4, no. C 39.

Oriel, S. S., 1950, Geology and mineral resources of the Hot Springs window, Madison County, North Carolina: North Carolina Dept. Conserv. Devel. Bull. 60.

Reed, J. C., Jr., 1955, Catoctin formation near Luray, Virginia: Geol. Soc. America Bull., v. 66, p. 871–896.

Rodgers, John, 1952, Absolute ages of radioactive minerals from the Appalachian region: Am. Jour. Sci., v. 250, p. 411–427.

———, 1953, Geologic map of East Tennessee with explanatory text: Tennessee Div. Geology Bull. 58, pt. 2.

Scotford, D. M., 1951, Structure of the Sugarloaf Mountain area, Maryland, as a key to Piedmont stratigraphy: Geol. Soc. America Bull., v. 62, p. 45–75.

Stose, A. J., and G. W. Stose, 1944, Geology of the Hanover–York district, Pennsylvania: U.S. Geol. Survey Prof. Paper 204.

Stose, A. J., G. W., Stose, and others, 1946, Carroll County and Frederick County: Maryland Department of Geology, Mines, and Water Resources.

Stose, G. W., 1909, Description of the Mercersburg–Chambersburg district: U.S. Geol. Survey Geol. Atlas, Folio 170.

———, 1932, Geology and mineral resources of Adams County, Pennsylvania: Pennsylvania Geol. Survey Bull., ser. 4, no. C 1.

Stose, G. W., and Florence Bascom, 1929, Description of the Fairfield and Gettysburg quadrangles: U.S. Geol. Survey Geol. Atlas, Folio 225.

Stose, G. W., and A. I. Jonas, 1933, Geology and mineral resources of the Middletown quadrangle, Pennsylvania: U.S. Geol. Survey Bull. 840.

———, 1939, Geology and mineral resources of York County, Pennsylvania: Pennsylvania Geol. Survey Bull., ser. 4, no. C 67.

Van Horn, E. C., 1948, Talc deposits of the Murphy marble belt: North Carolina Dept. Conserv. Devel. Bull. 56.

Whitaker, J. C., 1955, Geology of Catoctin Mountain, Maryland and Virginia: Geol. Soc. America Bull., v. 66, p. 435–462.

Physical History and Evolution of the Grand Cañon District

C. E. DUTTON
1882

Of the earlier Paleozoic conditions prevailing in the Plateau Province we know as yet but little. Already many perplexing problems have arisen which will require much study to solve, and their solutions promise to be extremely difficult. Within the boundaries of the province exposures of rocks older than the middle Carboniferous are very few and far between. Those which have received attention hitherto are confined to the Uinta Mountains and the lowest deeps of the Grand Cañon [Figure 47.1]. Limiting our attention to the latter region, we find beneath that system of strata which we have thus far treated as Carboniferous a great variety of beds which range in age from the Archæan to the Devonian. Throughout the Kaibab and Sheavwits divisions we find the so-called Carboniferous resting sometimes upon highly metamorphic schists of undoubted Archæan age, sometimes upon the eroded edges of strata which have yielded Cambro-Silurian and Silurian fossils. In a single instance in Kanab Cañon Mr. Walcott found in a similar situation a very limited exposure of beds bearing fossils of Devonian age. In general, the rocks classed as Carboniferous rest upon the Archæan, while the older Paleozoic beds come in only at intervals. The contact is always unconformable and usually in a high degree. The horizontal Carboniferous [actually Cambrian] beds appear to have been laid down upon the surface of a country which had been enormously eroded and afterwards submerged. In the Grand Cañon this single fact is indicated to us throughout the length of a long, narrow, and tortuous cut thousands of feet in depth. But if we pass westward or southward, beyond the limits of the great Carboniferous mass, we find a vast region where a similar state of facts is presented. The Sierra country of central and western Arizona, of Nevada, and western Utah shows remnants of the Carboniferous resting with great unconformity upon older Paleozoic rocks and upon the Archæan.

I have spoken of the great unconformity displayed at the head of the Grand Cañon.

From *Tertiary History of the Grand Cañon District* (USGS Monograph 2), pp. 206–229. United States Geological Survey, 1882.

FIGURE 47.1
Key to the Grand Canyon panorama from Point Sublime. Looking south. *A*, Bill William's Peak; *B*, Tower of Babel; *C*, Colorado River; *F*, Mount Floyd; *G*, Mount Sitgreaves; *I*, Inner Gorge; *TT*, Twin Temples; *WC*, West Cloister. [Approximate modern stratigraphic equivalents for the following units are given in brackets.] *1*, Cherty limestone [Kaibab limestone], 240 feet; 2, Upper Aubrey limestone [Toroweap Formation], 320 feet; 3, Cross-bedded sandstone [Coconino sandstone], 380 feet; *4*, Lower Aubrey sandstones [Permian: part of

Supai Formation under Hermit Shale], 950 feet; 5, Upper Red Wall sandstones [Permian: lower part of Supai Formation], 400 feet; 6, Red Wall limestones [Lower Carboniferous: Redwall Limestone], 1.500 feet; 7, Lower Carboniferous sandstones [Middle Cambrian: Bright Angel Shale and Muav Limestone], 550 feet; 8, Quartzite base of Carboniferous [Lower Cambrian: Tapeats Sandstone], 180 feet; 9, Archaean [pre-Paleozoic].

Probably there is no instance to be found in the world where an unconformity is revealed upon such a magnificent scale, and certainly none amid such impressive surroundings. It is all the more suggestive because it is the type and symbol of a great fact which prevails over a region large enough for an empire. It assures us that in early Silurian time this region received enormous deposits of detritus which were faulted and flexed; that they were afterwards raised above the waters with the accompaniment of volcanic action; that they were ravaged by an erosion commensurate with the grander examples of that process which are proven to have occurred in much later stages of the world's history; and that the region was again submerged.

With the Carboniferous began that long era of deposition which extended without any real break into Tertiary time. The record of each period seems to be complete in the strata, and the deposition was apparently continuous over the area of the Plateau Province taken as a whole, though here and there we may detect evidence of a brief interruption in some small areas. There are some general facts connected with this process of accumulation of strata which merit special notice.

(1) The strata of each and every age were remarkably uniform over very large areas, and were deposited very nearly horizontally. In the interior spaces of the province we never find rapid increments or decrements of the strata. They do indeed vary in thickness, but they vary in the most gradual manner. Around the old shore lines, however, which form the present borders of the Plateau Country, we find the volumes of the strata much larger than elsewhere. But as we depart from them towards the heart of the province, we observe, in the course of two or three leagues, a considerable diminution in their thickness, and thenceforward the attenuation is so slow that we discover it only by comparing correlative sections many leagues apart. Very analogous is the constancy of lithological characters. As we trace the individual beds from place to place, we find their composition to be as persistent as their thickness. The sandstone of a given horizon is always and everywhere a sandstone, the limestone a limestone, the shale a shale. Even the minuter structure of the beds is similarly maintained, and features which are almost abnormal are equally constant. The Jurassic and Triassic sandstones are everywhere cross-bedded after their own marvelous fashion. The singular cherty limestones at the summit of the Carboniferous are quite alike on the brink of the Grand Cañon, at the junction of the Grand and Green rivers, and in the borders of the great Black Mesa at the south. The curious Shinarump conglomerate is the same in Pine Valley Mountains, in the terrace at Kanab, at the base of the Echo Cliffs, and in the Land of the Standing Rocks. The lower Triassic shales and upper Permian shales, with their gorgeous belts of richest colors and beautiful ripple-marks, and with their silicified forests, have hardly varied a band or a tint from the brink of the Sheavwits to the pagoda-buttes of western Colorado. Still there are exceptions. The great Jurassic white sandstone fades out from northwest to southeast, and we are in doubt, at present, whether it failed of deposition or is blended with the Trias. Other members might be mentioned which undergo slow changes from place to place. But such changes are always very gradual. Nowhere have we found thus far what may be called local deposits, or such as are restricted to a narrow belt or contracted area.

All of these strata seem to have been deposited horizontally. Even the base of the Carboniferous has a contact with unconformable rocks beneath, which was but slightly roughened by hills and ridges. In the Kaibab division of the Grand Cañon, while the great body of Carboniferous strata was horizontal, we may observe near the brink of the inner gorge a few bosses of Silurian strata rising higher than the hard quartzitic sandstone which forms the base of the Carboniferous [actually Cambrian]. These are [pre-]Paleozoic hills, which were buried by the growing mass of sediment. But they are of insignificant mass, rarely exceeding two or three hundred feet in height, and do not appear to have ruffled the parallelism of the sandstones and limestones of the massive Red Wall group above them.

(2) Another consideration is as follows: as we pass vertically from one formation to another in the geological series, we observe the same diversity of lithological characters as is

found in other regions. The limestones occur chiefly in the [true] lower Carboniferous, and in very great force. At the summit of the Carboniferous also are 700 to 800 feet of calcareous strata [Permian]. But in the Mesozoic system limestones are rare, and constitute but a very small portion of the volume. By far the greater part of the entire stratigraphic column is sandstone, and the various members of this class show great diversity of texture and composition. Some are excessively hard adamantine quartzites, very many are common sandstones in massy beds. By small gradations these pass into shady shales, containing more or less argillite, and such shales form a large proportion of the bulk of the Permian and Trias. These shales in turn pass into marly beds, which have vast thickness in the Cretaceous and form a considerable portion of the Eocene. Beds of gypsum are also frequent, forming thin separating layers in the shaly divisions, and sulphate of lime is a very important ingredient of the arenaceous strata from the base of the Carboniferous to the summit of the Jurassic. Besides its occurrence in distinct bands of nearly pure gypsum, it plays the part of a cement in the sand rock, and is also richly disseminated in the form of selenite in the sandy shales. On the other hand, there is a marked absence of such rocks as clay-slate. The slaty structure and composition has not hitherto been observed anywhere, so far as I know, and though argillaceous rocks are very voluminous in the Cretaceous they are charged with calcareous matter, and are very distinct from the ordinary clay-slates of the Appalachians.

Thus it will be noted that while the strata are remarkably homogeneous in their horizontal extensions, they are very heterogeneous in vertical range. And this heterogeneity is found not only in the chemical constituents, but also in the texture and in the mechanical properties of hardness, compactness, and solubility. This consideration is an important one, since upon it depends the result which is obtained by the attack of the eroding elements—the architecture of the cliffs and profiles.

(3) Another general fact of importance is, that during the Mesozoic ages the surface of deposition was maintained very nearly at sea-level throughout the entire province. With regard to the Carboniferous strata it does not yet appear that the same was true. From such meager knowledge as we possess, there may be some reason for the opinion that the Carboniferous sea had a considerably greater depth during the earlier and middle portions of that age than during the later portion. The lower Carboniferous strata (Red Wall group) consist chiefly of limestones, and the over-lying lower Aubrey group [see Figure 47.1] corresponding to the coal measures is a series of sandstones of exceedingly fine texture and often gypsiferous. There is a notable absence in these beds of signs of very shallow water, such as ripple marks, cross-bedding, coarse clastic material, and littoral remains, organic or otherwise. The fauna, as usual, is an unsafe guide, and must be regarded as non-committal. On the other hand, there is no reason to suppose that the depth was at all profound. It is rather by contrasting the total absence of the signs of very shallow water with the presence of decisive signs of it in the Mesozoic and Permian, that we are drawn to the inference of somewhat greater marine depths in the early and middle Carboniferous.

In the upper Aubrey series we come upon some indications of shallow water, and from the base of the Permian upwards these are ever present. In the Permian, Trias, and Jura we find instances of those peculiar unconformities by erosion without any unconformity of dip in the beds. Perhaps the most widely spread occurrence of this kind is the contact of the summit of the Permian with the Shinarump conglomerate which forms the base of the Trias. Wherever this horizon is exposed this unconformity is generally manifest. Between the base of the Permian and the summit of the Carboniferous a similar relation has been observed in numerous localities, and there is a similar instance in the lower Trias. It has also been detected between the Trias and Jura, and between the Jura and Cretaceous. We are tempted to ask here, whether such unconformities, without the slightest trace of permanent displacement in the strata, may not have been due to oscillations in the regional sea-level rather than to movements of the land?

One of the more striking features of the lower Trias is the occurrence of a vast abundance of silicified wood. It is not uncommon to find large tree trunks imbedded in these shales in good preservation. They are also found in a fragmental condition among the pebbles of the Shinarump conglomerate. These petrifactions are found over a wide extent of country from the Sheavwits Plateau along the front of the Vermilion Cliffs to the Paria, and again far to the northward at the base of Thousand Lake Mountain in the district of the High Plateaus.

These occurrences and others, which will soon be specified, point decisively to the inference that during the great era of accumulation, lasting from the closing stages of the Carboniferous to the Eocene, the surface of deposition never varied far from sea-level, and now and then the waters retreated from it, but only for very brief periods. On the whole the deposition proceeded almost continuously. It necessarily follows that in the long run the underlying beds sank deeper and deeper as the newer ones were piled upon them. This fact is but a repetition of what is found in other regions where the deposition has been very heavy. The strata subsided as rapidly as they were formed. It was true of the Appalachians, of the Pacific coast, of western and central Europe, and I think the same is true of all the areas of great deposition throughout the West.

When we reach the Cretaceous age we find that a little more light may be thrown upon the physical condition of the province, though much less than might be wished. So large are the areas where this series is the surface of the country, and so readily does the mind restore it to the places from which it has been denuded, that we feel almost as if we saw this great formation in its entirety. Wherever we turn in the Plateau Province the Cretaceous tells us the same story. All over its extent it is a lignitic and coal-bearing formation. We find coal or carbonaceous shales from the base of the series to the summit. Very abundant also are the remains of land plants in recognizable fossils, and these fossils occur not only in the carbonaceous layers but in the sand-rock and marls as mere casts or impressions of wood and leaves. Intercalating with these are many calcereous layers which yield marine mollusca in the lower and middle Cretaceous, and brackish water mollusca in the upper Cretaceous. In a word, the parallelism, so far as physical and organic conditions are concerned, between the Cretaceous of the Plateau Country and the Carboniferous coal measures of England, Pennsylvania, and Nova Scotia, seems perfect. What the Carboniferous age was to the Appalachian region, such was the Cretaceous age to the great mountain region of the West.

A careful scrutiny of the facts presented by the Cretaceous strata of the Plateau Country brings up before us some very curious and perplexing problems. No one would hesitate to say that during the accumulation of these strata the surface of deposition must have been very nearly at mean sea-level. Yet the Cretaceous system varies from 3,500 to 8,000 feet in thickness in different parts of the province. The continuous area which they covered south of the Uintas surely exceeds 100,000, square miles, in which not a single mountain chain, not a hill, not even a perceptible undulation of the strata is known to have then existed. It seems at first very difficult to understand how so vast a mass of strata could have accumulated in such shallow waters and over so wide an area. And the difficulty becomes considerably greater when we recall the fact that coal was also accumulated at different horizons throughout the entire province. If the sea were everywhere so shallow and if notable portions of its area were raised above the surface sufficiently to permit the growth of land vegetation, it would seem difficult to account for the transportation and diffusion of so large a mass of sedimentary materials over the entire expanse. Possibly some of the difficulties will be lightened by the following suggestions.

Although to the eye the strata show no marked inclinations excepting such as we know have been produced in later periods, still there may have been, and probably were, very feeble slopes too small to be detected by the eye, and these feeble slopes if continued for any great distance would carry the surface down hundreds of feet. A slope of one degree means a difference of level of a thousand feet in less than eleven miles. Hence there is no difficulty in imagining that while some tracts were exposed just above the water level, there were still larger ones where there may have been more than a hundred fathoms of water. But it should seem that shallow water, provided the shallowness be not very extreme, would tend to a wider and more uniform distribution of sediments than waters which run off into great depths. The currents having less depth of cross-section would move more rapidly and constantly, while currents moving outward into deeper water lose velocity and transporting power. So far, then, is the shallowness of the Plateau sea from being an obstacle to our comprehension of the state of facts which the region presents, that it may be the key to the mystery. One of the most striking facts to be explained is the persistency of lithological characters over large areas and the very slight and gradual variations in the masses of strata from place to place. If these sediments had been brought down by rivers to a shore from which the waters steadily and rather rapidly deepened seawards, we might have looked for enormous masses of littoral beds which rapidly thinned out as they receded from the shores; for the moving currents might be expected to lose themselves in the deepening water. But with shallow waters, whatsoever currents might be generated—whether from tides, from large rivers, from oceanic drift, or from prevailing winds—would persist as far as the depths remained shallow. Some such explanation as this, if it be tenable, would greatly assist us in explaining the wide diffusion of cross-bedding displayed in the Jura-Trias. It is generally accepted as an explanation for ripple marks that they are formed in shallow and moving water, and ripple marks are almost as abundant here as cross-bedding.

It would be extremely interesting to know what was the relative distribution of land and water over the western part of our continent in the closing periods of the Cretaceous. In a general way we know that the greater portion of the West was submerged. We also know that considerable land areas existed there. Sometimes we can point with confidence to a particular area and assert that it was land in Cretaceous time, but as a rule we are in doubt about the land areas. The largest piece of terra firma which is known was the Great Basin area, and even here we are unable to fix more than a small part of its shore line. We are reasonably confident that some and perhaps most of the great mountain platforms of the eastern ranges were above the waters with submerged valleys between them. We also know, and the fact is a momentous one, that nearly the whole of the vast region of the West corresponded in its physical condition to what we have inferred for the Cretaceous age of the Plateau Country. But detailed knowledge of the geography of the land areas in that age is exceedingly meager. Perhaps, however, we may make some very general statements which are not without value.

We cannot as yet affirm confidently that the Cretaceous ocean stretched from the lower Mississippi to the Pacific Ocean; but the facts now known indicate that if the two oceans were separated in that age the separation was only by a very narrow land area. We can travel from the Mississippi to the Pacific, between the thirty-fourth and thirty-seventh parallels, without being at any time more than fifty miles distant from some known mass of Cretaceous beds. If some gaps in existing knowledge could be filled up, we might be able to close up the vacant spaces in the distribution of the Cretaceous, and say that strata of that age once stretched continuously between the termini just mentioned. Indeed the only gap of importance is in the extreme southern part of Nevada and southern California. Every indication we now have raises a presumption in favor of this complete connection; but it is unnecessary to speculate when the facts can be learned by observation.

North and south of this unexplored locality, where it is supposed that an arm of the Cretaceous sea reached out to join the Pacific, there lay land areas of considerable extent. The northern was the old mainland of the Great Basin; the southern was the Arizona land, of which such frequent mention has been made in this work. The northern area was much larger than the southern. It still remains possible that the two were one continuous area joined by an isthmus, or that the Arizona mass was a long Malacca-like peninsula projecting southeastward from the former.

At the close of the Cretaceous important vertical movements were inaugurated, which finally revolutionized the physical condition of the region. Around the borders of the Plateau Province some important flexures were generated at this epoch, and portions were uplifted sufficiently to undergo a large amount of denudation. Perhaps the most striking instance of this is the one described in the work on the High Plateaus extending from the eastern and southern flanks of the Aquarius southward to the Colorado. This area consists of Jura-Trias strata, from which the Cretaceous had been eroded before the deposition of the Tertiary. Beneath the lava-cap of the Aquarius the lower Eocene may be observed resting upon the Jurassic sandstone, and a little further westward it lies across the basset edges of the Cretaceous. Southeastward from the Aquarius and along the course of the Escalante River the same relation is inferred to have existed, but the great erosion has swept everything bard down to the Jura-Trias, and the evidence of the extension of the Eocene here is mainly indirect. But the two monoclines are in full view, between which the Escalante platform was hoisted, and their age is unquestionably pre-Tertiary and post-Cretaceous. These relations are repeated in many other localities, and they indicate to us very decidedly that the Cretaceous closed amid important disturbances.

Still the deposition of strata was not yet ended. It went forward with seemingly undiminished rapidity, but under circumstances somewhat different from those hitherto prevailing. Soon after the advent of the Eocene the waters became fresh, and remained so until they disappeared altogether. This change was not limited to the Plateau Country, but appears to have been general over the greater part of the western mountain region. In truth, I know of no more impressive and surprising fact in western geology than the well-attested observation that most of that area has been covered by fresh-water lakes, and that the passage from the marine to the terrestrial condition seems to have been through an intermediate lacustrine condition. The marvel is not in the fact that here and there we find the vestiges of a great lake, but that we find those vestiges everywhere. The whole region, with the exception of the mountain platforms and pre-existing mainlands, has passed through this lacustrine stage.

When we take account of the peculiar circumstances our surprise may diminish in some measure, and the facts thus described may seem natural enough. The uplifting of the western region was a movement which acted unequally over the continent. Some portions were raised more than others. It is also to be considered that some of the inequalities of the surface existed before this general uplifting began. The result of this inequality must necessarily have been the production of depressed basins and intervening watersheds. Whether these basins would be completely closed, so as to form great lakes, or whether they should have drainage freely to the ocean, would depend of course upon the relations of the new axes of displacement to the older topography. If the new displacements merely accent and increase the older features, we should hardly look for the formation of lake basins. But if the new displacements are in any marked degree independent of the old ones, and if their axes lie transverse or oblique to the older axes, the formation of lake-basins in a newly emerging country is inevitable; and if the area affected be very extensive the chances are that the basins will be either very large or very numerous—in any event covering the greater part of the area. Without speculating as to the cause, it may be laid down as a general fact that the broader displacements of the West which began in early Tertiary time are quite independent of the older topographies, and the production of lake-basins by the new emergence seems a necessary consequence.

It is apparent in any event that the Plateau Country formed one continuous lake south of the Uinta Mountains. The vertical movements which followed the close of Cretaceous time shut it off from access to the sea. If we are at liberty to go on as we have done and to draw broad inferences from the drainage channels concerning the mode of evolution, we can very quickly frame a theory of the distribution of those vertical movements. Thus we know that during Cretaceous time the Plateau area was wide open to the ocean towards the southeast, or towards the Gulf of Mexico. For the Cretaceous system stretches from the heart of the province clear across New Mexico and into Texas, with no other interruptions than some short mountain ranges, (themselves largely composed of Cretaceous strata), and such gaps as have very plainly been produced by Tertiary erosion. Let us assume that at the beginning of the Eocene, or very soon thereafter, the western and northwestern part of New Mexico was uplifted slightly more than regions either east or west of it; the axis of elevation trending nearly north and south. The effect would have been to make an almost, if not completely, closed basin of the Plateau Country.

With this hypothesis we are able to frame a very simple and intelligible account of the manner in which the Plateau Province finally was isolated in Eocene time from the ocean. In truth, three-fourths or more of its boundary had been marked out long before, perhaps as far back as the beginning of the Trias; and in the following way. On the northwest lay the Mesozoic mainland, now forming the Great Basin area. In some form or other the Wasatch was then in existence as a mountain range. So, also, the Uinta chain on the north of the province then existed, but probably did not project so far eastward as at present, and left a gap in the boundary along the course of the Green River. On the northeastern side of the basin some of the great Park ranges of Colorado were standing, though the sea may have washed their bases. But to the southeast the area was wide open to the Cretaceous ocean. On the southwest and south lay the Arizona mainland so often spoken of in this work. Whether this mainland was continuous with the Great Basin mainland we do not know as yet, nor is it material just here. If, now, the first effort of the elevating force which has raised the continent had acted with more effect upon the eastern than upon the western side of the basin, the result would have been to make this basin a land-locked area like the Euxine. Its outlet would necessarily have been along the lower courses of the Colorado to the Gulf of California, or, perhaps, straight westward to the Pacific.

Having thus obtained a consistent view of the manner in which the great Eocene lake of the Plateau Province may have originated, it now remains to follow out such changes as are indicated in its subsequent history. It should seem that the passage from the brackish water to the fresh water condition was quite sudden, and as the same is true of widely extended areas outside of this region, we are apparently obliged to assume that the movement of which this was a result affected the entire western portion of the continent, and that it was one of elevation. A considerable number of large lakes being formed, the next process was the desiccation of these lakes and the evolution of river systems. So long as the region occupied a low altitude this process, we may infer, would be very protracted. Before a large lake can be drained its outlet must be cut down. But several causes in the present instance would combine to render this action very slow and feeble. The elevation being small, the declivity and consequent corrasive power at the outlet must be correspondingly small. Moreover, the waters issuing from a large lake contain little or no sediment; and sediments—sand, grit, &c.—are the tools with which rivers chiefly work in corrading their beds. Corrosion by clear water is an exceedingly slow process.

It is not surprising, therefore, to find that the lakes produced by the first action of the elevating forces persisted for a very long time. This persistence is a general feature of the Eocene lakes of the West. The Plateau lake seems to have been one of the largest and most enduring, for it did not wholly vanish until the close of the Eocene. The volume of sediment accumulated upon its bottom was very large, ranging from 1,200 to more than 5,000 feet in thickness, and these deposits represent Eocene time exclusively. Here we are confronted by the same paradoxes as those we encountered in viewing the Cretaceous condition of the region: a tract which is rising yet sinking; a basin which is shallow, which receives great thickness of deposits, and yet is never full.

At length we detect evidence of the gradual cessation of deposit and of the progressive upheaval of the country. In the southern portion of the lake basin only the lower Eocene was deposited, while in the northern portion around the Uintas the whole Eocene formation is present. Whence we infer that the final desiccation of the lake began in its southern or southwestern portions, and that the lake shrank away very slowly towards the north, finally disappearing at the base of the Uintas at the close of Eocene time.

We must also infer that upon the floor of this basin, as it emerged, a drainage system was laid out. Such a drainage system would necessarily conform to the slopes of the country then existing. Taking the supposition already made, that the uplift was somewhat greater upon the eastern than upon the western side of the province, the configuration of the principal drainage channels would be very much like that now existing. The trunk channel would flow southwestward and westward, while the tributaries would enter it on either hand very much as the larger and older tributaries now do. The affluents on the south side are the San Juan, the Little Colorado, and Cataract Creek, which seem to be due to just such an original surface. On the north side of the Colorado the arrangement of the tributaries also seems to conform to the assumption. On this side the later movements of the strata have been such that the prevailing courses of the streams are almost always against the dips. But when we restore these displacements and deduce from them as nearly as we may the original conformation of the country, the positions of the tributaries at once become natural and easy of explanation.

The argument here adopted concerning the origin of the drainage system affords little scope for discussion. Rivers originated somehow. It seems almost a truism to say that they originated with the land itself, and that their courses were, in the first instance, determined by the slopes of the newly emerged land surface. No doubt there are many causes which may have changed the courses of rivers, and in the subsequent changes of position the original arrangement may have been lost and left no intelligible trace. On the other hand, there are certain conditions under which we may look for the highest degree of stability in the positions of drainage channels, and when we find such conditions to have prevailed continuously the question of origin becomes at once important, for it indicates to us an initial configuration of the surface, which must be taken account of and never violated in all subsequent discussion. All inferences or speculations concerning later displacements and many other groups of facts must be kept in strict subordination to it.

The Plateau Country is one in which the conditions have been remarkably favorable to the stability of the larger drainage channels. On the other hand, it has been singularly unfavorable to the stability of smaller or local drainage channels. The Colorado and its larger tributaries—those tributaries which head in the highlands around the border of the province—exhibit everywhere incontestible evidence that they are flowing to-day just where they flowed in Eocene time. But the smaller tributaries are wanting altogether in some large tracts, and where they do exist they usually disclose the fact that they are of very recent origin and have been determined by surface conditions of recent establishment. In the remainder of this discussion these facts assume great importance.

With the final desiccation of the Grand Cañon district began the great erosion, which has never ceased to operate down to the present time. Concerning the details of that process we know but little, and we can only guess at its general character during the earlier stages. Erosion is here associated with a large amount of uplifting, and we may conjecture that as the uplifting went on the inequalities produced by erosion became greater and greater, the valleys grew deeper, and the intervening mesas stood in higher relief. This is merely an application of the general law that the higher the country the more deeply is it engraved by erosion and the greater are its sculptured reliefs. Much, however, must depend upon climate. But the Eocene climate of the West, so far as it is indicated by the strata and organic remains of that age, was moist and subtropical, and presumably the climate of the Grand Cañon district was similar.

During the latter part of Eocene time the degrading forces no doubt made great progress in destroying and removing the Mesozoic deposits, which I have shown originally covered the region. We cannot, however, in this district find any epoch separating the later Eocene from the Miocene. To all intents and purposes they formed here a single age. From the time when the great erosion was begun until it reached a certain stage (to be spoken of speedily) not a single detail can be pointed to beyond the principal facts of elevation and erosion. We are, so to speak, passing a long interval of time in the dark. We must, therefore, stride at once from the middle Eocene to an epoch which may be provisionally fixed at the close of the Miocene. From this epoch looking backward the total change wrought upon the region up to that time breaks into view. But we know only the beginning and the end. The intermediate stages are discerned only by the imagination. Yet I am tempted here to view this period in a way which may be in some measure speculative, though not wholly so. Some deductions may be made from established principles governing erosion which may fairly claim to be something more than mere speculation.

At the close of the Miocene, or thereabout, the greater part of the denudation of the Mesozoic should have been accomplished, and it is worth while to inquire in what manner this work may have been done. In the fourth chapter of this book I have spoken of the general fact that the attack of erosion is directed chiefly against the edges of the strata and the steeper slopes, and operates but feebly upon flat surfaces. The entering cuts are made by the corrading streams. The whole region had, during the long interval of Eocene and Miocene time, undergone a great amount of uplifting, and this progressive movement itself constitutes a condition highly favorable to corrasion; for the higher the country rises the greater become the declivities of the streams, and of those factors which determine a stream to corrade the most potent by far is declivity. While the country rises, therefore, the streams are making the reliefs greater—are creating larger surfaces of edgewise exposure and longer and steeper slopes. Thus, every advantage is given the agents of erosion.

The area thus exposed to rapid denudation was a very large one, and the corrasion of streams apparently went on over its entire expanse, without any very great local variations of amount, except perhaps near the borders of the watershed. While the normal method of decay is expressed in the recession of cliffs, we must not suppose that single and comparatively straight lines of cliffs stretched across the whole region and slowly wasted backwards. We should rather conceive of the platforms as being cut by a labyrinth of drainage channels, ramifying over their entire expanse, and as being attacked within and without, and all around—as a great conflagration spreads through every square, street, and alley of a city. A state of affairs quite similar to that suggested here seems to prevail at the present time in the interior spaces of the Plateau Province. The drainage basins of the Escalante River, of the San Juan, and indeed of that entire part of the Colorado which reaches from the junction of the Grand and Green to the head of Marble Cañon, are wonderfully dissected by countless cañons, which I am confident were in existence at this very epoch, though they have since been greatly deepened and otherwise modified.

It may also be of interest to inquire whether it is probable that cañons, architectural cliffs, buttes, and mesas existed in the Miocene, similar to those now occurring. The answer to this must be largely conjectural, but it seems to me that the probabilities are against such a topography. The present features of the region are no doubt favored greatly by an arid climate. Still we know that cañons and cliffs may be generated in moist climates. But under a moist climate, other circumstances and conditions must be of a very exceptional nature to produce such features, and even if produced, they are evanescent. And arid climate not only tends to produce, but also tends to maintain them. Under a moist climate the tendency is to reduce them to normal forms. Further than this it seems useless to speculate.

The first indications of specialized events are associated with the beginning of the present Grand Cañon. About the time that the river began to cut into the Carboniferous strata, some important physical changes in the condition of the region took place, which have left their imprints upon the topography. The climate appears to have changed from moist to arid. In preceding chapters we have noted particular instances where this change manifests itself in the drying up of lateral streams. Perhaps the most instructive one is De Motte Park, on the Kaibab. A considerable number of others are still distinguishable. These indicate that as the Colorado began to sink into the Carboniferous strata, some cause dried up their very fountains, and they ceased to flow. No explanation seems at all adequate except the advent of an arid climate. If, then, we could fix the period at which this change of climate occurred, we should have strong presumptive reasons for selecting the same period as the one in which the present Grand Cañon originated.

We know that the Miocene climate of the West was moist and subtropical. This indicated by the great extent of fresh-water lakes in some portions of the West, their abundant vegetable remains, and the exuberance of land life. But the remnants of Pliocene time are usually of a different character. In the Great Basin we have many proofs of the arid character of that age, and it is equally evident throughout the Plateau Country that the Pliocene climate was in the main very much like the present. We cannot, it is true, correlate with precision any definite boundary between Miocene and Pliocene; but, with no unreasonable latitude, I think we may still say that the Miocene climate of the Plateaus was a moist climate, while the Pliocene was arid, and that the transition from one climate to the other occurred near the close of the former age or near the beginning of the latter.

At the epoch when the cutting of the present Grand Cañon began, no doubt the district at large presented a very different aspect from the modern one. While the greater part of the denudation of the Mesozoic had been accomplished, there were some important remnants still left which have been nearly or quite demolished in still more recent times. The basalts of the Uinkaret and Sheavwits have preserved some extensive Permian [Triassic] outliers, and even these must have shrunken greatly by the waste of erosion during the long period occupied in the excavation of the Grand Cañon. Although the basalts which cap Mounts Logan and Trumbull are certainly very ancient, and are older than the faults—or at least older than a great part of the faulting movements—there is no assurance that they are as old as the origin of the present cañon. Still I do not doubt that they go back nearly as far, and they are certainly much more ancient than the inner gorge at the Toroweap. At the time of their outpour large masses of Permian strata overspread the region. These are not limited to the few remnants described on the Uinkaret, but we find the summit of the Permian similarly protected by basalt in many widely separated localities. Thus the Red Butte south of the Kaibab division of the cañon has a basaltic cap which seems to be about as ancient as that of Logan. In the San Francisco Mountains may be found remnants of the same formation protected by lavas, though our knowledge is not yet sufficient to give us any opinion as to how great an antiquity should be assigned to those eruptions. No doubt they are Tertiary, but whether Miocene or Pliocene is unknown. In the valley of the Little Colorado some Permian masses have been similarly protected by basalt and still reveal nearly or quite the entire series. The Sheavwits Plateau contains these remnants with basaltic coverings more abundantly and upon a larger scale than any other plateau. Thus there is a general accord of testimony that at the period of the older basaltic eruptions very large bodies of Permian strata lay upon the Carboniferous platform. In truth, it seems as if the summit of the Permian [Triassic] then constituted the surface of the country, just as the summit of the Carboniferous [Permian] does now. The fact that the older basalts wherever found rest upon the same geological horizon, viz, the summit of the Permian, suggests to us the further inference that the region near the river was then flat and destitute of deep cañons and valleys, such as now exist there, and, therefore, destitute of great hills, buttes, or mesas. The meaning of this is a base-level of erosion. The rivers could not corrade, because they had reached for the time being their limiting depth in the strata. The work of erosion would then be confined to leveling the sculptural inequalities without the power to produce new ones or to augment the relief of old ones. This, it is true, looks at first like drawing a very broad and rather remote inference from a very slender basis, and would not be justified at all if it were not in general harmony with a wide range of facts. Many facts take form and coherence around it which would otherwise seem mysterious. Let us illustrate.

The condition of base-level is one in which the rivers of a region cannot corrade. As a general rule it arises from the rivers having cut down so low that their transporting power is fully occupied, even to repletion. This, in turn, involves the correlative fact that no elevating force has acted upon the region for a long period of time. For the most part base-levels are prevalent during a cessation of the uplifting force. The recurrence of upheaval terminates the condition of base-level. The declivities of the streams are increased, their energy augmented, and their corrasive power renewed. New features are then carved out of the topography, or older ones are embossed in higher relief. A period of upheaval, then, is one in which the sculptural features of the land are generated and increased; a period of quiescence or cessation of vertical movement is one in which these features are obliterated. Now, in trying to form some conception of the process by which the great denudation of the Mesozoic was accomplished, we may suppose that the uplifting of the region went on (1) either at a constant or a slightly varying rate, or (2) through alternating periods of activity and quiescence. The results would be widely contrasted in the two cases. The former would give us an exceedingly rough and hilly country at all periods of the erosion; the latter would give us just such a country as we see at present. The inequalities produced during a period of upheaval would be smoothed off during the period of repose. As a matter of fact we may be confident that the upheaval in its later stages has been of the paroxysmal character. Of this the proofs are abundant.

We may then conjecture the reason for the somewhat remarkable fact that the same stratum or geological horizon is almost everywhere the surface of the interior platform of the Grand Cañon district. Before the last upheaval we may conceive of the region occupying the situation of a base-level in which the inequalities which may have existed were obliterated. We shall see more of this subject of base-level hereafter.

I have shown that we find at this epoch the first indications of the existence of the great faults. It does not appear, however, that these faults all originated at exactly the same epoch, and it is certain that their respective amounts of displacement have increased very slowly and gradually with the lapse of time. Again, we cannot be sure that all parts of one and the same fault were begun at the same epoch. Indeed, the evidence is overwhelming that the development of these dislocations has been a very slow and gradual process, and all that can be said concerning their condition in the particular epoch of which we are treating (close of the Miocene) is that they first betray their existence at that time. Before this epoch we know nothing of them; and at the time in question they were of inconsiderable dimensions for the most part. Their formation seems to have been incidental to the uplifting of the platform which took place about the time the present Grand Cañon began to cut. But concerning the nature of this association it is useless to speculate. In all the range of geological phenomena I know of none more perplexing than a great fault, and until we have some semblance of a working hypothesis which may serve or help to explain them, it is useless to speculate upon the causes of particular cases.

We may also note the coincidence of the earlier basaltic eruptions with this period of uplifting and faulting. It has been noted as a fact of very general application, that volcanism is active during periods of upheaval, and becomes quiescent during subsidence. The relations of the two classes of phenomena in the Grand Cañon district appear to conform to the general rule.

The amount of upheaval which took place at the epoch in question may also be roughly estimated. It varies from 2,000 to 3,000 feet. The uplifting forces then suspended operations for a time, and the drainage system sought a new base-level. During this paroxysm of upheaval the outer chasm of the Grand Cañon was cut; the river corrading down to the level of the esplanade in the Kanab and Uinkaret divisions, but below that horizon in the Kaibab. The corrasion was probably done as rapidly as the country rose, or very nearly so. At first we may presume that only a narrow gorge was cut—like the upper portion of the Marble Cañon. But the river found its base-level soon after the uplifting ceased, and the cañon slowly widened by the recession of the cliffs. In this stage of the development an arid climate reigned throughout the district. Its effect is apparent chiefly in two ways: 1st, in the paucity of lateral tributaries and in the meagerness of small details in the land sculpture, and 2d, in the sharpness and abruptness given to all the cliffs, valleys, and mesa profiles.

(1) Allusion has been made to the first mentioned effect of an arid climate. The only tributaries which remained during this period were the large and more powerful ones which had their sources far away in the highlands, around the margin of the watershed. Within the inner platform of the district no streams took their rise. The large tributaries continued to sink their lateral gorges in unison with the corrasion of the main river, but no new chasms

were generated. On the contrary, some of the lateral tributaries, which for a time valiantly sustained a doubtful struggle for existence, at last succumbed and dried up, leaving their troughs opening into the main gorge far up near the summit of the cañon wall.

(2) The sharpness and abruptness of profiles which characterizes the plateau scenery is not of recent origin, but dates back no doubt to the beginning of the Pliocene. An arid climate is an important factor in producing this effect. In such a climate weathering proceeds slowly. If the conditions are such as to produce a high efficiency in the agencies which transport the débris, the rocks will be left comparatively naked; little soil and talus will be formed, and little will be left. The attack upon the edges of the horizontal strata will thus be facilitated and the profiles will be determined chiefly by undermining. Such profiles are invariably cliffs.

We come now to the final upheaval which has brought the region to its present condition. The Colorado River, after remaining without corrasion at the level of the esplanade of the cañon during the greater part of Pliocene time, at length resumed the operation of sinking its channel. A new paroxysm of upheaval set in; the faults increased their displacement; the volcanic vents reopened. This time the upheaval was greater than before, amounting probably from 3,000 to 4,000 feet. The narrow, inner gorge at the Toroweap was swiftly cut, and it is in this respect a type of the lower deeps of the entire cañon. Everywhere the rapid corrasion of the deeper gorges is revealed. The epoch at which this latest upheaval took place, is no doubt a very recent one in the geological calendar. It began most probably near the close of the Pliocene. That it has now ceased is almost certain. No trace of present movement can be detected in any of the faults, and it is certain that no movement tending to increase them has taken place in those portions which have been scrutinized. In the Uinkaret some lava flows cross the Hurricane fault, and though they must be thousands of years old they are not dislocated. If any vertical movement is now in progress it is nowhere betrayed, and is unaccompanied by any of those collateral movements of faulting, which are usually associated with upheaval.

During the last stage of the evolution of the region we have to consider a very interesting episode. The glacial period here intervenes between the arid climate of the Pliocene and that of the present time. As has been already remarked, the glacial period here was not icy, but rainy, and very probably colder than the present. In some localities it began to excavate systems of local drainage channels and to carve out minuter details of topography. In truth the amount of this work which was done in that period was quite considerable. The most striking instance is to be found in the ravines of the Kaibab. The smaller drainage of the Paria Plateau is another instance. West of the Kaibab we fail to find such conspicuous traces of the glacial period. The explanation of their absence or feebleness may be the fact that those western plateaus have scarcely any slopes upon which such a drainage system could readily find foothold, while the slopes of the Kaibab summit and of the Paria platform are very considerable. The glacial period appears to have been of too brief duration to achieve any very great results in this district. It may have increased the corrasive power of the Colorado and tributaries by furnishing a larger water supply and there is decided reason for thinking that some of the cañons in the terraces were rapidly corraded and deepened at this time. Most of those lateral cañons in the terraces are slowly filling up with alluvium at the present time, but very plainly they were much deeper at no remote epoch in the past. The lower talus in some of them is completely buried and the alluvium mounts up on the breasts of the perpendicular scarps. In some cases a smooth floor of alluvium extends from side to side of what was originally a cañon valley. The recurrence of a climate sufficiently moist to sustain a vigorous perennial stream would probably sweep out all this unconsolidated alluvium, and return the valley to its former condition of an ordinary cañon.

48

The Tectonic Evolution of the Western United States

JAMES GILLULY

1963

From *Quarterly Journal of the Geological Society of London*, vol. 119, pp. 133–174, 1963. Reprinted with permission of the author and the Geological Society of London.

For the purpose of this review I define the western United States as that part west of the meridian of 104° W, which traverses the Great Plains immediately east of nearly all the Cainozoic orogenic structures of the country. The area between this meridian and the Pacific Coast includes more than a million square miles. Discussion must obviously be highly selective if it is to be in reasonable compass; the salient features of the history are here briefly outlined and then consideration is given to several special topics and their bearing on the larger tectonic and plutonic problems.

GEOLOGICAL HISTORY

PRE-CAMBRIAN HISTORY

The Pre-Cambrian history of the western United States is decidedly fragmentary: less than nine per cent of the area exposes rock so old, and of this only small parts of the plutonic areas have been mapped on other than reconnaissance scales.

The age-determinations so far obtained are for plutonic minerals. The oldest dates (2800 to 2500 m.y.) form a considerable cluster in Wyoming and Montana. This group is followed by a wide gap, equivalent to the whole of Phanerozoic time, unrepresented by any dates, then by almost a dozen values between 1500 and 1800 m.y., sporadically distributed from Montana through the Black Hills, Wyoming, Colorado, Nevada, California, and Arizona, without apparent trend; another scattering between 1300 and 1500 m.y., in all the areas between Montana and Arizona; a scattering of 1100- to 1300-m.y. dates in Colorado, New Mexico, Arizona, and Nevada; some 980- to 1100-m.y. dates in Colorado, California, and Arizona. The only date less than 980 m.y. is one of 700 m.y. from western Nevada. It has been suggested that the 900–1100-m.y. dates outline part of a transcontinental belt extending north-east to Ontario, but I can see no more consistency in this trend than in an arc of 1500–1800-m.y. ages. I think it is too early to make generalizations about the meaning of such an alignment—if one indeed exists—let alone to postulate a transcontinental mountain chain on the basis of its supposed reality. As Wasserburg, Wetherill & Wright (1959) have pointed out, there is no evidence of continental accretion in southern California since 1.7×10^9 years ago.

The areas of exposed Pre-Cambrian rocks are shown in Figure 48.1 In the past it was common to refer to the plutonic rocks on this map as of 'Archaean age' and to the sedimentary rocks as 'Algonkian.' Radiometric dating has shown this classification, which was always philosophically indefensible, to be wholly misleading.

Many of the sedimentary rocks formerly called 'Algonkian' have been shown by radiometric dating to be as old as many of the plutonic rocks that had been classed as 'Archaean.' The Belt Series of the northern Rockies was long correlated with the so-called 'Eocambrian' of the Caledonides and was considered to be essentially conformable with the Cambrian and to be its continuation downward. There are still, indeed, a few supporters of this view, but it seems to me that the weight of the evidence, both on the Belt and on the somewhat analogous Apache Series of Arizona, is overwhelmingly opposed to it. In the northern Rockies, map-patterns show that the homotaxial basal quartzites of the Cambrian (Lower Cambrian in Washington and British Columbia, and Middle Cambrian in Idaho and Montana) overlie a regional unconformity along which many thousands of feet of Belt strata are overlapped (Campbell, 1959; Deiss, 1935; Walcott, 1899; Weiss, 1958). Furthermore, in British Columbia the thick Windermere Series intervenes between Belt and Lower Cambrian rocks and is unconformable with both (Little, 1960, p. 13). Radiometric dates for mineral veins that cut the

FIGURE 48.1
Precambrian areas of the western United States. (Slightly modified from *Geologic Map of the United States*, U.S. Geological Survey, 1933.)

Belt Series in northern Idaho are more than 1000 m.y. (Eckelmann and Kulp, 1957, p. 1130); similar evidence places the Apache Group as older than 1200 m.y. (Shride, 1958; Silver, 1960). Although we have no clear-cut evidence on the Uinta Sandstone of northern Utah, it seems likely that this, too, is older Pre-Cambrian rather than younger. Lack of metamorphism is no criterion of age; conversely, some of the Early Cretaceous of Arizona has been so highly metamorphosed as to be almost inseparable from known older Pre-Cambrian rocks (Gilluly, 1956, pp. 81–2).

The only rocks of the region that appear actually to be very late Pre-Cambrian are those of the southern Great Basin of California and Nevada that conformably underlie the *Olenellus* zone in the Inyo, Nopah, and neighbouring ranges. The strata between the *Olenellus* zone and the first notable unconformity below are up to 8000 ft thick (Hazzard, 1938); unconformably beneath these lies another sedimentary section of only slightly metamorphosed rocks 7000 ft thick that rest unconformably on a plutonic basement (Hewett, 1956, pp. 25–8).

Of Pre-Cambrian orogenies, only fragments have so far been recognized. Strong disturbances along north-east trends are common in Arizona, Colorado, and Wyoming (Cohee and others, 1961; Wilson, 1937; Anderson, 1951; Case and Joesting, 1961; Tweto and Pearson, 1958). It is possible that these trends reflect in part the hypothetical transcontinental chain, but the rocks concerned range in age from 1055 to 1700 m.y. (radiometric dating), spanning more time than the whole of the Phanerozoic, and other trends are also common. Pre-Cambrian granitic stocks that cut previously metamorphosed rocks, and others that blend through migmatites into their wall-rocks, have been found in many areas, but it seems fruitless to try to reconstruct regional chains when none can be confidently traced across a single State. Later structures obscure our reading of the older.

EARLY PALEOZOIC HISTORY

From Cambrian until the end of Devonian times the western Cordillera was geosynclinal. The eastern margin of the geosyncline fluctuated somewhat, but in general lay along a line from eastern Nevada through western Utah, eastern Idaho, and western Montana; the area of the present Cordillera farther east received shelf sediments intermittently. The Early Cambrian sea began to encroach on the continent from both the south and the north, and by late Middle Cambrian times had covered essentially all the geosyncline; many parts of the shelf were not reached until Late Cambrian times, and some remained emergent. The encroaching sea everywhere deposited a basal sandstone, locally many thousands of feet thick; the deposits received subsequently by the eastern, miogeosynclinal, part of the Cordillera were mainly carbonates. The western part, on the other hand, was eugeosynclinal, and abundant volcanic rocks and thick sandstones, shales, and cherts are represented in every system from the Cambrian to the Devonian (Figure 48.2). Whether the eugeosyncline and miogeosyncline formed parts of the same trough or were separated by a welt or an island chain is unknown; the contact between the two facies is everywhere a tectonic one. A welt may have persisted within the miogeosyncline in north-western Utah and Idaho (Stokes, 1952).

The Pacific border of the Palaeozoic and later geosynclines is quite unknown; indeed, if the largest movement postulated for the San Andreas fault is correct (Hill and Dibblee, 1953) the Pre-Cambrian rocks to the southwest of this fault lay far to the south of their present locations in pre-Cretaceous time.

From the Cambrian to the Devonian, each system contains many thousands of feet of eugeosynclinal rocks; perhaps 10,000 ft of Cambrian, 25,000 ft of Ordovician, and comparable thicknesses of Silurian and Devonian strata. Concurrent deformation and large-scale magmatic activity nearby are thereby demanded, but a thick arkose—a textbook example of a molasse deposit—of Late Cambrian age in central Nevada supplies the only direct evidence of orogeny.

The eugeosynclinal clastic rocks came either from welts within the basin or from highlands to the west, for after the Cambrian transgression the eugeosyncline was separated from the craton to the east by a wide belt of carbonate deposition (Nolan, 1943). Inasmuch as all the eugeosynclinal rocks in Nevada appear to be allochthonous, neither the site of their accumulation nor of their provenance is known, except that both lay somewhere to the west or north-west of central Nevada.

THE ANTLER OROGENY

The Antler orogeny, the first well-documented one of Palaeozoic time, took place in the Early Mississippian in central Nevada; its effects become obvious a little later both to north and south. Although Nolan (1928), on the basis of extremely limited information, had brilliantly inferred a late Palaeozoic geanticline in its approximate position, and Kirk (1933) suggested from facies contrasts of juxtaposed Middle Ordovician rocks that there had been telescoping by thrusts, it was not until about twenty years ago that the first clear-cut structural evidence for a major Palaeozoic orogeny in this area was discovered. Merriam and Anderson (1942) mapped a thrust in the Roberts Mountains of central Nevada in which eugeosynclinal Ordovician rocks were thrust eastward over miogeosynclinal rocks of Cambrian to Devonian age. They did not have diagnostic relations in the area of their map, and did not therefore recognize that the thrust was of Mississippian age. Subsequently, however, the work of many geologists has demonstrated that the deformation was truly alpine, involving recumbent folds and thrusts that travelled a minimum of 60 miles, probably much more. The Antler orogeny has been recognized from direct and indirect evidence throughout an arc 500 miles long, of extent comparable to that of the Alps, extending from west central Nevada to central Idaho (Figure 48.3). It probably extended still farther, but is cut off at either end by great Mesozoic batholiths, beyond which it has not yet been recognized.

This great orogeny telescoped contrasting

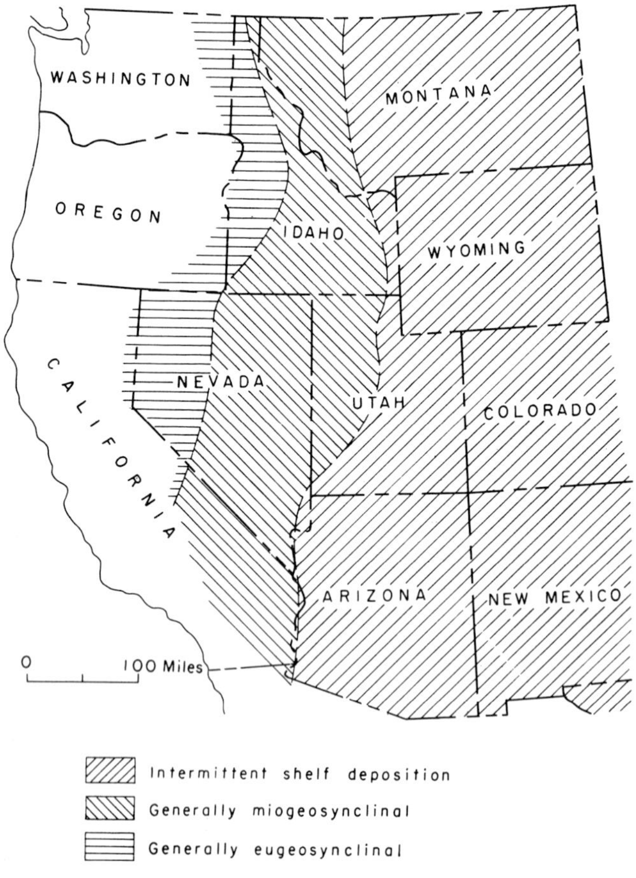

FIGURE 48.2
Early Paleozoic paleogeography of the Cordillera

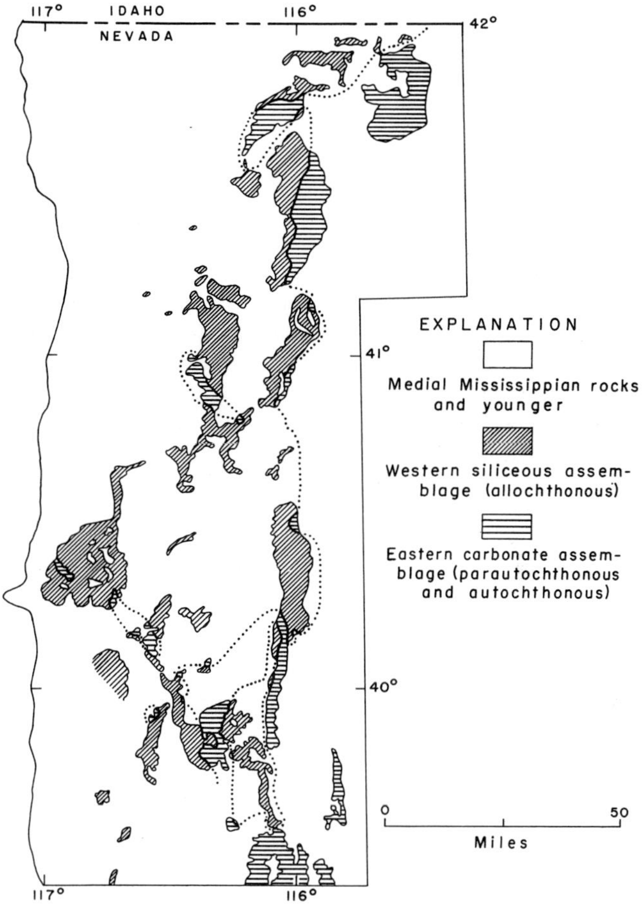

FIGURE 48.3
The distribution of eugeosynclinal and miogeosynclinal facies of Devonian and older Paleozoic rocks in northern and central Nevada. The two facies are separated everywhere by the Roberts thrust. (After Roberts and others, 1958.)

facies of rocks ranging from the Cambrian to the Devonian over a width of several scores of miles (Roberts and others, 1958). Representative structure-sections of the thrust-zone are shown in Figure 48.4.

Although there may have been renewed movement on some segments of the structure at later times (Nolan, Merriam & Williams 1956), the main movement of the thrust was of Early Mississippian age near the Fortieth Parallel, for Smith and Ketner of the U.S. Geological Survey have found fossiliferous Early Mississippian rocks both beneath the distal end of the thrust-sheet and unconformably overlying both plates (J. Fred Smith, Jr., oral communication, 1961). Cobbles and pebbles derived from the thrust-sheet abound in the thick coarsely clastic beds of middle Mississippian age to the east, both in Nevada and Idaho (Westgate and Ross, 1930; Skipp, 1958; Thomasson, 1959; Churkin, 1960; Dott, 1955).

Despite the fact that the thrusts carried thicknesses of several miles of strata for distances of several scores of miles, neither metamorphism nor plutonism of any consequence has been recognized as associated with this orogeny, nor is the Pre-Cambrian basement anywhere involved. Presumably the thrusts are décollement structures that involved only the shallower crustal layers, even though the deeper crust and mantle must also have been somehow affected, for the geanticline formed at that time has been a dominantly positive area ever since.

Far to the west of the Antler thrust-zone, in the Klamath Mountains of northern California, an angular unconformity between shale and siliceous volcanic rocks of Middle Devonian age and coarse clastic rocks of Early

Mississippian age records an orogenic disturbance at about the same time as the Antler orogeny (Albers and Robertson, 1961, pp. 16–18; Diller, 1906; Kinkel, Hall, and Albers, 1956, pp. 35–41; Hinds, 1940).

LATER PALEOZOIC OROGENIES

With the more complete exposure of the younger systems, evidence of deformation becomes increasingly abundant. A geanticline formed during the Antler orogeny, and although it was locally flooded at times between the Pennsylvania and Early Triassic, it generally persisted. Thus, until mid-Mesozoic time there were two troughs of major sedimentation, one about 100 miles east of the pre-Antler geosynclinal axis, the other about the same distance to the west. The western trough was eugeosynclinal; the eastern miogeosynclinal, receiving some clastic sediments near the geanticline but chiefly carbonates farther east.

The western, eugeosynclinal, trough and the geanticline east of it underwent considerable tectonic disturbance in Late Pennsylvanian and Permian time, but the trends and tectonic details are obscured by younger intrusions and overlying rocks. For the most part the record is one of thick coarsely clastic orogenic sediments rather than of unconformity. At three well-dated times during the Permian there were episodes of folding and thrusting in Nevada,

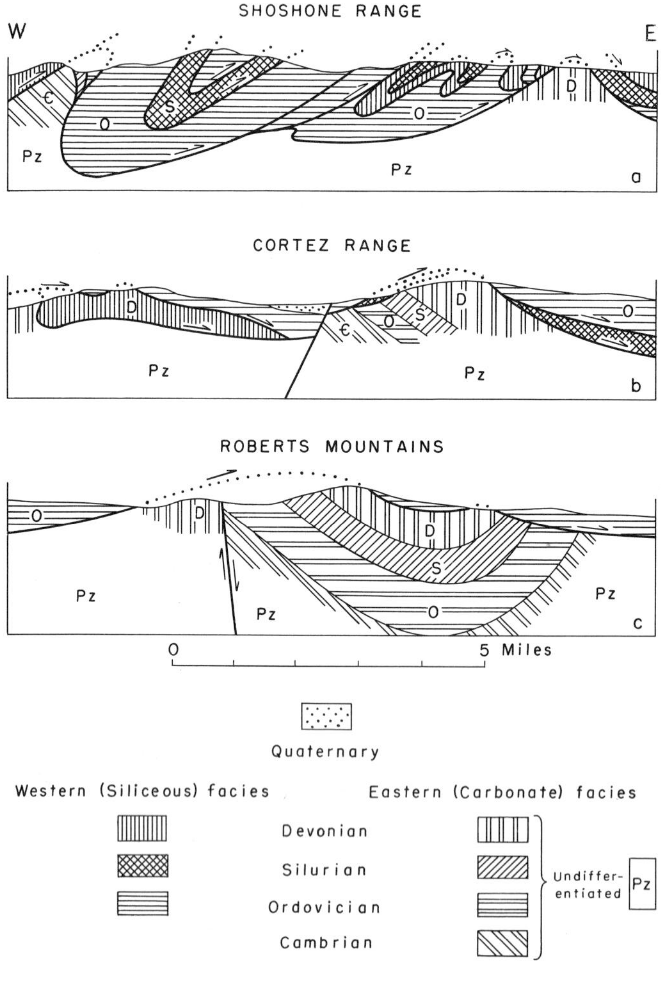

FIGURE 48.4
Diagrammatic structure-sections through the Roberts thrust zone. From the Shoshone Range, at the northwest, through the Roberts Mountains, at the east of the zone. Note greater complexity towards the west, more simple structures towards the east. (After Gilluly and Gates, 1967; Gilluly and Masursky, 1967; Merriam and Anderson, 1942.)

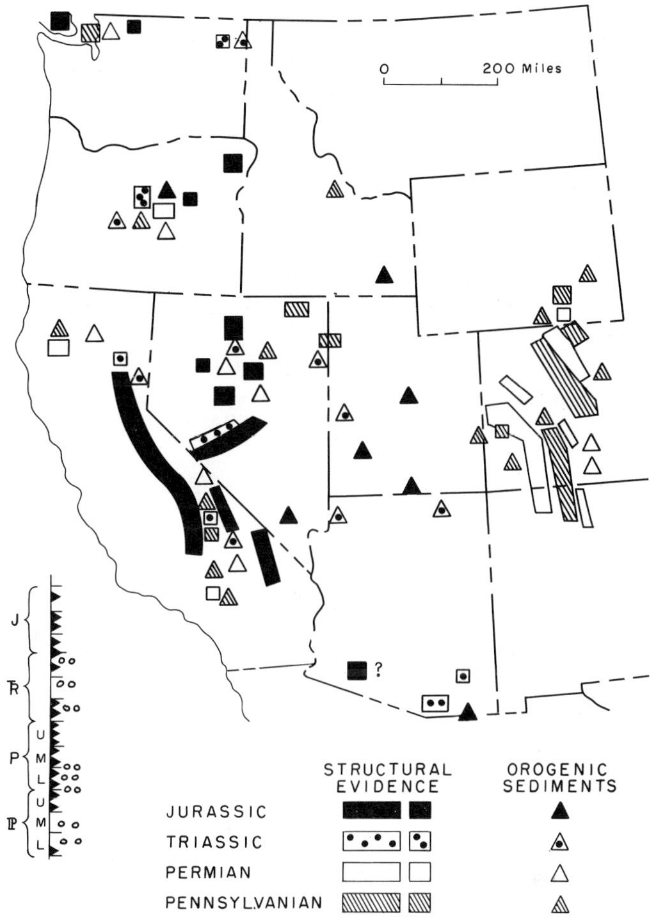

FIGURE 48.5
Localities of identified unconformities and orogenic sediments of Pennsylvanian to Jurassic age. The diagram indicates the distribution in time of unconformities (*wedges*) and orogenic sediments (*circles*).

and in California yet a fourth episode is recorded by unconformity (Figure 48.5).

A sedimentary anomaly that has not yet been associated with any particular orogenic episode came into existence in north-western Utah in middle Mississippian time. A dramatic subsidence began here, in an area perhaps 100 miles across and 150 miles long, which had been either mildly geosynclinal or even part of the stable shelf. In later Mississippian time as much as 6000 ft of carbonates with subordinate clastic rocks accumulated in it; in the Pennsylvanian as much as 18,000 ft of carbonate and well-washed quartz sandstone; and in the Permian, another 4000 ft: a total of more than five miles of sediment, although adjoining areas only a few miles from the border of the basin received a mere fraction of these thicknesses (Gilluly, 1932; Nolan, 1935). Presumably the sand—a mature sediment—was derived from a welt in the miogeosyncline somewhere to the north-west.

In the Permian a salt basin formed in eastern Nevada, but its extent and palaeogeographical relations are little understood.

The best known of the post-Antler Palaeozoic orogenies took place in Colorado and Wyoming, where the former shelf area was broken by huge normal faults and block uplifts to form the Ancestral Rockies (Mallory, 1960). Most of these tilted horsts and trap-door uplifts exposed Pre-Cambrian plutonic bodies from the beginning, and some of those that originally had thin carapaces of Palaeozoic sedimentary rocks were soon denuded. From the uplifts huge volumes of coarse arkose spilled into the bordering lowlands, to form deposits, partly continental, partly marine, as much as several thousand feet thick. Some of the narrow straits in this fault-block archipelago were only 10 miles wide, yet accumulated more than 10,000 ft of beds; in some of the deeper basins the total thickness, which includes an unknown thickness of Permian beds, is as much as 13,000 ft (Brill, 1952; Burbank and Goddard, 1937). The uplifts began in Early Pennsylvanian times and continued through Early Permian times, at different rates in different places. Immediately south-west of the horsts as much as 6000 ft of evaporites accumulated in a saline basin, chiefly in Mid-Pennsylvanian time.

EARLY MESOZOIC OROGENIES

At some time between late Permian and Early Cretaceous the formerly relatively stable area of southern Arizona was strongly deformed and widely invaded by plutonic rocks. Inasmuch as it became a source of clastic sediment in Early Triassic time, I assume that deformation began then. A date of 163 to 178 m.y. (Creasey and Kistler, 1962) obtained for one of the large intrusive bodies suggests that active plutonism was occurring in latest Triassic or early Jurassic time. The widespread cover of younger rocks and plutonic intrusions and metamorphism obscure the trends and positions of the orogenic belts near the Pacific, but some intrusions there also yield Triassic radiometric dates; orogenic sediments and volcanic rocks are common in all the coastal States and in Idaho and Nevada.

During the Lias large thrusts formed in a belt at least 20 miles wide and 40 miles long in southern Nevada. Late Triassic rocks in the upper plate rode southward over boulder-bearing detritus spilled from the advancing thrust-plate into the Liassic sea. The still-unconsolidated sediments were injected diapirically into the upper plate as it advanced (Ferguson and Muller, 1949).

This orogenic zone has been followed for about 40 miles along a north-east–south-west trend, almost at right-angles to the better-known Sierra Nevada trend; in both directions it disappears under Cainozoic cover. This belt may have been arcuate, veering north towards the east, for the Liassic (the latest marine) beds in west central Nevada are folded along meridional trends in the Eugene Mountains, about 150 miles farther north.

THE NEVADAN OROGENY

The main folding of the Sierra Nevada was in late Kimmeridgian time (Taliaferro, 1943, p. 134). This orogeny has long been known and it has become customary to refer any disturbance in the coastal States between early Jurassic and mid-Cretaceous times to it, but there are in fact several closely bracketed disturbances in this interval at various places in the western United States; indeed, the Jurassic strata of the Sierra itself have undergone at least two episodes of folding (P. C. Bateman, private communication, October 1962).

THE ROCKY MOUNTAIN GEOSYNCLINE

The two depositional troughs that had been formed in Mississippian time on either side of the Antler geanticline were drastically modified as a result of the Jurassic deformations. The western trough was displaced still farther westward; the eastern one was eliminated or perhaps in part migrated eastward to form the Rocky Mountain geosyncline, whose western boundary was near the former transition zone between geosyncline and shelf. Thence it extended far to the east over what had formerly been shelf and craton. The Rocky Mountain geosyncline began to form in Early Cretaceous time and reached its maximum during the Cenomanian, after which it slowly shrank as orogenic belts encroached on it from the west and it became filled with sediment. It was finally drained during the Palaeocene.

The Rocky Mountain geosyncline eventually came to hold more than a million cubic miles of dominantly clastic sediment, about five-sixths of it of Cenomanian and younger age (Reeside, 1944; Gilluly, 1949). Only a relatively small part of this volume was of juvenile volcanic rocks; the overwhelming bulk was derived from erosion of older rocks. The ostensible source-area, that is, a large part of the area between the Rocky Mountain geosyncline and the Pacific geosyncline, was only about

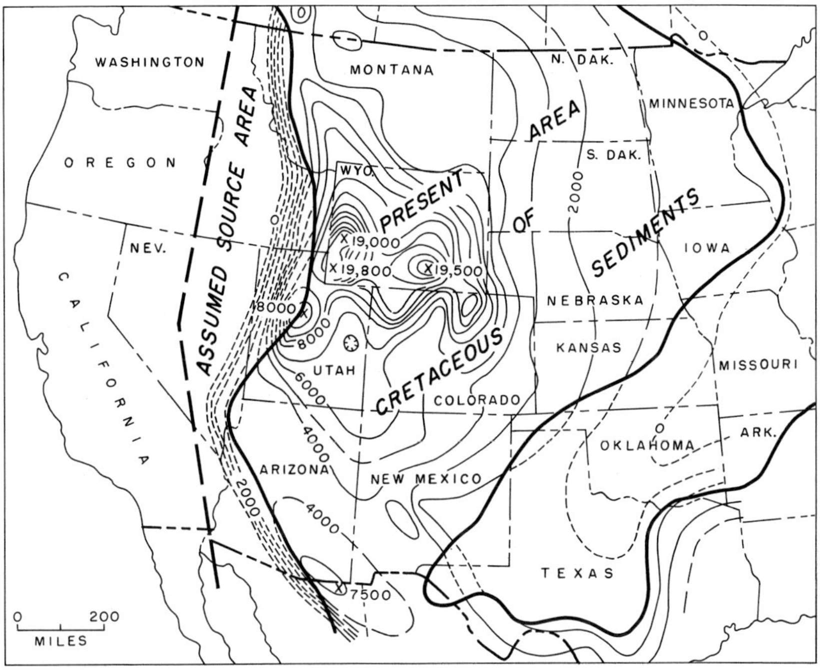

FIGURE 48.6
The Rocky Mountain geosyncline. Shows thickness of Upper Cretaceous sediments and the ostensible source-area. (Modified slightly from Reeside, 1944.)

160,000 square miles—at the most generous estimate 200,000 square miles (Figure 48.6). If this were indeed the whole source, an average denudation of about five miles is implied. The bulk involved is tremendous; it is equal to that which would be furnished by slicing 1600 ft from the entire area of the United States. While this huge volume was accumulating in the eastern part of the Cordilleran region, clastic beds of comparable or perhaps even greater thickness were accumulating in the Pacific geosyncline, west of the Sierra Nevada. Part—and perhaps a large part—of the western trough-filling was supplied from beyond the present coastline to the west, but some came from the east, thus limiting the area contributing to the Rocky Mountain geosyncline (Taliaferro, 1943).

The depth of erosion—an average of five miles—implied by such volumes of sediment is hard to reconcile with the known geology of the presumed source-area. One would expect far larger areas of Pre-Cambrian rocks to be exposed than are seen, for the fill of the Palaeozoic and earlier Mesozoic geosynclines, even at the most generous estimates, could not have sufficed to feed the Cretaceous troughs and still leave the widespread and thick inliers now exposed through the Cainozoic cover in the source-area. The difficulty is increased by the fact that much of the section in the presumed source-area was carbonate, whereas practically all the fill of the Rocky Mountain geosyncline was of siliceous clastic rocks. Nearly all the carbonates eroded from the source-area must have by-passed the Cretaceous geosyncline.

It seems necessary to postulate either: (1) erosion of the presently exposed batholithic areas to extreme depths (a possibility suggested by the sillimanite-kyanite grade of metamorphism around parts of the Idaho batholith); (2) erosion of former volcanic piles (of which there is little other evidence); or (3) a stream-pattern parallel to the fold-belt, like that of present-day Burma, by which much of the sediment was brought from Mexico or Canada.

THE 'LARAMIDE' OROGENY

The most intense shortening of the surficial rocks during the Cretaceous and early Tertiary in the eastern Cordillera took place along the western border of the Rocky Mountain geosyncline (Figure 48.7). Here, great thrusts telescoped the sedimentary cover but nowhere were more than trivial quantities of plutonic basement rocks involved. Although the larger thrusts must have moved several scores of miles and cumulatively shortened the outer strata by much greater amounts, all seem to have been simple décollement structures. In northern Montana a single thrust, the spectacular Lewis thrust, carried Belt rocks eastward over Late Cretaceous rocks for several tens of miles; farther south, in eastern Idaho and western Wyoming, several thrusts formed in succession from west to east. Still farther south, in the Basin Range province, the wide cover of alluvium prevents us from tracing individual structures from one range to another, but great thrusts are present to the southern point of Nevada. The thrusts in southern Arizona do not seem to belong to the same belt, but only reconnaissance geology has been done in most of the intervening country, and this is therefore uncertain.

East of the main thrust-belt in several parts of Montana, Wyoming, Colorado, and Utah, the deformation consisted chiefly of differential vertical displacements in which anticlinals were uplifted and the intervening synclinals depressed many thousands of feet, producing structural relief as great as six or even ten miles, within a few miles horizontally. Much of the differential movement was by flexure, but some high-angle reverse faults emerged at the borders of the uplifts. Several of these

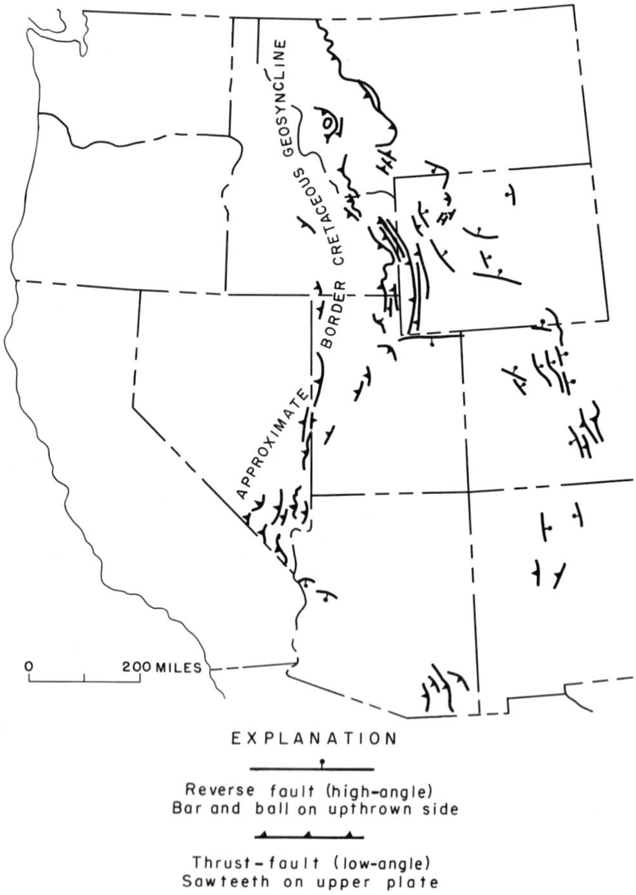

FIGURE 48.7
Thrust faults of the Late Cretaceous and Early Tertiary of the eastern Cordillera. (Modified from Cohee and others, 1961.)

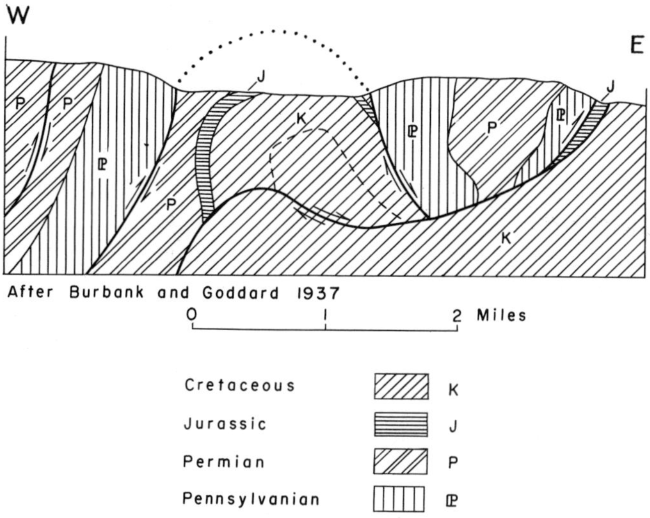

FIGURE 48.8
Section through one of the thrusts in Huerfano Park, Colorado. (Based on section by Burbank and Goddard, 1937.)

activated considerable surficial slides that have sometimes been interpreted as thrust-faults.

The trend of several of the uplifts, the great Uinta Range, the Owl Creek Range, the Sweetwater and Stillwater uplifts, is nearly normal to that of the Cordillera as a whole, and their steep reverse and gravity faults are also transverse to the general grain.

In the Colorado Rockies steep reverse faults are common along the flexures and there are a few low-angle thrusts, most of which have much smaller displacements than the faults of the western belt, although, unlike these, they involve both basement rocks and their sedimentary cover.

One noteworthy structure in Wyoming, the Heart Mountain detachment thrust, moved Mississippian and younger rocks for more than 28 miles to emplace them on middle Eocene rocks (Dake, 1918; Hewett, 1920; Pierce, 1957).

The remarkable folded late Eocene thrust mapped by Burbank and Goddard (1937) in Huerfano Park (Figure 48.8) is exceptional in bringing about several miles of superficial crustal shortening at the very border of the plains. It travelled several miles and carries a completely inverted syncline of Cretaceous and older rocks over Cretaceous of the lower plate.

The Rocky Mountain orogeny that has long and misleadingly been called 'Laramide' may have begun in Albian time in Utah (Spieker, 1946) and certainly began in Turonian time in Montana, Idaho, Utah, and southern Nevada (Cobban and Reeside, 1952; Hutchinson, 1956; Hewett and others, 1936). Several well-dated pulses marked by unconformities and orogenic sediments occur in late Campanian time in central Utah (Spieker, 1946, p. 145; Lautenschlager, 1954), in Maestrichtian time in Wyoming (Veatch, 1907; Rubey, Oriel, and Tracey, 1961), in Maestrichtian-Montian-Thanetian times and several times during the Eocene in Wyoming (Thomas, 1949, p. 27; Keefer, 1960), in Thanetian-Sparnacian time in Montana (Spieker, 1946, p. 143), and at many other places during the Palaeocene and Eocene.

As many as seven angular unconformities within the Eocene have been found in New Mexico (Johnson, Dixon, and Wanek, 1956). In places there are unconformities between Palaeocene and Oligocene and between Oligocene and Miocene; even Pliocene rocks are tilted (DeVoto, 1961). The major deformation ended, however, with the late Eocene. But the time-span of the pre-Oligocene episodes of orogeny that have geen grouped as 'Laramide' was thus by no means limited to the span of the 'Laramie Formation'—say, Maestrichtian to Montian—and immediately later time, as has generally been assumed, but included all the long interval from Turonian to late Eocene, at least 60 m.y.

THE PACIFIC GEOSYNCLINE

The Pacific geosyncline (Figure 48.9) is less well known than the Rocky Mountain because of abundant intrusions, metamorphism, and the widespread cover of younger rocks. Throughout Cretaceous time clastic and volcanic rocks accumulated in great thickness. Although there is abundant indirect evidence in the sedimentary record of crustal deformation through the western Cordillera, direct evidence such as is furnished by closely bracketed folds, thrusts, and unconformities is of only sporadic occurrence. Well-dated orogenic pulses took place in early, in middle, and (twice) in late Cretaceous time in California (Taliaferro, 1943; Jones, 1959), twice during the late Cretaceous in Nevada (Willden, 1958; Hewett and others, 1936; Nolan, Merriam, and Williams, 1956), and in the mid-Cretaceous in Oregon. In California, angular unconformities have been mapped at the base of the Palaeocene, between lower and middle Eocene, between middle and upper Eocene, at the top of the Oligocene, and at several other horizons in the early Cainozoic (Hoots, Bear, and Kleinpell, 1954). More than forty separate pulses are recorded during Miocene and later time in California, where the marine record is more complete than anywhere else in the region (Figure 48.10). Doubtless many other of the Pacific areas were similarly active, but much of the record has been lost through erosion or burial.

The depositional basins along the present Pacific littoral during the late Mesozoic and Cainozoic were much more interrupted by islands and peninsulas than the broad geosynclines of the Palaeozoic and of the eastern Cordilleran Cretaceous. Even so, many basins were large; the Ventura Basin of southern California, for example, is almost as large as the early Palaeozoic geosyncline of England and Wales. Space does not permit detailed discussion of the tectonic evolution of so complex an area; I can mention only a few features that seem to me especially interesting and instructive.

The hazard of extrapolating the age of one geological structure to a near neighbour is well illustrated in the Los Angeles basin. The early Pleistocene beds of the Signal Hill anticline were tilted to dips of 60° or even 80° in Mid-Pleistocene time while the parallel Wil-

FIGURE 48.9
Areas of Cretaceous or Tertiary marine invasion of the Pacific States

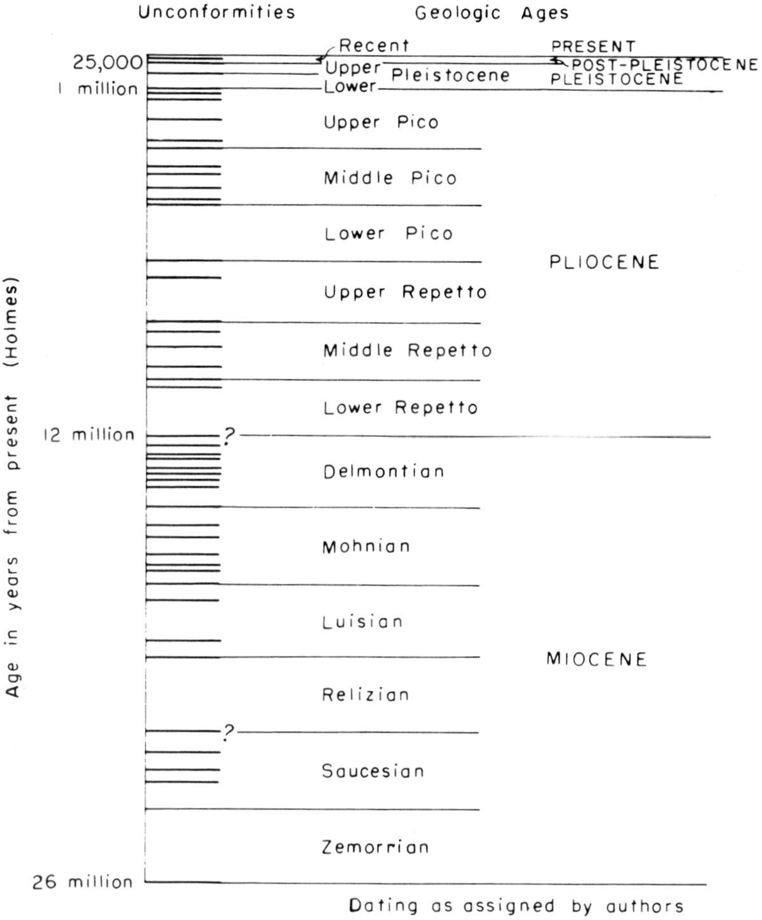

FIGURE 48.10
Unconformities reported in 60 oilfield descriptions in California. (Data from *Calif. Div. Mines Bull.*, v. 118, 1943.)

mington anticline, only three miles away, whose structural relief of more than 1000 ft was acquired in mid-Pliocene time, remained completely dormant (Figure 48.11).

Long-continued tectonic activity is convincingly demonstrated in the transverse range north of Los Angeles (Figure 48.12). The Ridge Basin, a graben 6 to 10 miles wide, that crosses the trend of the Ventura Basin for more than 20 miles, began to sink in middle Miocene time. More than 40,000 ft of beds accumulated before the faulting stopped in late Pliocene time and both bounding faults were buried beneath unbroken sediments. A talus- and fan-breccia along one of the bounding faults is more than five miles in stratigraphical thickness, but extends basinward along the strike only about 4000 ft before it interdigitates with fine-grained lacustrine and fluviatile beds. Its thickness is almost ten times its length along the strike. The relations can only mean that the downfaulting of the graben was so nearly continuous that the facies change from fan- to valley-sediment remained always within a few hundred feet of a constant distance from the scarp. The scarps continued to yield coarse fan-gravels but were never so high as to flood the entire graben with them at any time between mid-Miocene and late Pliocene time (Crowell, 1954).

The duration of this graben subsidence thus spans the time of several compressional phases

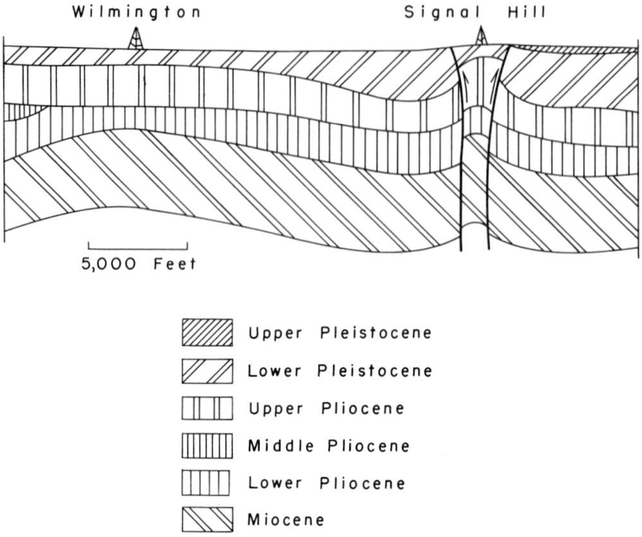

FIGURE 48.11
Cross section through the Wilmington and Signal Hill anticlines, Los Angeles basin, California. (From data in *Calif. Div. Mines Bull.*, V. 118, 1943.)

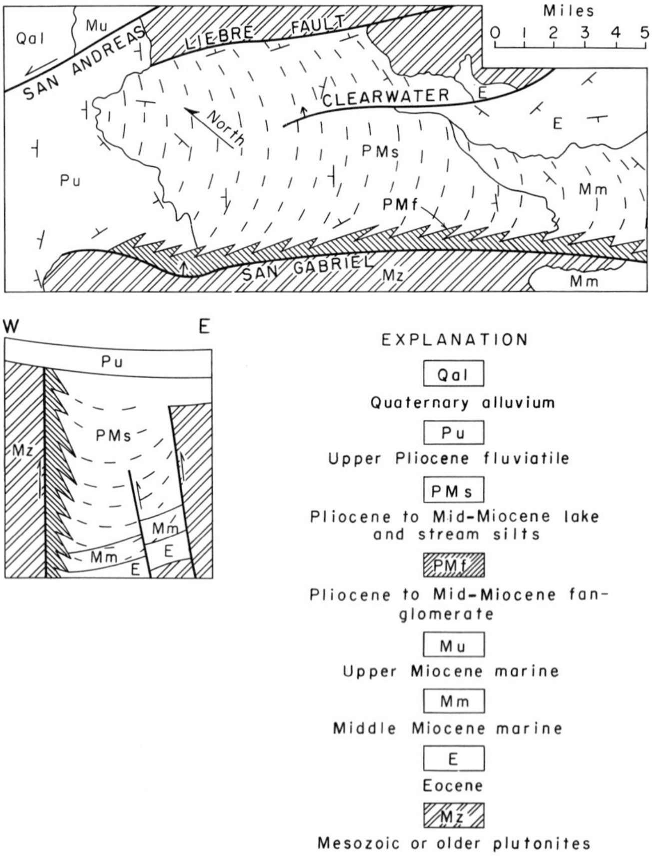

FIGURE 48.12
Diagrammatic map and section of the Ridge basin area, Los Angeles and Ventura Counties, California. (Simplified after Crowell, 1954.)

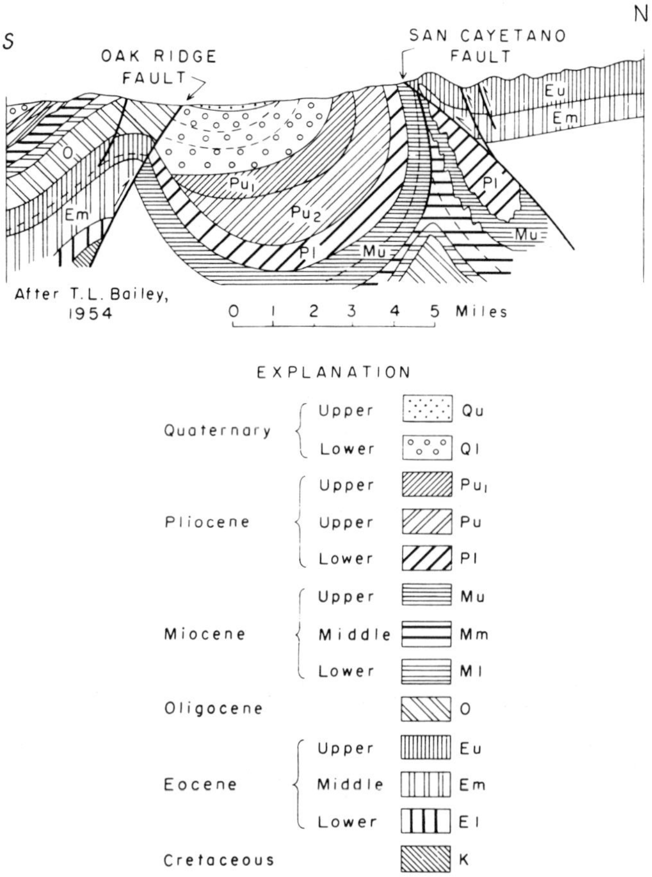

FIGURE 48.13
Cross section of the Santa Clara River valley, southern California. Shows the Oak Ridge and San Cayetano faults. (After T. L. Bailey, *in* Bailey and Jahns, 1954.)

nearby, proving again what so much of the Cainozoic history of California demonstrates: the assumption of world-wide episodes of compression alternating with others of tension is quite untenable. Crustal deformation in the past, like that of the present day, was compressional in one area at the same time that it was tensional a few miles away.

The Ventura anticline formed in mid-Pleistocene time in the Transverse Ranges northwest of Los Angeles. It appears from surface observations to be a normal anticline, but the many scores of oil-wells that penetrate the structure at depth have shown that thrust-faults of several thousand feet displacement face each other from either side of the fold and, indeed, interfere at depth. Both limbs of a contemporaneous syncline in the Santa Clara valley are overturned and overridden by thrust-faults that face each other within a mile or two and, but for the erosion of their emerging prows, would interfere with each other (Figure 48.13). A similar thrust in the neighbourhood (Aliso Canyon), is still growing. The thrust emerges on the surface and folds the terrace gravels in front of its advancing prow.

A similar example of a still-active thrust is the well-known one in the Buena Vista oilfield on the west side of the Great Valley of California (Koch, 1933; Wilt, 1958). This fault is growing at the rate of nearly seven feet per century, and since it was first recognized about thirty years ago has shortened the span between power-line supports on opposite sides by almost two feet. Oil-wells that penetrate the fault at depths of almost 800 ft have been sheared off so that they have had to be redrilled, and it is apparent that this is not a superficial slump but an active thrust-fault.

In the Los Angeles basin, stream-terraces and wave-cut surfaces of very late Pleistocene age are folded into anticlines and synclines whose relief is several hundred feet. Precise levelling in connexion with engineering projects has shown several of these anticlines to be rising now at a rate of a foot in 75 years (Stone, 1961). Some synclinal areas are subsiding even faster, but their lowering might be partly due to dewatering of aquifers at depth so that the tectonic significance of subsidence is ambiguous.

It is nevertheless obvious that this rate of uplift, even if continued for only a relatively brief time geologically, is adequate to make mountains comparable to any on earth. The present is an active orogenic time in California.

With the foundation of this very incomplete geological history and cursory comment I should like now to turn to a series of topics of special interest to western American geologists, but I hope of wider interest also. The first of these is the plateau problem.

SOME SPECIFIC TOPICS

THE COLORADO PLATEAU

An area in the southern Cordillera about 400 miles across and 500 miles long—the site of the future Colorado Plateau—although bordered on the north, south, east, and west by belts of Cretaceous and early Tertiary folds and thrusts, remained undeformed except by some simple monoclines of pre-Sparnacian age, and a few younger normal faults like those of the adjoining Basin Range province. The uplift of the plateau was long delayed, perhaps until Pliocene or even early Pleistocene time, but its structural character was established before the close of the Eocene (Figure 48.14).

That the plateau uplift resulted from subcrustal processes is certain. At the close of the Cretaceous and during the Palaeocene the area must have lain nearly at sea-level. Today the average elevation of any reference surface over

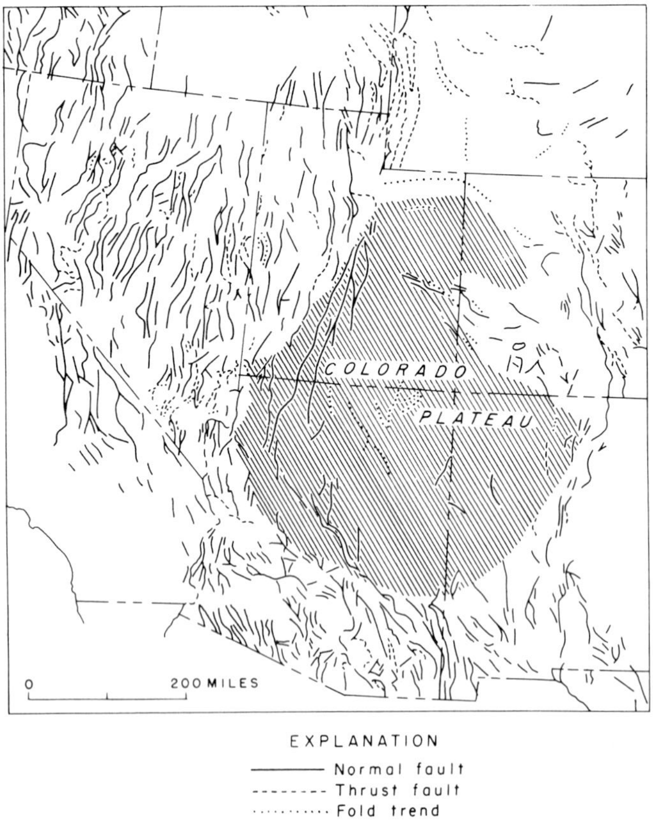

FIGURE 48.14
The structural setting of the Colorado Plateau. (From Cohee and others, 1961.)

the plateau (the top of the Permian, for example) is nearly a mile higher than it was at the close of Cretaceous time.

Although there were several episodes of continental deposition and erosion, only small volumes of rock were involved, except for the Eocene rocks on the north and north-west parts of the plateau. On the assumptions of isostasy and the usually chosen density contrasts between mantle and crustal rocks, the erosion of beds above the reference surface can account for only a few hundred feet of this uplift. It can readily be shown that thermal expansion of a normal crust could not account for such an elevation without a temperature increment sufficient to melt the crust.

Explosion seismometry has recently demonstrated that the crustal thickness beneath the Basin Range province is somewhat less than 30 km (Berg and others, 1960; Diment, Stewart, and Roller, 1961), whereas that beneath the plateau is nearly 45 km, the one less than, the other much greater than, the average for the western United States (L. C. Pakiser, U.S. Geological Survey, written communication, 1962). The many thermal springs of the Basin Range province and the widespread evidence of Quaternary volcanism suggest that the area is one of unusually high heat flow. If the Mohorovičić discontinuity marks a phase change, higher-than-normal heat flow should tend to favour inversion to the low-density phases, and thereby to thicken rather than to thin the crust.

These facts suggest that the Mohorovičić discontinuity is here due to a chemical contrast rather than to a phase inversion. The geology shows that the Basin Range province (or at least the part immediately west and south of the plateau) has been more deeply eroded than the plateau so that formerly it must have stood higher than the plateau, yet now it is several thousand feet lower. These relations suggest that the crust beneath the Basin Ranges has been thinned, permitting its relative subsidence, while that beneath the plateau has thickened, giving rise to the uplift.

The differences in elevation and crustal thickness of the two provinces are compatible with the uplift of the plateau having resulted from isostatic response to the transfer of deeper crustal material from beneath the Basin Range province to a position beneath the plateau. The crustal thickening beneath the plateau seems reasonably to account for its uplift. I suggest that such a transfer might have come about through currents in the mantle. Several other features of western geology seem also to suggest currents in the mantle and perhaps even to permit our considering the somewhat unorthodox idea of subcrustal erosion and deposition.

THE BASIN RANGE PROBLEM

The Basin Ranges, which characterize large areas in Arizona, New Mexico, eastern California, Nevada, Utah, eastern Idaho, western Montana, and southern Oregon, have puzzled geologists for ninety years, ever since their structure—dominated by great normal faults—was recognized as different from that of many other ranges. Although local groups of these ranges are roughly parallel, the trend varies widely from one part of the province to another; in New Mexico and south-eastern Arizona the trend is generally meridional, but in south-western Arizona it swings to west–north-west. In much of Nevada and western Utah the trend is again north, but the most westerly ranges, the Sierra and Inyo, and others nearby, trend north-west, and some of those in the north of the province in Oregon trend due west.

The ranges have been developing for a long time; some may have started their growth in the Eocene, though the evidence is indirect (Gilluly, 1932). Certainly some of the great normal faults were formed in Oligocene time (Stock and Bode, 1935), and many more in the Miocene and Pliocene. The present ranges owe much of their relief to Pliocene and younger faulting (Blackwelder, 1931; Axelrod, 1957; Thompson, 1960). Several have risen many feet in historic time (Page, 1935; Slemmons, 1956); others seem to have become dormant; they rise above broad pediments rather than debris fans (Bryan, 1922).

The origin of these structures has long been debated. Some have thought that the faults represent the response of the brittle upper part of the crust to plastic deformation at depth, and thus are forming in response to crustal compression (Gilbert, 1875). This view, which I formerly held, seems inconsistent with the normal displacement shown on nearly every fault. On the other hand, the thrust-faulting of probable Pliocene age in the southern Great Basin (Noble, 1941; Hewett, 1954, 1956) was both preceded and followed by strong normal faulting. Nolan (1935) adduced good evidence for an alternation of thrust-faulting and normal faulting episodes in western Utah. The Basin Range faults seem to demand crustal extension in directions normal to their trends, which means, at one place or another, in all points of the compass, though chiefly east–west for the belt as a whole (Russell, 1883).

Because of a local converging or even intersecting plan of some faults in southern Oregon, the suggestion has been made (Allison, 1949; Donath, 1959) that the faults have formed as shear failures caused by north–south compression in the crust. It is difficult to reconcile the near-vertical attitude of the faults with such a mechanism; one would expect failure under compression to take place by shearing toward the free surface of the earth, with strike nearly normal to the axis of compression. East–west-trending normal faults of the same age just a few score miles to the north, and faults with circular graben not far to the east (Fuller and Waters, 1929), do not seem to accord with the stress orientation suggested.

Still another suggestion is that the faults are indeed due to tension in the crust arising from a clockwise torque embracing the entire western part of the continent (Becker, 1934). On this hypothesis one might expect to find the greatest concentration of faults where the torque would seem to have been greatest, that is, near the great rifts like the San Andreas. It is clear that there is no such concentration.

It has been plausibly suggested that the eruption of the vast masses of siliceous lavas and tuffs of the Cainozoic of the western United States—estimated at 50,000 cubic miles and doubtless derived from the melting of the crust itself—led to the crustal collapse reflected in the Basin Range faults (Mackin, 1960). Because there are both large areas of Basin Range structure many miles from the nearest siliceous eruptive rocks and large areas of siliceous eruptive rocks in which Basin Range structures are subordinate or absent, this suggestion seems unsatisfactory by itself.

Another suggestion, prompted by the likelihood that the Basin Range province is one of high heat flow (as attested by its many thermal springs and signs of relatively recent volcanism), is that the crust in this area is thickening and expanding laterally because of phase transitions converting mantle to crust at the Mohorovičić discontinuity (Thompson, 1960). Unfortunately for this theory, explosion seismometry has shown that the crust beneath the province is probably considerably thinner than the continental average, and almost certainly much thinner than that beneath the Colorado Plateau (L. C. Pakiser, written communication, 1962).

My personal preference borrows from both these ideas: it is that the Basin Range faults are the result of lateral transfer of crustal material from beneath the province to the area of the plateau. Both this movement and the formation of the siliceous lavas may be connected with extraordinary heat flow because of subcrustal currents.

TRANSCURRENT (STRIKE-SLIP) FAULTS

The fame of the San Andreas fault and the demonstrated components of strike-slip on many other faults have aroused much interest in such structures. Figure 48.15 shows the faults along which major strike-slip movement appears to have been demonstrated. Many others have been so interpreted, but on evidence that seems to me weak or non-existent.

One of the major strike-slip faults of the Cordillera is the Osburn fault of northern Idaho and western Montana (Hershey 1916; Umpleby & Jones 1923; Wallace & others 1960). Although the evidence is inconclusive, this and the branching Hope fault (J. E. Harrison, oral communication, 1962), one with about 16 miles, the other with 8 miles of right-lateral movement indicated, both seem to have been active in Pre-Cambrian time. Their Palaeozoic history is unknown for lack of record, but the Hope fault offsets the earliest batholithic intrusions of mid-Mesozoic age, and feather-faults splitting from it are occupied by later (but still probably Cretaceous) intrusions. These and the more southerly Placer Creek fault do not seem to have been

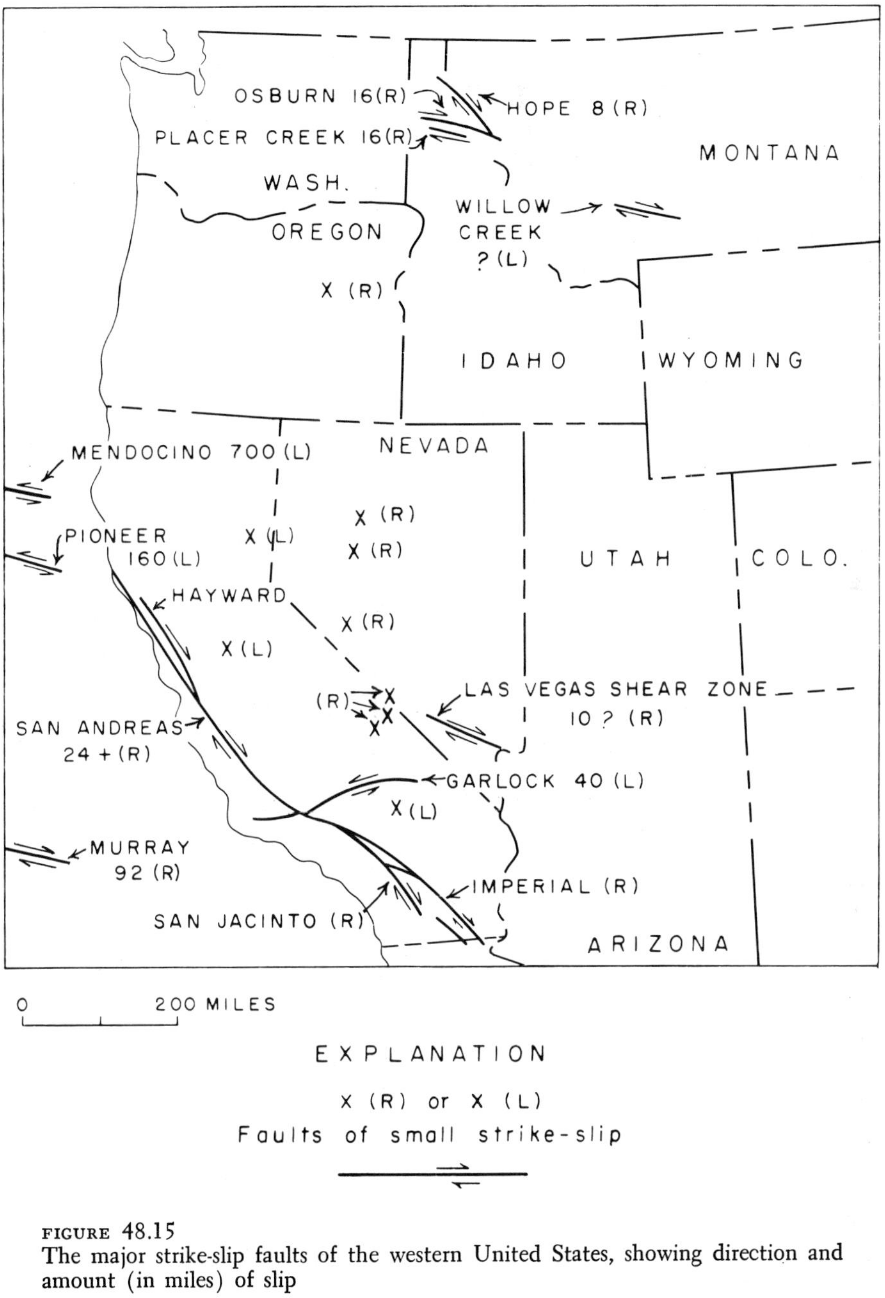

FIGURE 48.15
The major strike-slip faults of the western United States, showing direction and amount (in miles) of slip

active since late Miocene time, when their western extremities were flooded by the Columbia River lava. Toward the east, Cainozoic cover buries them, but these faults do not appear to have extended across the Cordillera, as has sometimes been suggested.

All the other demonstrated strike-slip faults of large displacement are in California and Nevada. Right-lateral displacement of a few miles is strongly suggested in southern Nevada (Longwell, 1950) and modern earthquake faults have shown a similar strike-slip component farther north-west (Callaghan and Gianella, 1935; Gianella and Callaghan, 1934; Slemmons, 1956), so that it has been suggested that a major strike-slip fault, called the 'Walker

Lane,' comparable to the San Andreas fault, trends almost parallel to the Nevada–California boundary in its northwestern course. Such a fault, if it exists, cannot, however, have had movement remotely comparable to that of the San Andreas fault, for it fails appreciably to offset structures transverse to it in the Hawthorne area (Ferguson and Muller, 1949).

A so-called 'Texas Lineament' has been postulated to trend from southern California far to the east in Texas, but there is no evidence in either Palaeozoic or younger rocks of its existence.

By any criterion the greatest of the recognized strike-slip faults is the San Andreas fault in California, which extends for more than 600 miles from the Gulf of California to the Pacific north of San Francisco. Near San Francisco it is paralleled by the Hayward and Calaveras faults, and toward the south the San Jacinto and Imperial faults split off as branches. Estimates of the age and displacement of the San Andreas fault vary from pre-Cretaceous, with possible cumulative right-lateral displacement of 350 miles (Hill and Dibblee, 1953; Crowell and Walker, 1961; Hamilton, 1961), to late Pleistocene, with a cumulative movement of less than a mile (Taliaferro, 1943, p. 161). Noble's (1926) estimate of 24 miles displacement since the Palaeocene seems very likely to be conservative; it is by no means impossible that the movement has been as great as the largest figures suggested, but as yet these are based on 'spot' correlations and not on consistent comparisons of the intervening transects. The minimal estimates seem explicable only by a very narrow definition of the fault and by ignoring its branches. For the intersecting Garlock fault, a left-lateral displacement of 40 miles since mid-Mesozoic time, based on offset dyke-swarms (Smith, 1960), seems reasonable; if accepted, it would account for the notable change in trend of the San Andreas fault near the junction of the two.

Geodetic measurements and offset building foundations prove that deformation is now proceeding on the San Andreas fault at the rate of nearly 5 cm a year near San Francisco (Whitten, 1948), 1 cm a year near Hollister, about 100 miles to the south, and 2.5 mm per year near Cholame, 75 miles still farther southeast (Whitten and Claire, 1960). The San Andreas fault reaches the coast near the east end of the Pioneer fracture-zone of the Pacific door, or, if one assumes an eastern branch from the main trend, close to the Cape Mendocino fracture-trend. Both these fracture-zones in the Pacific floor have great displacement, one about 160, the other perhaps 700 miles, judging from apparent offsets of magnetic anomalies (Vaucquier and others, 1961). It is not, however, apparent how they can be related to the San Andreas fault, for their apparent displacements are all left-lateral. There is no evidence of the further extension of the oceanic fractures through the continent nor of the continental fault into the ocean basin. Although it is highly probable that very great movement has occurred along the rift, the continental border shows no apparent offset. Where has the wedge of the continent west of the rift gone? And how have these huge differential movements been so smoothly accommodated? The tectonic unconformity between continent and ocean seems to demand that the two crustal segments are completely uncoupled; the interface between them must be a zone of great differential movement.

Consideration of the mechanical properties of a crustal segment more than 600 miles long and not more than 20 or 25 miles thick seems clearly to imply that the San Andreas rift is due to differential movement within the mantle, with the two segments of the crust riding passively past each other. No conceivable set of forces within the crust could permit shearing on an essentially vertical interface and at notably different rates in different segments along a boundary of this length. To my mind this is another of many lines of evidence that the tectonic and plutonic processes are closely related to currents in the mantle, and that truly gigantic differential movements between continental and oceanic crustal segments are implied.

VOLCANIC HISTORY

Submarine volcanic rocks appear in great volume in Early Cambrian time in Nevada and abound in the western part of the Cordilleran geosyncline in each of the systems of the Palaeozoic and Mesozoic and in the Tertiary.

The Cambrian and Ordovician volcanic rocks are chiefly andesitic and basaltic but many of those of Silurian and later time are rhyolites or quartz-keratophyres. In the Devonian, siliceous and subsiliceous lavas are closely associated.

Although absolute continuity cannot be proved, one of the greatest volcanic fields of all geological time existed in the Pacific States and Canada during the Permian and Early Triassic (Figure 48.16). Wherever rocks of these ages are exposed between south-eastern California and Alaska, great thicknesses of submarine spilites, keratophyres, and related volcanic rocks are found. The total volume of these rocks must be many times that of the great Columbia River flood-basalts.

There are thick Jurassic andesitic volcanic rocks in California (Taliaferro, 1943), Oregon (Dickinson, 1961), north-eastern Washington (R. G. Yates, written communication, 1962) and British Columbia (Little, 1960). Neocomian and Late Cretaceous volcanic rocks are present in northern Washington (Barksdale, 1960).

The eastern Cordillera had little volcanism in the Palaeozoic; the earliest volcanic rocks of note are ashes of Triassic and Jurassic ages. The first lavas appear in the Early Cretaceous of Arizona (Brown, 1939; Bryant and Kinnison, 1954; Gilluly, 1956) and New Mexico (Lasky, 1947). Volcanism began in the middle Albian of Montana (Gwinn, 1960; Klepper, Weeks, and Ruppel, 1957), was more active in the Late Cretaceous (Lyons, 1944; Weeks and Klepper, 1954), and persisted into the Palaeocene (Iddings and Weed, 1894; Rogers, 1913; Larsen and Cross, 1956).

In the Eocene, volcanic rocks spread widely over most of the western Cordillera (Waters, 1955), and indeed over much of the eastern Cordillera as well (Hague, 1896; Larsen and Cross, 1956) (Figure 48.17). A great field of submarine eruptions extended along the present coast of Washington and Oregon for more than 400 miles and for more than 100 miles inland, perhaps much more, for the eastern limit is overlapped by the great flood of Columbia River basalt. In the Olympic Mountains of Washington, where these volcanic rocks are exposed in a huge overturned fold, they are as much as 50,000 ft thick; their volume is greater than that of the better-

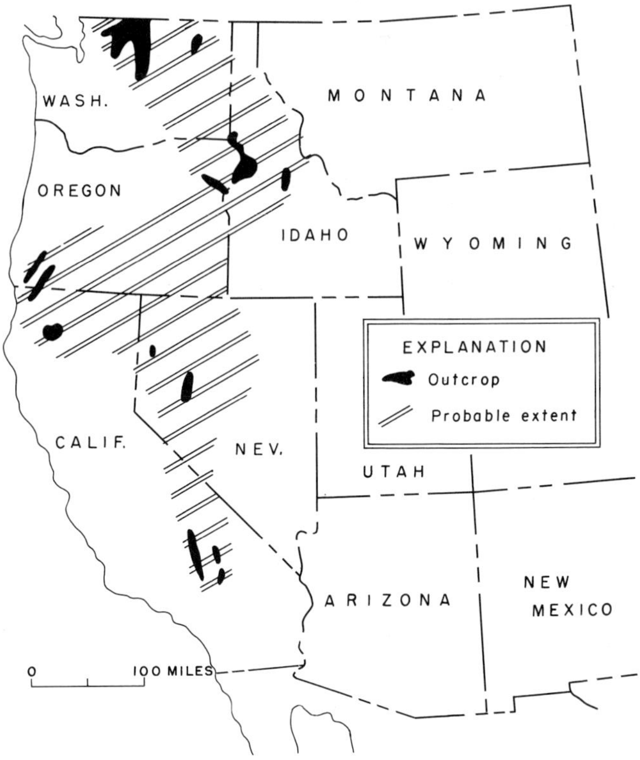

FIGURE 48.16
Exposed areas and probable extent of the Permian–Early Triassic submarine lava field in the western United States. The field actually extended as far north as Alaska. (Modified from *Geologic Map of the United States*, U.S. Geological Survey, 1933.)

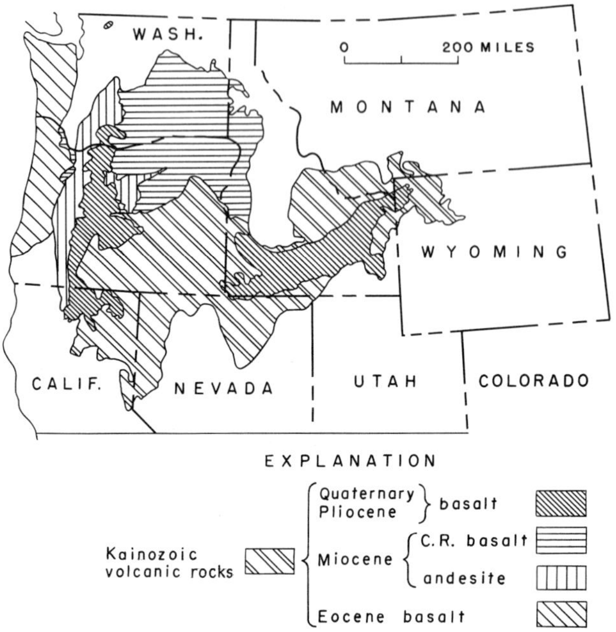

FIGURE 48.17
Cenozoic volcanic fields of the northwestern United States

known Columbia River basalts, of Miocene and possible Pliocene age (Waters, 1955), and very much larger than that of the Pliocene and Pleistocene basalts of southern Idaho.

There is a noteworthy contrast between the composition of the Cainozoic volcanic rocks of the coastal States and those farther east. Although rhyolitic pyroclastic rocks abound in the Oligocene of both eastern Washington (Waters, 1955) and eastern Oregon (Hay, 1961), the overwhelming bulk of the volcanic rocks of these States is basaltic and andesitic (Callaghan, 1951). In all the other States in the area here dealt with, the volcanic rocks are dominantly siliceous—quartz-latites and rhyolites; andesite and basalt are common, but subordinate. Siliceous ash-flows are particularly abundant in the eastern and southern parts of the Great Basin; their aggregate bulk is certainly fully as great as that of the Columbia River basalt and has been estimated at 50,000 cubic miles (Mackin, 1960).

PHANEROZOIC PLUTONISM

Although we have clear evidence of several very large-scale orogenic episodes in Mississippian, Pennsylvanian, and Permian times, there are no definitely dated Palaeozoic plutons in the western United States; the oldest granitic intrusion of the Phanerozoic is Late Triassic, in southern Arizona (Creasey and Kistler, 1962). It is likely that several granites of south-western Arizona that have been called Pre-Cambrian in reconnaissance work are also of late Triassic or early Jurassic age.

Radiometric studies (Curtis, Evernden, and Lipson, 1958; Creasey and Kistler, 1962; Larsen and others, 1958) and field-relations (Taliaferro, 1943) suggest that there were three main periods of plutonic activity during the Mesozoic, one in the Late Triassic (about 175 m.y.), one extending from late Jurassic to early Cretaceous (about 140 m.y.), and one in the Middle Cretaceous (about 110 to 80 m.y.). The geological evidence in the Sierra, though not sharply decisive, suggests somewhat greater ages than these numbers would imply on the Holmes scale (Paul C. Bateman, written communication, 1962). The Holmes scale need not, however, require revision on this account. The radiometric dates may not be those of the emplacement of these gigantic intrusions of the Sierra, Peninsular Ranges, and the Idaho batholith (all of which must have been at very great depth to judge from their metamorphic aureoles), but the dates at which the rocks cooled to temperatures at which the mica lattice could retain argon.

The volume of the early Late Cretaceous plutons must be several hundred times that of all the other granitic masses of the western United States, a fact long ago emphasized by Lindgren (1915) but not often stressed in the literature although Knopf (1955) has recently re-emphasized this (Figure 48.18). The intrusions of latest Cretaceous to Eocene age, which have been called 'Laramide,' are trivial in bulk (except perhaps in southern Arizona) and some of those shown in Figure 48.18 as of this age may well belong to the later and considerably more voluminous mid-Tertiary group. The mid-Tertiary plutons are chiefly in the north-west, where the Snoqualmie granodiorite and associated intrusions have long been known to be of Miocene age (Smith and Mendenhall, 1900). It is very likely that some of these mid-Tertiary intrusions of Washington and northern Oregon may prove to be mere cupolas of a very much larger batholith, not yet reached by erosion (A. C. Waters, oral communication, 1962). Some smaller bodies in the Colorado Plateau and in south-eastern Arizona are probably also of this age, as are some that have been injected into both the Idaho batholith and some of the intrusions of north-eastern Washington. There is no question that the mid-Tertiary intrusions are second only to the early Late Cretaceous batholiths in bulk. They far exceed the 'Laramide' intrusions (70 to 50 m.y.) in bulk.

The plutonic rocks of the region exhibit three noteworthy features. First, there is no close association of tectonics with plutonism. For example, the great Antler orogeny of Mis-

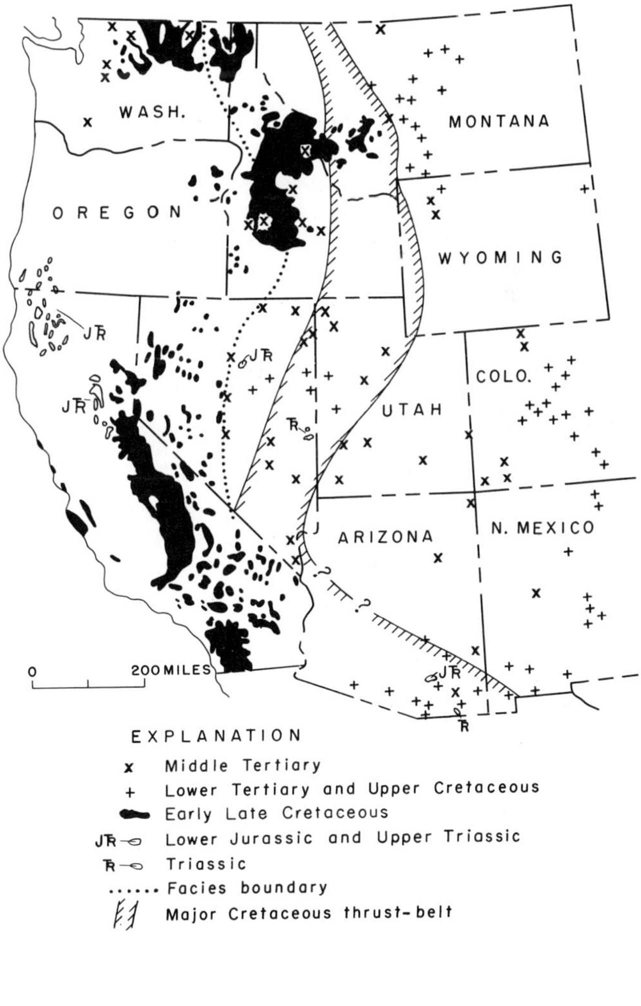

FIGURE 48.18
The Phanerozoic granitic rocks of the western United States. Age assignments of many small plutons are arbitrary. (Compiled from the *Tectonic Map of the United States*, 1961, and with consideration of all published radiometric data to 1962.)

sissippian age, the Ancestral Rockies of Pennsylvanian age, and the many episodes of thrusting and folding of the Permian and Early Triassic of the Great Basin, are all without associated plutonic activity or metamorphic phenomena of note. The great belt of Cretaceous thrusts has few and small plutons, and the mid-Tertiary plutons do not seem to be at all closely related to any tectonic disturbance, except perhaps in southern Arizona and more definitely in northern Washington. One of the general assumptions of geology has been that there is a close association of tectonism and granitic intrusion. In the western United States, we can assert that plutonism is indeed associated with orogeny, but the converse is quite as certainly not true.

The second noteworthy fact is that although structural and sedimentary evidence, considered together, show that crustal deformation and surface volcanism were both proceeding throughout Phanerozoic time in a quasi-continuous (though doubtless episodic) way, plutonic activity was anything but uniform in time. The complete lack of known Palaeozoic plutons may perhaps be explained by concealment of critical contacts or by inadequate radiometric sampling, but there is no doubt that they are really disproportionally deficient in both number and bulk as compared to those of later time.

Furthermore, the overwhelming majority of the great granitic intrusions—fully a hundred times and perhaps a thousand times the bulk of all the rest together—were emplaced in an interval of perhaps 30 million years, say five per cent of Phanerozoic time. The plausible assumption that magmatic activity as revealed by volcanism at the surface should be accompanied by plutonic phenomena at depth can, of course, be supported by evidence at many individual localities, but quite certainly it is not supported by the history of the area as a whole. No major plutons correspond to the great Palaeozoic, early Mesozoic, or (except perhaps in southern Arizona) to the early Tertiary volcanic rocks. It has long been recognized that flood-basalts are not generally associated with either plutonism or orogeny, but it is indeed surprising to me to find vast eruptions of andesite and more siliceous volcanic rocks to which no plutonic intrusions can reasonably be referred as parental. This absence of related plutonic rocks does not seem to be a matter of depth of erosion, again with the possible exception of southern Arizona. The history of the segment of the continent as a whole is one of uniformitarianism where both tectonism and volcanism are concerned, but of catastrophism as far as plutonism is concerned.

The third fact is that the great late Mesozoic intrusions have formed on the eastern border of an area that throughout Phanerozoic time had been dominantly eugeosynclinal. Although quartz-bearing keratophyres and rhyolites are interspersed through many of the older volcanic rocks, and the Jurassic volcanic province of central Oregon is largely andesitic (Dickinson, 1961), most of the volcanic rocks of the eugeosynclines contain little silica. The idea has frequently been advanced that eugeosynclines form on an originally oceanic crust. Quantitative considerations of silicate equilibria, as well as much geological evidence, seem clearly to demand that granitic batholiths should be derived from remobilization of a sialic crust. It is impossible to reconcile the evolution of such a tremendous volume of siliceous plutonic rocks as that of the Idaho, Sierra, and Peninsular masses—exposed over nearly 150,000 square miles—with the common assumption that eugeosynclines develop on a simatic crust, unless one at the same time grants that sial in great quantities can be transferred laterally beneath this crust. Subcrustal flow of gigantic volumes of differentiating mantle or the overriding of smaller but still huge masses of foundering sialic crust would seem to be demanded.

THE PACIFIC LITTORAL

One of the most striking things about the Pacific coast of the United States is the narrowness of the continental shelf (Figure 48.9)· Off southern California the basin-and-ridge topography is very marked and resembles that of the Basin Range province. Farther north the 500-ft sub-sea contour is nowhere more than 40 miles from the coast, and for long stretches it is not half as far. Much of the Cretaceous and Tertiary sediment of the coastal States was derived from the west, from areas that have since vanished beneath the Pacific. What has happened to these source-areas? And what has become of the products of denudation of the continent that must have gone to the Pacific during late Mesozoic and Tertiary time? Gravity and seismic data show that the Pacific floor is oceanic right up to the edge of the shelf, yet many Tertiary formations of the Pacific coast are thousands of feet thick at the coast-line. The volume of the sediment in the continental terrace falls far short of the volume that must have been deposited, assuming a reasonable 'feathering-out' of sediment fans from the shore. The unaccounted-for sediment surely cannot have disappeared through phase changes that gave it the density of mantle material. It seems to me that we must account for the missing sial and the wedge displaced by the San Andreas fault by carrying them under the continent by currents in the upper mantle.

CONCLUSIONS

The generalizations that seem to me to be justified from the history of the western United States include the following:

(1) The visible structures of the region do not imply shortening of the crust as a whole at any time within the Phanerozoic; all can be considered as involving only the outer part of the crust.

(2) The vast masses of siliceous plutonic and volcanic rock now occupying the former eugeosynclinal area near the Pacific cannot have been formed by mobilizing merely the material of the geosyncline and its pristine basement; they demand accretion from a differentiating mantle or from former sialic lands to the west.

(3) The position of the great plutonic belt near the ocean suggests relative motion of mantle material, dragging with it sial to founder beneath the continent, there to be remobilized. More likely, the continent is drifting westward over the oceanic floor, as has been suggested by Hess from other data, and as seems implied by the relatively small thicknesses of pelagic sediment that appear to characterize nearly all the ocean floors. The concentration of quartz-diorite plutons near to the Pacific and of granodiorite and quartz-monzonite plutons farther east (Moore, 1959), may reflect a more emphatic eugeosynclinal composition of the crust toward the west and a more mature (siliceous) composition farther east.

(4) The uplift of the Colorado Plateau suggests subcrustal transfer of sial from other areas, perhaps from the present area of the Basin Range province.

(5) No simple time-relation can be established between tensional and compressional forces in the crust; at present thrust-faults are active in one part of California while normal faults are active in another only a hundred miles away. The idea of world-wide epochs of compression alternating with others of tension is simply not supported by present-day events nor by the geological record of Cainozoic time—the part of geological history we can read most clearly.

(6) The history of the area taken as a whole has been one of essential uniformity in tectonic and volcanic activity throughout the Phanerozoic, but of catastrophic plutonism, not closely related to either of the other processes.

Plutonism must depend on processes whose time-scale is of an entirely different order of magnitude from those of volcanism or tectonism. There is no obvious correlation of tectonics either with metamorphism or with granitic intrusion, though both metamorphism and granite are obviously associated with tectonism. To judge from both sedimentary and structural records volcanism and orogeny have been active at one place or another in the region throughout Phanerozoic time, though of course being highly episodic locally. Plutonic processes, on the other hand, have been highly concentrated in the Cretaceous, less so in the Miocene, and almost trivial at all other times during the Phanerozoic whose record we can read.

If this difference in habit is substantiated in other regions, it means that radiometric dates yield, not the times of orogenic activity, but of those orogenic episodes that were accompanied by plutonism. Judged by tectonic criteria, these episodes were not more intense than many orogenic episodes that were not so accompanied. Cannon and others (1961, p. 21) have deduced from isotope ratios that the evolution of ore leads seems to have been episodic, on a time-scale measured in hundreds of millions of years. Such a distribution in time, if confirmed, is not evidence of episodic diastrophism but of episodic plutonism.

SUMMARY

The Pre-Cambrian history of the western United States is fragmentary, and the radiometric dates so far measured give no obvious clues to ancient orogenic belts or to systematic continental accretion.

From Cambrian until Devonian time the western part of the area of the present Cordillera was geosynclinal, the eastern part the site of intermittent shelf seas. The geosyncline was compound, the western part eugeosynclinal, the eastern miogeosynclinal.

In Early Mississippian time the Antler orogenic belt rose near the axis of the geosyncline through Nevada and Idaho in an alpine mountain chain at least 500 miles long. The former geosyncline was split into two, the western segment remaining eugeosynclinal, the eastern miogeosynclinal. Notable orogenies took place in the western area in Pennsylvanian, Permian, Triassic, and Jurassic time, across Colorado in Pennsylvanian to Early Permian time, and across southern Arizona in Triassic time. At the end of the Jurassic, after the Nevadan orogeny, the western geosyncline was displaced still farther to the west, the eastern one was drained, and a new one formed on the site of the former craton, in the area of the present eastern Cordillera. Over a million cubic miles of largely clastic sediment accumulated in this new geosyncline.

In mid-Cretaceous time orogenic pulses began on the western side of the Cretaceous geosyncline and gradually extended eastward until by the end of the Eocene the entire belt was involved. On the west side of the trough great thrusts were formed from Arizona and Nevada to Montana and beyond into Canada; toward the east, uplift of anticlinal areas and depression of synclinal ones occurred, shortening the surficial crust only slightly but creating structural relief as great as eight or ten miles.

The western trough has frequently been much disturbed and broken up by orogenic episodes since the beginning of the Cretaceous. Some structures formed by the 'Mid-Pleistocene' Pasadenan orogeny are still highly active.

The Colorado Plateau became established as a structural unit by mid-Eocene time but its uplift was delayed until Pliocene and Quaternary time. It may owe its elevation to an isostatic response to the transfer of crustal material by currents in the mantle.

The Basin Range structural province is dominated by normal faulting and extends far beyond the region of internal drainage. The distension of the crustal segment indicated by the normal faults may also be attributed to differential drag by currents in the mantle.

Transcurrent (strike-slip) faults are important only in California, Nevada, and Idaho. The great San Andreas fault in California (whose movement may have begun in Cretaceous time and is still continuing) seems to demand drag of crustal segments by differential movements in the mantle as the immediate cause.

Volcanic activity has occurred in the western part of the area during every period of the Phanerozoic. The Cambrian and Ordovician extrusive rocks are chiefly andesitic or basaltic, but siliceous lavas became abundant during the Silurian and have since been conspicuous. The greatest volcanic field (Permian–Lower Triassic) was submarine; eruptions extended from southern California to Alaska. The extrusion of the flood-basalts of the north-west began in Eocene time, when the greatest outpouring took place. The Columbia River basalts are Miocene and early Pliocene; basaltic flows continued in the Snake River region until Pleistocene or even Recent time. Most of the Tertiary volcanic rocks of the Great Basin are siliceous; the total bulk of the rhyolitic welded tuffs and lavas of this area probably equals that of the Columbia River flood-basalts.

Plutonic activity has been dominated by the great batholiths of the Peninsular Range, the Sierra Nevada, and Idaho, with their satellitic intrusions. Most of the radiometric dates are Cretaceous, but many small intrusions are Triassic, Jurassic, and Eocene. The youngest large granitic intrusions are of Miocene age.

In Cretaceous time plutons probably a thousand times larger than those of all the rest of the Phanerozoic were emplaced. The records of sedimentation, tectonics, and surface volcanism are uniformitarian, but plutonic activity has been catastrophic—completely lacking during the Palaeozoic and since trivial except during the mid-Cretaceous and Miocene. Plutonic activity is evidently not a necessary accompaniment of normal orogenic processes.

The great plutons have arisen on the site of a persistently eugeosynclinal crustal segment. Their volume demands supply either from huge volumes of differentiating mantle or by remelting of large volumes of sial; either mechanism requires differential movement of crust and mantle on a vast scale.

The abrupt boundary of the continent against the ocean basin and the complete independence of the large strike-slip faults of the two domains also suggest relative movement of continental crust and mantle. Either the continent is drifting westward over the ocean floor, or the ocean floor (with the sialic segments that formerly lay off-shore) is moving eastward under the continent. The local mechanics would be the same in either case, though the wider mechanisms would be quite different. It is probable that the continent as a whole is moving away from a widening Atlantic.

REFERENCES

Albers, J. P., and J. F. Robertson, 1961, Geology and ore deposits of East Shasta copper-zinc district, Shasta County, California: U.S. Geol. Survey Prof. Paper 338.

Allison, I. S., 1949, Fault pattern of south-central Oregon: Geol. Soc. America Bull., v. 60, p. 1935.

Anderson, C. A., 1951, Older Precambrian structure in Arizona: Geol. Soc. America Bull., v. 62, p. 1331–1346.

Axelrod, D. I., 1957, Late Tertiary floras and the Sierra Nevada uplift: Geol. Soc. America Bull., v. 68, p. 19–45.

Bailey, T. L., and R. H. Jahns, 1954, Geology of the Transverse Range province, southern California: California Dept. Nat. Resources Div. Mines Bull., v. 170, p. 83–106.

Barksdale, J. D., 1960, Late Mesozoic sequences in the north-eastern Cascade Mountains of Washington: Geol. Soc. America Bull., v. 71, p. 2049.

Becker, Hans, 1934, Die Beziehungen zwischen Felsengebirge und grossem Becken im westlichen Nordamerika: Deutsche geol. Gesell. Zeitschr., v. 86, p. 115–120.

Berg, J. W., Jr., and others, 1960, Seismic investigation of crustal structure in the eastern part of the Basin and Range province: Seismol. Soc. America Bull., v. 50, p. 511–536.

Blackwelder, E., 1931, Pleistocene glaciation in the Sierra Nevada and Basin Ranges: Geol. Soc. America Bull., v. 42, p. 865–922.

Brill, K. G., Jr., 1952, Stratigraphy in the Permo-Pennsylvanian zeugogeosyncline of Colorado and northern New Mexico: Geol. Soc. America Bull., v. 63, p. 809–880.

Brown, W. H., 1939, Tucson Mountains, an Arizona Basin Range type: Geol. Soc. America Bull., v. 50, p. 697–760.

Bryan, Kirk, 1922, Erosion and sedimentation in the Papago country, Arizona: U.S. Geol. Survey Bull. 730, p. 19–90.

Bryant, D. L., and J. E. Kinnison, 1954, Lower Cretaceous age of the Amole arkose, Tucson Mountains, Arizona: Geol. Soc. America Bull., v. 65, p. 1235.

Burbank, W. S., and E. N. Goddard, 1937, Thrusting in Huerfano Park, Colorado, and related problems of orogeny in the Sangre de Cristo Mountains: Geol. Soc. America Bull., v. 48, p. 931–976.

Callaghan, Eugene, 1951, Distribution of intermediate and basic igneous rocks in the Tertiary of western United States: Geol. Soc. America Bull., v. 62, p. 1428.

Callaghan, Eugene, and V. P. Gianella, 1935, The earthquake of January 30, 1934, at Excelsior Mountains, Nevada: Seismol. Soc. America Bull., v. 25, p. 161–168.

Campbell, A. B., 1959, Precambrian-Cambrian unconformity in northwestern Montana and northern Idaho: Geol. Soc. America Bull., v. 70, p. 1776.

Cannon, R. S., and others, 1961, The data of lead isotope geology related to problems of ore genesis: Econ. Geology, v. 56, p. 1–38.

Case, J. E., and H. R. Joesting, 1961, Northeast-trending Precambrian structures in the central Colorado Plateau: Geol. Soc. America Spec. Paper 68, p. 85.

Churkin, Michael, Jr., 1960, Early Paleozoic sedimentation in central Idaho: Geol. Soc. America Bull., v. 71, p. 1842–1843.

Cobban, W. A., and J. B. Reeside, 1952, Correlation of the Cretaceous formations of the western Interior of the United States: Geol. Soc. America Bull., v. 63, p. 1011–1043.

Cohee, G. V., and others, 1961, Tectonic map of the United States: U.S. Geological Survey and American Association of Petroleum Geologists.

Creasey, S. C., and R. W. Kistler, 1962, Age of some copper-bearing porphyries and other igneous rocks in southeastern Arizona: U.S. Geol. Survey Prof. Paper 450D, p. D1–D5.

Crowell, J. C., 1954, Geology of the Ridge Basin area, Los Angeles and Ventura Counties, California: California Dept. Nat. Resources Div. Mines Bull., v. 170, map sheet 7.
Crowell, J. C., and J. W. R. Walker, 1961, Displacement of anorthosite and related rocks by the San Andreas fault, southern California: Geol. Soc. America Spec. Paper 68, p. 157.
Curtis, G. H., J. F. Evernden, and J. I. Lipson, 1958, Age determination of some granitic rocks in California by the potassium-argon method: California Dept. Nat. Resources Div. Mines Spec. Rept. 54.
Dake, C. L., 1918, The Heart Mountain overthrust and associated structures in Park County, Wyoming: Jour. Geology, v. 26, p. 45–55.
Deiss, C. F., 1935, Cambrian-Algonkian unconformity in western Montana: Geol. Soc. America Bull., v. 46, p. 95–124.
DeVoto, R. H., 1961, Tertiary stratigraphy of South Park, Colorado: Geol. Soc. America Spec. Paper 68, p. 87.
Dickinson, W. R., 1961, Jurassic andesitic province along the Pacific margin of North America: Geol. Soc. America Spec. Paper 68, p. 19.
Diller, J. S., 1906, Redding, California, folio: U.S. Geol. Survey Geol. Atlas, Folio 138.
Diment, W. H., S. W. Stewart, and J. C. Roller, 1961, Crustal structure from the Nevada Test Site to Kingman, Arizona, from seismic and gravity observations: Jour. Geophys. Research, v. 66, p. 201–214.
Donath, F. A., 1959, Basin range structure of south-central Oregon: Dissert. Abs., v. 19, p. 2318–2319.
Dott, R. H., Jr., 1955, Pennsylvanian stratigraphy of Elko and northern Diamond Ranges, northeastern Nevada: Am. Assoc. Petroleum Geologists Bull., v. 39, p. 2211–2305.
Eckelmann, W. R., and J. L. Kulp, 1957, Uranium-lead method of age determination. Part II, North American localities: Geol. Soc. America Bull., v. 68, p. 1117–1140.
Ferguson, H. G., and S. W. Muller, 1949, Structural geology of the Hawthorne and Tonopah quadrangles, Nevada: U.S. Geol. Survey Prof. Paper 216.
Fuller, R. E., and A. C. Waters, 1929, The nature and origin of the horst and graben structure of southern Oregon: Jour. Geology, v. 37, p. 204–238.
Gianella, V. P., and Eugene Callaghan, 1934, The Cedar Mountain, Nevada, earthquake of Dec. 20, 1932: Seismol. Soc. America Bull., v. 24, p. 345–384.
Gilbert, G. K., 1875, U.S. Geographical and Geological Surveys west of the 100th Meridian: U.S. Geol. Survey Rept. 3, p. 62.
Gilluly, James, 1932, Geology and ore deposits of the Stockton and Fairfield quadrangles, Utah: U.S. Geol. Survey Prof. Paper 173.
———, 1949, Distribution of mountain-building in geologic time: Geol. Soc. America Bull. v. 60, p. 561–590.
———, 1956, General geology of central Cochise County, Arizona: U.S. Geol. Survey Prof. Paper 281.
Gilluly, James, and Olcott Gates, 1967, Tectonic and igneous geology of the northern Shoshone Range, Nevada: U.S. Geol. Survey Prof. Paper 465.
Gilluly, James, and Harold Masursky, 1967, Geology and ore deposits of the Cortez Quadrangle, Nevada: U.S. Geol. Surv. Bull. 1175.
Gwinn, V. E., 1960, Cretaceous Colorado group west of the Boulder batholith in Montana: Geol. Soc. America Bull., v. 71, p. 1877.
Hague, Arnold, 1896, The age of the igneous rocks of the Yellowstone National Park: Am. Jour. Sci., ser. 4, v. 1, p. 445–457.
Hamilton, Warren, 1961, Strike-slip control of tectonics of coastal California: Geol. Soc. America Spec. Paper 68, p. 30.
Hazzard, J. C., 1938, Paleozoic section in the Nopah and Resting Springs Mountains, Inyo County, California: California Jour. Mines and Geology, v. 33, p. 273–339.
Hay, R. L., 1961, Diagenetic facies in the John Day formation of Oregon: Geol. Soc. America Spec. Paper 68, p. 31–32.
Hershey, O. H., 1916, Origin and distribution of ore in the Coeur D'Alene: San Francisco.
Hewett, D. F., 1920, The Heart Mountain overthrust, Wyoming: Jour. Geology, v. 28, p. 536–557.
———, 1954, General geology of the Mojave Desert region, California: California Dept. Nat. Resources Div. Mines Bull., v. 170, p. 5–20.
———, 1956, Geology and mineral resources of the Ivanpah quadrangle, California and Nevada: U.S. Geol. Survey Prof. Paper 275.
Hewett, D. F., and others, 1936, Mineral resources of the region around Boulder Dam: U.S. Geol. Survey Bull. 871.
Hill, M. L. and T. W. Dibblee, Jr., 1953, San Andreas, Garlock, and Big Pine faults, California: Geol. Soc. America Bull., v. 64, p. 443–458.
Hinds, N. E. A., 1940, Paleozoic section in the southern Klamath Mountains, California: Pacific Sci. Assoc. 6th Cong. Proc., v. 1, p. 273–287.
Hoots, H. W., T. L. Bear, and W. D. Kleinpell, 1954, Geological summary of the San Joaquin Valley, California: California Dept. Nat. Resources Div. Mines Bull., v. 170, p. 113–129.
Hutchinson, R. M., 1956, Structural geology of the Browne Lake area, northern Beaverhead County, Montana: Geol. Soc. America Bull., v. 67, p. 1796–1797.
Iddings, J. P., and W. H. Weed, 1894, Livingston, Montana: U.S. Geol. Survey, Folio I.
Johnson, R. B., G. H. Dixon, and A. A. Wanek, 1956, Upper Cretaceous and Tertiary stratigra-

phy of Raton Basin of New Mexico and Colorado: Geol. Soc. America Bull., v. 67, p. 1797.

Jones, D. L., 1959, Stratigraphy of the Upper Cretaceous rocks in the Yreka-Hornbrook area, northern California: Geol. Soc. America Bull., v. 70, p. 1726–1727.

Keefer, W. R., 1960, Magnitude of crustal movement and deposition during latest Cretaceous and Early Tertiary time in the Wind River Basin, Central Wyoming: Geol. Soc. America Bull., v. 71, p. 1901.

Kinkel, A. R., W. E. Hall, and J. P. Albers, 1956, Geology and base-metal deposits of the West Shasta copper-zinc district, Shasta County, California: U.S. Geol. Survey Prof. Paper 285.

Kirk, Edwin, 1933, The Eureka quartzite of the Great Basin region: Am. Jour. Sci., ser. 5, v. 26, p. 27–44.

Klepper, M. R., R. A. Weeks, and E. T. Ruppel, 1957, Geology of the southern Elkhorn Mountains, Jefferson and Broadwater Counties, Montana: U.S. Geol. Survey Prof. Paper 292.

Knopf, A., 1955, Bathyliths in time: Geol. Soc. America Spec. Paper 62, p. 685–702.

Koch, T. W., 1933, Analysis and effects of current movement on an active fault in Buena Vista Hills oilfield, Kern Co., California: Am. Assoc. Petroleum Geologists Bull., v. 17, p. 694–712.

Larsen, E. S., Jr., and C. Whitman Cross, 1956, Geology and petrology of the San Juan region, southwestern Colorado: U.S. Geol. Survey Prof. Paper 258.

Larsen, E. S., Jr., and others, 1958, Lead-alpha ages of the Mesozoic batholiths of western North America: U.S. Geol. Survey Bull. 1070-B.

Lasky, S. G., 1947, Geology and ore deposits of the Little Hatchet Mountains, Hidalgo and Grant Counties, New Mexico: U.S. Geol. Survey Prof. Paper 208.

Lautenschlager, H. K., 1954, Tectonic influence on sedimentation in central Utah: Geol. Soc. America Bull., v. 65, p. 1344.

Lindgren, W., 1915, The igneous geology of the Cordilleras and its problems, *in* Problems of American Geology: New Haven, Conn., p. 234–286.

Little, H. W., 1960, Nelson Map area, west half, British Columbia: Geol. Survey Canada Mem. 308.

Longwell, C. R., 1950, Tectonic theory viewed from the Basin Ranges: Geol. Soc. America Bull., v. 61, p. 413–433.

Lyons, J. B., 1944, Igneous rocks of the northern Big Belt Range, Montana: Geol. Soc. America Bull., v. 55, p. 445–472.

Mackin, J. H., 1960, Eruptive tectonic hypothesis for origin of Basin-Range structure: Geol. Soc. America Bull., v. 71, p. 1921.

Mallory, W. W., 1960, Outline of Pennsylvanian stratigraphy of Colorado; Guide to the Geology of Colorado: Denver, Colorado, Rocky Mountain Association of Geologists, p. 23–33.

Merriam, C. W., and C. A. Anderson, 1942, Reconnaissance survey of the Roberts Mountains, Nevada: Am. Jour. Sci., ser. 5, v. 16, p. 1675–1727.

Moore, J. G., 1959, The quartz-diorite boundary line in the western United States: Jour. Geology, v. 67, p. 198–210.

Noble, L. F., 1926, The San Andreas rift and some other active faults in the desert region of southeastern California: Carnegie Inst. Washington Yearbook, v. 25, p. 415–428.

———, 1941, Structural features of the Virgin Spring area, Death Valley, California: Geol. Soc. America Bull., v. 52, p. 941–999.

Nolan, T. B., 1928, A late Paleozoic positive area in Nevada: Am. Jour. Sci., ser. 5, v. 16, p. 153–161.

———, 1935, The Gold Hill mining district, Utah: U.S. Geol. Survey Prof. Paper 177.

———, 1943, The Basin and Range province in Utah, Nevada, and California: U.S. Geol. Survey Prof. Paper 197-D, p. 141–196.

Nolan, T. B., C. W. Merriam, and J. S. Williams, 1956, The stratigraphic section in the vicinity of Eureka, Nevada: U.S. Geol. Survey Prof. Paper 276.

Page, B. M., 1935, Basin-range faulting of 1915 in Pleasant Valley, Nevada: Jour. Geology, v. 43, p. 690–707.

Pierce, W. G., 1957, Heart Mountain and South Fork detachment thrusts of Wyoming: Am. Assoc. Petroleum Geologists Bull., v. 41, p. 591–626.

Reeside, J. B., Jr., 1944, Maps showing thickness and general character of the Cretaceous deposits on the western interior of the United States: U.S. Geol. Survey Oil and Gas Inv. (Prelim.) Map 10.

Roberts, R. J., and others, 1958, Paleozoic rocks of north-central Nevada: Am. Assoc. Petroleum Geologists Bull., v. 42, p. 2813–2857.

Rogers, G. S., 1913, A study in the petrology of sedimentary rocks: Jour. Geology, v. 21, p. 714–727.

Rubey, W. W., S. S. Oriel, and J. I. Tracey, Jr., 1961, Age of the Evanston formation, western Wyoming: U.S. Geol. Survey Prof. Paper 424-B, p. 153–154.

Russell, I. C., 1883, A geological reconnaissance in southern Oregon: U.S. Geol. Survey Rept. 4, p. 431–464.

Shride, A. F., 1958, Younger Precambrian geology in southeastern Arizona: Geol. Soc. America Bull., v. 69, p. 1744.

Silver, L. T., 1960, Age determinations on Precambrian diabase differentiates in the Sierra Ancha, Gila County, Arizona: Geol. Soc. America Bull., v. 71, p. 1973–1974.

Skipp, Betty A., 1958, Significant sedimentary features in Mississippian rocks in Custer County, Idaho: Geol. Soc. America Bull., v. 69, p. 1744.

Slemmons, D. B., 1956, Geologic setting for the

Fallon-Stillwater (Nev.) earthquakes of 1954, *in* The Fallon-Stillwater earthquakes of July 6, 1954, and August 23, 1954: Seismol. Soc. America Bull., v. 46, p. 4–9.
Smith, G. I., 1960, Estimate of total displacement on the Garlock fault, southeastern California: Geol. Soc. America Bull., v. 71, p. 1979.
Smith, G. O., and W. C. Mendenhall, 1909, Tertiary granite in the northern Cascades: Geol. Soc. America Bull., v. 11, p. 223–230.
Spieker, E. M., 1946, Late Mesozoic and early Cenozoic history of central Utah: U.S. Geol. Survey of Prof. Paper 205-D, p. 117–161.
Stock, Chester, and F. D. Bode, 1935, Occurrence of lower Oligocene mammal-bearing beds near Death Valley, Calif.: [U.S.] Natl. Acad. Sci. Proc., v. 21, p. 571–579.
Stokes, W. L., 1952, Paleozoic positive area in northwestern Utah: Geol. Soc. America Bull., v. 63, p. 1300.
Stone, Robert, 1961, Geologic and engineering significance of changes in elevation revealed by precise leveling, Los Angeles area, California: Geol. Soc. America Spec. Paper 68, p. 57–58.
Taliaferro, N. L., 1943, Geologic history and structure of the central Coast Ranges of California: California Dept. Nat. Resources Div. Mines Bull., v. 118, p. 119–163.
Thomas, H. D., 1949, The geological history and geological structure of Wyoming: Wyoming Geol. Survey Bull., v. 42.
Thomasson, M. R., 1959, Late Paleozoic stratigraphy and paleotectonics of central and eastern Idaho: Geol. Soc. America Bull., v. 70, p. 1687–1688.
Thompson, G. A., 1960, Crustal structure and Cenozoic deformation in the Basin and Range province: Geol. Soc. America Bull., v. 71, p. 1992–1993.
Tweto, Ogden, and R. C. Pearson, 1958, Great Precambrian shear zone, Sawatch Range, Colorado: Geol. Soc. America Bull., v. 61, p. 1748.
Umpleby, J. B., and E. L. Jones, Jr., 1923, Geology and ore deposits of Shoshone County, Idaho: U.S. Geol. Survey Bull. 732.
Vaucquier, V., A. D. Raff, and R. E. Warren, 1961, Horizontal displacements in the floor of the northeastern Pacific Ocean: Geol. Soc. America Bull., v. 72, p. 1251–1258.
Veatch, A. C., 1907, Geography and geology of a portion of southwestern Wyoming: U.S. Geol. Survey Prof. Paper 56.
Walcott, C. D., 1899, Pre-Cambrian fossiliferous formations: Geol. Soc. America Bull., v. 10, p. 199–244.
Wallace, R. E., and others, 1960, Tectonic setting of the Coeur d'Alene district, Idaho: U.S. Geol. Survey Prof. Paper 400-B, p. 25–27.
Wasserburg, G. J., G. W. Wetherill, and L. A. Wright, 1959, Ages in the Precambrian terrane of Death Valley, Calif.: Jour. Geology, v. 67, no. 6, p. 702–708.
Waters, A. C., 1955, Volcanic rocks and the tectonic cycle: Geol. Soc. America Spec. Paper 62, p. 703–722.
Weeks, R. A., and M. R. Klepper, 1954, Tectonic history of the northern Boulder batholith region, Montana: Geol. Soc. America Bull., v. 65, p. 1320–1321.
Weis, P. L., 1958, Probable Cambrian-Precambrian unconformity in northeastern Washington: Geol. Soc. America Bull., v. 69, p. 1710.
Westgate, L. G., and C. R. Ross, 1930, Geology and ore deposits of the Wood River region Idaho: U.S. Geol. Survey Bull. 814.
Whitten, C. A., 1948, Horizontal earth movement, vicinity of San Francisco, California: Am. Geophys. Union Trans., v. 29, p. 318–323.
Whitten, C. A., and C. N. Claire, 1960, Creep on the San Andreas fault: Seismol. Soc. America Bull, v. 50, p. 404–416.
Willden, C. R., 1958, Cretaceous and Tertiary orogeny in Jackson Mountains, Humboldt County, Nevada: Am. Assoc. Petroleum Geologists Bull., v. 42, p. 2378–2398.
Wilson, E. D., 1937, Precambrian Mazatzal revolution in central Arizona: Geol. Soc. America Bull., v. 50, p. 1113–1163.
Wilt, J. W., 1958, Measured movement along the surface trace of an active thrust fault in the Buena Vista Hills, Kern County, California: Seismol. Soc. America Bull., v. 48, p. 169–176.

49

Late Paleozoic Cyclic Sedimentation in Central United States

RAYMOND C. MOORE
1950

From *Rhythm in Sedimentation* [Reports of the 18th International Geological Congress, pt. IV (Proceedings of Section C)], pp. 5–16. 18th International Geological Congress (Great Britain, 1948), 1950. Reprinted with permission of the author.

During the past two decades or more, attention of students of sedimentation and stratigraphy has been drawn to rhythmic sedimentation observable in many parts of the column and many parts of the world. The observed features offer many interesting but difficult problems.

The purpose of this paper is to describe and discuss briefly evidence of cyclic sedimentation which is clearly shown in Kansas and immediately adjacent parts of the central United States. Perhaps nowhere in the world are some features of such deposition better displayed than can be seen in Pennsylvanian and Permian strata of this region. The rocks can be studied in innumerable outcrops, and during late years, much information on the subsurface character and distribution of cyclic deposits has been obtained. . . . I wish both to emphasize the actuality of various sorts of cyclic repetitions in the northern mid-continent Pennsylvanian-Permian succession, representing a depositional environment in which marine sedimentation predominated, and especially to draw attention to problems in interpreting the significance of observed features satisfactorily in terms of geologic history.

TERMINOLOGY

It is appropriate, before giving attention to the details of cyclic deposition in the region considered, to take up the subject of terminology. I note a tendency among geologists to ascribe such widely diverse sorts of sedimentary variations to cyclic sedimentation that, in my view, there is danger of obscuring and depreciating the evidence of best defined examples of this phenomenon. Those who have made field studies of repetitive sequences of several kinds of strata are well aware that recognition of cycles is by no means a subjective affair, but it is also true that cyclic features of sedimentation may be overlooked entirely by casual observers and unskilled stratigraphers.

In the first place, distinction is required

between sporadically recurrent oscillations in the nature of sedimentary deposition, and systematic deviations in type of sedimentation which are repeated. The occasional spreading of clastic materials over an area of organic limestone accumulation or of saline precipitation as result of storms, shifting of currents or some such cause represents an oscillation of sedimentary deposition that surely is not cyclic in nature. On the other hand, any series of events or conditions which is repeated with constancy of pattern may be definable in terms of a cycle, whether repetition is regular in time (and thus rhythmic in the root sense) or irregular. Waves of the open sea, movement of a pendulum, advance and retreat of tides, seasonal oscillations of temperature or precipitation, changes associated with sun-spot activity —all these and many others are both cyclic and rhythmic in that there are successive (a) minimum, (b) rising, (c) maximum, and (d) falling phases, and these are regularly periodic. Constancy of arrangement of phases defines the cyclic aspect, whereas regularity of recurrence constitutes rhythm. By extension of meaning, the latter word has come to embrace almost any orderly disposition of things, but I lean toward feeling that rhythmic and cyclic should not be used synonymously in geology. Banded strata, such as varves, record sedimentation that is both cyclic and rhythmic, but alternating glacial and inter-glacial or marine and non-marine sedimentation in which cyclic aspects may be discerned are probably not rhythmic because no regularity of duration (or motion) is involved.

The main distinction between late Paleozoic sedimentation cycles and simple alternations of rock types, which likewise may be cyclic in origin, is the presence in the former of far greater diversity of lithologic and paleontologic components. Whether numerous and complex or few and simple, each distinguishable element in a cyclic succession may be termed a *phase*. It denotes a combination of physical and biological conditions which belong to the temporarily existing environment of sedimentation. The stratum or succession of strata is the record of paleoecology. Wells (1947) has introduced the term *lithotope* for such sedimentary record of different environments. Using this word, we may say that some cycles consist of only two distinguishable lithotopes which may be repeated in alternation almost endlessly. Most Pennsylvanian and Permian cycles contain many different lithotopes. Each phase of a cycle consists of a lithotope, and hence the two terms are essentially synonymous as applied to cyclic sedimentation.

The term *phantom* (Reger, 1931), or phantom phase, has been proposed to designate an element in a cyclic succession, which is theoretically expectable but commonly absent. For example, a phase which is very persistent in some cycles may be lacking in another, and in the latter it may be reckoned to be a phantom. Such phantoms assume substance locally and thus establish validity of their claim to recognition.

Deposits of a single sedimentary cycle, as represented by the interrelated phases of Pennsylvanian and Permian sedimentation associated with a landward-and-seaward oscillation of the strand line, have been called a *cyclothem* (Weller, 1930) or cyclic formation. These are recognized as units of stratigraphic classification and mapping in Illinois. Cyclothems are not so treated in the mid-continent or most other regions, because boundaries commonly cannot be defined exactly and, where determinable, they are generally less suited to geologic mapping than combinations of beds having limits that fall within a given cycle.

The term *megacyclothem* was introduced by me (Moore, 1936) for strata belonging to a group of successive sedimentary cycles which exhibits regularity of occurrence in sequence, each constituent cyclothem being marked by some distinctive character or characters. Such megacyclothems are exceptionally well shown in Upper Pennsylvanian rocks of Kansas.

GENERAL CHARACTERS OF LATE PALEOZOIC CYCLIC DEPOSITION

As based on observations in central United States, cyclic sedimentation in the sense here indicated, is definitely recognized in Upper Mississippian, in Pennsylvanian, and in Lower Permian rocks. The rocks of each cycle normally consist of coarse clastic sediments in the lower part, which commonly rests disconformably on underlying rocks. The coarse beds, generally sandstone, are followed by finer grained materials, a coal bed, and then marine sediments, which prove invasion of a shallow sea. After deposition of marine shale and limestone, the retreat of this sea is recorded by the reappearance of non-marine deposits. This generalized sequence of sediments clearly indicates, both by lithologic and paleontologic characters, a major oscillatory shift of the strand line. Referring especially to Pennsylvanian and Permian rocks of the Kansas region, simple and complex types of these sequences may be distinguished.

SIMPLE SEDIMENTARY CYCLES

Simple sedimentary cycles, as represented in the late Paleozoic section of Kansas, consist of the record of a single marine advance and retreat. Different types of such records appear in the lower and higher parts of the column. Ignoring minor variations, these may be identified as the Cherokee type, Wabaunsee type, and Council Grove type, named from groups of strata in which each is well shown.

CHEROKEE TYPE

Strata belonging to the Cherokee group, of Desmoinesian age, make up the lower-most 500 feet, approximately, of the Pennsylvanian deposits in Kansas. The group contains several local sandstones, a few persistent sandstones, many coal beds and some thin limestones, but it is predominantly composed of several sorts of shale (Figure 49.1). Cyclic sedimentation is shown by repeated sequences of deposits in constant order. Ten of the 14 cycles which have been recognized (Abernathy, 1937) are marked by a sandstone (or conglomerate) phase at the base, that of some cycles being very extensive sheet-like bodies which denote widespread deposition of coarse materials disconformably on underlying deposits; the sandstone of other cycles is local and found to fill channels carved in the subjacent beds. The sandstone phase of some cycles exceeds 50 feet in thickness throughout an area of many square miles, as shown both by surface and sub-surface tracing. The sandy deposits are non-marine, as is shown by absence of marine fossils and in some by local presence of land plant remains and tracks of land animals. The sandsone is succeeded by sandy shale, which likewise is non-marine. Then comes an underclay and coal, although in one cycle no underclay is seen. The coal beds are relatively prominent and many of them are of minable thickness. The coal is overlain by marine strata consisting invariably of black shale, which locally is calcareous and grades to black shaly limestone containing marine fossils. A few marine layers are found to yield fusulines but generally these fossils are absent. A varied assemblage of brachiopods, bryozoans, corals, and various other invertebrates occurs at several horizons. The marine deposits are not very thick on the average and are succeeded conformably by unfossiliferous shale that is interpreted as brackish to non-marine. This terminates the cycle.

Characteristic features of the Cherokee type of cycle are the relative thinness of marine

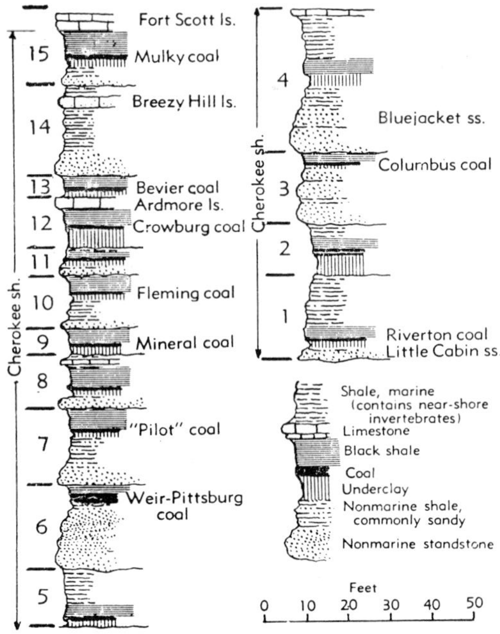

FIGURE 49.1
Middle Pennsylvanian cyclothems. Generalized section of the Cherokee group, Desmoinesian Stage, southeastern Kansas. (Modified from G. E. Abernathy.)

phases, especially limestone beds. Individual cyclothems are traceable for long distances. The most persistent elements are the coal beds and overlying black shales. Attention may be directed especially to the occurrence in every recognized cycle of a coal bed and black platy shale, whereas other phases are less regular in development. Also noteworthy is the organic content of the black shales, which in many places comprises not only shells of marine invertebrates and remains of fishes but fairly well preserved impressions of land plants and somewhat macerated land plant remains. Williams (1938) reports on several black shales of the Cherokee in south-eastern Kansas, noting that in non-calcareous, "papery" or platy beds of this type, the common fossils are conodonts, *Orbiculoidea*, and plant fragments; less common are fish remains, consisting of teeth and bones, pectinoid clams, and small coiled cephalopods. Some of the latter fossils occur only in small phosphatic concretions. In calcareous black shale (and thin black limestone which occurs locally in some zones) is a varied marine assemblage containing fusulines (uncommon); corals (*Lophophyllidium*); bryozoans (*Rhombopora, Septopora, Fistulipora*); inadunate crinoids (columnals, cup plates, brachials); brachiopods (*Lingula, Orbiculoidea, Derbyia, Chonetes, Mesolobus, Dictyoclostus, Linoproductus, Marginifera, Neospirifer, Crurithyris, Squamularia, Hustedia, Composita*); pelecypods (*Aviculopecten, Pernopecten*); gastropods; cephalopods (*Pseudorthoceras*, unidentified coiled forms); trilobites; plant remains.

WABAUNSEE TYPE

Uppermost Pennsylvanian rocks of the northern mid-continent region are classed as the Wabaunsee group. These beds, of Virgilian age, show cyclic sedimentation which may be termed the Wabaunsee type. The section consists mainly of alternating shale, containing thin sandstone locally, and very persistent thin beds of limestones. Cyclic deposition is shown by the regular succession of phases ranging from initial sandstone of rather fine texture and micaceous character, through non-marine shale, underclay and coal, to marine shale and limestone. Many of the limestones, although thin, contain fusulines (Figure 49.2). Other limestone beds are characterized mainly by abundance of algal deposits. Differentiation of the marine parts of the cycle into several phases is possible on basis both of lithologic features and assemblages of fossils.

The initial sign of presence of the sea is the occurrence of phosphatic inarticulate brachiopods associated with other brachiopods, like *Derbyia, Juresania*, and thick-shelled clams, such as *Myalina*. These marginal deposits presumably were laid down in somewhat brackish waters, for corals, echinoderms, many genera

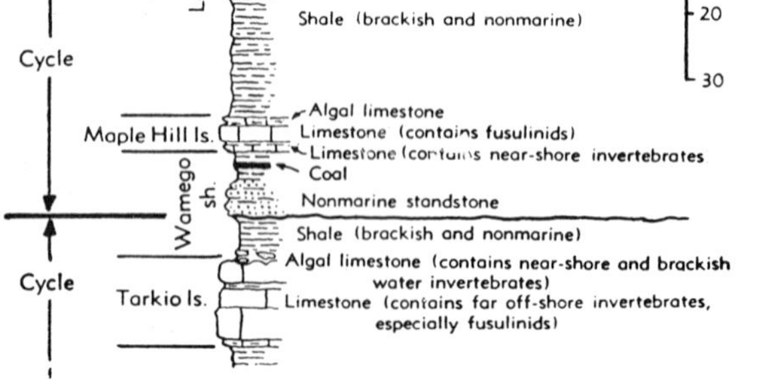

FIGURE 49.2
Upper Pennsylvanian cyclothems. Section of typical Wabaunsee cyclothems, Virgilian Stage, central Kansas.

of brachiopods, bryozoans, and other invertebrates of normal sea water are lacking. Overlying beds of the cycle are shale and limestone containing a varied assemblage of brachiopods and mollusks, the most important feature being the relative abundance of molluscan shells. The establishment of typical shallow water marine conditions is indicated by this normal population of invertebrates belonging to an offshore environment; we find crinoidal remains, corals, brachiopods, bryozoans, and some mollusks. Deposits that may be distinguished as having been laid down farthest offshore, although by no means in deep water, are limestones containing abundant fusulines. Many such deposits contain almost no other organic remains than numerous fusulines and their shells may form much of the rock volume. The marine beds of a higher part of the cycle tend to repeat the lower ones in reverse order, but the terminal one is unlike the first marine deposit in that it contains abundant remains of various sorts of algae. Commonly, this is known as the algal limestone phase. Associated with the algae are a special group of organisms, such as the brachiopod *Composita*, ramose bryozoans and certain mollusks. Evenly bedded unfossiliferous shale which overlies the algal limestone of many Wabaunsee cyclic successions, probably represents deposition in water, for it is well laminated and fairly uniform. Possibly it was laid down in shallow pools or on broad tidal flats. These unfossiliferous shales belong presumably with the cycle containing the fossiliferous limestone just below. The shale is overlain by sandy beds, with or without indication of disconformity, which are interpreted as belonging to the next higher cycle. That these higher beds are another cycle is established by occurrence of a coal bed and other non-marine deposits beneath marine layers.

The distinguishing attributes of the Wabaunsee type of cycle are absence of black platy shale phases, extreme persistence of very thin coal beds, and especially the sequence of limestone and shale beds in the marine part of the cycles, beginning with invertebrates of nearest shore, following through farther and farther offshore assemblages to the fusuline-marked maximum, and then reverse arrangement of phases to the close of marine sedimentation. Fifteen distinct cyclothems are observed in the Wabaunsee group, many of which contain phase subdivisions identifiable for a distance of 300 miles or more along the outcrop. Some distinctive beds thus traced are less than 1 inch in thickness.

COUNCIL GROVE TYPE

Characteristically developed in Lower Permian rocks of the Kansas-Nebraska region is a type of cycle that corresponds closely to the Wabaunsee type, differing mainly in having persistent red shale, associated with variegated colours, in place of sandy deposits. It may be termed the Council Grove type, from the name of the group in which it is best shown. Parts of this group, however, exhibit a more complex sort of cyclic pattern.

Fossiliferous shale and limestone, representing normal marine deposition, overlie the red shale and define the culminating part of the cycle. Inasmuch as red shale is found to be equivalent to the sandstone phase of some Pennsylvanian cyclothems and is devoid of fossil remains, it is interpreted as subaerial in origin, but red muds washed into the sea would be water-laid and some of the red sediments of the Lower Permian in the central part of the western Kansas basin may be marine. Even so, this red shale definitely corresponds to emergent phases of other cyclic successions.

The Council Grove type of simple sedimentation cycle is mainly distinguished by persistent unfossiliferous red shale which occurs between the marine phases of adjacent cycles. Most of these red shale units are very persistent, both along the outcrop and in subsurface distribution. By means of drillers' logs and well samples, several of the red shales and intervening limestones have been traced 300 miles down dip.

COMPLEX SEDIMENTARY CYCLES

An outstanding feature of cyclic sedimentation in parts of both Pennsylvanian and Permian strata of the northern mid-continent area is repetition of a long complex sequence of varied sorts of deposits and fossils representing a number of distinct individual cycles. This is actually a cycle of cyclothems and I have applied to such groups of cyclic deposits the term megacyclothem.

SHAWNEE TYPE

The most complete representation of this orderly arrangement of sets of cyclic deposits is observed in the Shawnee group of Virgilian age, in the Upper Pennsylvanian section of Kansas. The characters are typically shown by Figure 49.3. The only fairly prominent persistent coal bed is near the base of the sequence. The marine limestones are characterized by the brown ferruginous nature of the first, the thin blue dense nature of the second limestone, the light grey wavy-bedded, comparatively thick nature of the third limestone, and by less distinctive characteristics of the fourth and fifth limestones which, though thin, are very persistent. Each of the five limestones is characterized by presence of fusulines and by other phases which are diagnostic of individual cyclothems. The intervening shaly deposits also are identifiable elements of simply cyclothems in which emergent phases, including underclays and coaly zones, are found. Accordingly, the conclusion seems very well supported that the whole sequence of beds included in the megacyclothem indicates a number of completely or partly developed cyclothems, each of which differs from associated cycles in one or more characters.

The basis for identifying this sequence as a cycle of cycles is the recurrence of almost identical sequences of cycles at higher levels at least four times. The duplication of characters between corresponding cycles of each mega-

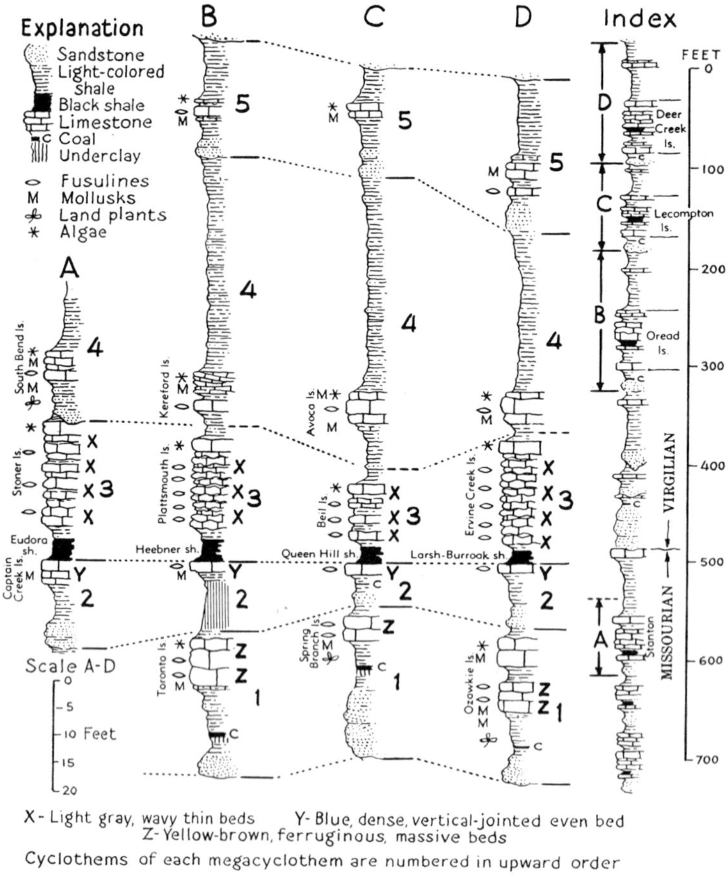

FIGURE 49.3 Upper Pennsylvanian megacyclothems. Shawnee group, Virgilian Stage, and Lansing group, Missourian Stage, Kansas.

cyclic sequence is so striking that good stratigraphers can readily mistake the identity of beds in isolated outcrops unless attention is paid to minor marks which study shows may be relied on for making distinction, or unless the strata are traced from known outcrops, or a long stratigraphic section containing marker beds is examined in the field. Not only are lithologic features repeated with fidelity, but average thicknesses of corresponding units are much the same, and faunal peculiarities are likewise duplicated. Recent detailed study of the microfaunas of all fossiliferous phases of two Shawnee megacyclothems confirms the repetition of environmental settings denoted by the phases of each cyclothem; certain assemblages of ostracodes and foraminifers, which occur in a specified phase of the second cyclothem of the lower megacyclothem, are found to be duplicated closely in the same phase of the second cyclothem of the higher megacyclothem, whereas intervening fossiliferous strata of various cyclothems differ in faunal content.

The Shawnee type of complex sedimentary cycle, or megacycle, is approximately duplicated in upper Desmoinesian (Marmaton group) and Missourian (Kansas City and Lansing groups) parts of the northern mid-continent section. That is to say, sequences of cycles corresponding to the second, third and fourth cycles of the Shawnee type occur again and again in these lower rocks, but the first and fifth are only doubtfully distinguished or they definitely are lacking (Figure 49.3). An important marker phase which is readily found belongs to the second cyclothem of the Shawnee megacyclothem; it is black platy shale which bears conodonts and locally *Lingula, Orbiculoidea,* and a few other fossils. No black shale occurs in any other of the five cyclothems of the megacyclothem.

CHASE TYPE

Megacyclothems are distinguishable in Lower Permian rocks of Kansas. These may be defined as the Chase type on the basis of their representation best in the Chase group. Chief differences from the Shawnee type are the absence of any black platy shale and prominence of chert in the dominant limestone elements of the cycles. Like the Shawnee type, however, there are prominent, closely associated limestone deposits representing certain cycles and these alternate with relatively thick clastic deposits, which include red shale and thin persistent limestone, belonging to other cycles.

LATERAL EXTENT OF RECOGNIZED CYCLIC DEPOSITS

Individual phases of various Pennsylvanian and Permian cyclothems in the northern mid-continent have been traced along the outcrop for distances of 400 miles or more. Many of them have been identified down dip into basins for distances of at least 300 miles from the outcrop. Thus, many of the cyclic elements have very wide lateral extent, not only along the present strike of outcrops but at right angles to this line.

The black platy shale of some Pennsylvanian cyclothems, but by no means all, is highly radioactive and thus in deep well sections it may be recorded with precision by radioactive logging techniques. Figure 49.4 shows a series of correlated sections of such radioactive logs from the subsurface of central and north-western Kansas (see map, Figure 49.5). They represent part of the Oread limestone in which the black shale (Heebner shale member) can be distinguished definitely by the sharp deflection indicating gamma ray frequency. A regional picture of deposits representing a considerable part of a typical megacyclothem—the Oread, which is lowermost of those in the Shawnee group—is given in Figure 49.6. This shows selected sections distributed along the outcrop from southern Kansas to south-western Iowa, an airline distance of 300 miles, and subsurface sections in central and western Kansas, and south-eastern Nebraska. The limestones are those representing the culminating marine phases—in most places, as seen at the outcrop, consisting of the fusuline-bearing farthest offshore phase—which belong to the first, second, third and fourth cyclothems of the Oread megacyclothem. A single black shale (Heebner) is

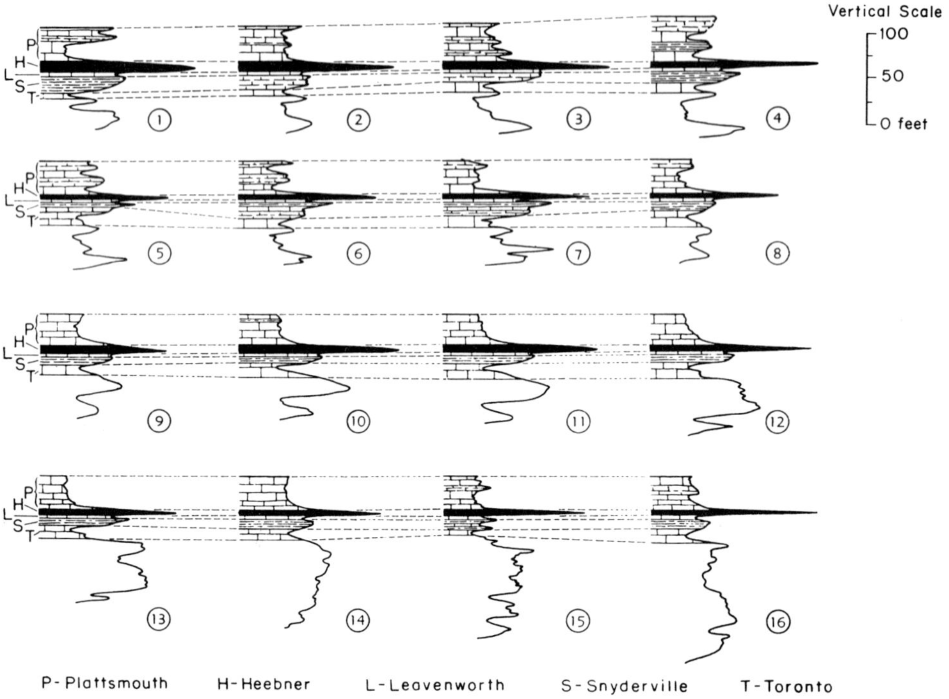

FIGURE 49.4
Correlated subsurface sections of strata in northwestern Kansas belonging to the Oread megacyclothem. Based on gamma ray radioactive well logs. Radioactivity well logs furnished by the Layne Wells Company, Wichita, Kansas.

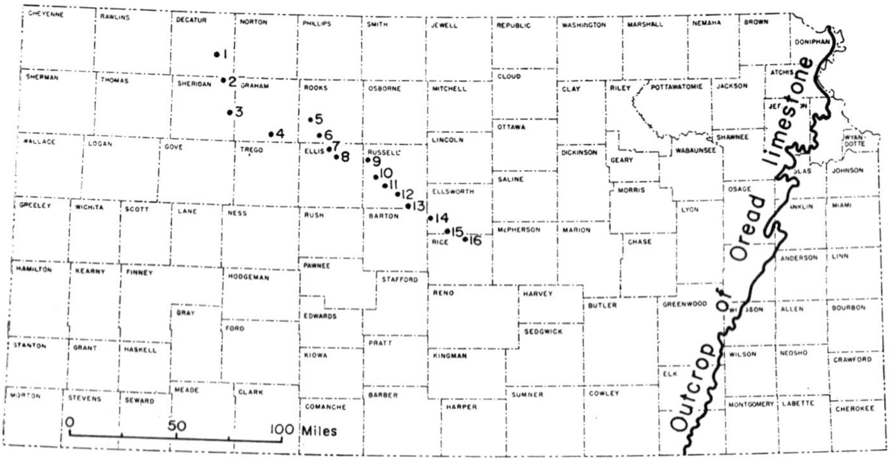

FIGURE 49.5
Location of wells plotted in Figure 49.4 and of the Oread limestone outcrop in eastern Kansas

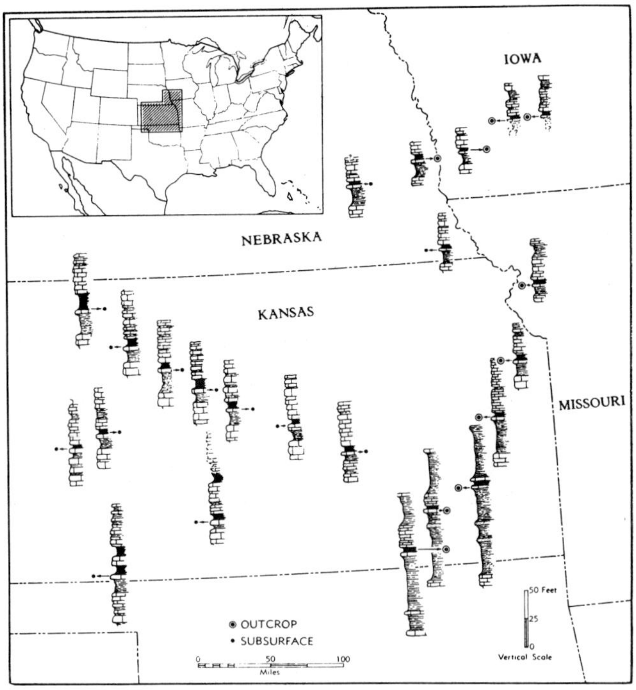

FIGURE 49.6
Surface and subsurface sections of the major part of the Oread megacyclothem in Kansas, Missouri, Iowa, and Nebraska, showing presistence of cyclic elements

present in each section just above the limestone of the second cyclothem (Leavenworth), except in one south-western Kansas subsurface section where another shale of strongly radioactive character (and therefore like the Heebner black shale, presumably) occurs a few feet higher in the section. Along the outcrop, limestones of all cyclothems are close together in the north, but they become separated southward (except the second and third, which are separated by the black shale). This increase in thickness of clastic strata southward accompanies a change in type of sedimentation which expresses late Pennsylvanian paleogeography. The southern Oklahoma region was an area of dominant subaerial sedimentation during this part of Paleozoic time, whereas shallow seas more or less persistently occupied the mid-continent region farther north. All of the Shawnee limestones disappear southward.

The foregoing discussion is concerned only with part of the northern mid-continent area. It should be observed that several cyclic units of this region can be correlated confidently with units in the Illinois-Indiana area, and these in turn with cyclic deposits farther east. This indicates a truly enormous lateral continuity of cyclic sedimentation.

SIGNIFICANCE OF CYCLIC SEDIMENTATION

The historical meaning of the cyclic succession of beds which is observed throughout the Pennsylvanian and Lower Permian sections of the northern mid-continent is obviously an oscillatory movement of the strand line marking the edge of shallow seaways. That the seas retreated from time to time so as largely or entirely to uncover areas of sedimentation is indicated definitely by occurrence of coal beds and of non-marine conditions which in many places are recorded by deposits containing abundant land plants and by disconformities. The persistence of marine layers between these continental deposits and disconformities shows expansion of the shallow seas. This much is elementary and obvious.

An evident conclusion derived from study of many cyclic deposits also is that several sorts of environments are recorded by the respective phases, both marine and non-marine. The nature and setting of some of these can be inferred with reasonably reliable judgment by their placement in the cycle and their relations to one another. For example, the initial marine and the terminal marine parts of the successions must represent marginal parts of the shallow sea. Also, the culminating marine phase, represented by the fusuline-bearing limestone, clearly indicates a most offshore environment. The underclays and the coal beds also may be understood, even though some of the very thin coals are surprisingly persistent, denoting an areal extent of coal-forming conditions in closely contemporaneous portions of the record that is amazing.

The significance of some types of deposits is not understood. For example, the cause of variation in types of limestones, which are repeated in constant relation to the cyclothems, is largely unknown. The persistent compositional and textural variations include the abundance of ferruginous material in certain beds, the largely siliceous nature of others, and types of bedding, such as the massive, blocky nature of some beds and thin wavy bedding of other limestones. There is need to make comparison between different parts of a unit which is known to be physically continuous over a very large area.

One of the phases which is least well understood is the black platy shale, which is found to have greater persistence laterally than almost any of the limestones. Explanation of the highly radioactive nature of this particular phase is not known. This shale cannot reasonably be interpreted as an accumulation of fine clastic detritus on the unoxygenated floor of a deep water body like the Black Sea. All of the Pennsylvanian marine deposits of the Kansas region must have been formed in shallow water bodies—in temporarily submerged parts of the continent. Presence of marine fossils in some of the black shales, especially the varied invertebrate assemblages found in some Cherokee black shale deposits, shows that environment of deposition was not such as repels normal life of shallow seas. But along with invertebrates and fishes are found poorly marked traces or well preserved remains of land plants, and the carbon content of the shale is very high. Extreme evenness of bedding and fineness of grain point to accumulation of sediment in very quiet water. Waves and currents could not have stirred up the black mud effectively. It seems to me that all these observations accord best with the concept of a kind of marine swamp in which seaweeds grow so thickly that disturbance of the bottom by wind and waves is nil. The abundance of vegetation may account satisfactorily for the carbonaceous content of the shale, and one may conceive readily how in some places the anomaly of marine organisms associated with land plants may be explained. The occurrence of black platy shale beds having all described characters directly overlying coal beds in each of the Cherokee cyclothems and in some of the higher Desmoinesian (Marmaton group) cyclothems, suggests drowning of a coal swamp by marine inundation. The relationship of black shale on coal is not that of the complete cycle, however, as shown in innumerable sections of Pennsylvanian beds in Kansas, Missouri, Illinois and other States. A thin limestone almost invariably lies between the black shale and coal, even though such deposit does not occur normally in the Cherokee group in this position. Lateral extent of some of the black shale bodies is more than 100,000 square miles, but this may not be greater than extent of some thin coal beds and thin limestone layers.

Is the black shale a strictly contemporaneous deposit throughout its discovered area of distribution? Are other phases of cyclothems also laid down simultaneously, or do all represent shifting belts—perhaps very broad belts—in which a particular sedimentary environment prevails while that belonging to another phase coexists in neighbouring territory? Evidence on which answers to these questions can be given is not easy to find. Stratigraphic observations in the field support the most exact sort of parallelism of many sedimentary units over very large areas. Yet regional changes do exist and these point to lack of exact contemporaneity of homologous phases in sections of the same cyclothem observed at widely separated exposures. This accords with *a priori* judgment.

What explanation can be offered for the arrangement of cyclothems of differing character in regularly repeated order? If relationships ascribed to megacyclothems are real—and they are—what do these mean? From the standpoint of observations in the Kansas region alone, the only suggestion by way of answer is that centrally placed cyclothems of the megacyclic sequence are dominant as record of important marine invasion; these cyclothems (second and third of the Shawnee type) have weakly developed non-marine phases, even though normal marine conditions are clearly interrupted between the cycles. Subaerial deposition is prominent and marine phases (even though they attain the fusuline phase, as commonly they do) are less widely and strongly expressed in other parts of the megacyclothem. These point to interpretation of megacyclic sequences of cyclothems as a sedimentary record of major seaway fluctuation on which minor advances and retreats of the strand line are superposed. Correlation of Kansas and Illinois cyclic successions is not well enough established to warrant positive conclusions, but Wanless and others now think that beds assigned to a megacyclothem in the northern mid-continent are equivalent to a single cyclothem as recognized in Illinois. Inasmuch as marine invasions of Pennsylvanian time reached eastward from Kansas, which was more persistently and frequently flooded by the sea than Illinois, it is very possible that the main marine phase of an Illinois cyclothem is equivalent to the dominant marine cyclothems of a Kansas megacyclothem, and that the marine parts of subordinate cyclothems belonging in the latter are not represented by marine equivalents in Illinois. It must be said, however, that this hypothesis offers no explanation for the peculiar distinctions which so strikingly differentiate homologous phases of successive cyclothems in the Kansas megacyclothem. This question I must leave unanswered.

CONCLUSIONS

Study of the Late Paleozoic deposits here briefly described supports the following conclusions, among which are some not based on discussion given in this paper. (1) The continental surface in central United States during Late Paleozoic time was mostly just above or below sea level and over very large areas was so lacking in relief that a slight relative change of sea level was sufficient to produce vast inundation or equally large emergence. (2) The dominant character of sedimentation was cyclic accumulation of varied sorts of clastic and calcareous deposits which can be differentiated and traced with confidence for hundreds of miles. (3) The phases of each cyclic succession are record of environments which prevailed and which spread over areas of sedimentation as seas advanced and retreated. (4) Cyclic successions in different parts of the column show divergence of expression but follow the same general pattern, and are all interpreted as representing an advance of the sea followed by retreat. (5) In parts of the Kansas Pennsylvanian and Permian section, cyclothems having individual peculiarities of expression are arranged in constant order which is repeated. These define megacyclothems. (6) During sedimentation, there was gradual subsidence which resulted in maintenance of the surface of sedimentation approximately at the mean sea level. (7) The cause of the oscillatory movements of the sea is not definitely known, but seemingly the controlling factor was change of sea level rather than movements of the continental masses. Main evidence of this is appearance of cyclic sedimentation in rocks of corresponding age in widely separated parts of the world. (8) The periodicity and long persistence of cyclic sedimentation, extending from Late Mississippian well into Permian time, as recorded in the central United States, are evidence opposing assignment of sea level fluctuation to glaciation and the resulting changes of oceanic volume through waxing and waning of ice sheets. (9) The wide lateral distribution and number of cyclic sequences in the central United States provides a laboratory of stratigraphic and sedimentational study which may serve to throw light on fundamental problems of paleoecology, because features of environment may be inferred more reliably than in many other studies of ancient sediments.

REFERENCES

Abernathy, G. E., 1937, The Cherokee group of south-eastern Kansas: Kansas Geol. Soc. 11th Ann. Field Conf. Guidebook, p. 18–23, figs. 5–6.

Moore, R. C., 1936, Stratigraphic classification of the Pennsylvanian rocks of Kansas: Kansas Geol. Survey Bull., v. 22, p. 1–256, figs. 1–12.

Reger, D. B., 1931, Pennsylvanian cycles in West Virginia: Illinois Geol. Survey Bull., v. 60, p. 217–239, figs. 1–2.

Weller, J. M., 1930, Cyclical sedimentation of the Pennsylvanian period and its significance: Jour. Geology, v. 38, p. 97–135, figs. 1–6.

Wells, J. W., 1947, Provisional paleoecological analysis of the Devonian rocks of the Columbus region: Ohio Jour. Sci., v. 47, p. 119–126, fig. 1.

Williams, J. S., 1938, Pennsylvanian invertebrate faunas of south-eastern Kansas. Kansas Geol. Survey Bull., v. 24, p. 92–122, pls. 10–12, figs. 12–13.

50

Note on Mississippian and Permian Reef Suites

JOHN W. WELLS
1952

From *Journal of Geology,* vol. 60, no. 1, pp. 97–98, 1952.

The July, 1950, number of the *Journal of Geology* is devoted to a number of papers on past and present reef structures. The first paper is an able and illuminating summary by Adams and Frenzel of the environment and sedimentation of the now famous Capitan Reef and associated suite of deposits of Upper Permian (Guadalupian) age in Texas and New Mexico. The second paper is an equally important, but less impressive, analysis of the Upper Mississippian (Viséan) reef suite of the Pennine region of northern England. The apparently fortuitous juxtaposition of these two papers suggests that a comparison of these two Paleozoic reef areas should be mutually useful to students of stratigraphy.

But even a casual survey of the extensive literature on the two areas (see King, 1948, containing many references; Bond, 1950, containing many references to British reef structures; Pugh, 1950, a very useful paper, although several significant British papers are omitted) shows that their interpretation has developed independently, with modern reefs, which are not entirely homologous, as the only common frame of reference. One is surprised to find no mention of similar Paleozoic reef-bordered basins in the definitive papers of P. B. King on the Permian area, and very little in the papers by our British friends on the Mississippian Basin of northern England (Parkinson, 1943) and it comes to mind that the work of each might have been eased by study of what the others had done and thought. The purpose of this note is not to make the suggested extended comparison but rather to point out the remarkable similarities of these two great structures, in the hope that others who are closer to these special stratigraphic-paleoecologic-sedimentologic problems may profit by and extend the work of one another.

The diagram (Figure 50.1) emphasizes the homology between the reef-bordered basins of the Mississippian of England and the Permian of Texas and New Mexico. North-south generalized sections of the critical part of each, to

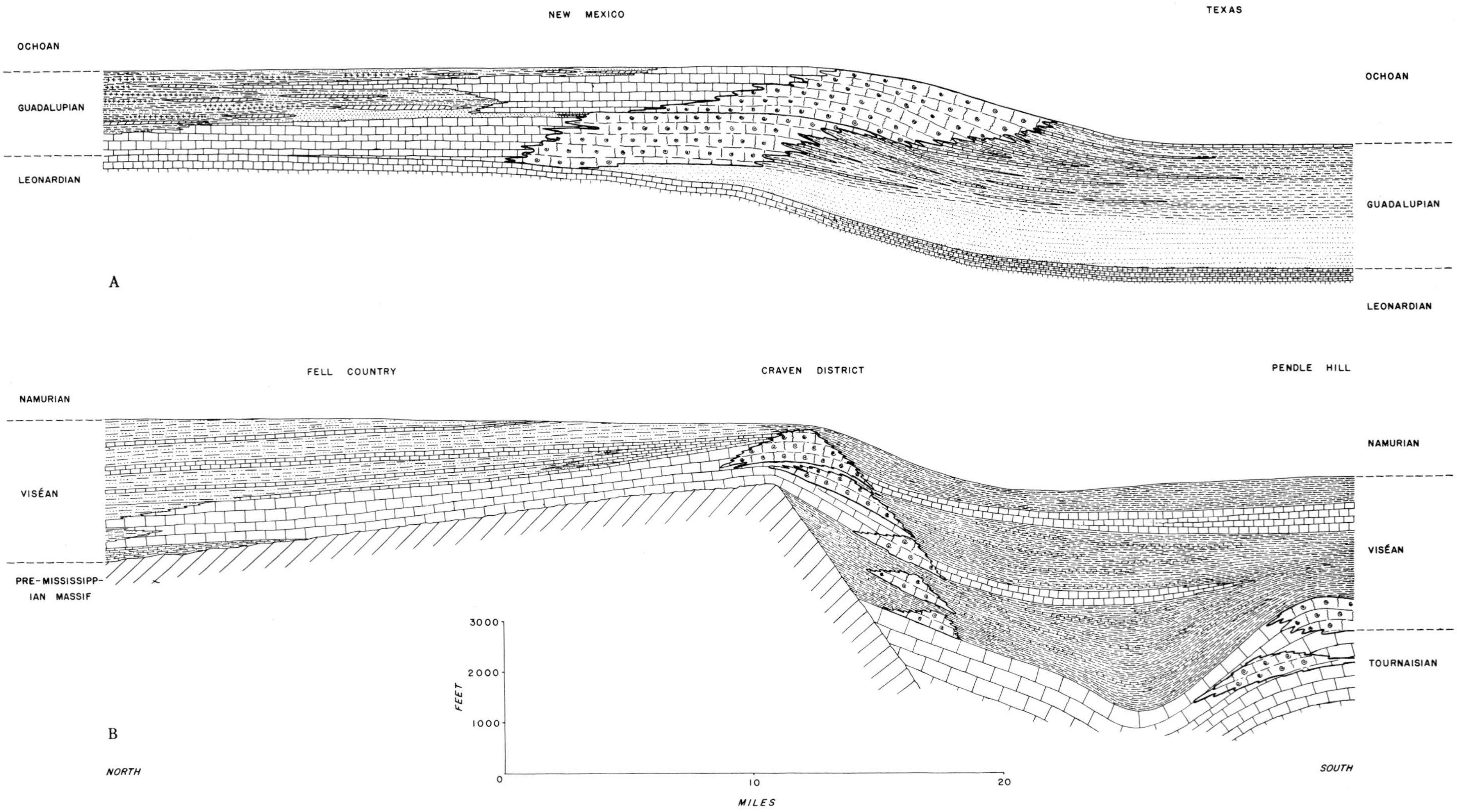

FIGURE 50.1
British Mississippian and American Permian reef suites. North-south sections of same horizontal and vertical scales of A, Upper Permian (Guadalupian) reef suite of Delaware Basin, Texas and New Mexico (adapted from Lang, 1937), and B, Upper Mississippian (Viséan) reef suite of northern England (Pennines) (adapted from Wray, 1948).

the same horizontal and vertical scales, indicate their similar magnitude both in time and in space. The Permian Delaware Basin, however, is larger areally, enclosing at least 10,000 square miles to the Mississippian Pennine ("Central Province") Basin's 4,000 square miles. Both are of structural origin, the Pennine Basin being dominated on the north by the Craven fault system and bordering rigid pre-Mississippian massifs, whereas the Delaware Basin was apparently controlled by local downward flexing without fracturing of earlier Permian rocks. In both cases, however, results were similar: deep euxinic (Pennine Basin) or para-euxinic (Delaware Basin) marine basins, more or less completly enclosed by steep slopes leading to shallow shelves extending toward more or less distant shore lines. Organic reefs grew in the optimum environment presented by the edges of the shelves bordering the basins, with the result that three main ecological and depositional situations, stressed by all workers on both areas, were established: (1) the lagoonal shelves (to the north in the particular sections, fig. 1), (2) the reef tracts (central in the sections), and (3) the deep basins (to the south in the sections), each with its characteristic sedimentary and faunal phase.

The shelves and basins were separated, and to a great extent their sediments were controlled, by the marginal reef tracts. The sediments and faunas of the reef phase are very similar in both basins, as expected because the environment in both cases was similar: massive, poorly bedded to unbedded complexes of various types of limestones, more or less lenticular in section, normal to the margin of the shelves, and more or less continuous as knolls or banks parallel to them. Fossils, other than algae and sponges, occur only in a few lenses; corals and bryozoans are uncommon.

The sediments on the shelves ("back-reef facies," "massif facies") behind the reefs and extending shoreward are not wholly alike in the two areas because of different climatic and geographic conditions. In both, however, "normal" fossiliferous limestones, pisolites, and chinastones extend back for some distance, passing into marine shales and sandstones (Yoredale group) in the Pennine Basin, and into dolomites, sandstones, shales, evaporites (Chalk Bluff group), and eventually continental beds in the Delaware Basin.

Basinward from the reef tracts the sediments are, at first, those characteristic of steep slopes: conglomerates, breccias, granular limestones, etc., becoming less massive and finer grained outward and passing or lensing into the basin-bottom deep-water deposits. In the Delaware Basin the latter are largely cyclic sequences of flat-lying fine sandstones and siltstones, with some bituminous limestones. The fauna is characterized by ammonites, but it is not clearly pelagic. The origin of these deep-basin clastics has not yet been satisfactorily explained. They are present in immense quantity, although somewhat thinner than the equivalent reef and shelf deposits, and apparently contain no shale or clay-sized particles except bentonites. If they represent material carried somehow from the shelf over the reef tracts, what became of the finest particles? The relationship of water composition, temperature, and circulation to sedimentary and organic environments has yet to be satisfactorily resolved. The studies now in progress by N. D. Newell and associates should be significant in this connection.

In the Pennine Mississippian Basin the deposits are more genuinely of the euxinic ("pontic") phase than in the Delaware Basin and are much thicker than their equivalent reef and shelf phase sediments. They consist of thin-bedded black bituminous shales and limestones, carrying a pelagic goniatite and thin-shelled pelecypod fauna. Their source is perhaps more obvious than that of the basin beds of the Delaware Basin: the by-passing of fine clastics across the incompletely enclosing marginal reef tract into a deep stygian basin.

REFERENCES CITED

Adams, J. E., and H. N. Frenzel, 1950, Capitan barrier reef, Texas and New Mexico: Jour. Geology, v. 58, p. 289–312.

Bond, G., 1950, The Lower Carboniferous reef limestones of northern England: Jour. Geology, v. 58, p. 313–329.

King, P. B., 1948, Geology of the southern Guadalupe Mountains, Texas: U.S. Geol. Survey Prof. Paper 215.

Lang, W. B., 1937, The Permian formations of the Pecos Valley of New Mexico and Texas: Am. Assoc. Petroleum Geologists Bull., v. 21, p. 833–898.

Parkinson, D., 1943, The age of the reef-limestones in the Lower Carboniferous of North Derbyshire: Geol. Mag. [Great Britain], v. 80, p. 121–131.

Pugh, W. E., ed., 1950, Bibliography of organic reefs, bioherms, and biostromes: Tulsa, Okla., Seismography Service Corp.

Wray, D. A., 1948, British regional geology—the Pennines and adjacent areas: London, Geol. Survey and Museum.

51

Permian Faunas

A Study in Facies

CARL O. DUNBAR

1941

Approximately 140 years ago William Smith discovered the use of fossils in correlation. Most of his life had been spent as a surveyor crossing and recrossing the Jurassic rocks of England where the structure is simple and many of the formations are easily identified by lithology. Distinctive beds can be traced along the outcrop from quarry to quarry where Smith was wont to hunt fossils, and thus he came to realize that each formation has distinctive species by which it can be identified without the trouble of tracing.

It is no accident that within the half century following Smith's discovery the entire geologic column was securely established and all the systems were correctly identified, not merely in England but across the whole of Europe and eastern North America, for no other conception has ever become such an open sesame to the secrets of Earth's history. Without it we should still have no general time scale, and correlations of the younger rocks would even now be as uncertain as those of the pre-Cambrian.

But the use of fossils is by no means as simple as William Smith then believed. Perhaps the greatest obstacle—not suspected by Smith—is the influence of changing facies.

In his address before the Geological Society a year ago, President Vaughan analyzed the ecology of modern marine organisms, seeking criteria by which to reconstruct the physical and chemical conditions prevalent in the seas of the past. He showed how both animals and plants are limited by depth, currents, sunlight, chemical features of the water, and physical character of the sea floor. As a result of such factors, faunal assemblages, largely distinct, live side by side, each restricted to some special environment. Doctor Vaughan focused attention on the paleogeographic significance of these facts and strove to lay a firmer basis for interpreting the records made by the ancient seas. It is proposed here to discuss another aspect of the picture, namely the difficulties that such faunal restrictions present in stratigraphic correlation.

From *Geological Society of America Bulletin*, vol. 52, pp. 55–81, 1941. Reprinted with permission of the author and the Geological Society of America.

The subject of facies change is not novel. Within 40 years after Smith had discovered that he could correlate the Jurassic rocks across England by fossils, Gressly had found that in Switzerland some of the Jurassic horizons change character along the strike, both in lithology and in faunas. For these distinct aspects of each horizon, based on either lithologic or biologic characters, he introduced the term *facies*. Moreover, he found the same facies locally in different horizons and thus foresaw clearly the difficulties involved in using fossils for accurate correlation. Mojsisovics encountered the same difficulties in the Tirolean Alps in 1879, and most subsequent students of alpine geology have appreciated the significance of facies, as shown by Diener in 1925 and by Pia in 1930. . . .

Such changes of facies occur in every geologic system but perhaps nowhere on a scale more impressive than in the Permian. I have chosen to use the Permian as a basis for discussion partly from personal interest and partly because it provides instances of lateral change so abrupt and so profound as to be easily demonstrated and analyzed. . . .

LATERAL CHANGE FROM MARINE TO NONMARINE FACIES

THE KAZANIAN SERIES OF THE RUSSIAN PLATFORM

The most obvious change in the *biologic* facies is seen where marine deposits grade laterally into nonmarine. A magnificent illustration was studied by members of the Permian excursion of the Seventeenth International Geological Congress when we followed the Kazanian horizon from the city of Perm across the Russian Platform to Kazan. In this 300-mile stretch (Figure 51.1), the nearly horizontal Kazanian beds are more or less continuously exposed in the bluffs of the Kama River, which rise at many places from 100 to 200 feet above the valley floor.

About Perm this series is represented by bright red, unfossiliferous sandstone and siltstone some 500 feet thick. This is the nonmarine, Ufimian facies, so called for the city of Ufa which is on the strike south of Perm. In conspicuous contrast, the equivalent beds in the environs of Kazan are richly fossiliferous white limestone. Our 3-day journey by steamer down the Kama, stopping repeatedly to examine and collect, gave us ample opportunity to observe the gradual change in lithology.

For the first several hours below Perm the bluffs were monotonously red, and then gray lenses of channel sands were seen in increasing numbers. We stopped to examine one of these at Babka and another at Saigatka, finding in both the leaves of a large fern, *Odontopteris*, and petrified driftwood. At near-by Ischajewo, stegocephalians and reptiles (*Ulemosaurus, Titanophoneus, Moschops*) have been found and recently were described by Efremov. During the second day's journey we saw tongues of gray siltstone and shale within the red beds, increasing in number and thickness toward the west. At Tikhye Gori we found in one of these gray tongues the first elements of a marine fauna—a few cypriid ostracods, small clams, and rare specimens of a small spiriferoid brachiopod. Associated layers yielded fossil insects and fragments of land plants. At Yelabuga thin beds of oölitic limestone were added to the section, and the marine fauna was somewhat more varied; and by the time we had reached Vandovka, some 80 miles east of Kazan, the bluffs appeared more gray than red, and three distinct tongues of impure limestone were observed. The limestones increased rapidly toward the west, and fossils became more abundant and more varied at successive stops. Thus, in a journey of some 300 miles, we saw the lateral transition from the deep red, unfossiliferous sandstones at Perm into the white limestones at Kazan, a transition marked by deep intertonguing of marine and non-marine zones.

The Kazanian faunas occurring along this route have been monographed by Netschaeva, who records 180 species in the environs of Kazan. Even here the fauna is somewhat restricted in its scope, having no fusulines and no ammonites and very few corals or echinoderms; but it does include 10 species of bryozoans, 27 of brachiopods, and lesser numbers of several other groups, in addition to a large number of pelecypods. In contrast to this, the marine tongues exposed about Yelabuga and from there to the east yielded only 31 marine

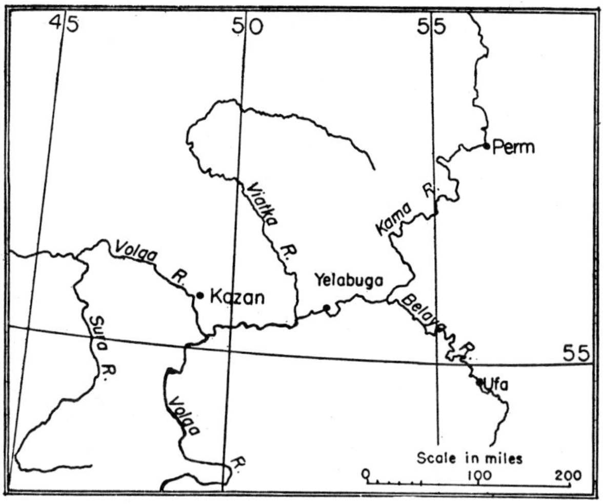

FIGURE 51.1
Sketch map of part of the Russian platform

invertebrates. These included 1 species of Foraminifera, 1 of sponges, 3 of worms, 1 linguloid and 4 articulate brachiopods, 2 gastropods, 1 nautiloid, 1 brachiopod, 3 ostracods, and 14 small clams.

An analysis of the changing faunas indicates that the marine tongues which reach so far east into the Ufimian red beds represent more and more brackish water toward the east until finally they grade over into fresh-water deposits. With this gradual change two things happen to the fauna. The first is a screening out of more and more of the species until there are left a few of the most hardy, the most ubiquitous, and therefore probably the longest-ranging forms. Toward the eastern limit of these tongues there is progressive reduction of the number of species and a dwarfing of those that persist, a phenomenon also observed by Goldring in her study of the postglacial faunas of the Champlain embayment. A second change involves the addition to the fauna of brackish-water elements, such as *Estheria* and *Liebea*, and fresh-water or terrestrial forms, such as insects and land plants. The net result is that, in tongues reaching far out in the nonmarine facies, the faunas are limited in variety, they lack most of the diagnostic elements of the equivalent marine deposits, the species present are in part ubiquitous and long-ranging and therefore of limited value in detailed correlation, and they contain elements of unknown value which are not represented in the standard marine sequence.

EXAMPLES FROM THE AMERICAN PERMIAN

The Phosphoria formation in Wyoming presents a close parallel to the Kazanian relations just described, but the exposures there are less favorable. Thomas has succeeded in tracing several tongues of the Phosphoria limestone eastward into the Chugwater red beds, as represented in Figure 51.2. The Sybille tongue has now been identified as the Minnekahta limestone in the rim of the Black Hills. There, it is for the most part strangely barren of fossils, but abundant small clams occur locally near its base. These have been known and collected by a number of paleontologists, but in the present state of our knowledge they do not justify correlation with other formations, nor do they indicate clearly whether the beds are Pennsylvanian or Permian.

A comparable fauna of small clams occurs locally in dolomite beds in the Blaine group of central Oklahoma. For the most part this is a red-bed and gypsum-bearing group of strata now correlated on the basis of physical stratigraphy with the upper part of the Leonard series of Texas. The Leonard faunas are large and varied, including fusulines, ammonites, and brachiopods, but the few fossiliferous tongues that extend into the Blaine of Oklahoma carry only a few "nondescript" little clams.

The fauna of the Whitehorse sandstone of west-central Oklahoma and the panhandle of

Texas illustrates again the influence of environment on a marine assemblage. Newell's recent study has confirmed the belief that the Whitehorse sandstone is equivalent to the Capitan horizon of the Guadalupe region. For the most part the Whitehorse is made of red beds, presumably nonmarine; but a few thin lenses of calcareous beds carry a limited marine fauna. Newell records 32 species, of which 26 are pelecypods and small gastropods, most of them unknown elsewhere. Of bryozoans there is a single species and of brachiopods 4, none of them common. The contemporaneous marine fauna of the Delaware Basin, on the contrary, is large and varied, with ammonites, fusulines, and abundant brachiopods.

Even though intertonguing of beds or the presence of identical species may prove the correct correlations, there is more *general resemblance* among the faunas of the Minnekahta limestone, the Blaine gypsum, the Whitehorse sandstone, and the Ufimian beds of Russia then there is between any one of these and its nearest, normally marine equivalent!

VERTICAL CHANGES FROM MARINE TO NONMARINE

TYPE SECTION OF THE PERMIAN SYSTEM

Thus far we have considered only the lateral changes of facies due to local inequalities in the environment at a given time. But there are also instances in which the environment over a large area changed gradually from marine to nonmarine conditions during a considerable lapse of geologic time. An illustration is afforded by the Permian section in Kansas and Nebraska, where the basal part (Council Grove group) is mostly marine and has a varied fauna, while the upper part is entirely nonmarine and consists of unfossiliferous red beds. If studied in ascending order, the faunas of successive formations show an irregular but progressive change, comparable to the lateral change displayed in the Kazanian faunas. The Council Grove group of Kansas, for example, is marine and generally fossiliferous, but the succeeding Chase group includes alternating fossiliferous and barren formations in which the higher marine faunas are progressively more limited in scope and eventually consist largely of small pelecypods.

The type section of the Permian system, unfortunately, presents such a change in facies, as shown in Figure 51.3. The Sakmarian and Artinskian horizons are largely marine and richly fossiliferous; but the Kungurian, with its vast salt deposits, has very limited faunas; the Kazanian series marks a return of marine waters over the western part of the Russian Platform, but even this fauna is limited in facies, having no fusulines and no ammonites and but few of the distinctly Permian genera of brachiopods; the Tartarian includes only nonmarine red beds with land plants and fossil reptiles and stegocephalians. In short, the lower part of the section is normally marine and carries an immense fauna including ammonites, fusu-

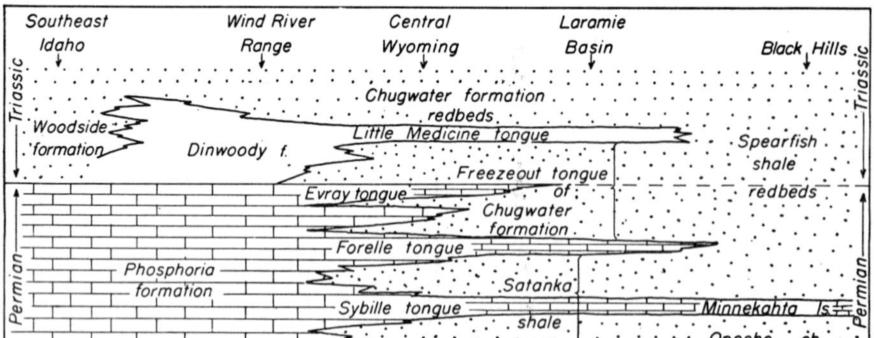

FIGURE 51.2
Idealized stratigraphic section of the Phosphoria Formation and its red bed equivalents in Wyoming. (Slightly modified from Horace D. Thomas.)

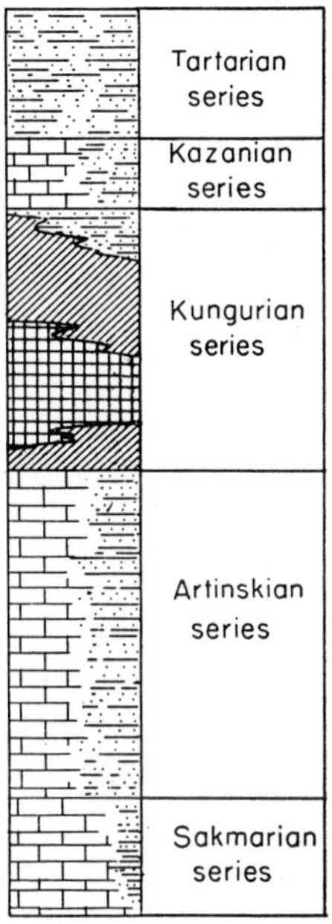

FIGURE 51.3
Generalized columnar section of the type Permian of Russia. The Kungurian includes vast thicknesses of anhydrite (*oblique shading*) and salt (*quadrille shading*).

lines, a great variety of brachiopods, mollusks, corals, and bryozoans, but the middle part has much restricted and only partly normally marine faunas, and the upper part is wholly nonmarine.

In spite of its historical importance, therefore, this is a poor standard for international correlation, just because so much of it is nonmarine. Murchison originally included only the Kungurian, Kazanian, and Tartarian, basing his system largely on the evidence of fossil reptiles and plants and referring the underlying normally marine beds (Artinskian and Sakmarian) to the Carboniferous. The *original* Permian thus contains but few distinctive genera of brachiopods and no fusulines or ammonites. It was Karpinsky who added the Artinsk to the Permian because his analysis of its ammonite fauna showed closer relation to the Permian than to the Carboniferous. This may sound strange in view of the fact that the original Permian has never to this day yielded a single ammonite! But by 1889, when Karpinsky made his study, the Trogkofel limestone of the Carnic Alps, the Sosio beds at Palermo, the *Productus* limestone of the Salt Range, and other marine formations had come to be recognized as Permian, and on the basis of these faunas, outside of Russia, Karpinsky revised the original Permian in its type region.

OBSTACLES TO CORRELATION, EXEMPLIFIED BY THE PERMIAN OF EAST GREENLAND

The practical bearing of these facts on correlation with other regions is illustrated by recent studies of the Permian faunas of East Greenland. Large collections have been made there by Lauge Koch and his assistants, who recognize two quite distinct marine facies, one of limestone rich in brachiopods and bryozoans and the other of shales bearing clams and rare ammonites (Figure 51.4). Recognizing that these faunas belonged to the Russian province, Frebold correlated the Brachiopod limestone of East Greenland with the "Schwagerinakalk" of the Ufa Plateau, and the ammonite-bearing shales with the Artinsk of the Urals. This was but natural, for the general resemblances between the beds thus correlated are striking. But in both he was correlating facies with like facies. The fact remains that we do not know a typical marine brachiopod fauna of Kungurian, Kazanian, or Tartarian age in European Russia, and there is little basis for a direct comparison of the Greenland beds with that part of the type section of the Permian.

Fossil fishes from the Posidonomya shales have been monographed by Neilsen and Aldinger, and the latter (1935) has reviewed the evidence of this group and pointed out close resemblances and possibly identical species in the fish faunas of the Zechstein of Germany, the Phosphoria of North America, and the Kazanian of Russia. Furthermore, restudy of the ammonite *Gothabites* from the Martinia shales of Greenland has convinced A. K. Miller (personal communication) that it is approximately at the cyclolobine stage of evolution and should be high instead of low in the Permian. It appears necessary, therefore, to restudy the brachiopods of Greenland critically

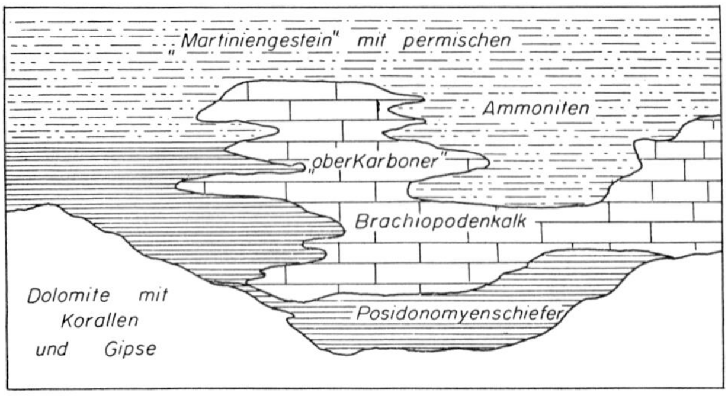

FIGURE 51.4
Idealized stratigraphic diagram of lithologic facies in the Permian of East Greenland. (After Hans Frebold.)

and to compare them with the higher marine faunas of other parts of the world as well as with the basal part of the type Permian.

LATERAL CHANGES OF FACIES WITHIN A MARINE PROVINCE

MODERN EXAMPLES

Modern studies of marine ecology have presented striking illustrations of the extent to which bottom faunas are limited by the physical character of the sea floor. Two instances may be cited by way of illustration.

Near the famous marine biological station at Naples there is a tiny shoal, known as Pigeon Bank, standing about 115 feet above the adjacent muddy floor of the bay. On the bank Walther found 296 species of shell-bearing animals (*i.e.*, those capable of fossilization), whereas but 31 were found on the adjacent muddy bottoms. Moreover, only 14 species were found to share the two environments. If these two types of sediments were preserved as limestone and shale, respectively, their faunas would have but little in common in spite of the fact that they accumulated side by side. Surely our Paleozoic record is full of instances of this sort.

A striking case of a different nature is that of Great Bahama Bank, one of the largest areas of modern limy deposits (Figure 51.5). With an area of nearly 7000 square miles, it presents a remarkably flat surface over which the water is mostly less than 20 feet deep. Andros Island rises as a low rim along its eastern margin, and the bank stands as a great limy platform with steep slopes, rising out of deep water. About 5000 square miles of its surface, west of Andros Island, has a bottom composed of fine limy mud. During storms this sediment is partly lifted into suspension, making the water turbid and milky, but with the return of fair weather it settles back like a fall of fine snow, smothering and killing nearly all kinds of sessile bottom life. As a result, the fauna of the mud-covered area is amazingly limited for a shallow limy sea floor in a subtropical region. The chief animals of the mud-covered area are crustaceans, notably *Crangon*, a form that burrows in during storms and digs out afterward. Corals are [almost] lacking, and marine mollusks are rare and of few kinds. . . .

During storms, the sediment in suspension is partly carried beyond the edge of the bank where it settles over the steep marginal slope, reaching as far out as the center of Florida Strait. Parts of the bank have a solid floor of somewhat older limy deposit, where the currents prevent the present lime-mud from coming to rest. In these areas a more normal and varied benthonic fauna exists.

CAPITAN REEF AND RELATED FACIES

The water is now so shallow over Bahama Bank that probably little of the sediment comes to rest there permanently, but if slow subsidence were going on, a limy deposit would form having many of the features of the great Permian "reefs." Such limestone masses as the Capitan reef, for example, clearly stood well above the surrounding sea floor (Figure 51.6). The massive deposits of the reef proper are for the most part strangely unfossiliferous, though fossils occur abundantly in spots and at certain levels; but the biostromes that descend

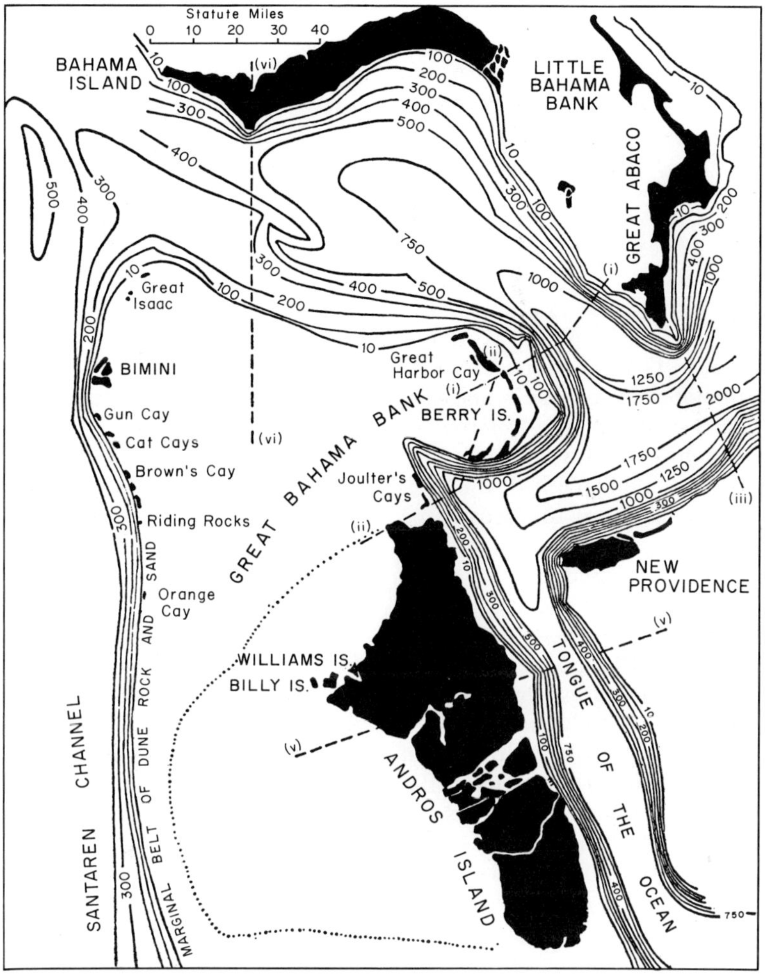

FIGURE 51.5
Map of Andros Island (*black*) and a part of Great Bahama Bank. Shows the area of thick lime mud (*within dotted line*) west of Andros Island. (After R. M. Field.)

from its seaward margin into the Delaware Basin are richly fossiliferous, as is the well-bedded Carlsbad limestone on the lagoonal side of the reef. Probably the scarcity of fossils in the massive core of the reef is due to the fact that the bottom there was inhospitable to benthonic animals. A fascinating problem still awaiting critical study in connection with such great Permian reefs is the actual distribution of fossil organisms in different parts of the reef and in the adjacent and contemporaneous deposits of other facies. The Capitan exposures afford an unusual opportunity for such study.

THE ARTINSK AND ITS LIMESTONE EQUIVALENTS

The troublesome problem of the Pennsylvanian-Permian boundary arose largely because of changes of facies in the type region of the Permian. When Karpinsky added the Artinskian to the Permian in 1889, his arguments were generally accepted, and the typical Artinsk has been placed in the Permian by practically all subsequent students, including the Geological Survey of Russia. The typical Artinskian is a detrital facies of sandstones, siltstones, and shale with interbedded conglomerate, distributed in a rather narrow belt along the western flank of the Urals. It bears an extensive fauna from which Krotow was able to identify 293 species, but the fossils are largely restricted to certain zones interbedded with barren shales or sandstones. . . .

To the west of the Artinskian facies, however, lies the Ufa Plateau, presenting a great thickness of limestones, in part well bedded and in part reefy. These also contain a very large fauna, chiefly of brachiopods, bryozoans, fusulines, and corals. The brachiopods mostly belong to "Carboniferous genera," and the limestones which carry them were referred to the Carboniferous by Murchison. Moreover, when Tschernyschew monographed the brachiopods in 1902, he assumed the beds to be Upper Carboniferous, and this was adopted as the official usage of the Geological Survey. Only within the last decade or so has it been discovered that the "Upper Carboniferous" limestones of the Ufa Plateau and the Artinskian detritals farther east are only distinct facies and that they are largely equivalent in age. The stratigraphic relations are obscured in this instance by the scarcity of exposures in the transition zone where intertonguing should provide a certain clue. The evidence for equivalence rests in part on regional stratigraphic relations and in part on the presence of zone fossils not restricted to either facies. Such, for example, are the shark, *Helicoprion bessonowi*, found in the Artinsk facies on Sylva River and in the limestone facies at Upper Tschussovaya village; or the Artinskian types of ammonites recently found in the Shikhans near Sterlitamak; or the fusulines also recently found in the lower part of the Artinsk facies about Sim Works.

Even within the limestone facies of the Ufa Plateau there are striking restrictions of the faunas, recently described by Tolstikhina. She recognizes four distinct stratigraphic horizons, each divisible locally into several organic-lithologic facies. For example, she finds that the Jurezan horizon includes a bryozoan reef facies, a hydroid reef facies, and a facies of well-bedded limestone with corals and fusulines; and the succeeding Chernaia Rechka horizon includes coralline-algal reefs grading laterally into stratified limestone with brachiopods and fusulines.

DISTINCT PROVINCIAL FACIES

MODERN EXAMPLES

The existence of well-defined faunal provinces in the modern oceans is well known. In some instances the faunal distinctness is apparently due largely to isolation, as by a land barrier. For example, Dall found on the Pacific side of the Isthmus of Panama a fauna of 805 species of shell-bearing invertebrates and on the Caribbean side 517 species, yet only 24 of these are common to the two regions.

Such distinct faunal provinces may also be caused by differences in temperature in a continuous shelf sea. For example, Dall recorded a fauna of 180 species of shell-bearing mollusks off the coast of Greenland, 277 in the Gulf of Maine, 305 off the Carolina coast, 681 off the west coast of Florida, and 517 along the coast of Panama. The total of these figures is 1960

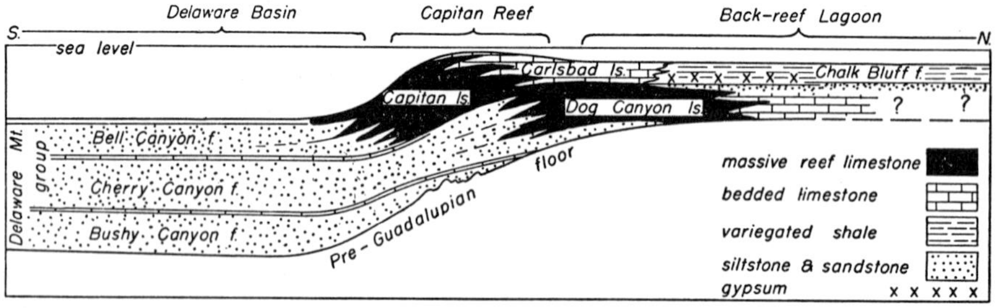

FIGURE 51.6
Diagrammatic section across the Capitan reef. Shows relations of the reef (*black*) to related facies. (Adapted from Walter B. Lang.)

and by actual count there are 1772 species involved. In other words, less than 200 species out of 1772 have appeared in two or more of the provinces mentioned, and the overwhelming majority of them are restricted to a single province. Here temperature appears to be the most important limiting factor.

Differences in salinity obviously account for the contrast between the fauna of the Baltic and that along the west coast of Norway.

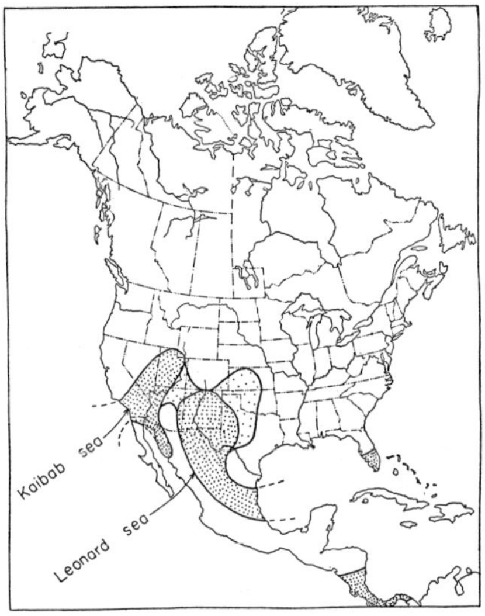

FIGURE 51.7
Paleogeographic map showing inferred relations of the Leonard and Kaibab seas. *Close stipple,* normally marine areas; *sparse stipple,* nonmarine or abnormally marine parts of the basin. (After Charles Schuchert.)

There are, however, some faunal restrictions in the modern oceans for which no simple explanation is apparent. The majority of shallow-water articulate brachiopod species now living are confined to the Australian region, and most of the living crinoids are confined to the Indian Ocean. Each of the other oceans presents an equal range of environments but almost lacks representatives of these two great stocks.

Now, whatever the cause of such restrictions, it is evident that epeiric seas derived from two distinct faunal provinces may have little in common, or at least may show striking differences in their faunas.

CONTRAST BETWEEN THE LEONARD AND KAIBAB FAUNAS

An illustration from the Permian is that of the contrast between the Leonard and the Kaibab faunas, which are known to be contemporaneous but which represent two embayments, more or less completely separated (Figure 51.7). The Leonard faunas contain abundant fusulines, many ammonites, and such distinctive Permian brachiopod genera as *Leptodus, Prorichthofenia, Geyerella, Aulosteges, Scacchinella,* and *Waagenoconcha* (King described 30 genera and 81 species of brachiopods); the Kaibab, on the contrary, has never yielded a fusuline or an ammonite, and, with the exception of a rare species of *Waagenoconcha,* its brachiopods are all of long-ranging Carboniferous genera. (McKee records 15 genera and 22 species of which all but two genera occur in the Pennsylvanian.) There is little about the Kaibab fauna to indicate a Permian rather than a Pennsylvanian age, except the presence of zone species, such as *Dictyoclostus bassi,* which are identical with those in the Leonard. For some reason, not understood, the distinctive elements of the Permian faunas largely failed to exist in the Kaibab sea.

COMPARISON OF WORD AND PHOSPHORIA FAUNAS

The Phosphoria formation of Utah and Wyoming is probably equivalent to part, at least, of the Word formation of Texas. Both are marine, and each has a fairly extensive fauna, yet there are few species in common, and the general composition of the Word fauna is quite different from that of the Phosphoria. The Word has abundant ammonites and fusulines, and its brachiopods include such characteristic Permian genera as *Waagenoconcha, Aulosteges, Prorichthofenia,* and *Leptodus,* whereas the Phosphoria has thus far yielded no fusulines, only three genera of ammonites, and none of the last three brachiopod genera. Nevertheless, according to R. E. King, at least seven species of the Phosphoria brachiopods occur also in the Word. The ammonite species are believed by Miller and Cline to be of

Word age, but none are quite identical with forms from Texas. If the Word and Phosphoria seas were contemporaneous, they were only indirectly connected, or else some conditions in the Phosphoria sea prevented most of the Word fauna from entering. The phosphate deposits suggest that chemical conditions may have been abnormal during at least a part of the time when the Phosphoria deposits were forming.

THE ECHINODERM OF THE PERMIAN OF TIMOR

One of the most amazing local peculiarities known among Permian faunas occurs in the Island of Timor in the Netherlands East Indies, whence a blastoid fauna of 14 genera and 32 species and varieties was described by Wanner. With this exception, no blastoids are known in any part of the world in rocks younger than the Lower Carboniferous. All the species and all but two of the genera of Timor are distinct from Lower Carboniferous types, and the extreme specialization of some of the genera reflects their younger age. There is likewise a large and specialized crinoid fauna in the Permian of Timor, from which Wanner originally described 28 new genera and 105 new species out of a total fauna of 44 genera and 123 species. After later expeditions Wanner (1924) indicated that a total of 75 genera and 239 species of crinoids could be recognized.

Most of the crinoids and all the blastoids are limited, so far as now known, to Timor. This appears the more remarkable because the abundant representatives of other groups, such as ammonites, bryozoans, and brachiopods, do not display a marked provincial character. Most of the ammonite species are local, but the genera are widespread in other parts of the world and permit satisfactory interregional correlation. The brachiopods and bryozoans, likewise, show no more than local specific distinction from contemporaneous faunas in Europe, Asia, and America.

As yet there is no evidence as to the nature of the environmental factors that gave asylum

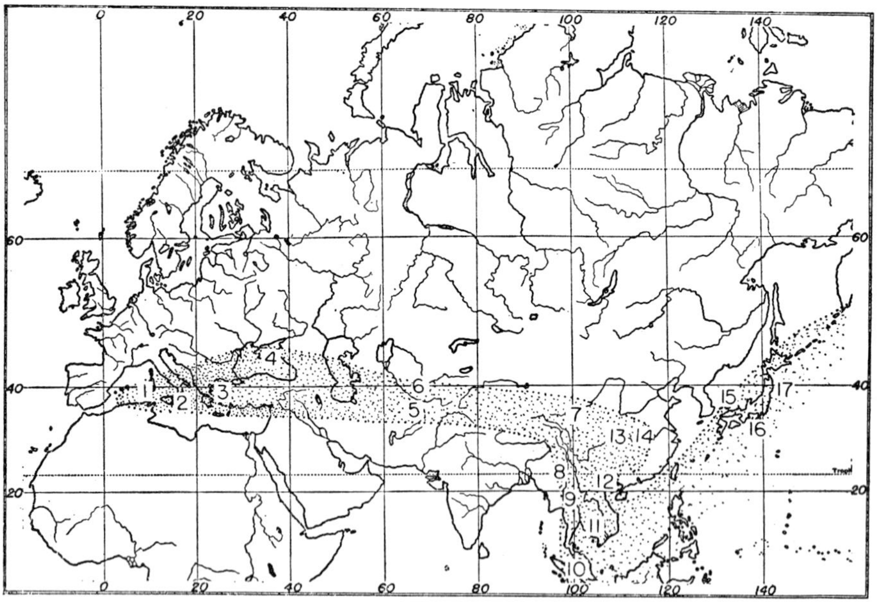

FIGURE 51.8
Map showing seaway (*stippled*) in which Neoschwagerine faunas of the Oriental realm flourished in Middle Permian time. The numerals indicate significant fossil localities: *1*, Tunisia; *2*, Palermo, Italy; *3*, Greece; *4*, Crimea; *5*, Afghanistan; *6*, Darwas; *7*, Mt. Omei, China; *8*, northern Burma; *9*, northern Siam; *10*, Cambodia; *11*, Tonkin; *12* and *13*, Yangtze River, China; *14*, Nagato, Japan; *15*, Alasaka, Japan; *16*, Kitakami Mountainland, Japan.

here to the blastoids and produced such a burst of evolution in both blastoids and crinoids, at the same time preventing the migration of all the blastoids and most of the crinoids to other parts of the world. It can hardly have been a physical barrier, since other groups of animals show no evidence of such isolation. But the very existence of blastoids in the Permian of Timor is clear proof that they had an asylum somewhere throughout Upper Carboniferous time, and their appearance in faunas of that age should not be a great surprise.

THE ORIENTAL REALM AND ITS NEOSCHWAGERINE FAUNAS

One of the notable peculiarities of the Middle and Upper Permian of the Orient is the presence, commonly in great abundance, of fusulines of the subfamilies Neoschwagerininae and Verbeekininae. These characteristic faunas are found farther westward along the old Tethian geosyncline in Darwas, Afghanistan, Crimea, Greece, Sicily, and Tunis (Figure 51.8). None of these has been found in the Salt Range of India or in Persia or in the Permian basin of Russia or in the Alps, and, with a local exception, they did not reach America. That exception must be made for the occurrence of neoschwagerines in a narrow belt extending from near Kamloops, British Columbia, into Washington and Oregon. It seems to mark a western trough that was temporarily reached by the Oriental faunas. So far as the fusulines go, the neoschwagerines characterize a great faunal realm which, in Middle and Late Permian time, was sharply isolated from the rest of the world. Nevertheless, other groups, such as the brachiopods and ammonites, do not indicate the same restrictions and seem to prove that the oriental fusulines were not limited in their distribution by land barriers alone.

CONCLUSIONS

We have focused attention thus far on the difficulties presented by changes of facies. The purpose has been to emphasize the fact that formations and faunas essentially different may be of the same age and that others, generally similar, may actually not be equivalent.

Time does not permit a development of the other side of the problem—namely, means of establishing correlation between contemporaneous facies regardless of their differences. Some obvious aids are (1) the intertonguing of distinct facies as seen either in outcrop or in subsurface well records, (2) the presence in distinct facies of certain zone fossils not limited by bottom ecology or by other restrictions which affected the majority of the fauna, (3) the stage of evolution represented in progressively changing stocks, and (4) correlations through a third area where the faunas of two distinct provinces or facies mingle or intertongue.

The objective fact of contemporaneous but distinct facies will probably be generally admitted; but it is important to carry the conception into actual use in field problems in stratigraphy.

The illustrations reviewed now seem evident, yet scarcely more than 10 years ago the relations of the Capitan reef were not understood and the limestone facies of the Artinsk was still considered Carboniferous while the detrital facies was classified as Permian. Yet these cases, because of the very magnitude and abruptness of the facies changes, are relatively obvious. The earlier Paleozoic, especially that of the Appalachian trough, must be full of examples of changes in facies less spectacular and therefore less easily detected that still confuse our stratigraphic interpretations.

REFERENCES

Aldinger, Hermann, 1935, Das Alter der jungpaleozoischen Posidonomyaschiefer von Ostgrönland: Medd. Grønland, v. 98, no. 4, p. 1–24.

Dall, W. H., and G. D. Harris, 1892, Neocene correlation papers: U.S. Geol. Survey Bull. 84, p. 22–31.

Diener, C., 1925, Grundzüge der Biostratigraphie: Leipzig and Vienna, p. 174–214.

Dunbar, Carl O., 1940, The type Permian—its classification and correlation: Am. Assoc. Petroleum Geologists Bull., v. 24, p. 237–281.

Efremov, J. A., 1940, *Ulemosaurus svijagensis* Riab. —ein Dinocephale aus den Ablagerungen des

Perm der U.S.S.R.: Nova Acta Leopoldina, n.f., v. 9, no. 59, p. 155–205.
Field, Richard M., 1931, Geology of the Bahamas: Geol. Soc. America Bull., v. 42, p. 759–783.
Frebold, Hans, 1932, Marines Unterperm in Ostgrönland: Medd. Grønland, v. 84, no. 4, p. 1–33.
Goldring, W., 1922, The Champlain Sea: New York State Museum Bull., v. 239–240, p. 153–194.
Gressly, A., 1838–1841, Observations géologique sur le Jura soleurois: Soc. helvetique sci. nat. Mém., Extr. nouv.
Karpinsky, A., 1889, Über die Ammoniten der Artinsk-Stufe: Acad. sci. [St. Petersbourg] Mém., ser. 7, v. 37, no. 2.
King, Philip B., 1934, Permian stratigraphy of Trans-Pecos Texas: Geol. Soc. America Bull., v. 45, p. 697–798.
King, Robert E., 1930, Geology of the Glass Mountains, Texas. Part II, Faunal summary and correlation of the Permian formations with description of the Brachiopoda: University of Texas Bull. 3042, p. 1–245.
Krotow, P., 1885, Artinske Étage, geologisch-paleontologische Monographie des Sandsteins von Artinsk: Univ. Kazan Soc. Nat. Proc., v. 13, p. 1–314.
Lang, Walter B., 1937, The Permian formations of the Pecos Valley of New Mexico and Texas: Am. Assoc. Petroleum Geologists Bull., v. 21, p. 833–898.
McKee, Edwin, D., 1938, Toroweap and Kaibab formations of Arizona and Utah: Carnegie Inst. Washington Pub., v. 492, p. 1–264.
Miller, A. K., and L. M. Cline, 1934, The cephalopods of the Phosphoria formation of northwestern United States: Jour. Paleontology, v. 8, p. 281–302.
Mojsisovics, E., 1879, Die Dolomitriffe von Südtirol und Venetien: Vienna,
Netschaeva, A., 1894, Die Fauna der permischen Ablagerungen des östlichen Theils des europäischen Russlands: Univ. Kazan Soc. Nat. Studies, v. 27, p. 1–503.
Newell, Norman D., 1940, Invertebrate fauna of the Late Permian Whitehorse sandstone: Geol. Soc. America Bull., v. 51, p. 261–336.
Pia, J., 1930, Grundbegriffe der Stratigraphie: Leipzig and Vienna.
Ruzhencev, V. E., 1938, Ammonoids of the Sakmarian stage and their stratigraphic significance: Moscow Univ. Problems Paleontology, v. IV, p. 187–285.
Thomas, Horace D., 1934, Phosphoria and Dinwoody tongues in lower Chugwater of central and southeastern Wyoming: Am. Assoc. Petroleum Geologists Bull., v. 18, p. 1655–1697.
Tolstikhina, M. M., 1935, Carboniferous deposits of the central part of the Ufa Plateau: Central Geol. and Prospecting Institute, fasc. 65, p. 1–35.
Vaughan, T. Wayland, 1940, Ecology of modern marine organisms with reference to paleogeography: Geol. Soc. America Bull., v. 51, p. 433–468.
Walther, J., 1919, Allgemeine Paleontologie: Berlin, Borntraeger, p. 55–62.
Wanner, J., 1916, Die permischen Echinodermen von Timor, pt. 1: Paläontologie von Timor, v. 11, no. 6, p. 1–329, pls. 96–114.
———, 1924, Die permischen Echinodermen von Timor, pt. 2: Paläontologie von Timor, v. 23, no. 14, p. 1–79, pls. 199–206.

52

Sedimentary Facies and Associated Diastrophism

in the Upper Cretaceous of Central and Eastern Utah

E. M. SPIEKER

1949

From *Sedimentary Facies in Geologic History* (GSA Memoir 39), edited by Chester R. Longwell, pp. 55–81. The Geological Society of America, 1949. [Ten photographs deleted.] Reprinted with permission of the author and the publisher.

The mountains, plateaus, and deserts of central and eastern Utah present a display of Upper Cretaceous rocks which for completeness of exposure and clarity of stratigraphic record is possibly not excelled in North America. For nearly 200 miles along the Book Cliffs and over 75 miles along the eastern front of the Wasatch Plateau the entire Upper Cretaceous succession is exposed in barren cliffs and desert stretches almost without interruption, and westward into the High Plateaus and the eastern margin of the Great Basin the conditions of exposure are only slightly less favorable. This point is brought into emphatic relief at the very outset of this discussion because it is important to understand that the facts here presented, and especially those of lateral stratigraphic relationship are not subject to the reservation normal for a region in which any considerable part of the rock mass described is in any way obscured.

These Upper Cretaceous rocks embody a group of sedimentary facies which, as regards range in environment, orderly development, and relation to regional diastrophism, present a remarkably clear and stimulating picture of regional stratigraphy. The facies range in variety from coarse rubble and associated heterogeneous sediments of the piedmont environment to fine muds of the offshore sea bottom. Between these two extremes a normal sequence of continental and marine environments is clearly represented in both vertical and horizontal succession, in a record eloquent of conditions shifting with the passage of time. Details as well as regional features of stratigraphy reveal unmistakably the effects of crustal movement, both epeirogenic and orogenic.

The facts and conclusions presented in this paper result from work which in the western districts is still in the pioneering stage, elsewhere is just emerging from the later stage of detailed mapping, and only locally has gone into the stage of highly detailed study which will be necessary before all the rich material available can yield fully mature results. This paper must by force of scope deal almost solely with larger features, but beyond that it must be understood that thoroughgoing studies in modern techniques of the many special branches of sedimentation and stratigraphy remain yet to be completed, and a vast deal of desirable factual detail is not yet available. It is only fortunate that the larger facts of stratigraphy are so favorably disposed that "he who runs may read," and in consequence that the order of subject matter here to be presented may be offered with a degree of confidence for which in less favored regions much more detailed and thoroughgoing field work would be necessary. . . .

EXTENT AND GENERAL CHARACTER OF AREA

The area covered (Figure 52.1) extends from the longitude of the Juab Valley, in central Utah, on the eastern margin of the Great Basin, through the Wasatch Plateau and along the Book Cliffs, in the northern part of the Colorado Plateaus, across the eastern half of Utah and into western Colorado as far as the general environs of the Grand Mesa. In most of the Wasatch Plateau and all the country to the east the structure is simple, and the nearly flat-lying rocks undulate gently around the western and northern margins of the San Rafael Swell, and the northern and eastern margins of the Uncompaghre uplift. The exposures here, in the Wasatch Plateau and the Book Cliffs, and the adjacent valleys, form the sweeping rim of the Colorado basin. In the western part of the Wasatch Plateau, however, and the valleys and ranges to the west, the structure is complex, and the various stratigraphic units are less continuously exposed. In these districts much more detailed and extended work has been necessary than to the east for determinations of stratigraphic relationship that are not so obviously certain.

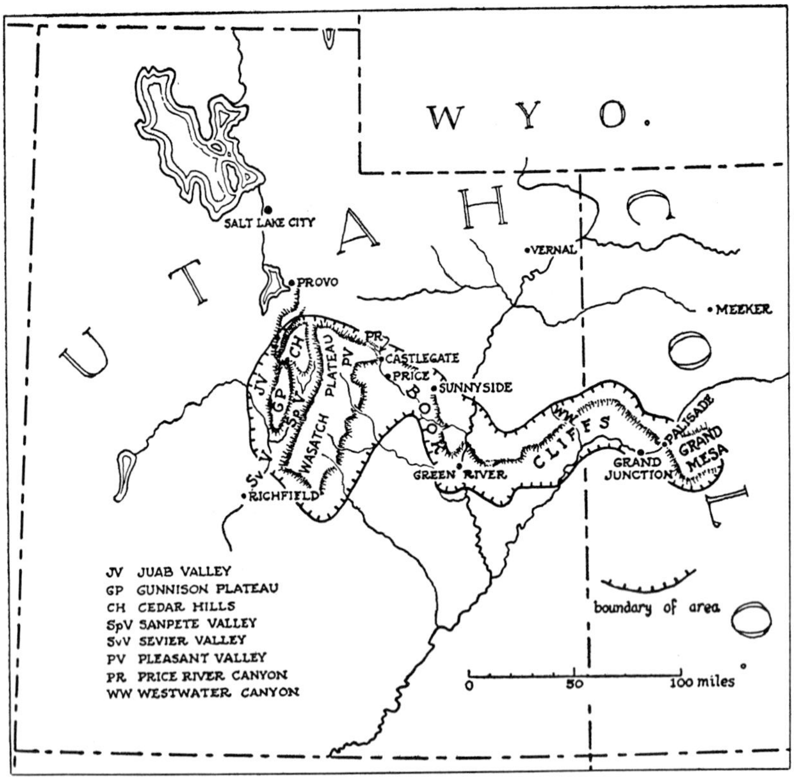

FIGURE 52.1
Index map: Utah and western Colorado

TABLE 52.1
Stratigraphic sections, central and eastern Utah

	Age	Formation		
		Central Utah		Eastern Utah
	PALEOCENE			
UPPER CRETACEOUS	Lance	*North Horn* Variegated shale, sandstone, fresh-water limestone, conglomerate; abrupt facies changes in west: 1500–6700 feet		*North Horn* (and equivalents) Variegated shale, sandstone, some fresh-water limestone and conglomerate; fairly uniform 400–500 feet
UPPER CRETACEOUS	late Montana	*Price River* Sandstone, conglomerate, little shale, no coal: 1000–2000 feet angular unconformity grading eastward to discomformity		*Price River* Sandstone, shale, coal; no coarse sediments: 1000–2500 feet no uncomformity; gradation
UPPER CRETACEOUS	medial Montana		*Blackhawk* Sandstone, shale, coal; no coarse sediments: 700–1500 feet	
UPPER CRETACEOUS	medial Montana	Not known west of Wasatch Plateau (eroded) but probably all sandstone	*Star Point sandstone* Littoral marine sandstone 350–700 feet	*Mancos shale*: Gray marine shale with thin beds of sandstone and limestone 3000–4000 feet
UPPER CRETACEOUS	early Montana		*Mesuk shale* (upper Mancos) Gray marine shale: 600–1000 feet	
UPPER CRETACEOUS	early Montana		*Emery sandstone* Littoral marine sandstone: 50–800 feet	
UPPER CRETACEOUS	Colorado	*Indianola group* West of Sanpete Valley coarse conglomerate, red beds, fresh-water limestone; some marine beds east of Sanpete Valley sandstone, conglomerate, some marine shale: 8000–15,000 feet	*Blue Gate shale* (middle Mancos) Blue marine shale, some thin sandstone locally; 1600–3000 feet	
UPPER CRETACEOUS	Colorado		*Ferron sandstone* Littoral marine sandstone (coal-bearing locally) 200–500 feet	
UPPER CRETACEOUS	Colorado		*Tununk shale* (lower Mancos) Dark-gray marine shale: 600 feet	
UPPER CRETACEOUS	Dakota	?	Dakota (?) sandstone	Dakota (?) sandstone

GENERAL NATURE OF STRATIGRAPHIC SECTION

In the eastern part of the area, within the province of the Colorado Plateaus, the Upper Cretaceous section is divisible physically into two major parts, the lower of which is a thick marine shale, the Mancos, with a thin and discontinuous sandstone beneath it that has generally been identified as Dakota, and the upper a succession of sandstones with some shale and one or more coal-bearing units, the Blackhawk, the Price River, and the North Horn formations, or their equivalents in the terminology of some workers. (Stratigraphic nomenclature is by no means settled in the eastern part of the area, and it is not to be discussed specifically in this paper; for the general purposes concerned the nomenclature of central Utah will suffice.) These rocks span the entire Upper Cretaceous, possibly excepting part or all of the Cenomanian stage (the identification of the Dakota is uncertain, and the sandstones assigned to it are poorly known); in western American terms the equivalents of the Colorado and Montana groups and the Lance formation are all present, and the passage to the Tertiary is transitional and apparently complete. In the western districts, in central Utah, the rocks are generally much coarser and thicker. Here the Indianola group, the part of the section equivalent to the lower 2000 to 2500 feet of the Mancos shale, comprises 8000 to 15,000 feet of conglomerate with minor amounts of sandstone, shale, and fresh-water limestone, the Price River formation is mainly coarse conglomerate locally over 2000 feet thick, and the North Horn is likewise thicker, highly variable, and in places much coarser. These westward changes are all normal functions of passage into an orogenic belt which was at times actively geosynclinal and at others the site of rising mountains.

The essentials of this stratigraphic comparison are given in Table 52.1.

One outstanding feature of this westward progression is the rapidity with which the sediments coarsen and change otherwise in facies as they enter the geosynclinal belt. On the east side of the Wasatch Plateau the lower part of the Mancos, Colorado in age, is marine shale with one fine to medium sandstone unit, the Ferron; on the west side of the plateau, 20 miles or less away, the same time interval is represented mainly by sandstone, with much conglomerate, and 5 to 6 miles farther west it is nearly all conglomerate, much of which is very coarse and all of which is evidently rubble from near-by mountains.

FACIES AND INTERTONGUING RELATIONSHIPS

The westward change from marine and lowland deposits to those of highland areas is not one of simple lateral gradation; there is exten-

TABLE 52.2
Facies and corresponding environments in the Upper Cretaceous of Utah

Sedimentary facies	Environment
1. Conglomerate, red-bed, fresh-water limestone.	Piedmont, highland.
2. a. Conglomeratic sandstone. b. Variegated beds, clay shale, fresh-water limestone, and sandstone. c. Buff sandstone and gray shale.	Inland flood plain, channel, and lake
3. Coal-bearing successions of buff to gray sandstone and shale.	Lowland (mainly near shore), flood plain and swamp.
4. Buff to white massive and evenly bedded medium to fine sandstone.	Littoral marine.
5. Gray shale and siltstone, evenly bedded.	Offshore marine.*

* The term offshore marine is here used to designate the open-water environment away from the littoral zone in which, mainly as a function of depth but also in part of distance from the strand, mud and potentially lime are the dominant sediments, as opposed to the sand of the littoral belt. This usage is not approved by some workers, but it is not without acceptable precedent and for reasons not to be discussed here it is applied in the present paper as arbitrarily defined.

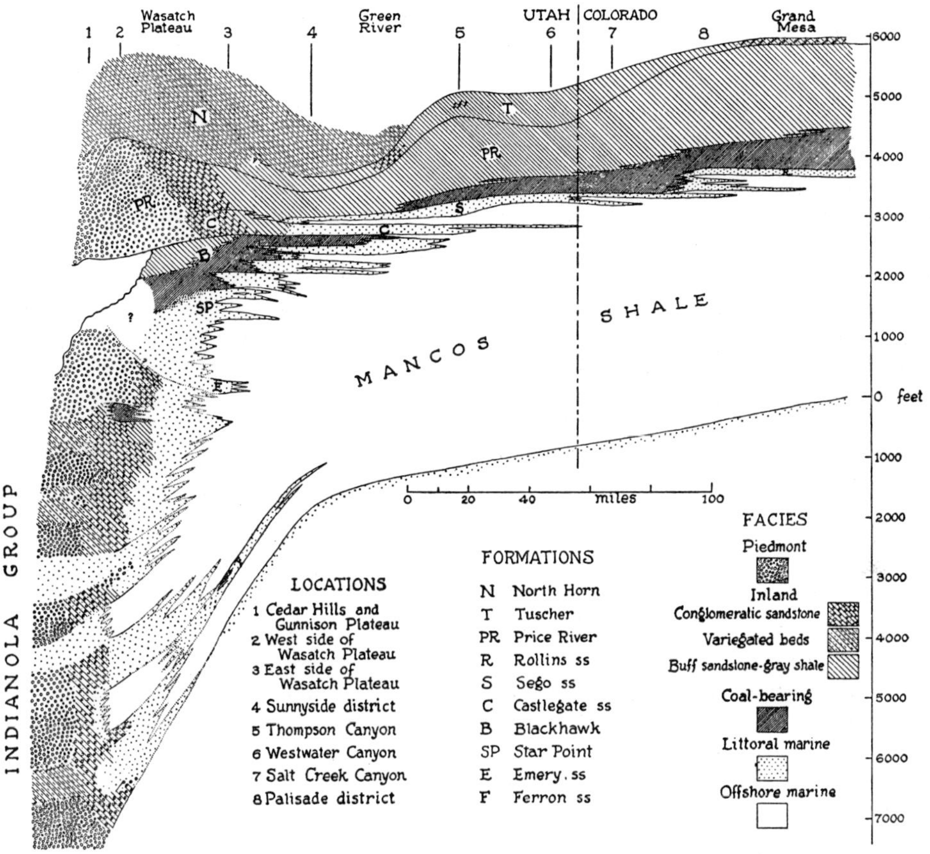

FIGURE 52.2
Section showing distribution of facies in Upper Cretaceous between central Utah and western Colorado

sive intertonguing, indicative of shifting environments, almost throughout the section. This intertonguing not only emphasizes facies relationships and affords an unusual opportunity to study critical features of sedimentary distribution in both space and time, but in much of the area it also involves cyclic relations that invite thoughtful consideration of fundamental principles governing this common and much-discussed phenomenon.

Finical contemplation of the sedimentary bodies involved might easily result in the recognition of a dozen or more facies, and the problem of classification is difficult, especially for the varied continental beds, but in the large five natural groupings may be recognized, as shown in Table 52.2.

From this point on these facies will be designated in environmental terms, with modification where necessary for the several variants of No. 2.

These five facies are present in normal order of vertical succession throughout the area, as shown in Figure 52.2. The succession is partially repeated where lateral oscillations of environment have produced intertonguing, but the order is always the same, and the only distinctive element locally missing is the coal, in a few places where extensive swamps did not thrive during the prevalence of lowland flood plains. The extremes in the group of facies are generally absent or not well developed at the extremes of the area; the piedmont facies is generally absent in the eastern part, and the offshore marine in the westernmost part.

The five facies are also traceable laterally, in normal order and along given time lines from piedmont on the west to offshore marine on the east. This condition affords excellent opportunity for the study of interrelationship in space as well as time. Here again the order of succession is normally complete, and on given horizons it is possible to progress westward from offshore marine deposits in eastern Utah through the intermediate facies to highland continental and piedmont deposits in the center of the State.

It is evident in a glance at Figure 52.2 that through the Upper Cretaceous continental conditions gradually advanced eastward, blotting out the shallow sea before latest Montana time. It is also evident that this eastward encroachment was not steady, but wavered in its progress as the sea temporarily advanced westward and the successive environmental belts on the land fell back in good order, only to resume their eastward march, generally but not always gaining notably in their conquest of the sea. The eastward movement of the strand and associated belts of sedimentation was due to invasion of debris from the erosion of positive areas to the west, ultimately controlled by uplift; westward movements were caused by diastrophism outright. Before considering the interrelationships here demonstrated among diastrophism, physical environment, and sedimentation, it may be well to examine some phases of the intertonguing in exemplary detail.

NATURE AND SIGNIFICANCE OF THE INTERTONGUING

The several facies all interfinger, and full consideration of the phenomena involved would demand description of the relationships at every contact between the deposits of adjacent environments. Even if it were satisfactorily possible, such treatment would exceed the space requirements of this paper; one example with some collateral reference must suffice. The most obvious intertonguing, the best known, and perhaps the most significant is that between the littoral marine sandstones and the marine shales.

Taking first a general view of the whole picture, it may be seen on Figure 52.2 that in the eastern part of the Wasatch Plateau the littoral marine facies immediately below the coal measures is embodied in the Star Point sandstone, which splits eastward into three subsidiary tongues that feather out into the Mancos shale about halfway between Castlegate and Sunnyside (Figure 52.3). Above the Star Point the coal-bearing facies of the Blackhawk formation intertongues with more littoral marine sandstone, the Aberdeen (Figure 52.3), which in its turn behaves like the Star Point and disappears in the vicinity of Sunnyside. The phenomenon continues; the next body of littoral marine sandstone, not yet individually named, disappears near Green River, and the next, which is contemporaneous with the upper part of the Blackhawk formation, tongues out west of Thompson Canyon. The Castlegate sandstone becomes of littoral marine facies and extends eastward to the Colorado boundary; this tongue is of special significance and is individually described farther on. Above the Castlegate the sequence is repeated, and the Sego sandstone, the next of littoral marine origin, penetrates eastward to the Grand Mesa, there to be succeeded upward by another unnamed group and finally, in the southern part of the Grand Mesa, by the Rollins sandstone.

Figure 52.3 shows in detail the intertonguing between Castlegate and Sunnyside, a distance of about 25 miles. Here the tongues of littoral marine sandstone projecting eastward into the marine shale are plainly evident, and it is equally obvious that the principal sandstone tongues are overlain in westward succession by marine shale, more littoral sandstone, and then coal measures, with a strong coal bed at the base either immediately overlying the sandstone or separated from it by a thin layer of carbonaceous shale or fireclay. It is also clear that the principal coal beds are opposite the tips of the principal shale tongues. This pattern of distribution, examined in detail, affords evidence that the sequence of environments at principal coal-forming times was, in order from west to east, inland flood plain, swamp, sandy beach, and shallow sea, with the littoral sand extending out to a certain depth at which it graded into mud. It also shows that the sandstone tongues were built out into the sea as successive accumulations of beach sand. The evidence for this

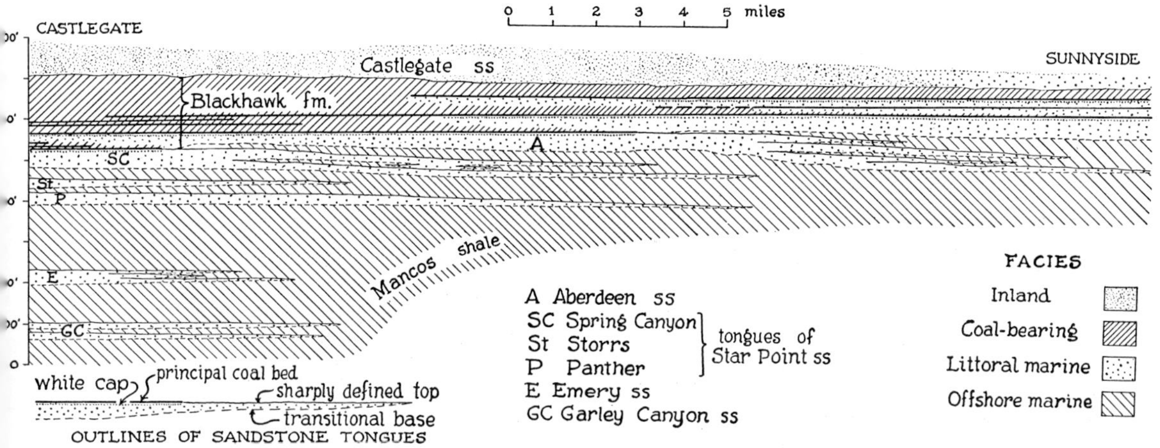

FIGURE 52.3
Section showing details of intertonguing between Castlegate and Sunnyside, Utah. (After F. R. Clark, 1928.)

lies in the character of the littoral marine sandstones and their relation to the adjacent shales and coal measures.

The littoral marine sandstones are of type common in the Cretaceous of the western states; they consist of fine to medium buff to gray sandstone, fairly massive but generally showing considerable internal bedding. Where overlain by coal beds they are commonly white near the top, owing to leaching out of iron by swamp waters. Where they are overlain by shale, contrariwise, there is normally a ferruginous zone at the top which in relative resistance to weathering causes the upper surface to stand out clearly. At the base, however, there is no such sharp boundary; with rare and generally local exception these sandstones grade imperceptibly into the underlying marine shale. This produces, in the weathering and erosion forms of the desert, the familiar step-like profile, with sharply defined top, vertical cliff, and curving base leading into the shale slopes below.

The clear-cut tops of the sandstones are subaerial gradation planes developed across successive beach and littoral bottom planes as the sand from adjacent land areas was swept into the sea and reworked by waves. The transitional bases represent the horizon of the sand-mud transition in the offshore zone, which migrated seaward at essentially constant level as the sand beaches were built into the sea. The bedding planes within the sandstones represent successive bottom surfaces, and they pass gently outward from the sandstones into the shales, where they generally become vague and difficult to follow. The beach and shallow bottom gradients were commonly too gentle for this phenomenon to be easily detectable among the minor irregularities normal in such accumulations of sediment, but locally where the beaches were steeper the relations may be clearly seen. In Price River Canyon at the mouth of Panther Canyon, for example, individual bedding planes in the Panther sandstone, the basal member of the Star Point, may be traced gently downward from the points where they are truncated by the sharp top of the sandstone completely through the unit and out into the underlying shale.

On this interpretation, the production of a given sandstone tongue may be visualized as shown in Figure 52.4A. During the extension of the littoral zone (here arbitrarily defined as the onshore belt, with sandy bottom) the local basement must have remained stable, with little or no diastrophic movement. For the production of the next shale tongue, however, the basement must have subsided, allowing reinvasion of the sea, and if the next sand tongue were formed like the foregoing another period of stillstand must have ensued. This phase of the succession is depicted in Figure 52.4B. The whole picture across eastern Utah and into western Colorado fits such interpretation, and the general conclusion here offered is that the intertonguing resulted from natural, steady transport of sediment eastward across flood plain and other lowlands into the sea during a time of dominant crustal quiet punctuated by episodes of fairly sudden subsidence. The unit bodies of sediment, each sand tongue and its underlying opposite of mud, were formed during the quiet periods, and the zigzag pattern was produced by the pulses of subsidence. The sandstone and shale tongues, then, instead of being distinct and separate, really originated in pairs.

Other interpretations may be considered, but exhaustive study of the possibilities seems to leave them untenable. The problem is the basic one of relation and balance between supply of sediment and space for its reception. Space exists at any given time during the passage of time by diastrophic movement and the effects thereof on the dynamics of erosion and sedimentation. The form of a body of sediment, its physical relations to others adjacent, and the positions of the time lines in the assemblage will depend fundamentally on the three possible relations between space and supply: (1) Supply may be less than space made available by diastrophism; (2) the two may exactly balance; and (3) supply may exceed space. Ancillary modification of the conditions involved may be classified in terms of the three possible diastrophic conditions—namely, uplift, quiet, and subsidence—, and for complete examination of the possibilities it is necessary to complicate the statistical picture by introduction of these three variables. This is not the place for full examination of the principles involved, and the foregoing stipulations are given here merely to prepare the way for consideration of at least one possibility alternative to the interpretation presented in this paper that is likely to occur first of all to some critics.

The outstanding feature plainly indicated by the sandstone tongues is the alternating recession and advance of the strand. On analysis of the problem the critical element turns out to be recession of the sea, and this may be caused by one of three conditions (or combinations thereof): (1) uplift; (2) eustatic depression of sea level; and (3) the feeding of sediment into a static basin. The first two of these will produce essentially the same effects on sedimentation (primarily governed by the position of base level), and they are therefore here considered together, as the effective equivalent of uplift. Many students of this problem have contemplated retrogression of the sea solely as a result of uplift, and have interpreted all

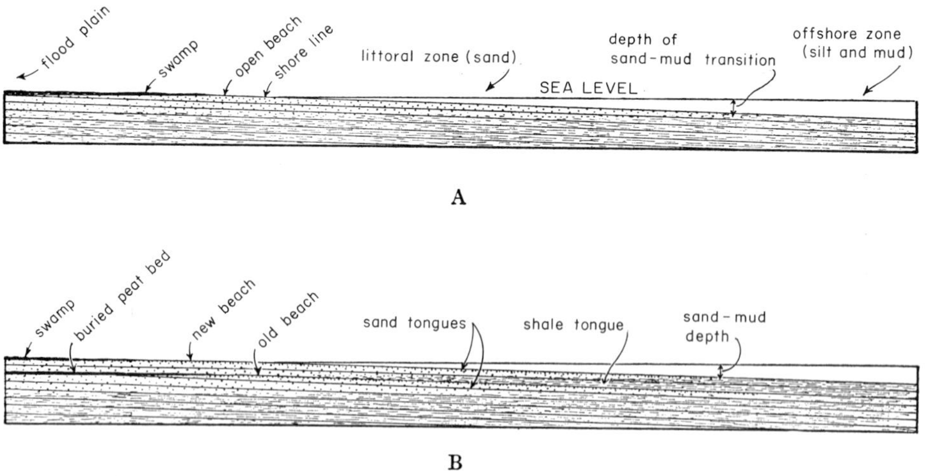

FIGURE 52.4
Origin of sandstone tongues and associated strata. *A*, section showing probable conditions in shore zone of Upper Cretaceous in Utah (no diastrophic movement has taken place during deposition of the sandstone); *B*, section showing results of sudden subsidence: the sea bottom has dropped about 100 feet, and normal sedimentation has continued.

sandstones of retrogression as due to uplift, in simple contradistinction to transgressive sandstones resulting from subsidence. No profound study of the realities in the situation is necessary to show that littoral marine sandstone of retrogression could hardly develop, to great extent transverse to the shore, from uplift—the body of sand would be eroded and reworked as uplift proceeded, and the transverse extent of the resulting marine sandstone could hardly exceed by much the width of the littoral marine belt at the end of the uplift.

A sandstone of transgression, on the other hand, is a different case. It must result from subsidence or eustatic rise of sea level with a supply of sediment inadequate to fill the space made available in the effective basin of sedimentation as rapidly as it develops. Such a sandstone would not have a sharply defined top, but would grade upward into the overlying marine shale. Sandstones of this sort may exist in the Upper Cretaceous section here considered, but so far none has been clearly discerned. Some of the sandstone tongues might possibly be interpreted to consist of retrogressive sand in the lower part and transgressive in the upper, but more detailed study is necessary before this possibility may be evaluated. Dominance among the sandstones of the characteristic profile and other features already described argues against extensive occurrence of such a dual type. It must be noted, however, that many students of regional stratigraphy have visualized this sort of origin for all sandstones of this type.

In an excellent study of intertonguing relations among the Upper Cretaceous formations of northwestern New Mexico, Sears, Hunt, and Hendricks (1941) have presented an interpretation of the littoral marine sandstone tongues basically similar to that here offered but differing in certain respects, one of which is the assumption of transgressive as well as retrogressive elements in the sandstone tongues. Tongues of dual nature may therefore be common in the New Mexico Cretaceous.

Should the supply of sediment from the land balance the space made available by subsidence, there would result between any two time lines a body of continental sediments grading laterally throughout the vertical section to littoral marine sandstone which would grade in similar fashion to marine shale. Some littoral marine sandstone in the Utah Cretaceous doubtless has originated in this fashion, but it does not figure in the facies distribution considered in this paper, and here again more detailed studies should be made before the phenomenon is discussed.

Turning again to the total picture presented by the intertonguing across eastern Utah, it is evident on study of Figure 52.2 that, whatever horizons or time lines are chosen for horizontal depiction on such a diagram, others in the marine part of the section will converge strongly eastward. The horizons chosen for horizontal datum lines are the tops of the most prominent sandstone tongues. These, in the interpretation of origin just given, are probably nearly coincident with time lines and are logical datum lines on that account; they were chosen, further, instead of other possible lines (for example the base of the Mancos shale, which is probably contemporaneous throughout) because so used they afford a design that approximates a realistic picture of the tongues as they are. The thickness of the Mancos shale in western Colorado is about 1000 feet less than in central Utah, and, when the whole stratigraphic diagram is so drawn up, the base of the Mancos rises sharply eastward, following the overall trend of the contact between the marine shale and the main body of overlying sandstone. The convergence of time lines involved has the significance usual in diagrams of this sort—it means differential sedimentation, and might be dismissed with that simple observation, but there are some features of the picture that will bear brief discussion.

Between the east front of the Wasatch Plateau and the west front of the Grand Mesa the contact between the Mancos shale and the overlying littoral marine sandstone rises stratigraphically about 2700 feet. If the cross section is extended farther west, through the Wasatch Plateau where the strata concerned are not continuously exposed, the ascent of the contact in the column is much greater, but the present examination is restricted to the stretch in which perfect exposure leaves no doubt as to the nature of the lateral relationships. Thanks to the intertonguing and the consequent zigzag pattern of the contact, fossils are not necessary to show that the ascent of 2700 feet exists and is stratigraphically real. Being an actual rise through stratigraphic horizons, it is also a rise in the time scale, and the conclusion is inescapable that the upper part of the Mancos shale in the Grand Mesa is coeval with at least the middle and perhaps the upper part of the Price River formation of central Utah. Whether or not this observation is self-evident from the general picture, it may be wise to clinch it by the simple demonstration that each tongue of littoral marine sandstone must contain a time line, or, to put it perhaps more effectively, no time line can cut completely through a sandstone tongue from one shale tongue to the next. In Figure 52.5 if A, B, and C represent the times when the sand-mud transition was at the three places shown, then it is obvious that time B, when the tip of the tongue was formed, must be represented in the root of the tongue somewhere between A and C. On the interpretation of origin here offered the line BB must lie near, if not at the top of each tongue.

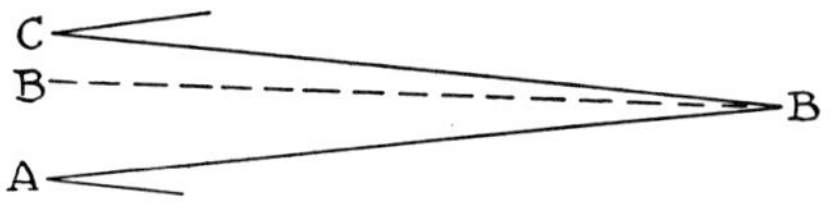

FIGURE 52.5
Time relations in a sandstone tongue

The basal beds of the Mancos shale contain hroughout this region the lower Turonian marine fauna characteristic of the Graneros-Greenhorn zone of the plains section, and the contemporaneity of these fossil occurrences, subject to discussion not feasible here, seems . . . to be fairly sure. The westward ascent of the base of the Mancos in the overall stratigraphic diagram (Figure 52.2) then means that during the progress of the strand from central Utah to western Colorado sedimentation was less heavy, to aggregate extent by more than 3500 feet, in the center of the marine basin than it was on the margins. Detailed evidence of such peripheral concentration of sediment is seen in Figure 53.3, where between Castlegate and Sunnyside subsidiary tongues of the Star Point and Aberdeen sandstones project downward into the Mancos when the tops of the main tongues are taken for horizontal datum lines. The tip of the uppermost tongue of the Aberdeen sandstone, for example, is about opposite the top of the Star Point sandstone farther west; this indicates some 200 feet of differential sedimentation in 10 to 15 miles. Evidently during medial and part of late Montana time the offshore bottom of the Mancos sea was receiving little or no sediment for considerable stretches of time. Some record of this condition is seen in parts of the Mancos of eastern Utah, in the form of thin beds of ferruginous limestone and ironstone, many of which appear to be concretionary in origin and but for this evidence would probably not be regarded offhand as primary deposits. . . .

The continental facies followed the marine in crude zigzag pattern, as may be seen in Figure 52.2, but the piedmont and parts of the other highland facies were controlled to considerable extent by mountain building, as discussed further on, and the regularity in the oscillatory succession is generally broken up somewhat in the western part of the area. Exactly what the time relations were between the several components of the coal measures and the littoral marine sandstones is one of many problems for which still more detailed field study is necessary. . . .

CYCLIC ELEMENT AND PRINCIPLES OF CORRELATION

In almost any stretch of the Book Cliffs it is possible to start in marine shale of the uppermost Mancos and go upward in order through littoral marine sandstone and coal measures to clastic beds barren of coal, and from the same point to go laterally westward, following contemporaneous beds, through the same succession of facies. The oscillation, furthermore, has introduced vertical repetitions of parts or all of this sequence, and nearly every section measured will show some cyclic pattern. The entire picture affords basis for consideration of principles governing some aspects of cyclic sedimentation and problems of correlation involved.

Let us consider first a practical case of correlation that involves a spectacular possibility of deception. In addition to the features above described, the part of the cycle directly associated with the coal beds (the underlying littoral marine sandstone and the overlying coal measures, which is the part generally repeated) very commonly has prominent white sandstones at the tops of the littoral marine units, overlain by principal coal beds which are about 200 feet (the range is 180 to 220) apart. In the Castlegate district the Spring Canyon and Aberdeen sandstones, overlain respectively by the Hiawatha and the Castlegate A coal beds, afford an excellent example of this occurrence. In the Sunnyside district, about 25 miles due east, the section embracing the Kenilworth and Sunnyside coal beds is identical in general appearance, and the sandstone beneath the Kenilworth coal is underlain by the Upper Mancos exactly as is the Spring Canyon (Figure 52.3). The similarity is so impressive that few geologists seeing only the Castlegate and Sunnyside districts and nothing in between would hesitate to correlate the two sections, yet the Sunnyside section is bodily more than 400 feet higher and the coal beds there are totally independent of the similar beds at Castlegate. When F. R. Clark first discovered this relationship mining men who were widely and minutely acquainted with the coal of the region refused to believe him.

Other instances might be cited, but it will suffice to point out here in general that stratigraphic sections in this and other similar areas have been miscorrelated in the past on the assumption that the characteristic succession above the Mancos shale, and especially the basal littoral marine sandstone, was everywhere of the same age. . . .

The fallacy involved in such correlation, and especially between such identical sections as those of Castlegate and Sunnyside, is basically statistical. In any given correlation if two variables agree the force of the conclusion is much more than twice that for agreement as to one variable, and for three or more the certainty of the correlation mounts at an imposing rate. In the present stratigraphic case there are at least five major variables in perfect agreement, and many more minor ones can be aligned. The statistical case would seem to be virtually proved, but the fallacy is that the variables are not independent; on the contrary they are intimately dependent and for purposes of logical analysis they must be treated as one. Even so, in general stratigraphic practice, such groups of variables are potentially worthless for correlation because they are not rigorous functions of time. The detailed picture of lateral relationships in the Book Cliffs may well serve as a warning to stratigraphers who are accustomed to matching peculiar lithologic sequences across stretches of terrain in which the rocks are not exposed. The general principle is that any lithologic succession, however peculiar and apparently distinctive, whose units were deposited in environments that naturally exist side by side is untrustworthy as an independent or unique criterion for correlation.

This principle bears on the general use of sedimentary cycles in correlation. Any cycle consisting of units which might have existed side by side, and especially any one whose several units form a natural or common lateral succession should be used in correlation with full apprehension of the possibilities here presented. One may even go further and say that what exists in cyclic vertical succession must potentially exist side by side. For any group of internally varied cycles to be contemporaneous across a region of any size would require a uniformity in succession of sweeping and sudden changes that is hardly credible. To assume such a complicated pattern of regionally regimented performance is to revert to catastrophism. None of this is intended to deny the possibility of using cyclic phenomena of any sort in stratigraphic correlation, but it is intended to recommend searching examination of all evidence in light of the known principles of historical geology before reaching conclusions. As a matter of fact, in normal uniformitarian outlook it is much more likely for any group of sedimentary cycles to interfinger laterally across the region occupied than for it to simulate a Wernerian layer-cake.

EFFECTS OF OROGENY

CASTLEGATE SANDSTONE AND THE EARLY LARAMIDE OROGENY

One of the most striking individual features of the general stratigraphic diagram (Figure 52.2) is the great tongue of the Castlegate sandstone, which extends unbroken across the eastern half of Utah, and east of Green River is enclosed between beds of the Mancos shale.

The Castlegate tongue differs from its fellows in that it resulted from a strong pulse of orogeny, the early Laramide (Spieker, 1946), which produced a range of mountains in central Utah; its very size stands in partial evidence of this distinctive mode of origin. Were there no other evidence available, the predominating penetration of this great body of sand into the marine muds of the Mancos sea would argue significant uplift to the west.

The evidence for the orogenic origin of the Castlegate, however, lies in other and more substantial quarters. The sandstone may be traced westward into the body of conglomerate that overlies the margins of the folded mass in angular unconformity and laps up on the slopes of the late Cretaceous Wasatch Mountains. The principal facts of this occurrence as known up to 1940 have already been published (Spieker, 1946, p. 120–121, 130–132, 152, 153, 157, 159–160), and it is not possible to go fully into detail here, but, to give basis for a brief discussion of the sedimentary facies involved and especially to incorporate the benefit of the knowledge gained in central Utah since 1940, a brief resumé of the critical facts is necessary.

As its type locality in the canyon of Price River, the Castlegate sandstone, the basal member of the Price River formation, comprises about 500 feet of massive, cliff-making sandstone, much of which is coarse and all of which has a sugary appearance and a slight pinkish cast as well as other features that distinguish it from the ledge-making sandstones of the underlying Blackhawk formation. It lies disconformably on the Blackhawk, and at many places where the contact has been seen (it is commonly covered by rubble from the cliffs) there is obvious relief, albeit of low order, on the Blackhawk surface.

Elsewhere to the south and southwest in the Wasatch Plateau the Castlegate is consistent and characteristic in appearance, and in many districts it contains notable quantities of conglomerate whose pebbles average an inch or more in diameter. It decreases in thickness, but there is only one small area at the southern end of the plateau where it is locally absent. In the northern part of the plateau it becomes coarser westward, gradually at first, but rapidly in the western half, and about midway across the plateau it loses its identity, becoming indistinguishable from the overlying beds of the Price River formation; here it is a conglomerate dominated by cobbles 3 to 4 inches in diameter, still essentially parallel to the Blackhawk formation, but set off by pronounced disconformity. In the northwestern part of the plateau the whole formation is a mass of coarse rubble 900 to 2000 feet thick, commonly containing boulders several feet in diameter, and locally deep red, lying in pronounced angular unconformity on ancient pediments and higher foothill surfaces cut across all the other folded and thrust rocks of the Wasatch Range. In some parts of the southern Wasatch Mountains the Price River conglomerate wedges out against the old erosion surface, which is overlapped by the North Horn and younger formations. All these features are direct functions of the early Laramide orogeny.

Investigations of recent years show that in the part of central Utah west of Sanpete and Sevier valleys on the eastern margin of the Great Basin and at considerable but yet unknown distances from the late Cretaceous mountain front, the Price River conglomerates commonly lap and abut against relief features on the early Laramide surface, the North Horn and later formations extending on above the angular contact. The absence of the Price River thus involved is in some districts the effect of later orogeny, but much of it is clearly discernible as evidence of extensive rolling terrane of moderate to low relief in the belt fronting the early Laramide mountains.

In view of the statement made at the beginning of this paper it might be well to remark here that along the eastern margin of the Great Basin these formations have been subjected along some lineaments to intense deformation later than the early Laramide, and this complication, plus the fact that in the orogenic belt several formations both below and above the Price River contain conglomerate exasperatingly similar in type, locally makes the working out of stratigraphic relations very difficult. The conclusions respecting these western districts therefore rest on no such obvious and certain data as those for the eastern. . . .

In the western districts, then, the orogenic origin of the Price River formation is clear. The rocks are of true piedmont facies in the general environs of Sanpete Valley and to the west, and in the north-central part of the Wasatch Plateau they are intermediate between true highland facies and those of the lower land. Let us now return to the type locality and follow the formation through its facies changes to the east.

In the vicinity of Castlegate the sandstone is of inland floodplain facies, but it contains much coarse sand and some grit, remnant sorting differentiates from the piedmont rubble that were spread by fairly active currents. East of Castlegate, in the western Book Cliffs, the sandstone gradually becomes finer, and remains so throughout its extent across the state. The disconformity at its base disappears not far east of the Wasatch Plateau, and in the western Book Cliffs the sandstone becomes more like that of the Blackhawk formation, distinguishable mainly by its cliff-forming habit, and not set off by a distinct break. Here it is of lowland floodplain facies, but nowhere does it contain coal, and it is evident that neither the inland nor the coastal swamp environments developed here during Castlegate time. The intense flood of sediment unleashed by the orogeny, perhaps abetted by a small amount of associated crustal instability, may have prevented the delicate balance necessary for persistent existence of coal-forming swamps.

Between Sunnyside and Green River the facies changes gradually from floodplain to littoral marine, and at the Green River the Castlegate is overlain by marine shale of the next westward transgression. The remnants of the Blackhawk formation beneath it disappear, eastward, and between Green River and Grand Junction the Castlegate becomes a clear-cut tongue of fine-grained littoral marine sandstone penetrating into the Mancos shale, and, like the other such tongues, grading at the base in downward transition to the marine shale beneath. Here without much question the disconformity beneath the Castlegate has disappeared. It may be present but not evident in the western Book Cliffs, as are many such disconformities, but in the eastern stretch the relations between the Castlegate and the underlying Mancos seem to rule out the possibility of a significant break. The sandstone continues across Utah, gradually thinning and losing its prominence, until at the Colorado boundary it is an insignificant sandstone some 300 feet beneath the top of the Mancos that would not be noticed especially in a study of that section alone. Eastward into Colorado it disappears, and the horizon of its tip is lost in the monotonous gray shale of the upper Mancos.

In eastern Utah and western Colorado, then, the profound pulse of the early Laramide orogeny had little or no effect. Even in the Wasatch Plateau, hard by the actual mountain front, the effects were by no means as strong as might normally be expected; the disconformity between the Blackhawk and the Castlegate not only shows very low local relief where evident, but in some places is hardly recognizable as such, and regionally does not invade the Blackhawk formation to noticeable extent. This phenomenon apparently was common in the orogenic history of the region, and in some of the episodes of folding both before and after the early Laramide was even more striking. . . .

But even if the early Laramide orogeny did fail to produce the normally expectable kind of physical effect in the stratigraphy of eastern Utah, it will be noticed that the Castlegate sandstone, in addition to its dominating eastward extension, does completely interrupt the eastward and upward migration of the coal-bearing facies across eastern Utah; this is one of the most obvious of the larger features evident in Figure 52.2.

As partly suggested in a foregoing paragraph, this additional prominence of the Castlegate is probably a function of its orogenic origin.

The Price River formation, and especially the Castlegate sandstone, present the most extensive connected picture of facies development so far known in the region, and invite further study directed toward the understanding of principles in various quarters of stratigraphic science. The Castlegate, in its great extent and perfection of exposure, naturally promises much in the determination of mineral distribution, textural and other physical characters, detailed lateral chronology, and other aspects of its physical stratigraphy, not to mention paleontologic problems of great import which have barely been touched. Material has been collected for some such studies, and laboratory work is partly done, but it is yet too soon to announce any conclusions beyond the generalities given in this paper. The Castlegate has one deficiency in its lack of well-developed coal-bearing facies, and it may be that higher zones in the Price River formation will afford even more fruitful material for study. After the post-Castlegate invasion of the sea coal-forming swamps again appeared, east of Green River, and in the upper part of the Price River formation the lateral sequence of facies goes in full order from offshore marine to highland continental, but the lateral relations of these strata are by no means so obvious as those of the Castlegate, and more detailed field work is necessary for the precise determination of physical continuities. Prospects for such work are mixed; even this geologist's paradise has disadvantages. Contrary to many regions where the geology is easy to reach but hard to see, in this case the rocks are easy to see but hard to reach.

POSSIBLE OROGENIC SIGNIFICANCE OF SANDSTONE TONGUES

The striking case of the Castlegate sandstone prompts at once the question whether all prominent sandstone tongues of the sort may not signify pronounced uplift, if not orogeny. Any answer to this question must at present be strongly qualified. The evidence in Utah is yet somewhat confusing, but considering the notorious difficulty that commonly invests the dating of orogenies, and the strong need for sound principles of any sort, the problem may well bear further and more general examination.

Elementally, and in terms of the mode of origin discussed earlier in this paper, any sandstone tongue means essentially dominance in supply of sand over available space in the basin of sedimentation, and a distinctly extensive tongue such as the Castlegate simply means extension of that dominance. Such extension might result from uplift in the source area, but if so the question would still remain whether such uplift were truly orogenic, or merely upwarping of epeirogenic order. Conceivably, indeed, such a tongue might result from nothing more than a period of protracted quiet in the marine basin. Collateral evidence in the tongue itself—for example, the sudden appearance of a new suite of minerals—might strengthen the case or even prove the point, but if we restrict the evidence to the field of gross stratigraphic relations it is clear that no sharply defined principle can be sustained. On the other hand it should be equally clear that an occurrence like that of the Castlegate, and not necessarily by any means so prominent would afford due cause for suspicion, and should bring on aroused and enlightened examination of other pertinent regional facts which in turn might bring out evidence, otherwise not noticed or thought of, in favor of orogeny at the time concerned.

OROGENY OF COLORADO AGE AND RELATED FACIES DEVELOPMENT

The appeal to basic principle thus yields nothing more solid than suggestive guide; this, however, need not be scorned, for it may well lead to advance over pre-existing facility. Let us now turn to the empirical approach, for which the stratigraphic picture presented in Figure 52.2 affords further material. There were orogenic episodes in the region during Colorado time, and in the Mancos shale of eastern Utah there are at least two prominent sandstone tongues, the Ferron and the Emery. Here would seem to be a first-class opportunity to test the hypothesis, in the very same region where the Castlegate makes its outstanding display. However, the results of such empirical test are hardly more satisfactory than is the consideration of principles. As is so commonly the case with geological hypotheses, the evidence here does not fit together as nicely as for the Castlegate sandstone, and viewed from some angles it seems to suggest that the hypothesis will not work at all. The grave difficulty in these older instances is that the strata concerned cannot be traced through in the critical zone; they pass under the Wasatch Plateau and change so rapidly in that interval that even with good fossil evidence for part of the section it is impossible to be sure of the lateral relationships that must be known.

The evidence bearing on these earlier orogenies as such has already been presented and discussed as known up to 1940 (Spieker, 1946,

p. 126–130, 150–152, 158), and a brief statement here will suffice to outline the general case and add certain knowledge gained since 1940. The westernmost conglomerates of the Indianola group are so much like those of the Price River that it transcends merely reasoning by analogy to conclude they are of similar origin. They contain local marine intercalations of Colorado age and are regionally so homogeneous as a unit that despite their great thickness they are interpreted at present to be mainly if not entirely of that age.

In extant published statement (Spieker, 1946, p. 152) the possibility is ventured that the Indianola signifies two distinct orogenic pulses. Field investigations of recent years have turned this possibility into a virtual certainty, granted that the conglomerates mean orogeny at all. The upper Indianola conglomerates are not only separated from the lower in the Wasatch Plateau by a notable thickness of finer sediments, including marine shales and sandstones, but regionally to the west they show in pebble—and boulder—count a striking difference in composition, and in many sections in the Gunnison Plateau they are set off sharply from the lower conglomerates. The outstanding difference is that the upper conglomerates contain mainly quartzite pebbles, cobbles, and boulders, with limestone rare or absent, whereas the lower contain abundant identifiable Paleozoic limestone. This change would be a natural result of erosion through the Paleozoic limestones into the pre-Cambrian quartzite core of the ancient range, and in itself might not signify a second orogenic pulse, but the sudden appearance of the quartzite rubble leaves no conclusion possible but sudden uplift followed by a period of nondeposition in the piedmont area, and these conditions, without going into the whole argument, can hardly mean anything other than renewed folding and thrusting in the west.

To connect these two orogenies with the Ferron and Emery sandstone tongues, however, is precarious business. The Ferron tongue would be a good candidate for representation of the early Colorado orogeny, but for the fact that abundant marine fossils seem to show that Ferron time is represented in the western Wasatch Plateau and elsewhere to north and south by marine shale, the Allen Valley (Spieker, 1946, p. 127–128). There is also the disturbing fact that the lower part of the Sanpete formation, the basal unit of the Indianola group in the western part of the Wasatch Plateau, contains conglomerate which is putatively equivalent to part of the lower Indianola conglomerate farther west. The Sanpete formation contains a good basal Colorado fauna, and the basal Colorado is uniformly represented across the eastern deserts by a black to gray marine shale, the Tununk or its equivalent. If the basal Sanpete conglomerates reflect the first pulse of Colorado orogeny, the resulting sandstone tongue was puny compared with the Castlegate. If the Ferron tongue resulted from orogeny it is difficult to account for the barrier of marine shale completely across the path westward to the Indianola conglomerates; there is only the outside possibility that sandstones above or below the Allen Valley shale are actually equivalent to the Ferron. As at present interpreted the Ferron was formed as a broad, persistent peninsula of sand probably derived from the north, but this may be wrong. The Ferron extends fairly far out into the marine basin, and represents a strong supply of sediment, but in southern Castle Valley and the Henry Mountains area it contains a well-developed coal-bearing facies, and this might argue against orogenic origin. To sum up, the case for the early Colorado orogeny is unsatisfactory, and no definite conclusion is possible, but as matters stand the Ferron sandstone seems rather likely not to be of orogenic derivation.

The Emery sandstone would be in much better case but for the fact that it is early Montana in age. The upper Indianola conglomerates have nowhere been certainly dated, however, and their Colorado age has been simply imputed from the lack of any apparently significant stratigraphic change above the beds of known Colorado, probably Niobrara age. As an argument this of course bears no weight; the passage from Colorado to Montana time need not anywhere have been marked by change in sedimentation. Furthermore, there is a change locally in the western Wasatch Plateau from fine-grained coal-bearing sediments of Colorado age to the coarse conglomerates above. The possibility that the Emery sandstone represents the later of the two Indianola orogenies is much more promising than that for the Ferron, but no correlation will be made until the upper Indianola conglomerates are shown to be early Montana in age. Detailed mineral studies might help, but present knowledge seems to rule out any possibility of physical connection.

Even if the two orogenies of Indianola age should turn out to have produced no extensive tongues penetrating the Mancos shale, the contradistinction to the case of the early Laramide orogeny and the Castlegate sandstone might well be explained in terms of difference in physical setting. The Indianola conglomerates are regionally geosynclinal in origin, whereas the Price River are only locally so and by no means so profoundly. The observed westward changes in the sediments of Colorado age are much more abrupt than those for the Price River; in the environs of Sanpete Valley they occur in such short stretches as to startle and shock the geologist accustomed to well-behaved stratigraphy. Marine beds penetrate well into the Indianola where it is mainly thousands of feet of coarse rubble; during early Price River time the open sea was never much closer to the early Laramide mountains than the present longitude of Green River, and brackish-water embayments (post-Castlegate) were never nearer than Price River Canyon. The Indianola conglomerates and associated sediments were deposited in a geosynclinal trough that must have been a foredeep fronting the belt of rising mountains, and may have been dynamically related in origin to the folding and thrusting. Although the Price River rubble is locally very thick, there was evidently no such extensive foredeep at the time of the early Laramide orogeny.

There is another difference between the Indianola and the Price River in relation to their respective orogenies. The distance westward from the first appearance of coarse conglomerate in the Indianola to angular unconformity beneath them, although not yet known, is certainly greater than for the Price River. The fact has already been published (Spieker, 1946, p. 150) that nowhere had angular unconformity been unmistakably observed beneath the Indianola conglomerates up to 1940. Extensive work since then has verified this condition throughout the Gunnison Plateau and has brought into view the possibility that the angular unconformities involved, unlike that beneath the Price River, have suffered the fate common to such structural features and have been eroded away. In any event this evidence suggests that the increased volume of sediment from the newly rising mountains concerned was mainly dumped into the foredeep instead of being spread far eastward into a shallow marine basin. . . .

PIEDMONT AND OTHER RELATED INLAND FACIES

AGE RELATIONS IN COARSE PIEDMONT DEPOSITS

The great masses of coarse conglomerate in the Price River formation are dated with reference to fossiliferous beds in the type section, in Price River Canyon (Spieker and Reeside, 1925, p. 446–447). In the western districts, where the coarse piedmont facies prevails, extensive search has so far produced no diagnostic fossils, and the question of age relations in lateral succession of changing facies has become serious. In natural development coarse conglomerates such as the Price River might well become distinctly younger as they transgress the old erosion surfaces into the piedmont districts. They would normally be somewhat younger in any case, but the practical question here is whether they are so in terms of recognizable geologic time divisions.

This question is amplified by the fact that in some districts, notably in the Gunnison Plateau and adjacent territory, conglomerates much like those of the Price River occur in the lower part of the North Horn formation, and locally it is difficult to separate the two. To the north, in the central Wasatch Mountains, Baker (personal communication) has found it impossible to distinguish the Price River and North Horn formations, and has been forced to map the two as a single unit without definite knowledge of the time range embraced. In its type area the North Horn formation bridges transitionally the Cretaceous-Tertiary boundary and includes the equivalents of the Lance and the lower two-thirds, approximately, of the Fort Union. It has been carefully traced and mapped throughout the districts in question, but physical evidence of lateral age relations is restricted so far to lithologic continuity, commonly but often mistakenly accepted to indicate contemporaneity. The same stipulation may be made for the Price River formation. . . . The most that should be said now is that the Price River conglomerates in the western districts may well be younger than those of the Wasatch Plateau, and all the beds of the North Horn formation likewise.

VARIEGATED BED FACIES

Assemblages of varicolored shale and sandstone, with or without some conglomerate and fresh-water limestone, of the type common in the Wasatch and other Tertiary formations of the North American Cordillera, were universally thought during early studies in Utah to be distinctive of Tertiary time. Other occurrences of this facies were known, as a matter of fact, in formations such as the Morrison and the Chinle, but all such beds anywhere in the column clearly above the Jurassic were at once diagnosed as Tertiary. It is one of the surprising results of more recent study (Spieker, 1946) to find that in parts of central Utah this distinctive type of lithologic assemblage occurs throughout the Upper Cretaceous as well as the Tertiary.

This merely brings out what should have been recognized in the first place—namely, that the variegated bed facies is not inherently a function of time, but rather of environmental conditions in which heterogeneous lots of clastic sediment including much red and other brightly colored material were deposited more or less irregularly under oxidizing conditions, or at least conditions in which reduction, a common function of aqueous environments rich in organic matter, was not completely effective. Such environmental conditions obtained, it is now seen, in the piedmont and adjacent aggradational areas of the orogenic belts, and the variegated beds, thus interpreted, were naturally more extensive in the eastern parts of the Cordilleran province during Tertiary time, when the effects of orogeny were first prominent there.

The highly colored beds in this facies were mainly and perhaps entirely derived from true red beds of the older Mesozoic that were exposed to erosion in the Cretaceous and Tertiary orogenies. This is demonstrated in many parts of central Utah where beds in the North Horn formation, for example, are deep red close to demonstrable Jurassic and Triassic sources and gradually fade in color eastward. In some cases the loss of color intensity is remarkably rapid. In general, the pale, washed-out nature of the colors and the delicate blending of many tints and hues argues derivation from red source rocks.

LATERAL CHANGES IN FACIES

The common rapidity with which all the stratigraphic units change in facies within the orogenic belt has already been brought out, but it is desirable to add brief mention of this phenomenon as peculiarly a characteristic of the variegated bed facies. In formations like the North Horn the juxtaposition of contrasting facies is in some places so abrupt as to bewilder the observer in spite of the fact that the evidence is all clearly before him. In the central part of the Gunnison Plateau, for example, the North Horn formation occurs in the vicinity of Wales in what might be called its normal facies—about 2500 feet of variegated shales with subordinate sandstone and a prominent member of fresh-water limestone containing coal beds. In Peach Canyon, not more than a mile south of this facies, the whole 2500 feet and more is solid buff sandstone with many conglomerate beds. The coal-bearing zone continues through. A few miles farther south the whole formation is different again—here light-gray shale with fine siltstone beds and fresh-water limestones, and very little pale pink shale. Across the divide to the west from Peach Canyon the formation consists largely of deep red beds to the northwest and is dominantly bright yellow and calcareous to the southwest; there is no sign of the massive sandstone. All this would merely add up to a first-class geologic puzzle were the rocks not so fully exposed as to leave no doubt concerning detailed lateral relationships; most of the changes can be traced through.

Even with nearly all the facts available,

many features of this facies distribution are difficult to interpret and to render into a reconstruction of the environments, their relations to one another and to the known surroundings, and their progress through time. Evidently there must have been remarkable persistence in a close quartering of several different kinds of sedimentation for more than 2500 feet of beds to embody such complete lateral change.

The foregoing example has been selected for mention to indicate the kind of occurrence that invests these particular facies in the orogenic belt. Admittedly it is the most striking example so far found, but there are others throughout the section that are almost as difficult to accept. This is not the place for further excursion into detail; the purpose of this whole paper is to set forth significant aspects of facies development in the large, and it must suffice to reiterate that the facies in the orogenic belts are characterized throughout by the kind of heterogeneity to be expected in such areas of relatively disturbed condition. Patient unravelling of the tangled mess is gradually bringing into shape pictures of conditions in Cretaceous time that may serve not only to elucidate the geologic history of central Utah, but also point the way toward interpretations in orogenic regions where the evidence is obscured or not so well preserved.

NOMENCLATURE

Stratigraphic nomenclature in rock assemblages such as those discussed in this paper is no easy matter, either in local or regional concern. The attempt to find a logical scheme which will most expressively incorporate and encompass desirable features of chronology and facies distribution bogs down here and there in morasses of inconsistency, and yet with the picture of Upper Cretaceous stratigraphy now before us it surely seems not only desirable but possible, if it is ever going to be, to devise a system of regional nomenclature which will at once do justice to the significance of local features and at the same time express the real relations of the various sedimentary masses more effectively than does the present array of stratigraphic names. Even if the way were fully prepared, which it is not, the present paper is not the place to introduce new names, or even change applications of old ones, but it does seem desirable to discuss a few principles and to indicate the trend of studies in the attempt now under way.

The stratigraphic names now accepted for the Upper Cretaceous of Utah have resulted from the time-honored and undoubtedly necessary process of piecemeal recognition. In the early stages of this process the name applied, such as Mancos, Mesaverde, and Laramie, had only gross significance, and the tendency to generalize led next to the spread of such names as far afield as possible, so that for example the name Mesaverde has been used from northern Wyoming to New Mexico for strata that range between early Colorado and late Montana, possibly even Lance in age, and the Mancos of the eastern Book Cliffs turns out to contain the equivalent of the Lewis shale, which in the type area of the Mancos is separated from it by the whole Mesaverde group. Furthermore, the shale called Lewis in northwestern Colorado is almost certainly younger than some of the sandstone formations overlying the Lewis in its type area. These cases are cited at random merely to indicate one aspect of the problem that pervades the whole stratigraphic picture. Homogenetic equivalency as defined by Lee (1915, p. 29) may in some instances be recognized and invoked in support of the American principle of sticking to lithologic continuity in extension of stratigraphic names, but physical range through the column as well as purely chronologic interests must have some consideration, and there would seem to be limits beyond which absolute lithologic continuity may not be pushed without doing violence to the desired simplicity and stratigraphic logic that are among the expressed ends of our system.

The next stage of advance in nomenclature, arising in part out of recognitions such as the foregoing, has been the cautious application of local names, with or without suggestion as to correlation with other established sections but definitely with the intent of avoiding erroneous implication as to regional relationships and also with the laudable purpose of doing justice to the local lithologic sequence. This procedure has brought matters to their present status, and has resulted in a plexus of names which in part gives little direct expression of the regional stratigraphic values involved, as for example the present nomenclature in central Utah, and in other part introduces seemingly unnecessary complications between contiguous or otherwise related areas, as for example the opposing sets of names for the same beds across the Utah-Colorado boundary (Fisher, 1936; Erdmann, 1934).

In a body of rock such as the Upper Cretaceous of Utah, with its intricate and widespread interwedging and intergrading of various facies, as well as other complexities of lateral distribution, simplicity of nomenclature is impossible. It is necessary to use individual names for units such as the Star Point sandstone, and their several tongues, where such exist and are prominent enough to require general recognition. It is unlikely that many such units are either sufficiently widespread in acceptable stratigraphic integrity or, if so, certainly recognizable over areas extensive enough to warrant general use of individual names over entire stratigraphic provinces. There seems to be no escape from a controlled multiplicity of names; the stratigraphy itself is complex, and its nomenclature must logically also be.

It does seem possible, however, to unify the necessary complexity and to give it meaning by relating as many as possible of the units in the scheme to encompassing assemblages of kindred facies which may themselves bear a simple set of names regional in significance and application. In the whole stratigraphic province during much of Upper Cretaceous time there was a body of open epicontinental sea in which marine muds and associated calcareous sediments, dominantly typified by the Mancos, were deposited. Bordering this sea were land areas ranging from broad flood plains and other flat lowlands to rugged mountains on which a great variety of sediments, dominantly but by no means entirely coarser, was spread out, and some of the coarser material, mainly sand, was washed and worked by waves and currents to varying distances into the shallow sea. As a result, in the center of the former marine basin there is a distinctive marine facies, and all around the bordering lands a continental facies to which the littoral marine sandstones are closely related. It should be possible to set up a comprehensive Mancos facies on the one hand, for example, and an Indianola facies on the other, each representing its extreme of environmental range, with subsidiary interpenetrating or intergrading units such as tongues, formations, or members, each bearing a local name to be extended as far as logically possible but always related to its parent mass. For example, there might be the Blue Gate tongue of the Mancos, the Ferron tongue of the Indianola, and so on.

The attempt to put this idea into practical effect is beset at once by many difficulties of which two may be mentioned here in contribution to the sum of suggestion which is the main aim of these remarks. How shall the comprehensive and regional units be designated—as facies, or by some other term? The subsidiary terms, tongue, member, formation, might well be ordered and applied in accordance with existing rules of nomenclature, but how should they be related to the name of the general unit? These and other questions must be reasonably settled before any definite plan may be proposed.

Perhaps more serious is the question of allowable chronologic extent for the major facies units, and the general relation of the stratigraphic scheme to the time scale. If the term Indianola facies is to be used, should it extend upward in the column beyond the stratigraphic range of the present Indianola group, which makes an excellent opposite to the lower two-thirds or more of the Mancos? The Price River-North Horn succession constitutes another first-class highland continental facies and is separated from the Indianola in its heart-land by a pronounced angular unconformity; it should probably be recognized as a separate major unit, and utter simplicity seems impossible. More important still, the continental deposits of the late Cretaceous grade upward into those of the Tertiary, and in the lower part of the Tertiary section lacustrine deposits begin to be extensive. Here there is an excellent opportunity to apply the principle by recognizing a Wasatch facies, on the one hand, and a Green River on the other. Six different intertonguing formations, three of Wasatch type and three of Green River, are now recognized in central Utah, and for this part of the section a unified classification would now be possible, but it would have to extend down into the Cretaceous, involving the North Horn formation, which as already pointed out merges locally with the Price River and cannot be distinguished from it. Boundaries of some sort are after all necessary in any system of classification, and here it would be difficult to select one which would be regionally usable. The transgression of the Cretaceous-Tertiary boundary would be of no moment, but the differentiation between Price River and North Horn would. To incorporate the Wasatch-like succession, opposed to the Green River, with the Price River, partly opposed to the Mancos, is manifestly out of reason.

The purpose of these suggestions is to stimulate thought on the general problem, not only as regards the Upper Cretaceous of Utah but for any other regional section in which similar conditions prevail. The principal difficulties are the time-honored ones of placing arbitrary lines where no sharp divisions exist in nature, and of selecting the most significant elements in the natural scheme for dominant expression. . . . But the case is by no means so hopeless; larger elements of order, even if not perfect regularity, stand out clearly in the Upper Cretaceous, and they should be openly distinguished in the nomenclature whose semantic power exerts no mean influence in our thinking.

REFERENCES CITED

Clar, Frank R., 1928, Economic geology of the Castlegate, Wellington, and Sunnyside quadrangles, Carbon County, Utah: U.S. Geol. Survey Bull. 793.

Erdmann, C. E., 1934, The Book Cliffs coal field in Garfield and Mesa counties, Colorado: U.S. Geol. Survey, Bull. 851.

Fisher, D. J., 1936, The Book Cliffs coal field in Emery and Grand counties, Utah: U.S. Geol. Survey Bull. 852.

Lee, Willis T., 1915, Relation of the Cretaceous formations to the Rocky Mountains in Colorado and New Mexico: U.S. Geol. Survey Prof. Paper 95-C.

Sears, Julian D., C. B. Hunt, and T. A. Hendricks, 1941, Transgressive and regressive Cretaceous deposits in southern San Juan Basin, New Mexico: U.S. Geol. Survey Prof. Paper 193-F.

Spieker, Edmund M., 1931, The Wasatch Plateau coal field, Utah: U.S. Geol. Survey Bull. 819.

———, 1946, Late Mesozoic and early Cenozoic history of central Utah: U.S. Geol. Survey Prof. Paper 205-D.

Spieker, Edmund M., and John B. Reeside, Jr., 1925, Cretaceous and Tertiary formations of the Wasatch Plateau, Utah: Geol. Soc. America Bull., v. 36, p. 435–454.

53

Limnology and the Eocene Lakes of the Rocky Mountain Region

W. H. BRADLEY
1948

From *Geological Society of America Bulletin*, vol. 59, pp. 635–648, 1948. Reprinted with permission of the author and the Geological Society of America.

For many years I have felt that the title of a paper, or address, should be brief, informative, and self explanatory. Now I have violated my own tenet by using the relatively unfamiliar word limnology, and some explanation is due. Limnology is the science of lakes, just as geology is the science of the earth, but that simple definition is neither satisfying nor adequate for my present purpose. Limnology is indeed the science of lakes, and streams too, but it depends heavily on the facts and principles of chemistry, physics, biology, hydrography, geology, and meteorology. The central theme that binds all these into an organized science is ecology—the ecology of lakes—for one of the principal objectives of limnology is to explain the organic productivity of lakes and, more especially, the great differences between the capacity of lakes to produce living matter. . . .

I propose to review certain principles of limnology and then to show how these can be used, both directly and integrated with geology, to interpret the deposits of several large middle Eocene lakes of the Rocky Mountain Region. These lake deposits extend over a considerable area in Wyoming, Colorado, and Utah, and are collectively known as the Green River formation.

As we are to approach this problem from a limnological point of view it may not be amiss to review some of the physical properties of water. Water is a truly remarkable liquid and its various properties are of the utmost importance to the characteristics of lakes.

In Figure 53.1 are shown the changes of density and viscosity of water with increasing temperature. The rate of change with temperature is significant for limnology. Note that the difference of density between 22° and 25°C. is approximately three times as much as it is between 9° and 12°C. This means that about three times as much wind energy is required to mix two layers of water in a lake when the upper layer is at 25° and the lower 22° as when the upper layer is 12° and the lower 9°. The viscosity decreases with increase of temperature. The slope of this curve is significant but, so far as I know, the rate of change of slope is not.

SOME PRINCIPLES OF LIMNOLOGY

It is commonly taken for granted that a lake is a simple homogeneous body of water, but let us take a lake in the temperate zone and see what it is like and how it changes with the seasons (Figure 53.2). We'll start in the spring when the ice has melted off and has begun to warm up so that the whole water body has the same temperature. The wind blowing across it sets up a slow circulation. The oxygenated surface waters are carried to all parts of the lake. But as summer comes along the surface water warms up, and as it warms, its density and viscosity decrease until a distinct upper layer of relatively warm, light, less viscous water, known as the epilimnion, is established. This rests on a deeper, colder, denser body of water known as the hypolimnion. Actually there is a relatively thin transitional zone, or thermocline, between them, which might be thought of as a zone of shear. The wind blowing across the lake now sets in motion only the epilimnion whose light warm water flows easily and resists being pushed down into and mixed with the hypolimnion. This surface layer acts as a seal, for the oxygenated surface water is not carried below the thermocline into the hypolimnion. In the hypolimnion the respiration of organisms and the decay of organic matter continue to use up the dissolved oxygen and increase the quantity of dissolved carbon dioxide. If this stagnation continues for a long summer all the oxygen may be used up and then the water becomes progressively more charged with hydrogen sulphide.

In the autumn the epilimnion is cooled until it reaches the temperature of the hypolimnion whereupon the whole lake goes into circulation again as in the spring. These times of full circulation are known as overturns. The deeply circulating water brings up from the bottom new supplies of dissolved nutrients like phosphates and nitrates, which give rise to temporarily great increases in the growth of certain microscopic plants and animals. And these, in their turn, impart bad tastes and odors to the water in the spring and fall. As winter comes on the surface water gets cooled below the maximum density. Then a layer of colder but lighter water makes up the epilimnion and we have what is known as an inverse stratification. The same changes go on in the hypolimnion as

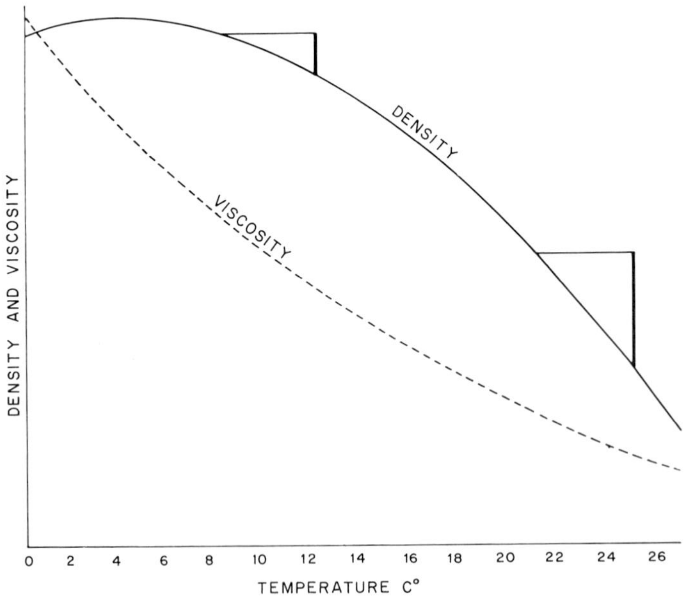

FIGURE 53.1
Curves showing the changes of density and viscosity of fresh water with changes of temperature

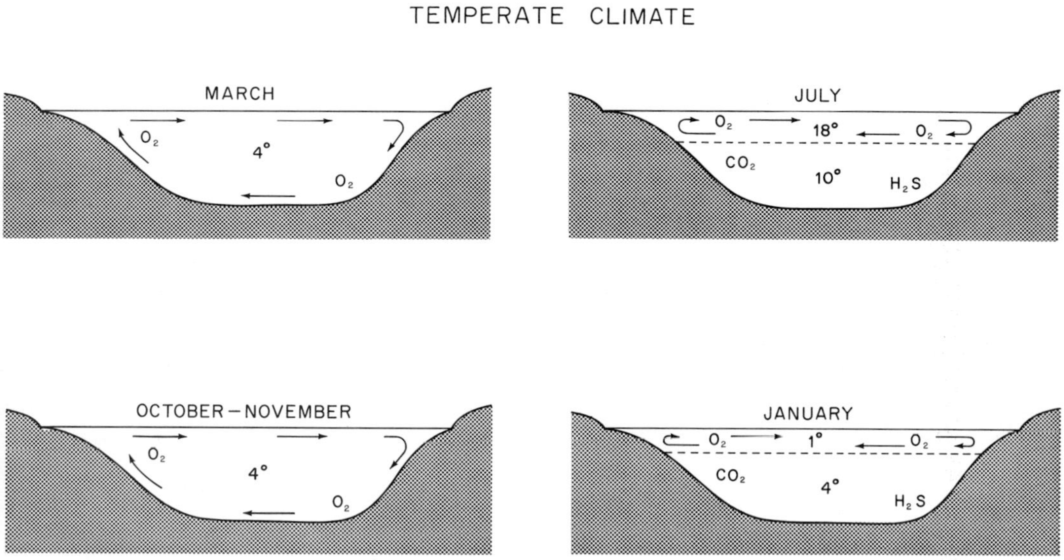

FIGURE 53.2
Schematic cross section of a fresh water lake in the Temperate zone. Shows seasonal variations of temperature distribution, circulation, direct and inverse stratification, and, in part, changes in the content and distribution of dissolved gases.

in the summer stagnation period. Indeed, if the lake freezes over and stays frozen a long time even the epilimnion may be depleted of its oxygen. When that happens there results a catastrophic mortality of fish and other organisms in the lake.

In subtropical climates there is generally only one overturn a year. The sequence of events illustrated in the top two diagrams of Figure 53.3 is much the same as for lakes in the Temperate zone except that by reason of higher temperatures, the hypolimnion becomes charged with hydrogen sulphide much more quickly and stays that way a considerable part of the year. The result is that the lake bottom in the hypolimnion is barren of virtually all living organisms except anaerobic bacteria. In the subtropics the thermal stratification is more stable—more durable than in the Temperate lakes because the warm surface water is so much less dense than that in the hypolimnion, even though the temperature differential is not great. In equatorial regions where there are no definite temperature seasons lakes become stratified but may overturn almost any time if the temperature stays a few degrees below normal for several days. A sudden cooling of subtropical or warm temperature thermally stratified lakes may cause so sudden an overturn that the hydrogen sulphide cannot be oxidized as it comes up. When this happens there is a great mortality among the fish and other organisms.

In lakes that have a complex life history we sometimes get another kind of stratification—a chemical one. If the lake is fed by highly mineralized springs or has gone down to a very low stage so that the dissolved salts become concentrated there can come to exist a saline hypolimnion—one that is denser than the overlying water because of its salinity. Soda Lake in Nevada, Lake Edward in Africa, and Lake Ritom in Switzerland are lakes of this kind. The Black Sea, although essentially marine, has a chemical stratification on a grand scale.

A saline hypolimnion once established is extremely stable and long lived. Hutchinson (1937, p. 116–127) has shown that the loss of salinity by diffusion upward into the overlying water is very slow and that because of the sharp density difference, there is a marked resistance to any tendency for the two water bodies of different salinity to mix. Indeed, he has shown that, paradoxical as it may seem, the fresher the water of the upper layer and the more of it there is moved across the saline hypolimnion the more nearly permanent is the chemical stratification.

In the relatively fresh water body above a saline hypolimnion the usual type of thermal stratification may, of course, develop as is shown in the lower part of Figure 53.3. Organisms that grow in this upper water body and, by one means or another, settle into the saline hypolimnion are likely to be well preserved, for no scavengers live there—only the slow process of decay by anaerobic bacteria goes on. The deposits that accumulate there are never worked over by mud feeders as they are at the bottoms of lakes and seas that are well oxygenated, or ventilated.

By productivity the limnologists mean simply the total quantity of organic matter of all kinds that grows in the lake—everything from bacteria to fish and all kinds of plants from diatoms and planktonic algae to the large forms that grow in the marginal shoals. Productivity is usually measured in metric tons per hectare—that is per 10,000 square meters. Lakes differ tremendously in their capacity to produce organisms. At one extreme are lakes like Crater Lake, which despite its great beauty is nearly barren of life. At the other end of the spectrum, in virtually all respects, would probably come small farm ponds that receive farmyard drainage. These are literally green and soupy with organisms.

What factors contribute to a lake's productivity? Moderate depth for one thing—that is, roughly 10 or more times wider than deep. But more important is a long shore line and extensive shoals around the margins, for in these warm, well-lighted waters much plant material is synthesized and many aquatic organisms prosper. Decomposition of these organisms adds dissolved nutrients to the lake as a whole. Another factor is a drainage basin containing an abundance of limestone and limy rocks from which the streams can bring lime and phosphates to the lake. The opposites of these factors, of course, determine lakes of low productivity.

So much for the principles of limnology. This cursory review leads now to a consideration of how these principles can be either applied directly or integrated with geologic evidence to interpret deposits laid down in the large Eocene lakes of the Rocky Mountain Region. To me, the interpretation of a sedimentary formation is essentially a problem of reconstructing environment as fully as possible and then deducing the physical, chemical, and biological processes that were taking place at

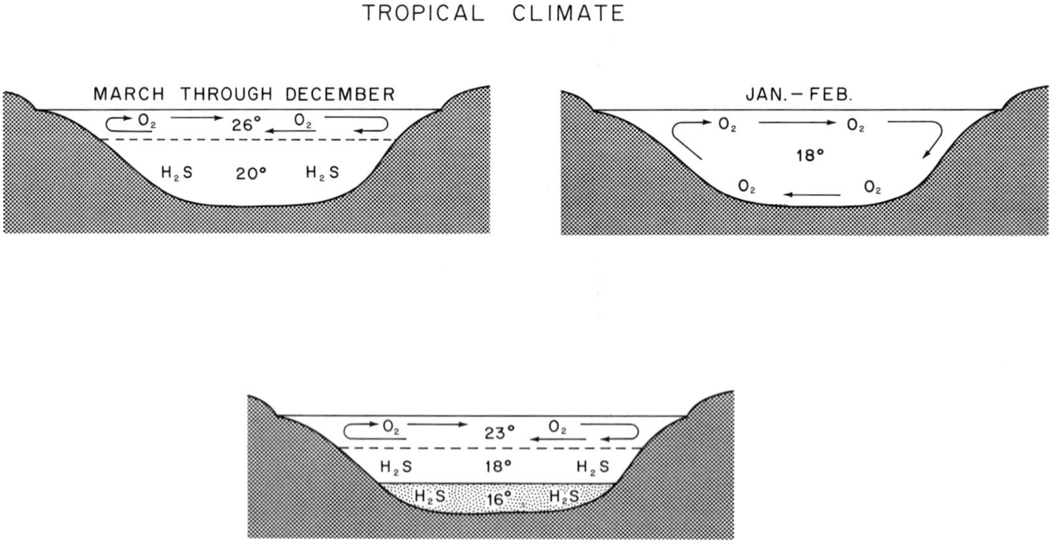

FIGURE 53.3
Schematic cross section of a fresh water lake in the Tropical zone. Shows seasonal variations of temperature distribution, circulation, thermal and chemical stratification, and, in part, changes in the content and distribution of dissolved gases.

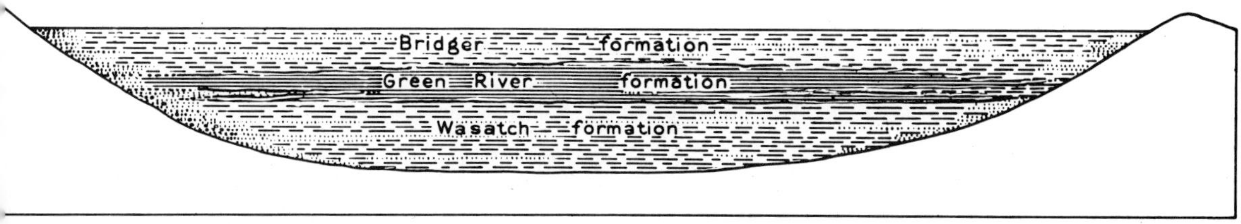

FIGURE 53.4
Schematic cross section of the Bridger Basin of Wyoming. Shows the relationship of the lacustrine Green River Formation to the enclosing fluviatile deposits of the Wasatch and Bridger Formations.

the time. The quality and fullness of that reconstruction are measures of our understanding of how that formation came to be and what its constituent elements mean. The test of such a reconstruction is met if all the parts of the resulting picture are consistent not only with one another but also with what we know of analogous features and processes of the earth that we can observe today.

The first steps in this reconstruction are to establish the origin and form of the lake basin, to review the bare outlines of its geologic history, and to determine its climatic environment.

PALEOLIMNOLOGY OF THE EOCENE LAKES

For the present purpose the origin of the basins in which the Green River formation was deposited can be considered superficially. I conceive that at the end of Upper Cretaceous time when the Rocky Mountain ranges were upfolded and the intermontane basins were formed the average altitude of the basin floors may have been several hundred feet above sea level, possibly a thousand. Under these conditions, no matter how perfectly the drainage to the sea was integrated, the streams eroding these new mountains would not only fill the basins with sediment but would continue to aggrade their beds all the way to the sea until they established a gradient adequate to transport their loads. The post-Cretaceous topography of the Rocky Mountain region was so far from graded that this conclusion appears to follow without regard to what the climate happened to be. The same cause would have accounted for the aggradation of the great frontal blanket of Tertiary sediments that slopes away from the east front of the Rocky Mountains.

This is unquestionably an oversimplified picture but it will suffice for the present, provided that we add that there is evidence in the Eocene sediments of these basins for intermittent slight downwarp during the early Tertiary. The lake basins of Green River time owed their origin, then, to downwarp and, although I have no compelling evidence, I believe that the lakes themselves owed their long existence to a progressive downwarp that exceeded both the rate of deposition in the basin and the rate of erosion of the axial ridge at the east end of the Uinta Range, where the outlet was.

The Green River formation itself makes up a huge lens of lacustrine beds some 1,500 to 2,000 feet thick within the mudstone of the Wasatch and Bridger formations (Figure 53.4). Its interfingerings with these enclosing formations reflect a long sequence of changes in the size and shape of the lake. At a comparatively few places the lake waters reached the edge of the basin and came in contact with the pre-Tertiary rocks. Marlstone, which is limy mudstone or muddy limestone, is the predominant rock type. Most of it contains organic matter and these organic marlstones grade into oil shales. All are thin bedded and regularly bedded. Most of the oil shale is restricted to the central two-thirds of the lens. Also occupying the central part of the basin is a saline facies some 6 or 8 hundred feet thick. To a large extent the saline facies and the oil shale deposits coincide though not wholly; oil shale occurs higher and lower in the formation and locally has a wider lateral extent than the saline facies. Marginal facies of the Green River formation are generally muddy and sandy though in them too lime is a conspicuous constituent. Locally the shore facies contain extensive beds and reefs of algal limestone, oölite, and shell beds. Locally also the formation is conglomeratic and at other places highly carbonaceous.

Toward the end of the lake's existence, the feeding streams brought in an abundance of sand and mud, which gradually filled the lake and made it shrink progressively to extinction.

Actually, there were three Green River lakes: Lake Uinta, the largest, south of the Uinta Mountains, in Utah; Gosiute Lake, the next largest, in Wyoming; and an as yet unnamed lake that occupied the relatively small basin in extreme western Wyoming now known as the Fossil Syncline. In speaking of one lake I have had in mind Gosiute Lake whose inferred maximum area was about 12,000 square miles. According to an estimate I made some years ago Gosiute Lake and the Fossil Syncline lake, at their maximum extent, occupied about 36% of their combined hydrographic basins. There is good evidence to indicate that many times in its history Gosiute Lake maintained a static stage during which it lost by evaporation from its surface as much as it received from rainfall and inflow. An analysis of the probable rates of evaporation and transpiration from vegetation and other factors involved (Bradley, 1929, p. 88–95) led me to conclude that the average annual rainfall of the region was between 30 and 40 inches. The same report gives an analysis of the probable ecology of the large Green River flora as interpreted by Roland Brown, E. W. Berry, and F. H. Knowlton. These paleobotanists concluded that the Green River flora would find a congenial environment along our present Gulf Coast and in the south Atlantic States. Accordingly, the average annual temperature may have been about 65°F. However, since Gosiute Lake was in the interior of the continent the temperature probably departed rather widely from this mean. It probably stayed above freezing and the summers were probably long and hot.

The geologic characteristics of the hydrographic basin were of significance to the ancient lake. The mountain ranges have an abundance of limestone and limy rocks and in several localities there are bedded rock phosphates. Under the inferred warm, moist climate these, and the associated rocks, were probably deeply weathered and the soils on the foot hills and lowlands were probably deep and fertile. A moderate amount of geologic and paleontologic evidence supports this inference but it can not conveniently be compressed into small enough compass to be presented here.

We have just considered the setting—the framework—within which can be reconstructed all the events of the Green River epoch. To attempt anything like a complete reconstruction, however, would be folly. Consequently, I have selected three distinctive features of the Green River formation to interpret in terms of the paleolimnology of the Eocene Green River lakes. These are the carbonate sediments and carbonate minerals, the oil shales, and the varved sediments.

PREDOMINANCE OF CARBONATES

The bulk of the deposits making up the Green River formation are marlstones. . . . These are slightly magnesian. In the shore facies limy algal deposits and oölites are common. How does it come about that the whole formation is so rich in carbonates? The explanation seems to me to run like this: Nearly all the streams that drained into the lake crossed upturned limestones or limy formations in the neighboring mountains. We have deduced that the climate of the area was warm and relatively moist. In such regions the streams are characterized by carbonates in solution. In the rivers of the eastern Gulf Coast States calcium carbonate makes up about 40 per cent of the total dissolved solids. Silica comes next and sulphates and chlorides run a poor third and fourth respectively. The lake therefore had an abundance of carbonates brought to it. Now the lake occupied so large a portion of its hydrographic basin and the temperature was such that each year most of the accession of water was lost by evaporation rather than by overflow. Indeed, for long intervals the lake had no outlet. This means that most of the dissolved carbonates were caught and held in the lake basin. Within the lake two factors tended to precipitate the calcium and magnesium carbonates: 1) the summer warming of the water, which decreases the solubility of these carbonates, and 2) the photosynthesis of the algae, which takes carbon dioxide out of the system and thereby raises the pH values, which increases the concentration of normal carbonates until the solubility product is exceeded and the calcium and magnesium carbonates are thrown down. . . . Thus it came about that through thermal effects alone calcium and magnesium carbonates were precipitated from the surface waters all over the lake, and particularly in the shoal waters, for there the water temperatures reached a maximum. In addition, photosynthesis of the planktonic algae accounted also for carbonate precipitation all over the lake and, near the margins, it accounted for the deposition of massive and bedded algal reefs.

CARBONATE MINERALS

At times during the lake's history its volume was so reduced that sodium carbonate minerals were deposited either as evaporites or as crystals that grew in the muds.

Saline Minerals from the Green River formation

Shortite	$Na_2CO_3 \cdot 2CaCO_3$
Trona	$Na_2CO_3 \cdot NaHCO_3 \cdot 2H_2O$
Pirssonite	$Na_2CO_3 \cdot CaCO_3 \cdot 2H_2O$
Northupite	$Na_2CO_3 \cdot MgCO_3 \cdot NaCl$
Gaylussite	$Na_2CO_3 \cdot CaCO_3 \cdot 5H_2O$
Bromlite	$(Ca,Ba)\ CO_3$
Bradleyite	$Na_3PO_4 \cdot MgCO_3$

Observe the general aspect of the group. They are all carbonates—no sulphates. Only one contains chloride as part of a three component mixed salt. Four of the seven are anhydrous. The trona is probably an evaporite as it occurs in a bed 8 to 10 feet thick. Shortite occurs as crystals that clearly grew in the mud and is exceedingly abundant through nearly 800 feet of beds in the central part of the Gosiute Lake Basin. It is a new mineral discovered by J. J. Fahey (1939, p. 514–518) of the Geological Survey and is known only at this locality. The system $Na_2CO_3 - CaCO_3$ has been studied to some extent by chemists and, I am told, at least one man is on record that this compound cannot exist. It seems to me another illustration of the remarkable phenomenon of geology wherein a rare combination of factors provides the necessary environment for the formation of an unusual mineral and then persists without significant change until huge quantities of the rare product have formed. The great cryolite deposit of Greenland is another example and so are the borate deposits of California where kernite was formed in great abundance. The montan wax deposits in the brown coals of Germany might also be added. I confess that contemplation of these laboratories of nature where a complex dynamic system remains so long in apparent perfect balance fills me with something very close to childlike wonder.

Northupite is also a rare mineral but is abundant in the Green River formation. Bromlite is another rare one. Bradleyite is a curious combination of sodium phosphate and magnesium carbonate (Fahey and Tunell, 1941, p. 646–650). . . .

The presence of these saline minerals is good evidence that Gosiute Lake at times, during its life of some 5 million years, was reduced to rather small size. When the water level rose again, through change of climate or possibly by enlargement of the drainage basin by stream capture, I infer that a body of relatively saline water remained in the deeper part of the basin. Indeed, some limnologists think that only a stratification made by a saline hypolimnion is stable in a large lake.

ORGANIC SEDIMENTS

Many of the beds of the Green River formation contain organic matter and some contain so much that they are classed as oil shale. The organic content ranges from a trace to more than 80 per cent by volume. The organic matter itself is not black carbonaceous stuff but hard, reddish yellow material that has somewhat the consistency of certain plastics or vulcanized rubber. On distillation it yields oil similar to crude petroleum. In the oil shales of the whole Green River formation, in all three states, the reserves of crude shale oil have been estimated at more than 75 billion barrels (Winchester, 1928, p. 13) [1965 estimates approach 1500 billion barrels in shales that yield 10 to 25 gallons per ton; of which 80 billion gallons are believed "recoverable under present conditions"]. Whether it is ever used will depend upon the economics and technology of the oil industry.

Our problem at the moment, however, is to answer the questions why the great abundance of organic matter and how did it come to be preserved? The distribution of the organic matter and its lack of the remains of large plants indicates rather clearly that it originated in the lake and that it was derived from small organisms and micro-organisms that lived in the lake. The great abundance of the organic matter, apart from any other consideration, is compelling evidence that Gosiute Lake was highly productive. This means that the water not only was rich in dissolved calcium and magnesium carbonates, as we have already seen, but that it had continuing supplies of dissolved phosphate and nitrates. Presumably the phosphate was derived from the small but ever present amounts in the thick sections of sedimentary beds in the adjacent mountains and the nitrates from the lush vegetation and the large animal population that lived on the land and in the streams and marshes along the lake margin. Crocodiles, large turtles, and birds are known to have been plentiful. Nitrogen was probably fixed from the air by some of the algae that lived in the lake. Judging by analogy with modern lakes the nitrogen was probably carried down and preserved in the bottom sediments in the cell walls of certain bacteria. The nitrogen content of the oil shale is directly proportional to the total amount of organic matter and in some rich shales runs up to as much as 1¼ per cent by weight of the rock. This implies a large continuing supply of nitrates to, and within, Gosiute Lake though the quantities of all the nutrients were probably increased periodically by shrinkage of the lake volume.

To explain the preservation of the organic matter we can turn again to modern lakes where abundant organic matter is preserved only in the stagnant parts where oxygen is scarce or absent and the water is charged with hydrogen sulphide. Only if Gosiute Lake were stratified, therefore, would it have been likely to preserve so much organic matter. Moreover, the observed saline minerals make it probable that the stratification was a chemical one and that most of the organic matter accumulated in a saline hypolimnion that persisted for thousands of years. On the other hand, since some oil shale was formed without saline minerals, Gosiute Lake probably was thermally, rather than chemically, stratified at some of its highest stages.

All the elements of this picture seem consistent—the geologic evidence agrees with the conditions inferred from the paleolimnology. One further geologic fact, however, supports the inference that the organic matter of the oil shale accumulated in a stagnant hypolimnion. The oil shale contains a considerable amount of pyrite that was deposited in the muck before compaction and diagenesis.

Entombed in the organic matter are many kinds of complete or fragmentary organisms (Bradley, 1931, p. 22–54). Among these are fungus spores, most of which were probably carried into the lake by the wind. At times wind carries incredible numbers of fungus spores. Records are available of times when as many as 1,000 spores per square centimeter fell (Durham, 1942, p. 42–44). This is enough to make a virtually continuous layer one cell thick of fungus spores. Spores of higher plants and pollen grains in the oil shale were surely wind borne. Pine and spruce pollen grains are common and distinctive. They are fitted with relatively large air sacks that enable them to float in the air for many miles. Although pine and spruce pollen is abundant, seeds are rare in the Green River formation. I conclude that pine and spruce grew high in adjacent mountains. With the spores and pollen grains are microscopic algae that grew in the lake and that closely resemble living forms. The compound eyes of minute adult insects—a few with the partially crushed wings and body parts attached are common in some oil-shale beds. The soft lens parts of the eyes were decomposed leaving only the netlike supporting tissue which presumably consisted of cuticular protein. Along with all these other or-

FIGURE 53.5
Varved marlstone from the Green River Formation, Fossil, Wyoming. Each varve, or annual increment of sediment, consists of one light-colored layer of microgranular carbonates and one dark-colored layer of organic matter. *a,* fossil fish in cross section; *b, c,* fish coprolites.

ganic remains are wing scales from mosquitoes, probably the most trivial things in the world, for what could be more trivial than a few microscopic scales from the wing of a mosquito that has been dead some 30 or 40 million years? I like to think of the violent contrasts that this formation offers—at one extreme these dustlike remnants of a long dead mosquito and at the other potential billions of barrels of oil. . . .

Preserved in the organic marlstone under somewhat less well understood conditions are other remarkable fossils, including enormous numbers of fly maggots that lived in decomposing organic matter, presumably in shallow water, and a large fauna of finely preserved adult insects.

VARVED SEDIMENTS

Figure 53.5 shows a thin section of the varved marlstone in the small unnamed Green River lake west of Gosiute Lake, where the varves are better developed. Each varve, or annual deposit, consists of a layer of microgranular carbonates and a thinner, darker layer of organic matter.

The problem is to identify these rhythmic sediments with the annual cycle. Once more we can turn to the sediments in modern lakes for an analogy—this time to the lake of Zürich in Switzerland where Friedrich Nipkow (1927, p. 71–120), a student of diatoms studying the cyclic variations in the growth size of the plankton diatoms, took core samples of the mud in the deep central part of the lake. These sediments, he observed, were laminated —one thin layer of microgranular carbonates and one layer of organic matter. He surmised that these were annual deposits because he had observed that each summer particles of calcium carbonate were precipitated out of the surface waters of the lake in sufficient abundance to clog his plankton nets. Then he counted the pairs of layers downward in the core until he came to a very thick muddy layer. According to his count this corresponded to the year when a large part of the lake shore had caved off and slid into the lake making it muddy. He counted back several more years to another cave-in and its corresponding thick mud layer. And farther down to a third one. Next he sliced each thin organic layer into 5 or 10 thin slices and studied the diatoms in each slice. Indeed, he measured 100 specimens in each so as to get statistics on the size variations. He found the spring diatoms, the summer diatoms, and the autumn diatoms! Then he plotted their size distribution and compared the uppermost 8 years of their variations obtained from the sediments with similar measurements made from his past 8 years of collections from the surface waters. The curves agreed. Thus he did two things: he obtained his statistics on the cyclic growth of diatoms and unwittingly gave geologists a most convincing demonstration of the existence of nonglacial varves. I feel that such demonstrations are of the utmost value to geology—they are unequivocally objective. May I reinforce this with another example. By far the best paper on the origin of oölites that I know was written by Heinrich Schade (1909, p. 263–265), a physician who was studying the formation of bladder stones. He was well founded in physical chemistry, biochemistry, and colloid chemistry and, fortunately, was quite ignorant of the geological literature on oölites.

Nipkow made another significant observation. He found the varved sediments only in the deep parts of the hypolimnion of the lake of Zurich where dissolved oxygen was absent and where no bottom fauna lived that could work over the mud and so spoil the lamination.

I think the analogy with Nipkow's laminated lake sediments adequately identifies these paired laminae in the Green River formation as varves. But there is abundant additional evidence, were it needed.

In Figure 53.6 I have tried to reconstruct the paleolimnology of the small unnamed

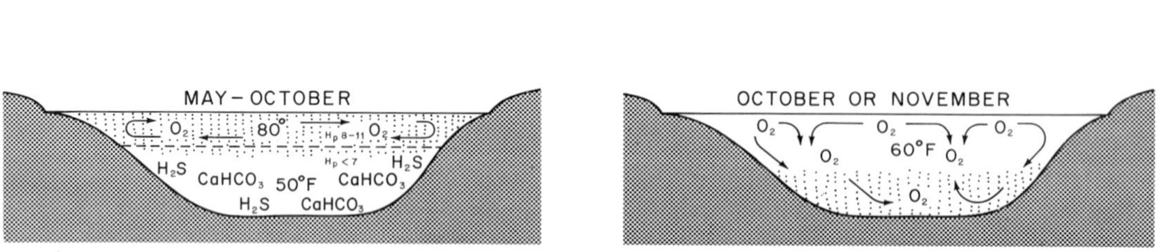

FIGURE 53.6
Schematic cross section of the ancient Eocene lake that once occupied the Fossil Syncline in western Wyoming. Shows seasonal variations of temperature distribution, circulation, thermal and partial chemical stratification, and, in part, changes in the hydrogen ion concentration, content and distribution of dissolved gases, and solid and dissolved carbonates.

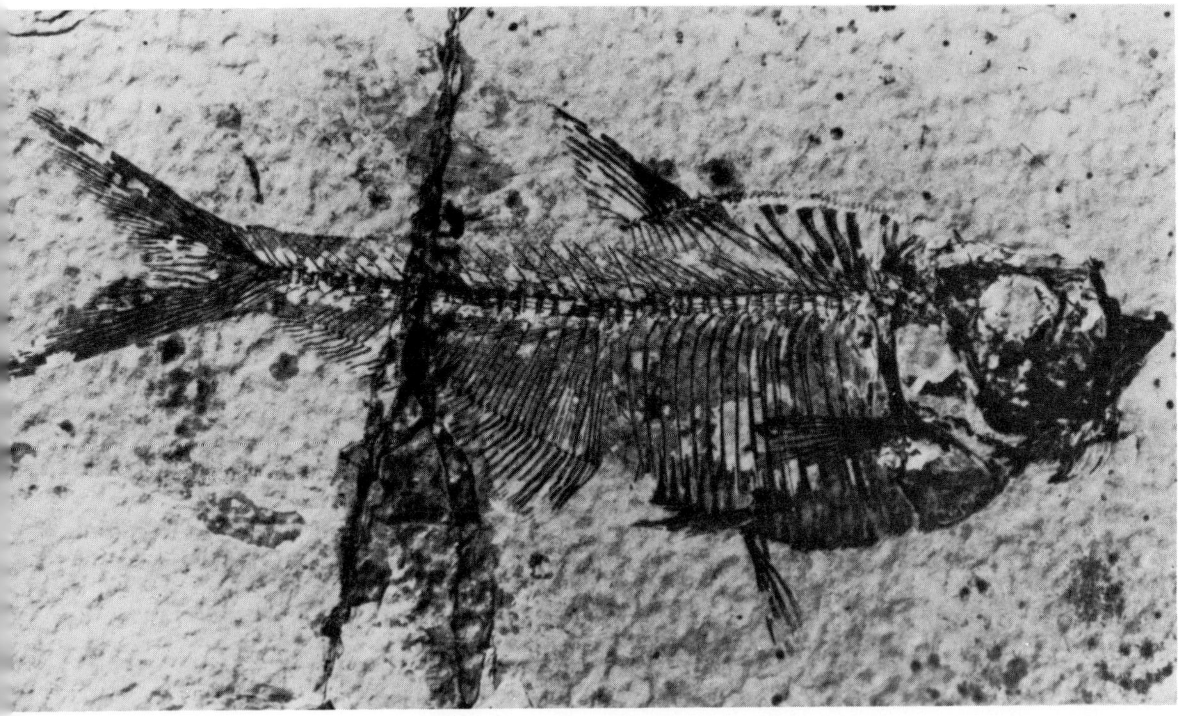

FIGURE 53.7
The undisturbed arrangement of delicate bones and tail and fin rays. In life, these were held in that arrangement by tissues rather than by articulation of the skeleton.

Green River lake in extreme western Wyoming. The lake basin was relatively deep and nearly free from saline minerals, hence I conclude that it was thermally stratified for the long summer during which calcium and magnesium carbonates were precipitated from the surface waters by summer warming and by photosynthesis. When these particles reached the hypolimnion, which was acid because of its content of carbon dioxide and hydrogen sulphide much of the carbonate went back into solution and was held so until the one overturn of the year. According to Strøm (1945, p. 1–16) dissolved carbonates may well enhance the stability stratification. During the period of complete circulation the pH value of the hypolimnion was raised by dissipation of the hydrogen sulphide and excess carbon dioxide and also by mixing with the more alkaline surface water. At that time also, the bulk of the normal carbonates were precipitated. This is admittedly an extreme picture and probably some of the carbonate came down to the bottom throughout the greater part of the summer. This stage was followed by the much slower settling of the organic matter during the rest of the year.

In this basin (Fossil, Wyo.) hundreds of thousands of beautifully preserved fish are entombed in the varved sediments. Even the delicate fin and tail rays and other bones originally held in place only by tissue are virtually undisturbed (Figure 53.7), and even the scales are in place almost completely undisturbed (Figure 53.8). It seems to me that the picture of this lake as a thermally stratified water body provides nearly all the necessary information to account for the excellent preservation of these fish. Only in the stagnant hypolimnion could they have escaped being torn to pieces by scavengers or disturbed by bottom feeders. It is significant that all the well preserved fish are in varved sediments. Those in nonvarved sediments are a disordered mass of broken and chewed up bones.

The only part of the story lacking now is

how the fish died and got into the hypolimnion. Limnology offers two possible explanations. Sometimes when the surface of a lake gets excessively warm, fish will plunge into deep water and might thus penetrate the hypolimnion, be overcome by hydrogen sulphide, and also have the gas in their swim bladders chilled so that they sank at once to the bottom. Once there, only anaerobic bacteria would attack them. The other hypothesis is that the thermally stratified lake was suddenly chilled so that it overturned more rapidly than the hydrogen sulphide could be oxydized and so killed off large numbers of fish. This seems a little more probable as the fossil fish are of all ages and kinds.

CONCLUSIONS

The foregoing consideration of a brief portion of earth history has prompted me to look inquiringly at the science of geology. Like limnology, geology is a derived science. It takes much of its substance from physics, chemistry, and biology. It also draws on oceanography, volcanology, and climatology. But what is the central theme peculiar to the science of geology—that core which is not derived from any of the sister disciplines? Perhaps you will agree that it is the history and constitution of the earth. And how do we reach an understanding of the history and constitution of the earth? Very largely by observing earth processes that

FIGURE 53.8
The arrangement of scales only slightly modified during decay, burial, and fossilization of the fish

FIGURE 53.9
Restoration of the southern shore of the Eocene Gosiute Lake

are going on today—volcanic and glacial action, geochemical and geophysical changes, marine and terrestrial ecology, or geobiology if you will. All these we can observe and measure, either in nature or as scale models in the laboratory. We, as geologists, however, are doing far too little of this kind of work—and to the detriment of geology. It is one of the sure ways we can carry a quantitative approach right into the heart of geology; and today geology needs that quantitative attribute. . . .

I have digressed from my principal theme. In closing let me return to it briefly—you will see by this sketch (Figure 53.9) that in attempting to use limnology to interpret the deposits of the Eocene Green River formation I have let my imagination run freely. This represents, in my imagination, a tranquil day some 30 or 40 million years ago on the south shore of Gosiute Lake where two four-toed horses are mildly startled by the rumbling of a distant volcano. . . . I wish to impress on you, however, that what I have depicted here is not all imagination. The four-toed horses and the handsome tree near which they stand I cribbed shamelessly from a painting by Charles R. Knight (1935, p. 72, 83) of the American Museum.

REFERENCES CITED

Bradley, W. H., 1929, The varves and climate of the Green River epoch: U.S. Geol. Survey Prof. Paper 158-E, p. 88–95.

———, 1931, Origin and microfossils of the oil shale of the Green River formation of Colorado and Utah: U.S. Geol. Survey Prof. Paper 168, p. 22–54.

Durham, Oren C., 1942, Air-borne fungus spores as allergens, *in* Aerobiology: Am. Assoc. Adv. Sci. Pub. 17, p. 42–44.

Fahey, J. J., 1939, Shortite, a new carbonate of sodium and calcium: Am. Minerologist, v. 24, p. 514–518.

Fahey, J. J., and George Tunell, 1941, Bradleyite, a

new mineral, sodium phosphate–magnesium carbonate: Am. Minerologist, v. 26, p. 646–650.
Hutchinson, G. E., 1937, A contribution to the limnology of arid regions, primarily founded on observations made in the Lahontan Basin [Nevada]: Connecticut Acad. Arts Sci. Trans., v. 33, p. 47–132.
Knight, Chas. R., 1935, Before the dawn of history: New York, McGraw-Hill, p. 72, 83.
Nipkow, H. Friedrich, 1927, Über das Verhalten der Skellete planktonischer Kiselalgen im geschichteten Tiefenschlamm des Zurich und Baldeggersees: Rév. Hydrol., IV ann., p. 71–120.
Schade, Heinrich, 1909, Zur Entstehung der Harnsteine und ahnlicher konzentrisch geschischteter Steine organischen und anorganischen Ursprungs: Zeitschr. Chemie und Industrie der Kolloide, v. 4, p. 263–265.
Strøm, K. M., 1945, Lakes with stagnant deeps: Norske Vidensk.-Akad. Skr., no. 7, p. 1–16.
Winchester, D. E., 1928, Report 2 of the Federal Oil Conservation Board to the President, p. 13.

54

Caribbean Land and Sea through the Ages

W. P. WOODRING
1954

Paleogeography starts as a concoction of essential ingredients, generally too meager, and winds up as a heady essence distilled through the imagination of the perpetrator. It therefore is an art. It is practiced—and too frequently abused—by geologists, paleontologists, and biogeographers. It is a simple matter to make paleogeographic generalizations, but it is something else to lay them down on a map, even on a small-scale map, and practically all paleogeographic maps are of very small scale. On a map your ideas look up at you coldly, knowing full well they will come back to taunt you.

For the most part published paleogeographic maps of the Caribbean region are based on the premise that almost the entire Caribbean Sea has indeed been sea since the earliest dated events in the geological history of the region. Schuchert's (1935) well-known and widely used maps, for example, show land of varying width extending from Central America northeastward to Jamaica and Cuba, but the remainder of the Caribbean Sea is enduring sea. That premise has been challenged during recent years (Bucher, 1947, p. 100; Eardley, 1952). It is not my intention to present a long series of paleogeographic maps: that would be dull for any audience. I propose to present a few maps representing intervals of time selected to test the validity of the premise on the basis of what is now known about the geology of the Caribbean region.

Almost any conclusions, at least concerning the pre-Tertiary history, are bound to be tentative. Our knowledge of the pre-Tertiary geology of the Greater Antilles is meager. There has been plenty of reconnaissance, and generalized small-scale maps are available, but very little real mapping has been published. In all of the Greater Antilles, an area of 80,000 square miles, geological maps of pre-Tertiary areas on a scale of a mile to the inch or better are available for about 600 square miles (Flint, de Albear, and Guild, 1948, Pl. 18; Matley, 1951). To be sure, the pre-Tertiary rocks of Puerto Rico are shown on maps having a scale of 1 : 62,500 or 1 : 50,000, published during the period 1919–1931. Despite the scale, they

From *Geological Society of America Bulletin*, vol. 65, pp. 719–732, 1954. Reprinted with permission of the author and the Geological Society of America.

are reconnaissance maps. Though ultramafic rocks crop out in all the provinces of Cuba, one of the maps just cited (Flint, de Albear, and Guild, 1948, Pl. 18) is the only published detailed may showing any part of them, and it covers a minute segment. Another map (Koschmann and Gordon, 1950 [1951], Pl. 19), covering 350 square miles, is the only map on any scale showing a considerable number of pre-Tertiary units in the entire island of Hispaniola. It represents reconnaissance mapping on a scale of 1 : 100,000. It is based, however, on mapping and not on generalizations from hasty road and trail traverses.

Though the Caribbean region includes Central America and northern South America, this account deals principally with the Antilles.

GEOGRAPHIC AND STRUCTURAL SETTING OF CARIBBEAN REGION

About 90 per cent of the Caribbean region, exclusive of the continental mainland, is under water. All that is known about that part is its general configuration; the results of gravity observations at about 100 stations; and the results of geophysical probing of the thickness of sediments in one area: the Puerto Rico Deep.

Figure 54.1 shows the gross submarine features. The greatest depths are in the Puerto Rico Deep (4350 fathoms) and in the Bartlett Trough (just short of 4000 fathoms), directly south of the highest range in Cuba (the Sierra Maestra) and directly south of the highest peak in that range.

Figure 54.1 also shows areas of pronounced negative gravity anomalies—anomalies greater than 100 milligals. The isogams of Figure 54.1 are based on de Bruyn's (1951) 1 : 10,000,000 25-isogam map, the most recent compilation of gravity data covering the Caribbean region. The Vening Meinesz narrow belt of strong negative anomalies extends from eastern Cuba to the eastern Venezuelan basin. The largest anomalies are just south of the bottom of the Puerto Rico Deep (−219 milligals) and in the eastern Venezuelan basin (a little more than −200 milligals). According to de Bruyn's map, the narrow belt of negative anomalies north of the Venezuelan coast, shown by an incomplete −100 isogam on Figure 54.1, evidently is not continuous with the Vening Meinesz belt. Though data are still lacking, the belt off the Venezuelan coast may bend northeastward and flare out up the Aves Swell.

The Precambrian areas of Figure 54.1 are at the far south border of the Caribbean region. The metamorphic rocks of the Guianan Shield, the counterpart of the Canadian Shield, in the extreme southeastern part of the map, are overlain by lower Paleozoic deposits 600 miles to the southeast in Brazil. The smaller of the two areas in the Venezuelan Andes evidently is older than the Middle Ordovician near by (Leith, 1938, p. 337–339) and therefore is presumably Precambrian. The larger area is assumed to be of the same age, but the oldest fossiliferous strata overlying the metamorphic rocks are of Devonian age. The metamorphic rocks of the Cordillera Central of the Andes in Colombia are overlain by Middle Cambrian to Middle Ordovician 125 miles south of the south border of Figure 54.1 (Harrington and Kay, 1951, p. 655–657 and by Lower Ordovician within the area of Figure 54.1 (Botero Arango, 1942, p. 24). The metamorphics of the Cordillera Oriental may possibly be Paleozoic. The oldest dated deposits overlying them are nonmarine strata of early Mesozoic age.

The late Cenozoic volcanics of Central America (Figure 54.1) form a distinct geological province. They are likely to remain the chief obstacle in attempts to integrate the geology of southern Central America with that of northern Central America.

The trend and relative structural relief of folds are represented on Figure 54.1. Faults, however, are omitted. Many faults mapped on land could not be adequately shown on the scale of that illustration. Some of the submarine faults that have been suggested need confirmation.

OUTLINE OF GEOLOGICAL HISTORY OF CARIBBEAN REGION

PRE-JURASSIC

The oldest part of the Caribbean region proper is not in the Antilles; it is in the folded mountain ranges of northern Central America.

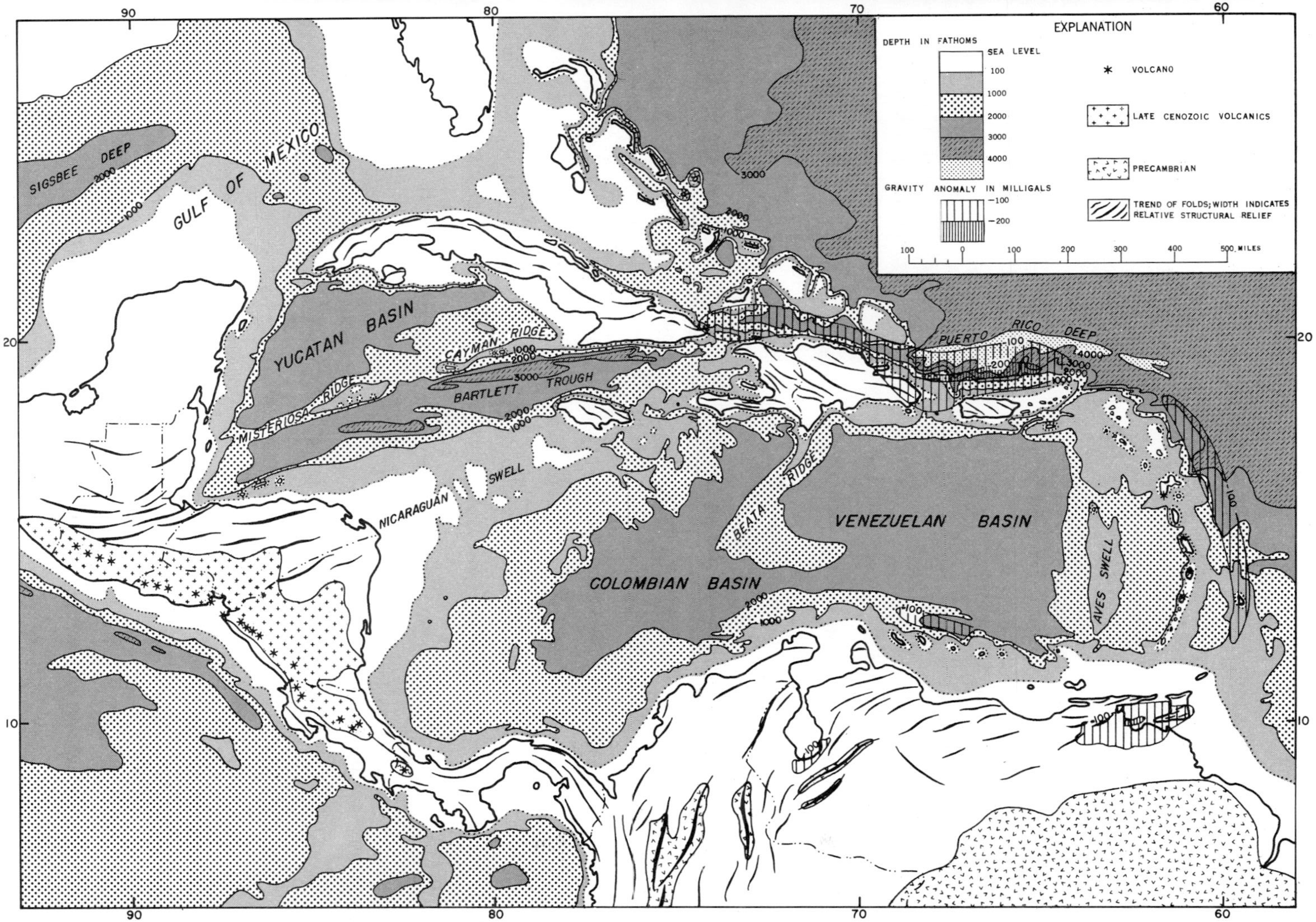

FIGURE 54.1
Geographic and structural setting of Caribbean region. Base, submarine contours, and isogam contours from de Bruyn (1951), by permission of E. J. Brill, Leiden.

Gneiss, schist, and other metamorphic rocks, exposed in the cores of anticlines in central Guatemala, northern Honduras, and northern Nicaragua, are the oldest rocks in northern Central America. They have been assigned to the Precambrian since the pioneer work in that area. All that is now known about their age is that they are older than the 2000 feet or more of Permian(?) and Lower Permian marine strata resting on them. These ancient-appearing rocks may indeed be of Precambrian or early Paleozoic age. In view, however, of the geological history of the entire region, it is more probable that they are not older than middle Paleozoic. They have been through two periods of deformation and batholitic intrusion and therefore are strongly metamorphosed. The Permian(?) and Lower Permian rocks themselves appear to be progressively metamorphosed eastward: shale to phyllite to schist (Roberts and Irving, 1957).

In the entire Caribbean region and its borders marine Triassic deposits are lacking. Marine Upper Triassic, interbedded with red beds, has been found in the eastern foothills of the Cordillera Central of the Andes in Colombia, 75 miles southwest of Bogotá (Trumpy, 1943, p. 1297–1299), but not farther north. The widespread nonmarine strata of Colombia and Venezuela, which overlie marine upper Paleozoic and underlie marine Lower Cretaceous, are thought to represent much of Triassic and Jurassic time.

Sometime during the interval between Middle Permian and Late Triassic, the pre-Permian and Permian strata of northern Central America were deformed and intruded by ultramafic and granitic rocks (Roberts and Irving).

JURASSIC

After the deformation in northern Central America just mentioned, nonmarine deposits were laid down in that area north and south of the folded ranges, which trend east-northeastward in an arc of gentle curvature, and in intermontane basins. These nonmarine deposits contain plants of Early and Middle Jurassic age. In Guatemala and the adjoining Mexican state of Chiapas, the upper part of the nonmarine strata include gypsum and salt (Sapper, 1937, p. 27), suggesting that marine Middle or Upper Jurassic underlies northern Guatemala and Yucatán. There is a still undocumented report of marine Upper Jurassic in Honduras (Imlay, 1952, p. 969–970).

Marine Lower and Middle Jurassic, like marine Triassic, is unknown in the Caribbean region proper. Marine Lower Jurassic has been found at a locality along the south border of the region in Colombia: near the north end of the Cordillera Central of the Andes (Trumpy, 1943, p. 1299).

By middle Late Jurassic time (late Oxfordian; Imlay, 1952, p. 969) geosynclinial deposition reached the Greater Antilles, but only the westernmost island, Cuba. Thick marine deposits of that age, including rocks mildly metamorphosed to phyllite and quartzite, are found in westernmost Cuba. The much more strongly metamorphosed rocks of Isla de los Pinos (L. M. R. Rutten, 1934; Page and McAllister, 1944, p. 181–184), off the south coast of western Cuba, and the similar pre-ultramafic rocks of central and eastern Cuba, may possibly be of the same age. If they are, deformation and intrusion of diorite, now more or less gneissic, took place during a span from early Kimmeridgian to early Portlandian time, corresponding to a gap in the Cuban sequence (Imlay, 1942, p. 1439–1440). Late Portlandian (Imlay, 1942, p. 1433–1440; 1952, p. 969) is represented in western, central, and eastern Cuba by 2000 feet of limestone, shale, chert, and some tuff.

EARLY CRETACEOUS

Early Cretaceous geosynclinal deposition took in all of Cuba and Hispaniola, probably Jamaica, and possibly Puerto Rico. If it included Jamaica, the deposits are represented in the metamorphic rocks of the Blue Mountains. This is the beginning of enormously thick volcanics: mostly pyroclastics in Cuba, mostly flows (including submarine flows) in Haiti, mostly pyroclastics in the Dominican Republic.

All the major subdivisions of the Lower Cretaceous are reported to be represented in Cuba (MacGillavry, 1937, p. 7–13; Maync, 1949, p. 531–532), but no records of a well-dated sequence have so far been published. Both the late Portlandian and the earliest Lower Cretaceous (Neocomian) of Cuba—the Aptychi limestones or Aptychi formation of Dutch geologists (MacGillavry, 1937, p. 7–8; M. G. Rutten, 1936, p. 10–12; van Wessem, 1943, p. 6–8)—contain concentrations of ammonite opercula, radiolaria, and pelagic foraminifera. They evidently are fairly deep-water deposits. The presence of land-plant debris is not opposed to that interpretation. Great quantities of decomposed land-plant debris were dredged by the ALBATROSS in deep water off the Pacific coast of Central America (Agassiz, 1892, p. 11–12). The Cuban deposits are typically geosynclinal, typically eugeosynclinal, if that term is preferred.

The Lower Cretaceous of most of Cuba is mad up principally of marine pyroclastics, with which minor flows are interbedded: part of the Tuff formation or Tuff series of Dutch geologists (de Vletter, 1946, p. 11–15; Hermes, 1945, p. 3–5; MacGillavry, 1937, p. 8–10; M. G. Rutten, 1936, p. 7–10; Thiadens, 1937, p. 11–18; van Wessem, 1943, p. 8–12; Vermunt, 1937, p. 15–17). Along the north coast of the island, in the northwestern part of Camagüay Province, van Wessem's (1943, p. 7–8) Aptychi formation includes thick beds of gypsum. Northward from the north coast of Cuba, in the subsurface strata of the Bahamas and peninsular Florida, the Lower Cretaceous consists of carbonate rocks. The only deep well so far drilled in the Bahamas penetrated almost 4000 feet of presumably Lower Cretaceous carbonate deposits and did not reach their base. Some of the dolomite of the carbonate deposits contains blebs of anhydrite. The subsurface Lower Cretaceous carbonate rocks of peninsular Florida include minor amounts of bedded gypsum or anhydrite (P. L. and E. R. Applin, 1944, p. 1721).

The ultramafic rocks of Cuba probably were emplaced at an early date in Early Cretaceous time; that is, they probably are younger than the Central American ultramafics. In the east-central part of the island, where the ultramafics have been mapped (Flint, de Albear, and Guild, 1948, p. 43–45), they engulf schist and gneiss of unknown age and are overlain by volcanics that appear to range in age from Early to Late Cretaceous, but the lower, presumably Early Cretaceous, part is not yet dated. The late Upper Cretaceous deposits contain serpentine debris (L. M. R. Rutten, 1940, p. 542).

Much of what has been assigned to the Lower Cretaceous in Haiti, with varying degrees of qualification (Woodring, Brown, and Burbank, 1924), p. 86–93), is now known to be Upper Cretaceous. Nevertheless some of the lavas, particularly the earlier basalt of the northern part of the country and the basalt of the southern peninsula, may be Lower Cretaceous. Limestone between pillows of basalt, in the extensive area of basalt southwest of Port-au-Prince, shows sections of [caprinids] comparable to those from Lower Cretaceous limestone in the Dominican Republic.

The metamorphic rocks of the Cordillera Central of the Dominican Republic have been claimed to be pre-Cretaceous, possibly Paleozoic (Weyl, 1940, p. 5, 28–29; and other publications by the same author). In the only area that has been mapped, however, a great thickness of sericite schist, altered tuff, and greenstone—all estimated to represent a thickness of 20,000 feet, if there is no duplication—overlies more or less altered limestone containing [caprinids] and other fossils of Cretaceous age, probably late Early Cretaceous (Koschmann and Gordon, 1950 [1951], p. 317–325). Ultramafic rocks form a sill-like mass, between altered tuff and greenstone in the upper part of the sequence. Limestone 70 miles southeast of the mapped area contains the [caprinids] found in the mapped area and also *Orbitolina concava texana*, which occurs in the Aptian-Albian of Cuba, northern Central America, Colombia, and Venezuela.

Matley (1929, p. 465; 1951, p. 22) was convinced that the metamorphic rocks of the Blue Mountains in eastern Jamaica are pre-Cretaceous. They are now thought, however, to be Cretaceous or possibly Jurassic (Zans, 1953, p. 2). If they are Cretaceous, they are likely to be Lower Cretaceous.

LATE CRETACEOUS

Late Cretaceous geosynclinal deposition spread still farther eastward to include all of the Greater Antilles, the Virgin Islands, and St.

Croix. Figure 54.2 is a representation of Late Cretaceous paleogeography. Like most paleogeographic maps, it takes in too great a time span and therefore is composite.

Throughout the Greater Antilles, the Virgin Islands, and St. Croix the Upper Cretaceous deposits include basaltic and andesitic pyroclastics and flows of great thickness. They are everywhere strongly deformed and practically everywhere are intruded by batholiths of quartz diorite or granodiorite, near some of which they are altered to schist. It was on St. Thomas, one of the Virgin Islands, where the Swedish naturalist Cleve (1871, p. 5) was able to show almost 85 years ago that the metamorphic rocks are altered Cretaceous.

The latest dated Upper Cretaceous of the Greater Antilles includes, or consists mostly of, detrital deposits of late Campanian and Maestrichtian age (Imlay, 1944, p. 1013–1015). They include thin beds of limestone containing a distinctive fauna, characterized by the remarkable [rudistid] *Barrettia,* which has been found in Cuba, Jamaica, Haiti, Puerto Rico, and northern Guatemala.

Deformation and intrusion of quartz diorite or granodiorite took place in the Greater Antilles and the Virgin Islands toward the close of Cretaceous time. The deformation was the first of several episodes of varying intensity during the interval from late Cretaceous to Eocene. In Cuba quartz diorite intrudes volcanics of early Late Cretaceous age, apparently Cenomanian to Coniacian (part of the Tuff formation or Tuff series of Dutch geologists; Imlay, 1944, p. 1011–1012) and contributed debris to the Campanian-Maestrichtian detrital deposits. The deformation and intrusion therefore is middle Late Cretaceous, approximately Santonian (Imlay, 1944, p. 1012). This deformation produced the arc of islands shown on Figure 54.2 where Cuba now is located. Discordance between the volcanics and the detrital deposits, however, is by no means uniform. At some localities there is no appreciable discordance, but the volcanics, the quartz diorite, and the ultramafic rocks were shedding debris into the late Campanian-Maestrichtian sea.

In Jamaica granodiorite intrudes the still undated metamorphic rocks of the Blue Mountains. Pebbles of granodiorite, however, are found in conglomerates of early Eocene age, but not in conglomerates interbedded with Upper Cretaceous limestone (Zans, 1953, p. 3). In Hispaniola, Puerto Rico, and the Virgin Islands deformation and plutonic intrusion took place at about the end of the Cretaceous, but the dating is not within narrow limits.

Altered basaltic and andesitic flows and tuffs, intruded by diorite, form the pre-Tertiary basement in Panamá (Woodring and Thompson, 1949, p. 227). The tuffs, like those in the Antilles, contain radiolaria and are altered to schist near some of the stocks of diorite. These volcanic rocks are shown as Tertiary volcanics on the current edition of the geological map of North America. At least part of the volcanics is dated as Late Cretaceous, on the basis of foraminifera found in siliceous limestone in northwestern Panamá near the Costa Rican border.

Though the little Dutch islands off the coast of Venezuela (Aruba, Curaçao, Bonaire) are separated from the Greater Antilles by the width of the Caribbean Sea (a distance of 400 miles), their geology is Antillean. Their basement consists of a thick pile of volcanics overlain by detrital Upper Cretaceous (Molengraaff, 1929, p. 15–25; Pijpers, 1933, p. 7–38; Westermann, 1932, p. 11–37). Tuffs and cherts in the volcanic sequence contain radiolaria, as in the Greater Antilles. The three islands show a westward increase in intensity of deformation, in the size of exposed stocks of quartz diorite, and in degree of metamorphism.

The highly metamorphosed rocks of the Cordillera de la Costa in northern Venezuela (Bucher, 1952, p. 39–62, 73–84) include altered volcanics and apparently represent a transition from the volcanic sequence of the Dutch islands to the nonvolcanic sequence farther south and southwest in Venezuela. Late Cretaceous (Turonian) foraminifera have been found in limestone interbedded with schist, and the entire sequence of metamorphic rocks is now thought to be of Cretaceous age, or possibly both Cretaceous and Late Jurassic. Both Late Jurassic and Cretaceous fossils have been found in the metamorphic rocks of the Northern Range of Trinidad (Sutter, 1951–52, p. 189–191, 1951), the

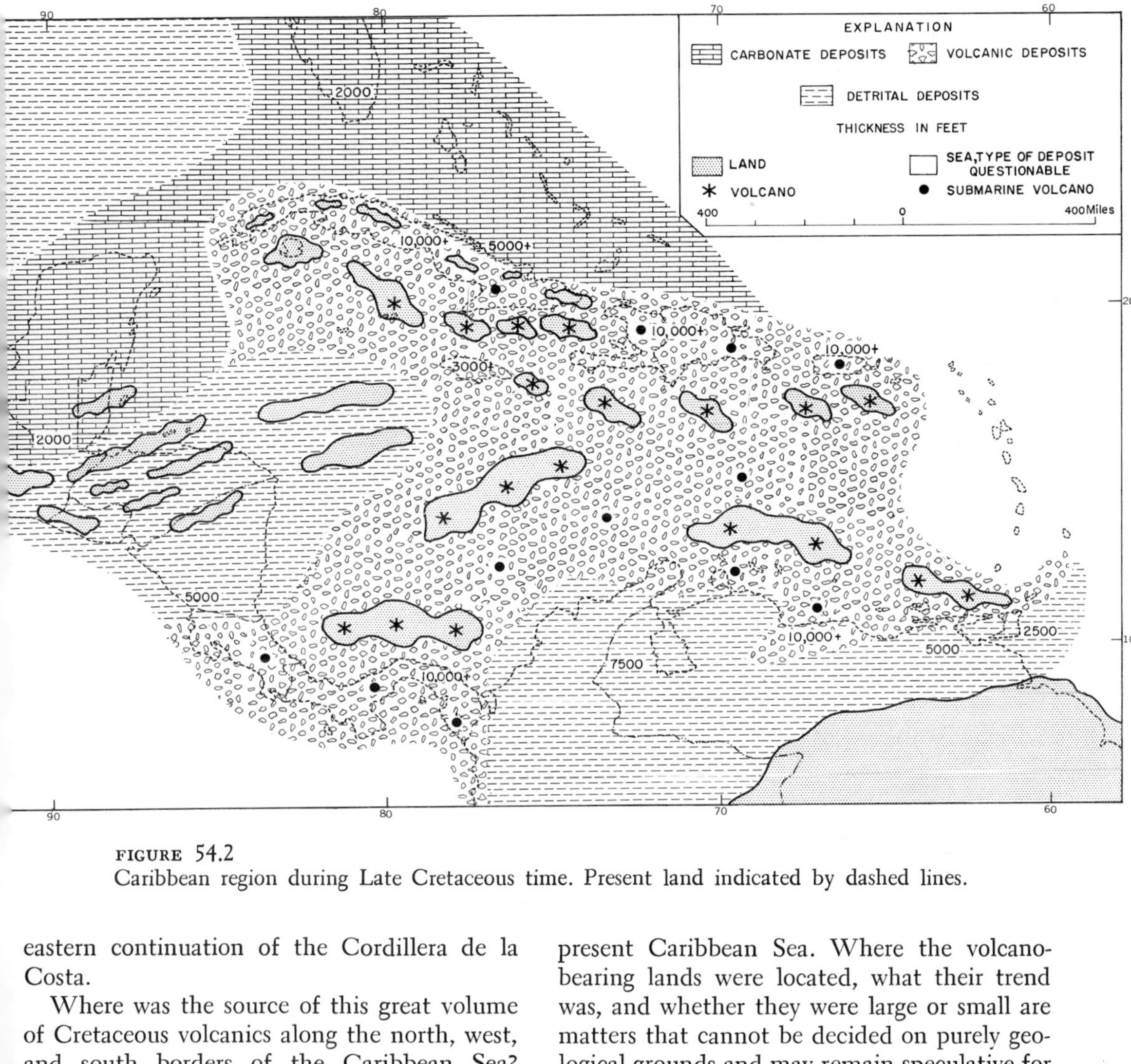

FIGURE 54.2
Caribbean region during Late Cretaceous time. Present land indicated by dashed lines.

eastern continuation of the Cordillera de la Costa.

Where was the source of this great volume of Cretaceous volcanics along the north, west, and south borders of the Caribbean Sea? Though data are too meager for estimates, pyroclastics evidently are thicker and more widespread than flows. There doubtless were some minor volcanic centers in the present Greater Antilles, but they apparently were submarine. A northern source for the pyroclastics is at once eliminated. The entire Cretaceous sequence in the Bahamas and peninsular Florida, revealed by deep wells, consists of carbonate deposits. In north-central Cuba, the widespread Upper Cretaceous volcanic facies is replaced northward by a carbonate facies (de Albear, 1947, abstract; M. G. Rutten, 1936, p. 21–24). The only source for the pyroclastics is not in sight, it is under the waters of the present Caribbean Sea. Where the volcano-bearing lands were located, what their trend was, and whether they were large or small are matters that cannot be decided on purely geological grounds and may remain speculative for an indefinite time. The representation of the volcano-bearing lands on Figure 54.2 is one of several possible interpretations.

PALEOCENE AND EARLY EOCENE

Paleocene deposits are mostly thin and of limited extent. In western Cuba the Paleocene is detrital (Bermúdez, 1950, p. 218–225), in southeastern Cuba volcanic (Lewis and Straczek, In preparation), in Haiti carbonate (Butterlin, 1953, p. 285). No Paleocene has been recognized so far in Jamaica or Puerto Rico.

Lower Eocene deposits, like the Paleocene,

are mostly thin and not widely distributed. The lower Eocene of western and central Cuba consists of detrital and carbonate deposits (Bermúdez, 1950, p. 227–238), but in southeastern Cuba the lower Eocene is made up of volcanics, with which some limestone is interbedded (Bermúdez, 1950, p. 238–239; Lewis and Straczek). Carbonate deposits are the prevailing type in Hispaniola (Bermúdez, 1949, p. 19, 32; Butterlin, 1953, p. 285). The lower Eocene of Jamaica consists chiefly of detrital marginal marine-nonmarine deposits, and includes gypsum (Zans, 1953, p. 3). Land was near by, and the distribution of coarse detrital material suggests a source to the northeast (Trechmann, 1924, p. 4).

Strong deformation, stronger than the middle Late Cretaceous deformation, took place in western Cuba in early Eocene time (Palmer, 1934, p. 132, 141); none whatever in southeastern Cuba (Lewis and Straczek). In eastern Jamaica lower Eocene deposits are involved in intense folding (Trechmann, 1924, p. 5; 1929, p. 484; Zans, 1953, p. 3).

MIDDLE AND LATE EOCENE

Carbonate deposits of middle and late Eocene age are widespread in the Greater Antilles and northward (Figure 54.3). Both middle and late Eocene are strongly transgressive, particularly late Eocene. The carbonate deposits are thin in Cuba (Bermúdez, 1950, p. 239–263), moderately thick in Jamaica (Zans, 1953, p. 4), very thick in Hispaniola (Bermúdez, 1949, p. 10–11, 19–21, 32; Butterlin, 1953, p. 285; Woodring, Brown, and Burbank, 1924, p. 99–145*). If represented in Puerto Rico, they are overlapped.

The volcanic islands of the Late Cretaceous (Figure 54.2) have disappeared, with the exception of remnants south of Cuba, where the deep Bartlett Trough is now located. In southeastern Cuba the entire Paleocene and lower and middle Eocene are almost wholly volcanic —pyroclastics and relatively minor flows—representing an estimated thickness of 13,000 feet (Bermúdez, 1950, p. 238–239, 245–246; Lewis and Straczek; Taber, 1934, p. 576–581; Woodring and Daviess, 1944, p. 363–374†). The upper Eocene is mostly detrital (Bermúdez, 1950, p. 251–258; Lewis and Straczek; Taber, 1934, p. 584–585; Woodring and Daviess, 1944, p. 374–375). The Paleocene and Eocene pyroclastics are coarser southward, and flows are more numerous in the same direction, indicating a southward source. In northwestern Haiti pillow basalts are interbedded with limestone of middle or late Eocene age. It is fashionable—or perhaps was fashionable—to name hypothetical lands, despite the frequency with which some of these lands become unfashionable. The hypothetical land south of the Sierra Maestra of Cuba has been casually named Bartlett Land (Keijzer, 1945, p. 13, 86).

The middle Eocene of Jamaica is the Yellow Limestone of British geologists (Trechmann, 1923, p. 337–347). The fresh limestone is dark gray and contains small cubes of pyrite, oxidation of which produces the "yellow" color. Lithologically and faunally similar limestone, the Plaisance limestone, is found in northern Haiti (Woodring, Brown, and Burbank, 1924, p. 99–107). Elsewhere in Haiti middle Eocene limestone is ordinary white limestone, like the overlying upper Eocene limestone. The Cretaceous and Tertiary geology of Jamaica and northern Haiti, not southern Haiti, are similar in other features. This similarity does not support the recent proposition that Jamaica and southern Haiti have been moved 500 miles eastward to their present position along a hypothetical left-lateral fault (Hess and Maxwell, 1953, Fig. 2).

The volcanic foundation of at least the northern part of the outer sedimentary arc of the Lesser Antilles apparently was built during middle Eocene time, presumably from submarine volcanoes that later became volcanic islets, located immediately east of the arc. The French island of St. Bartholomew, near the north end of the sedimentary arc, has a foundation of andesitic pyroclastics, with which limestone of middle Eocene age is interbedded (Christman, 1953, p. 67–73). The volcanics are intruded by quartz diorite. The quartz dio-

* The upper Eocene of this publication has been found, during recent years, to include middle and even lower Eocene.

† The part of the Cobre formation covered by this publication and the Charco Redondo limestone member are now assigned to the middle Eocene, not upper Eocene.

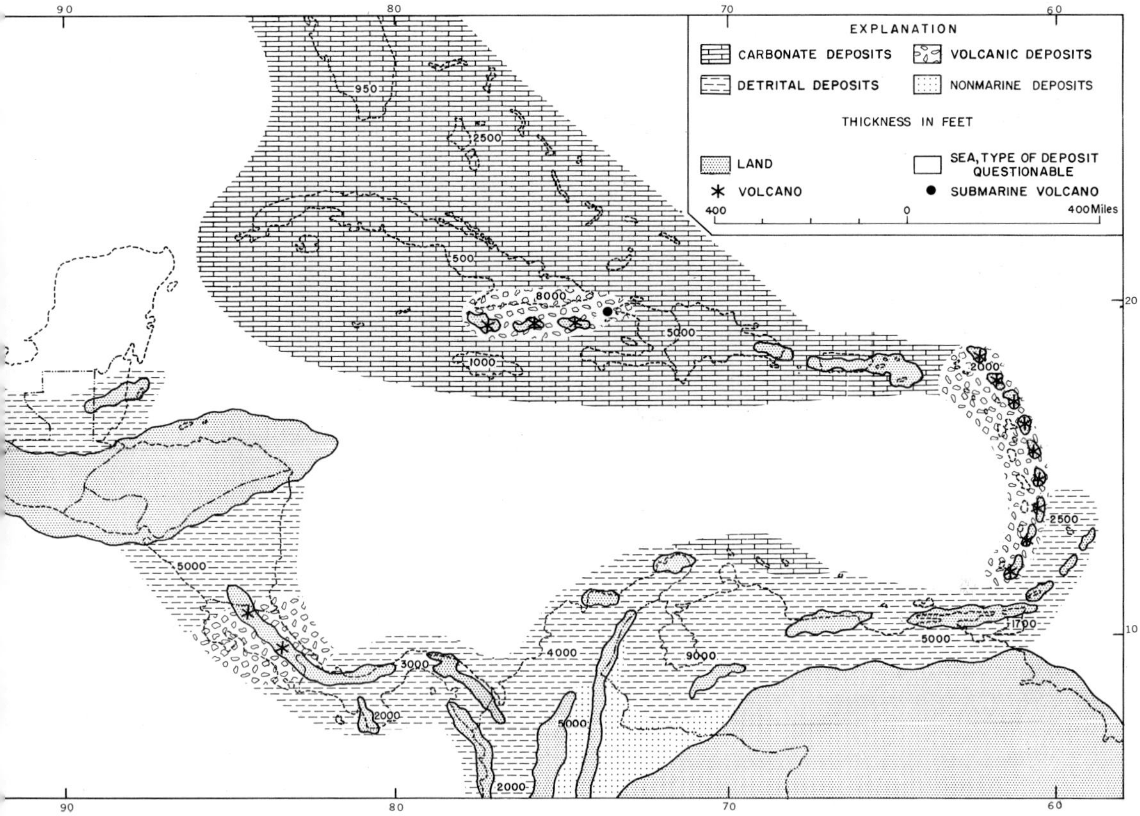

FIGURE 54.3
Caribbean region during Middle and Late Eocene time. Present land indicated by dashed lines.

rite of the Lesser Antilles, heretofore recorded only as blocks in tuffs of middle-Tertiary age in Guadeloupe and Martinique, was formerly thought to indicate an Upper Cretaceous foundation for the sedimentary arc of the Lesser Antilles (Woodring, 1929, p. 416).

The detrital lower and middle Eocene of Barbados thickens southeastward and therefore suggests a source in that direction (Senn, 1940, p. 1557). Metamorphic rocks like the Cretaceous(?) metamorphics of Tobago would be suitable source rocks (Senn, 1940, p. 1561–1562).

EARLY OLIGOCENE

Lower Oligocene is much more restricted in distribution than upper Eocene. Where represented in the Antilles, the lower Oligocene consists of carbonate deposits. They are thin in Cuba (Bermúdez, 1950, p. 264–270) and moderately thick in Hispaniola (Bermúdez, 1949, p. 21–23; Butterlin, 1953, p. 286). Though the White Limestone of Jamaica ranges in age from late Eocene (or possibly middle Eocene) to early Miocene, an early Oligocene part has not yet been faunally defined.

LATE OLIGOCENE AND EARLY MIOCENE

Upper Oligocene and lower Miocene strata are widespread and strongly transgressive. Carbonate deposits are widely distributed (Figure 54.4).

Deformation of varying intensity took place in some areas in the Greater Antilles toward the close of Oligocene time, and in southern Central America toward the close of early Miocene time. The thin early Miocene Güines limestone, the most widespread formation in Cuba (Bermúdez, 1950, p. 293–295; Palmer,

1934, p. 134–135; 1945, p. 17–18), was deposited after this period of deformation. Locally it overlies upper Oligocene marl and limestone without discordance, but it is widely transgressive. The anticlinal fold of the Sierra Maestra of southeastern Cuba, only the north limb of which is now visible, was formed sometime during the Oligocene. By early or middle Miocene time (the dating depending on the age of the La Cruz formation), the anticline was disrupted by faulting. The thin coastal carbonate deposits of the La Cruz formation rest with marked unconformity on Eocene volcanics (Lewis and Straczek; Woodring and Daviess, 1944, p. 381–382). A fault along the southeast coast of Cuba, long advocated, therefore is supported by observable geological evidence. This fault has been interpreted as an extensive left-lateral fault (Hess, 1938, p. 86–87, fig. 6; Bucher, 1947, p. 109–111).

The Cordillera Central of the Dominican Republic and its continuation in Haiti, the Massif du Nord, were deformed, or at least uplifted, at approximately the end of the Oligocene. Along the borders of the newly emerged land the lower Miocene deposits are detrital, in contrast with the Eocene and Oligocene carbonate rocks (Bermúdez, 1949, p. 13–14, 27–29, 33–34; Woodring, Brown, and Burbank, 1924, p. 161–206). Marked discordance between upper Oligocene and lower Miocene, however, is rare. Farther from the newly emerged land the lower Miocene is made up of detrital and carbonate deposits.

Perhaps the foundation of the volcanic inner arc of the Lesser Antilles began to grow from submarine volcanoes in middle Tertiary time.

MIDDLE AND LATE MIOCENE

Hispaniola is the only Antillean island that has thick middle and upper Miocene strata; middle Miocene are more extensive than upper Miocene (Bermúdez, 1949, p. 14–17, 29–31, 35–36; Woodring, Brown, and Burbank, 1924, p. 219–223). Detrital deposits are the prevailing type, but carbonate and evaporite deposits are represented.

With few exceptions, formations younger than early Miocene in Cuba, Jamaica, and Puerto Rico are thin and marginal. Also, with few exceptions, they are mildly deformed or practically undeformed. In fact, the lower Miocene itself, again with few exceptions, is only mildly deformed, and in Puerto Rico no deposits of Tertiary age are strongly deformed.

PLIOCENE

The marine Pliocene deposits of the Caribbean region and its borders are of very limited extent and for the most part are thin. At the present time two divisions can be recognized: lower and upper. The lower Pliocene is represented, for example, by the Cabo Blanco formation of Venezuela, by marine strata near Cumaná, Venezuela, and by the Matura formation of Trinidad; the upper Pliocene by marine coralliferous strata at Limón, Costa Rica. In Haiti the marine deposits referred to the Pliocene (Butterlin, 1953, p. 286; Woodring, Brown, and Burbank, 1924, p. 239–243) may prove to be of late Miocene age, or to include upper Miocene, when the faunas are adequately studied.

The deformation at about the end of the Oligocene and at about the end of the early Miocene heralded stronger deformation that reached a climax during the Pliocene and during the Pleistocene, apparently early in the Pleistocene.

PLEISTOCENE

Thin marine deposits on coastal terraces assigned to the Pleistocene are widely distributed. They may be almost entirely of late Pleistocene age. At the present time, however, there is no satisfactory basis for differentiating early Pleistocene, late Pleistocene, and Recent in the Caribbean region on a faunal basis, despite the availablity of large faunas at numerous localities. Reef corals are as abundant in the deposits referred to the Pleistocene as in the present meager reefs. In areas at the far margin of the Caribbean region, like the Bahamas, or at the far margin of the Antillean faunal province, like Bermuda, restriction of range affords a basis for differentiating Pleistocene from Recent. Restriction of range in Ber-

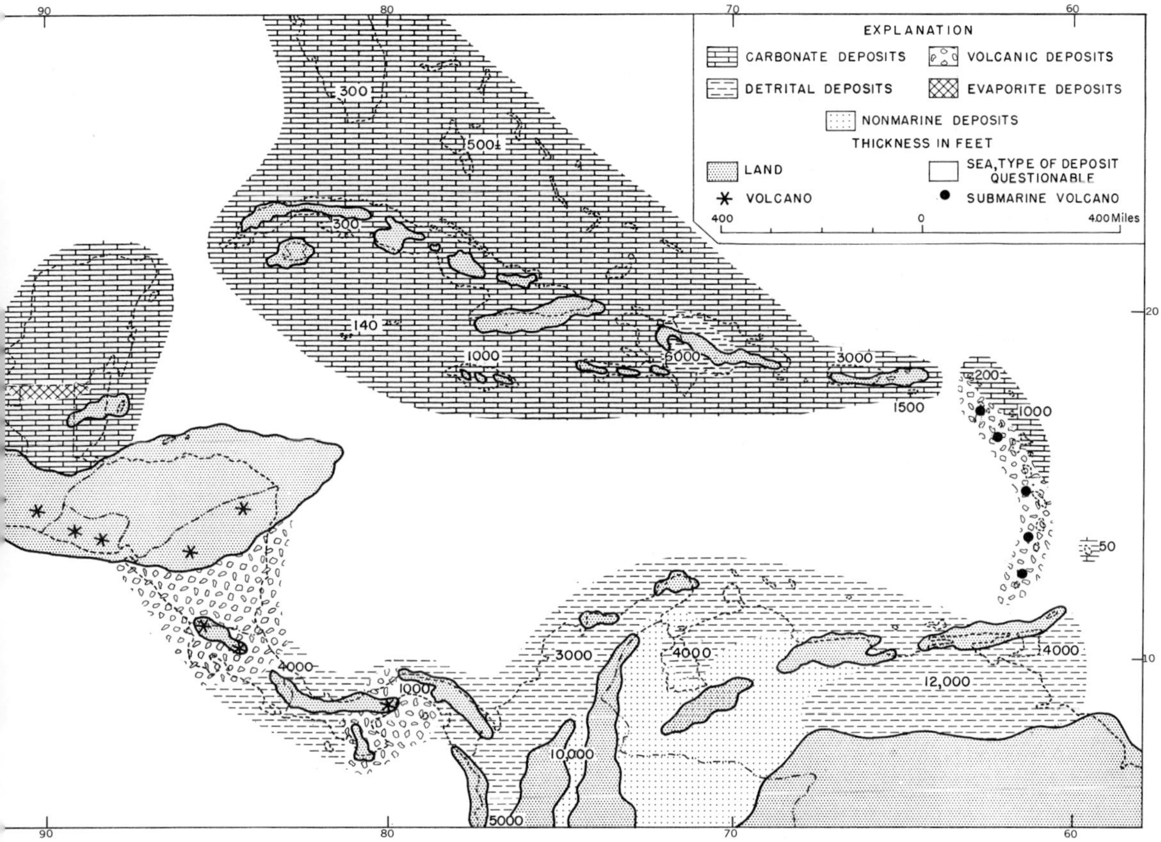

FIGURE 54.4
Caribbean region during Late Oligocene and Early Miocene time. Present land indicated by dashed lines.

muda is illustrated by the Antillean terrestrial hermit crab (*Cenobita diogenes*). Throughout the Antilles the preferred shelter of this hermit crab is the large heavy shell of *Livona pica*. That species of marine snails lived in Bermudan waters during Pleistocene time but is now extinct there. In Bermuda the hermit crab seeks out Pleistocene specimens of *Livona pica* to use as a shelter (Haas, 1950).

According to current age assignments, during Pleistocene time the present island of Hispaniola was divided into two islands by a strait along the Cul de Sac-Lago Enriquillo trough. The practically complete submergence of Cuba, shown by Schuchert (1935, Pl. 16), is without foundation.

Marine deposits assigned to the Pleistocene reach great altitudes in southeastern Cuba (700 feet), northwestern Haiti (1300 feet), and Barbados (1000 feet).

UNRESOLVED PROBLEMS

Much remains to be done in the Caribbean region in an attempt to resolve problems, some of which involve fundamental matters in geology. First of all, detailed mapping is essential, particularly in pre-Tertiary areas, such as has been undertaken recently along the south border (Dengo, 1953; Smith, 1953). For the establishment of a standard Cretaceous sequence, Cuba offers great possibilities. A standard Cretaceous sequence and more data on the Jurassic sequence in Cuba are needed to determine the relations in space and time of the volcanic and plutonic rocks. There appear to be five periods of intrusion of granitic and dioritic rocks, ranging from late Paleozoic to early Miocene, including well-dated late Oligocene-early Miocene quartz diorite in Panamá and quartz diorite of probable Miocene age in

Haiti. Absolute dating of these plutonic rocks would fix an upper limit for the age of the invaded sediments and would furnish data on the age of the metamorphic rocks. Is the apparent eastward spreading of geosynclinal deposition real, or is it an illusion resulting from inadequate dating?

What is the foundation of the Nicaraguan Swell, stretching from northern Nicaragua and southern Honduras to Jamaica? Why are the folds of southern Central America practically at right angles to those of northern Central America? What does the sigmoid curve of Panamá mean? It does not help much to call it an isthmian link and to attribute it to subsidence of the adjoining oceanic basins on both sides. To be sure, it is in fact an isthmian link. But why is it an outrageous isthmian link?

So much of the Caribbean region is under water that close co-operation between geologists and geophysicists is essential. What is the meaning of the anomalous combination of positive gravity anomalies and deep water in the Caribbean Sea and the Gulf of Mexico? The Puerto Rico Deep at the north end of the Vening Meinesz belt of strong negative anomalies has been found by Ewing and Worzel (1954, p. 168–169) to contain very thick unconsolidated sediments. At the south end the belt broadens to coincide with a basin containing 40,000 feet of Cretaceous and Tertiary sediments. In the intervening area, does the belt mark a sialic downbuckle, as postulated for the entire belt by Vening Meinesz and as elaborated by Hess? If the strong negative anomalies are due to great thickness of sediments along the length of the belt, what produced the long deep arcuate trough in which the sediments accumulated?

It is quite evident on ordinary geological grounds that a considerable part of the Caribbean Sea was land during the Cretaceous, and that at least some of this land was still land during the Eocene. How extensive was the land and how long-enduring? Geophysical data may aid in resolving that question.

REFERENCES CITED

Agassiz, Alexander, 1892, General sketch of the expedition of the *Albatross* from February to May, 1891: Mus. Comp. Zoology Harvard Coll. Bull., v. 23, p. 1–89, 22 pls.

Albear, J. F. de, 1947, Stratigraphic paleontology of Camagüey district, Cuba: Am. Assoc. Petroleum Geologists Bull., v. 31, p. 71–91, map.

Applin, P. L., and E. R. Applin, 1944, Regional subsurface stratigraphy and structure of Florida and southern Georgia: Am. Assoc. Petroleum Geologists Bull., v. 28, p. 1673–1753, 5 pls., 38 figs.

Bermúdez, P. J., 1949, Tertiary smaller Foraminifera of the Dominican Republic: Cushman Lab. Foraminiferal Research Spec. Pub. 25, 322 p., 26 pls., 6 figs.

———, 1950, Contribución al estudio del Cenozoico cubano: Soc. Cubana Hist. Nat. Mem., v. 19, no. 3, p. 205–375.

Botero Arango, Gerardo, 1942, Sobre el Ordoviciano de Antioquia: Am. Sci. Cong. 8th Sess. Proc., v. 4, p. 19–25, 2 pls.

Bruyn, J. W. de, 1951, Isogam map of Caribbean Sea and surroundings and of southeast Asia: World Petroleum Cong. 3d Sess. Proc., sec. 1, p. 598–612, 2 maps.

Bucher, W. H., 1947, Problems of earth deformation illustrated by the Caribbean Sea basin: New York Acad. Sci. Trans., ser. 2, v. 9, no. 3, p. 98–116, 1 fig.

Bucher, W. H., 1952, Geologic structure and orogenic history of Venezuela: Geol. Soc. America Mem. 49, 113 p., 5 figs.

Butterlin, Jacques, 1953, Données nouvelles sur la géologie de la République d'Haiti: Soc. Géol. France Bull., ser. 6, v. 3, p. 283–291, 1 fig.

Christman, R., 1953, Geology of St. Bartholomew, St. Martin, and Anguilla, Lesser Antilles: Geol. Soc. America Bull., v. 64, p. 65–96, 4 pls., 4 figs.

Cleve, P. T., 1871, On the geology of the northeastern West India Islands: Kgl. Svenska Vetenskapsakad. Handl., v. 9, no. 12, 48 p., 2 pls., unnumbered figs.

Dengo, Gabriel, 1953, Geology of the Caracas region, Venezuela: Geol. Soc. America Bull., v. 64, p. 7–40, 2 pls., 3 figs.

Eardley, A. J., 1952, Surficial and deep-seated tectonics of the Gulf of Mexico and Caribbean region (Abstract): Geol. Soc. America Bull., v. 63, p. 1361–1362.

Ewing, Maurice, and J. L. Worzel, 1954, Gravity anomalies and structure of the West Indies, pt. 1: Geol. Soc. America Bull., v. 65, p. 165–174, 2 figs.

Flint, D. E., J. F. de Albear, and P. W. Guild, 1948, Geology and chromite deposits of the Camagüey district, Camagüey Province, Cuba: U.S. Geol. Survey Bull. 954, p. 39–63, pls. 18–19, figs. 1–3.

Haas, Fritz, 1950, Hermit crabs in fossil snail shells in Bermuda: Ecology, v. 31, p. 152.

Harrington, H. J., and Marshall Kay, 1951, Cambrian and Ordovician faunas of eastern Colombia: Jour. Paleontology, v. 25, p. 655–668, pls. 96–97.

Hermes, J. J., 1945, Geology and paleontology of

east Camagüey and west Oriente, Cuba: Utrecht Univ. Geog. Geol. Mededeel., Physiog.-Geol. Reeks, ser. 2, no. 7, 75 p., 6 pls., 3 figs.

Hess, H. H., 1938, Gravity anomalies and island arc structure, with particular reference to the West Indies: Am. Philos. Soc. Proc., v. 79, p. 71–96, 2 pls., 6 figs.

Hess, H. H., and Maxwell, J. C., 1953, Caribbean research project: Geol. Soc. America Bull., v. 64, p. 1–6, 2 figs.

Imlay, R. W., 1942, Late Jurassic fossils from Cuba and their economic significance: Geol. Soc. America Bull., v. 53, p. 1417–1478, 12 pls., 4 figs.

———, 1944, Correlation of the Cretaceous formations of the Greater Antilles, Central America, and Mexico: Geol. Soc. America Bull., v. 55, p. 1005–1046, 3 pls., 1 fig.

———, 1952, Correlation of the Jurassic formations of North America, exclusive of Canada: Geol. Soc. America Bull., v. 63, p. 953–992, 4 figs.

Keijzer, F. G., 1945, Outline of the geology of the eastern part of the Province of Oriente, Cuba: Utrecht Univ. Geog. Geol. Mededeel., Physiog.-Geol. Reeks, ser. 2, no. 6, 239 p., 12 pls., 34 figs.

Koschmann, A. H., and Mackenzie Gordon, Jr., 1950 [1951], Geology and mineral resources of the Maimón-Hatillo district, Dominican Republic: U.S. Geol. Survey Bull. 964, p. 307–359, pls. 18–19.

Leith, E., 1938, A Middle Ordovician fauna from the Venezuelan Andes: Am. Jour. Sci., ser. 5, v. 36, p. 337–344, 9 figs.

Lewis, G. E., and J. A. Straczek, 1955, Geology of south-central Oriente, Cuba: U.S. Geol. Survey Bull. 975D, p. v, 171–366.

MacGillavry, H. J., 1937, Geology of the province of Camagüey, Cuba, with revisional studies in rudist paleontology: Utrecht Univ. Geog. Geol. Mededeel., Physiog.-Geol. Reeks, no. 14, 169 p., 10 pls., 1 fig.

Matley, C. A., 1929, The basal complex of Jamaica, with special reference to the Kingston district; with petrographical notes by Frank Higham: Geol. Soc. London Quart. Jour., v. 85, p. 440–492, pls. 23–25, 5 figs.

———, 1951, Geology and physiography of the Kingston district, Jamaica: Jamaica Geol. Survey Pub. 2, 141 p., 20 pls., 14 figs.

Maync, Wolf, 1949, The foraminiferal genus *Choffatella* Schlumberger in the Lower Cretaceous of the Caribbean region (Venezuela, Cuba, Mexico, and Florida): Eclogae Geol. Helvetiae, v. 42, p. 529–547, pls. 11–12, 1 fig.

Molengraaff, G. J. H., 1929, Geologie en geohydrologie van het eiland Curaçao: 126 p., 28 pls., maps.

Page, L. R., and J. F. McAllister, 1944, Tungsten deposits, Isla de Pinos, Cuba: U.S. Geol. Survey Bull. 935, p. 177–246, pls. 32–43.

Palmer, R. H., 1934, The geology of Habana, Cuba, and vicinity: Jour. Geology, v. 42, p. 123–145, 6 figs.

———, 1945, Outline of the geology of Cuba: Jour. Geology, v. 53, p. 1–34, 6 figs.

Pijpers, P. J., 1933, Geology and paleontology of Bonaire (D. W. I.): Utrecht Univ. Geog. Geol. Mededeel., Physiog.-Geol. Reeks, no. 8, 103 p., 2 pls., 155 figs., map.

Roberts, R. J., and E. M. Irving, 1957, Mineral deposits of Central America, with a section on manganese deposits of Panamá: U.S. Geol. Survey Bull. 1034, x and 205 p.

Rutten, L. M. R., 1934, Geology of Isla de Pinos, Cuba: Koninkl. Nederlandse Akad. Wetensch. Proc., ser. B, v. 37, p. 401–406, 1 fig.

———, 1940, On the age of the serpentines in Cuba: Koninkl. Nederlandse Akad. Wetensch. Proc., ser. B, v. 43, p. 542–547, 1 fig.

Rutten, M. G., 1936, Geology of the northern part of the Province Santa Clara [Las Villas], Cuba: Utrecht Univ. Geog. Geol. Mededeel., Physiog.-Geol. Reeks, no. 11, 59 p., 3 pls., 12 figs.

Sapper, Karl, 1937, Mittelamerika: Handbuch der regionalen Geologie, v. 8, pt. 4a, no. 29, 160 p., 10 pls., 15 figs.

Schuchert, Charles, 1935, Historical geology of the Antillean-Caribbean region: New York, John Wiley and Sons, 811 p., 16 pls., 107 figs.

Senn, Alfred, 1940, The Paleogene of Barbados and its bearing on history and structure of Antillean-Caribbean region: Am. Assoc. Petroleum Geologists Bull., v. 24, p. 1548–1610, 4 figs.

Smith, R. J., 1953, Geology of the Los Teques–Cua region, Venezuela: Geol. Soc. America Bull., v. 64, p. 41–64, 3 pls., 3 figs.

Sutter, H. H., 1951–52, The general and economic geology of Trinidad, B. W. I.: Colonial Geol. and Mineral Resources, v. 2, no. 3, p. 177–217, pl. 1, figs. 1–2, 1951; v. 2, no. 4, p. 271–307, pls. 2–5, figs. 3–11, 1951; v. 3, no. 1, p. 3–51, pl. 6, figs. 12–15, 1952.

Taber, Stephen, 1934, Sierra Maestra of Cuba, part of the northern rim of the Bartlett Trough: Geol. Soc. America Bull., v. 45, p. 567–619, pls. 57–85, 4 figs.

Thiadens, A. A., 1937, Geology of the southern part of the Province Santa Clara [Las Villas], Cuba: Utrecht Univ. Geog. Geol. Mededeel., Physiog.-Geol. Reeks, no. 12, 69 p., 4 pls.

Trechmann, C. T., 1923, The Yellow Limestone of Jamaica and its Mollusca: Geol. Mag. [Great Britain], v. 60, p. 337–367, pls. 14–18.

———, 1924, The Carbonaceous Shale or Richmond formation of Jamaica: Geol. Mag. [Great Britain], v. 61, p. 2–19, pls. 1, 2.

———, 1929, Fossils from the Blue Mountains of Jamaica: Geol. Mag. [Great Britain], v. 66, p. 481–491, pl. 18, 1 fig.

Trumpy, D., 1943, Pre-Cretaceous of Colombia: Geol. Soc. America Bull., v. 54, p. 1281–1304, 1 pl., 6 figs.

van Wessem, Aart, 1943, Geology and paleontology of central Camagüey, Cuba: Utrecht Univ. Geog. Geol. Mededeel., Physiog.-Geol. Reeks, ser. 2, no. 5, 9 p., 4 pls., 3 figs.

Vermunt, L. W. J., 1937, Geology of the Province of Pinar del Rio, Cuba: Utrecht Univ. Geog. Geol. Mededeel., Physiog.-Geol. Reeks, no. 13, 60 p., 3 pls.

Vletter, D. R. de, 1946, Geology of the western part of middle Oriente, Cuba: Utrecht Univ. Geog. Geol. Mededeel., Physiog.-Geol. Reeks, ser. 2, no. 8, 101 p., 4 pls., 2 figs.

Westermann, J. H., 1932, The geology of Aruba: Utrecht Univ. Geog. Geol. Mededeel., Physiog.-Geol. Reeks, no. 7, 129 p., 3 pls., 24 figs., map.

Weyl, Richard, 1940, Bau und Geschichte der Cordillera Central von Santo Domingo: Deutsch-Dominikanischen Tropenforschungsinst Hamburg Veröffentlichungen, v. 2, 60 p., 9 pls., 2 maps, 12 figs.

Woodring, W. P., 1929, Tectonic features of the Caribbean region: Pan-Pacific Sci. Cong. 3d Sess. [1926] Proc., v. 1, p. 401–431, map.

Woodring, W. P., and S. N. Daviess, 1944, Geology and manganese deposits of Guisa–Los Negros area, Oriente Province, Cuba: U.S. Geol. Survey Bull. 935-G, p. 357–386, pls. 68–77, figs. 19–20.

Woodring, W. P., and T. F. Thompson, 1949, Tertiary formations of Panama Canal Zone and adjoining parts of Panama: Am. Assoc. Petroleum Geologists Bull., v. 33, p. 223–247, 2 figs.

Woodring, W. P., J. S. Brown, and W. S. Burbank, 1924, Geology of the Republic of Haiti: Port-au-Prince, Haiti Geol. Survey, 631 p., 40 pls., 37 figs. (French ed., 1924).

Zans, V. A., 1953, Geology and mineral deposits of Jamaica: Kingston, Jamaica Geol. Survey Dept., 8 p., map.

ADDITIONAL PUBLICATIONS USED IN COMPILING MAPS BUT NOT CITED IN TEXT

Brodermann, Jorge, J. F. de Albear, and A. Andreu, 1946, Croquis geológico de Cuba: Cuba Inst. Nac. Hidrología y Climatología Medicas, Sec. Geología (scale 1–1,000,000).

Bucher, W. H., 1950, Geologic-tectonic map of the United States of Venezuela: Geol. Soc. America (scale 1–1,000,000).

Cederstrom, D. J., 1950, Geology and ground-water resources of St. Croix, Virgin Islands: U.S. Geol. Survey Water-Supply Paper 1067, 117 p., 6 pls., 11 figs.

Earle, K. W., 1923, Report on the geology of Antigua: St. Johns, Antigua, Government Printing Office, 28 p.

Hedberg, H. D., 1950, Geology of the eastern Venezuelan basin (Anzoategui–Monagas–Sucre–eastern Guarico portion: Geol. Soc. America Bull., v. 61, p. 1173–1215, 11 pls., 6 figs.

Imlay, R. W., 1944, Cretaceous formations of Central America and Mexico: Am. Assoc. Petroleum Geologists Bull., v. 28, p. 1077–1195, 16 figs.

Matley, C. A., 1926, The geology of the Cayman Islands (British West Indies): Geol. Soc. London Quart. Jour., v. 82, p. 352–387, 13 figs.

Mencher, E., H. J. Fichter, H. H. Renz, W. E. Wallis, H. H. Renz, J. M. Patterson, and R. H. Robie, 1953, Geology of Venezuela and its oil fields: Am. Assoc. Petroleum Geologists Bull., v. 37, p. 690–777, 39 figs.

Müllerried, F. G. K., 1944, El mapa geológico de la América Central: Inst. Panam. Geog. Hist. Rev. Geog., v. 4, nos. 10–12, p. 36–64, map (scale 1–5,000,000).

Nygren, W. E., 1950, Bolivar geosyncline of northwestern South America: Am. Assoc. Petroleum Geologists Bull., v. 34, p. 1998–2006, 3 figs.

Olsson, A. A., 1942, Tertiary deposits of northwestern South America and Panamá, Am. Sci. Cong. 8th Sess. Proc., v. 4, p. 231–287.

Pilsbry, H. A., and A. A. Olsson, 1935, Tertiary fresh-water mollusks of the Magdalene embayment, Colombia, Acad. Nat. Sci. Philadelphia Proc., v. 87, p. 7–39, pls. 2–5, 1 fig.

Sutton, F. A., 1946, Geology of Maracaibo basin, Venezuela: Am. Assoc. Petroleum Geologists Bull., v. 30, p. 1621–1741, 9 pls., 11 figs.

Wegemann, C. H., 1931, Geology of southern Nicaragua (Abstract): Geol. Soc. America Bull., v. 42, p. 194.

Zapp, A. D., H. R. Bergquist, and C. R. Thomas, 1948, Tertiary Geology of the coastal plains of Puerto Rico: U.S. Geol. Survey Oil and Gas Inv. (Prelim.) Map 85, 2 sheets, maps, text.

55

Switzerland and the Prealps

E. B. BAILEY
1935

From *Tectonic Essays* by E. B. Bailey, pp. 30–35, 57–72. The Clarendon Press, 1935. Reprinted with permission of The Clarendon Press, Oxford.

SWITZERLAND

Switzerland, as all the world knows, is divided into three parts: the Jura Mountains in the north, the Swiss Plain in the middle, and the Alps in the south.

The Juras are but a half-extended wing of the Alps, and articulate lightly with the main body a little south-west of Geneva. They consist for the most part of a succession of closely compressed steep folds, very beautifully displayed in the scenery. The Jura folds often break, with a development of thrusts, some of which are quite important; but a succession of steep compressed folds remains the outstanding superficial character of the district, and is taken as constituting the *Jura type* of structure. It is doubtful whether this type is ever developed, in the Juras or elsewhere, without a considerable amount of thrusting of the chain as a whole over a relatively unmoved basement. The amount of sub-chain thrusting varies greatly in different occurrences. Thus, in the Alps, the Jura type of folding is conspicuous in the Prealps, south of Lake Geneva, where there has been immense thrusting, most of it of rather earlier date than the folding. Similar, though less extreme, conditions prevail in the Säntis, west of the Rhine, south of Lake Constance. In the Ardennes of Belgium the Jura type of folding is once more found in connexion with sub-chain thrusting, but here much of the thrust movement is of later date than the folding. In the Juras themselves sub-chain thrusting is pictured as entirely contemporaneous with folding, and as increasing from zero at the north-west front of the chain to a fairly large measure along the inner margin of the arc. Comparable additive movement has probably occurred in the Southern Uplands of Scotland and in parts of the Appalachians.

The stratigraphical name, Jura Formation, or Jurassic as we now commonly say, was early introduced by Alexander von Humboldt. It is singularly appropriate, for the main rocks of the Jura Mountains are Jurassic limestones, marls, &c., which range up to 1,500 m. in thickness. Less than 400 m. of Cretaceous, along with some Oligocene and Miocene, appear in synclines, while Trias shows through in anticlines. The compacted pre-Triassic complexes, exposed in the Black Forest, Vosges, and Central Plateau, must continue under the Jura folds relatively unbent, for they are never brought to the surface. In fact, even the lower half of the Trias seems to have escaped the folding.

In the theoretical interpretation of the Juras we may note three main stages. Two are well represented in the writings of Thurmann, who devoted his life to a study of these mountains . . . in 1830 and 1836 he ascribes the parallel arches to independent vertical uplifts; while in a report published in 1857, shortly after his death, he discards this notion and folds the Juras by lateral push acting from the Swiss side. H. D. Rogers, of Appalachian fame, had already, in 1849, moved the Juras laterally, but in the opposite direction, towards the Alps. The meaning of these descriptions, and their differences, will be discussed in the next paragraph. Here we pass on to Buxtorf's great contribution to the subject, in which he supplements natural sections with underground information supplied by tunnels, &c. Since 1907 he has argued that the folded rocks of the chain have parted company with the unfolded foundation along a thick plastic clay of Middle Triassic age, the Anhydrite Group of the Muschelkalk. This group has served as a lubricating medium and has permitted of northward overhead movement of the folding thrust-mass. Buxtorf's section (Figure 55.1) conveys his meaning at a glance. It may be pointed out in this connexion that the lubricating virtue of the Trias was fully realized by Schardt in his descriptions of the Prealpine thrusts dating from 1893 and earlier. In fact, it is now clear that the Trias often plays a part in Swiss tectonics equivalent to that of the Gault, or 'Blue Slipper,' in landslip phenomena of southern England.

We now return to the question of what is meant, in tectonics, by saying that the movement illustrated in Figure 55.1 has come from the south, that is, from the direction of the Alps. This figure shows the upper layers, those that constitute the folded Jura Mountains, as having travelled northwards *relatively* to their Black Forest (Schwarzwald) foundation, or, in other words, it shows the foundation as having travelled southwards *relatively* to its folded cover. It was open to the founders of tectonics to speak of this relative motion either as northward, if they thought of the surface, or southward, if they thought of the depths. As man lives on the surface, it is natural that he should take the former alternative; and accordingly almost all tectonists speak of *northward movement* when they mean *northward relative movement of more superficial layers*. Occasionally a tectonist adopts the other alternative; but he runs the same risk of confusing his readers that a physicist would who interchanged the names positive and negative in regard to electricity.

Thurmann and Rogers were both agreed as to what they meant by northward or southward movement. How then did Thurmann interpret the Juras as having moved northwards, after Rogers had expressed exactly the opposite view? The reader must understand that most of Buxtorf's section, Figure 55.1, depicts what is buried out of sight. The direction of movement has had to be deduced from those portions that are visible. In the close steep folds of the Juras there is often very little asymmetry, and that asymmetry is not always of the same sort. If all the Jura anticlines were overthrown towards the north, Rogers would have come to the conclusion that the movement had been northward. As it is, however, he based on exposures such as those illustrated at Moutier and Graitery in Figure 55.1 and deduced southward movement with a heaping up of folds at the edge of the great Swiss Plain. It was left to Thurmann, who lived among the Jura Mountains, instead of merely walking across them, to perceive the general indication of overfolding towards the north, which had escaped his American contemporary. Later research, more particularly as it has been concerned with the development of thrusts (cf. Grenchenberg, Fig. 8, and Dottenberg, Fig. 9), has abundantly confirmed Thurmann in a field of inquiry by no means destitute of difficulty.

The Swiss Plain is floored by a huge thickness of marine and fresh-water deposits of Middle Tertiary date—Miocene, with Upper and Middle Oligocene. To this great assem-

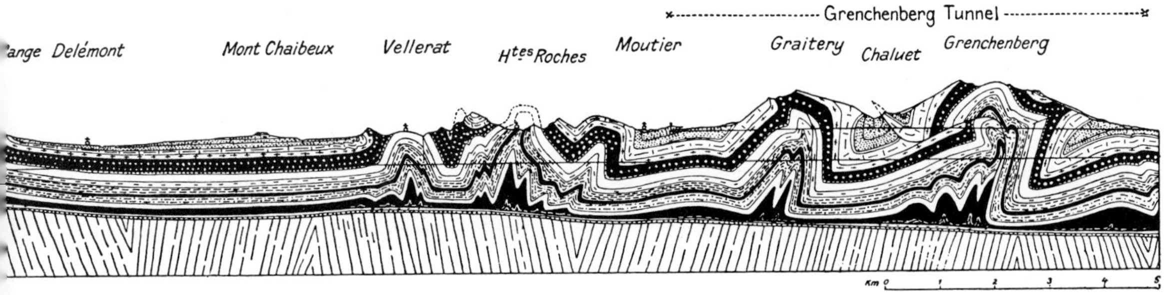

FIGURE 55.1
Section showing *décollement* (ungluing) of the folded Jura. [After Buxtorf, 1916 (see Collet, 1927).]

blage the term *Molasse* is now applied. To begin with, Molasse was a dialect name for *soft* sandstone; but Studer, in 1853, expanded its meaning to include all the sandstones, conglomerates, coals, and limestones, of the Swiss Plain. Molasse conglomerates figure very prominently in the sub-Alpine belt, and also to some extent along the foot of the Juras. Here again a local term has found its way into the literature. The conglomerates of the molasse are called *Nagelfluh*, because conglomerate exposures often look as though studded with the round heads of giant *nails*.

The Molasse, in the main, is disposed in a gentle flat syncline, which in its setting between the Juras and the Alps acquires a special tectonic interest. The lubricated sub-Jura thrust, that Buxtorf has introduced to notice, increases in displacement from north to south. It is at its maximum where it passes below the relatively unfolded Swiss Plain. It seems necessary, therefore, to consider the Molasse of this plain as forming part of a thick thrust-mass, or nappe,* the taper edge of which has buckled to produce the Jura Mountains.

Another tectonic interest of the Molasse is the derivation of most of its material, conglomerates, sandstones, &c., from the Alps, although these latter marginally overfold and overthrust it. The same sort of story can be made out for the early Tertiaries, now wholly incorporated in the Alps. We are beginning to learn more and more of the Alpine chain, not only as it stands today, but also as it pushed its way forward over its own frontal detritus.

On entering the Alps the observer at once encounters manifest complications of folding and thrusting. The sorting out of these phenomena went slowly until 1893, but since then has proceeded at an amazing pace. It has been found necessary to group the nappes into systems according to superposition. The main structural divisions adopted by Staub in his 1924 memoir, *Der Bau der Alpen*, are as follows in descending order:

Austrides appearing from beneath Suess's Dinarides.
Pennides.
Helvetian { Helvetides.
Helvetian { Parautochthon and Autochthon.

Figure 55.2 sufficiently explains the outcrops of these zones. A few words may be added regarding the derivation and meaning of the various names employed.

Helvetian (Suess) and *Helvetides* are derived from the Latin *Helvetia*, meaning Switzerland. The adjective *Helvetian* is naturally applied to rocks which, occurring in Switzerland, can be shown on close examination to have travelled comparatively little from their place of sedimentation. The same term is also quite properly extended beyond Switzerland into the French and Austrian portions of the Alps, and carries with it the notion of comparatively small displacement.

* The French word *nappe* means *sheet* and is familiar in this sense to non-technical readers in its diminutive *napkin*. In tectonics a *nappe* is a sheet of rock brought forward over *relatively* unmoved rock by recumbent folding or thrusting. Most named nappes lie on thrust-planes, so that the term *nappe* is generally translatable by *thrust-mass*.

Autochthon (Lugeon) is derived from two Greek words meaning the *land itself*. Autochthonous is an adjective commonly applied in ethnology with the significance indigenous or aboriginal. In tectonics, an *autochthonous fold* is one that is made of *untravelled indigenous rocks*, the rocks, that is, of the *country itself*. In *parautochthonous* folds and thrust-masses (Arnold Heim) the travel of the rocks has been considerable or great, according to ordinary standards, but small in the Alpine scale of magnitudes. The separation of structural systems is just as arbitrary as that of stratigraphical systems.

The *Helvetides* are a group of nappes overlying the Parautochthon and underlying the Pennides. Their travel is great, but the stratigraphical characters of their rocks have still much in common with that of the underlying portions of the Helvetian assemblage. They are approximately equivalent to the Lower and Upper Glarus Nappe-groups. The farthest-travelled Helvetides are called *Ultrahelvetides*.

The *Pennides*, above the Helvetides, take their name from the well-known *Pennine Alps* that include the Matterhorn (Mt. Cervin), south-east of the Rhone. The Pennine Alps are continued north-eastwards across the Simplon Pass by the *Lepontine Alps*. Steinmann and Suess's Lepontine Nappes, however, include higher elements than Argand's *Pennine Nappes* (Staub's *Pennides*).

Austrides is based, presumably, upon the term *austro-alpin* or South Alpine, that one finds in Schardt's tectonic writings; but it is explained by Staub as an abbreviation for *Ostalpinendecken*, or East Alpine Nappes. No confusion arises from this ambiguous derivation, for, standing on the Austride outlier that constitutes the Prealps, one naturally thinks of the *southern* origin of the mass and *also* of the great *eastern* spread of continuous Austride outcrops beyond the Rhine (in the Austria of the Romans and ourselves). . . .

PREALPS

The Prealps, or more fully *les Préalpes romandes*, are shared by France and Switzerland. In France they lie entirely on the north-east side of the river Arve and overlook Lake Geneva from the south. On reaching Switzerland they cross the Rhone and continue to Lake Thun—there to cease. The north-western front of the Prealps runs more or less along the thousand-metre contour, while their south-eastern boundary is marked externally by a line of snow-clad summits, mostly over 3,000 m. in height (Figure 55.4). The names of these giant sentinels disposed outside the line from west to east are all familiar—Mt. Buet, the Tour Salières, Dent du Midi, Dent de Morcles, Grand Muveran, Diablerets, Wildhorn, and Wildstrubel. The tops of the Prealps themselves often reach well above 2,000 m.

In keeping with their title, the Prealps jut out somewhat beyond the general frontier of the Alpine chain. Contours do small justice to this advance; it is much more evident in the scenery and materials of the district: as may be gathered from any general geological map of Switzerland, the Prealpine outcrops of Mesozoic and early Tertiary formations project conspicuously north-westwards among the comparatively late subalpine Tertiaries of the great Swiss Plain. A closer scrutiny of the evidence emphasizes the anomaly of the situation. The Mesozoic crags of the Prealps are not mere deflected continuations of those met with in the Helvetian High Limestone Alps on either side: Triassic and Jurassic rocks are very widely displayed in the Prealps, whereas in the neighbouring Helvetian Alps these formations are restricted to a complicated outcrop which passes unconcerned behind the Prealps through the south-eastern slopes of the snow-capped mountains already enumerated. The Triassic and Jurassic rocks of the Helvetian Alps are everywhere separated by Cretaceous and Tertiary outcrops from anything of the same age in the Prealps.

Moreover, though Triassic, Jurassic, Cretaceous, and Tertiary rocks are firmly established by fossil evidence in the Prealps, each system is distinguished by its character, or facies, from its counterpart in the adjoining Helvetian Alps. The differences affect the thickness as well as the nature of the formations, and in one particular are recognizable even on small-scale geological maps: the Cretaceous of the Prealps is often extremely thin, whereas in the adjacent Helvetian Alps it is of mountainous proportions (Figure 55.3).

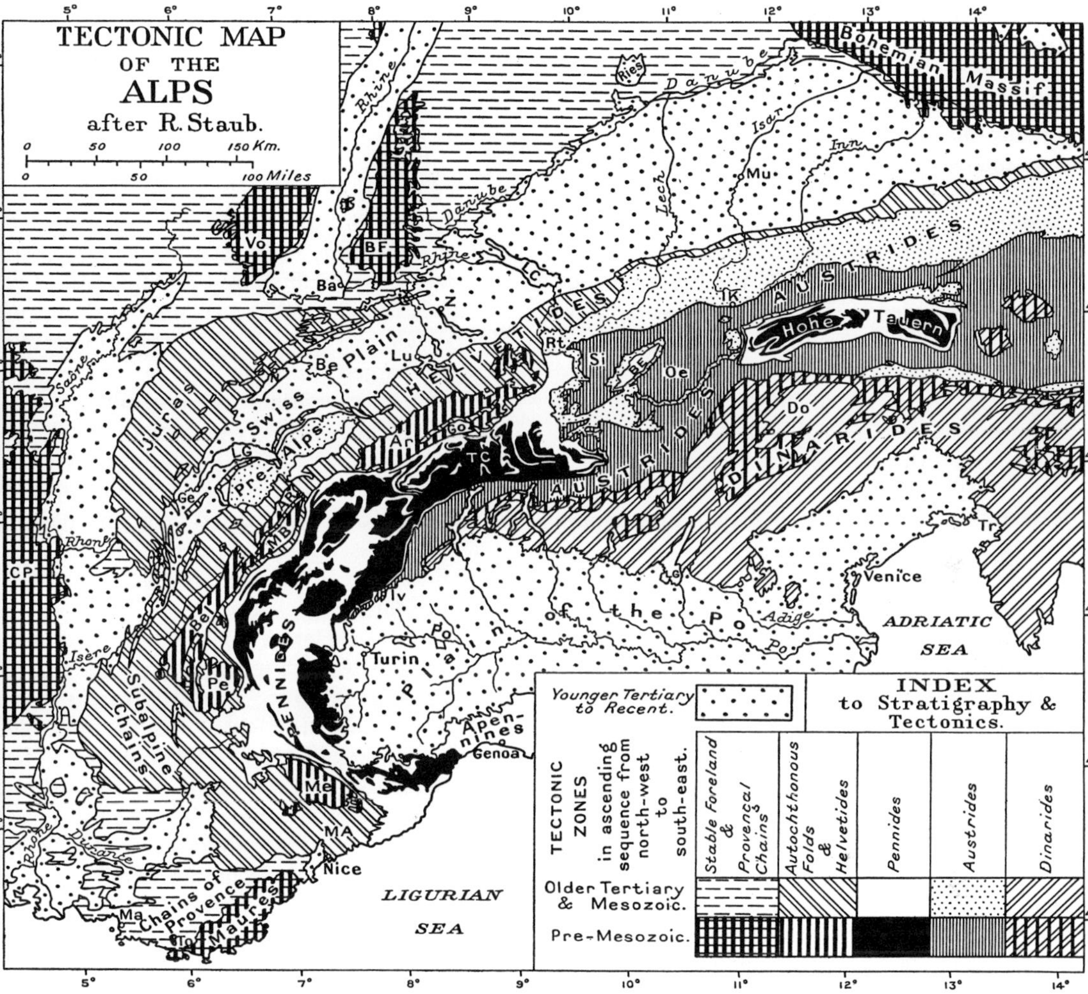

FIGURE 55.2
Tectonic map of the alps. (After R. Staub.) *Ar*, Aar massif; *AR*, Aiguilles Rouges; *Ba*, Basle; *Be*, Berne; *Bel*, Belladonna; *BE*, Basse Engadine; *BF*, Black Forest; *CP*, Central Plateau of France; *Do*, Dolomites; *Ge*, Geneva; *Go*, St. Gothard massif; *Ik*, Innsbruck; *Iv*, Ivrea; *LC*, Lake Constance; *LG*, Lake Geneva (in west), Lake Garda (in east); *Lu*, Lucerne; *Ma*, Marseilles; *MA*, Maritime Alps; *MB*, Mt. Blanc; *Me*, Mercantour; *Mu*, Munich; *Oe*, Oetzthal; *Pe*, Pelvoux; *Rt*, Rhaeticon; *Si*, Silvretta; *Tc*, Ticino; *To*, Toulon; *Tr*, Trieste; *Vo*, Vosges; Z, Zürich.

All the points that have been emphasized up to the present were more or less recognized by Studer as early as 1834; and, in 1880, they led Renevier to introduce the name *Préalpes romandes*. Still, there were few in the 80's who paid any attention to this little group of mountains. It presented stratigraphical and structural complications more bewildering perhaps than were common even in the Alps; but experience had taught Alpine geologists to endure such difficulties. They groped their way, allotting rocks to their formations, making maps, and recording dips. The time for distant views seemed to have passed; as a matter of fact the twilight was of dawn. Suddenly, in 1893, Hans Schardt found himself standing in the full sunlight, a sunlight that penetrated to the foundations of the Prealps and illuminated their past history as well as their present position.

There before him stretched the Prealps, a complex of all the post-Palaeozoic formations, entirely underlain by the local Tertiary; an immigrant countryside fashioned of alien rocks that bespeak a southern origin; an erratic, as truly as any of the great blocks of Mt. Blanc granite that lie upon the flanks of the Juras—but an erratic 120 km. long and 40 broad!

Fortunately the revelation came to one who had struggled on for fourteen years in the semi-darkness of the times. Schardt was able to appreciate at once not only the broad outline of the phenomenon, but also the co-ordination of its detail. The Prealps are a composite erratic formed of a succession of superimposed nappes, each one of which has travelled farther than its underlying neighbour and has brought with it its own particular stratigraphical facies. When Schardt first wrote on the subject he was able to point out that the various nappes of the Prealps, considered from below upwards, must have come from sources ever farther to the south. According to later research, which will be considered in subsequent chapters, the superimposed nappes of the Prealps furnish an epitome of all the major tectonic zones of the Alps—in Staub's nomenclature they rest upon the Autochthon, Parautochthon, and Helvetides, and are themselves referable to the Ultrahelvetides, Pennides, and Austrides.

Another point that Schardt realized in this great moment was that the Prealps, extensive as they seem, are but a relic left by erosion. They occupy a huge depression, under which the Mesozoic rocks of the Helvetian High Limestone Alps pass below sea-level. On either side of this depression, both on the south-west and north-east, stand the mysterious klippes, in the heart of comparatively restricted Tertiary synclines. The German word *Klippe* means a cliff, and was early applied by Austrian geologists to certain abrupt crags, distributed along the grassy northern front of the Carpathians and interpreted as islands of older rocks emerging from beneath later deposits. In Switzerland the klippes most talked about in geological literature number about a dozen, and include Mt. Sullens, 35 km. south-west of the Prealps, and the Mythen with its fellows, 90 km. north-east of the same. Of all the klippes the Mythen is the best known, since it rises abruptly from grassy slopes that overlook a bend of Lake Lucerne and is a landmark familiar to numberless tourists. In these klippes, Triassic, Jurassic, and Cretaceous rocks present the facies characteristic of one particular nappe of the Prealp assemblage. Together with it they form parts of an obvious entity, the continuity of which has been destroyed by erosion. Now, in front of the line of klippes, from Lake Thun to Lake Lucerne, and beyond that to the Rhine, lie immense conglomerates, the so-called nagelfluh of the Molasse. They are of Miocene and, to a small extent, of Upper Oligocene age. These conglomerates were discharged from the Alps by ancient rivers, and they contain a surprisingly large amount of water-worn material of what we may term Klippe facies. Their origin ceases to be enigmatical once the klippes are understood as remnants of a widespread overlying nappe, and not as essentially local phenomena, such as islands, horsts, or broken domes.

The conglomerates of which we have spoken belong to a late stage in the history of the emplacement of the Prealps. Nevertheless they pass for some distance beneath these mountains; in fact, near the Rhone, certain grits and red planty marls of Upper Oligocene age—the Red Molasse—actually underlie the whole breadth of the erratic chain. The Red Molasse is the oldest of the Tertiaries of the Swiss Plain exposed anywhere in the vicinity of the Prealps. Prior to its deposition there is a distinct gap in the local stratigraphy, for the Middle Oligocene appears to be represented merely by erosion. On the other hand, marine marls, shales, and sandstones, referable to the Lower Oligocene (and perhaps Eocene), and collectively styled Flysch, play a very important rôle in the Prealp complex and also in the Helvetian folds, among and upon which this complex partly lies. The Flysch, like the Molasse, formed in front of the Alps, but in course of time its basin of deposition has been almost completely incorporated or overwhelmed by the advancing chain. In the comparatively untravelled Flysch there is little or nothing to correspond with the nagelfluh of the Molasse; but in the lower nappes of the Prealps, which consist largely of Flysch detached from the sea bottom and dragged forward wholesale by the upper nappes, there is abundant debris of Mesozoic rocks, which Schardt claims as of Prealpine (meaning

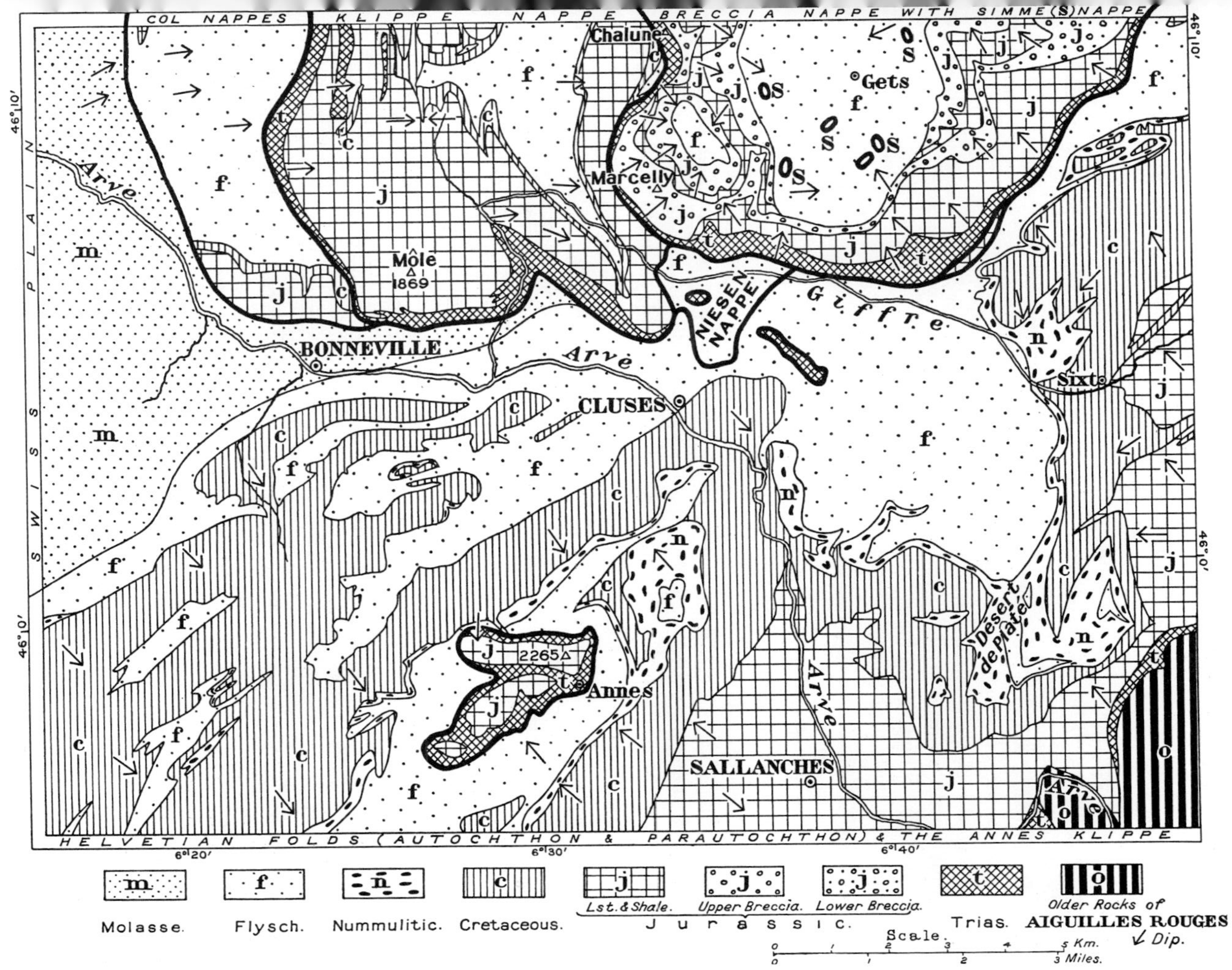

FIGURE 55.3
Map of southern border of the Prealps

Klippe) type. The debris in this case is generally more angular than the comparable material enclosed in the nagelfluh. Schardt pictures it as scree and landslip reaching down from the frontal cliff of the advancing nappe to be washed over by more normal marine sediment and eventually to be buried deeply beneath its parent mountain.

Those readers who are already conversant with Alpine geology may well be astonished to find the *sedimentary* pebbles and boulders, contained in the Molasse and Flysch, singled out for attention in the two preceding paragraphs. As a matter of history, interest was first aroused by numerous crystalline erratics, consisting of granite, &c., which accompany the sedimentary debris in both formations. Studer discussed these crystalline rocks as early as 1825, while it was not until 1863 that Bachmann raised the problem of the sedimentary *remanié* by disclosing its Prealpine facies in many unexpected situations. Schardt's explanation, which may perhaps require a little modification, has the great merit of embracing both phenomena; but it is easier to deal with the sedimentary boulders in a general statement, such as has been attempted up to the present, and to reserve the treatment of their crystalline companions until the constitution of the Prealps has been set out in a little more detail.

As a first step we shall enumerate the main nappes of the complex from above downwards (Figure 55.5):

Name	*Class*
Simme Nappe	Austrides
Breccia Nappe	Austrides
Klippe Nappe	Austrides
Niesen Nappe	Pennides
Col Nappes	Pennides and Ultrahelvetides

A few words are required regarding these names.

The Simme Nappe was rechristened by Heim after the river Simme that drains into Lake Thun. It is only preserved in patches and was first identified as a unit of the Prealp

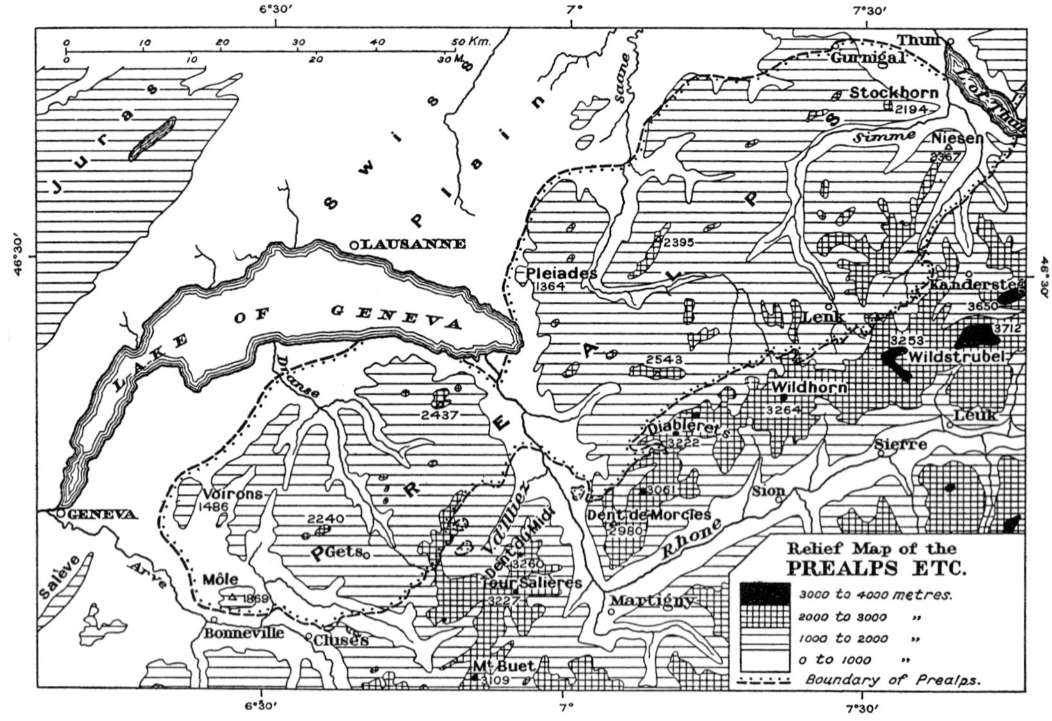

FIGURE 55.4
Relief map of Prealps

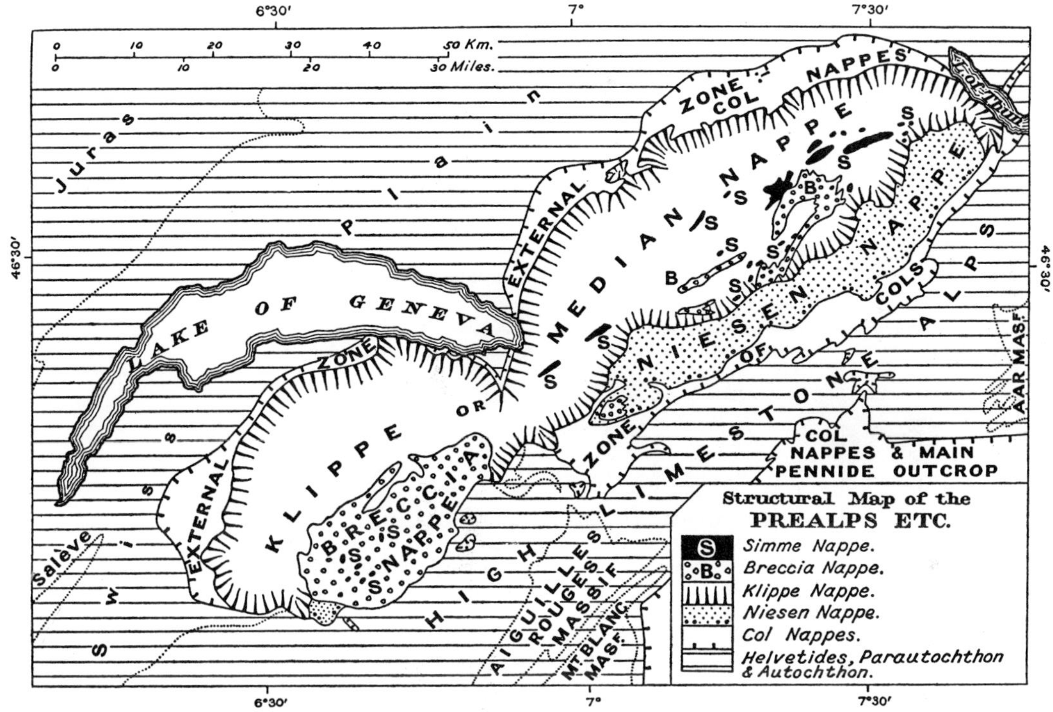

FIGURE 55.5
Structural map of the Prealps

complex by Steinmann in 1905 (publication 1906). Steinmann called it the Rhaetic Nappe; but so much confusion has attended the application of this title in other parts of the Alps that it has more or less disappeared from the tectonic vocabulary.

The Breccia Nappe is a descriptive term based upon the occurrence within it of very thick sedimentary breccias or conglomerates of Jurassic age. If more precise definition is required, the nappe is often styled the Breccia Nappe of the Prealps, or more particularly of Chablais or Hornfluh—the two last are Prealp localities lying respectively west and east of the Rhone.

The Klippe Nappe is named after its famous outliers known as klippes, near Lake Lucerne. It is sometimes also spoken of simply as the Prealp Nappe, but this is apt to puzzle a reader. More frequently it is styled the Middle Prealp Nappe, because its outcrop occupies a middle position with regard to the external, or north-western, and internal, or south-eastern, outcrops of the underlying nappes. It is also sometimes called the Stockhorn Nappe, after one of its mountains, the Stockhorn, a great landmark on the shores of Lake Thun.

The Niesen Nappe is named after the Niesen, another mountain conspicuous from Lake Thun.

The Col Nappes are an extremely moved complex, of which the main outcrop occurs along the internal (south-east) margin of the Prealps, east of the Rhone. Here erosion has fashioned a line of cols, or passes, from which has been derived the designation Col Nappes. When Schardt first wrote on the subject, in 1893, he treated the Niesen and Col Nappes together, as an excessively involved, far-travelled, basal complex. Our fuller knowledge is mainly due to discoveries by Lugeon in 1900 and 1914.

The distribution of the various Prealp nappes is indicated in Figure 55.5. We shall now pass on to a discussion of their composition and structural relations.

Viewed as a whole, the Prealp nappes differ from the neighbouring and underlying Helvetian nappes in having no nummulitic limestone—except to some extent in the Col

TABLE 55.1
Sedimentary facies of nappes in the Prealps compared with the adjacent Helvetian facies

Age of Rocks	Helvetian	Col Nappes	Niesen Nappe
Older Tertiaries	Flysch Nummulitic limestones and marls	Flysch, rich in exotic blocks Nummulitic limestone	Flysch, mostly grits with great basal breccias
Upper Cretaceous	Senonian and Turonian marls Cenomanian limestones Albian greensand	Senonian and Turonian thin shales and marls, locally reddish Cenomanian and Albian unidentified	Erosion Gap
Lower Cretaceous	Aptian greensand and shales on limestone (Upper Urgonian) Barremian limestone (Lower Urgonian) Hauterivian limestones Valangian marls and limestones	Aptian blue marls Barremian, Hauterivian and Valangian represented by an ammonite-bearing set of shaly marls and thin-bedded limestones (*Néocomien á Céphalopodes*)	
Upper Jurassic	Malm limestone Argovian limestone Oxfordian shale	Malm limestone Argovian marl Oxfordian shale	
Middle Jurassic	Limestones and shales	Shales, sandstones, limestones, some conglomerate (*Zoophycos* Dogger)	
Lower Jurassic (Lias)	Toarcian shale Middle and lower Liassic limestone	Toarcian shale Middle and lower Liassic limestone	Sandstone with breccia beds, shale, and limestone
Trias	Rhaetic shell-bed (local) Dolomitic limestone, cargneule, green shales, quartzite, and arkose	Rhaetic shell-bed Shale, gypsum, and red dolomite	Dolomite, cargneule, shale, and quartzite
Pre-Triassic	Permian Upper Carboniferous conglomerate, etc. Granite, gneiss, and schists	Granite in one exposure	Casanna Schists

Klippe Nappe		Breccia Nappe	Simme Nappe
north part	south part		
Flysch	Flysch, with some conglomerate	Flysch	?
Red foraminiferal limestone	Red and grey foraminiferal marl and limestone	Local red and green foraminiferal limestone and shale with basement conglomerate	Foraminiferal shale and limestone Gosau Beds consisting of breccia, sandstone, and conglomerate
Grey aptychus limestone with chert	Almost absent	Absent	Limestone with aptychus, belemnites, and radiolaria
Malm limestone with shale towards base	Malm limestone Thin shale	Upper breccia	
Limestones and marls (*Zoophycos* Dogger)	Impersistent limestone with basal breccia and sandstone and local coal (*Mytilus* Beds)	Thick but impersistent slate group	Red and green radiolarian chert with basic eruptives
Toarcian shaly marl Middle and lower Liassic encrinital and cherty limestones	Toarcian absent Middle and lower Lias dies out southwards	Lower breccia with shale and sandstone beds towards base Local fossiliferous limestones	Limestones and cherts with Cephalopods and *Posidonomya*
Rhaetic shell- and bone-beds Marl, dolomitic limestone, cargneule, and gypsum	Rhaetic shell- and bone-beds, and limestones Marl, dolomite, cargneule (sometimes fossiliferous), and gypsum	Rhaetic shell-bed Marl, dolomite, cargneule, red and green shale, gypsum, arkose, and quartzite	
		Permian polygenous conglomerate. Carboniferous sandstone, shale, and anthracite	

Source: condensed from the writings of Schardt, Jeannet, Heim, etc. (Fossil contrasts are much more fully stated in the originals.)

Nappes—and in possessing a comparatively thin and featureless Cretaceous. These two general features are well illustrated in Figure 55.3. On the ground, the failure of the Urgonian limestone, of the Lower Cretaceous, is one of the most arresting scenic peculiarities of the Prealps. In the Helvetian country, on three sides of the district, this Barremian-Aptian limestone is continually attracting attention by its abrupt scarps, sometimes 200 m. in height. Inside the Prealps there is no comparable band.

Beyond this point it is more satisfactory to consider the nappes one by one, rather than to contrast them, as an *ensemble*, with their foundation.

The Simme Nappe occurs in exceedingly involved patches of inconsiderable bulk. West of the Rhone, these generally lie upon the Flysch of the Breccia Nappe, while, east of the Rhone, they rest on, or in, the Flysch of the Klippe Nappe. In the latter position their structural relations are so complicated that they were not guessed at until after the general story of the Prealps had been read. Even today they are conveniently treated as a corollary of this story, rather than as evidence leading up to it. We shall therefore baldly state: (1) the Simme Nappe was thrust from the south onto, and beyond, the Breccia Nappe so that its frontal portion overlapped the latter and came to rest directly on the Flysch of the Klippe Nappe; (2) the Breccia Nappe moved once more and buried the advance guard of the Simme Nappe, pinching it into compressed synclines of the Klippe Flysch. In spite of its maltreatment the Simme Nappe still preserves a recognizable individuality—high testimony indeed to the peculiarity of its Mesozoic sequence! This is marked by a very thin development of materials that are absent from the Breccia and other nappes of the district. Their characters are sufficiently outlined in Table 55.1.

When we come to the Breccia Nappe we arrive at something that is comparatively easy to understand. The nappe has a main outcrop, west of the Rhone, and a series of minor outliers east of that river. The main outcrop lies partly upon the Flysch of the Helvetian Alps, and partly upon the Klippe Nappe; the minor eastern outcrops lie almost wholly on the Flysch of the Klippe Nappe. We are therefore concerned with distinguishing the facies of the Breccia Nappe from that of its two main neighbours. It is scarcely necessary to repeat that its Tertiary and Cretaceous have a non-Helvetian character. Its Jurassic is not only non-Helvetian, but is also utterly unlike anything in the Klippe Nappe. The Jurassic of the Breccia Nappe is upwards of 3,200 m. thick, and 1,600 m. of this great mass are essentially breccia, made of pebbles of Triassic dolomite and limestone; while the remaining 1,600 m. contain many layers of similar breccia. It is a wonderful experience to walk among great mountains made of such material, and then to search the 2,000 m. of Jurassic limestones and shales of the Klippe Nappe and to find nothing more than a couple of insignificant bands of breccia in the whole succession! Breccia is also practically unknown in the neighbouring Helvetian Jurassic.

A geologist can be trusted to understand that in well-exposed country, with the greater part of the Breccia Nappe constituted of an absolutely distinctive rock type, it is an easy matter to map the boundary of the nappe. Such border zones of Trias (and occasional patches of older rock) as evidently belong to the same stratigraphical assemblage as the breccia are of course included within the mapper's line. West of the Rhone the rocks of the Breccia Nappe are disposed in broad open folds. A novice can see the structure on the hill-sides (Figures 55.6 and 55.7). There are three main outliers of Flysch belonging to the Breccia Nappe and they occupy gentle basins. If we walk outwards from any one of these Flysch exposures we almost always pass in the clearest possible manner across successively lower and lower zones of the Jurassic breccia, and then, with or without the interposition of Trias, we step abruptly on to something quite different. In the great majority of cases this underlying material is Flysch or Cretaceous. We have evidently walked over the outcrop of the basal thrust-plane. We have reached, according to the direction of our traverse, either the Klippe Nappe or the Helvetian folds. We do not meet with the great Jurassic breccia again unless we re-enter the obvious synclinal depression in which it reposes. There are local complications of interest, as for instance the

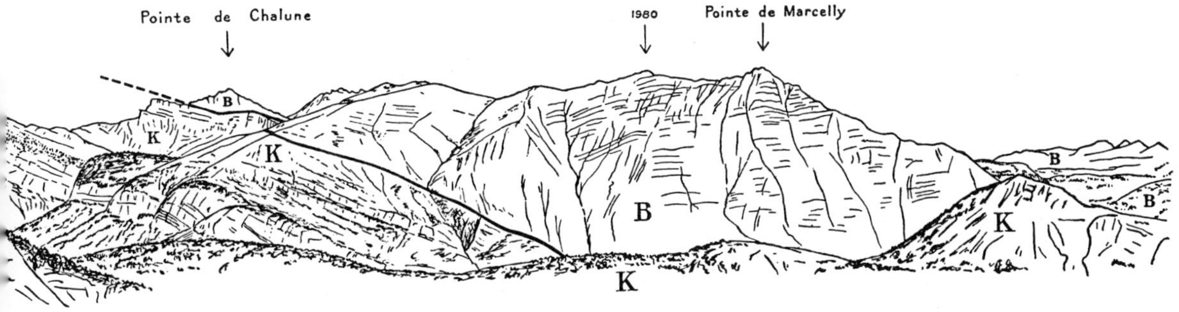

FIGURE 55.6
Contact of Klippe Nappe (*K*) and Breccia Nappe (*B*). Viewed across the Arve from above Bonneville. (After photo by E. Joukowsky.)

celebrated 'plunging head' of the nappe revealed in one of the great northern corries (above Abondance); but these complications are subsidiary. The emplacement of the Breccia Nappe, west of the Rhone, has all the grandeur of simplicity. There it stands, as Schardt has so aptly remarked, with one foot on the Helvetian Alps and the other on the Klippe Nappe.

East of the Rhone the Breccia Nappe has, on the whole, suffered more from folding. To compensate for this, it has been reduced by erosion to a number of outliers, some of them very small, and its superposition upon the Flysch of the Klippe Nappe remains exceedingly obvious.

The compositional and structural features of the Breccia Nappe have been discussed in some detail because they make it particularly easy to realize that this nappe is a far-travelled thrust-mass. Let us summarize the evidence:

(1) The Breccia Nappe consists essentially of Triassic, Jurassic, Cretaceous, and Tertiary sediments.
(2) The facies of many of its components is strikingly different from that of the surrounding country.
(3) Its rocks are disposed in open folds, and its basal members, Jurassic or Triassic according to the locality, rest, in the great majority of cases, upon much younger rocks, Tertiary or Cretaceous.

Older rocks were never stratigraphically deposited upon younger. Therefore we infer that the Breccia Nappe has been thrust into its present position. Moreover, as its materials differ in kind from those of corresponding age in the neighbourhood, it is safe to conclude that they have been transported a considerable distance.

As already explained, it is often said that outliers of thrust-masses have no roots, or that they are separated from their roots. The outliers of the Breccia Nappe are typical of this conception.

Now let us summarize quite briefly the corresponding evidence in regard to the Klippe Nappe.

(1) The Klippe Nappe consists of Tertiary, Cretaceous, Jurassic, and Triassic sediments.
(2) The facies of its Tertiary and Cretaceous is so different from that of the Helvetian Folds that even a tyro can appreciate the distinction. The peculiarities of its other members are vouched for by experts.
(3) Its rocks are disposed in compressed folds—of the simple type familiar to geologists in the Jura Mountains. There is no difficulty in distinguishing anticlines and synclines; and it is found that the cores of the former invariably consist of relatively old rock—there is within the limits of the nappe no really important inversion. In keeping with this, we find an almost continuous band of Trias outcropping at the margin of the nappe *where it usually rests upon adjacent Tertiary.*

Again the inference is clear. We are dealing with an outlier of a thrust-mass which has lost connexion with its root.

There are some who find a difficulty in focusing at one and the same time all the evidence required for the reading of large-scale structures, when that evidence happens to be dispersed over so wide an area as is occupied by the Klippe Nappe in the Prealps. Nature fortunately has anticipated this difficulty. The outliers known as klippes supply a convenient epitome of the story, for instance at Annes (Figure 55.3) and near Lake Lucerne.

Passing downwards from the Klippe Nappe into the basement complex that forms the external and internal zones of the Prealps, we enter a field of great confusion. This basement complex is in the main composed of Flysch which is often much contorted, and, locally, is almost inextricably mixed up with lenticles and cores of Mesozoic sediments. The latter have their main outcrops in the Zone of Cols, which forms the most south-easterly belt belonging to the Prealps in the district between the Rhone and Lake Thun.

The basement complex may be interpreted as a thrust-complex because:

(1) Its Flysch and its Mesozoic rocks, Cretaceous, &c., where present, have distinctive facies.
(2) All along its north-western margin its Flysch lies upon Molasse.
(3) In the Zone of Cols its Mesozoic, though intimately interfolded with the Helvetian Mesozoic, is separated from the latter by a layer of Flysch. On close examination it is seen that the Mesozoic of the Col Nappes, along with Flysch, sometimes occupies the cores of broken synclines closing to the south-east, whereas the Mesozoic of the Helvetian folds occupies intervening anticlinal cores closing towards the north-west.

The obvious inferences are:

(1) The Col Nappes once spread as a fairly flat sheet over the Helvetian Flysch and forward on to the Molasse of the Swiss Plain.
(2) The rear portion of this sheet has been greatly complicated by important folding and has locally been overridden for considerable distances by the Helvetian substratum.

Another very interesting structural feature of the basement complex is its complete separation into an external and an internal zone. This can safely be ascribed to the drag of the overlying Klippe Nappe, which has pulled or pushed the complex into two.

So far we have treated the basement complex as a unit, very much as Schardt did in his original description. The division of the complex into an overlying Niesen Nappe and an underlying group, provisionally styled the Col Nappes, has followed from Lugeon's researches. The Niesen Nappe consists almost wholly of Flysch which is of immense thickness and is largely made of bedded breccias. Even as compared with the rest of the Flysch of the basal Prealp complex the Niesen Flysch possesses a fair measure of individuality. Its outcrop is mostly restricted to an extensive area between the Rhone and Lake Thun, where it separates Trias of the Klippe Nappe from complicated Mesozoic outcrops of the Zone of Cols. Accordingly Argand in 1911 suggested that the Niesen Flysch was a definite structural unit intermediate in position between the Klippe and Col Nappes, and ascribed it to the Pennides. In 1914 Lugeon found exposures of the Niesen Flysch where the breccia was separated only by a few metres of Lias and Trias from crystalline Casanna Schists—a group well known in the pre-Triassic cores of the Pennine Alps. The approximate conjunction of Flysch and Casanna Schist cannot be accidental, for fragments of the latter are abundant in the bedded breccias of the former. One realizes that the Niesen Flysch has unconformable relations unparalleled elsewhere in the Prealps. It is obviously an independent nappe, and, when all the evidence is considered, it can safely be assigned to the Pennides. Staub nowadays places it at the very top of this group.

Even when we exclude the Niesen Nappe, the Col Nappes remain a complex. Arnold Heim and Staub group the upper members with the Pennides, while the lower members belong definitely to the Ultrahelvetides. . . .

We are now in a position to return to the question of the exotic blocks enclosed in the Prealpine Flysch. The phenomenon is so extraordinarily interesting that the reader will probably welcome the following free translation from an account published by Schardt in 1899.

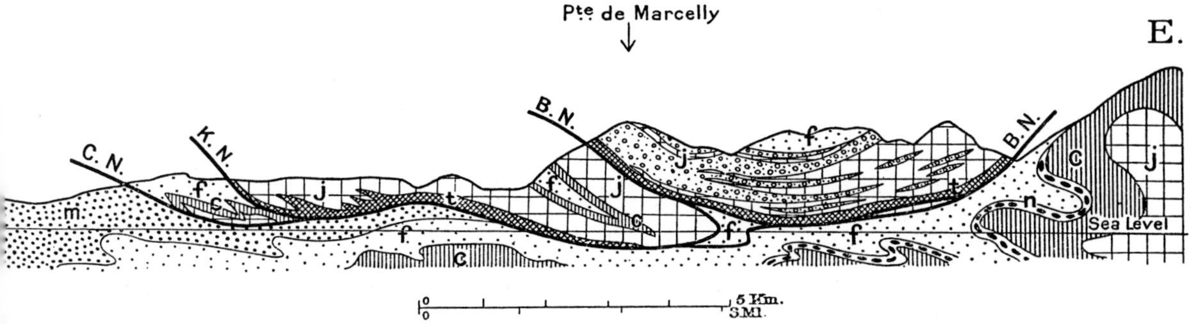

FIGURE 55.7
Section across Prealps. *m*, Molasse; *f*, Flysch; *n*, Nummulitic; *c*, Cretaceous; *j*, Jurassic (with breccias separately ornamented); *C.N.*, Col Nappes; *K.N.*, Klippe Nappe; *B.N.*, Breccia Nappe.

The Flysch is of great thickness throughout the Prealpine district. It is an arenaceous detrital formation, alternating in regular beds with shales or marls. Over wide tracts, it presents a very characteristic appearance due to its grit bands passing into coarse breccioidal grits (the Gurnigel Grit and Niesen Grit) that contain debris of granite, gneiss and other crystalline rocks, along with fragments of Prealpine Triassic and Jurassic limestones [Schardt means by this statement limestones of Klippe facies].

Locally, the Flysch conglomerates develop into breccias containing materials of gigantic volume. Instead of meeting with fragments of ordinary size, we come upon huge blocks that are often quite angular and measure several metres in length. Although distributed pell-mell these blocks constitute very regular layers, always separated by beds of shale and marl.

In the conglomerate banks, great boulders of granite or gneiss lie cheek by jowl with fragments of fragile, sometimes fossiliferous, Liassic shale, just as angular as themselves. It is impossible to invoke a long transport by water, since water currents soon disintegrate shale. Moreover, several of the blocks exceed 1,000 cubic metres in volume.

Schardt puts aside his early conception of iceberg transport and adopts instead a theory of landslips and screes from the front of the advancing Klippe Nappe. At first sight a fundamental difficulty appears to exist in the absence of crystalline rocks from the Klippe Nappe as at present preserved. Schardt met this difficulty by a fine exercise of imagination. His idea is very clearly expressed in 1898, when he pictures the Klippe Nappe "gliding forward on its Triassic base and pushing in advance considerable masses of crystalline rocks torn from ridges arrayed in its path." Lugeon's work on the Niesen Nappe has given reality to this conception, in so far, at any rate, that it proves the existence of a crystalline ridge exposed in Early Tertiary times in the position required by Schardt's hypothesis. We have already seen how Flysch of the Niesen Nappe is separated, in certain available exposures, by only a few metres of Lias and Trias from Casanna Schists. In the near neighbourhood the Casanna Schists and accompanying granite must have stood bare over considerable areas, since they have yielded abundant debris to the great basal breccias of the Flysch. If Schardt is correct in recognizing a Klippe facies among the limestone fragments of the Niesen breccias, then his views seem substantiated even in detail. On the other hand, Lugeon's brief notes half suggest that the Niesen breccias may have come entirely from erosion of a Pennide anticline at a time when the Klippe Nappe stood well in the background. We may be content for the moment with this minor uncertainty.

REFERENCES

Buxtorf, A., 1907, Zur Tektonik des Kettenjura: Oberrheinischen geol. Ver. Vers. Ber. 40, p. 29.

———, 1908, *in* Geologische Beschreibung des Weissensteintunnels und seiner Umgebung: Beitr. geol. Karte Schweiz, n.f., v. 21, no. 51.

———, 1911, Bemerkungen uber den Gebirgsbau

des nordschwiezerischen Kettenjura im besondern der Weissensteinkette: Deutschen geol. Gesell. Zeitschr. v. 63, p. 337.
———, 1916, Prognosen und Befunden beim Hauensteinbasis und Grenchen bergtunnel und die Bedeutung der letztern fur die Geologie des Juragebirges: Naturf. Gesell. Basel Verbandl., v. 27, p. 184.
Collet, L. W., 1927, The Structure of the Alps: London, Arnold.
Heim, Albert, 1919–22, Geologie der Schweiz: Leipzig, C. H. Tauchnitz, v. 1 and 2. (The section "Das Romanische Deckengebirge, Prealpes und Klippen" was written by A. Jeannet, and edited by A. Heim.)
Jeannet, A., 1913, Monographie géologique des Tours d'Aï et des régions avoisinantes (Préalpes vaudoises), pt. 1: Bern, Mat. carte géol. Suisse.
———, 1918, Monographie géologique des Tours d'Aï et des régions avoisinantes (Préalpes vaudoises), pt. 2: Bern, Mat. carte géol. Suisse.
Lugeon, M., 1900, Sur la découverte d'une racine de la "zone des cols" (Préalpes suisses): Soc. géol. France Bull., ser. 3, v. 28, p. 998.
———, 1901, Sur la découverte d'une racine des Préalpes suisses: Acad. sci. [Paris] Comptes rendus, v. 132, p. 45.
———, 1902, Les grandes nappes de recouvrement des Alpes du Chablais et de la Suisse: Soc. géol. France Bull., ser. 4, v. 1 (1901), p. 723.
———, 1914, Sur la présence de lames cristallines dans les Préalpes et sur leur signification: Acad. sci. [Paris] Comptes rendus, v. 159, p. 685.
———, 1914, Sur quelques conséquences de la présence de lames cristallines dans le soubassement de la zone du Niesen (Préalpes suisses): Acad. sci. [Paris] Comptes rendus, v. 159, p. 778.
———, 1916, Sur l'origine des blocs exotiques du Flysch préalpin: Eclogae Géol. Helvetiae, v. 14, p. 217.
Rogers, H. D., 1850, On the structural features of the Appalachians, compared with those of the Alps and other disturbed districts of Europe: Am. Assoc. Proc., rept. 2 [1849], p. 113.
Schardt, H., 1893, Sur l'origine des Alpes du Chablais et du Stockhorn, en Savoie et en Suisse: Acad. sci. [Paris] Comptes rendus, v. 117, p. 707.
———, 1893, Sur l'origine des Préalpes romandes: Archives Sci. [Geneva], ser. 3, v. 30, p. 570.
———, 1898, Les régions exotiques du versant nord des Alpes suisses: Soc. vaudoise sci. nat. Bull., v. 34, p. 113. (This is Schardt's standard description.)
———, 1899, Les Préalpes romandes: Soc. neuchâteloise géog. Bull., v. 11, p. 5.
Staub, R., 1924, Der Bau der Alpen: Bern, Mat. carte géol. Suisse.
Steinmann, G., 1906, Geologische Beobachtungen in den Alpen. II. Die Schardt'sche Überfaltungstheorie: Naturf. Gesell. Freiburg im Breisgau Ber., v. 16, p. 18.
Thurmann, J., 1832–36, Essai sur les soulèvements jurassiques du Porrentruy: Strasbourg and Porrentruy.
———, 1857 (posthumous), Essai d'orographie jurassique: Inst. genevois Mém.

SECTION VIII

GLIMPSES OF PHANEROZOIC LIFE

The race of man shall perish,
but the eyes of trilobites eternal be in stone.

T. A. Conrad

The grand panorama of evolution began far back in pre-Paleozoic time, after the appearance of a hydrosphere and atmosphere, and presumably after a period of chemical evolution during which a supply of the primary biochemical building blocks evolved abiogenically. The first cells were anaerobic and procaryotic, but the eventual evolution of efficient oxygen-mediating enzymes, followed by the accumulation of free oxygen in the atmosphere beginning about 1.8 aeons ago, provided the impetus for the appearance of the mitosing or eucaryotic cell. Primitive eucaryotic ancestors gave rise to the Metazoa—differentiated multicellular animal life—near the beginning of Paleozoic time, perhaps 0.64 aeons ago.

Metazoa are the "index fossils" of the Phanerozoic Eon. Although single-celled organisms are also abundant throughout, the Phanerozoic is essentially the time of the diversification of metazoans and metaphytes. In effect, the really basic events of biologic evolution as we know it were completed with the arrival of the Metazoa, marking the dawn of Phanerozoic time; the rest was elaboration.

Nevertheless, it was a fascinating elaboration, and many conspicuous changes accompanied it. Vertebrates, in the form of fishes, appeared early in Ordovician time. They diversified, and eventually gave rise to the first amphibians in Late Devonian time. With the appearance of the amniote egg, protected by a shell against desiccation, certain amphibians were able to bypass the larval stage of ancestral forms and, being freed from their tie to the water, to evolve into reptiles—a transition that seems to have occurred in the Early Pennsylvanian. The reptiles, then, eventually gave rise to mammals near the end of the Triassic, and to birds in the Jurassic. Although mammals were few and inconspicuous at first, they underwent extensive adaptive radiation during the Cenozoic, following the decline of reptilian dominance at the end of the Cretaceous, which opened for exploitation various ecological niches that previously had been filled by reptiles. The engrossing stories of horse, camel, elephant, and anthropoid evolution are features of the Cenozoic era: anthropoid elaboration, of course, led to recognizable hominids perhaps 12 million years ago; to the genus *Homo*, to which man belongs, maybe 2 million years ago; and to *Homo sapiens* himself perhaps 200,000 years ago, during a warm interval in the latter part of the Pleistocene ice ages.

While the vertebrates were evolving, other great developments were taking place. The oldest unequivocal records of tracheophytic, or vascular, plants (plants with authentic root systems, branches, and leaves) are those of Devonian time, and are contemporaneous with extensive nonmarine deposits. The marine uniserial graptolite *Monograptus*, with which the ancestral tracheophyte *Baragwanathia* occurs in Australia, is now known to represent an Early Devonian graptolite zone—and not to be a Silurian precursor, as was earlier believed. The vascular plants may well have had a long pre-Devonian ancestry, but that remains conjectural. It has been suggested that their appearance, as well as that of the first insects (a little later, in the Middle Devonian Rhynie Chert of Scotland), was related to an increase of free oxygen in the atmosphere. That, too, remains conjectural, for we have not, as yet, recognized any strong correlations with events in lithospheric evolution. The insects and other land animals may, of course, have evolved at least partially in response to the availability of tracheophytic plant food. Later, during the late Early Cretaceous, the true flowering plants (angiosperms) were to appear with similar abruptness, but also with a possible prior evolution of some duration. As, however, their appearance in the record also precedes, and probably correlates with, an episode in arthropod evolution—the appearance of the social insects—the evolution of the flowering plants may well have been rather abrupt, as such things go. Grasses finally appeared at the very end of the Cretaceous, and the spread and diversification of that source of fodder during the Tertiary evidently had something to do with the evolution and dispersal of horses and other grazing mammals at that time.

The Phanerozoic was also a time of exuberant diversity and changing patterns of evolution among marine invertebrates—a subject fascinating to specialists, although often not so appealing to others. Some exposure to the subject, however, will serve to illustrate one of the most characteristic features of science: how intrinsically interesting the most ordinary-seeming things can become once we begin to observe them attentively (a feature beautifully illustrated by T. H. Huxley's essay "On a Piece of Chalk," listed under Supplemental Reading for Section VII).

As with the preceding section on the physical history of the Phanerozoic, space simply doesn't permit the introduction of many of the excellent writings on Phanerozoic life and evolution. A few examples, selected from the many available, must suffice to illustrate the kinds of things that geologists must deal with in seeking to comprehend the evolutionary record of the many-celled animals and plants.

The student who has not studied evolution would be well-advised to preface his reading of Section VIII with some appropriate introductory material, such as George Gaylord Simpson's brief and elementary essay "The Course of Evolution," from his book *The Meaning of Evolution* (1949, Supplemental Reading). Choosing examples mainly from the vertebrates, Simpson shows how change of biologic composition may take place over geologic time as a consequence of adaptive radiation, substitution, extinction, and addition. His examination of biologic change through the more than half an aeon of Phanerozoic time shows no fixed plan in detail, but rather a tendency for life to expand and fill up the earth as far as possible.

Section VIII begins with a broad overview by paleontologist Norman Newell of Columbia University and the American Museum of Natural History. Newell's survey, "The Nature of the Fossil Record" (Reading Selection 56), was prepared for the centennial of the publication of *The Origin of Species*. Aptly enough, the discussion begins with Darwin's concepts (see Reading Selection 14) of the incompleteness of the geological record of organic evolution. Newell observes that, although quite a few gaps have been filled since Darwin worried about them, many others still remain. He sees two kinds of gaps: "casual" ones that can be bridged by more exploration, better fossil collecting, and improved techniques of preparation; and general "systematic" deficiencies in the record. These "systematic" gaps are exemplified by the seemingly abrupt appearance of major categories of plants and animals, such as the sudden variety of invertebrate forms early in Phanerozoic time, the appearance of tracheophytic land plants in the Early Devonian (*not* Sulurian) of Australia, and the marked diversification of the angiosperms (flowering plants) in the Upper Cretaceous. Bias in reconstructing the evolutionary record arises from, among other things, the rarity of preservation of soft-bodied organisms. Very few of the organisms that ever live have good prospects of leaving their mark on the geological record. Our knowledge of the record is much more complete than it was in Darwin's time, however, and is getting better all the time. Newell discusses many of the problems of the study of Phanerozoic life, such as determining rates of evolution and the nature and distribution of fossil populations, discovering parallelisms, and reconstructing phylogenies and paleoecology.

Against the background provided by Newell, we may now consider the first differentiated multicellular animals and plants, as described in Reading Selection 57 by the late Percy Raymond of Harvard University. Since this paper was written in 1947, some of the details have been modified by new finds (the Ediacaran fauna of South Australia, for example, and some newly discovered primitive echinoderms from eastern California), but a better general statement in plain words has yet to be written. Raymond tabulated all the Lower Cambrian fossils then known: about 455 species in 7 phyla, mostly trilobites, brachiopods, sponges, and monoplacophorans (called gastropods by Raymond for lack of a better available name). He emphasizes that those species did not all appear instantaneously, but gradually; and that the 455 species then known could be only a fraction of the fauna that actually inhabited the Early Cambrian seas. Any way one looks at the picture, though, the primordial metazoan fauna was not as highly differentiated as casual reading might make it appear. Raymond briefly considers how that fauna might have arisen, and also discusses its later Cambrian evolution. The time factor, he supposes, has been overemphasized; but then, there must have been, he infers, some interval of pre-skeletal metazoan evolution. "We are not driven," he concludes "to belief in an ancient special creation, but to further research on the genealogy of organisms."

We cannot consider the genealogy of organisms in detail here, but it is instructive to look at what is known of some of the early generalized molluscs and their descendants. The dredging, shortly after World War II, of the "living fossil" *Neopilina*—a limpet-like mollusc with muscle pattern like that of the many-segmented chitons, or coat-of-mail shells —helped to provoke a reappraisal of molluscan phylogeny. Space does not permit us to consider here all the details of that reappraisal, but the Supplemental Reading includes a whimsical essay by Ellis Yochelson (1967, "*Quo Vadis, Bellerophon?*") wherein the confusing parallel evolution of some early limpet-like and planispirally coiled molluscs of different ancestry is discussed. The primitive molluscs—the Protogastropoda—showed a remarkable diversity of musculature and shell form from the very beginning. The Class Monoplacophora (*Neopilina* and its ancient relatives), with paired muscle scars, appears to be primitive: most of its members were extinct by the end of the Early Ordovician, although several are known from rocks as young as Devonian and at least two species inhabit modern seas. Torsion of the nervous system and other soft parts (a critical phylogenetic development recognizable by a non-paired arrangement of muscle scars) had occurred well before the end of the Cambrian, eventually giving rise to the true gastropods (snails) and pelecypods (clams).

One of the most interesting invertebrate connecting links we know of is a bivalved mollusc of early Middle Ordovician age that appears to be transitional from the molluscan root stock, the Monoplacophora, to the Pelecypoda. This genus, *Babinka*, is discussed in Reading Selection 58 by Yale University paleontologist A. Lee McAlester. In its general morphology *Babinka* resembles the long-enduring family of lucinid clams, characterized by the genus *Lucina*. However, it has a complicated set of muscle scars reminiscent of the Monoplacophora. McAlester discusses the functional morphology of *Babinka*, its systematic relations, its implication for phylogeny, and the general structure and musculature of eight related superfamilies of living pelecypods. The paper is included here to introduce the reader to the intricacies, pitfalls, and potentialities of comparative invertebrate morphology and phylogeny, by means of a suitable molluscan example from the early Paleozoic.

For the Paleozoic as a whole, however, the brachiopods are the most characteristic fossils. Members of the phylum Brachiopoda have bivalved shells, like clams (to which they are unrelated), but with the plane of bilateral symmetry splitting each valve into right and left parts, instead of running between them as it does in clams. Further, the calcareous shells of brachiopods are usually in the crystallographic form of calcite, rather than of aragonite, as is usual with clams. From the fossil evidence, we know that many thousands of species of brachiopods swarmed the Paleozoic seas before dwindling to the mere 200 or so species found in modern seas. Many fascinating evolutionary trends are shown by those fossils, and many stratigraphic applications are known for them, but the one brief selection on the Brachiopoda included here illustrates a different point. In his paper titled "Silurian Marine Communities and Their Environmental Significance" (Reading Selection 59), paleontologist A. M. Ziegler of the University of Chicago shows how the Middle Silurian brachiopods of Wales and the Welsh Borderland of England can be segregated into five communities that give striking clues to the depth of the shelf seas and to the fluctuations of the shoreline. Those communities follow linear trends parallel to, and at increasing distances from, the shoreline. They occur most characteristically in certain sedimentary facies, but are not restricted to an particular type of sediment. Their displacement by contemporaneous submarine lava flows at several places demonstrates that they in fact denote depth zones whose characteristic bathymetry can be worked out in terms of meters of water on the basis of displacements observed. This in turn gives the basis for a more detailed picture of the advances and retreats of the Middle Silurian sea in England and Wales. Thus we have one of the rare examples of a paleobathymetry expressible in numbers, rather than in general terms such as *shallow* and *deep*. Since similar brachiopod communities occur in other regions, moreover, the opportunities to infer a parallel depth zonation are many. The story is expanded in a later paper by Ziegler, co-authored with L. R. M. Cocks and R. K. Bambach (1968, see Supplemental Reading).

Although much earth history can be inferred from the record of the fossils and rocks themselves, inference about life associations and behavior is limited where we do not find features that can be correlated with those of living organisms, or where we do not know how far organic remains may have been transported to reach their places of burial. For that reason the study of the works or traces of organisms reflecting life processes at specific sites takes on special interest. That study is known as palichnology, and the biogenic sedimentary structures with which it treats—the tracks, trails, burrows, body imprints, and the like—are know as ichnofossils, or trace fossils. Their interpretation, nomenclature, and uses as paleoecologic indicators are discussed in Reading Selection 60 by the palichnologist Adolf Seilacher of the University of Tübingen. Generally similar forms of those "fossils" occur in similar environments over a wide range of Phanerozoic time, implying mechanistic ecologic response and permitting relatively confident interpretation of broad habitat conditions over much longer time spans than is possible from most fossil evidence.

The rest of Section VIII is devoted to the consideration of four broad evolutionary sequences, beginning with A. S. Romer's inimitable summary of "Major Steps in Vertebrate Evolution" (Reading Selection 61), his presidential address to the American Association for the Advancement of Science. Romer, professor emeritus of vertebrate paleontology at Harvard University, gives us a highly condensed tour of vertebrate evolution from the earliest records to the origin of man, with brief excursions into chordate origins and vertebrate paleoecology. He rejects the time-honored notions that cartilage is primitive and bone advanced, and that fish originated in the sea and only later migrated into fresh water. Assessment of other structural relations simply requires that the early heavily armored fishes were ancestral to later forms, some of which, like the highly evolved sharks, underwent nearly complete reduction of the bony impregnation of the skeleton, probably beginning as an embryonic adaptation. Likewise a survey of the occurrences and associations of early fishes, as well as the kidney structure of living fishes, suggests to Romer that they arose in fresh water, together with their suspected primitive enemies, the pincered and joint-legged eurypterids, only later migrating to the sea. The first tetrapods, the amphibians, evolved from the lobe-finned (crossopterygian) fishes—as a consequence, according to Romer, of adaptation to conditions of seasonal drought. Anything that would facilitate getting from one water hole to another would then be selected for. The amniote egg, which opened the door to reptilian evolution by freeing certain ancient amphibians from their aquatic ties, is seen by Romer as another protection against seasonal drought, as it eliminated the water-dependent larval stage. Romer also sketches the emergence of the mammals from the mammal-like reptiles (Therapsida), and, finally, the emergence of primates and man. Those discussions link with Reading Selection 63, a paper by E. C. Olson on the origin of mammalian characters, and with the papers in the final section of this book.

At this point, however, we pause to consider a subject that no treatment of earth history can totally bypass. The dinosaurs, although now known to every grade-school student, remain a subject of never-ending fascination. Reading Selection 62, by the leading American student of the dinosaurs, E. H. Colbert of the American Museum of Natural History and the Museum of Northern Arizona, briefly outlines the major features of dinosaur evolution. The term dinosaur loosely designates two not very closely related orders of so-called giant reptiles. Although not all reptiles called dinosaurs were true giants, about 150 of the 250 or so described genera attained adult heights of 20 feet or more and weights exceeding 2 tons. Most Triassic dinosaurs were small, but the Jurassic and Cretaceous genera included many giants. Colbert discusses the disadvantages and advantages of gigantism, and the implications of globally mild climates inherent in the dominance of large, widely distributed, cold-blooded animals. He calls attention to the many unusual adaptations of bone and jaw structure that accompanied the attainment of exceptionally large size among both herbivorous and carnivorous dinosaurs. Why did the dinosaurs become extinct? Not because they grew too big, for dinosaurs of a variety of sizes (including the largest of all, the sauropods) prospered until near the end of Cretaceous time. Colbert thinks it "probable that we shall never reach a satisfactory solution to the problem of dinosaurian extinction."

For the story of mammalian evolution, we turn to Reading Selection 63, "The Evolution of Mammalian Characters," by University of California paleontologist E. C. Olson. Olson does not elaborate the full course of mammalian evolution, but focuses on when and how mammals, as such, arose. He uses a number of systematic and anatomical terms that may be unfamiliar, but, as their precise definitions are not essential to the general picture, they need not detain the reader (they are, however defined in the Glossary). New data on the transition from reptile to mammal, gathered largely by Olson himself, points to a polyphyletic origin of the Mammalia in latest Jurassic time, with the main mammalian roots among the therapsid reptiles. Regulation of blood temperature is seen as having been a primary physiological "goal," going along with a reduction of the bony elements of the jaw and with the emergence of other characteristics of mammality. But the transition was gradual. Some intermediate forms might, with equal reason, be assigned either to Reptilia or Mammalia. Taxonomic convenience then becomes the arbiter, revealing nomenclature as a human artifice, treating an actual continuum as a series of separate parts to make it easier to handle. Olson also raises a number of questions about interpreting observed evolutionary patterns that provide the framework for some searching discussion.

Section VIII closes with an essay titled "Evidence of Climatic Change in the Geologic Record of Plant Life," by Harvard University paleobotanist Elso Barghoorn (Reading Selection 64). Although our particular concern in this paper is with the evolutionary record of plant life, climate is as good a perspective to examine it from as any, and it sets the stage for a consideration of paleoclimatology in the next section. Barghoorn sees both morphological and physiological change in the characteristics of plants through time. He sees a broad evolutionary trend toward an increasing sensitivity of plants to the physical features of their environment as the explanation for the contrast between the cosmopolitan nature of earlier floras and the more localized habitats of modern plants. Above all, he sees plants as the response to, and the revealers of, climatic change, and as important conditioners of animal evolution.

It would have been useful in this section to have included an example of biometrical methods in paleontology, but lack of space forbade it. The interested reader will find no better brief introduction to the subject than John Imbrie's 1956 paper on "Biometrical Methods in the Study of Invertebrate Fossils," cited below under Supplemental Reading. The fundamental source book for paleontologists is the treatise by Simpson, Roe, and Lewontin (1960).

Supplemental Reading

Bell, W. C., 1941, Cambrian Brachiopoda from Montana: Jour. Paleontology, v. 15, p. 193–255.

Boucot, A. J., J. G. Johnson, and Wolfgang Struve, 1966, *Stringocephalus*, ontogeny and distribution: Jour. Paleontology, v. 40, p. 1349–1364.

Brinkman, Roland, 1929, Statistisch-biostratigraphische Untersuchungen am mitteljurassischen Ammoniten über Artbegriff und Stammesentwicklung: Gesell. Wiss. Göttingen Abh., N.F., v. 13, no. 3, 249 p.

Cloud, P. E., Jr., 1959, Paleoecology—retrospect and prospect: Jour. Paleontology, v. 33, p. 926–962.

Durham, J. Wyatt, 1967, Notes on the Helicoplacoidea and early echinoderms: Jour. Paleontology, v. 41, p. 97–102.

Easton, W. H., 1960, Invertebrate paleontology: New York, Harper and Row, 701 p.

Flower, R. H., 1961, Montoya and related colonial corals—organisms attached to Montoya corals: New Mexico Bur. Mines and Mineral Resources Mem. 7, 124 p.

Flower, R. H., and Bernhard Kummel, Jr., 1950, A classification of the Nautiloidea: Jour. Paleontology, v. 24, p. 604–616.

George, T. N., 1958, The ecology of fossil animals: Sci. Prog., v. 46, p. 677–690.

Glaessner, M. F., 1966, Problems of palaeontology: Geol. Soc. India Jour., v. 7, p. 14–27.

Grant, Richard E., 1968, Structural adaptation in two Permian brachiopod genera, Salt Range, West Pakistan: Jour. Paleontology, v. 42, p. 1–32.

Imbrie, John, 1956, Biometrical methods in the study of invertebrate fossils: Am. Mus. Nat. History Bull., v. 108, p. 215–252.

Imbrie, John, and N. D. Newell, 1964, Approaches to paleoecology: New York, John Wiley and Sons, 432 p.

Moore, R. C., ed., 1953 *et seq.*, Treatise on invertebrate paleontology: Boulder, Colo., Geological Society of America, 24 pts. planned.

Olson, E. C., 1966, Community evolution and the origin of mammals: Ecology, v. 47, no. 2, p. 291–302.

Romer, A. S., 1945, Vertebrate paleontology: Chicago, University of Chicago Press, 687 p.

———, 1946, Early evolution of fishes: Quart. Rev. Biology, v. 21, no. 1, p. 33–69.

Seilacher, Adolf, 1967, Fossil behavior: Scientific American Offprint 872, 9 p.

Simpson, G. G., 1945, The principles of classification and a classification of mammals: Am. Mus. Nat. History Bull., v. 85, 350 p.

———, 1949, The meaning of evolution: New Haven, Conn., Yale University Press, 364 p.

———, 1951, Horses: London, Oxford University Press, 247 p.

———, 1951, The species concept: Evolution, v. 5, p. 285–298.

Simpson, G. G., Anne Roe, and R. C. Lewontin, 1960, Quantitative zoology: New York, Harcourt, Brace and World, 440 p.

Smith, H. W., 1961, From fish to philosopher: Garden City, N.Y., Doubleday, Anchor Books, 293 p. (Reprint of 1953 edition.)

Whittington, H. B., 1966, Phylogeny and distribution of Ordovician trilobites: Jour. Paleontology, v. 40, p. 696–737.

Yochelson, E. L., 1967, *Quo vadis, Bellerophon?*: Univ. Kansas Dept. Geology Spec. Pub. 2, p. 141–161.

Ziegler, A. M., L. R. M. Cocks, and R. K. Bambach, 1968, The composition and structure of Lower Silurian marine communities: Lethaia, v. 1, p. 1–27.

56

The Nature of the Fossil Record

NORMAN D. NEWELL
1959

When Charles Darwin turned to the geological implications of his theory of evolution, his first major concern was to learn the nature of the fossil record. It is a measure of his genius that two geological chapters, ten and eleven, in *The Origin of Species* demonstrate a profound grasp of the subject far beyond that of any paleontologist of his time. It is the purpose of the present discussion to undertake briefly an evaluation of the fossil record in the light of a century of discovery since publication of *The Origin of Species.*

Darwin argued that the fossils known to science in his day represented a very small part of the potentially available record. He also understood that all of the fossils that ever existed must constitute only a very incomplete and fragmentary record of past life. These conclusions we still endorse, even though we now know immeasurably more about fossils than did Darwin. We cannot learn everything about past life from fossils, but we have learned much and the potentially knowable record is still far greater than the known record for most fossil groups. Paleontological exploration of the past is a sampling procedure in which provisional estimates of the whole are made from small, frequently biased, samples. Knowledge is cumulative and sampling errors are gradually corrected as the process is repeated over and over again by independent workers.

DARWIN'S GEOLOGICAL BACKGROUND

It is perhaps often overlooked that during his youth Darwin was by interest and training as much geologist as biologist, and it must be granted that his conclusions about organic evolution would have been significantly different had he not learned to view organisms against the historical background provided by geology. At Cambridge University he had studied under Adam Sedgwick, who, with Murchison, was shortly to work out the British early Paleozoic sequence of rocks and fossils; but his greatest

From *Proceedings of the American Philosophical Society,* vol. 103, no. 2, pp. 264–285, 1959. Reprinted with permission of the author and the American Philosophical Society.

inspiration in geology undoubtedly came from Charles Lyell whose ideas were sweeping across Europe in the 1830's and bringing about a revolution in geology that had been quietly started half a century before by James Hutton.

It is important that Darwin thought as a geologist. His enthusiasm for the science of the earth is revealed in a letter from South America to his sisters:

> I wish any of you could enter into my feelings of excessive pleasure which Geology gives me as soon as one partly understands the nature of a country. . . . There is nothing like Geology. The pleasure of the first day's hunting cannot be compared to finding a fine group of fossil bones which tell their story of former times with almost a living tongue.

On an Argentine pampa he collected remains of extinct mammals of gigantic size and he pondered deeply on the fact that, although they clearly belonged to extinct forms, they were constructed on the same basic plan as the small living sloths and armadilloes of the region. This experience started him thinking about the fossil sequence of faunas and floras, the causes of extinction, and the origin of new forms that have replaced successively old ones in the fossil record.

In 1859 the fossil record still was poorly sampled and practically all paleontologic studies had been concerned with the description and stratigraphic documentation of fossil assemblages. Nevertheless, many important generalizations could be made. Although it often is denied, the known record gave strong support to Darwin and he made full use of available knowledge of fossils. The evidence that he gleaned from the fossil record showed that the prevalent theory of multiple special creations and catastrophic extinctions could not possibly explain [it]. . . .

THE STRATIGRAPHIC SUCCESSION

Late in the eighteenth century Cuvier, Alexandre Brogniart, William Smith, and many others had shown the value of fossils as indicators of stratigraphic position and geologic age. Out of their observations there quickly developed the conception of a geological time scale, and the stage was set for the organization of a scientific history of the earth. In the first two decades of the nineteenth century, paleontologists were recognizing a sequence of three great time-stratigraphic units, Primary, Secondary, and Tertiary, based mainly on their fossils; and by the time Darwin returned to England from his voyage, the broad outlines of the time-stratigraphic system now in general use had been worked out in Great Britain and on the Continent [see front endpapers].

Lyell had shown that the recent biota had not appeared abruptly in its entirety, as required by special creation, but gradually, a few species at a time in the Tertiary rocks, replacing one after another species that are now extinct; and these new species and their near relatives were commonly widely distributed, making their appearance in different regions at nearly the same stratigraphic position. Darwin was deeply impressed by this and by the discoveries of de Verneuil, d'Archiac, Barrande, Adolph Brogniart, and others. They showed that there is a characteristic succession of fossil forms through time in all studied rock sequences in various parts of the world. Darwin wrote:

> Scarcely any paleontological discovery is more striking than the fact that the forms of life change almost simultaneously throughout the world. . . . Thus, as it seems to me, the parallel, and, taken in a large sense, simultaneous, succession of the same forms of life throughout the world, accords well with the principle of new species having been formed by dominant species spreading widely and varying. . . . As new and improved groups spread throughout the world, old groups disappear from the world; and the succession of forms everywhere tends to correspond both in their first appearance and final disappearance.

Fossils structurally intermediate between distantly related living animals were known in Darwin's day and they, of course, influenced the strictly morphological taxonomy of the time. Many paleontologists had noted that fossil forms in some cases join together living families and even orders. For example, the fossil *Zeuglodon* was regarded as intermediate between whales and aquatic carnivores, and, after its discovery in 1861, *Archaeopteryx* was

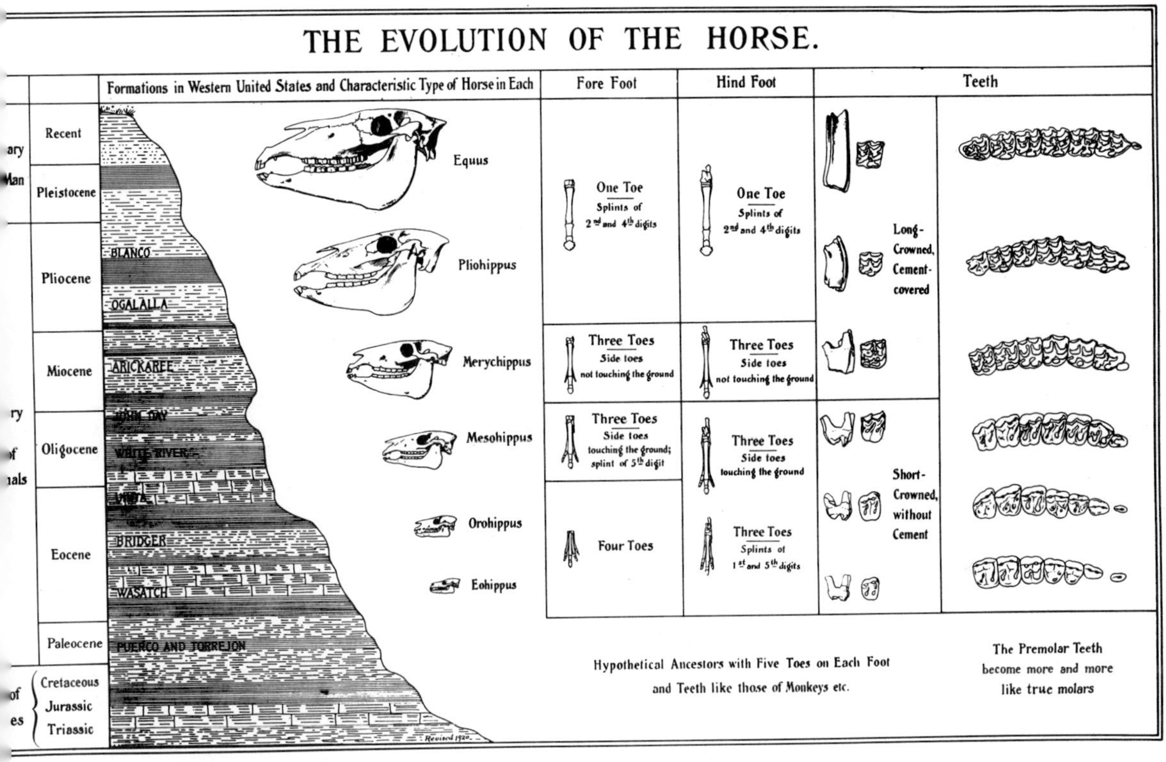

FIGURE 56.1
The fossil record of the horse family. Illustrates gradual but comparatively rapid morphological change during some 60 million years. (Matthew and Chubb, *Guide Leaflet Ser.* 36, Am. Mus. Nat. History, 1921.)

properly placed in a position intermediate between reptiles and birds, but before Darwin there was little reason to consider the phylogenetic implications of these discoveries.

CASUAL GAPS IN THE RECORD

Two kinds of interruptions in the fossil record attracted Darwin's attention and the attention of every paleontologist since. One of these is a local, or casual, deficiency which results from insufficient collecting, migrations of original organisms, unfavorable biotic environment, nondeposition, nonpreservation after burial, or destruction by erosion. With continued and geographically extended search aided by improved techniques of collecting and preparing fossils, these gaps in the record gradually are filled in as "missing links" are discovered.

Within ten years of the publication of *The Origin of Species,* Waagen had published evidence in support of an ammonite phylogeny and five years thereafter Kowalevsky had worked out a graded sequence of fossil horses in Europe. The record of horse evolution was quickly improved and amplified by Marsh's discoveries in America (Figure 56.1). Thus, Darwin lived to see the support from paleontology that he had confidently expected. There are now innumerable illustrations of graded temporal series of fossils from both animal and plant kingdoms, and there are few paleontologists in the world today who doubt that the fossil record gives convincing support to Darwin's thesis that species gradually become modified with time (Figure 56.2).

SYSTEMATIC GAPS IN THE RECORD

The second kind of paleontological break is systematic. That is, it reflects a genuine deficiency of the record not dependent on insufficient collecting or chance factors of sedimentation. The earliest members of higher categories, phyla, classes, orders, and superfamilies generally have all of the basic characteristics of those categories rather than dominantly ancestral characters. Thus, the higher categories tend to be separated sharply from other related groups with little or no tendency for intergradation. The meaning of this morphological isolation of higher categories has troubled students of the fossil record and was explained by pre-Darwinian paleontologists as indicative of special creation. It is true that a few stratigraphic levels are characterized by the "simultaneous" appearance of several higher categories, for example, at the base of the Triassic system; but for the most part the first appearances are scattered through the stratigraphic record. The idea of piecemeal special creations was not what most of the early paleontologists had in mind. A very few modern students have attributed these sudden appearances of group characteristics as evidence of large gene mutations, macroevolution, but there are alternatives that are considered more acceptable to the majority of modern evolutionists. This is the problem of the origin of higher categories.

From time to time discoveries are made of connecting links that provide clues to the relationships, as between fishes and amphibians, amphibians and reptiles, and reptiles and mammals. These isolated discoveries, of course, stimulate hope that more complete records will be found and other gaps closed. These finds are, however, rare; and experience

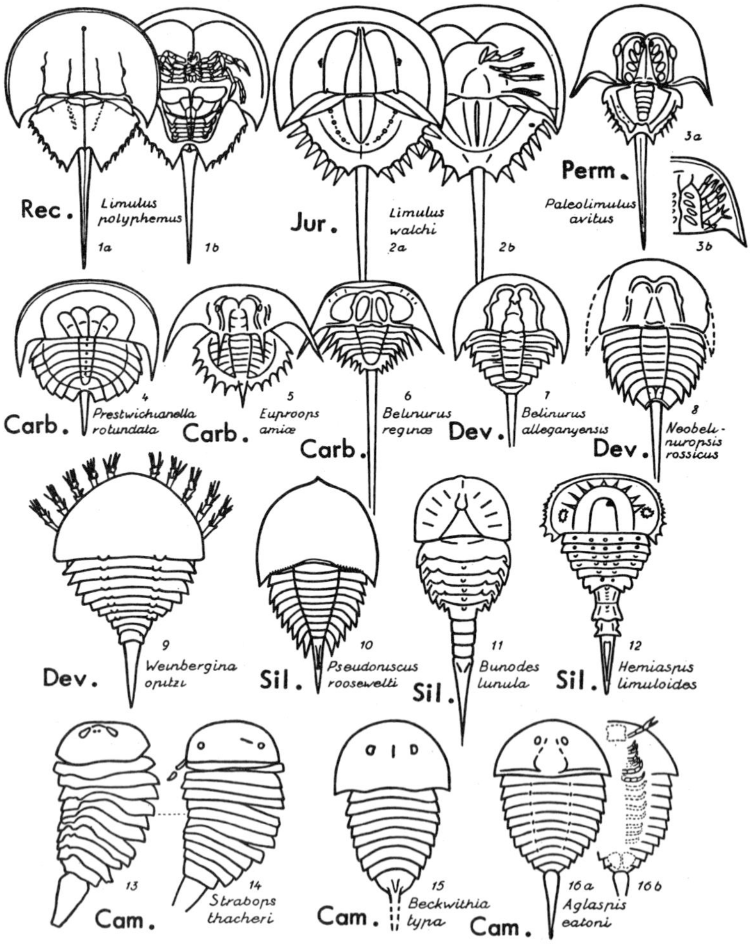

FIGURE 56.2
Merostome arthropods. These highly organized arthropods have evolved very slowly during 450 million years. (Størmer, 1944.)

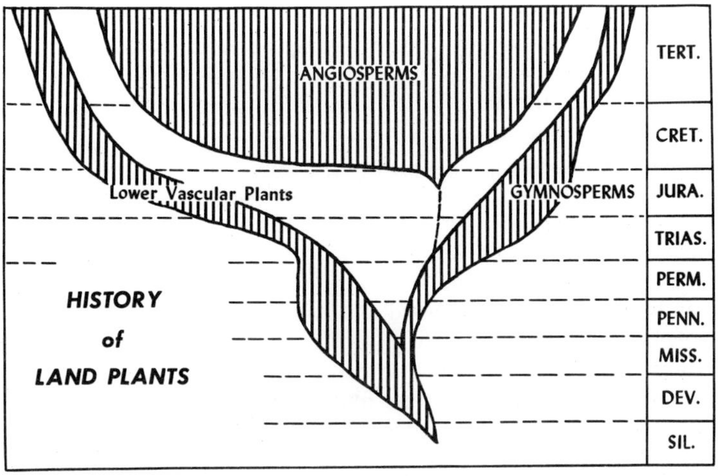

FIGURE 56.3
The flowering plants, or angiospersms. Of uncertain ancestry, they appear abruptly in the fossil record and almost immediately become the dominant flora. (Dorf, 1955.)

shows that the gaps which separate the highest categories may never be bridged in the fossil record. Many of the dicontinuities tend to be more and more emphasized with increased collecting.

The early history of the flowering plants, the angiosperms, is a case in point. Their rich fossil record begins with great abruptness in the lower Cretaceous rocks (Figure 56.3). The first angiosperm flora of some sixteen families appears almost simultaneously in such remote places as Transcaucasia, Portugal, England, Maryland, Texas, and New Zealand; and before the close of the Cretaceous period the flowering plants had become the dominant land vegetation probably occupying most of the present niches. In spite of their initial diversity, a long and determined search for Jurassic ancestors of the angiosperms has produced only a few doubtfully related forms. We can conclude only that the character of terrestrial vegetation throughout the world underwent a radical change within a period of time that was quite brief geologically but sufficient for differentiation and worldwide spread of the angiosperms, or that a long antecedent history of these plants took place in upland habitats that have not been preserved (Axelrod, 1952).

The trilobites of Paleozoic seas also illustrate very well the phenomenon of the systematic discontinuity. Judging from their fossils, the trilobites may well have been the most highly organized, abundant, and diverse animals during the first 100 million years of their existence. Several superfamilies comprising many families appear abruptly near the base of the lower Cambrian; others are introduced somewhat higher in the lower Cambrian (Figure 56.4). Of the ten superfamilies of lower Cambrian trilobites, not a single ancestor is known. Several of these major groups drop out at the top of the Cambrian without known descendants. Among the post-Cambrian forms ten of the superfamilies have long and well-documented records in the later Paleozoic. But of these, seven cannot be related confidently to any of the known Cambrian groups by means of intermediate fossils. Continued collecting has only emphasized the separation of these groups in the known record.

The abrupt appearance of the trilobites near the base of the Paleozoic rocks is part of a larger problem of the origin of the Cambrian fauna. A majority of the major invertebrate phyla comprising some five hundred known species, many of which belonged to highly organized animals, are known in this fauna.

On the other hand, most pre-Cambrian rocks are unfossiliferous and very few pre-Cambrian fossils are on record. Many of these have been discredited either as inorganic in origin or younger than pre-Cambrian in age. . . .

Students of trilobites, impressed by the advanced state of evolution of the earliest trilobites of the lower Cambrian, believe with Darwin that they must have had a long antecedent history in the pre-Cambrian when their skeletons may have contained little or no calcium carbonate (Whittington, 1954). It is a well-known fact that the chitinous exoskeletons of *Limulus* and other arthropods are destroyed quickly by certain bacteria and only those groups that have heavily calcified skeletons are common fossils even in Tertiary and Quaternary rocks. This explanation, however, does not take into account the fact that unequivocal fossils of soft-bodied invertebrates, although by no means common, are known in many places and should have turned up in pre-Cambrian rocks by now. The mid-Cambrian Burgess shale of British Columbia has yielded thousands of specimens of upward of 130 species of soft-bodied animals, most of which are unknown elsewhere. They are preserved with minute details as tissue-thin films of carbon imprinted on bedding planes. Many of these fossils (trilobitomorphs) are similar to trilobites but they did not possess calcareous skeletons.

A clue to the meaning of some of the systematic deficiencies of the fossil record is provided by the recent discovery of living coelacanth fishes and monoplacophoran molluscs long known from the fossil record and supposed to be extinct since the Cretaceous and Devonian periods, respectively. There are many such illustrations in the fossil record of stragglers from once widespread and abundant groups that have become greatly restricted geographically, living on in some isolated area for millions of years after their disappearance in other areas. For example, blastoids died out in early Pennsylvanian times over most of the world, but they survived well into the Permian period in Indonesia, a time span of forty or fifty million years. These facts simply mean that probabilities of discovery of a fossil record or a living population are poor in those groups that are not abundant and widely distributed.

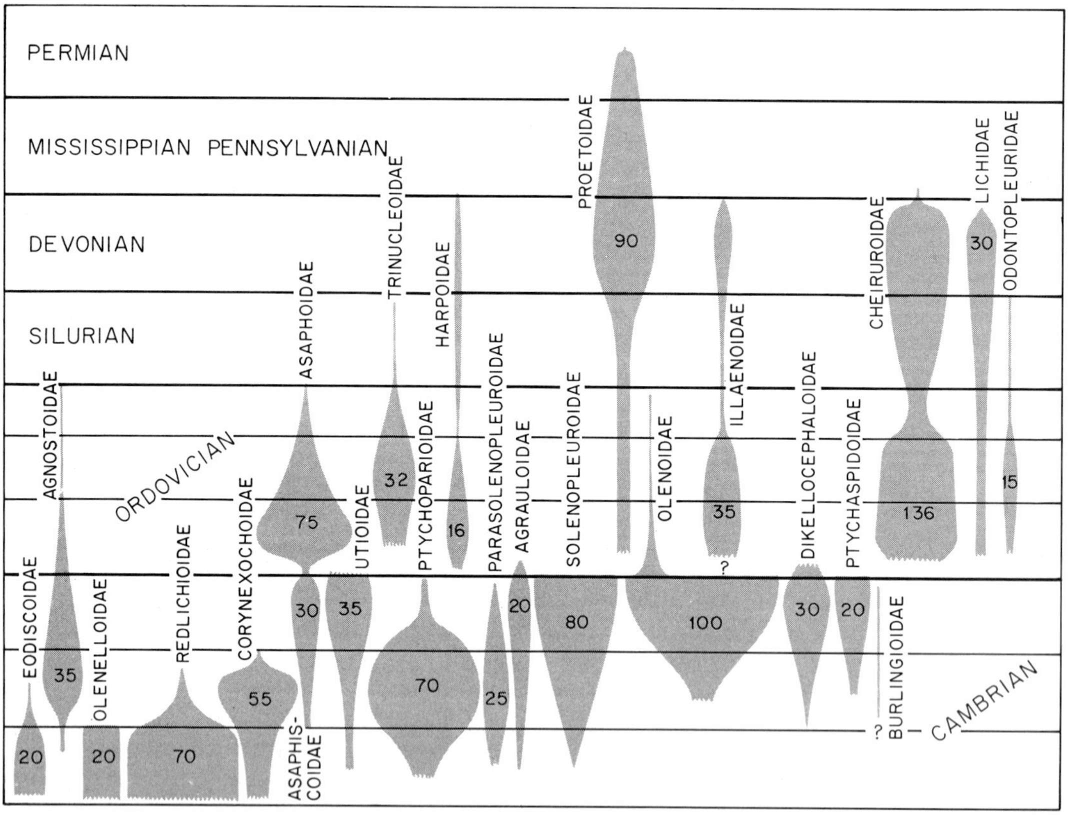

FIGURE 56.4
Stratigraphic distribution of superfamilies of trilobites in the fossil record with numbers of known genera. Noteworthy are the contrast in composition of Cambrian and Ordovician assemblages, abrupt extinction of great groups at top of the Cambrian, and restriction of post-Devonian trilobites to a single superfamily. (From Moore, after Whittington, 1953.)

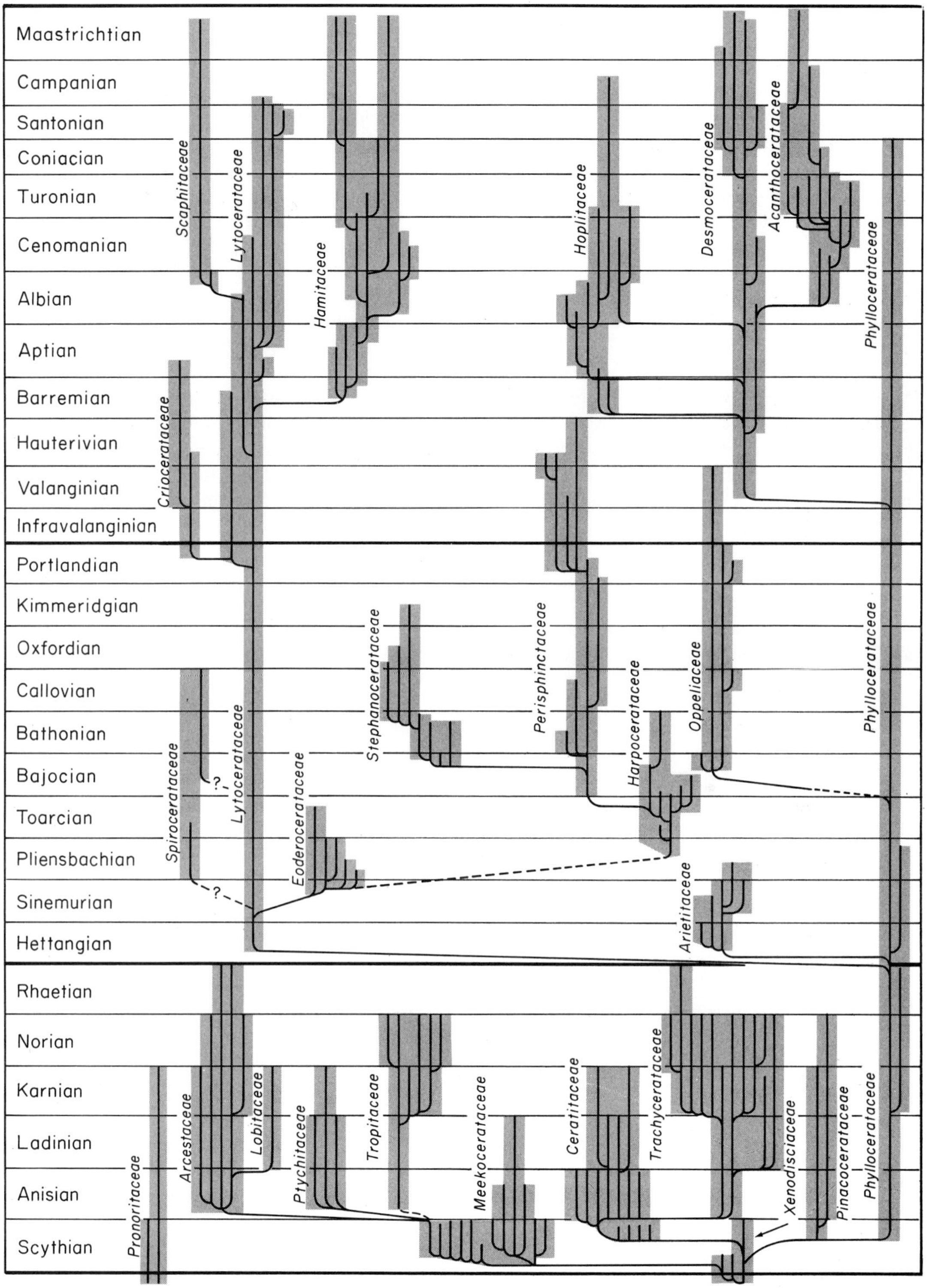

FIGURE 56.5
Stratigraphic distribution and inferred phylogeny of Mesozoic ammonites. Heavy horizontal bars separate Triassic, Jurassic, and Cretaceous systems and shaded areas represent superfamilies and family subdivisions. The Triassic ammonites originated from two, and the Jurassic forms from a single superfamily. (From Moore, 1955.)

Darwin noted that our fossil record is pretty much limited to sedimentary basins. That is, low swampy areas, deltas, lakes, the sea. Organisms of upland areas and other ecological zones characterized by erosion . . . are rarely represented in the fossil record. It has often been suggested that the angiosperms may have diverged from the gymnosperms in upland areas subject to persistent denudation. . . .

Simpson (1953*a*) has shown that the systematic discontinuities in the fossil record are most satisfactorily explained as an effect of sampling error in small, isolated populations. Many of these populations were in rapid transition, undergoing "quantum evolution" between adaptive zones. Sampling is less reliable for very rapidly evolving than for slowly evolving groups. Thus, while a few connecting links are discovered between higher categories, these are relatively rare and many systematic gaps tend to persist in spite of continued collecting.

In contrast to the many fossil groups that display innumerable gaps in the record, there are a few in which the known record is relatively complete and inferred phylogenies are secure, e.g., the ammonites (Figure 56.5).

ABUNDANCE OF FOSSILS

One of the earliest discoveries about the paleontologic record is that fossils actually are more abundant in fossil-bearing rocks than might be assumed from cursory inspection. In many cases it may be suspected that even those forms represented in collections by a few specimens, or only one, are numerous or abundant within the rocks.

Now, the problem of locating fossils is enormously complicated by the fact that fossiliferous strata are partly or wholly concealed in most areas by a cover of superficial rubble, soil, and vegetation. Consequently, our ideas about the abundance of fossils usually are colored by the character and extent of suitable rock exposures.

Strata considered to be only sparsely fossiliferous as judged from superficial inspection actually may be abundantly so. The degree to which this is true is clearly shown by methods of mass collecting fossils, wherein a volume of fossiliferous clay or marl is dug by hand shovel, or power machinery, washed with water, and sieved for fossils. This method has long been used widely for microscopic fossils such as spores and Foraminifera, but it also is coming into use for larger invertebrates and bones and teeth of small vertebrates. The number of fossils thus obtained is usually greater per unit volume of rock than per unit surface and fossils collected in matrix have an advantage that they are damaged less frequently by weathering than those found at the surface.

Small fossils are incredibly numerous in certain strata, where they may be a major component of the rocks. Leidy once estimated a quarter of a million Foraminifera in an ounce of marine sediment. A cubic inch of diatomaceous earth contains as high as fifteen million diatoms . . . and there are many cubic miles of pure diatomite in the Tertiary rocks of California alone. Robert Broom, the distinguished South African paleontologist estimated that there are about eight hundred billion skeletons of vertebrate animals in the Karroo formation. While such estimates are not really meaningful in themselves, they stress the vast difference between the paleontological sample and the astronomic numbers of fossils remaining in the rocks. The abundance of individual fossils is, of course, not directly related to their diversity. Teichert (1956) has undertaken an interesting estimate of the total number of fossil species of animals and plants. He has taken as a premise that those organisms with skeletal parts make up most of the fossil record and he omits consideration of soft-bodied organisms or insects as quantitatively unimportant. In this he errs on the side of conservatism because very many of these are known as fossils. Among living organisms the numbers of species most susceptible to preservation as fossils are:

Invertebrates	170,000
Vertebrates	49,000
Vascular plants	350,000
"Preservable species"	569,000

Taking twelve million years as the average longevity of a species, he concludes that the number of species of animals and plants preserved in the rocks may reach a total of ten million. According to an estimate made by

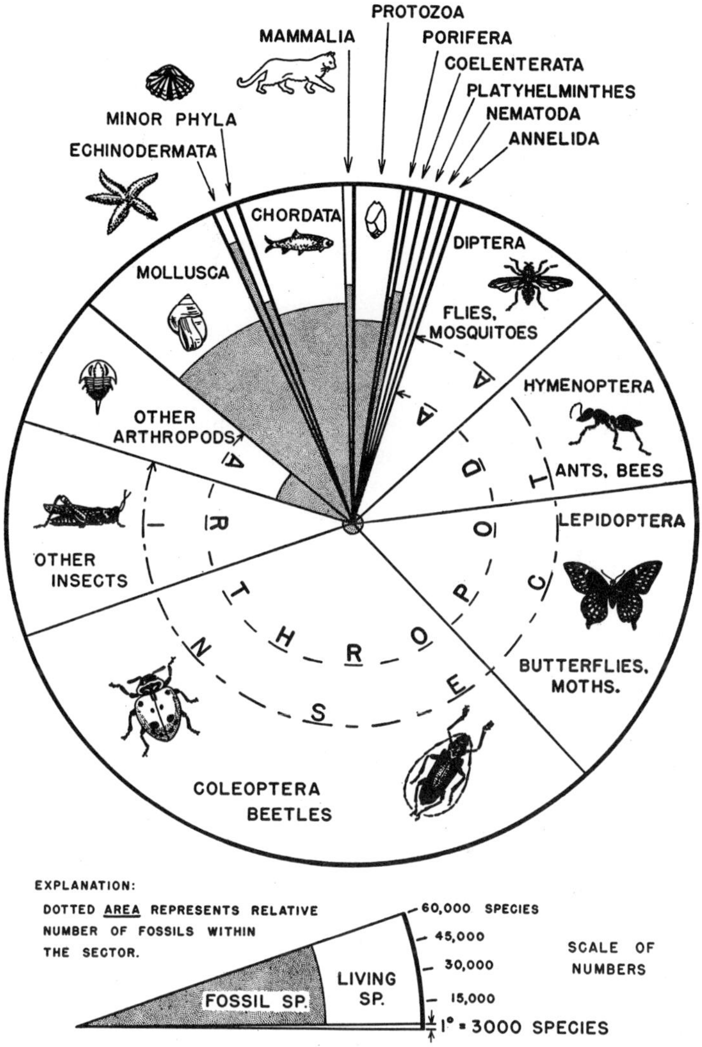

FIGURE 56.6
Relative numbers of known species of animals. (Muller and Campbell, *Systematic Zoology*, 1954.)

Muller and Campbell (1954), about ninety-two thousand fossil species of animals are now described (Figure 56.6), and I think that the plants would bring the total to around one hundred thousand or only one per cent of Teichert's estimate of the ultimate richness of the fossil record. These speculations are useful in stressing the fact that the fossil record still is poorly known, and they indicate something of the magnitude of the opportunities and the task ahead.

Publication rates provide a rough measure of the rates of discovery of new categories of fossils (Figure 56.7). A long sustained or increasing rate of publication of new genera, for example, is strong circumstantial evidence that there has not been a decline in the rate of new discoveries. Minor fluctuations in publication rates are produced by the sporadic appearance of monographs, by differences in initiative and taxonomic philosophy among authors; and larger fluctuations are caused by war, depression, and other vicissitudes of life. Long term trends may be significant in terms of the development of knowledge about fossil groups. Figure 56.7 indicates that discovery rates in Foraminifera and fossil mammals seem to be expanding. There is no indication from this evidence that most of the distinctive kinds of fossils have been discovered. On the other hand, discovery of new living mammals has about ceased, and there is a suggestion that the rate of discovery of new ammonoids is declining. This may indicate that most of the basically different kinds of ammonoids have been found, but it is too early to be sure of this.

BIAS IN THE FOSSIL RECORD

It is an exciting experience to sit in a canoe quietly drifting down a stream surrounded by a tropical forest teeming with life or to submerge oneself along a coral reef and to inspect closely this biota. To the paleontologist these are momentary situations in a changing scene—single frames in the motion picture of earth history. How much is likely to be preserved in the fossil record? I have examined the alluvial deposits of the tropical river bank for recently deposited organic remains and I have studied broken fragments of living coral reefs piled above sea level by great storm waves. In both cases, the contrast between the living and the dead is very great. Practically all of the organic substances readily decomposable by aerobic bacteria and fungi disappear within days or weeks. In the river alluvium there are remains of perhaps ten or fifteen species of the total of ten thousand. In the reef limestone fifty to seventy-five species of the living three thousand are recognizable after depredations of bacteria and scavengers. But note this: even though the living communities are not preservable in the aggregate, the few preserved species, studied in context with the sediments, tell eloquently of a specific habitat.

Darwin showed clearly that the fossil record probably is never [simply] a random sample of life of the past. . . .

Aside from extremely rare examples of preservation of animal tissues in comparatively young rocks and small arthropods and spores in fossil amber, nearly all fossil remains consist

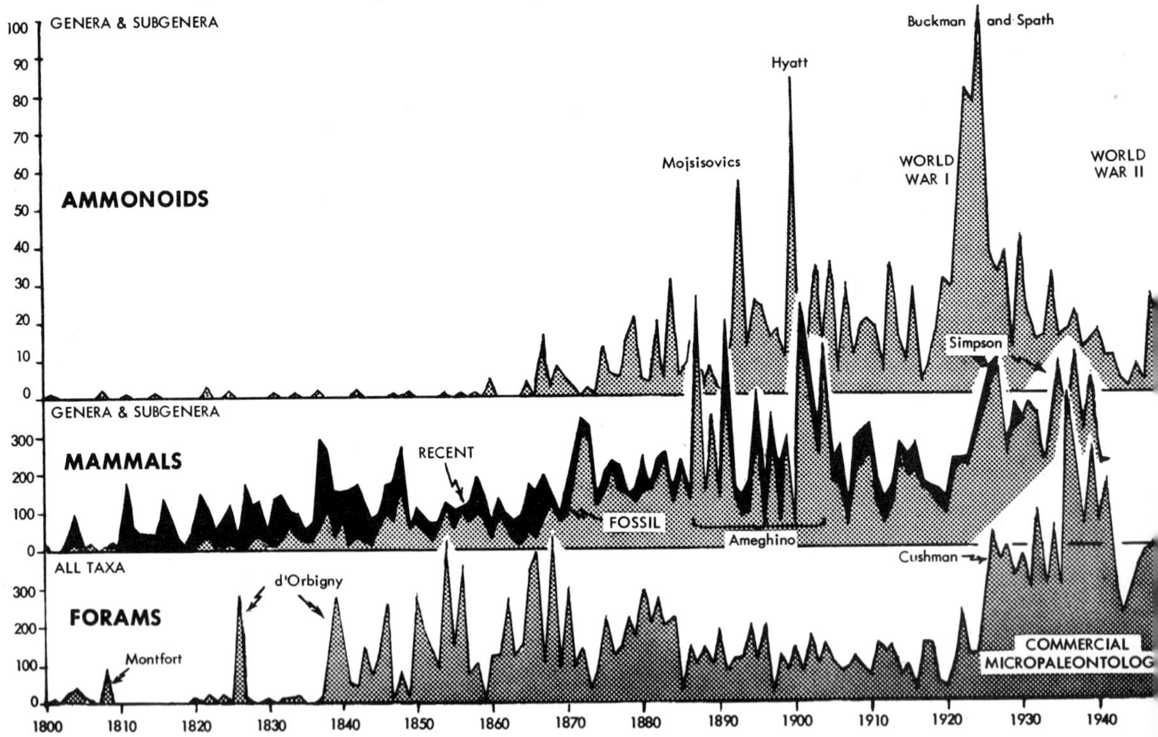

FIGURE 56.7
Publication rate as a measure of discovery rate of new fossils. Minor fluctuations result from initiative of a few authors, larger cycles reflect economic and political conditions. The data suggest that most living mammals are now known but fossil mammals and Foraminifera are being discovered at increasing rates. New ammonite discoveries possibly are decreasing in frequency. (Ammonite data from Arkell, Wright, and Kummel, *Treatise on Invertebrate Paleontology*, 1957; mammals from Simpson, 1945; Foraminifera from Messina, 1952.)

of comparatively resistant hard parts. Complete skeletons with all of the parts in position of articulation are on the whole exceptional or even unknown for many groups of plants and animals, so that paleontological studies usually are based on scattered and fragmentary parts of skeletons. Although there are exceptions, the organs and other tissues, details of form, coloration, behavior, and many other characteristics of living organisms commonly are not preserved. The great hosts of soft-bodied plants and animals that make up a large part of any biota likewise rarely are preserved so that their very existence in the past must be inferred by analogy with communities of organisms of the present.

There are puzzling systematic deficiencies in the records of many groups of organisms with skeletal parts well adapted for fossilization. The incompleteness of the record in many cases probably originates in low population density, location of habitat far from sites of deposition of sediments, and in the habits of organisms. For example, as already noted, the fossil record throughout the world is very poor in remains of upland animals and plants. Probabilities of quick and permanent burial of these forms are slight because they live at a distance from the low places where sediments finally come to rest in depositional basins. Likewise, arboreal mammals and birds tend to be consumed by scavengers before burial and they are poorly represented as fossils. There is scarcely any record of desert plants. Desert deposits are deficient in fossils of all kinds because of a characteristic sparseness of desert life, and oxidizing conditions and leaching reach far below the surface. Organic remains are destroyed here about as fast as they are buried; desert deposits tend to be coarse-grained. The sediment fragments grind up organic remains as they are transported in violent floods that characterize stream deposition in the desert.

Without going into all the various factors operative in these systematic deficiencies in the fossil record, it seems safe to conclude that very many organisms did not frequent sites of persistent and quiet accumulation of sediments. For one reason or another they did not occur in abundance in places where they might be buried quickly. The extreme rareness of fossil remains of early man is a case in point. Man and many other mammals make use of their intelligence in escaping flood waters and in avoiding quicksands and bogs.

On the other hand, aquatic organisms and those that live near water are in close association with the deposition of sediments and are favorably situated for quick burial before they are consumed. Consequently, the greatest part of the fossil record consists of the skeletal remains and traces of organisms that lived in water, especially in the sea, or near the margins of streams, lakes, or swamps. Thus, in a very real sense, most of the fossil record is the record of lowland or marine basins of aqueous sedimentation. Even under the most favorable conditions, however, quick burial and preservation of organic remains must be a rare event as compared with the total number of organisms that live at one time.

BIOLOGICAL FACTORS

Population density and distribution must also be an important factor affecting the frequency with which organisms have been preserved. It seems certain that preservation of organisms in the fossil record is such a very rare event that thousands or millions of individuals are destroyed for each one that is incorporated in the record. Thus, organisms that are abundantly represented in an environment favorable for quick burial have a better chance of preservation than those that are not so abundant. In general, small organisms reproduce more rapidly and produce larger populations than do large organisms. . . .

The structure of the plant body is not well adapted to preservation as a single unit and the most common plant fossils are detached spores, pollen leaves, stems, or fragments of wood. Well-preserved seeds, fruits, and particularly flowers are rare. There also is occasionally a close resemblance of form among the leaves of different families and orders. These difficulties are overcome by careful consideration of all the fine details of shape, texture, character of margin, and apex of leaves, character of primary and secondary venation, and particularly by the microscopic structure of the cuticle of leaves and reproductive organs. Epidermal characters are often well preserved and directly comparable to those of living plants.

Thus, conclusions are not based solely on a few leaves but on a whole complex of characters and on the plant associations which, although incomplete, are nevertheless composed of dominant members of harmonious communities and therefore indicative of specific habitats.

PHYSICAL FACTORS

Fossils may be destroyed quickly by weathering or gradually by changes that take place after burial. These changes are more rapid in certain kinds of skeletons than in others so that there is selective preservation of some fossil groups over others.

The processes of sedimentation in many cases complicate interpretation of the associations of fossils, particularly the small forms that are easily moved by wind or water. The dead remains of various forms may be transported from diverse habitats and deposited together in associations that do not reflect any single life environment. Under these conditions there is much winnowing and sorting of organic remains by size, shape, and effective specific gravity. The remains of young and small organisms thus may be separated from those of older and larger forms. Less commonly, the fossils of an older rock formation are weathered free of rock matrix and become incorporated in a younger formation in association with fossil forms that lived much later and under quite different conditions. . . .

In spite of the shortcomings of the fossil record, many extinct animal and plant groups favored by the factors of preservation are becoming quite well known. The record provides documents of organic evolution and still incomplete but very meaningful histories of many important groups of organisms through hundreds of millions of years. It serves as the basis for a scale of geologic time that has been adopted generally and found accurate in broad outline throughout the world. The sequence of fossil faunas and floras enables the paleontologist to date rock formations in terms of this standard geologic scale and thus to correlate contemporaneous strata and geological events in widely separated regions.

RELIABILITY OF THE RECORD

I have discussed at some length the shortcomings of the fossil record as a representative sample of past life. Darwin understood very well most of the cited limitations. He was optimistic about the future of paleontology, and the remarkable advances in the past century of discovery and collecting surely have far exceeded his expectations. But how can we evaluate our knowledge of the record? What are the confidence limits of our present inferences? How much will we have to modify our conclusions as more information is gathered? These questions cannot be answered readily, but past experience may help us in formulating tentative judgments.

Experience from past discoveries shows that our ideas still are changing rapidly in some areas of knowledge as new evidence accumulates. In other areas, there has been little or no fundamental change in broad perspective for several decades in spite of continuous study. For example, the early nineteenth century paleontologists knew that the trilobites were quite varied and complex at their first appearance in the lower Cambrian, that they soon deployed greatly in the higher Cambrian and Ordovician rocks, and that they then gradually diminished in variety until their disappearance from the record near the top of the Paleozoic.

Even if the known range of the trilobites is extended through future discoveries of pre-Cambrian or Triassic trilobites, it would be unreasonable in the present advanced state of knowledge to consider seriously the possibility that the new finds would reveal widespread and diverse faunas at the new limits of range that had been completely overlooked previously. Such new discoveries are not likely to affect greatly our present conclusions about the presently known record.

Studies of fossils over the past century have confirmed many generalizations held in Darwin's day, and, in retrospect, we can recognize steady confirmations as well as refutations of general conclusions. We still believe that the dinosaurs, marine reptiles, and the ammonites dropped out in the late Cretaceous. Gymnosperms are still considered dominant in Jurassic and Triassic rocks; angiosperms and mammals

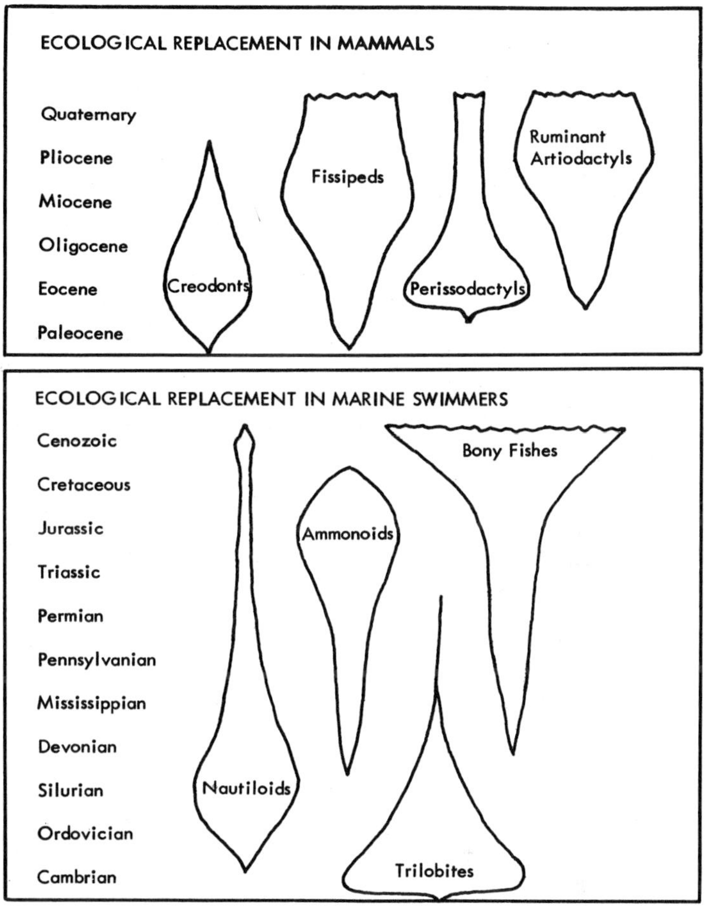

FIGURE 56.8
Replacement among competing major groups of animals. The patterns of increasing and decreasing diversity suggest progressive ecological displacement of less successful by more successful groups. (Data on mammals after Simpson, 1953, Columbia Univ. Press.)

are dominant in Tertiary rocks. Of course, revolutionary discoveries occur from time to time, but usually they result in modification and adjustment of details, not in wholesale abandonment of broad generalizations arrived at empirically after much sampling. The known record is spotty indeed, but it is very good for the more abundant and well-preserved groups of fossils. When fossils are rare or poorly preserved, conclusions are more tentative and they vary greatly in order of probability.

The great times of expansion and recession of the better-known major groups have been known for a long time and the general outlines of knowledge here are not likely to undergo major revision. Some major groups display what appears to have been a sort of ecological incompatibility, successively and gradually replacing one another in time as more successful groups wrested one niche after another from competing inferior groups. Darwin anticipated this phenomenon and suggested how competition could lead to the extinction of all of the less well-adapted organisms without concurrent changes in the inorganic factors of the environment. Illustrations of replacement in competing groups are the trilobites, shelled cephalopods, and bony fishes; the creodonts and fissipeds; and the perissodactyls and ruminant artiodactyls (Figure 56.8). Among plants, the expansion of the angiosperms was accompanied by restriction and elimination of many groups of gymnosperms and lower land plants (Figure 56.3).

Studies by G. G. Simpson and others have shown that the known fossil record now is sufficient for accurate measurement of rates of evolution, a subject of great importance in connection with understanding evolutionary mechanisms and also of interest from the standpoint of geological chronology (Simpson, 1953*a*). It now is well established that rates of evolution vary greatly within and between related groups. Furthermore, there is no simple correlation between reproduction rate and evolutionary rate. Certain groups of small Foraminifera, with reproductive rates thousands of the times those of mammals, have evolved very much more slowly than the latter, but other Foraminifera have evolved as fast as any group of mammals. High, intermediate, and low rates are recognized and these are dependent on the Darwinian factors of variability and selection pressure (Figures 56.1, 56.2, and 56.5).

Phylogenies in paleontology are inferred from morphological series distributed chrono-

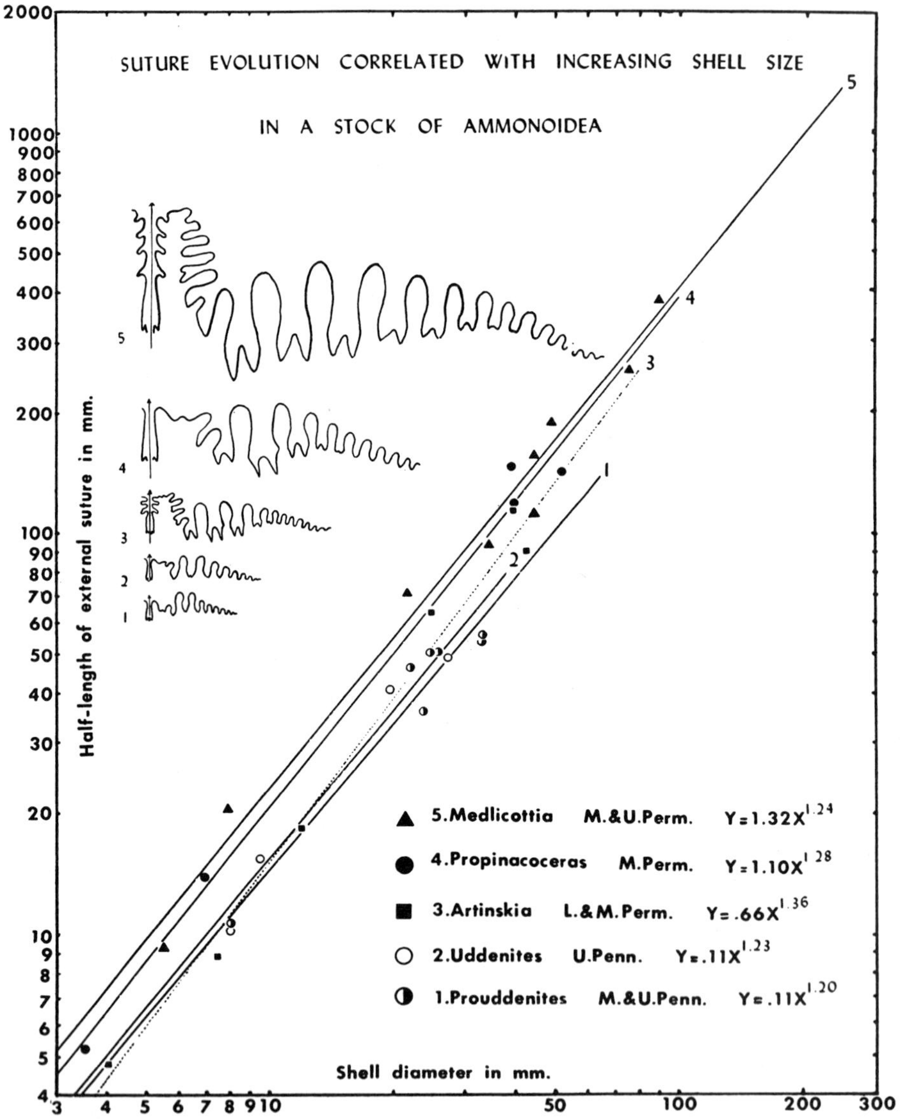

FIGURE 56.9
Correlated trends in evolution of certain ammonites. There is a simple mathematical (allometric) relationship between the tendency for shells to increase in size and increased complexity of suture pattern during evolution. A close relationship is found between size and complexity during growth of the individual. (Newell, *Evolution,* 1949.)

logically through the stratigraphic succession. Innumerable examples have been worked out for Foraminifera, corals, molluscs (Figure 56.5), echinoderms, arthropods, hemichordates, vertebrates, and vascular plants. The evidence in many fossil groups is so well documented and voluminous that few neontologists would think of ignoring paleontologic data in making phylogenetic interpretations. For example, Florin (1944) has shown that the mutual relationships among modern conifers can be understood only by taking into account the many extinct Permian forms which had fructifications unlike those of any living forms. It has been shown many times that modern animals and plants are the ends of evolutionary lines which usually are more specialized in at least a few characters than the most closely related ancestral forms in the fossil record. Thus, hypothetical phylogenies based solely on living genera and species cannot express the true relationships. In order to understand the ancestry of, and connections between, living genera and families, it is necessary to know the fossil record. Conversely, the evidence from fossils is incomplete without reference to distributions, ecology, anatomy, and adaptations of living forms.

Paleontologists have pioneered studies of growth and morphogenesis and they have provided many illustrations from the fossil record of correlated growth (allometric) gradients in both ontogeny and phylogeny (Figure 56.9).

One outstanding contribution of paleontology that would otherwise be completely unknown is the repeated demonstration of long evolutionary trends in which two or more separate but related lineages pass independently through the same sequence of morphological changes, either simultaneously or at different times (Figure 56.10). Many illustrations are known among both animals and plants. For example, there was a persistent tendency for many lines of primitive graptolites to change direction of colony growth from downward or horizontal to vertical. This trend extended through several families and it frequently enables the stratigrapher to determine the general geological age of a graptolite assemblage from evolutionary stage without identification of the particular genera at hand (Bulman, 1955). Likewise, many families of the great groups of corals have evolved along a characteristic sequence from solitary or dendritic forms to tightly packed colonies with prismatic individuals (Wells, 1956). The independent development of saber-toothed "tigers" and carnivores in placental and marsupial mammals, the closely parallel changes in horse and horselike litopterns, the common trends for increased body size and brain size in mammals are other examples of parallel evolution recognizable as such only in the fossil record (Colbert, 1955).

Stebbins notes that "the great majority of evolutionary trends toward increased specialization in vascular plants can be explained as a result of three types of morphological trends, acting either separately or in conjunction with each other. These are reduction, fusion, and change in symmetry. The most widespread of these trends has been reduction" (Stebbins, 1950).

These parallel trends no longer have orthogenetic or vitalistic implications to the majority of paleontologists who now recognize the

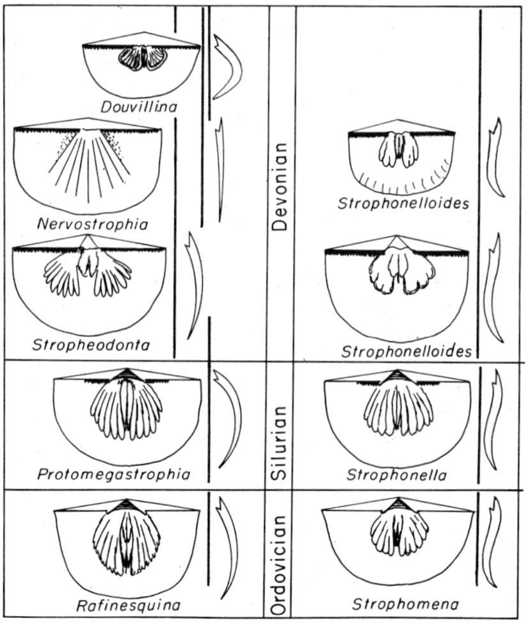

FIGURE 56.10
Parallel evolution in two families of early Paleozoic brachiopods. In both lines the hinge margin becomes increasingly subdivided by interlocking teeth. Note that the rates of change were about the same in the two stocks. (Dunbar and Rodgers, *Principles of Stratigraphy*, John Wiley and Sons, 1957.)

probability that these patterns are an adaptive expression of similar genetic organization in closely related lineages.

FOSSIL POPULATIONS

The fossil record supplies a wealth of data on changes in time and space in both populations and entire biotas during long spans of time. Thus, paleontology contributes evidence bearing on many principles of evolution and gives the paleontologist an advantage of an abundance of time that is denied the student of living organisms.

Many fossil samples are adequate for quantitative studies of various kinds. For example, Kurten (1953), Deevey (1955), and others have shown that relatively undisturbed fossil assemblages may be used effectively in studies of population dynamics. Samples suitable for the studies of population variability are quite easily obtained for some groups, especially microfossils; and statistical methods are used increasingly to refine discrimination and to establish the limits of fossil subspecies and species (Imbrie, 1957).

PALEOECOLOGY

Much attention has been given in recent years to ecological interpretations of fossil assemblages in order to learn about the mutual relationships between past organisms and their environments. This requires a disciplined synthesis of paleontology, stratigraphy, petrology, geochemistry, and sedimentation for the most complete utilization of all available evidence from fossils, rocks, and stratigraphy. By attacking paleoecological problems along all available lines of evidence, surprisingly detailed interpretations of past environments are possible and the fossils themselves acquire much added significance whenever they are studied in the full context of their geologic setting (e.g., Imbrie, 1955; Newell, *et al.*, 1953; Bradley, 1931).

Fossils have provided most of the evidence for a quite detailed history of changes in distributions of land and sea, and many generalized paleogeographic maps have been published showing the location of major seaways and lands for the successive epochs of time (Dunbar, 1949). These maps are helpful in summarizing knowledge of the distributions of marine and nonmarine deposits and in working out hypothetical times and routes of migrations of organisms (Simpson, 1953*b*).

The evidence from fossil plants is in some respects less complete than that available from fossil animals, but plants tell us much more than animals do about past climates and there is an excellent record of the succession and migration of floras during geologic history.

The oldest known fossils are the remains of filamentous algae and fungi, but the record of past floras is quite poor before the upper Silurian by which time the continents of the world had become clothed with a diverse vegetation of vascular plants (Figure 56.3). Cosmopolitan floras of extraordinarily wide distribution of the middle Paleozoic are thought to indicate much milder world climates than at present with remarkably little zonation. The late Paleozoic and Triassic floras increasingly marked zonation roughly parallel with the present equator. This is succeeded in Jurassic and Cretaceous rocks by comparatively uniform floras throughout the world. Evidence of latitudinal floral zones is again apparent throughout the Tertiary period which was a time of gradual cooling from generally subtropical conditions at intermediate latitudes to the present conditions (Figure 56.11). The zonal distribution from fossil floras argues for stability of the poles and continents throughout the latter part of earth history (Chaney, 1940; Edwards, 1955), as opposed to extensive polar migrations or continental sliding as suggested by studies of paleomagnetism. The record of fossil invertebrates has been used in arguments for (Ma, 1957) and against (Stehli, 1957) migration of poles or continents. . . .

Fossil spores long have been known in coal beds (Figure 56.12 A), and in the past few decades plant micropaleontology, or palynology, as it is now termed, has produced . . . thousands of papers on fossil spores and pollen, bearing particularly on stratigraphic zonation and correlation in coal basins and Quaternary nonmarine deposits. These fossils have assumed a significance for correlating and dating continental deposits comparable to that of

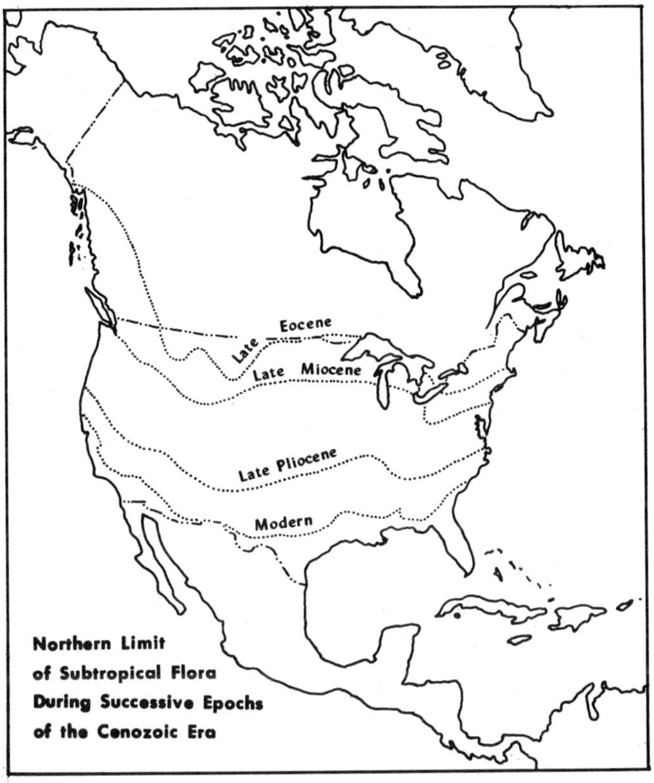

FIGURE 56.11
Evidence from fossil plants of progressive cooling of climate since the Cretaceous period. The glacial climates of the Pleistocene are not represented. (Dorf, 1957.)

the Foraminifera of marine rocks. The tiny plant fossils are chemically resistant and may be extracted successfully from rocks by chemical means. In 1900 the Swedish botanist Logerheim showed that the stratigraphic succession of spores and pollen in Quaternary deposits provided a detailed record of floral migrations under the influence of strong climatic changes. With the aid of these tiny plant remains, the complex climatic fluctuations of the Quaternary glacial and interglacial stages have been worked out in great detail.

Shortly after World War II, H. C. Urey showed that the ratio of the isotopes of oxygen O^{18}/O^{16} contained in unmodified calcium carbonate skeletons of aquatic organisms is a delicate indication of the temperature of the water in which the skeletons were secreted. Paleotemperatures of ancient marine molluscs as old as Cretaceous thus have been measured, but the greatest application of this chemical method has been to work out the detailed stratigraphy and temperature zonation of the Globigerina ooze that blankets much of the floor of the north Atlantic (Emiliani, 1958*a*). The records of climatic fluctuations over the north Atlantic basin throughout the glacial and interglacial stages of the past 300,000 years have been worked out in detail and correlated with climatic cycles in Europe and America determined by means of pollen analyses (Emiliani, 1958*b*).

QUALITY OF FOSSILS

Much has been written and said about the imperfections of fossils which, for the most part, consist of incomplete, weathered, or fragmentary skeletons, or their impressions in matrix from which the skeletal remains have been dissolved by ground water. Fortunately, we do not have to depend solely on fossils of inferior quality for our information about past life. Steady improvement in techniques of collecting and of extracting fossils from rock matrix has effected a minor revolution in paleontology and has shown that there is a bountiful supply of well-preserved material available for study provided that it can be suitably prepared for study. The great impediment to progress in paleontology is not the imperfections of the fossil record, but rather the difficulties involved in freeing fossils from matrix or otherwise preparing them for study. . . .

Animal skeletons and shells originally composed of phosphate or carbonate of lime, or of silica, and leaves, spores and the woody parts of plants form the bulk of the fossil record and these may be well preserved (Figures 56.12 A, B, and 56.13 A, B), but there are also examples of preservation of chitinous skeletons and soft tissues which provide valuable information not available in the more common fossils (Figures 56.12 C and 56.13 C).

For example, frozen mammoths with parts of the flesh and skin preserved have been reported from more than fifty localities in northern Siberia, and thousands of ivory tusks have been obtained from this source and marketed for the manufacture of art objects in China. In this case, continuous refrigeration since death has prevented bacterial decay. Fossils preserved in this way are limited to quite young fossils of the far north. A much more important mode of preservation is the embalming action of stagnant, oxygen-deficient waters of certain swamps, lakes, and marine basins. . . .

Animal tissues decompose very slowly in the bottom sediments of stagnant waters. For example, a large number of human cadavers more than two thousand years old have been found within peat deposits of Denmark and Holland. Many of these are remarkable for the excellent preservation of tissues and organs which have suffered hardly any shrinkage or deformation. . . .

Incompletely decayed plant remains accumulate in bogs as peat, and if the peat becomes buried by sediments, it may eventually form coal through a succession of chemical changes. Remains of bottom animals are not abundant in these deposits because bog waters are usually anaerobic and even toxic, but occasional insects and land animals find their way into bog deposits where, free from the depredations of scavengers, they may become preserved as fossils.

One of the most remarkable examples of preservation of organic tissues in antiseptic swamp waters is a "fossil graveyard" in Eocene lignite deposits of the Geisel Valley in central Germany. This was systematically studied by Johannes Weigelt of Halle University and his associates (Weigelt, 1935). Many animals, including groups rarely found as fossils, lower

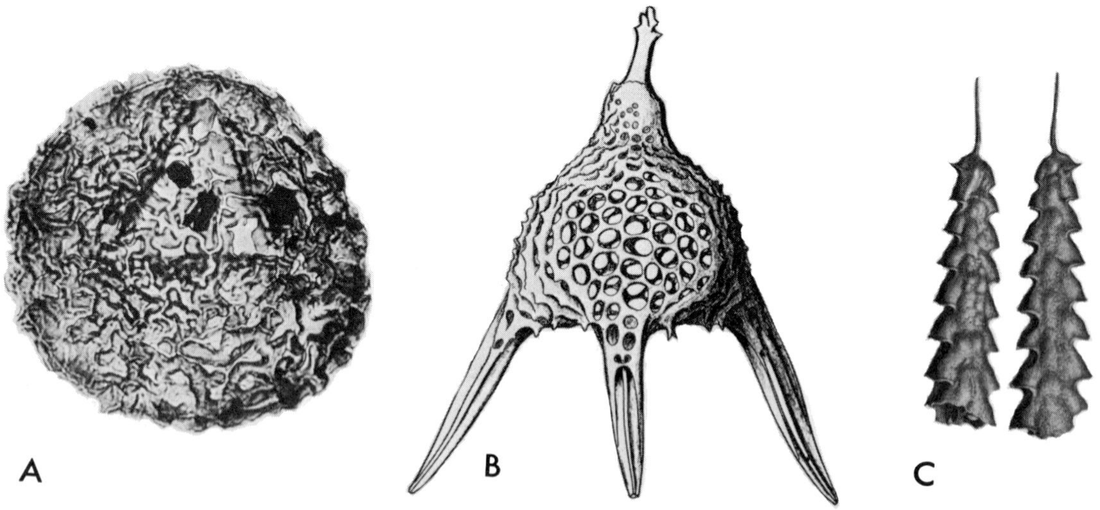

FIGURE 56.12
Microscopic fossils. A, a plant spore, × 250, of Mississippian age, Nova Scotia (Hacquebard, 1957, *Micropaleontology*); B, a silica radiolarian, × 250, late Tertiary, Rotti (Riedel, *Jour. Paleontology*, 1953); C, an uncrushed graptolite colony of original chitinoid material, × 8, Ordovician of Öland (Bulman, *Archiv för Zoologi*, 1936.)

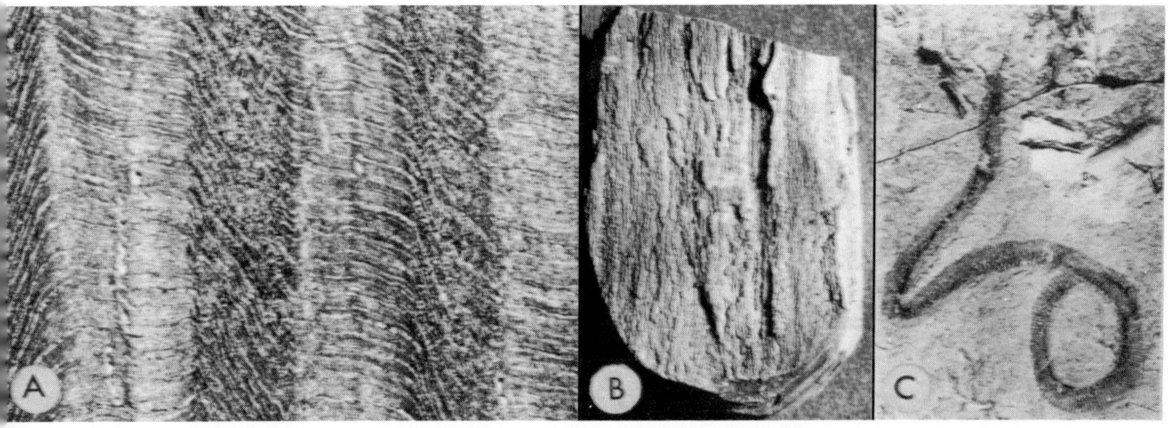

FIGURE 56.13
Cretaceous wood and Cambrian worm. *A*, *B*, fossil wood of Araucaria tree more than 100 million years old. The microscopic structure of this early Cretaceous fossil from New Jersey is perfectly preserved. The wood has not been mineralized or otherwise appreciably modified. *A*, × 16; *B*, × 1. *C*, Fossil annelid worm with details preserved as carbonaceous film on clay shale, × 3, Upper Cambrian (Tremadocian) of England (Whittard, *Geol. Soc. London Quart. Jour.*, 1953).

primates, snakes, and birds were trapped in several small, scattered bogs where they accumulated and were preserved from bacterial attack in stagnant oxygen-poor waters. More than six thousand remains of vertebrate animals and great numbers of insects, molluscs, and plants were found over a period of several years as the lignite was being mined.

The fossils that had been collected when Weigelt made his report in 1935 included more than fifteen hundred fish of many kinds, twenty frogs, a salamander, fifty-two crocodiles, two hundred tortoises, several snakes, and tree lizards, twenty different kinds of birds, seventeen species of lemuroids, five rodents, six archaic carnivores, three early horses, a bat, and many primitive herbivores.

The flattened and dessicated remains of soft tissues of these animals in many cases showed details of cellular structure. Some of the specimens had undergone little chemical modification, but among the frogs there are specimens in which the bones were leached away while the brain and spinal cord were preserved as *adipocere*, a calcium compound of fatty acids. This is a very unusual case of preservation of soft anatomical structures after destruction of the hard skeleton. Epithelial cells showing the nuclei were preserved in the skin of frog specimens. Small details of fly larvae and beetles, including the chitinous exoskeleton, muscular tissue, and tracheae were preserved. Muscular tissue, connective tissue showing microscopic details, and cartilage were found in fishes, frogs, salamanders, lizards, and mammals.

Several fossils contained remains of fat cells and pigment cells (chromatophores) with animal pigment. Well-preserved bits of hair, feathers, and scales probably are among the oldest known examples of essentially unmodified preservation of these structures. Stomach contents of beetles, amphibia, fishes, birds, and mammals provided direct evidence about eating habits. Bacteria of two kinds were found in the excrement of crocodiles and another on the trachea of a beetle. Fungi were identified on leaves, and the original plant pigments, chlorophyll and coproporphyrin, were found preserved in some of the leaves. From such ample fossil evidence it is possible to reconstruct the Eocene life of the Geisel Valley in considerable detail.

Fossil wood buried under the anaerobic conditions of stagnant swamps has in some cases endured with only little decay for amazingly long periods of time. For example, logs found in the Eocene lignites of Germany and in early Cretaceous clays of New Jersey are composed of unaltered wood and show perfectly preserved microscopic cellular structure of the original trees (Figures 56.13 A, B). They resemble ordinary wood and do not exhibit significant mineralization in spite of the fact that they are approximately fifty million years old in the first case, and one hundred million years old in the second.

The fossil amber deposits of the Baltic region are famous for the well-preserved insects and spiders found in the amber. These were trapped in tree gum long ago, in the Oligocene epoch, and have been protected from decomposition by the moisture-proof and air-proof cover.

Destruction of organic remains is retarded in impervious rocks which not only exclude oxygen but also prevent the circulation of ground water. Molluscs of Cretaceous age are abundant in the Coon Creek Clay of Tennessee. The mother-of-pearl shells and even chitinoid ligaments of clam shells are extraordinarily well preserved for faunas this old. Caster and Waering (1951) discovered many remarkable skeletons of eurypterid *Megalograptus* in a clay deposit of Ordovician age. The original chitin is but little altered in these fossils and still retains a scorpionid color pattern, and many of the skeletons are articulated. Since chitin usually is quickly destroyed by bacterial decomposition, the preservation of these eurypterids illustrates the influence of the type of matrix on preservation of fossils. The horny substance of graptolites still is preserved in calcareous rocks of fine grain (Figure 56.12 C).

The most effective preservative of fossils is fine-grained silica which may hermetically seal and protect organic remains from bacteria and ground water solutions for hundreds of millions of years. The most remarkable examples of this are filaments and spores of low algae and fungi found in the chert of the mid-Huronian Gunflint formation of Ontario. . . .

Until recently, the oldest known land flora was a lower Devonian peat bog, heavily impregnated with silica, found near Rhynie in the Scottish county of Aberdeen. Many species of beautifully preserved primitive vascular plants have been described from this locality together with the remains of many spiders, a mite, and a primitive wingless insect. Early Paleozoic protozoans (Chitinozoa) and graptolites are common in chert nodules. A great advance was made when Kozlowski discovered that many of these microscopic fossils are not appreciably altered from the original chitinoid condition and that they can be extracted from the hard matrix by means of hydrofluoric acid, which dissolves the silica but does not affect the fossils. Soft-bodied microscopic organisms, including the flagella of one-celled euglenoid forms, have been described in Cretaceous chert (Figure 56.14) in several well-documented reports by Wetzel (1933).

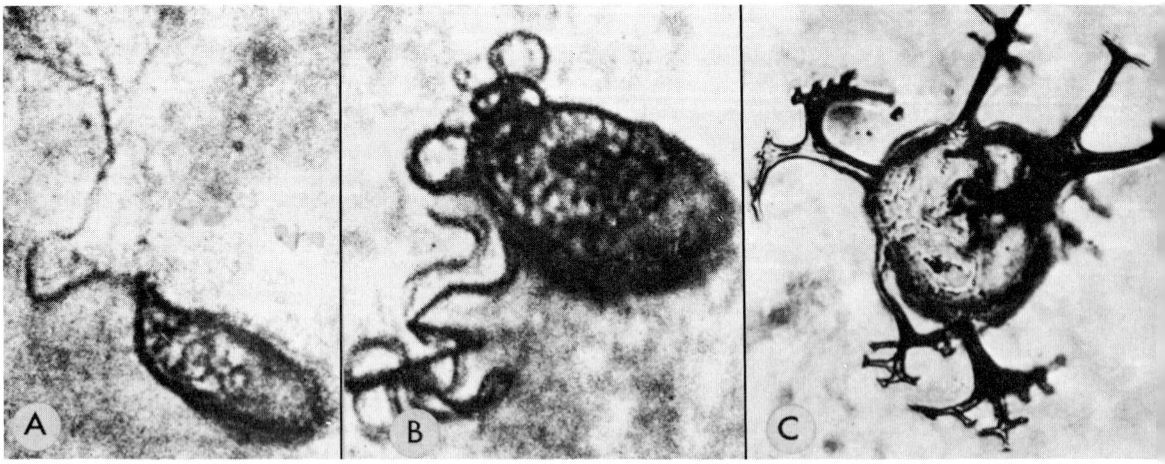

FIGURE 56.14
Cretaceous flagellate protozoans in chert, Germany. *A*, Euglenoid individual with flagellum, × 1,800; *B*, another individual with flagellum, × 1,055; *C*, hystrichospherid, × 700. (Wetzel, *Paleontographica*, 1933.)

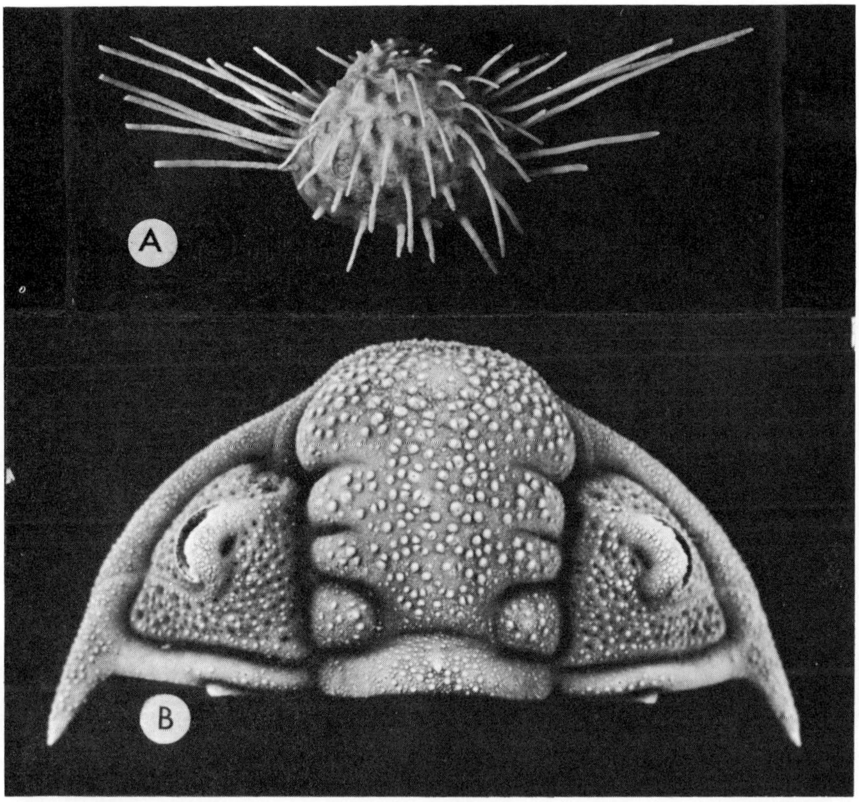

FIGURE 56.15
Invertebrate fossils in which the original calcareous skeletons have been replaced by silica. A, Spiny productid brachiopod, × 1, Permian, Texas (Cooper); *B*, trilobite, × 3, Ordovician, Virginia (Whittington, Geol. Soc. America, 1954.)

CHEMICAL PREPARATION OF FOSSILS

Long ago, in the latter part of the nineteenth century, it was known that certain fossils may be extracted without damage from hard rock matrix by means of acids which either dissolve the matrix without harm to the fossils, or dissolve the fossils without affecting the matrix. In the latter case, the resulting cavity could be used as a mold to restore perfectly the external form of the organism or skeleton. Perhaps because of the relatively high cost of commercial acids in those days, this method of preparing fossils was never thoroughly explored until the past three decades. G. Arthur Cooper of the U.S. National Museum, more than any other, is responsible for an important revolution in paleontology through the development of "chemical" methods of preparation of fossils. In certain rock formations many of the calcareous fossils have been selectively replaced by silica. This was owing, presumably, to the catalytic effect of contained organic substances on silica-bearing solutions. The matrix commonly was not affected by the replacement. Consequently, the more soluble rock matrix may be carefully dissolved away from the fossils with hydrochloric or acetic acid. Cooper has combined the advantages of mass collecting with chemical preparation. From 30 tons of Permian limestone collected in the Glass Mountains of Texas, he has extracted three million individual invertebrate fossils, almost all of which are exquisitely preserved with many delicate structures intact. The morphology of a large proportion of these fossils now can be worked out for the first time. A single control block of limestone weighing one hundred and eighty-six pounds yielded ten thousand excellent specimens of invertebrates, including Foraminifera, brachiopods (Figure 56.15 A), bryozoans, gastropods, and pelecypods. Only a very few of these fossils were exposed on the surface of the rock and none could have been completely cleaned of matrix by mechanical means. A whole new fauna of mid-Ordovician trilobites preserved in this way has been worked out by H. B. Whittington and others (Figure 56.15 B).

Extraordinarily well-preserved, uncrushed insects and other small arthropods with the body hairs and appendages clearly visible and some of the internal organs preserved were discovered by Bassett in calcareous nodules of Miocene age in the Calico Mountains, California. Palmer (1957) discovered that many of the insects have been impregnated, or coated, with silica so that they can be extracted in all exquisite detail from the matrix by means of acetic or formic acid (Figure 56.16). This discovery points the way to systematic examination and chemical preparation of calcareous nodules from other formations and areas. Bradley (1946) discovered well-preserved micro-organisms of several kinds in fossil coprolites of Eocene age in Wyoming. The fossil faeces belonging to reptiles and mammals contained a profusion of intestinal saprophytes closely similar to those of living forms. In addition, one of the mammalian coprolites contained large numbers of fresh-water algae. The bacteria and algae are preserved in silica and show fine structures in detail.

Calcium phosphate, the principal substance of vertebrate bones, conodonts, and certain brachiopods is nearly insoluble in acetic and formic acids which can, therefore, be used to dissolve calcareous matrix from these fossils. Many delicate and complex structures have been perfectly cleaned of hard matrix by this

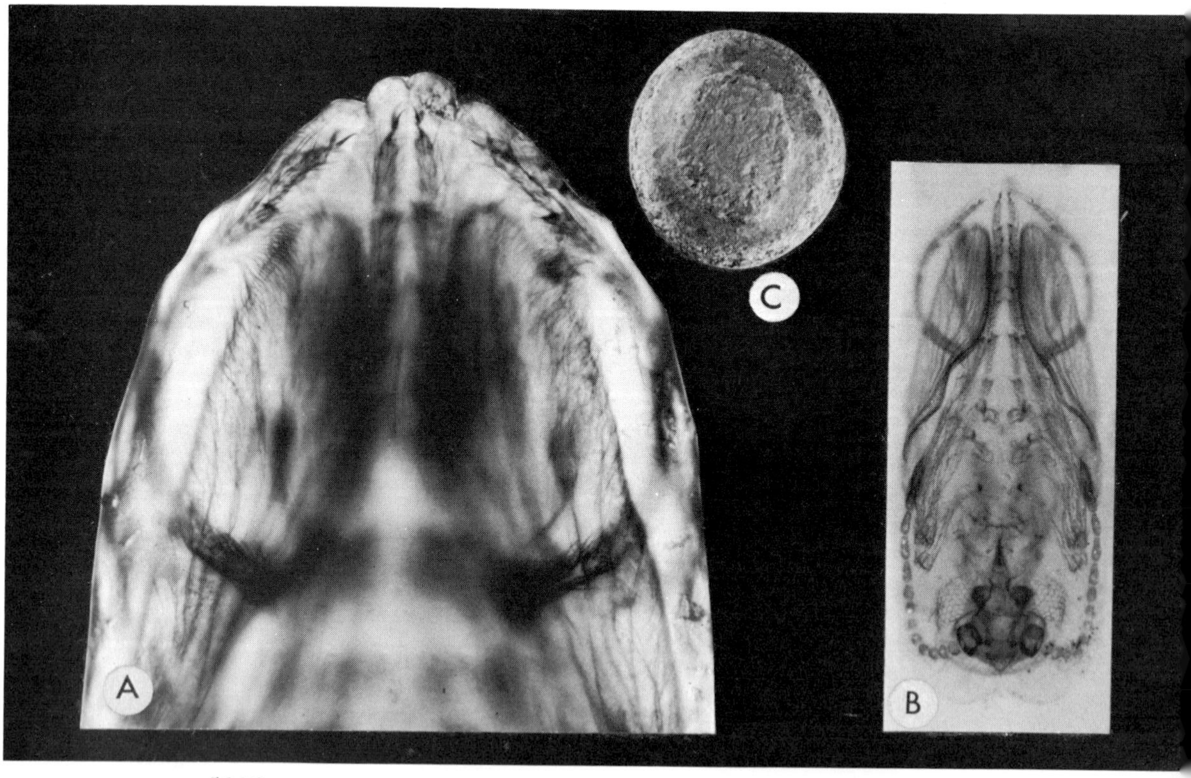

FIGURE 56.16
Perfectly preserved fossil insect impregnated with silica, a female midge in the pupa, Miocene, California. The fossil was freed with acid from a calcareous nodule. A, posterior end of midge showing genitalia and body hairs, × 150; B, ventral view, × 50; C, a typical calcareous nodule similar to that in which the fossil occurred, × 1. (Palmer, U.S. Geol. Survey, 1957.)

means. Usually the matrix contains much insoluble material so that chemical preparation must be supplemented with manual cleaning under a microscope.

SUMMARY

The known fossil record is characterized by systematic deficiencies as pointed out long ago by Charles Darwin; but as a record of preservable lowland and aquatic organisms, it is rich beyond the most optimistic predictions of nineteenth-century paleontologists. As collecting continues, it is becoming evident that the unsampled record in the rocks far exceeds the known record. Well-preserved fossils of some groups are abundant, and it may be confidently asserted that new discoveries made possible by new techniques of collecting and preparing fossils will necessitate revision of many present concepts about past life; but most of the revision will pertain to details of phylogeny and the accommodation of new categories not yet discovered.

REFERENCES

Axelrod, Daniel I., 1952, A theory of angiosperm evolution: Evolution, v. 6, p. 29–60.

Barghoorn, Elso S., 1957, Origin of life: Geol. Soc. America Mem. 67, p. 75–85.

Bradley, Wilmot Hyde, 1931, Origin and microfossils of the oil shale of the Green River formation of Colorado and Utah: U.S. Geol. Survey Prof. Paper 168, p. 1–58.

———, 1946, Coprolites from the Bridger formation of Wyoming, their composition and micro-organisms: Am. Jour. Sci., v. 244, p. 215–239.

Bulman, O. M. B., 1955, Graptolithina, *in* R. C. Moore, ed., Treatise on invertebrate paleontology, pt. V: Boulder, Colo., Geological Society of America.

Chaney, Ralph W., 1940, Tertiary forests and continental history: Geol. Soc. America Bull., v. 51, p. 469–488.

Colbert, Edwin H., 1955, Evolution of the vertebrates: New York, John Wiley and Sons.

Darwin, Charles, 1956, The origin of species (Reprint of the 6th ed.): London, Oxford University Press.

Deevey, E. S., Jr., 1955, Paleolimnology of the upper swamp deposit, Pyramid Valley: Canterbury Mus. Rec., v. 6, p. 291–344.

Dorf, Erling, 1955, Plants and the geologic time scale: Geol. Soc. America Spec. Paper 62, p. 291–344.

———, 1957, The earth's changing climates: Weatherwise, v. 10, p. 54–59.

Dunbar, Carl O., 1949, Historical geology: New York, John Wiley and Sons.

Dunbar, Carl O., and John Rodgers, 1957, Principles of stratigraphy: New York, John Wiley and Sons.

Edwards, Wilfred N., 1955, The geographical distribution of past floras: Adv. Sci., v. 12, p. 165–176.

Emiliani, Cesare, 1958a, Ancient temperatures: Scientific American, v. 198, p. 54–63.

———, 1958b, Paleotemperature analysis of core 280 and Pleistocene correlations: Jour. Geology, v. 66, p. 264–275.

Florin, R., 1944, Die Koniferen des Oberkarbons und des unteren Perms: Palaeontographica, v. 6, p. 365–456; v. 7, p. 457–654.

Imbrie, John, 1955, Quantitative lithofacies and biofacies study of Florena shale (Permian) of Kansas: Am. Assoc. Petroleum Geologists Bull., v. 39, p. 649–670.

———, 1956, Biometrical methods in the study of invertebrate fossils: Am. Mus. Nat. Hist. Bull., v. 103, p. 215–252.

———, 1957, The species problem with fossil animals *in* Ernst Mayr, ed., The species problem: Am. Assoc. Adv. Sci. Pub. 50, p. 125–154.

Kummel, Bernhard, 1954, Status of invertebrate paleontology, 1953, V. Mollusca—Cephalopoda: Mus. Comp. Zoology Harvard Coll. Bull., v. 112, p. 181–192.

Kurten, B., 1953, On the variation and population dynamics of fossil and recent mammal populations: Acta Zool. Fennica, v. 76, p. 5–122.

Ma, Ting Ying, 1957, Climate and the relative positions of continents during the upper Cretaceous, *in* Research on the past climate and continental drift: Taipei, World Book Co., v. 13, p. 1–69.

Matthew, W. D., and S. H. Chubb, 1921, Evolution of the horse: Am. Mus. Nat. Hist. Guide Leaflet, no. 36, p. 1–67.

Muller, Siemon Wm., and Alison Campbell, 1954, The relative number of living and fossil species of animals: Systematic Zoology, v. 3, p. 168–170.

Newell, Norman D., 1949, Phyletic size increase, an important trend illustrated by fossil invertebrates: Evolution, v. 3, p. 103–124.

Newell, Norman D., J. Keith Rigby, Alfred G. Fischer, Arthur J. Whiteman, John E. Hickox, and John S. Bradley, 1953, The Permian reef complex of the Guadalupe Mountains region, Texas and New Mexico: San Francisco, W. H. Freeman and Company.

Palmer, Allison R., 1957, Miocene arthropods from the Mojave Desert, California: U.S. Geol. Survey Prof. Paper 294-G, p. 236–280.

Robb, R. C., 1935, A study of mutation in evolution: Jour. Genetics, v. 31, p. 39–52.

Simpson, George Gaylord, 1953a, The major features of evolution: New York, Columbia University Press.

———, 1953b, Evolution and geography: Oregon State System of Higher Education, London Lectures.

Stebbins, G. Ledyard, Jr., 1950, Variation and evolution in plants: New York, Columbia University Press.

Stehli, Francis, G., 1957, Possible Permian climatic zonation and its implications: Am. Jour. Sci., v. 255, p. 607–618.

Størmer, Leif, 1945, On the relationships and phylogeny of fossil and recent Arachnomorpha: Norske Vidensk.-Akad. Oslo Mat.-Nat. Kl. Skr., v. 1944, no. 1, p. 1–58.

Teichert, Curt, 1956, How many fossil species?: Jour. Paleontology, v. 30, p. 967–969.

Tyler, S. A., and Elso S. Barghoorn, 1954, Occurrence of structurally preserved plants in pre-Cambrian rocks of the Canadian shield: Science, v. 38, p. 606–608.

Weigelt, Johannes, 1935, Some remarks on the excavations in the Geisel Valley: Research and Progress, v. 1, p. 155–159.

Whittington, Harry B., 1954, Status of invertebrate paleontology, 1953, VI. Arthropods—Trilobita: Mus. Comp. Zoology Bull., v. 112, p. 193–200.

57

The First Animals and Plants

PERCY E. RAYMOND
1947

The oldest aggregation of animals and plants which is adequately known is found in rocks of Cambrian age. This, [believed in 1947 to be] the first authentic record of life of the globe, is of more than usual interest. What sorts of organisms lived during those ancient times, hundreds of millions of years ago? Were they such as exist today, or sufficiently like them to fit into a classification based on modern animals and plants? Do they meet the expectation of believers in the doctrine of evolution in being exceedingly simple? . . .

Ever since the days of the great Franco-Bohemian paleontologist, Joachim Barrande, it has been customary to refer to the animals whose remains are found in the Cambrian rocks as the first or "primordial" fauna. But the ten thousand or more feet of Cambrian strata were not formed in a moment; their deposition is generally supposed to have occupied from ninety-five to a hundred million years. It is therefore absurd to consider all the faunas which succeeded one another during that long time as contemporaneous. All geologists recognize three distinctly different faunas in the Cambrian, one in the lower beds, another in the middle, and the third in the upper part of the strata. It would be just as logical to group together all the animals of the Upper Cretaceous, Cenozoic, and Recent as representing the state of evolution of life in the late Mesozoic as it is to say that the total Cambrian fauna is the congeries which was in existence at the beginning of that period.

The Lower Cambrian fauna of the world, so far as it is at present described, consists of about 455 species, distributed among the phyla as follows: Protozoa, none; Porifera, 18.5 per cent; Coelenterata (all jellyfish) and Echinodermata (cystids and edrioasteroids), taken together, 2 per cent; "Vermes" (tubes, trails, and burrows), 4.25 per cent; Brachiopoda, 27.5 per cent; Mollusca (all gastropods, and all but two bilaterally symmetrical forms), 11.5 per cent; and Arthropoda (84 per cent trilobites, 16 per cent other Crustacea), 36.25 per cent. These statistics probably give a more

From *Prehistoric Life* by Percy E. Raymond, pp. 19–28. Harvard University Press, copyright 1947 by the President and Fellows of Harvard College. Reprinted with permission of the publishers.

accurate idea of the shell-bearing members of the oldest Paleozoic fauna than those based upon the Cambrian as a whole. The proportion of sponges and free-swimming gastropods is relatively much higher, of arthropods considerably lower, and of brachiopods somewhat lower, than in the lists published by other writers.

It is evident that the oldest Cambrian fauna is diversified and not so simple, perhaps, as the evolutionist would hope to find it. Instead of being composed chiefly of protozoans, it contains no representatives of that phylum, but members of seven higher groups are present, a fact which shows that the greater part of the major differentiation of animals had already taken place in those ancient times. The other phyla not represented are the flat worms, wheel worms, round worms, Bryozoa, and Chordata the last the one which contains the most specialized of all animals. It is also apparent that the animals living in Cambrian times were not strikingly peculiar, since most of them can be assigned readily to phyla erected on the basis of modern ones.

What, then, are we to conclude? Are we to deny the special creation of the modern fauna, only to find that it is descended from animals specially created some millions of years ago? To answer this question, it is necessary to look further at the fauna under discussion. Diversified as it is, if analyzed further it proves to be simple as compared with that of the present day.

In the first place, the whole phylum Chordata, from fish to bird, is absent.

Although the Arthropoda are numerous, making up more than a third of the fauna, the only class represented is that of the Crustacea, the simplest of the arthropods, and 84 per cent of these are trilobites, the most primitive of the crustaceans. Very late in the Cambrian a few marine arachnids appeared.

The Mollusca are all gastropods, the simplest members of the phylum, and nearly all are of the most primitive type, their shells being simple, bilaterally symmetrical, uncoiled cones.

Next in importance to the Crustacea are the brachiopods, which make up 27.5 per cent of the fauna. Both the Inarticulata and the Articulata are present, but 80 per cent of the species belong to the former, which is the simpler group. Such of the articulates as are found are of the most primitive type.

The echinoderms are represented only by a few edrioasteroids and cystids, ancestral to all other members of the phylum.

The "Vermes," likewise poorly represented, probably because of lack of preservation, differ from the other animals that have been discussed in that most of the specimens found belong to the highest phylum, the Annulata, and, moreover, to the most highly organized class of the annulates, the Chaetopoda, or bristle worms.

Few specimens of Coelenterata have been recovered from the Lower Cambrian strata, but, curiously, those so far found belong to the Scyphozoa or jellyfish, one of the most specialized groups. These animals are absolutely without hard parts and are composed chiefly of water, yet Dr. C. D. Walcott found a few impressions of them in the Lower Cambrian shales of Vermont.

Spicules of siliceous sponges have long been known from Lower Cambrian rocks, but the oldest complete specimens are of Mid-Cambrian age. The most specialized of modern Porifera are the glass sponges, so called because their framework is made up of needles of glasslike amorphous silica. The living members of this division are classified according to the shapes of the spicules, whether straight and simple or arranged at various angles in two planes. It is interesting to note that some Lower Cambrian sponges are of the sort with siliceous spicules, and that they can be referred to modern orders on the basis of the forms shown by the elements of their skeletons. Much more common are the calcareous archaeocyathinids, the oldest known sessile organisms.

The Protozoa, instead of making up the whole of the oldest known fauna, are very poorly represented in it, if they are present at all. A few species of Lower Cambrian Foraminifera have been described from Russia and New Brunswick, but Dr. Joseph A. Cushman, the foremost student of this group at the present time, is doubtful if any of them really belongs to it. A few poorly preserved radiolarians were found in thin sections of rocks collected from the Cambrian of Thuringia, but even their describer was doubtful about them. This lack of specimens, however, cannot be taken as evidence of the absence of Protozoa from the faunas of this age. It must be remembered that the majority of these animals lack skeletons, and that all are small and ill adapted for preservation as fossils. The largest of the radiolarians are less than one millimeter in diameter; most of the Foraminifera are equally small, and many of the latter have exceedingly frail, agglutinated shells which could hardly have been preserved in any abundance in rocks millions of years old.

To complete the survey of primordial life it is necessary to say a word about the plants. Up to the present time no traces whatsoever of terrestrial plants have been found . . . which means not only that all of the higher types of vegetation but even such lowly things as ferns, mosses, and lichens were absent from the most ancient flora. The Algae (seaweeds) are the only plants known to have been present. A few of the most primitive unicellular forms happen to be preserved because they secreted calcium carbonate. Walcott described other plants, some of which are perhaps red algae, from his famous quarry in the Mid-Cambrian at Burgess Pass. . . .

No one thinks that the Lower Cambrian fauna contained only 455 species. Probably some already described have been overlooked in the present survey of the literature. Perhaps many are as yet unknown, after seventy-five years of search. The present number may be doubled within the next few years as keener observers split up the species already described or supplement the list from discoveries at new localities. Suppose we add another thousand to accommodate the various soft-bodied animals practically incapable of preservation. Even that brings the list to only two or three thousand species as compared with two or three million supposed to be in existence at the present time. However one looks at the picture, the "primordial" fauna was simple and undifferentiated.

Various writers have been so much impressed by the amount of differentiation shown by the Cambrian fauna that there may be a tendency to overemphasize the amount of time necessary to produce it. This is perhaps because one is apt to think of the great phyla as absolutely distinct from one another, each higher in the scale of organization than its predecessor, as shown in the tables in the textbooks. And one thinks of each step in advance as having been accomplished only after a long period of time. Yet it is a question whether time is a particularly important factor. It is natural to think of the phyla as they are represented today rather than as they were in Cambrian times. For example, the term "chordata" connotes fish, birds, mammals, et cetera, not the lowly backbone-less members of the group, animals so simple that some of them were for years supposed to be invertebrates. To estimate the real amount of differentiation which had taken place by the beginning of Cambrian times it is necessary to compare the most primitive members of the various phyla. If this is done, it appears that there were really only three great steps in the progress which led from the protozoans to the present great diversity of animals. How long it took to organize a unicellular creature we have no idea.

Starting from the unicellular Protozoa (Figure 57.1 A, B) there are obviously two possibilities. The new cells produced in reproduction may separate, thus continuing to be Protozoa, or they may remain attached to one another, forming multicellular animals, or Metazoa. This was a fundamental step in the progress, but there is no reason why it should not have occurred as soon as Protozoa began to reproduce. Why it happened may be a mystery, but the introduction of the factor of time does not facilitate the explanation.

Once the metazoan stage was reached, there were again two possibilities. The members of the colony might retain their individuality, although giving up much of their freedom, as in the case of the sponges (Figure 57.1 C). That this was a successful plan of coöperation is shown by the abundance of sponges at the present day, but it cannot be called a "great step," for it led nowhere. The other possibility involved the uniting of all the cells into one system, with complete coöperation but loss of individuality. One can imagine various ways in which the cells might have been arranged; what actually happened seems to have been the production of two layers forming a hollow sphere. The inner layer is the endoderm, the outer one the ectoderm, and the opening to the central digestive cavity is the mouth (Figure 57.1 D). Here we have the fundamental characteristics of the Coelenterata. But is this a change which requires time?

Comparing the coelenterates and the sponges, one finds that the primitive members of the former group were, theoretically, freely floating organisms. This belief is borne out by the presence of jellyfish in the Cambrian. Sponges, on the other hand, were sessile, as shown by attached specimens from the same formation. Freedom and progress thus contrast with stability and vegetative growth.

The coelenterates had acquired a digestive cavity. The next great step was the formation of the mesoderm and a body cavity (coelom). This is so profound a change in organization that one must admit that it may have required time, though this admission really expresses only our ignorance of the connecting links between the primitive coelenterates and the primitive coelomates. The transition appears to have been from a pelagic organism to one dwelling on the sea floor, from a swimming or floating to a crawling mode of existence. The physical change was from a more or less spherical form to an elongate one, from spherical to bilateral symmetry (Figure 57.1 E, F). The study of modern animals furnishes some clues to the possible history, but since the fossils give no information it will not be helpful to enter into a long discussion.

Once the coelomate stage (body cavity with a digestive tract within it) had been reached, all the "great steps" had been taken. Some groups, such as the bryozoans, brachiopods, echinoderms, and Mollusca, have gone downhill; only two, the arthropods and the chordates, have risen above the status of their ancestors. If one dares to put a summary of these remarks in the form of a diagram, it might be expressed as in Figure 57.2.

The inference is that if one should group the animals into super-phyla there would be only four, Protozoa, Porifera, Coelenterata, and Coelomata. There seems to be no reason why the protozoans, sponges, and coelenterates should not have been practically contempora-

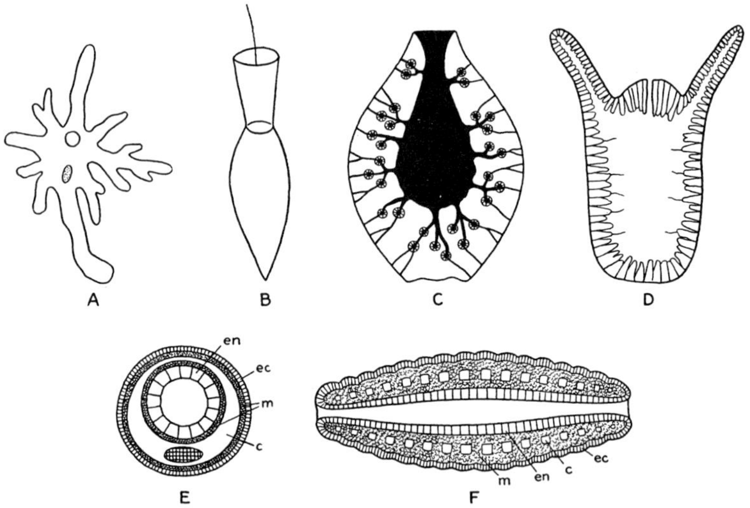

FIGURE 57.1
Fundamental steps in the differentiation of animals. *A*, amoeboid protozoan, with no definite shape; *B*, collared protozoan with vibratile cilium; *C*, a sponge, in which there are nonciliated ectodermal cells, and ciliated endodermal ones within the spherical cavities; *D*, section of a simple coelenterate, with mouth, digestive cavity, outer ectodermal and inner endodermal cells (which differ among themselves in form and function); *E,F*, transverse and longitudinal sections of a primitive coelomate; *ec*, ectodermal cells; *en*, endodermal cells; *m*, mesodermal cells; *c*, body cavity, or coelom. (*A*, *B*, *C*, *D*, redrawn and simplified from various sources; *E*, *F*, redrawn after Sedgwick and Wilson.)

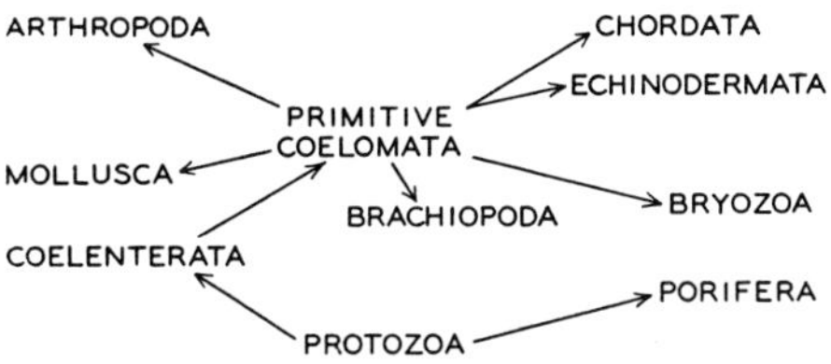

FIGURE 57.2
The relationships of the principal phyla of animals. The "worms" are excluded for the sake of simplicity. Their oldest representatives, the annelids, represent the most primitive coelomates now known.

neous in origin. Although there was a fundamental change, it was a simple one.

The later changes were more complex, but can they be evaluated as to time required? The structure of the brachiopod is much more complex than that of the bryozoan; yet brachiopods were well on their way at the beginning of the Cambrian, whereas bryozoans did not appear till the Ordovician. The primitive echinoderm is more "specialized" than the primitive chordate, but the former left skeletons in the Lower Cambrian rocks, whereas the latter do not appear in the record till the [Lower] Ordovician. It should, however, always be borne in mind that the earliest representatives of all phyla were probably without skeletons; hence the true chronology will probably never be known.

Glancing back over what has been said of the Lower Cambrian fauna and flora, it will be seen that the animals and plants of that time were, after all, simple. Backboned animals and other chordates and all the higher plants were as yet unknown. The Arthropoda, Mollusca, Brachiopoda, and Echinodermata, the higher groups of invertebrates, were represented by their simplest types only. On the other hand, the lower invertebrates, Annulata, Coelenterata, and Porifera, had representatives then which were almost as highly organized as any members of the same phyla today. An immense amount of evolution has taken place since the Cambrian. In other words, we are not driven to belief in an ancient special creation, but to further research on the genealogy of organisms.

Systematics, Affinities and Life Habits of *Babinka*

a Transitional Ordovician Lucinoid Bivalve

A. LEE McALESTER
1965

From *Palaeontology*, vol. 8, pt. 2, pp. 231–241, 246, 1965. [Plates and systematic descriptions deleted.] Reprinted with permission of the author and the Council of the Palaeontological Association.

Several students of molluscan phylogeny have recently called attention to the curious early bivalve genus *Babinka* (Barrande, 1881) from Ordovician rocks of Czechoslovakia. This rare monotypic genus is known only from the Bohemian Basin where it occurs in a formation (Šárka beds) that is probably of Llanvirn (lowest Middle Ordovician) age. Bivalve molluscs are extremely rare in Llanvirn or pre-Llanvirn rocks, and for this reason alone *Babinka* is of particular interest as one of the first known representatives of the Bivalvia. Further interest attaches to the genus because internal moulds preserve clear impressions of multiple pairs of muscle scars. These multiple muscle scars have led to the suggestion that *Babinka* is a primitive transitional form between the Bivalvia and some metameric molluscan ancestor (Vokes, 1954; Cox, 1959, 1960; Růžička and Prantl, 1960; Horný, 1960; Vogel, 1962; Merklin, 1962).

Although *Babinka* has been the source of much speculation regarding the early history of the Bivalvia, the genus has not been critically restudied since its first cursory description by Barrande almost a century ago. While preparing a review of the phylogeny and adaptations of Palaeozoic lucinoid bivalves, I have noted many characters of *Babinka* that suggest a relationship to the first lucinoid forms which appear abruptly in Middle Silurian deposits. The present study was prompted by this possibility of lucinoid affinities, and by the often suggested transitional evolutionary position of the genus. This paper has been prepared in order to: (1) review the systematics and morphology of *Babinka*; (2) further examine the functional and phylogenetic significance of the muscle scar pattern and other morphologic features of the genus; (3) suggest that *Babinka* is an ancestral lucinoid bivalve, and; (4) attempt to interpret the life habits of *Babinka* by analogy with recent lucinoid forms. More general phylogenetic and systematic conclusions which have resulted from the study will be treated in a separate paper (McAlester, 1965).

BABINKA AS A PRIMITIVE BIVALVE

Vokes (1954) appears to have been the first to call attention to the possible phylogenetic significance of the muscle scars in *Babinka*. He noted that the multiple scars of the genus, and the dissimilar multiple muscle scars of several Ordovician nuculoid species, are suggestive of the series of pedal muscle scars seen in fossil monoplacophorans, and he concluded (p. 236):

> The muscle scars shown by these Ordovician pelecypods can be shown to be close to those exhibited by primitive gastropods . . . they therefore may be interpreted as reflecting the musculature present in the ancestral stock from which the Pelecypoda were derived. Further, they suggest that the adductor muscles of the Pelecypoda are derived from discrete pairs of the ancestral musculature, rather than from the union of multiple pairs.

Vokes' suggestion was discussed by Cox (1959, 1960), who agreed in concluding (1959, p. 204) that *Babinka* 'could well have been newly evolved from the ancestral mollusc.' Cox further noted (1960, p. 71) that '*Babinka* appears to have approximated to the theoretical concept of the newly evolved bivalve mollusc. Little can be said about the role it played in bivalve phylogeny until it is better known.'

The idea that *Babinka* might be closely related to a monoplacophora-like ancestor was repeated by Růžička and Prantl (1960), and greatly expanded by Horný (1960), who regarded the genus as 'the phylogenetically initial form of the pelecypods' (p. 479). Because of this proposed phylogenetic position, Horný erected a new family (Babinkidae) and order (Diplacophora) for the genus. The latest discussions are those of Vogel (1962) and Merklin (1962), both of whom agree with Horný's conclusions.

Barrande's original descriptions, and all later discussions of *Babinka*, have not clearly established the nature and number of the multiple muscle scars which have aroused so much interest. In an attempt to clarify the generic morphology, I have restudied all specimens of *Babinka* in North American museums, and in the Národni Muzeum at Prague. This revision has provided several natural internal moulds which reveal for the first time the fine details of the muscle impressions. Of particular importance in showing the precise pattern is one extraordinarily clear internal mould of a right valve from the collections of the Národni Muzeum which was generously made available for study by Dr. Horný. These internal moulds show that *Babinka* has normal adductor muscle scars (Figure 58.1, *aam*, *pam*) and, in addition, a series of eight smaller scars above and between the adductor impressions. To avoid functional connotations, these eight scars will be temporarily referred to as the 'intermediate' muscle-scar impressions (Figure 58.1, *im*). Below some of these intermediate impressions is a series of about twenty-five still smaller scars. These will be temporarily called the 'small' muscle-scar impressions (Figure 58.1, *sm*). Finally, a large but obscure and faintly bounded 'elongate impression' (Figure 58.1, *ei*) extends ventrally from the anterior adductor scar, and a faint non-sinuate pallial line of mantle muscle attachment connects the adductors in the usual position (Figure 58.1, *pl*).

The first problem in interpreting the muscle scars of *Babinka* concerns the cross-sectional shape of the muscles which attached to the adductor, 'intermediate,' and 'small' scars. On well-preserved internal moulds these three groups of scars are strongest in sharply raised areas at their ventral extremities (the raised areas on the internal moulds represent strong depressions on the original shell interior). Extending dorsally from the raised extremities are more faintly raised 'tails,' which converge toward the umbonal region (Figure 58.1). These 'tails' are the traces of the position of the muscle scars at earlier stages of growth. In most bivalves the earlier muscle attachment sites are completely obscured by later deposition of inner shell material, but in *Babinka* this later deposition was not thick enough to cover completely the earlier trace of the muscle scars. Some workers have assumed that muscles attached along the entire elongate impression, but it is now apparent that the functional muscle at any one time occupied only the ventral extremity of each impression. The shape of the strongly raised extremities show that only the anterior adductor muscle was somewhat elongate in life. The muscles which attached to the posterior adductor scar and to all of the 'intermediate' and 'small' scars were approximately round in cross-section.

The two largest muscle scars in *Babinka* occupy anterior and posterior marginal positions along the line of pallial attachment, as do the adductor muscles in all isomyarian bivalves, and there is no reason to doubt that they are the attachment sites of typical isomyarian adductor muscles. The function of the muscles which attached to the 'intermediate' and 'small' scars is more problematical.

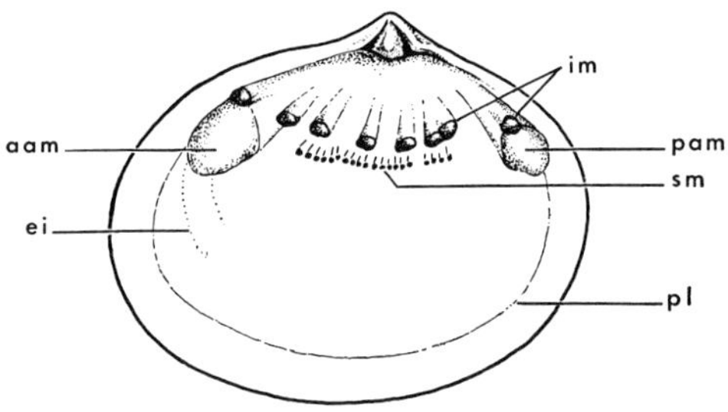

FIGURE 58.1
Muscle-scar pattern in *Babinka. aam*, anterior adductor muscle scar; *ei*, "elongate impression"; *im*, "intermediate" (pedal) muscle scars; *pam*, posterior adductor muscle scar; *pl*, pallial line; *sm*, "small" (gill) muscle scars.

The intermediate scars were considered by Barrande, Vokes, and Horný to represent the attachment sites of the pedal musculature. All recent isomyarian bivalves have paired pedal muscles, with one muscle of each pair attaching to each valve (Figure 58.2). These muscles commonly leave distinct shell impressions. In many recent isomyarian bivalves the foot is anchored by only two strong pairs which attach immediately above the adductor muscles (Figure 58.2; *Crassatella, Codakia, Mercenaria, Tellina*). Other groups have additional strong pedal muscle pairs which attach and leave scars in the central dorsal region. Living *Nuculana* and related protobranch forms commonly have five or six pairs of pedal muscles (Figure 58.2, *Nuculana*), some living Cardiacea have three strong pairs (Figure 58.2, *Cardium*), and some Mactracea have as many as five pairs (Figure 58.2, *Mesodesma*). Recent isomyarian bivalves thus show considerable variation in the number of pedal muscle pairs. Normally only two strong pairs attach above the adductor muscles, but in several unrelated groups there are from one to four additional pairs between the two principal pairs.

The 'intermediate' muscle scars of *Babinka* are similar in size and position to the pedal scars of recent isomyarian bivalves. As in recent forms, two pairs of pedal muscles attach directly above the adductors. The six additional pairs of muscles between the adductors in *Babinka* are almost certainly analogous to the additional strong pedal muscle pairs found in several unrelated recent superfamilies. These similarities strongly suggest that the 'intermediate' muscle scars of *Babinka* do in fact represent the attachment sites of pedal muscle pairs.

The pedal muscles of bivalves have completely different functions than do the adductor muscles, and it is most probable that the two kinds of muscles had separate evolutionary origins. Because both the pedal and adductor impressions in *Babinka* show a similar elongate shape, there has been a tendency to assume that the large adductors represent two additional pairs of pedal muscles which have become hypertrophied. It is much more likely, however, that the adductor muscles of the Bivalvia did not originate from modification of the pedal musculature, but instead arose independently by cross-fusion of the pallial attachment muscles, as has been convincingly stressed in the writings of Yonge (1953, 1957). If this reasonable conclusion is correct, then the adductor muscles in *Babinka* cannot be considered to represent additional pairs of modified pedal muscles.

The 'small' muscle scars and the faint 'elongate impression' have not been previously recognized in *Babinka*, and it is the 'intermediate' muscle scars (which will hereafter be termed the 'pedal muscle scars') which have led to the repeated suggestion that *Babinka* is related to some metameric ancestral mollusc. Similar multiple pairs of pedal muscles occur in several unrelated and divergently specialized groups of recent bivalves, and it is therefore evident that the mere presence of such muscles does not indicate a primitive condition. A strong suggestion of primitiveness is seen, however, from comparing the pattern of pedal and 'small' muscle scars in *Babinka* with the muscle at-

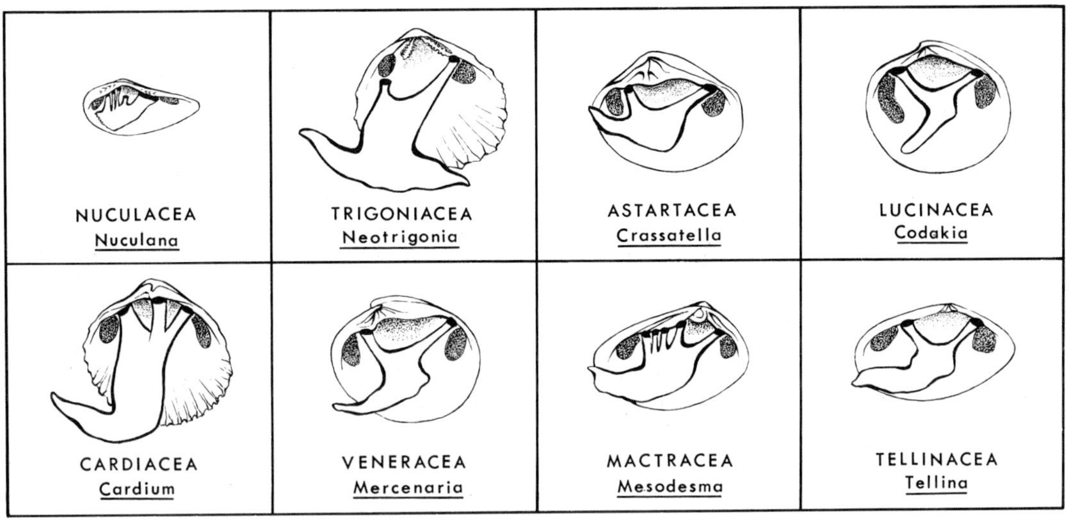

FIGURE 58.2
Pedal musculature of genera representing eight superfamilies of recent isomyarian bivalves. Pedal-attachment sites shown for right valves only. The pattern is repeated in the left valves making symmetrical right-left pairs of pedal muscles. Note the presence of 3 to 5 attachment sites in *Nuculana, Cardium,* and *Mesodesma.* (Data from Allen, 1958; Heath, 1937; Pelseneer, 1891, 1911; Yonge, 1939, 1949.)

tachment pattern of *Neopilina,* the only recent representative of the primitive molluscan Class Monoplacophora.

Lemche and Wingstrand have provided detailed descriptions of the pattern of muscle attachment to the shell of *Neopilina galatheae;* in that species the foot and visceral mass attach by eight strong pairs of pedal muscles (Lemche and Wingstrand, 1959, figs. 120, 121, 130). Associated with these eight pedal muscle pairs are a series of much smaller muscles having various functions, including pallial, ctenidial, radular, and visceral muscles. Among the strongest of these small muscles are the ctenidial muscles, which serve to attach the gills to the shell. *N. galatheae* has five pairs of gills which attach to the shell by many small muscles situated around the third through seventh pairs of larger pedal muscles (Figure 58.3).

Lemche and Wingstrand (1959, fig. 133) note that the muscle pattern in *N. galatheae* is closely analogous to the strong muscle-scar pattern of the Silurian monoplacophoran genus *Pilina.* Like *Neopilina,* this early fossil probably had eight strong pairs of pedal muscles and associated smaller ctenidial, radular, pallial, and visceral muscles. This eight-paired pattern is not universal in the Monoplacophora, for some other early Palaeozoic genera show fewer than eight pedal muscle pairs. It may be significant, however, that eight appears to be the maximum number of pedal muscle pairs found in any monoplacophoran, and in some species the smaller number of pedal scars appear to have resulted from fusion of originally more numerous pairs.

The pattern of pedal and 'small' muscle scars in *Babinka* shows an amazing similarity to the pattern of pedal and ctenidial muscle attachment in *Neopilina* (Figure 58.3). As in *Neopilina, Babinka* has eight pairs of pedal muscle scars. Even more strikingly, the 'small' muscle scars of *Babinka* occur under the third to seventh pairs of larger pedal muscle scars in the same position as the ctenidial attachment muscles in *N. galatheae.* Although it is tempting to draw immediate phylogenetic conclusions from these similarities, several facts suggest that the relationships may not be as simple as they first appear.

First, the detailed pattern of muscle impressions in *Babinka* is clearly visible on only one unusually well-preserved internal mould of a right valve from the collections of the National Museum at Prague. This is the only specimen which shows the 'small' muscle scars and all eight pedal muscle scars. The central pairs of pedal scars are preserved on many specimens, and these have been the source of the previous speculation regarding the muscle-scar pattern of the genus. A few specimens also preserve either the anterior or posterior pedal scar above the adductors, but only the single Prague specimen clearly preserves all eight pairs. It is therefore impossible to fully evaluate the variability in number and position of the pedal and 'small' muscle scars. Composite evidence from many specimens suggests a reasonably constant pedal muscle pattern, but the variability of the 'small' muscles is completely unknown.

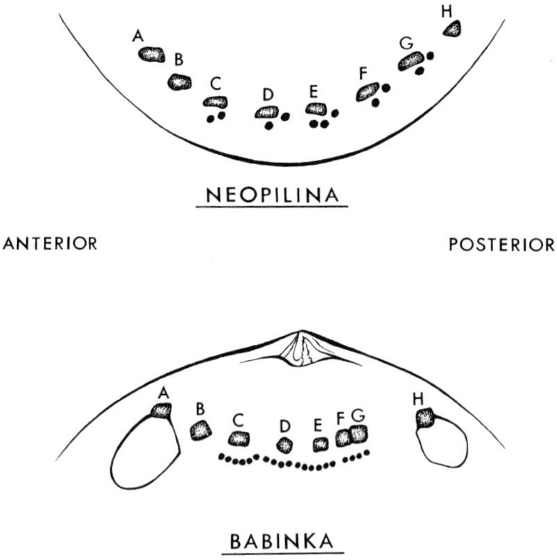

FIGURE 58.3
Comparison of muscle-scar patterns in *Babinka* and the recent monoplacophoran *Neopilina*. *A–H*, eight pairs of principal pedal muscles. The small dots below the pedal muscles show the position of gill attachment muscles in *Neopilina*, and the position of the "small" muscle scars in *Babinka*. (Data on *Neopilina* from Lemche and Wingstrand, 1959.)

Further difficulties are raised by the presence of fewer than eight pedal muscle pairs in many fossil monoplacophorans, and also by the occurrence of six instead of five gill pairs in a second recent species of *Neopilina*, *N. ewingi* Clarke and Menzies (1959). The anatomical details of this species have not yet been described, but it is probable that it has a somewhat different pattern of gill muscle attachment than does *N. galatheae*. In spite of these cautions and qualifications, I feel that the muscle patterns in *Neopilina*, *Babinka*, and some early fossil monoplacophorans are too similar to be entirely the result of chance, and I believe it is reasonable to infer that the pedal and 'small' muscle scars in *Babinka* do in fact represent an inheritance from some monoplacophora-like ancestor. It will be stressed later that in all features except the pedal and 'small' muscles, *Babinka* is a typical representative of the Class Bivalvia.

Implicit in the above comparisons is the suggestion that the 'small' muscle scars in *Babinka* represent the site of attachment of the gills. This possibility is raised not only by the similar position of these scars and the gill muscles of *Neopilina*, but also by the observation that no other large organs are likely to have been attached to the shell in the position of the 'small' scars. Direct gill attachment to the shell by many small muscles has no obvious analogue in recent bivalves, but the position of the scars in *Babinka* is geometrically correct to have supported a ctenidial structure in the mantle cavity. In addition, the many separate pedal scars of *Babinka* suggest that the animal still lacked the united pedal-visceral muscle system which supports the gills in most recent bivalves. A strong direct attachment of the gills to the shell may therefore have still been necessary. It is most probable that the 'small' scars were the sites of gill attachment, and they will henceforth be referred to as the 'gill muscle scars.' The many small muscles which attached to these scars may have supported a single large gill or, less probably, they might represent the attachment sites of several small gills.

The two final internal scars preserved in *Babinka* are the non-sinuate pallial line, and the faint 'elongate impression' below the anterior adductor. Both of these features suggest a relationship between *Babinka* and the bivalve Superfamily Lucinacea, and they will be considered in detail in the next section.

BABINKA AS AN ANCESTRAL LUCINOID BIVALVE

The oldest undoubted lucinoid bivalves are found in Middle and Upper Silurian limestones on the island of Gotland, Sweden. Two lucinoid species are found in abundance in the Gotland deposits (Hede, 1921; Munthe et al.,

1925; Haffer, 1959). One species, for which the correct name is probably *Paracyclas hisingeri* (Murchison and Verneuil), is a small, rounded, inflated form which is similar in shape to recent species of the lucinoid family Diplodontidae. The other Gotland species, *Ilionia prisca* (Hisinger), is a much larger, compressed form which closely resembles some recent species of the family Lucinidae. The internal morphology of *P. hisingeri* is poorly known, but the larger species, *I. prisca,* is found principally as internal moulds which preserve some muscle scar impressions. All of the morphologic features of *I. prisca* are strongly characteristic of recent Lucinacea (Allen, 1958). Among the similarities are: an extremely elongate anterior adductor muscle; an unusual anteriorly-expanded shell shape; and a unique radial shell groove near the dorsal valve margin which corresponds to the internal line of attachment of the gill to the visceral mass. The presence of these distinctive lucinoid characteristics in *I. prisca* makes it extremely probable that the species is closely related to recent Lucinacea. This superfamily was therefore fully established in mid-Silurian time. The group has a scattered but continuous fossil record after the Silurian, and is represented in modern oceans by about two dozen genera which are usually assigned to three families. This abrupt appearance of fully developed and essentially modern lucinoid bivalves in Middle Silurian deposits indicates that the group must have had a considerable evolutionary history before the Silurian, but as yet no possible ancestral or related fossil forms have been recognized in older deposits. Many morphologic features of *Babinka* strongly suggest lucinoid affinities and these, coupled with its occurrence in Middle Ordovician rocks, make it both morphologically and stratigraphically an ideal ancestor for such Silurian lucinoids as *Ilionia.* The morphologic features of *Babinka* which are strongly suggestive of lucinoid affinities are: (1) the characteristic anteriorly expanded shell shape, (2) the elongate anterior adductor muscle scar and associated 'elongate impression,' (3) the simple, non-sinuate pallial line, and (4) the typical lucinoid hinge, dentition, and ligament. In short, the only features of *Babinka* which are not typically lucinoid are the primitive patterns of pedal and gill muscle scars.

Comprehensive studies of living Lucinacea (Allen, 1958, 1960) have shown that the characteristic anteriorly-extended shape and elongate anterior adductor muscle are related to an unusual mode of life found in all recent representatives of the group. Instead of drawing respiratory and feeding currents into the mantle cavity through posterior siphons, as do most deeply buried infaunal bivalves, the Lucinacea construct a unique mucous-lined, anterior inhalent tube in the surrounding sediment by means of the elongate, cylindrical foot. The characteristic elongate anterior adductor muscle is directly related to this habit for the solid outer face of the muscle is ciliate and serves as a preliminary sorting area for food particles brought in by the anterior inhalent current (Figure 58.4). This unusual habit is universal in living lucinoids, and was almost certainly shared by Silurian and Devonian lucinoids which show the characteristic elongate anterior adductor scar.

The anteriorly expanded, flattened shell of *Babinka* is similar in shape to the Silurian species *I. prisca* (Figure 58.5). Even more suggestive is the pattern of the anterior adductor muscle and associated 'elongate impression' in *Babinka.* The anterior adductor scar of *Babinka* is considerably more elongate in a radial direction than is the posterior scar, although it

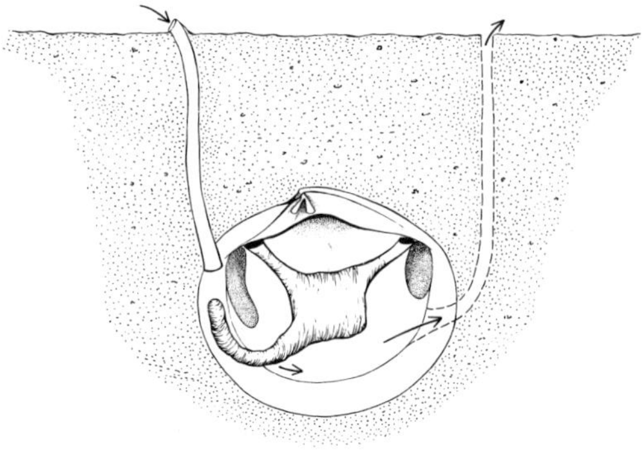

FIGURE 58.4
Life position of recent lucinacean bivalves. (Modified from Allen, 1958.) Nutrient-laden water is brought into the mantle cavity through a mucous-lined anterior inhalent tube constructed by the foot. In some genera the posterior exhalent current discharges directly into the sediment, in others it is channelled to the sediment surface through a retractable posterior siphon. The anterior face of the elongate anterior adductor muscle is covered with cilia and acts as a preliminary sorting area for incoming food particles.

does not yet show the extreme ventral elongation seen in *Ilionia* and most younger lucinoids. The radial elongation of this muscle in *Babinka* does, however, suggest the beginning of a trend toward increasing the surface area of the anterior adductor. Furthermore, several internal moulds of *Babinka* show a faint 'elongate impression' marking the site of an obscurely bounded depression extending ventrally from the anterior adductor on the original shell interior. This 'elongate impression' has exactly the same shape and position as the elongate anterior adductor muscle scar in *Ilionia* and most other lucinoids (Figure 58.5). The impression is too faint to represent an expansion of the actual adductor muscle, but it does indicate that there was some differentiation and specialization of the mantle in the region below the anterior adductor in *Babinka*.

The 'elongate impression' might reasonably represent the attachment surface of some kind of specialized ciliary sorting area which was similar in position and function to the elongate adductor muscle surface in later lucinoids. This sorting area would probably not have formed a connected partition between the valves and would have been less efficient than the sorting tube formed by the solid face of an elongate adductor muscle. It is not difficult, therefore, to visualize an evolutionary progression between *Babinka* and *Ilionia* involving an expansion of the adductor into the position of the 'elongate impression.' It is also worth noting that *Ilionia* shows a rounded posterior adductor scar with an elongate trace of the earlier growth position which is almost identical to that of *Babinka* (Figure 58.5). Regrettably, all of the internal moulds of *Ilionia* available for

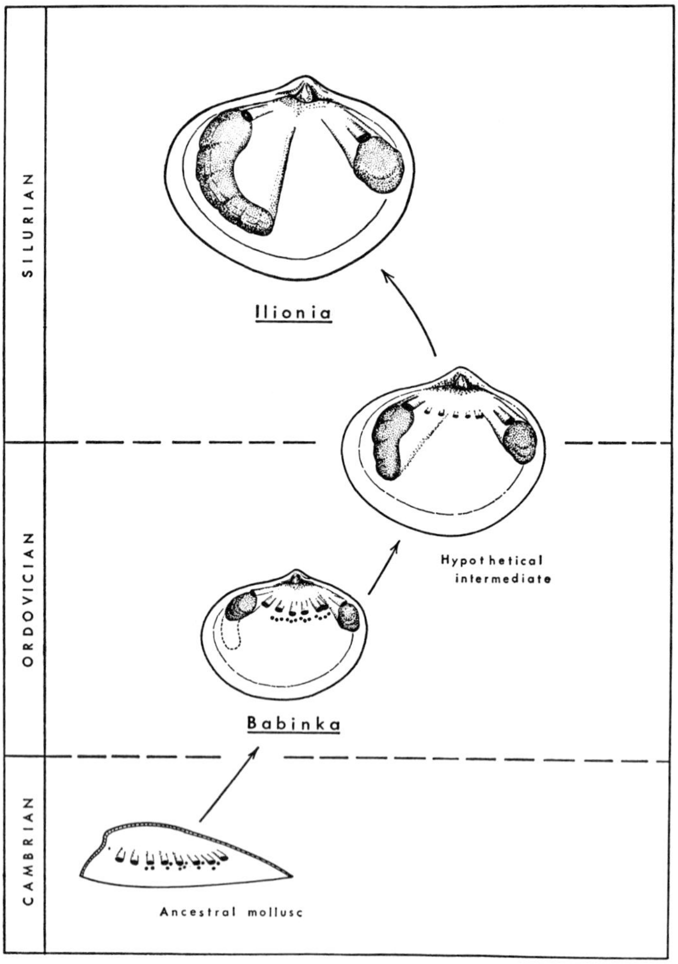

FIGURE 58.5
Proposed evolutionary relations of *Babinka*. Note the progressive reduction of the pedal muscles and the expansion of the anterior adductor muscle between *Babinka* and *Ilionia*.

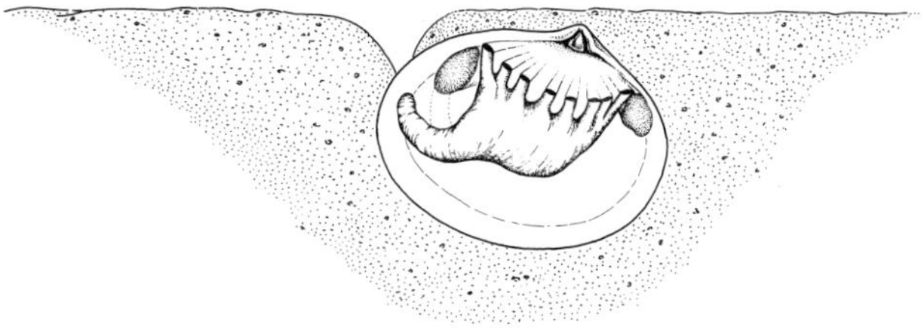

FIGURE 58.6
Inferred life position of *Babinka*. Compare with Figure 58.4.

comparison in the Yale Peabody Museum collections are too poorly preserved to show the details of the pedal muscle scars, but the genus most probably had the typical lucinoid pattern with one pair of strong pedal muscles above each adductor.

Because of the anterior inhalent tube and consequent absence of a posterior inhalent siphon, the Lucinacea are unusual among deeply buried infaunal bivalves in lacking a pallial sinus for siphon retraction. Some recent lucinoids do have a small posterior *exhalent* siphon, but this single siphon is retracted by a unique inside-out inversion which does not require an indentation in the line of pallial muscle attachment. True lucinoid bivalves all lack a pallial sinus, and it is suggestive that *Babinka* also shows a non-sinuate line of pallial muscle attachment.

In many fossil and recent lucinoid species the hinge teeth are poorly developed or absent, but when present the dentition consists of a large, commonly lobed, cardinal tooth in the right valve fitting between two smaller teeth in the left valve (Allen, 1960; Chavan, 1937–8, 1962). In some genera lateral teeth and an additional small cardinal tooth in the right valve are added to this basic pattern. Several internal moulds of *Babinka* preserve impressions of the dentition, and latex casts of these impressions clearly show the original dental pattern of the genus to have been identical to the basic dentition of the Lucinacea. As in recent lucinoids, *Babinka* has a large, lobed tooth in the right valve which fits between two smaller teeth in the left valve.

The ligament in the Lucinacea is opisthodetic; the principal ligament elements normally occupy an obscure groove in the hinge plate posterior to the cardinal dentition. In addition, the dorsal-hinge region posterior to the umbones normally shows a slight gape where elements of the ligament were exposed on the surface. Anterior to the umbones, recent lucinoids commonly show a well-developed lunule. The hinge region and ligament attachment area in *Babinka* show this same pattern. As in recent lucinoids, *Babinka* has a faint ligament groove and ligament gape posterior to the cardinal dentition, and the genus also shows the characteristic anterior lunule. In all features of the hinge and ligament, *Babinka* is a typical lucinoid bivalve.

LIFE HABITS

Silurian and younger fossil lucinoid bivalves almost certainly shared the adaptations for deeply buried suspension feeding seen in all recent Lucinacea (Allen, 1958) because the fossils show characteristic morphologic features, such as the elongate anterior adductor scar, which are directly related to that mode of life. Although the evidence is less conclusive for *Babinka*, it seems likely that it had similar habits.

The strong multiple pedal attachment muscles in *Babinka* suggest a large active foot which had probably only begun to develop the extremely extensible, cylindrical form of later Lucinacea. If this were the case, then *Babinka* would have been a rather shallow burrower, for the depth of burial in the Lucinacea is controlled by the degree of extensibility of the foot. *Babinka* may not have had the ability to form a distinct, mucuous-lined inhalent tube, but instead might have merely used repeated extrusions of the foot to maintain a crude anterior opening to the surface through a relatively thin cover of overlying sediment (Figure 58.6). Such habits would be a likely early stage in the development of the typical lucinoid anterior inhalent tube.

As discussed earlier, the 'elongate impression' below the anterior adductor in *Babinka* may represent a specialized area of the mantle which functioned as a preliminary ciliary sorting area for food particles brought in by the anterior inhalent current. A specialized sorting area on the mantle below the adductor is a likely preliminary step in the adaptive trend leading to dorsal extension of the adductor muscle in the same position. The gills of *Babinka* were probably already functioning as food-gathering organs which filtered particles directly from the incoming water, and which also received food from ciliary tracts on the surface of the mantle and visceral mass.

In summary, *Babinka* probably was a buried suspension feeder which lived just below the surface of the sediment, drawing in nutrient-laden water through an anterior depression in the sediment surface maintained by extrusion of the foot. The foot was probably strong and active, enabling the animal to burrow and move through the substrate with ease. The animal probably fed by ciliary trapping and sorting of small food particles on the surface of the mantle, visceral mass, and gills. . . .

SUMMARY

The rare bivalve genus *Babinka* from lowest Middle Ordovician rocks of the Bohemian Basin shows multiple muscle scars which have led several palaeontologists to suggest a relationship to some metameric molluscan ancestor. A systematic and morphologic revision reveals that *Babinka* is a typical bivalve in all features except the pedal and gill muscle-scar patterns. These scars are not like those of other bivalves, but are almost identical to the pattern found in the recent monoplacophoran *Neopilina,* and in some early Palaeozoic Monoplacophora. This close similarity confirms the suggestion that the muscle pattern in *Babinka* is an inheritance from a monoplacophora-like ancestral mollusc.

Babinka is among the first bivalves to appear in the fossil record. The genus is both chronologically and morphologically an ideal ancestor for the earliest lucinoid bivalves which appear abruptly in Middle Silurian deposits. Morphological features of *Babinka* which are strongly suggestive of lucinoid affinities are: the anteriorly-expanded shell shape; the elongate anterior adductor muscle with associated 'elongate impression'; the nonsinuate pallial line; and the typical lucinoid hinge, dentition, and ligament. *Babinka* provides the first direct evidence of an evolutionary transition between the Bivalvia and more primitive molluscs.

Functional comparison with recent lucinoid bivalves suggests that *Babinka* was a mobile, infaunal suspension feeder that received nutrient-laden water into the mantle cavity through an anterior inhalent opening maintained by extrusion of the foot.

REFERENCES

Allen, J. A., 1958, On the basic form and adaptation to habitat in the Lucinacea (Eulamellibranchia): Royal Soc. [London] Philos. Trans., ser B., v. 241, p. 421–484.

———, 1960, The ligament of the Lucinacea (Eulamellibranchia): Quart. Jour. Microscop. Sci., v. 101, p. 25–36.

Barrande, J., 1881, Système silurien du centre de la Bohême, v. 6. Classe des Mollusques, ordre des Acephales: Prague and Paris, Joachim Barrande (Imprimerie Charles Bellmann in Prague).

Chavan, A., 1937–38, Essai critique de classification des Lucines: Jour. Conchyliol., v. 81, p. 133–153, 198–216, 237–282; v. 82, p. 59–97, 105–130, 215–243.

———, 1962, Essai critique de classification des Ungulinidae: Inst. royal sci. nat. Belgique Bull., v. 38, no. 23.

Clarke, A. H., and R. J. Menzies, 1959, *Neopilina* (*Vema*) *ewingi,* a second living species of the Paleozoic Class Monoplacophora: Science, v. 129, p. 1026–1027.

Cox, L. R., 1959, The geological history of the Protobranchia and the dual origin of taxodont Lamellibranchia: Malacol. Soc. London Proc., v. 33, p. 200–209.

———, 1960, Thoughts on the classification of the Bivalvia: Malacol. Soc. London Proc., v. 34, p. 60–88.

Haffer, J., 1959, Der Schlossbau früh-heterodonter Lamellibranchiaten aus dem rheinischen Devon: Palaeontographica, ser. A, v. 112, p. 133–192.

Heath, H., 1937, The anatomy of some protobranch mollusks: Mus. hist. nat. Belgique Mem., v. 10, no. 2.

Hede, J. E., 1921, Gottlands silurstratigrafi: Sveriges Geol. Undersokning Årsbok Avh. Uppsatser, ser. C, v. 305, no. 7.

Horny, R., 1960, On the phylogeny of the earliest pelecypods (Mollusca): Věstn. geol. Úst. čsl., v. 35, p. 479–482.

———, 1963, Lower Paleozoic Monoplacophora and patellid Gastropoda (Mollusca) of Bohemia: Ústředního Úst. geol. Sborn., oddíl. paleontologický, v. 28.

Lemche, H., and K. G. Wingstrand, 1959, The anatomy of *Neopilina galatheae* Lemche, 1957 (Mollusca: Tryblidiacea): Galathea Rept., Copenhagen, v. 3, p. 1–71, pls. 1–56.

McAlester, A. L., 1965, Evolutionary and systematic implications of a transitional Paleozoic lucinoid bivalve (in preparation).

Merklin, R. L., 1962, Ob odnoy novoy siteme dvustvorchatykh mollyuskov: Soc. nat. Moscou Bull., otdel geologicheskiy, ser. 3, v. 37, p. 136.

Munthe, H., J. E. Hede, and L. Von Post, 1925, Gottlands geologi, en oversikt: Sveriges Geol. Undersokning Årsbok Avh. Uppsatser, ser. C, v. 331, no. 3.

Pelseneer, P., 1891, Contribution à l'étude des lamellibranches: Arch. Biol. Paris, v. 11, p. 147–312, pls. 6–23.

———, 1911, Les lamellibranches de l'expedition du Siboga, partie anatomique: Siboga-Expeditie Mon., v. 53a.

Růžička, B., and F. Prantl, 1960, Types of some of Barrande's pelecypods (Barrandian): Zvláštní Otisk Časopisu Národniho Mus., oddíl přírodovědý, v. 1, p. 48–55 (in Czech with English summary).

Thoral, M., 1935, Contribution à l'étude paléontologique de l'Ordovicien inférieur de la Montagne Noire et révision sommaire de la faune cambrienne de la Montagne Noire: Univ. Paris Fac. Sci. Theses, ser. A, v. 154, thesis 2.

Vogel, K., 1962, Muscheln mit Schlosszähnen aus dem spanischen Kambrium und ihre Bedeutung für die Evolution der Lamellibranchiaten: Akad. Wiss. Mainz. Math.-nat. Kl. Abh., Jahrg. 1962, v. 4.

Vokes, H. E., 1954, Some primitive fossil pelecypods and their possible significance: Washington Acad. Sci. Jour., v. 44, p. 233–236.

Yonge, C. M., 1939, The protobranchiate mollusca; a functional interpretation of their structure and evolution: Royal Soc. [London] Philos. Trans., ser. B, v. 230, p. 79–147.

———, 1949, On the structure and adaptations of the Tellinacea, deposit feeding Eulamellibranchia: Royal Soc. [London] Philos. Trans., ser. B, v. 234, p. 29–76.

———, 1953, The monomyarian condition in the Lamellibranchia: Royal Soc. Edinburgh Trans., v. 62, p. 443–478.

———, 1957, Mantle fusion in the Lamellibranchia: Sta. Zool. Napoli Pub., v. 29, p. 151–171.

59

Silurian Marine Communities

and their Environmental Significance

A. M. ZIEGLER

1965

Petersen [1], in a classic investigation in marine ecology, demonstrated that the benthonic animals of Danish waters tend to occur in several distinctive communities, and he produced maps showing the distribution of these communities. Other workers [2, 3] have followed Petersen's lead in treating the animal community as the basic ecological unit, and the general implication is that communities are ultimately controlled by environmental factors. If this is true, then maps showing the distribution of co-existing communities in remote geological times should reflect the different environments of those times; furthermore, the relationships of the communities to such geologically verifiable features as shorelines should provide a clue to the type of environmental factors responsible. Although some palaeontologists [4, 5] have defined specific fossil communities in Palaeozoic rocks, few have been able to map coexisting communities, probably because of the difficulties of stratigraphical control.

The early Silurian deposits of Wales and the Welsh Borderland contain fossil assemblages which fall naturally into several groups. The distinctions between some of the assemblages were noticed by earlier workers who invoked proximity to volcanoes [6], or submarine ridges [7] to account for the differences. At least five assemblages, or communities, may now be recognized and these are briefly defined in Table 59.1. In the column headed 'Characteristic Species' are the animals which normally occur abundantly in the community; the 'Associated Species' usually occur in the community, but are not as abundant or regular in their appearance. The communities are probably completely intergrading, and it should be emphasized that their recognition depends as much on relative abundances of species as it does on occurrences of particular species; thus *Eocoelia* is very abundant in its own community, but it frequently occurs in the *Pentamerus* community and is found occasionally in the other communities. The communities are widely distributed, and in fact,

From *Nature*, vol. 207, pp. 270–272, 1965. Reprinted with permission of the author and Macmillan (Journals) Limited.

TABLE 59.1
Welsh Silurian fossil communities

Community name	Characteristic species	Associated species
1. *Lingula* community	*Lingula pseudoparallela* "*Camarotoechia*" *decemplicata* "*Nucula*" *eastnori*	"*Hormotoma*" sp. "*Pterinia*" sp. *Cornulites* sp.
2. *Eocoelia* community	*Eocoelia* spp.* "*Leptostrophia*" *compressa* *Dalmanites weaveri*	*Howellella crispa* *Salopina* sp. "*Pterinia*" sp.
3. *Pentamerus* community (*Pentameroides* community)*	*Pentamerus* spp.* *Atrypa reticularis* *Dalejina* sp.	*Eocoelia* spp.* *Howellella crispa*
4. *Stricklandia* community (*Costistricklandia* community)*	*Stricklandia* spp.* *Eospirifer radiatus* *Atrypa reticularis*	*Resserella* sp.
5. *Clorinda* community	*Clorinda* spp.* *Dicoelosia biloba* *Cyrtia exporrecta* *Skenidioides lewisi*	*Plectodonta millinensis* *Coolinia applanata* *Plectatrypa marginalis*

* Chronological species or genera succeed one another in the same community.

the same associations occur in collections known to me from as far afield as Alabama and Hudson's Bay.

The five communities [(1) *Lingula;* (2) *Eocoelia;* (3) *Pentamerus;* (4) *Stricklandia;* and (5) *Clorinda*] are related to each other in a linear fashion; adjacent communities, for example, 1 and 2, or 4 and 5 have many species in common, while 1 and 4, or 2 and 5 are mutually exclusive. The communities defined, with the exception of the *Lingula* community, are dominated by articulate brachiopods which typically constitute more than 85 per cent of the fossil remains, so the distinctions between the communities are based largely on the brachiopods. In the case of the *Lingula* community, only one species of articulate brachiopod, a rhynchonellid, is present, and many groups such as the corals, crinoids, and trilobites are completely unrepresented. Because of the restricted nature of this community and because of its occurrence at the base of transgressive sequences, such as the Kenley Grit of Shropshire, or the Cowleigh Park Beds of the Malvern Hills, a coastal environment is postulated, similar perhaps to the environment inhabited by many modern lingulids [8].

Sediment type does not seem to have been a controlling factor in community distribution as each community has been found in a wide range of sedimentary rocks. But there is a general tendency for communities 1 and 2 to occur in sandstones, communities 3 and 4 in sequences of varying proportions of sandstone and shale beds, and community 5 in shale.

It is evident that a transgressing sea, such as the Upper Llandovery sea of the Welsh Borderland, would deposit stratigraphical sequences representing environments progressively farther from the shore. The Damery Beds of Tortworth show the stratigraphic sequence of communities 2, 3, and 4, whereas at May Hill the community sequence is 2 (Huntley Hill Beds), 3, 4 and 5 (Yartleton Beds). In the Malvern District the community sequence is at Eastnor 1 (Cowleigh Park Beds), 3, and 4 (Wyche Beds); at Gulley quarry it is 3 and 4 (Wyche Beds); and at Old Storridge Common it is 2 (Cowleigh Park Beds), 3, 4, and 5 (Wyche Beds). In Shropshire the general sequence is 1, 3 and 5 representing the Kenley Grit, *Pentamerus* Beds and Purple Shales respectively. Thus the communities, as numbered, represent progressively offshore environments, though the complete sequence of communities is not present in any one area.

The off-shore sequence of the communities may be clearly demonstrated with palaeogeographical maps showing two phases of the Upper Llandovery transgression (Figures 59.2 and 59.3). The communities of the Lower and Middle Llandovery have not yet been studied in detail, but a map of this time period has been included (Figure 59.1) to show the extent of the land area later flooded by the Upper Llandovery transgression, and also to contrast the widths of the shelf area during different times. The accuracy of these maps depends largely on the correlation of the various sections, and this has been accomplished by studying evolutionary trends in various brachiopod lineages [9]. The greywackes and the graptolitic muds are included on the maps; these deposits typically do not contain benthonic animals. The graptolites are largely restricted to these deposits, only because the environment of deposition was such that their delicate remains were preserved; they probably lived in the surface waters [10] and drifted wherever seas existed.

A first approximation of the depths at which the various communities existed may be derived from volcanic flows which occur both at Marloes, Pembrokeshire, and Tortworth, Gloucestershire [12]. At Renny Slip, near Marloes, a 20-foot thick pillow basalt flowed out on deposits containing an *Eocoelia* community. The water was apparently shallowed by an amount equal to the thickness of the flow and this was enough to displace the *Eocoelia* community by its neighbour, the *Lingula* community which occurs in the beds just above the flow. However, the duration of the *Lingula* community at this locality was short as the *Eocoelia* community occurs about 40 ft. higher in the succession, its return being due to the generally transgressive nature of the sea at this time. Two miles away, however, at Marloes

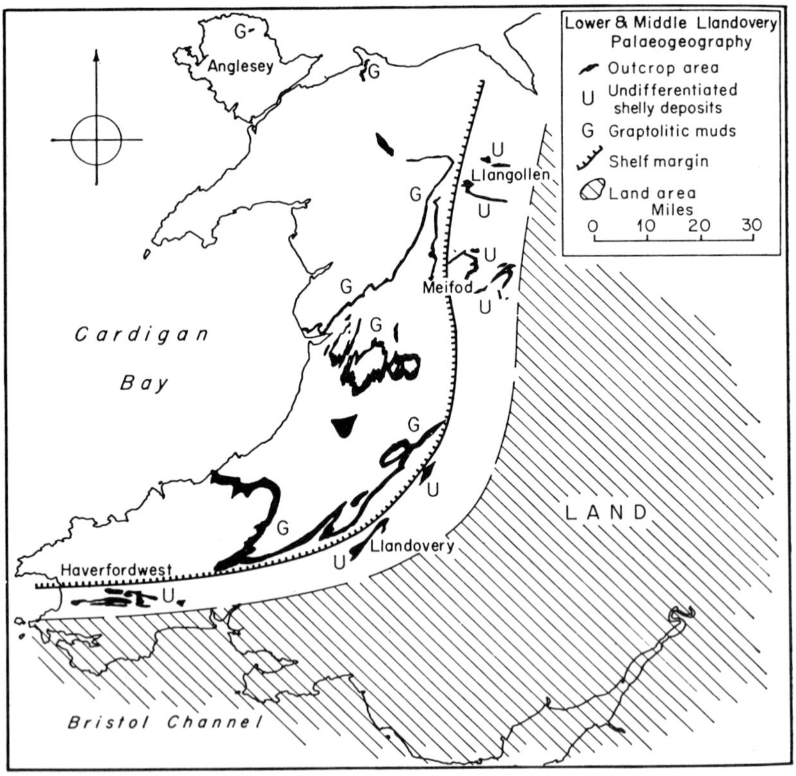

FIGURE 59.1
Lower and Middle Llandovery paleogeography

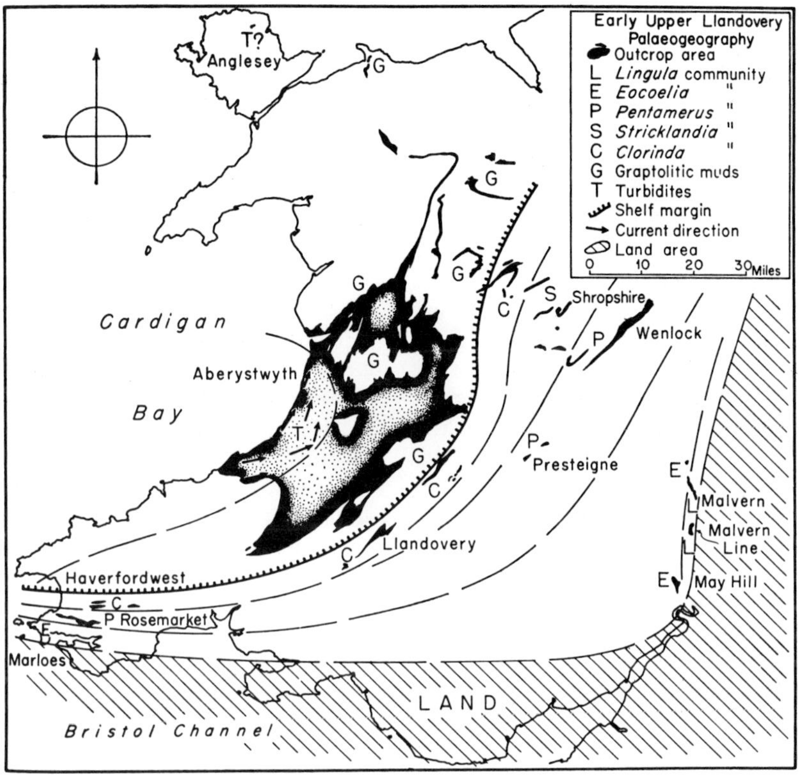

FIGURE 59.2
Early Upper Llandovery paleogeography

Bay, the basalt is much thicker (130 ft.) and therefore had a greater effect. Two flows occurred and the lower flow has a reddened surface [11], suggesting that deposition of the lower flow was at least in part subaerial. The *Lingula* community did not return until several hundred feet of conglomerates and sandstones had been deposited on top of the basalts. The relationship of these volcanic flows suggest that the depth ranges of these communities were of the order of tens of feet rather than hundreds of feet.

In the Tortworth inlier, an andesite flow of variable thickness occurs on top of deposits containing the *Costistricklandia* community. At Woodford, its thickness is small, perhaps 15 ft., and the *Costistricklandia* community is developed on top of the flow. However, less than two miles to the south, the flow is 150 ft. thick and the *Ecocoelia* community is developed in the sediments above the flow; here, both the *Costistricklandia* and *Pentameroides* communities were displaced. Relief of 135 ft., then, seems likely between the levels of the *Eocoelia* and *Costistricklandia* communities, and the *Pentameroides* community must have occupied some intermediate range.

In summary, the various lines of evidence on the community environments are: (1) comparison with modern communities in the case of *Lingula;* (2) sediment type; (3) stratigraphical succession; (4) areal relationships; (5) volcanic displacement. All these considerations point to an off-shore sequence of the communities, the *Lingula* community being the closest to the strand and the *Clorinda* community furthest from the strand. If this interpretation is correct, then several conclusions regarding the geological history follow.

The transgression of the Upper Llandovery sea occurred in two pulses. In early Upper Llandovery times the sea extended to cover much of South Wales and most of the Welsh Borderland. The record of its relatively rapid transgression is preserved in the *Eocoelia* community low in the succession of Presteigne and the *Lingula* community of the Kenley Grits of Shropshire. This was just a transient phase, however, and Figure 59.2 shows the relationships during much of early Upper Llandovery time, with the shoreline existing at the 'Malvern Line' [13]. About this time, turbidity currents began to deposit the Aberystwyth Grits in the geosyncline [14]. These turbidities are known to have extended further to the east and north with time, eventually covering much of central Wales [15]. It is a singular fact that there is a gap in the sequences of the shelf area which corresponds quite well with the deposition of the turbidities in the geosyncline; for example, northwest of Malvern at Old Storridge Common, Wyche Beds of C_5 age rest directly on Cowleigh Park Beds of C_1 or C_2 age. Possibly there was a slight regression causing much of the sediment that had accumulated on the shelf to be transported to the shelf margin where it was carried to the depths of the geosyncline by turbidity currents. Confirmation of this regression is found at Llandovery, about the only place where the sequence is continuous, where the *Stricklandia* community of C_4 beds succeeds the *Clorinda* community of C_2–C_3 beds.

The second pulse of the transgression occurred about C_5 time. It is perhaps significant that a transgression occurred on the north side of the geosyncline as well, in County Galway, Ireland [16], suggesting that the change of sea-level was eustatic. Much of south-east England became submerged, to judge by bore-hole information [17], turbidite deposition stopped abruptly, and fine-grained shales accumulated over much of the shelf and deeper area. By the end of Upper Llandovery times, the *Clorinda* community existed as far east as May Hill and Old Storridge Common, showing that subsidence continued at a faster pace than the accumulation of sediment.

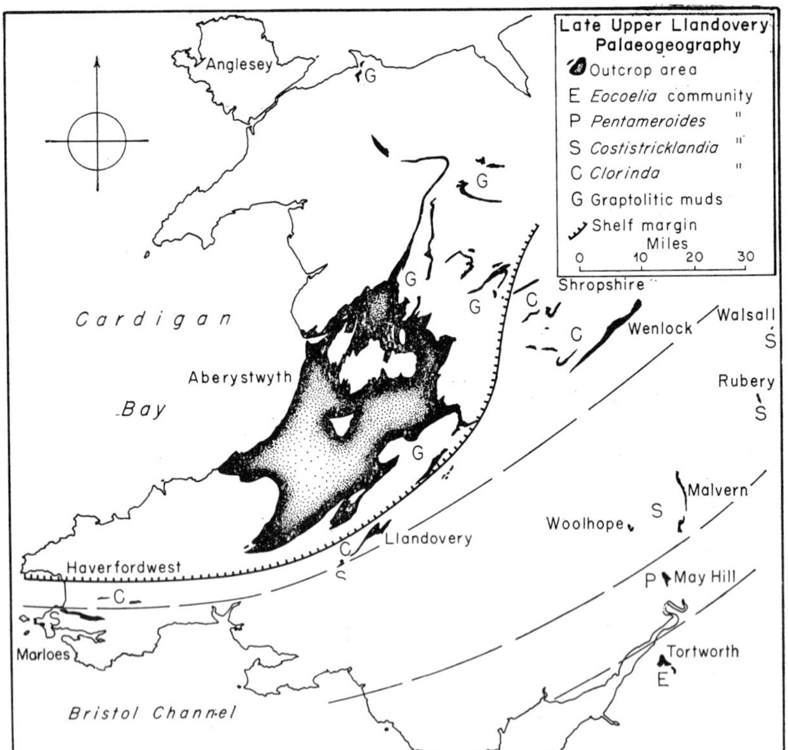

FIGURE 59.3
Late Upper Llandovery paleogeography

To conclude, it is clear that the animal community technique of the ecologists is applicable to fossil assemblages and can provide the basis for interpreting past environments. This article reports some preliminary results and is intended only as an announcement of a much more complete treatise, which would define the communities quantitatively, describe the various stratigraphical successions, and present a detailed geological history of the Llandovery of the British Isles.

REFERENCES

1. C. G. J. Petersen, *Am. Jour. Sci.*, ser. 5, v. 7, p. 343 (1924).
2. G. Thorson, *Geol. Soc. America Mem.* 67, p. 461 (1957).
3. R. H. Parker, *Dansk Naturh. Foren. Vidensk. Medd.*, p. 126 (1964).
4. R. S. Allan, *New Zealand Dept. Sci. Indus. Research Palaeontol. Bull.*, p. 14 (1935).
5. J. A. Fagerstrom, *Geol. Soc. America Bull.*, v. 75, p. 1197 (1964).
6. O. T. Jones, *Geol. Soc. London Quart. Jour.*, v. 77, p. 144 (1921).
7. W. F. Whittard, *Geol. Soc. London Quart. Jour.*, v. 83, p. 737 (1928).
8. G. Y. Craig, *Edinburgh Geol. Soc. Trans.*, v. 15, p. 110 (1952).
9. A. M. Ziegler, *Paleontology*, v. 9, pt. 4, p. 523 (1966).
10. O. M. B. Bulman, *Geol. Soc. London Quart. Jour.*, v. 120, p. 455 (1964).
11. T. C. Cantrill, E. E. Dixon, H. H. Thomas, and O. T. Jones, *Geol. Survey Great Britain Mem.*, Sheet 227 (1916).
12. M. L. K. Curtis, in *Bristol and its Adjoining Counties* (London: British Association for the Advancement of Science, 1955), p. 3.
13. A. M. Ziegler, *Geol. Mag.* [Great Britain], v. 101, p. 467 (1964).
14. A. Wood, and A. J. Smith, *Geol. Soc. London Quart. Jour.*, v. 114, p. 163 (1959).
15. D. A. Bassett, *Geol. Soc. London Quart. Jour.*, v. 111, p. 239 (1955).
16. W. S. McKerrow, and C. J. Campbell, *Royal Dublin Soc. Sci. Proc.*, ser. A, v. 1, p. 27 (1960).
17. E. C. Bullard, T. F. Gaskell, W. B. Harland, and C. Kerr-Grant, *Royal Soc.* [London] *Philos. Trans.*, ser. A, v. 239, p. 29 (1940).

60

Biogenic Sedimentary Structures

ADOLF SEILACHER
1964

From *Approaches to Paleoecology*, edited by John Imbrie and Norman D. Newell, pp. 296–313. John Wiley & Sons, Inc., 1964. Reprinted with permission of the author and the publisher.

TRACE FOSSILS AS PALEONTOLOGICAL OBJECTS

It is generally agreed that biogenic sedimentary structures are true fossils and that their study (ichnology or palichnology) is part of paleontology. Accordingly, they should be described, classified, and named like other fossils. The ordinary procedures of systematic paleontology, however, are difficult to apply to such structures, the shapes of which are controlled more by the depositional environment than by the shapes of the animals producing them. Therefore, some general considerations necessarily have to precede the paleoecological evaluation of these structures.

DEFINITION

Traces are sedimentary structures resulting from biological activity. This excludes agglutinated tests like those of Pectinaria and Foraminifera, as well as marks left by dead bodies drifting or rolling over the ground.

Preservation affects other fossils mainly in a negative sense, that is, by various degrees of secondary solution, disintegration, or deformation. Trace fossils, however, improve rather than suffer through diagenetic processes. Chemical differentiation tends to "develop" minor structural differences in originally more homogeneous sediments and to make them visible much as in photographic printing. Markings on bedding planes, almost inaccessible in recent cores, can be easily observed after selective cementation of the coarser layers. Even erosion, although usually destructive, may in certain cases preserve biogenic structures. For example, a mud structure may be eroded and a cast made by subsequent coarser sedimentation (Figure 60.1). In addition to secondary changes, a surprising variety of traces may result from the same activity of the one animal, depending on the plasticity of the sediment and the site of the activity at surface or inside the sediment. If such differences are

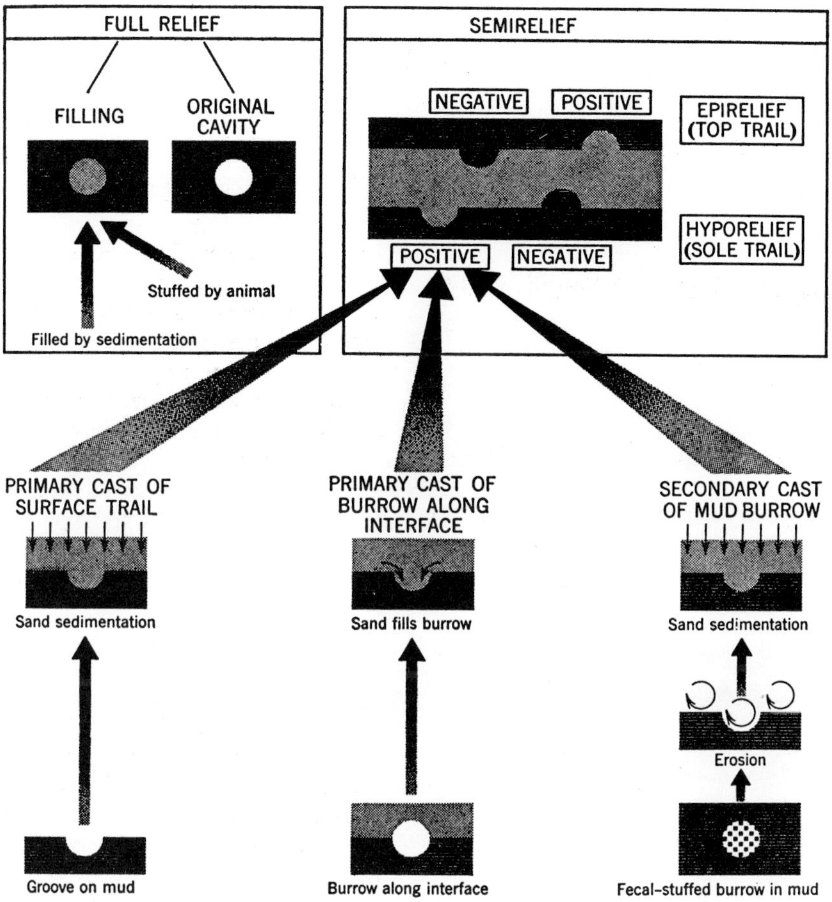

FIGURE 60.1
Preservation of trace fossils. Since the preparation of this chart a somewhat modified terminology has been suggested to the Committee for the Nomenclature of Sedimentary Structures. This includes the following new terms: "convex" for positive, and "concave" instead of negative, semireliefs; "exogene" for actual surface trails, versus "endogene" for primary casts of internal origin, and "pseudoexogene" for the secondary casts; "active" fill, if burrow was stuffed by the animal, and "passive" fill, if it was filled by sedimentation.

not realized and eliminated, nearly every specimen may be considered as a new "species." Some significant types of preservation and their possible origin are shown in Figure 60.1.

ETHOLOGICAL ELEMENTS IN TRACE MORPHOLOGY

Having sorted out accidental elements in trace morphology, we still have to separate features that express function from those reflecting the morphology of the animals. Since function is inherently involved in any trace, this separation is more difficult. The recognition of five ethological groups (Seilacher, 1953a) has so far proved to be satisfactory (Figure 60.2).

Repichnia: Trails or burrows left by vagile benthos during directed locomotion.

Pascichnia: Winding trails or burrows of vagile mud eaters which reflect a "grazing" search for food by covering a given surface more or less efficiently and avoiding double coverage.

Fodinichnia: Burrows made by hemisessile deposit feeders. They reflect the search for food and at the same time fit the requirements for a permanent shelter.

Domichnia: Permanent shelters dug by vagile or hemisessile animals procuring food from outside the sediment as predators, scavengers, or suspension feeders.

Cubichnia: Shallow resting tracks left by vagile animals hiding temporarily in the sediment, usually sand, and obtaining their food as scavengers or suspension feeders.

NONFUNCTIONAL (TAXONOMIC) ELEMENTS OF TRACE MORPHOLOGY

The final step in the analysis of trace fossils should be the recognition of features which are directly related to the morphology of particular animals. These features link the traces with other fossil remains and allow their identification in terms of systematic paleontology. While this goal is commonly reached in vertebrate ichnology, the analysis of invertebrate trace fossils can very rarely go that far, although it may happen that the body of an animal is preserved in its very track or burrow like *Limulus* in the Solenhofen Limestone (Caster, 1940). In other cases the body has left identifiable impressions, for instance, of cephalon and pleura in trilobite burrows or of distinctive claws in many arthropod tracks. Resting tracks of asteroids and ophiurians, which have long been mistaken for the bodies of the starfishes themselves, may be mentioned as another example (Seilacher, 1953b). Compared to the host of well-recognized, but systematically unidentified trace fossils, however, these are only rare exceptions. Even if by fur-

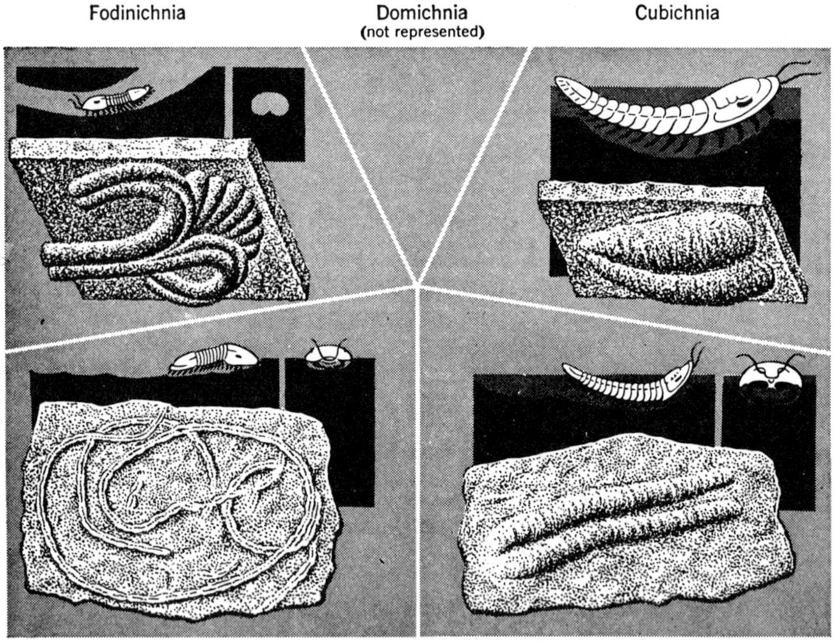

FIGURE 60.2
Main ethologic groups of trace fossils. Illustrated by trilobite burrows (sole faces of beds and restorations). *Cubichnia,* trace corresponds to outline of animal (*Rusophycus*); *Repichnia,* trace formed by repetition or extension of cubichnia (*Cruziana*); *Pascichnia,* a circling variety of repichnia, reflects search for food (from the Ordovician of northern Iraq); *Fodinichnia,* a branching burrow. (*Cruziana ancora* Lessertisseur from the Silurian of Equatorial Africa). Domichnia referable to trilobites have not been found so far.

ther studies, more and more revealing "fingerprints" are found, this situation will not essentially change in the future.

CLASSIFICATION AND NOMENCLATURE

A threefold determination including preservational, ethological, and taxonomic characters is necessary to describe any trace fossil adequately. As a base for nomenclature, however, only *one* classification can be used.

Hundt (1932), Desio (1940), and Lessertisseur (1955) have proposed ichnological systems, in which the main distinction is made between surface trails and burrows, while functional (ethological), ecological, or taxonomic differences are used for subordinate grouping. In practice these classifications are difficult to apply, because surface tracks and burrows are fundamentally different only to our eyes. For many benthonic animals it makes little difference whether they creep at the surface or along bedding planes inside the sediment, and for the paleontologist it is often impossible to differentiate these two types of motion. Therefore, most German authors (Richter, 1927; Krejci-Graf, 1932, and Abel, 1935) have based their classifications completely on ethology. A compromise solution was proposed by Seilacher (1953a). The higher categories of his ichnological system should be based on ethologic interpretations; the lower ones (ichnospecies) on taxonomic interpretations.

Meanwhile experience has shown that a hybrid system inevitably leads to difficulties. Preservation, ethology, and taxonomy do not have equivalent relative importance in different groups of trace fossils. Tetrapod tracks often reflect the morphology of their producers clearly enough to be placed in certain families, or even genera. Ethologically, however, they would all belong to the same group, Repichnia. "Worm" trails, on the other hand, very rarely permit further taxonomic distinction, but they show remarkable ethologic diversity. Other groups range between these two extremes. The burrows of Figure 60.2 are all made by trilobites. Some can be attributed even more specifically to Illaenids. This natural group must be split into four different genera if an ethological classification is rigidly applied. Ichnological names—not recognized according to the International Rules of Zoological Nomenclature—should express individual morphology rather than the interpretation of trace fossils. The recent issue, by W. Häntzschel, of the *Treatise on Invertebrate Paleontology*, has made the recognition of individual types much easier. Eventually, more and more taxonomic differences in trace morphology will emerge which may help to give invertebrate trace fossils a similar, though less defined, taxonomic status as tetrapod tracks have in vertebrate classification.

TRACE FOSSILS AS PALEOECOLOGIC GUIDES

GENERAL REMARKS

It is generally believed that ecological interpretation of fossil assemblages becomes more and more difficult as we go further back in geologic history. This rule does not fully apply to trace fossils. A Tertiary shell fauna can still be interpreted in terms of recent animals and their environments. Tertiary trace fossils, however, have little more resemblance to known Recent traces than do Mesozoic or even Paleozoic examples (Figure 60.3). Nevertheless there may be very close similarity between the Tertiary and Paleozoic trace fossils. This does not mean that the fossil types no longer exist in Recent seas. Rather, sedimentary structures, and particularly the internal ones, are much easier to study in consolidated rocks than in soft sediments where special preparations are needed to make them visible. What we know from Recent sea floors are mainly surface trails which would be rarely preserved as fossils, while internal structures have so far been inadequately studied, that is, in single sections (Reineck, 1958; Moore and Scruton, 1957). We could say that in ichnology the present has rarely provided actual keys to the past; however, it has taught us how the locks work. Here is still an open field for future exploration by marine geologists.

Although they cannot yet be directly translated into terms of recent taxonomy and biogeography, trace fossils nevertheless have considerable advantages.

(1) Long time range. Trace morphology reflects certain functions and behaviour patterns rather than body shapes. Different animals acting alike may leave almost the same type of traces. Partly for this reason many gross types of trace fossils occur through many periods, or even eras, of geologic history. This may be a disadvantage for stratigraphic use, but it considerably facilitates long-range facies comparison.

(2) Narrow facies range. The recorded actions are often direct responses to environmental conditions. Significant types of trace fossils therefore are restricted to certain facies, irrespective of what animals have produced them.

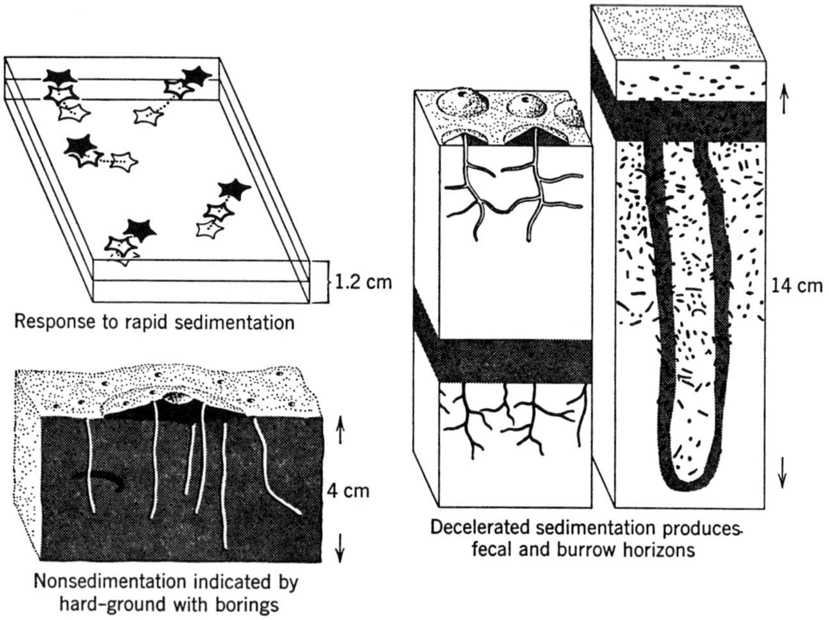

FIGURE 60.3
Trace fossils and relation to sedimentary rates. *Upper left*, reacting to fast deposition of new sand layers, epipsammonic ophiurans have followed the rising surface. They left corresponding, but not congruent, impressions (cubichnia of *Asteriacites* type) on subsequent laminae. Lower Triassic Seiser beds, Tyrol. In Rhaetic sandstone of southern Germany, corresponding impressions may be found on lower and upper face of beds up to 7 cm thick (Seilacher, 1953b). *Right*, during a time of retarded mud sedimentation, deposit feeders had a chance to riddle the top part of the mud with burrows (fodinichnia) and form a dark fecal layer at the contemporary surface. Note that *Chondrites* burrows (*small spots*) do not reach as deeply as the U-shaped *Corophioides*, except in the reworked septum ("Spreite") between the shafts of the latter. Deviations of burrows around mollusk shells indicate that the sediment was still soft. After a time interval, sedimentation continued at the original rate and formed the upper part of the calcareous mudstone bed in which the bioturbate layer is now included. (Lias γ, southern Germany.) Similar bioturbation zones have been observed in experiments with recent worms (Schäfer, 1952: left block). *Lower left*, simple burrows (domichnia) of suspension feeders originate from a sharp but uneven surface which was already hard enough to serve as a substrate for crinoid roots. These as well as shells in the sediment were pierced by the boring animals just as easily as the matrix. "Hard grounds" of this type indicate longer periods of nondeposition and form good marker horizons. From the Lower Muschelkalk (Middle Triassic). (From A. H. Müller, 1956.)

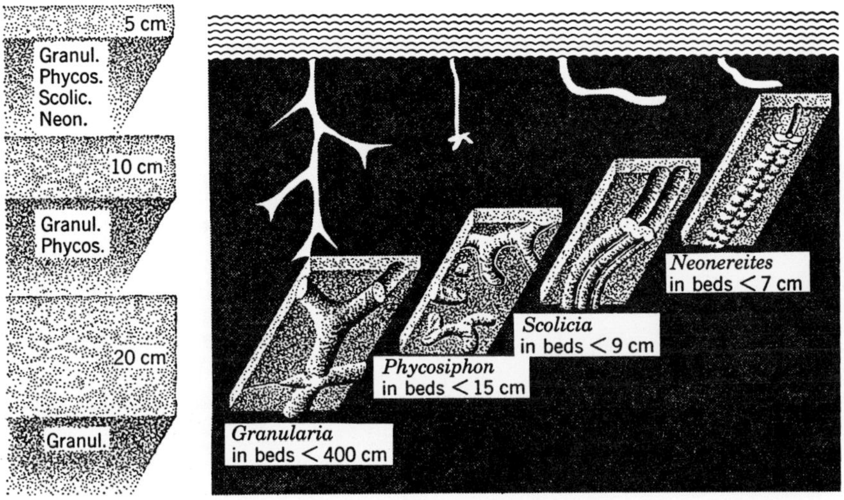

FIGURE 60.4
Trails indicating turbidity sedimentation. Among the sole trails of flysch greywacke beds the listed types are postdepositional. They are made by animals that penetrated the sand layer and moved along the interface between sand and mud. These trails are never found in beds beyond a certain thickness, probably corresponding to the depth to which the particular species used to burrow. This relation was tested in several hundred beds and is considered a proof for instantaneous sedimentation of each bed by a turbidity current. (Seilacher, 1962.)

(3) No secondary displacement. Sedimentary structures obviously cannot be reworked like other fossils. Every ichnocoenosis represents part of an actual benthic community that lived in a single area and usually at the same time.
(4) Preference for clastic sediments. Ichnofossils may occur in any type of sediment, but they are most abundant and best preserved in clastic series, particularly where sandy and shaly beds alternate.

All these circumstances together make trace fossils promising as paleoecologic guides. They will be particularly useful in clastic sediments poor in other fossils and in the more ancient rocks where other fossils are too different from Recent animals to justify the simple application of uniformitarianism.

For the purpose of this paper we may distinguish three main directions of research in this field. The first aims at recognition of individual environmental factors; the second is concerned about minor facies variations in limited sections; and the third tries to recognize general trace associations, or types of ichnocoenoses, representing certain facies with a long geologic range.

INDIVIDUAL ENVIRONMENTAL FACTORS

It is obvious that environmental conditions directly control animal actions to a large extent. In some cases individual environmental factors can be recognized in the fossil record of such actions.

AERATION

Whenever discussion arises about euxinic or noneuxinic origin of sediments, lack of trace fossils is a strong argument in favor of euxinic conditions, while their occurrence is the best possible proof against such conditions. The black Devonian Hunsrück Shales of Western Germany contain exceptionally well-preserved and complete fossils, and this fact was long considered to be a result of euxinic conditions.

In this particular case, euxinic origin was ruled out by Rudolf Richter, who discovered a variety of trails indicating a rich bottom life. Autochthonous benthos and complete preservation are not incompatible. For example, complete trilobite specimens with legs and even tiny preserved setae are associated with burrows of *Chondrites*, which must have been made when the trilobite body lay only 1 or 2 cm below the bottom surface (Seilacher, 1962).

On the other hand, the Liassic Posidonia Shales of Holzmaden (Western Germany), famous for skin-bearing Ichthyosaur fossils, contain no trails or burrows except in one or two distinct layers close to the upper and at the lower boundaries of the unit.

SEDIMENTATION

Trace fossils may tell about the relative speed of sedimentation in several ways; for example, by the response to sedimentary deposition shown by certain resting tracks of ophiuroids. Like most cubichnia, they are made by epipsammonic species that hide themselves in the sand just under the surface. If covered in experiments with more sand, ophiuroids dig their way up until the sensory organs (at the arm tips) reach the surface again. Vertical repetition of resting tracks, as occurs particularly in current-lineated sandstones, records such reaction to the deposition of a corresponding sand layer on top of the buried animal. As epipsammonic animals usually leave the sand to gather their food, this deposition must have happened between two meals—that is, rather rapidly.

Retarded sedimentation gives burrowing deposit feeders a chance to riddle the top layer more intensively. In addition, fecal pellets may accumulate at the surface. Both burrow horizons and fecal layers can be traced within otherwise homogeneous beds (Figure 60.3).

Periods of nondeposition produce in pelitic deposits more compact and firm surface layers

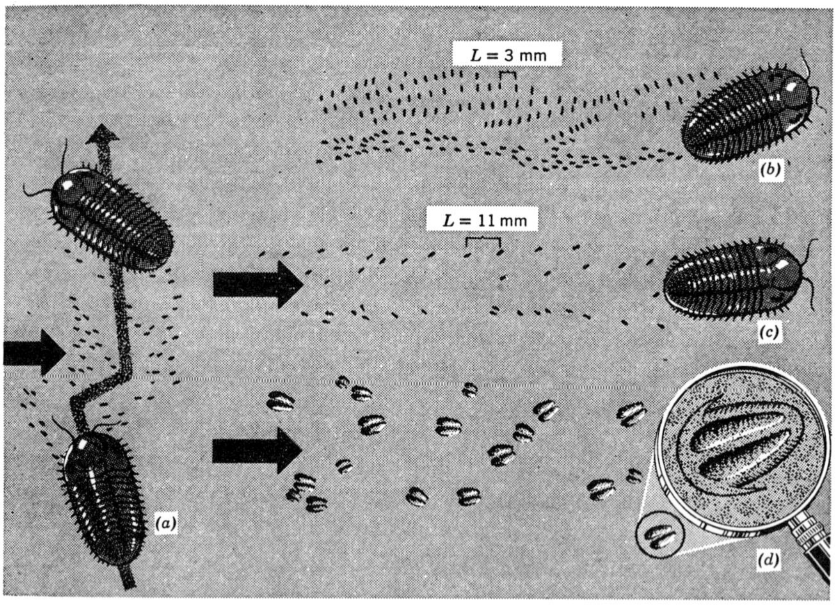

FIGURE 60.5
Arthropod tracks. *a–c*, trilobite tracks from Lower Devonian Hunsrück shales, Germany (Seilacher, 1960, Fig. 13): *a*, lateral current (recorded by groove casts) has displaced the walking trilobite from its original path; *b*, normal trackway; *c*, current from the rear (groove cast indication) has considerably increased the pace. *d*, coffeebean-shaped resting tracks from the Purple Sandstone (Lower Cambrian) of Pakistan (Seilacher, 1955): they record the rheotactic orientation of trilobites or phyllopods dug in the sand with their heads against the current (indicated by current lineation).

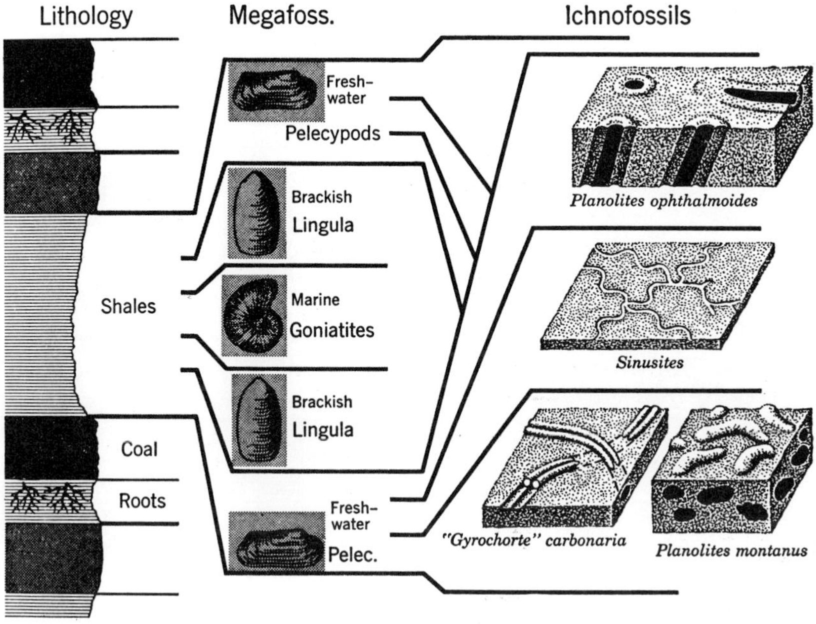

FIGURE 60.6
Trace fossils and stratigraphic subdivision. Within lithologic cyclothems in paralic deposits of the Ruhr Basin, more members can be recognized with the help of trace fossils. For this purpose it makes no difference that these trace fossils belong to rather insignificant types which in other formations may occur in dissimilar types of facies. (Based on data by Fessen and others.)

("hard grounds," Voigt, 1959). In hard grounds, suspension feeders have their burrows from which to feed in the turbulent water. These burrows, however, are mainly shelters (domichnia) dug or drilled perpendicular to the surface, rather than complicated feeding burrows (fodinichnia) as mentioned earlier.

An extremely rapid type of deposition has been suggested for sandy beds of the flysch, and other supposed turbidites. Figure 60.4 illustrates how this concept was confirmed ichnologically in the Spanish flysch. There is no contradiction in the fact that one type of sole trails (*Granularia*) occurs in beds up to 4 m. In modern deep-sea sands, which are aerated to a greater depth than shallow-water sands, worms actually dig that deeply (Bezrukov and Romankevič, 1960).

CURRENTS

Compared to the large number of inorganic current markings, biogenic indicators of current have no real importance. Nevertheless, they should be mentioned as a paleontological contribution to the study of paleocurrents. Currents not only affect the movements of animals crawling on the sea floor (Figure 60.5), but also control the orientation of suspension feeders and other animals hidden in the sand. Many crustaceans and gastropods tend to face the current, while some other crustaceans have filter mechanisms that require an orientation downstream, or even at right angles to the current (Seilacher, 1961). The umbo of digging pelecypods, if oriented at all, points downstream, so that the inhaling siphon faces the current. As a result, the resting tracks left on underlying bedding planes are subparallel to each other (Figure 60.5).

MINOR FACIES VARIATIONS WITHIN A GIVEN SERIES

In recent tidal flats the different types of burrows and surface trails and their relative abundance are used to distinguish and to map minor variations in sediment type, exposure,

GRAZING PATTERNS:
Meanders, Spirals, Branch- and Network

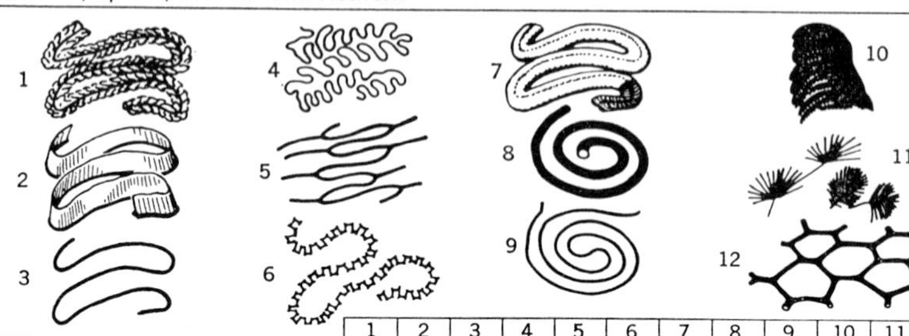

				1	2	3	4	5	6	7	8	9	10	11	12	TURBIDITE STRUCTURES
NEREITES FACIES	*T*	Eocene Flysch,	Austria				■	■	■	■	■	■	■		■	■
			Spain			■	■	■	■	■	■	■			■	■
	K	Cretaceous Flysch,	Alaska			■	■					■			■	■
			Italy	■		■	■	■	■						■	■
			N. Spain	■		■	■	■	■						■	■
	Ꞧ	Taurid Fm.,	Crimea												■	■
	P	Havallah Fm.,	Nevada										■			
	q	Johns Valley Sh.,	Okla.	■							■				■	■
	M	Kulm Sh.,	E. Germany	■	■					■	■		■		■	■
	D	Hemberg Sh.,	W. Germany	■	■										■	
		Nereites Sh.,	E. Germany	■			■						■			
	S	Aberystwith Sltst.,	Wales	■	■										■	■
	O	Barrancos Sh.,	Portugal	■	■			■					■	■		
		Sinat Sh.,	N. Iraq			■									■	■
		Taconic Sl.,	N.Y.	■												
	ϵ	Bray Ser.,	Ireland											■		
ZOOPH. F	*K*	Bänderkreide,	N. Germany													
	J	Wedelsandst,	S. Germany													
	ϕ	Atoka Fm.,	Arkansas													
	D	Chemung Gr.,	N.Y.													
		Gγ,	Bohemia													
	O	Dershish Fm.,	N. Iraq													
CRUZIANA FACIES	*T*	Burdigal-Molasse,	Switzerland													
	J	U. Malm Sst.,	N. France													
		Dogger β Sst.,	S. Germany													
		Lias α Sst.,	S. Germany													
	Ꞧ	Rhetian Sst.,	S. Germany													
		Muschelkalk,	S. Germany													
		Werfen Beds,	N. Italy													
		Verrucano,	Tuscany													
	M	Bedford Sh.,	Ohio													
	D	Taunus Qzt.,	W. Germany							■						
	S	Clinton Gr.,	N.Y.													
	O	Cincinnatian,	Ohio													
		Cobourg Beds,	Ottawa													
		Khabour Qzt.,	N. Iraq													
		Armorican Qzt.,	N. France													
		Phycodes Qzt.,	E. Germany													
	ϵ	Cambrian of Leon,	Spain													
		Magnesian Sst.,	Salt Range													
		Bright Angel Sh.,	Arizona													
		Mickwitzia Sst.,	Sweden													

FIGURE 60.7
Trace fossil communities. All communities of trace fossils, regardless of geologic age, can be assigned to one of three major types of ichnofacies which show parallel differences in lithology and inorganic sedimentary structures. See Table 60.1 for more details. The three facies represent major environments differing in depth and sedimentary regime. Sources of information: Hundt, 1941 (*Phycodes* Quartzite); Wilson, 1948

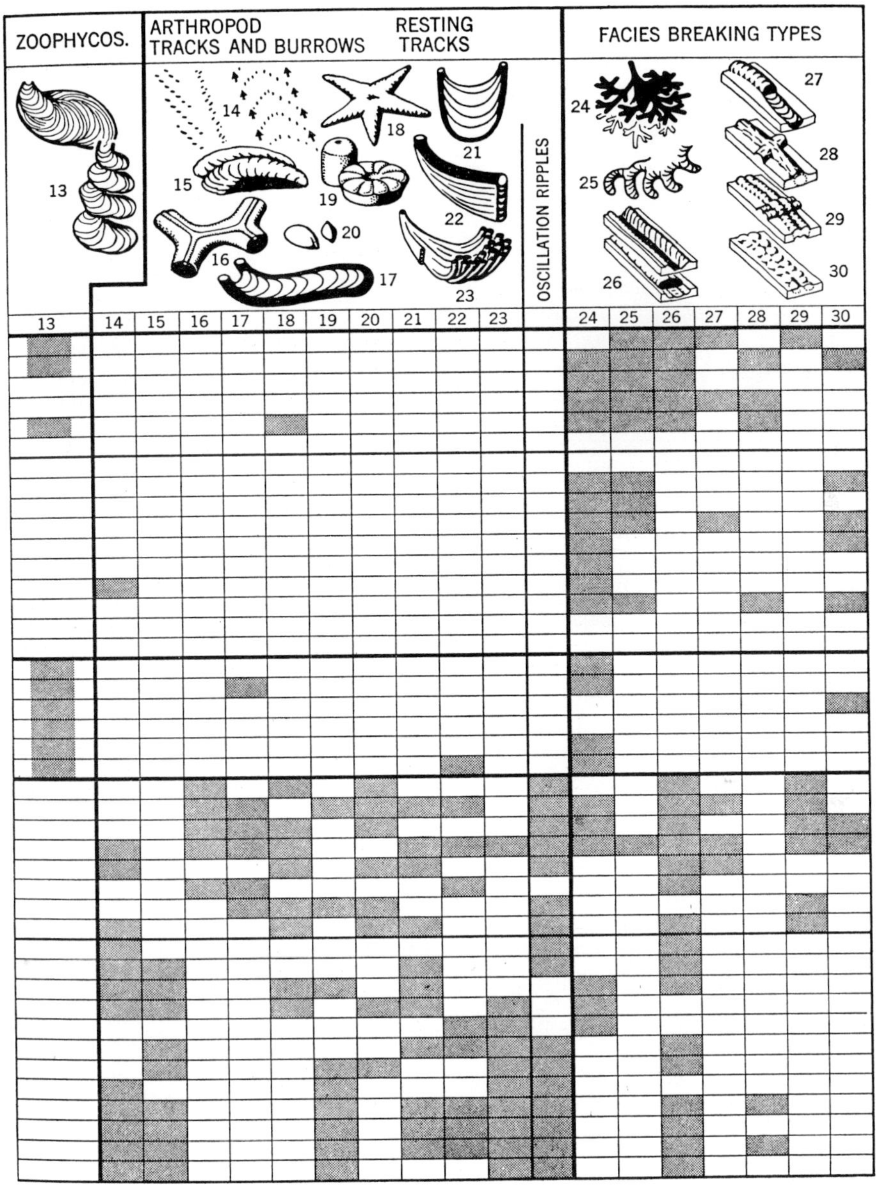

(Cobourg); J. Hall, 1850 (Clinton; *Asteriacites* in Albany museum); Fucini, 1936–38 (Verrucano); M. Schmidt, 1934; Leonardi, 1935 (Werfen); J. Hall, 1852 (Chemung); L. Henbest, 1960 (Atoka); Voigt and Häntzschel, 1956 (Bänderkreide); Emmons, 1844 (Taconic; similar types in Maine); Keeping, 1882 (Aberystwyth); S. W. Muller (unpublished specimens from Havallah); O. S. Vialov, 1960 (Taurid). Other data are based mainly on personal observations.

TABLE 60.1
Universal ichnofacies—their distinguishing characteristics

Characteristic	*Nereites*-Facies	*Zoophycos*-Facies	*Cruziana*-Facies
Diagnostic trace fossils (Figure 60.7)	Internal, meandering pascichnia: 1. *Nereites* (w. lateral flaps) 2. *Dictyodora* (w. vertical septum) 3. *Helminthoida crassa* 4. *Cosmorhaphe* (plain, sec. cast) 5. *Urohelminthoida* (w. appendices; sec. cast) 6. *Paleomaeandron* (sec. cast) 7. *Taphrhelminthopsis* (gastropod-trail, stuffed) Spiral pascichnia: 8. *Ceratophycus* (+ *Spirodesmos*) 9. *Spirorhaphe* (sec. cast) Branching pascichnia: 10. *Lophoctenium* (prim. cast) 11. *Oldhamia* (prim. cast; left: Cambr.; right: Ord.) 12. *Paleodictyon* (sec., rarely prim. cast)	Fodinichnia: 13. *Zoophycos* (only flat, nonspiral variety)	Arthropod tracks and burrows: 14. Tracks of Trilobites (left), Limulids (right), and other Arthropods 15. *Cruziana* and *Rusophycus* (Trilobite burrow, inverted cast) 16. *Thalassinoides, etc.* (Anomuran burrows) 17. *Rhizocorallium* (septate burrows, probably of crustaceans) Cubichnia (all inverted casts): 18. *Asteriacites* (of Asterozoans) 19. left: *Bergaueria;* right: *Solicyclus* (of Coelenterates) 20. *Pelecypodichnus* (of pelecypods) Septate Fodinichnia: 21. *Corophioides* (U-shaped with septum) 22. *Teichichnus* (similar, but irregular) 23. *Phycodes* (palmate)
Dominant groups	Pascichnia of vagile, endobiotic deposit feeders	Fodinichnia of deposit feeders	Cubichnia of epipsammon Domichnia of suspension feeders (mainly in shallow, turbulent zone) Fodinichnia of deposit feeders (mainly in deeper zone)
Diagnostic inorganic sedimentary structures	Load casts, convolute lamination and other turbidite structures	Bedding and lamination poor	Oscillation ripples
Dominant lithology	Lutites, alternating with graded greywackes or pelagic marls	Impure, crumbly siltstones to shales	Well sorted sandstones to shales, quartzites; detrital limestones to marls
Probable depth	Bathyal with turbidite sedimentation	Sublittoral to bathyal, below wave base and without turbidite sedimentation	Littoral to sublittoral, above wave base

Characteristic	*Nereites*-Facies	*Zoophycos*-Facies	*Cruziana*-Facies
Nondiagnostic trace fossils of Figure 60.7	24. *Chondrites* (root-like, branching fodinichnia) 27. *Münsteria* (stuffed linear burrows)	25. *Phycosiphon* (small, looped, and septate fodinichnia or pascichnia) 28. *Fucusopsis* (burrows cracking the interface; inverted) 30. *Scalarituba* (= *Neonereites*; burrows like No. 1, but without meanders; inverted)	26. *Scolicia* (gastropod trails like No. 7, but without meanders) 29. *Gyrochorte* (positive epireliefs, repeating in adjacent laminae)

etc. There is no reason why a similar procedure should not be applied to trace lateral and vertical changes in ancient sediments.

Particular associations of faunal and lithological elements occur in almost any series of sedimentary deposits. As recurrent facies types, they reflect certain conditions that have controlled either the original or postmortem distribution of organisms and their remains. Trace associations, or ichnocoenoses, however, may be destroyed but never secondarily changed by later events. They form a more adequate record of original benthic communities. For the given purpose it makes little difference whether the trace fossils dealt with are fully understood or not. They must not even belong to generally recognizable types, if they can only be told apart from other trace fossils of that particular formation.

Figure 60.6 illustrates an example from the Upper Carboniferous Ruhr Basin, where trace fossils have been successfully used to further subdivide the additional members of paralic cyclothems. None of the types represented is really diagnostic. *Planolites montanus* is a simple sand-filled burrow, *Gyrochorte carbonaria* a bilobate gallery that might occur in any formation. *Sinusites* trails may be formed through sinuose locomotion of almost any worm; they are found alike in Cambrian or Jurassic marine sandstones, as well as in Recent beach sands and pond muds. Even *Planolites ophthalmoides* becomes less diagnostic, if the eye-like halo is understood as a zone of slight alteration or cementation around a galley, made visible by subsequent tectonic compression. Nevertheless, within the limits of the Ruhr Basin and of the Pennsylvanian section, each type corresponds to a particular, though unknown, species of burrowing animal, each with distinct requirements as to salinity and other environmental factors.

UNIVERSAL TYPES OF MARINE ICHNOFACIES

In the preceding section, each trace fossil was considered as a substitute for the unknown species of animals from which it came. The conclusions, therefore, are not valid beyond the vertical and horizontal range of that particular species.

Comparison between many ichnocoenoses of various geologic ages has shown, however, that there is a more general, supraspecific relation between the ethological character of trace fossils and the geologic facies indicated by lithology and inorganic sedimentary structures. In a gross way, the difference is expressed by the ichnospectrum, that is, by the relative abundance in which the various ethotypes (domichnia, cubichnia, etc.: see Figure 60.2) are represented in each trace association (Seilacher, 1958, fig. 1). In a most general way, this relation may be described and interpreted as follows:

(1) To benthic animals of littoral and very shallow water environments, physical protection is a major concern. Vagile animals and suspension feeders which prevail in this turbulent zone either bury themselves temporarily under the surface, leaving shallow resting tracks (cubichnia), or they produce deep and vertical burrows (domichnia) for shelter. In a slightly deeper and quieter zone in which the food particles settle, deposit feeders become more important. Most of them are hemisessile and produce feeding burrows (fodinichnia). Cubichnia and domichnia are still found. Repichnia left by vagile epibenthos occur in either of the two zones.

(2) Deep-sea animals gain little by hiding in the sediment. Domichnia and cubichnia almost disappear from the trace spectrum. Instead, complicated fodinichnia and internal grazing tracks (pascichnia) with intricate patterns become more common. The deposit feeders that make them are largely vagile and have particular locomotion patterns to insure systematic coverage of possible food-rich layers.

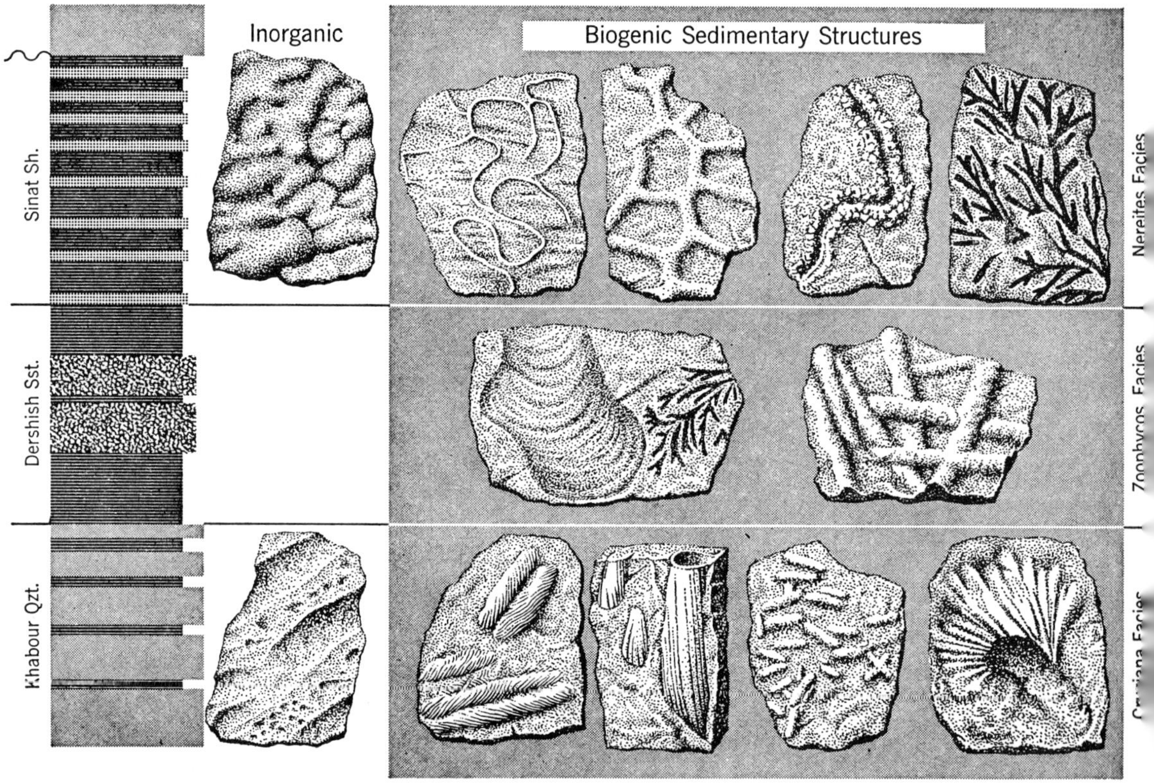

FIGURE 60.8
The Ordovician section of Sinat, northern Iraq. The section can be subdivided into three formations, named after nearby villages. These formations correspond by lithology as well as inorganic and biogenic sedimentary structures to the *Cruziana-*, *Zoophycos-*, and *Nereites*-facies and indicate the subsidence of the region from above wave base to deep geosynclinal conditions with turbidity currents in a relatively short time. Subsequent uplift is shown by lack of Silurian and deposition of littoral and continental Devonian beds on top. (For more details see Seilacher, 1963.) The illustrations of specimens were prepared from field photographs. KHABOUR QUARTZITE (*left to right*): oscillation ripples with flattened crests; *Cruziana*, $\times \frac{1}{10}$; *Daedalus halli*, $\times \frac{1}{3}$; basal parts of *Diplocraterion*, $\times \frac{1}{2}$; *Phycodes*, cf. *circinnatum* Richter, $\times \frac{1}{3}$. DERSHISH SANDSTONES (*left to right*): *Zoophycos* and *Chondrites*, $\times \frac{1}{7}$; *Teichichnus* (hyporelief), $\times \frac{1}{4}$. SINAT SHALES AND GREYWACKES (*left to right*): load casts, $\times \frac{1}{4}$; *Helminthoida* (secondary hyporelief), $\times \frac{1}{10}$; *Palacodictyon* (secondary hyporelief), $\times \frac{1}{4}$; *Neonereites* (primary epirelief), $\times \frac{2}{3}$; *Chondrites*, $\times \frac{2}{3}$.

The quantitative ichnospectrum is not the only way to classify a given ichnocoenosis. Most trace fossils are more or less restricted to one type of ichnofacies. In Figure 60.7 the diagnostic types are separated from the more ubiquitous forms, while the formations are grouped according to their lithofacies. In both respects three universal types of facies are recognized and named after significant trace fossils. These three facies are most obvious in psammitic rocks, but they apply also to pelitic sediments. The significant features of each are listed in Table 60.1.

It should be remembered that our ichnological facies concept was primarily derived from the comparison of given fossil ichnocoenoses. New discoveries have meanwhile confirmed this classification and its environmental interpretation.

A most striking example may be cited from the mountains of northern Iraq, where clastic Ordovician rocks crop out underneath thick limestones of the later Iranidian geosyncline. They have been considered so far as one single formation (Khabour Quartzites and Shales, Lexique Stratigraphique, Iraq, p. 147). At one place, however (Sinat), the Ordovician section consists of three distinct formations which clearly correspond to our *Cruziana-*, *Zoophycos-* and *Nereites*-facies, one grading vertically into the other (Figure 60.8). Sedimentary facies and associated volcanic rocks confirm the picture of a rapidly subsiding geosyncline that preceded the late Paleozoic and Mesozoic one in this place. No angular unconformity can be observed between the two cycles, but there is an abrupt change from the Ordovician turbidites (*Nereites*-Facies) to a very pure quartzite of unknown age that contains oscillation ripples and numerous vertical burrows. It is considered here as the littoral or fresh-water (*Scolithus*) facies that indicates the beginning of the new depositional cycle after a major uplift.

While the Iraq section illustrates a transition in time, lateral transition between the three ichno-facies can be most perfectly studied in the Paleozoic fold belts of the eastern and central United States and their forelands. In the Ouachita Mountains, for instance, the Johns Valley turbidites (Cline and Shelburne, 1959) correspond in every respect to our *Nereites* facies (Figure 60.7). North of the Ouachita Mountains, at Tenkiller Dam, Atoka siltstones of approximately the same age are impure and poorly bedded and contain *Zoophycos* ("*Taonurus*") and *Scalarituba*, a *Nereites*-like, but less-meandering burrow. There is no doubt that still further toward the craton this *Zoophycos* facies would eventually grade into the *Cruziana* facies including littoral deposits.

REFERENCES

[*For more complete bibliography, see Lessertisseur (1955).*]

Abel, O., 1935, Vorzeitliche Lebensspuren: Jena, Fischer.

Bezrukov, P. L., and A. Romankevič, 1960, Stratigraphy and lithology of the sediments in the northwest Pacific Ocean: Akad. Nauk SSSR Doklady, v. 130, p. 417–420, 3 figs., 12 pl.

Caster, K. E., 1940, Die sogenannten Wirbeltierspuren und die Limulusfährten der Solnhofener Plattenkalke: Paleont. Zeitschr., v. 22, p. 12–29.

Cline, L. M., and O. B. Shelburne, 1959, Late Mississippian–early Pennsylvanian stratigraphy of the Ouachita mountains, Oklahoma, *in* Ouachita Symposium: Dallas Geological Society, p. 175–207.

Desio, A., 1950, Sulla nomenclatura delle vestigia problematiche fossili: Riv. Italiana Paleont., v. 56, pls. 1–5.

Emmons, E., 1844, The taconic system: Albany, pl. II.

Fucini, A., 1936, 1938, Problematica verrucana I and II, *in* Palaeontographica Italica, v. 148: Pisa, Appendice I–II.

Hall, J., 1850, On trails and tracks in the sandstone of the Clinton group: Am. Assoc. Adv. Sci. Proc., v. 2.

———, 1852, Natural History of New York, v. 2. Palaeontology of New York: Albany, New York, Chas. van Beuthuysen (for the Geological Survey of the State of New York).

Häntzschel, W., 1962, Trace fossils and problematica, *in* R. C. Moore, ed., Treatise on invertebrate paleontology, pt. W: Boulder, Colo., Geological Society of America, p. W177–W245, figs. 109–149.

Henbest, L., 1960, Fossil spoor and their environmental significance in Morrow and Atoka series, Pennsylvania, Washington County, Arkansas: U.S. Geol. Survey Prof. Paper 400, p. 383–384, fig. 177.

Hundt, R., 1932, Eine Monographie der Lebensspuren des unteren Mitteldevons Thüringens: Leipzig, M. Weg.

———, 1941, Das mitteldeutsche Phycodesmeer: Jena, Fischer.

Jessen, W., G. Kremp, and P. Michelau, 1951, Gesteinsrhythmen und Faunenzyklen des Ruhrkarbons und ihre Ursachen: Cong. strat. géol. carbonifère, v. 3, p. 289–294.

Jessen, W., and G. Kremp, 1954, Feinstratigraphisch-mikrofaunistische Profilbeschreibung mit Fundstücken von *Gyrochorte carbonaria* Schleicher im Oberkarbon (Westfal A) am Niederrhein: Neues Jahrb. Geologie Palaontologie Monatsh., p. 284–286.

Keeping, W., 1882, on some remains of plants, Foraminifera and Annelida, *in* The Silurian rocks of Central Wales: Geol. Mag. [Great Britain], v. 9, p. 485–491, pl. 11.

Krejci-Graf, K., 1932, Definition der Begriffe Marken, Spuren, Fährten, Bauten, Hieroglyphen und Fucoiden: Senckenbergiana, v. 14, p. 19–39.

Lenoradi, P., 1937, Il trias inferiore delle Venezie: Ist Geol. Univ. Padova Mem., v. 11, 136 p., 8 pls.

Lessertisseur, J., 1955, Traces fossiles d'activité animale et leur signification paléobiologique: Soc. geol. France Mém., v. 74, p. 7–150, pl. 11.

Moore, D. G., and P. C. Scruton, 1957, Minor internal structures of some recent unconsolidated sediments: Am. Assoc. Petroleum Geologists Bull., v. 41, p. 2723–2751.

Müller, A. H., 1956, Weitere Beiträge zur Ichnologie, Stratinomie und Ökologie der germanischen Trias: Geologie, v. 5, p. 405–423.

Reineck, H., 1958, Wuhlbau-Gefüge in Abhängigkeit von Sediment-Umlagerungen: Senckenbergiana Lethaea, v. 39, p. 1–14, 5 pls.

Richter, R., 1927, Die fossilen Fährten und Bauten der Würmer, ein Überblick über ihre biologischen Grundformen und deren geologische Bedeutung: Paleontol. Zeitschr., v. 9, p. 193–235.

———, 1936, Marken und Spuren im Hunsrück-Schiefer, II; Schichtung und Grund-Leben: Senckenbergiana, v. 18, p. 215–244, 4 figs.

Schäfer, W., 1952, Biogene Sedimentation im Gefolge von Bioturbation: Senckenbergiana, v. 33, p. 1–12.

Schmidt, M., 1934, *Cyclozoon philippi* und verwandte Gebilde: Sitzungsber. Heidelberger Akad. Wiss. Math.-naturw. Kl. Abh., 31 p., 4 pls.

Seilacher, A., 1953, Studien zur Palichnologie, I. Über die Methoden der Palichnologie: Neues Jahrb. Geologie Paläontologie Abh., v. 96, p. 421–452, 14 figs., 2 pls.

———, 1953, Studien zur Palichnologie, II; Die fossilen Ruhespuren (Cubichnia): Neues Jahrb. Geologie Paläontologie Abh., v. 98, p. 87–124, 5 figs., pls. 7–13.

———, 1958, Zur ökologischen Charakteristik von Flysch und Molasse: Eclogae Geol. Helvetiae, v. 51, p. 1062–1078, 1 fig., 3 tables.

———, 1961, Krebse im Brandungssand: Natur und Volk, v. 91, p. 257–264, 8 figs.

———, 1962, Paleontological studies on turbidite sedimentation and erosion: Jour. Geology, p. 227–234.

———, 1963, Kaledonischer Unterbau der Irakiden: Neues Jahrb. Geologie Paläontologia Monatsh., p. 527–542, 3 figs.

Vialov, O. S., and B. T. Golev, 1960, K sistematike Paleodictyon: Akad. Nauk SSSR Doklady, v. 134, no. 1, p. 175–178.

Voigt, E., 1959, Die ökologische Bedeutung der Hartgründe ("Hardgrounds") in der oberen Kreide: Palaeontol. Zeitschr., v. 33, p. 129–147, 4 pls.

Voigt, E., and W. Häntzschel, 1956, Die grauen Bänder in der Schreibkeide Nordwest-Deutschlands und ihre Deutung als Lebensspuren: Geol. Staatsinst. Hamburg Mitt., v. 25, p. 104–122, pls. 15–16, 2 figs.

Wilson, A. E., 1948, Miscellaneous classes of fossils, Ottawa Formation, Ottawa–St. Lawrence Valley: Geol. Survey Canada Bull., v. 11, 116 p.

61

Major Steps in Vertebrate Evolution

ALFRED SHERWOOD ROMER

1967

In studies of animal form or function, there often seems to be an implication that the form studied was created *de novo* to fill the place which it occupies in the modern world. This is, of course, not the case. Every animal or plant living today has thousands of millions of years of history behind it and has been successively adapted to a long series of varied modes of existence; the structures and functions acquired by its ancestors as they passed through various stages have left indelible traces in its organization. It is my belief that the animals of today can be better understood and more reasonably interpreted if the investigator has an appreciation of their past history.

It is this evolutionary, historical approach, particularly as regards our own kin, the vertebrates, which has been the center of my research interests for half a century, and I propose here to give an outline of the present status of our knowledge of this field. The story is not, of course, fully known, but over the decades we have gained a fairly clear picture of most of its main events. There is general agreement as to the greater part of the evolutionary sequence. However, a number of points are still in dispute. Because space here is too limited for full discussion of them, I have selected, where there are alternatives, that interpretation which seems most reasonable in the light of current evidence.

The evidence in part is, of necessity, deduced from data obtained from the study of living animals. Their structures and functions often furnish suggestions of antecedent stages; the study of development can also give valuable information, for embryonic patterns in general tend to be conservative and to suggest the types of former adults to which these developmental processes once gave rise. But, early in their history, vertebrates acquired bony skeletons; this made it possible for them to be discovered in the fossil record. Particularly during the last half century, detailed studies have given important paleontological data on many crucial points of the evolutionary story which I wish to tell.

From *Science*, vol. 158, pp. 1629–1637, 1967. Reprinted with permission of the author and the American Association for the Advancement of Science.

It might be assumed that the evolutionary story is a straightforward one, beginning with simplicity and going on to increasing complexity and "advance." Not so; it is highly complex. What an organism becomes is not due purely to its inherent potentialities; its fate is strongly modified by physical and biological factors successively met with in its career. Vertebrate evolution has undergone strange shifts due to conditions at various stages; it is not simply an unfolding of innate potentialities. Those who desire a teleological interpretation argue that the evolutionary developments among the vertebrates are so remarkable that they are inexplicable under ordinary theories of evolution. For example, how can we understand such a major shift as that from fish life in the water to vertebrate life on land unless there is some supernatural, directing force behind it? Those who believe that the changes occurring during this transformation are of no immediate selective value feel that a teleological interpretation is necessary. A typical example of this point of view is du Noüy's popular work [1]. After demonstrating to his own satisfaction that no interpretation except a teleological one is possible, du Noüy discusses the future of man on the basis of supernatural direction in his development. However, I have failed to be interested in his discussion of our happy future; his conclusions are unsound, because his premises are faulty. Much of the evolutionary story which he believes to be insoluble except on the basis of design is readily interpretable under current neo-Darwinian theories of evolutionary progression.

Vertebrate history has been, of course, a continuum, a sequence of gradual changes and evolutionary development; but for present purposes we may divide this evolutionary story into about ten or so stages. And, abandoning any pretense of objectivity, let us direct the sequence of events toward the appearance of man.

SESSILE ARM-FEEDERS

I shall not attempt to follow our history down to the protozoan level. At the beginning of Cambrian times, some 500 million years ago, there first appeared in the fossil record a considerable variety of invertebrate metazoan animals—trilobites and other arthropods, lamp shells, molluscs, echinoderms, and so on. But of our own ancestors at this time there are no sure traces; quite certainly the vertebrate ancestors were then soft-bodied creatures, not normally to be found in the fossil record. We are forced to rely on clues obtained from surviving lowly relatives of the vertebrates, often included with them in a major animal group known as the phylum Chordata (or in part separated as a lower but related phylum Hemichordata) [2].

What type of organism should a simply built, early metazoan ancestor of the vertebrates have been? Vertebrates are dominantly active animals, seekers of food, bilaterally built forms, and we would expect the early forms to have been of this nature. But while there are, among the oldest fossils, numerous forms of this sort (notably the abundant trilobites), the evidence suggests that our early origins come from a more lowly level.

Today, and in the early fossil record, we find remains of metazoans of very different build and habits—simple sessile forms which do not seek their food, but wait for food particles to come to them. The body, attached by a stalk to the ocean bottom, consists of little except a digestive tract; above this, arms extend out hopefully, along which ciliated bands catch food particles drifting past in the water and direct them down to a receptive mouth. Animals of this sort include (i) the bryozoans, or moss animalicules; (ii) the lamp shells or brachiopods, in which the ciliated arms are enclosed in a pair of shells; and (iii) the crinoids, primitive echinoderms in which the stalk, body, and arms are encased in rings of armor. And present today, as well, although not seen in the fossil record, is a fourth type of arm-feeder, the pterobranchs, tiny and rare deep-sea forms with a few structures which definitely show their relationship to the vertebrate pedigree.

SESSILE FILTER-FEEDERS

The tiny sessile pterobranchs are a far remove from what we would expect in a vertebrate ancestor in body form or function. A further stage, it would appear, developed among early ancestral forms before we reach anything remotely resembling our expectations of vertebrate ancestors. The ciliated arms of a pterobranch are fairly well adapted to picking up passing food particles and bringing them down to the mouth; but this is not too good an adaptation for actually bringing the particles into the mouth and on the way to digestion. This was accomplished by the development of gill slits—paired openings leading on either side from the throat (pharynx) out to the surface; bands of cilia draw inward a current of water containing food particles; in the pharynx, the food materials are strained out, to be carried down the gut, while the water is passed outward through the gill slits. In larger and later types of chordates, the gills are important, as breathing organs, for the absorption of oxygen; in small early types, however, breathing could be satisfactorily cared for by the skin in general; the primary gill function was as a feeding aid. With the development of the gill current, the "arms" could be—and were—lost; in front of the mouth, there was only a noselike proboscis (already present as a sign of chordate relationship in pterobranchs). A simple pair of gill slits is present in one genus of living pterobranchs, and only an increase in number of slits was necessary to attain this new stage. Departing but little from what we believe to have been the truly primitive filter-feeders are the balanoglossids, or acorn worms, essentially sessile burrowers found in modern seas; their name is derived from the fact that the proboscis nestling into a bandlike neck resembles an acorn in its cup. Filter-feeding has been a successful, if lowly, way of making a living, and a further stage in developing a filtering apparatus occurs in the little tunicates, or sea squirts, rather common in modern seas either as solitary or colonial attached forms or as free-floating types. They carry the filtering apparatus to an extreme; in a typical member of this group, almost the entire animal consists of a barrel-shaped pharynx comprising a complex set of gill filters.

THE VERTEBRATE BODY PATTERN

The tunicates are terminal members of this sequence of particle-gathering sessile types—the end of the line. It would seem that nothing further could well develop in an evolutionary sequence beyond the adult of this stage. Nothing did. But from the larva of a tunicate, or presumably a pretunicate, there arose the body type from which the true vertebrates sprang (Figure 61.1).

We customarily think of evolutionary series in terms of adult animals; that change took place by gradual modifications in the structures and functions of mature individuals. But there is another possibility, that of paedomorphosis, emphasized especially by Garstang [3] as responsible for the further advance of the chordate-vertebrate series. Normally only a fully grown animal is capable of reproduction. But if immature forms should become sexually mature and reproduce, what then? It is quite possible that the previous adult stage might completely drop out of the picture, and a new evolutionary development might make its appearance.

In many tunicates, reproduction takes place by budding or by a normal direct development to the adult condition. But there is a different pattern in certain living types. Most tunicates make their livelihood where their parents live or where the local water currents carry them during their development. But some freedom of action has become available to certain tunicates by the introduction into the life cycle of a free-swimming, tadpole-like larva, so that the young have some freedom of choice to move to a favorable area for adult life. In a swollen "head" region, the gill apparatus, which is to constitute the major part of the adult body, develops. Behind, there is a muscular swimming tail, strengthened by a stout but flexible longitudinal cord, the notochord, predecessor of the vertebral column; the activity of the motile tail is supervised by a longitudinal dorsal nerve cord, which in the head region receives sensory information from rudimentary sense organs. The life of the larva is short; it swims about for a few hours or days and then settles down, to be attached to the sea bottom. Tail, notochord, nervous system, and sense organs degenerate and are resorbed, and the creature assumes the adult shape of a tunicate.

In this larva, we see the appearance, in simple form, of the typical body pattern characteristic of vertebrates, and it seems certain that we have here the beginnings of a new evolutionary series, radically different from that of the sessile series of which the adult tunicate is an end form. If, as seems surely to be the case, Paleozoic tadpoles of certain tunicates, or pretunicates, became sexually mature and no longer metamorphosed into sessile adults, a new mode of life opened up. Instead of passively waiting for food to come to it, the animal could go in search of food and could explore new areas or new habitats in which it might exist. *Amphioxus*, familiar to every student of biology, represents in slightly specialized fashion the stage in which sexual maturity of the tadpole has taken place, but not much progress toward higher evolutionary levels has occurred.

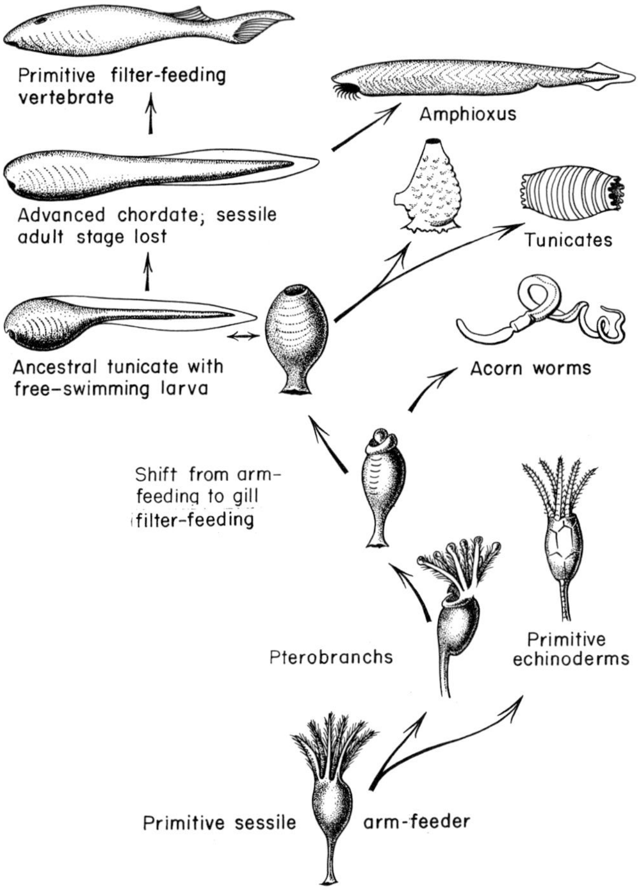

FIGURE 61.1
Diagrammatic family tree suggesting the possible mode of evolution of vertebrates. The echinoderms may have arisen from forms not too dissimilar to the little pterobranchs; the acorn worms may have arisen from pterobranch descendants which had evolved a gill-feeding system but were little more advanced in other regards. Tunicates represent a stage in which, in the adult, the gill apparatus has become highly evolved, but the important point is the development in some tunicates of a free-swimming larva with advanced features of notochord and nerve cord. In further progress to *Amphioxus* and the vertebrates, the old sessile adult stage has been abandoned, and it is the larval type that has initiated the advance. (From Romer, *The Vertebrate Story*, University of Chicago Press.)

FIRST VERTEBRATES—THE OSTRACODERMS

These earliest stages in the vertebrate pedigree occurred, at the latest, in very early Paleozoic times, for in the Ordovician, second of the Paleozoic periods, remains of fossil true vertebrates are present. Such remains become abundant by the end of the following Silurian period, where numerous specimens of varied types of lowly vertebrates termed ostracoderms are found. Our knowledge of them dates from the thorough studies (in the 1920's) of members of the *Cephalaspis* group [4]. No one of the late Silurian and early Devonian ostracoderms is to be regarded as a direct ancestor of "higher" vertebrates, but the cephalaspids, best known of ostracoderms, nevertheless show the general structure reasonably to be expected in an ancestral vertebrate. There is an expanded "head" region, exhibiting typical sense organs, and a powerful swimming tail. The "head," when dissected, is seen to be mainly occupied by an enormous gill chamber, terminated anteriorly by a small mouth. We have here, on a higher level, a structure not unlike that present in the tunicate tadpole. The ostracoderm was still a jawless filter-feeder, but it had the great advantage over its tunicate (or pretunicate) ancestor that the large feeding apparatus of the gill basket could be moved about to suitable food localities.

In what environment did the early vertebrates live? We assume that the ocean was the original home of life, and the seas are still the home of a great proportion of all animal types; further, the lower chordates and hemichordates are all marine forms. But many of the finds of early vertebrates are from sediments rather surely laid down in fresh waters, and I came to the conclusion, some decades ago, that early vertebrate evolution took place in lakes and streams rather than in the sea [5]. At about the same period, Smith [6] reached a similar conclusion from a comparative study of kidney function. Our conclusions have not gone uncontested [7], and it may be long before definite agreement is reached. But while I must defer further discussion of this question to some future occasion, it still seems clear to me that a freshwater origin fits best into the general picture. With the invasion of the continents by plant life in the Paleozoic, freshwater streams and ponds gave a new area where animals might find food. Few invertebrates have been capable of entering freshwater environments—for successful life inland, the animal must be an active swimmer to avoid being carried back down to the sea. The vertebrates and their advanced chordate ancestors, with the swimming powers given them by their tail development, were one of the few types competent to enter fresh waters and to enjoy them profitably. Upstream invasion by vertebrates took place rapidly and successfully, so that by the late Silurian and the following Devonian period, fishes had become prominent dwellers in inland waters.

Because the "lowest" of living vertebrates—lampreys, hagfishes, and sharks—lack bone and have skeletons of cartilage, and since in the development of higher vertebrates the skeleton is first formed in cartilage and is only later replaced by bone, it was long thought that cartilage was the original skeletal material of vertebrates, and that bone developed only at a relatively late evolutionary stage. But our present knowledge of the fossil record shows that the oldest of known vertebrates already had bone, at least as an external armor. As a consequence, most (but not all) students of the subject will agree with Stensiö's conclusion that bone developed at the base of the vertebrate series and that the boneless condition in cyclostomes and sharks is a secondary, degenerate one; the prominence of cartilage in the young vertebrate is an embryonic adaptation [8].

Except for improvement of sense organs, the appearance of bone is the only major advance made by the earliest vertebrates over their higher chordate ancestors. Why bone? Calcium is physiologically important, and it has been suggested that its appearance has to do with a functional need. However, bone, as we see it in the oldest vertebrates, is not simply a calcium deposit, but an external covering of plates arranged in a complex pattern. It looks like armor; and very probably it was. In the late Silurian and early Devonian, we find numerous faunas in which nearly the only animals present are small armored ostracoderms and eurypterids—a type of predaceous arthropod distantly related to the horseshoe crab of today. The average eurypterid was much larger than most contemporary vertebrates—some as much as about 2.5 meters in length, compared with ostracoderms generally but several centimeters long. It seems clear that the lowly ostracoderms were their food supply and that the development of bony armor was an adaptive protective device. In later times, fishes became more advanced, more skilled in swimming, generally larger, and often predaceous themselves. Parallel with these advances, eurypterids became rare and (robbed, it would seem, of their erstwhile prey) extinct before the end of Paleozoic days [9].

It seems probable, then, that bone first appeared in the form of dermal armor, laid down in membrane fashion in plates within the skin. In many ostracoderms, there is no bone except in the surface armor [10]. In the cephalaspids there is some development of internal bone within the head region, but even here it is of the same "membrane" pattern, laid down in sheets around the various internal canals and cavities. Only in higher fish groups, bone development progressed further, to the endochondral stage, when solid masses of bone are present in internal structure. It seems that, for the development of a bony skeleton, without which the evolution of the more advanced classes of vertebrates would have been impossible, we must thank the eurypterid enemies of our early ancestors.

The ostracoderms were, in general, small and feeble, doomed to extinction by the end of the Devonian period; they have survived only in the form of the degenerate and specialized lampreys and hagfishes in which the development of a peculiar, rasping, tonguelike structure has enabled them to persist in modest fashion as predators on other fishes. A new era in fish history opened with the development of jaws, formed by enlargement of a pair of skeletal bars which earlier had formed supports for gill slits. Armed with these new structures, fishes were released from the necessity of depending on filter-feeding for a livelihood, and a whole new series of potential modes of life was opened up for them. Early in the Devonian period we find, principally in fresh waters, a varied host of jawed fishes: placoderms, acanthodians, and, most especially, three major groups of advanced bony fishes which played an important role in later vertebrate evolution —the Actinopterygia (or ray-finned fishes), the Dipnoi (or lungfishes), and the Crossopterygii, of little account beyond Paleozoic days, but highly important as the progenitors of land vertebrates.

A persisting major gap in our paleontological record, however, is the almost complete absence of any trace of an earlier jawed fish. Although the common ancestor must have existed well before the Devonian, there is no earlier record of fish of this sort except for a few fragmentary remains of acanthodians in near-shore marine Silurian deposits. Why this gap? To one who believes that these early stages in fish evolution took place in salt water, there is no reasonable answer to this question. But to a believer in freshwater origins, the answer is simple. Earlier than the very late Silurian, continental strata are almost entirely absent from the known geological [Phanerozoic] record. Without question, continental deposits had been formed in the earlier geologic times, but it seems that subsequent erosion has resulted in the destruction of such older beds in which remains of truly ancestral jawed fishes might have been found.

AMPHIBIANS—THE BEGINNINGS OF LAND LIFE

With the radiation of jaw-bearing fishes, vertebrates had obtained a dominant position in life in the water. But a further major advance was presently to come—the conquest of the land, initiated by the amphibians and completed by their reptilian descendants. In recent decades, much of the general picture of this major evolutionary advance has been worked out (Figure 61.2).

What fish group gave rise to the early four-footed animals, tetrapods, represented today by the surviving orders of amphibians? Quite surely, all would agree, some type of the higher bony fish of the class Osteichthyes. One may immediately rule out the rayfinned fishes—the actinopterygians—for a variety of reasons; because of various specializations, the lungfishes, despite anatomical and embryological similarities to amphibians, are to be regarded as the "uncles" of the tetrapods rather than as actual

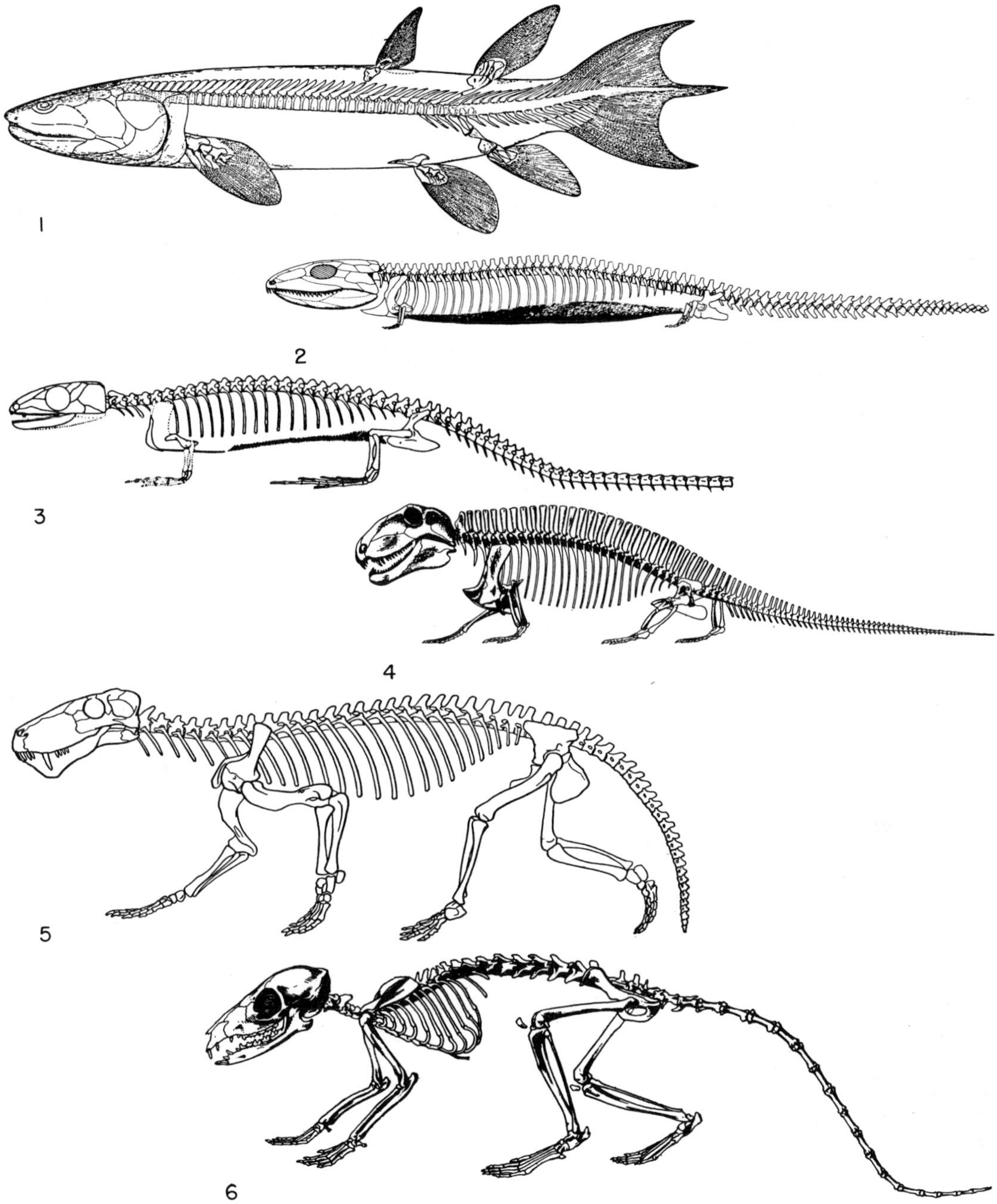

FIGURE 61.2
Series of skeletons in approximately true phylogenetic sequence from a rhipidistian crossopterygian to a placental mammal. *1*, crossopterygian *Eusthenopteron; 2, Pholidogaster*, an early labyrinthodont tending in a reptilian direction; *3*, *Hylonomus*, one of the oldest and most primitive of known reptiles; *4*, *Sphenacodon*, a Permian pelycosaur pertaining to the group from which therapsids were derived; *5*, *Lycaenops*, a generalized therapsid, with improved four-footed locomotion; *6*, the tree shrew *Tupaia*, a generalized planetal mammal. (*1* and *6* after Gregory, *3* after Carroll, *4* after Romer and Price, *5* after Colbert.)

ancestors. It has become increasingly certain in recent decades that the ancestors of land vertebrates lay among the Crossopterygii and, particularly, an early central group of crossopterygians, termed the Rhipidistia. The crossopterygians flourished during the Devonian but rapidly declined in numbers, and beyond the Paleozoic they survived only in the form of an aberrant side branch, the coelacanths, of which a single form, *Latimeria*, survives in the Indian Ocean. We know nothing firsthand of the soft anatomy or embryology of rhipidistians, but in regard to the skeleton, the evidence is clear that the older crossopterygians are proper ancestors for the tetrapods. The fin skeleton is of just the type to develop into a land limb, and, in general, a crossopterygian skull can be compared bone for bone not only with amphibians, but also with reptiles, mammals, and man.

The tie-in of crossopterygians with the Amphibia is close, not so much with the living orders as with a great group of forms, the Labyrinthodontia, which began their career at the end of the Devonian, abounded in the Carboniferous and Permian, and survived, before extinction, into the Triassic [11]. Over the last half century, a long series of finds has yielded a fairly complete story of the labyrinthodonts. They are of importance in their own right, but one group of them, the anthracosaurs, are especially important in that they show a series of stages leading onward to the reptiles [12].

But whereas we have a fairly clear story of the relationship of the crossopterygians to the labyrinthodonts and through them to the reptiles, the history of the surviving orders of amphibians is still obscure. These consist of (i) the Anura, frogs and toads; (ii) the Urodela, including newts and salamanders; and (iii) the Apoda or Gymnophiona, tropical wormlike forms. The three orders are quite diverse in structure and body form, but recent work suggests that they are, as the Lissamphibia, a phylogenetic unit [13]. Possibly related to their ancestry are small Carboniferous and early Permian amphibians known as the Lepospondyli [14]; but this does not solve the question, for the pedigree of the lepospondyls themselves is quite uncertain. This is a chapter of vertebrate evolution where further data are needed.

How did the major evolutionary step from water toward and to land take place? Those who favor teleological interpretations insist that some divine or mystical driving force must have underlain this radical shift in habitus and structure since, they say, the development of adaptations fitting the fish descendants for future life on dry land would have had no immediate adaptive value to a water dweller. Here, however, as in other cases, there is no need to call upon the supernatural, for it can be shown that under some special condition such adaptations could have been of immediate selective value. This special condition seems to have been seasonal drought [8]. More than half a century ago, Barrell [15] pointed out that the numerous red beds of the late Paleozoic (and Triassic) gave evidence of the widespread prevalence of regions subject to seasonal drought. At certain times of the year (as today in some tropical areas), rainfall would be abundant; at other seasons, the rains would cease, streams slow down, and ponds become stagnant.

There are many structural and functional changes necessary to turn a typical fish into an amphibian and, eventually into a reptile; let us merely take two of the most obvious "improvements" needed—lungs and land limbs. To a fish under normal climatic conditions, gills suffice for breathing purposes. But under drought conditions, with stagnation of waters and low oxygen content, it would be highly advantageous for a fish to be able to come to the surface and avail itself of atmospheric oxygen. Today only five genera of fish have retained true lungs (they live in seasonal drought areas), but our evidence suggests that in the late Paleozoic the great majority of freshwater forms possessed lungs.

But legs? Why should a water dweller have these structures, so essential for land life? The answer seems to be that legs did not evolve as a mystical "preadaptation" for a future life on land, but (seemingly a paradox) as structures which would aid a water-dweller, under drought conditions, to continue his life in his own proper element. In early stages of a severe drought, a fish with lungs would survive stagnant water conditions without trouble. But suppose the drought worsened and the water in a pond dried up completely? An ordinary fish would be literally stuck in the mud and would soon perish unless the rains soon returned. But a form in which there had been some trend for enlargement of fins toward the tetrapod limb condition might be able to crawl up or down a river channel, find a pond with water still present, happily splash in, and resume his normal mode of life. Most fossil amphibians had legs developed to at least a moderate degree. But as far as we can tell, most of them had no yen for life on land; legs were, for the time being, simply an adaptation for bettering the animal's chances for surviving in his proper aqueous environment [16].

THE FIRST REPTILES

Modern reptiles and modern amphibians can be readily told apart. But increased knowledge of the fossil record has brought us to the point where it is almost impossible to tell an advanced fossil amphibian from a primitive reptile on the basis of its skeletal structure. The first reptiles, it now seems clear, were a group of "stem reptiles" (cotylosaurs) known as the Captorhinomorpha, well known in the Permian and now known to have been present far back in Carboniferous times [17]. The real distinction, of course, between amphibians and reptiles lies in the mode of reproduction. The typical frogs, toads, or salamanders in our temperate regions gather in the spring in ponds where the eggs are laid and develop, as those of their fish ancestors did, into water-dwelling and water-breathing larvae. Only later, with metamorphosis, lungs develop, and land life becomes possible. In contrast, reptiles are notable in that they lay an amniote type of egg. This is prosaic to us (since it has been retained by the avian descendants of the reptiles), but it is actually the most marvelous "invention" in vertebrate history. This egg can be laid on land; the water stage of development is eliminated. Externally, there is a protective shell; internally, a complex series of membranes protects the growing embryo, and there is an abundant supply of nourishing yolk; a larval stage is eliminated, and the young reptile (or bird) hatches as a miniature replica of the parent, already well adapted to take up a fully terrestrial mode of life.

At what evolutionary stage did this new and revolutionary egg type enter the picture? Certain amphibians of ancient days had well-developed limbs and were apparently ready for a fully terrestrial existence. But they were chained to the water (splendid phrase) by the necessity of the old-fashioned aquatic mode of development. Finally (went the story as it was long told, and as I used to tell it myself), the amniote egg was developed, the chains were broken, and the reptiles burst forth upon the land!

A good story, but, it would now seem, a false one. It is probable that the egg came ashore before the adult was fully ready for land life [18]. Study of certain members of the oldest-known reptilian faunas seems to indicate that although they quite surely laid an amniote type of egg, the adults, like their amphibian ancestors, were still amphibious in habits, spending much of their time in the water, with a sustaining diet of fishes. Why, then, a land egg? A review of breeding habits of modern amphibians furnishes a clue. I have mentioned the "typical" mode of reproduction of frogs, toads, and salamanders. But if we survey these types as a whole, we find that the "typical" mode is really exceptional rather than common. Particularly in the tropics, modern amphibians adopt any device possible to avoid laying the eggs in the water. Why? Avoidance of enemies is probably a major objective; to a variety of forms, ranging from insects to other vertebrates, eggs in a pond are a desirable amphibian caviar. But to some degree among modern forms and, I think, to a major extent among the ancestral Paleozoic reptiles, the reason was seasonal drought; if eggs are laid in a pond, drought leads to larval death. Here again, an adaptation which was to be exceedingly useful in terrestrial life appears to have evolved, not with this end in view, but as an immediately useful adaptation to an animal still leading an amphibious life.

MAMMAL-LIKE REPTILES

Once lungs, limbs, and, finally, the amniote egg were developed, full terrestrial existence became possible. The early tetrapods were eaters of animal food; the rise of the insects toward the end of the Carboniferous furnished a basic food supply for early land-dwellers. Soon there was under way a great radiation of reptilian types which were to dominate the world during the Mesozoic era—a radiation leading not merely to the familiar surviving reptilian orders, but also to a host of forms now extinct, such as the great marine reptiles of the Mesozoic, dinosaurs, flying reptiles, and bird ancestors. Curiously, however, the first great development from the primitive reptilian stock was not the one that led to any of these forms, but was the rapid emergence of the Synapsida, a group from which the mammals were destined to evolve. The first synapsids appear in the record almost as early as the first reptiles of any sort, and from the late Carboniferous on through the Permian and into the early Triassic they were the commonest of land animals. From time to time, there sprang from this stock successful, herbivorous, side branches, but the main evolutionary line consisted of forms which were the dominant carnivores, large and small, of late Paleozoic and earliest Mesozoic times. The more primitive representatives of this group were the pelycosaurs, forms to which I have devoted a considerable part of my scientific life [19], and which are best known from the early Permian red beds of Texas. In structure, pelycosaurs had departed little from the most primitive reptiles; they still walked, quite inefficiently, with the sprawled-out pose of the limbs characteristic of all early four-footed animals. During the Permian, there developed from one pelycosaur group a more advanced mammal-like type, that of the therapsids. Here locomotion was greatly improved; the elbows were turned back, the knees forward, the trackway narrowed, the stride increased with resulting greater speed. These therapsids are best known from the Great Karroo deposits of South Africa, from which hosts of therapsids have been described by Broom, Watson, and many other scientists.

Therapsid dominance lasted until the Triassic. But as this period progressed, the therapsids dwindled in numbers and variety, to disappear completely in the Jurassic. The cause of their downfall appears to lie in the rise of a rival reptile group, the archosaurs, or "ruling reptiles." In this reptile subclass, there was a strong trend toward the solution of the problem of efficient locomotion in a fashion different from that adopted by the synapsids. Instead of evolving an improved quadrupedal gait, the front limbs were abandoned in locomotion, and fast bipedal running was attained by elongation and adaptation of the hind legs. This new stance came into being among archosaurs during the Triassic, when early carnivorous archosaurs, known as thecodonts, began a successful competition with the therapsids; by the late Triassic there had evolved carnivorous dinosaurs, which were to dominate the earth during the 100 million years or more which constituted the remainder of the Mesozoic era.

THE RISE OF MAMMALS

The mammal-like reptiles, then, disappeared from the scene, to give way to the dinosaurs, but not without having left behind, as their descendants, the mammals, small early representatives of which, not too far from therapsids in structure, have recently been found in deposits of late Triassic age. These mammalian descendants of the therapsids persisted through the next 100 million years of dinosaurian dominance, but survived only as small and inconspicuous forms. Their history during this long period [20] is sparse and fragmentary; except, perhaps, for the late Cretaceous, all known materials (should one treat them so irreverently) would probably little more than fill a derby hat. But this time of tribulation under the constant menace of the dinosaurs was not a wasted one. The first mammals were probably little above the reptilian level; by the close of the Cretaceous, when the dinosaurs became extinct, they had reached a high degree of organization and were competent to take over the rulership of the world.

If we were to attempt to define a mammal briefly, it could perhaps be done in two words —activity and intelligence. We mentioned earlier body improvements in therapsids which made them swift-running quadrupeds; in mammals generally, this four-footed gait is retained and improved. Maintenance of body temperature (toward which end a hairy or furry covering is one adaptation) enables a mammal to be active (quite in contrast to a reptile) at any temperature. Therapsids were active forms, but, as the fossils shows, still small-brained, still essentially thoughtless automata. By the end of the Mesozoic, the mammal brain had become highly developed; the cerebral hemispheres were large and complex; learning and training were possible, so that, in a broad sense of the world, intelligence had come into the world. Because the cerebral cortex is a complex organ, as much time as possible should be allowed in the development of the individual so that this important structure may reach its full potentialities before it is put to use. Reproductive improvements in mammals work toward this end. Mammals (except for two archaic types) bear their young alive, and in the higher mammals—generally termed the placentals—there had developed by the end of the Mesozoic a highly efficient nutrient connection, the placenta, between the mother and the fetus within her uterus, so that birth can be delayed until the young reach a much larger size and more mature structure than it was possible for them to do in an egg-laying form. The nursing habit extends further the time before the youngster is forced to live its own life. During this period, the young mammal can be trained and taught; in a sense, we can say that in the nursing habit we see the establishment of the world's first educational institution.

Some of these features, which were to be eventually responsible for mammalian success, were quite surely developed by their therapsid ancestors; most, however, appear to have been brought about as adaptations and advances necessary for the survival of our feeble mammalian ancestors under the reptilian tyranny. As mammals, we owe a debt of gratitude to the dinosaurs for their unintended aid.

LIFE IN THE TREES—PRIMATES

By the close of the Mesozoic and the dawn of Cenozoic times, the evolution of higher mammals had been completed, and there were forms well equipped to take over world dominance from the ruling reptiles. The small ancestral placental types of that day were (as their ancestors had been for innumerable millions of years) potentially carnivores, but we believe that, due to their modest size, they must have contented themselves with insects and grubs as food staples. Forms surviving today with similar diets are considered members of an order Insectivora, of which the shrews are the most characteristic representatives. But while the shrews, in their small size and inconspicuous habit, give us a picture of the life which the early placental mammals must have led under the reign of the dinosaurs, even they have developed certain specializations which remove them from a truly central position in placental evolutionary history. The actual ancestors, of 20 million or so years ago, are extinct; but if we look about us for living forms which appear to be closest to the primitive stock, the choice, I believe, falls on the tree shrews, *Tupaia* and related genera, of the Oriental region. These attractive little animals are often considered as possible ancestors of the primates; but there is little in their structure to prevent them from being considered as playing a still more important role, that of forms approaching most closely the parental stock of all higher mammals.

Once the dinosaurs passed from the scene, the ancestral placental mammals rapidly began a radiation into the varied mammalian types which are with us today—from rats to cats, to bats, to whales, to hoofed mammals of all sorts, and so on. All of these types have had interesting and often spectacular careers in the approximately 70 million years of the Cenozoic Era, the age of mammals. But if we wish (conceitedly) to continue our story in the direction of ourselves, the one mammalian order which comes into focus is that of the Primates, including lemurs, monkeys, apes—and men (Figure 61.3).

The primates are (with a few exceptions, such as men and baboons) tree-dwellers, and such success as man and his primate relatives have had can be attributed in great measure to features associated with arboreal life [21]. Locomotion in the trees, as practiced by primates, demands flexibility and agility, and the primate skeleton is much more generalized in nature than is that of most other mammals. Small tree-dwellers, such as squirrels, may climb trees by digging in their claws; primates, generally of rather larger bulk, have adopted another method—they have developed an opposable thumb and big toe, so that a branch may be grasped. Arboreal life has caused a marked change in the development of sense organs. In most mammals, smell is highly developed, while vision, as far as one can tell, is of a rather fuzzy nature. In the trees, olfaction is unimportant and is greatly reduced (as the snout is) in higher primates. Accurate vision, on the contrary, is essential for safe locomotion in the trees; we find that, in all but the lowest of primates, the eyes, primitively rather laterally directed, are turned forward so that the two fields of vision are identical, and stereoscopic vision, with depth effects and distance judgment, is developed. Further, higher primates have in each retina a central area in which detail is clearly perceived.

The brain of mammals is, in general, highly developed; in primates, its development is of a still higher type than in most other placentals. Locomotor agility in the trees demands a high development of motor centers in the cerebrum, and it is suggestive that the major brain area devoted to the highest mental faculties develops in an area (frontal) alongside the motor centers. Again, the development of good eyesight has rendered possible a far wider knowledge of their environment for primates than for forms which depend upon smell. Also important in primate mentality has been the development of the grasping hand as a sensory aid in the examination of objects. With the potential advantages to be gained from any trend toward increased mental ability, it is not surprising that, in monkeys, apes, and men, selection has resulted in the development of large brains and greatly extended areas of the gray matter of the cerebral cortex.

In early Tertiary times, numerous remains of primitive primates in the lemur stage of primate evolution were present in the fossil beds of both North America and Europe. In the lemurs, which today survive mainly in the protective isolation of Madagascar, primate evolutionary trends have but begun; for example, there is still a large muzzle, and the eyes are directed more laterally than anteriorly. But, early in the fossil record, there are remains of a more advanced primate type, of which the living *Tarsius* of the East Indies is a surviving member. *Tarsius* itself is a somewhat specialized little animal, but shows clearly the ad-

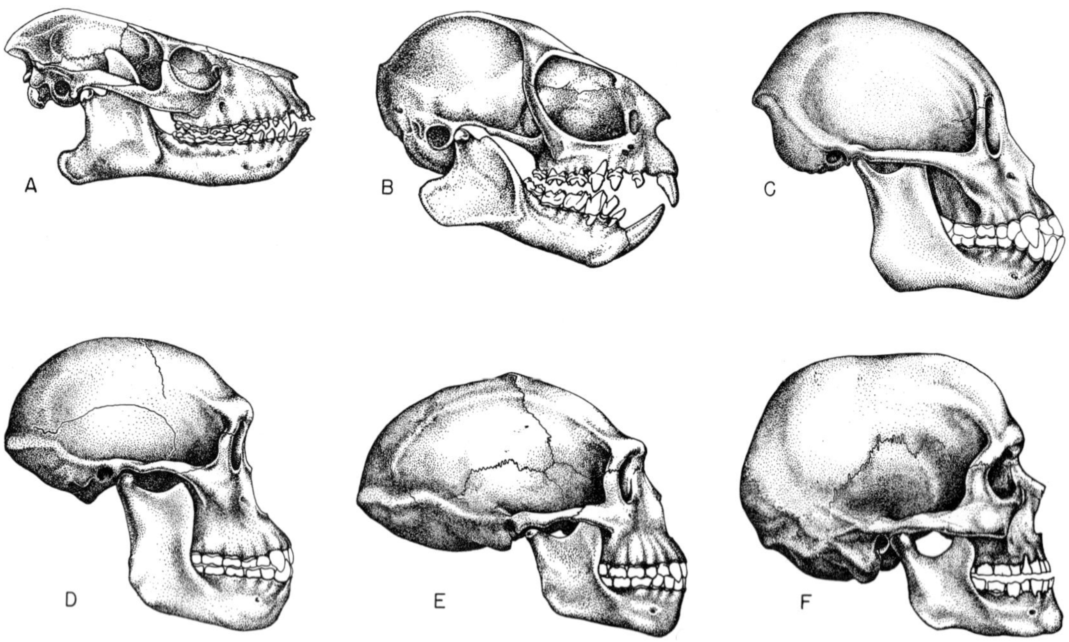

FIGURE 61.3
Series of skulls of primates. Essentially in phylogenetic sequence, the figure shows, particularly, forward turning of the eyes, reduction of the "nose," and braincase enlargement. A fossil lemur *Notharctus*; *B* Eocene tarsioid *Tetonius* (the dention is aberrant); *C*, Miocene dryopithecine ape "*Proconsul*"; *D*, *Australopithecus* of the early Pleistocene; *E*, "*Pithecanthropus*" (*Homo erectus*) of the middle Pleistocene; *F*, modern man. (*A* and *B* after Gregory, *C* after Napier and LeGros Clark, *D* after Robinson, *E* and *F* after McGregor.)

vances already present in its early Tertiary relatives. Smell is reduced, and the nose is a mere nubbin; the large eyes are turned straight forward, with the development of stereoscopic vision; the brain is quite large in proportion to body size.

Beyond the *Tarsius* stage, the evolution of higher primates occurred in two separate lines. The next higher level of organization, seen in the monkeys, was attained in one group of tarsioid descendants which migrated to South America and in a second group that developed in Eurasia. In Oligocene rocks of the Egyptian Fayum are found remains (if fragmentary) not only of ancestors of Old World monkeys, but also of small ancestors of the great apes which are man's closest relatives [22].

Of the living great apes, the gibbons and orang presumably split off at an early time. However, in mid-Tertiary rocks, widespread in Eurasia and Africa, there are found remains (mostly fragmentary, unfortunately) of a rather advanced type of great ape. The term *Dryopithecus*, the "oak ape," is generally applied to such remains; an East African member of the series is generally given the special name of *Proconsul*. In members of this group, we are dealing with apes of modest size which are relatively little specialized. As far as we know them, the oak apes appear to be potential ancestors of the chimpanzee, of the gorilla, and, not improbably, of man as well.

DOWN TO EARTH—MAN

Lower primates in general and even such higher apes as the gibbons and orang are definitely tree-dwellers. But the trend was reversed at the top of the primate series. The chimpanzee is less of an arboreal acrobat than the lower great apes, and the mountain gorilla of central Africa has almost completely abandoned tree-dwelling (but is essentially quadrupedal in locomotion on the ground). As yet, we know almost nothing of the late Tertiary history of the specific ancestors of man, but it is suggested, not unreasonably, that his abandonment of the trees may have been associated with reduction, in some of the Old World regions in which his ancestors lived, of a forest covering to a savanna-type of environment, with open areas between the copses; this would have encouraged ground locomotion and introduced prehumans to the possible advantages of terrestrial over arboreal life [23]. In recent decades, a part-way step from ape to man has become known with discovery of the australopithecines, whose remains are primarily from South African caves [24]. *Australopithecus* and his kin are, unquestionably, morphologically antecedent to man, and with one or two exceptions, all competent investigators in this field now agree that the australopithecines of the early Pleistocene are actual human ancestors. From mid-Pleistocene times, half a million or so years ago, we find remains of forms, such as *Pithecanthropus* and *Sinanthropus*, which are definitely human types, although with brains still well below modern levels and with many primitive features. Later in the Pleistocene, there appear more advanced forms and, toward the end of the Pleistocene Ice Age, some tens of thousands of years back, there appear in Eurasia and Africa representatives of our own species, *Homo sapiens*, fully as advanced as any living race.

SUMMARY

We have come to the end of our story—a long one, covering some half a billion years, it appears. A modern man or other higher vertebrate has traveled far from the simply built insensate type of creature seen in his ultimate metazoan ancestor among the pterobranchs. The course of this evolutionary progression is far from direct and simple, as some might believe to be the case; it is a trail with many twists and turns. Nor is there the slightest reason to attempt a teleological interpretation; there is no trace of design and direction toward an obvious goal. Quite in contrast, it seems clear in many stages of the series that the changes which have taken place are immediately beneficial ones, strongly subject to selection. Obvious, too, is the fact that special environmental factors, biological and physical, have added unexpected quirks to the story. The development of a motile "tadpole" larva at an early chordate stage led to a sharp shift in an evolutionary sequence which otherwise might have simply ended in a sedate filtering

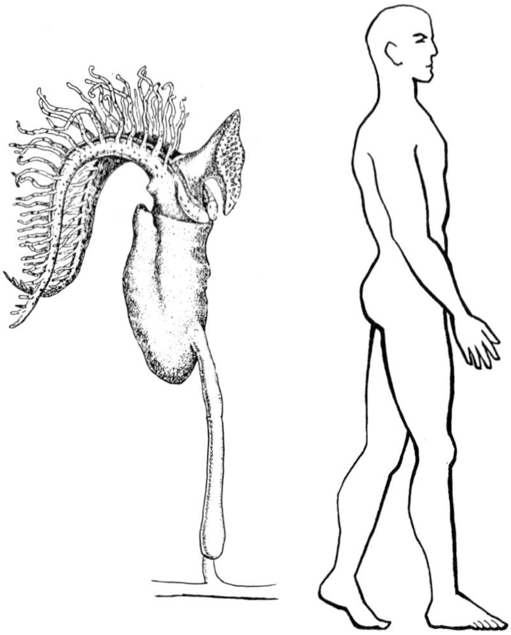

FIGURE 61.4
Beginning and end of the story. *Left*, pterobranch *Rhabdopleura*, much enlarged, showing the simply built, stalked body, with food-collecting arms above; *right*, modern man. (*Rhabdopleura* after Delage and Herouard.)

form of tunicate type. The development of plant life on the continents opened up to motile chordates a new environment into which few invertebrates could enter and in which the chordates flourished to progress to the vertebrate level. The need for armor as defense against eurypterid enemies appears to have initiated the development of bony skeletal structures, without which the higher vertebrates could never have developed. The widespread late Paleozoic condition of seasonal drought favored progressive developments which, with the attainment of a reptilian stage, had the happy accidental result of the vertebrate conquest of the land, a conquest aided by the emergence of the insects as a basic food supply. The long period of dinosaur dominance seems to have been responsible for the sharpened wits which made the mammalian descendants of the therapsids competent for terrestrial dominance when the reign of the ruling reptiles ended. The arboreal life of primates was finally abandoned by man, but tree-dwelling had endowed his ancestors with advances in brain, eyes, and hands that were highly advantageous when this relatively feeble creature descended to the ground. It has been a long and tortuous journey; but every stage of it shows its effects in the structures and functions of such an end product as ourselves (Figure 61.4).

REFERENCES AND NOTES

1. L. du Nouy, *Human Destiny* (New York: New American Library, 1947).
2. An excellent account of prevertebrates is given by C. Dawydoff in *Traité de Zoologie XI*, ed. P.-P. Grassé (Paris: Masson et Cie, 1948), p. 367.
3. W. Garstang, *Quart. Jour. Microscop. Sci.*, v. 72, p. 51 (1928); J. Z. Young, *The Life of Vertebrates* (London: Oxford University Press, 1950), chap. 3.
4. E. A. Stensiö, *Skr. Svalbard Nordishavet*, no. 12 (1927); *The Cephalaspids of Great Britain* (London: British Museum [Natural History], 1932).
5. A. S. Romer, *Am. Midland Naturalist*, v. 16, p. 805 (1935); *Deep-Sea Research*, v. 3 (suppl.), p. 261 (1955).
6. H. W. Smith, *Quart. Rev. Biology*, v. 7, p. 1 (1932).
7. For example, R. H. Denison, *Fieldiana Geology*, v. 11, p. 359 (1956); J. D. Robertson, *Cambridge Philos. Soc. Biol. Rev.*, v. 32, p. 156 (1957).
8. A. S. Romer, *Science*, v. 78, p. 114 (1933).
9. A. S. Romer, *Am. Naturalist*, v. 76, p. 394 (1942).
10. A. S. Romer, in *Bone Dynamics*, ed. H. M. Frost (Boston: Little, Brown, 1964), p. 13.
11. A. S. Romer, *Mus. Comp. Zoology Harvard Coll. Bull.*, v. 99, p. 1 (1947).
12. A. S. Romer, *Mus. Comp. Zoology Harvard Coll. Bull.*, v. 131, p. 129 (1964).
13. T. S. Parsons and E. E. Williams, *Quart. Rev. Biology*, v. 38, p. 26 (1963).
14. A. S. Romer, *Am. Jour. Sci.*, v. 248, p. 628 (1950); D. Baird, *Am. Jour. Sci.*, v. 5, p. 287 (1965).
15. J. Barrell, *Jour. Geology*, v. 16, p. 159, 255, 363 (1908); *Geol. Soc. America Bull.*, v. 23, p. 377 (1912).
16. A. S. Romer, *Am. Philos. Soc. Proc.*, v. 100, p. 157 (1956).
17. R. L. Carroll, *Linnean Soc. London Jour. Zoology*, p. 61 (1964); D. Baird and R. L. Carroll, *Science*, v. 157, p. 56 (1967).
18. A. S. Romer, *Sci. Monthly*, v. 55, p. 57 (1957).
19. A. S. Romer, and L. I. Price, *Geol. Soc. America Spec. Paper* 28, (1940); A. S. Romer, in *International Colloquium on the Evolution of Mammals* [Brussels, 1961], v. 1, p. 9.

20. Summarized by G. G. Simpson, in *International Colloquium on the Evolution of Mammals* [Brussels, 1961], v. 1, p. 57.
21. G. Elliot Smith, *The Evolution of Man* (London: Oxford University Press, 1927); W. E. LeGros Clark, *The Antecedents of Man—an Introduction to the Evolution of the Primates* (Chicago: University of Chicago Press, 1960).
22. E. L. Simons, *Am. Mus. Novitates,* no. 1976 (1959); *Am. Mus. Novitates,* no. 2051 (1961); *Postilla,* no. 64 (1964).
23. See, for example, G. Heberer, *Die Evolution der Organismen* (ed. 2) (Stuttgart: Gustav Fischer, 1959), p. 1110–1142.
24. An excellent review of this and later stages in the human story is by W. E. LeGros Clark, *The Fossil Evidences for Human Evolution* (ed. 2) (Chicago: University of Chicago Press, 1964).

62

Giant Dinosaurs

EDWIN H. COLBERT

1955

Almost all educated men know that there were dinosaurs on the earth in the far distant past, but not so many people know just what the dinosaurs were. Perhaps the most prevalent ideas about dinosaurs are that they were all gigantic animals (which is not strictly true); that, because of their great size, they became extinct many millions of years ago (which is almost surely not the reason for their extinction); and that they were "cold-blooded" reptiles (which is true).

Two orders of ancient reptiles, known as the Saurischia and the Ornithischia, contain the animals that we call dinosaurs. These two orders were related to the thecodonts, another reptilian group long since extinct; to the pterosaurs or flying reptiles, also extinct; and to the crocodilians, which are still with us. All of these reptiles had a common ancestry that dates back to the end of Paleozoic times, about 200 million years ago. The first dinosaurs appeared during the Triassic period of the Mesozoic era. From then on through the Jurassic period, and until the end of the Cretaceous period, the dinosaurs were destined to rule the earth's land masses. These reptiles were spectacularly dominant for a span of perhaps a hundred million years or more, but at the end of the Cretaceous period, they suffered complete extinction, as did various other groups of Mesozoic reptiles (Figure 62.1).

The dinosaurs were not all giants. Some of these ancient reptiles were no larger than turkeys or ostriches. Nevertheless, it is a fact that giantism was typical of their evolutionary history; so that of about 250 described genera of dinosaurs now known, at least 150 were giants. The fossil skeletons of some of these tremendous and impressive reptiles loom large in the halls of various museums, and create the general impression that all the dinosaurs were of great size.

What do we mean when we speak of the prevalence of giants among the dinosaurs? We are apt to think of ourselves as being of the "right size," so we regard as giants all those animals considerably larger than ourselves. If

From *Transactions of the New York Academy of Sciences*, vol. 17, no. 3, pp. 199–209, 1955.

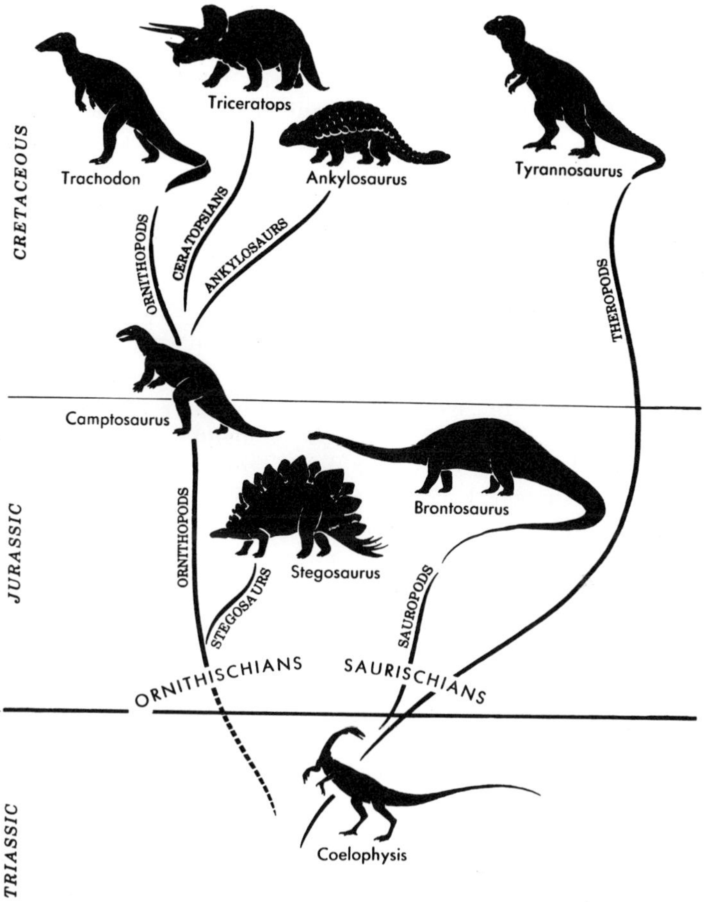

FIGURE 62.1
The evolution and relationships of the two orders and six suborders of dinosaurs. (From E. H. Colbert, *Evolution of the Vertebrates,* published by John Wiley and Sons, Inc., New York, 1955.)

we were the size of squirrels we would live in a world largely inhabited by giants. If we were the size of elephants we would live in a world populated for the most part by pygmies. Giantism is a relative term. For the purposes of the present discussion, let us define giants as animals having a minimum length of 20 feet and a probable minimum weight in life of two tons. In human terms, animals of this size are incontestably giants.

According to the terms of our definition, the early dinosaurs of Triassic days were rarely giants. With the progression of time through the Jurassic and Cretaceous periods, many of these reptiles evolved into giants, so that, among the later dinosaurs, the giants outnumbered the medium-sized and small forms by a wide margin. Middle and late Mesozoic times truly constituted an age of giants.

Why were so many of the dinosaurs giants? Before attempting to answer this question, let us examine some of the problems of giantism. Let us see, if we can, what are the advantages of being a giant and, conversely, what are the disadvantages.

The business of growing up to be a giant is not as simple in nature as it is in the fairy tales. The simple physical relationships of mass to linear dimensions and to bone strength make for definite limitations that restrict giants, particularly those that live on the land. As an animal increases in length, its mass increases roughly by the cube of the linear increase, while the strength of the supporting bones increases by the square of the linear increase. Therefore, when an animal gets progressively larger, its weight increases at a much faster rate than does the strength of its internal supports. Consequently, a point is finally reached where the animal cannot get any larger, because bones, ligaments, and muscles will not support its weight. It is very probable that the largest dinosaurs represent the top limits of size that a land-living animal can attain, and that the largest modern whales represent the greatest size attainable among water-living animals.

The problems of large size are not only those of physics, but are also problems of physiology and environment. For instance, a large animal requires a large area for its support. We know from the fossil evidence that extinct elephants, once inhabiting certain islands in the Mediterranean and off the California coast, were much smaller than their mainland relatives. The island areas were not extensive enough to support large mammoths. Again, we know from the study of modern animals that tigers in the East Indies do not occur on small islands. They require more area for their support than a small island affords.

Another problem that confronts the giant is one of protection from the elements. A small or medium-sized animal can get under cover when the weather is cold, or rainy, or when the sun is very hot. A giant cannot do this, but must stay out in the open and suffer. This problem of shelter was particularly important for reptilian giants such as the dinosaurs, whose temperature was directly proportional to the temperature of the environment.

The adverse physical effects of extremely large size, the need for large food-gathering areas, and the exposure to the elements that a giant must undergo, are some of the disadvantages of giantism. What, on the other hand, are some of the advantages?

As for physical relationships, the giant is fortunate in having a relatively small area of body surface in relation to mass. This factor is especially important for a reptile, which has no internal mechanism for maintaining body temperature. A large crocodile or alligator heats up slowly when exposed to the sun, and it cools off slowly when placed in the shade. Thus its body temperature fluctuates less than does the temperature of a small reptile, such as a lizard. Truly gigantic reptiles, such as the dinosaurs,

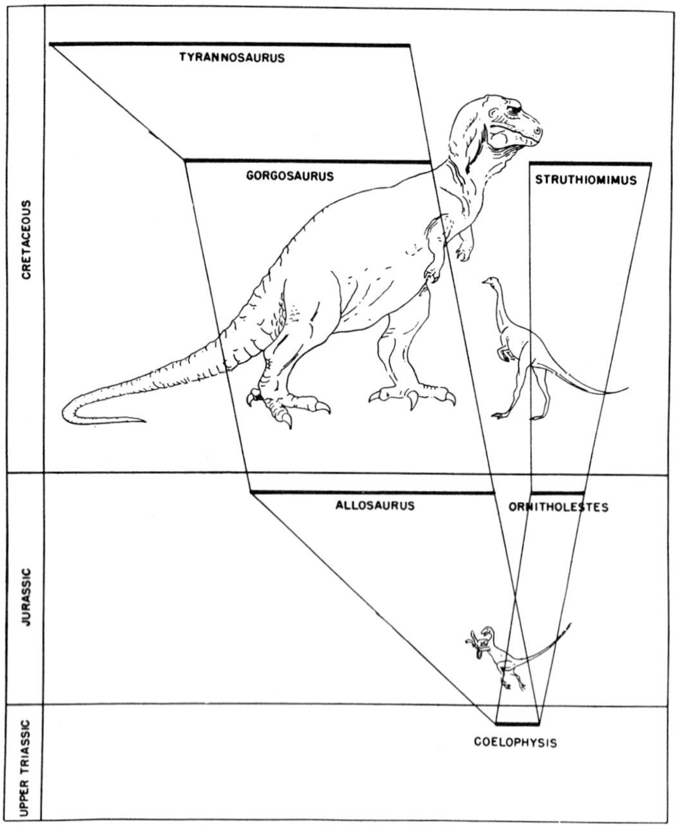

FIGURE 62.2
Size increase through time in two lines of theropod evolution. *Black lines* show comparisons of total lengths, all drawn to the same scale. The three restorations, drawn to scale, give an indication of the increase in mass of the culminating forms, *Tyrannosaurus* (*left*) and *Struthiomimus* (*right*), from an ancestral type (here represented by a drawing of *Ornitholestes*, a Jurassic theropod that was similar in size to *Coelophysis* and other Triassic dinosaurs). (From Colbert, 1949.)

must have had fairly constant body temperatures, and this factor might have given them some of the advantages that are generally enjoyed by the so-called "warm-blooded" animals.

Because of the relationship of surface area to mass, the giant is more economical of energy than is the small animal. Consequently, the giant eats much less food in relation to its size than the small animal. For instance, among the mammals a shrew may eat as much as double its own weight of food every day. It has to do so to stay alive, for the great amount of surface area in relation to weight in this tiny animal causes a rapid loss of heat and of energy. An elephant, on the other hand, does very well on a small fraction of its own weight in daily food intake. This factor is also of great importance to reptilian giants.

Although the giant is exposed to the elements, he is generally safe from other animals, except other giants. His size is his protection. A full-grown elephant on the African veldt need fear no animal except a gun-toting man. The giant reptiles of Mesozoic times had only other giant reptiles as enemies (Figure 62.2).

It is apparent, then, that there are various advantages in being a giant, especially a reptilian giant. And it would seem that, during the Mesozoic era, the advantages outweighed the disadvantages in the evolutionary history of the dinosaurs.

Most of the giant dinosaurs were plant-eating reptiles. This fact is one indication as to the abundance of plant food that was available to those reptiles during middle and late Mesozoic times. Being reptiles of such size that they were not able to retreat underground for protection against adverse temperatures, it seems obvious that the giant dinosaurs must have lived in tropical and subtropical environments, where there was generally an abundance of lush vegetation. With large amounts of plant food available, conditions were favorable for the rapid evolution and continued development of these reptilian giants.

The wide distribution of giant dinosaurs over all the continents during the Mesozoic era is one line of evidence that tropical and subtropical environments were general throughout the world in those ancient days. Dinosaurs are found from Canada almost to the tip of South America, and from northern Europe and Mongolia to the southern tip of Africa. Therefore, it is reasonable to assume that much of the world was warm when the dinosaurs were living, and that climates like the present climate of southern Florida prevailed in what are now regions of hot summers and severely cold winters.

Although most of the giant dinosaurs were plant-eating reptiles, the first dinosaurs of late Triassic age were predominantly carnivores that preyed upon other contemporaneous reptiles. These were the early saurischian theropods; small to medium-sized dinosaurs that walked in a semi-erect posture on strong, bird-like hind legs; using the front feet like hands to assist in gathering food; and possessing light, strong skulls and jaws furnished with sharp, bladelike teeth. Small, lightly-built carnivores such as these were the ancestors of the giant Jurassic and Cretaceous meat-eaters that preyed upon the huge plant-eating dinosaurs of those times. It is interesting to see the various adaptations that took place among the carnivorous dinosaurs during their growth to middle and late Mesozoic giants (Figure 62.3). The leg bones, which had been hollow, became solid and heavy. The hind feet, which had been narrow and of graceful construction, became broad to support the great weight of the body, and the metatarsals (the upper long bones of the feet), became closely appressed to form a solid structure. The skull was inordinately enlarged, and this increase in size allowed a very wide gape to the toothed jaws—a most useful adaptation for a gigantic animal that preyed upon other giants. The extreme enlargement of the skull in the late Mesozoic meat-eating dinosaurs would have been impossible had it not been for accompanying adaptations that lightened the skull, making of it an open structure of bony bars that afforded bases for strong muscle attachments, yet, at the same time, cut down the "dead weight" of bone where it was not needed. Even so, the skull in these predators was heavy and considerable weight was added by the powerful jaw muscles. Accordingly, the neck was short, to make a short but strong lever between the head and the body. Since most of the functions of predation seem to have been concentrated in the great jaws of these dinosaurs, the front limbs which, in the ancestral forms, had been like arms and hands to assist in the capture of food, were reduced to ridiculously small appendages.

We might say that, among the theropod dinosaurs, the adaptations of the progenitors were magnified so that the giant descendants were able to pursue and kill their giant cousins. And we might further say that the evolution of these carnivores was dependent upon the rise and development of varied plant-eating forms which, in turn, evolved in close correlation with the spread of middle and late Mesozoic tropical and subtropical jungles.

The sauropods were the saurischian dinosaurs that evolved in the direction of an herbivorous diet. These were the gigantic brontosaurs, the largest of all dinosaurs, the reptiles that typify to most people the great rulers of the Mesozoic world. The brontosaurs attained such immense size that they were of necessity quadrupedal, thus departing from the bipedalism of their ancestors. The legs were very heavy and the feet were broad. The body was massive. The neck and tail were long, and the head was comparatively small. The backbone in these dinosaurs was like a bridge truss between the heavy piers of the legs. It was composed of large vertebrae, strongly interlocked by rather complicated articulations and lightened by the development of open spaces or cavities to cut down "dead weight." The jaws

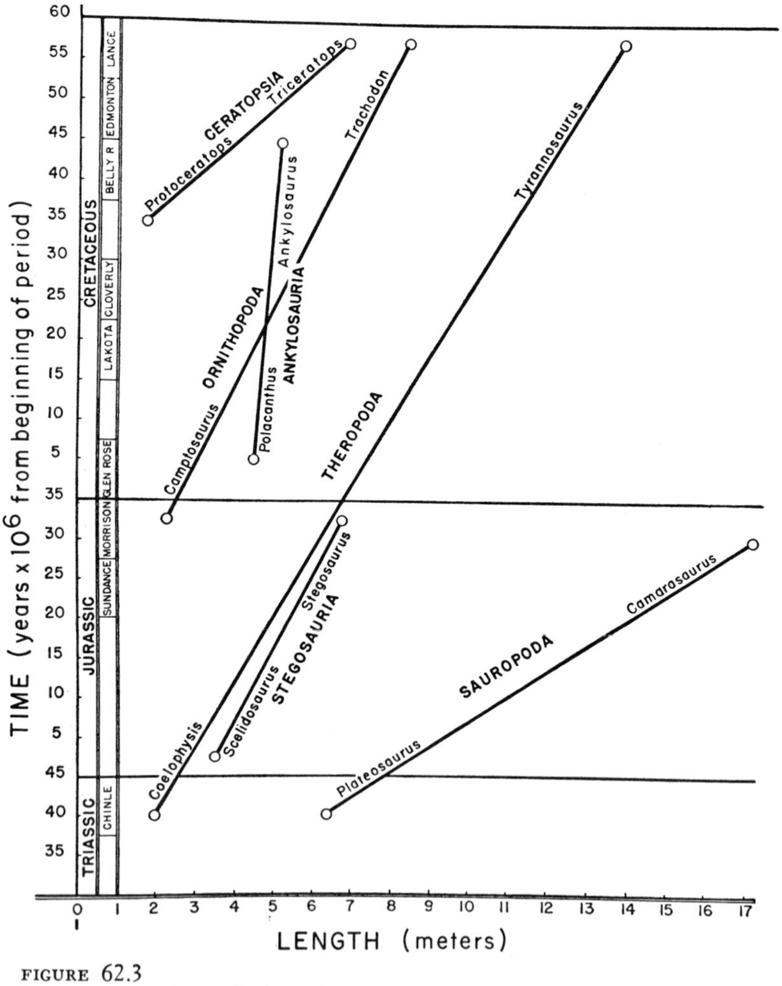

FIGURE 62.3
Increase in total length through time in the six suborders of dinosaurs. For each suborder a straight line connects an early, primitive genus and a late, specialized genus. The slope of the line gives some indication of the evolutionary growth rate in each suborder. (From Colbert, 1948.)

were furnished with rather weak rodlike or spoonlike teeth, capable of cropping soft vegetation, but nothing more. It seems evident that the sauropods, which must have commonly weighed 30 or 40 or 50 tons in life, were semiaquatic herbivores that usually waded in swamps, in rivers, or in lakes, where their great weight could be partially buoyed up by the water and where they might seek safety from the attacks of the giant predatory dinosaurs. These adaptations were highly successful, for the brontosaurs continued until near the end of Cretaceous times and were widespread throughout the world.

The saurischian dinosaurs, which have so far been described, were the meat-eaters and the giant brontosaurs. The ornithischian dinosaurs, seemingly arising at a later date than the saurischians, were all plant-eating animals. They were much more varied than the saurischian dinosaurs, evolving in four distinct lines during Jurassic and Cretaceous times. Among the ornithischians, the ornithopods began as small to medium-sized, partially bipedal dinosaurs, known as camptosaurs. The camptosaurs had low skulls and, in front, their jaws formed a sort of flat beak that must have been useful for cropping vegetation. On the sides of the jaws were small, cutting teeth for chopping up green stuff. From the camptosaurs, the later ornithopods evolved and, of these, the most numerous were the hadrosaurs or duckbills, so named because the front of the skull and jaws formed a great flat beak, like that of an outsized duck. These were gigantic water-loving dinosaurs that waded around in shallow water to feed and that probably swam away into deep water when they were attacked or threatened by the big carnivorous dinosaurs. They showed many of the adaptations for giantism that we have already seen: powerful, heavy hind limbs and broad feet, and a strengthened backbone (frequently braced in these dinosaurs by a lattice work of ossified tendons).

The ornithischian stegosaurs were, essentially, enlarged camptosaurs that had become so huge that they went about on all four legs. Their legs were heavy and rather straight. The feet were short and broad, something like the feet of elephants, clearly an adaptation for bearing weight. The curved back of the stegosaurian dinosaurs was decorated by a double row of huge triangular plates that ran from the head down to near the end of the tail. On the tail were long spikes, which these animals could use to spear their enemies at close range by whipping their tails around. Of all the larger categories of dinosaurs, the stegosaurs alone failed to live to the end of Cretaceous times.

The ankylosaurs were the armored ornithischians. They were stegosaurlike in the general build of the skeleton, but were broader in body. The top of the head and the entire upper surface and sides of the body were encased in a solid mosiac of heavy bony plates. The end of the tail was armed with a huge mass of bone forming a club, or sometimes armed with spikes. Again, we see adaptations for the support of weight in these giants, particularly in the strong limbs and the very broad feet.

The last of the ornithischians to evolve were the ceratopsians or horned dinosaurs, which probably did not appear until late Cretaceous times (Figure 62.4). These dinosaurs had a very rapid evolutionary history, developing from 6-foot long ancestors to 25-foot long descendants within the span of a few million years. They were quadrupedal types with solid bodies, strong legs, and broad feet. The head in these dinosaurs was enormous, generally constituting about a third or fourth of the total length. In front it was narrow, like the beak of a parrot; in the back it flared to form a great frill that extended back over the shoulders. Above the eyes and on the nose there were commonly horns; in some, a long nasal horn, in others, long brow horns. The large head, with its horns, formed a powerful combination of spear and buckler, with which these plant-eating dinosaurs could fight their enemies, the giant predatory dinosaurs. The large frill that made up the back portion of the skull in the horned dinosaurs was, to a considerable degree, an enlarged origin for strong jaw muscles, but it also served for the attachment of heavy neck muscles that gave great force to the thrust of the horns.

Except for the duck-billed dinosaurs, the ornithischians were predominantly "upland" dinosaurs that wandered around on dry land in search of a living. Therefore, they never reached the extremes of giantism that are seen in the swamp-living brontosaurs or even in the large hadrosaurs. They were preponderantly giants, nevertheless, and developed the varied adaptations that go along with giantism.

So it was that, at the end of Cretaceous times, a varied concourse of dinosaur giants inhabited the continents of the earth. There were huge brontosaurs, great duck-bills or hadrosaurs, heavy ankylosaurs or armored dinosaurs, and big, rhinoceroslike ceratopsians, all feeding upon the abundant vegetation of a tropical and subtropical world; and always in the offing were the giant meat-eaters, lurking in readiness to attack the plant-eaters. Then, these numerous and seemingly successful dinosaurs of late Cretaceous times were, in a geological sense, quickly and completely exterminated during the transition from Cretaceous to Tertiary times. What were the reasons for the extinction of the dinosaurs (Figure 62.5)?

It has frequently been said that the dinosaurs became extinct because they were "too big." They have been held up as fine examples of unsuccessful giants, of animals that grew to such huge dimensions they were unable to continue their struggle for existence. This easy explanation of the disappearance of the dinosaurs is to be found in many a sober textbook. It makes a nice story for moralists (Beware of the sins of bigness!), but it simply will not stand up under close scrutiny. Were the dinosaurs unsuccessful animals? They had an evolutionary history that ran for more than a hundred million years, which is a pretty good record, any way you look at it. Did they become extinct because they were giants? They were giants for many millions of years before their extinction, and there is no indication whatsoever that giantism was detrimental to their continued evolution. Indeed, the largest of the dinosaurs, the sauropods, had a particularly long evolutionary history, and they were seemingly prospering in late Cretaceous times, along with the various ornithischian dinosaurs so characteristic of that phase of geologic history.

No, the extinction of the dinosaurs cannot be attributed to giantism, for it is a fact that

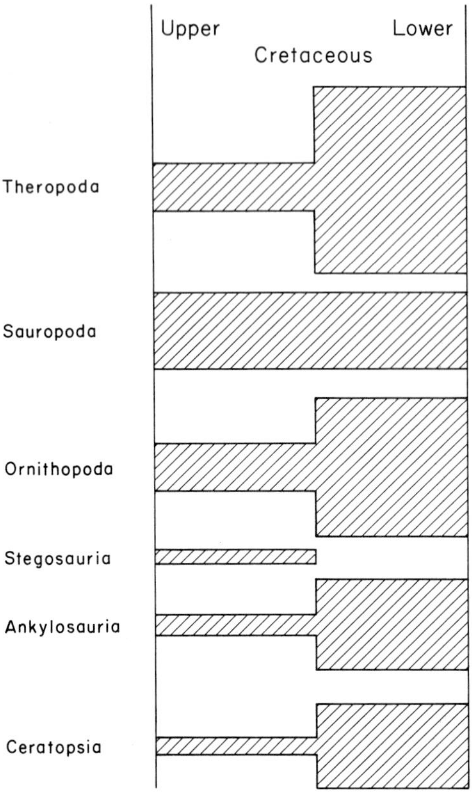

FIGURE 62.5
Extinction of the dinosaurs at the end of the Cretaceous period. The widths of the shaded areas are in proportion to known genera. (Modified from Colbert, 1949.)

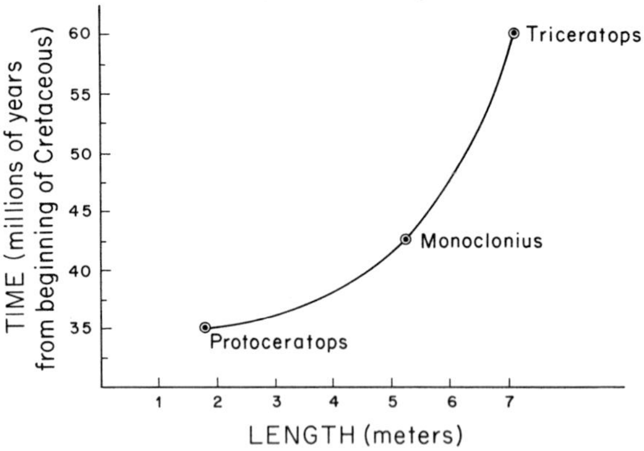

FIGURE 62.4
Increase in total length through time in the horned dinosaurs. This chart shows that most of the growth to giantism took place during the early phase of evolution, from *Protoceratops* to *Monoclonius*. Size increase from *Monoclonius* to *Triceratops* was comparatively slow. (From Colbert, 1948.)

all of the dinosaurs died out at the end of the Cretaceous period, not just the giants. Why, for instance, did not some of the small dinosaurs of late Cretaceous times live on into the Tertiary period, along with their crocodilian relatives?

Theoretically, the large size of the late Cretaceous dinosaurs might have been a factor for survival rather than for extinction. It was pointed out in a previous paragraph of this paper that, because of their great size, which would have caused slow, rather than rapid fluctuations of the body temperature, the giant dinosaurs might have had some of the attributes of "warm-blooded" animals. One might expect reptiles so favored to have lived on in a changing world. Yet all of the dinosaurs became extinct.

Extinction is one of the most difficult of all evolutionary phenomena to understand. Why was the whole series of extinctions that marked the end of the Cretaceous period along such strict taxonomic lines? Why did it affect not only the two orders of dinosaurs, but the flying reptiles as well, and, in addition, the dominant marine reptiles that flourished in the Cretaceous seas? Why did all of these animals disappear with such geological suddenness, when almost to the time of their extinction they were seemingly successful and flourishing organisms?

These are only a few of the many questions that can be asked in connection with the extinction of reptiles at the close of Mesozoic times. Extinction is obviously a complex phenomenon and, at times, a very subtle one. No single explanation is going to tell us why the dinosaurs and other reptiles vanished from the earth, and even a theory that involves multiple factors fails to satisfy us on many points connected with the extinction of these reptiles. It is indeed probable that we shall never reach a satisfactory solution to the problem of dinosaurian extinction.

Of this we can be sure: the dinosaurs were very successful giants through a long span of geologic time. Their sojourn as giants on the earth continued for as long a time as conditions favored the existence of such land-living giants. When they died, they left their bones in the earth. Today, one mammal, man, digs up these relics of the past and learns much from them and, at times, is confounded by them.

REFERENCES

Colbert, E. H., 1948, Evolution, v. 2, no. 2, p. 154–155.

———, 1949a, Sci. Monthly, v. 69, no. 2, p. 76.

———, 1949b, Early man in the Far East: Studies Phys. Anthropology, 1949, no. 1.

———, 1955, Evolution of the vertebrates: New York, John Wiley and Sons.

63

The Evolution of Mammalian Characters

EVERETT C. OLSON
1959

From *Evolution*, vol. 13, pp. 344–353, 1959. Reprinted with permission of the author and the Society for the Study of Evolution.

The problems of the origin of mammals have been under investigation for about one hundred years by comparative anatomists and paleontologists. Today, we can affirm with considerable confidence that the mammals arose from therapsid reptiles whose origins trace through pelycosaurian ancestors to the captorhinomorphs. The general patterns of morphological change are well understood, so far as osteology is concerned, and some attention has been given to inferences of the evolution of soft anatomical systems.

Interest in the origin of mammals has been renewed in recent years by new materials and restudy of older materials. Recent new finds in the Russian Permian along with restudies of older materials from beds of this age, and recent finds in the lower mid-Permian of Texas have added to our earlier picture the concept of faunal ecology in evolution. Efremov (1950, 1954, 1955) has stressed the distinctions between what he terms "archaic" and "advanced" faunas. The former represent modified persistent faunas of the Carboniferous type which maintained themselves on lowlands, primarily deltas. "Advanced" faunas, which in the present case are dominated by therapsid reptiles, have developed in the course of evolution on the continental areas away from the marginal lowlands and deltas. The San Angelo and Flower Pot formations, early mid-Permian of Texas (Olson and Beerbower, 1953), exhibit these two types in stratigraphic succession with "archaic" faunas in the mid-San Angelo and basal Flower Pot red shales, and an "advanced" fauna in the coarser clastics of the upper San Angelo. These beds are essentially contemporary with zones 1 and 2 of the Russian "Upper" Permian, but in the latter the two faunal types occur contemporaneously under different conditions of deposition. We know of no "advanced" elements in the lower Permian, apparently because the beds that carry fossils were formed only in very low lands and largely in deltaic areas. It is also important to realize that some elements were common to both types of faunas, especially certain captorhinids and sphenacodont pelycosaurs. . . .

New materials of very advanced therapsids and very early mammals are contributing importantly to knowledge of the critical intermediate reptilian-mammalian stage of development. Crompton (1958) has described an "ictidosaur," which he has named *Diarthrognathus,* and has emphasized the existence of a double articulation of the skull and lower jaw, involving both reptilian and mammalian elements. A recent publication of Kühne (1956) greatly increases the knowledge of the bienotheres by a detailed analysis of *Oligokyphus*. . . . Crompton and Ellenberger (1957) have made an important contribution in their description of the dentition of a cynodont of the Family Traversodontidae which shows strong resemblance for a cynodont-tritylodont relationship. The ictidosaurs, which appear to have arisen from scaloposaurid therocephalians, and the tritylodonts must be considered as separate groups, as these authors have suggested.

Two finds of Rhaetic or Liassic (uppermost Triassic or early Jurassic) mammals are most important additions to our knowledge of the reptilian-mammalian transition. . . . It would appear that these two suites of early mammals represent respectively docodonts and a different group with teeth remarkably like those of some of the "advanced" triconodonts. In each group there is some suggestion of the existence of more than a single element in the lower jaw. By every criterion, except that of the lower jaw, these new finds are mammalian. If we are to be rigid in application of the criterion of jaw structure, they probably would have had to be called reptiles, but if this is done, the idea of "reptile" must be stretched beyond all practical limits. If this is not done, what becomes of the position of the bienotheres, or the ictidosaurs: mammals or reptiles? Really, of course, this situation approaches the ideal for it shows that we are gaining an insight into the actual transition.

Finally, somewhat more remote from our central theme, the lower Cretaceous mammals of the Trinity formation of Texas, as described and discussed from Patterson (1957), provide vital information upon the early courses of mammalian evolution. The distinctness of early mammalian lines is emphasized and, in particular, the isolated position of the docodonts among the mammals is significant.

These finds and studies bring us to a position more favorable for consideration of various aspects of the problems of evolution of the mammals from their reptilian predecessors. In this paper, I shall consider very briefly the patterns of evolution of the mammalian predecessors. I will then turn to what appears to me to be the heart of the matter, the independent development of mammal-like characters in he various evolving lines of therapsids.

PATTERNS OF EVOLUTION OF MAMMALIAN PREDECESSORS

A phylogeny which represents the general patterns of evolution as they look to me at the present time is given in Figure 63.1. While this is undoubtedly incorrect in many details and will certainly be subject to both major and minor revisions in the future, it does serve well as a pictorial basis for brief consideration of certain key events in pre-mammalian evolution. Five "critical" stages are indicated by the letters "A" through "E" on the diagram.

"A" represents an adaptive shift from a primitive captorhinomorph. On the one hand there is an herbivorous line and on the other, one which is carnivorous. Ophiacodont and sphenacodont pelycosaurs represent derivatives of the carnivorous line. Whether the herbivorous pelycosaurs, the edaphosaurids, stemmed from an originally carnivorous line among the primitive pelycosaurs or, in fact, represent a group derived independently from captorhinomorphs is uncertain at present. The assumption of carnivorous habit is, to me at least, a critical affair, for by this step, the stage is set for initiation of increasing activity, which is a primary feature of the trend toward the condition we call mammalian.

There followed an adaptive radiation of the pelycosaurs with the development of advanced ophiacodonts, sphenacodonts, caseids, and edaphosaurids. The latter two groups assumed herbivorous modes of life. Two important points with respect to this radiation require emphasis. First, we know of it only from faunas from very low-lying areas that appear to have lain close to the oceanic margins of the continents.

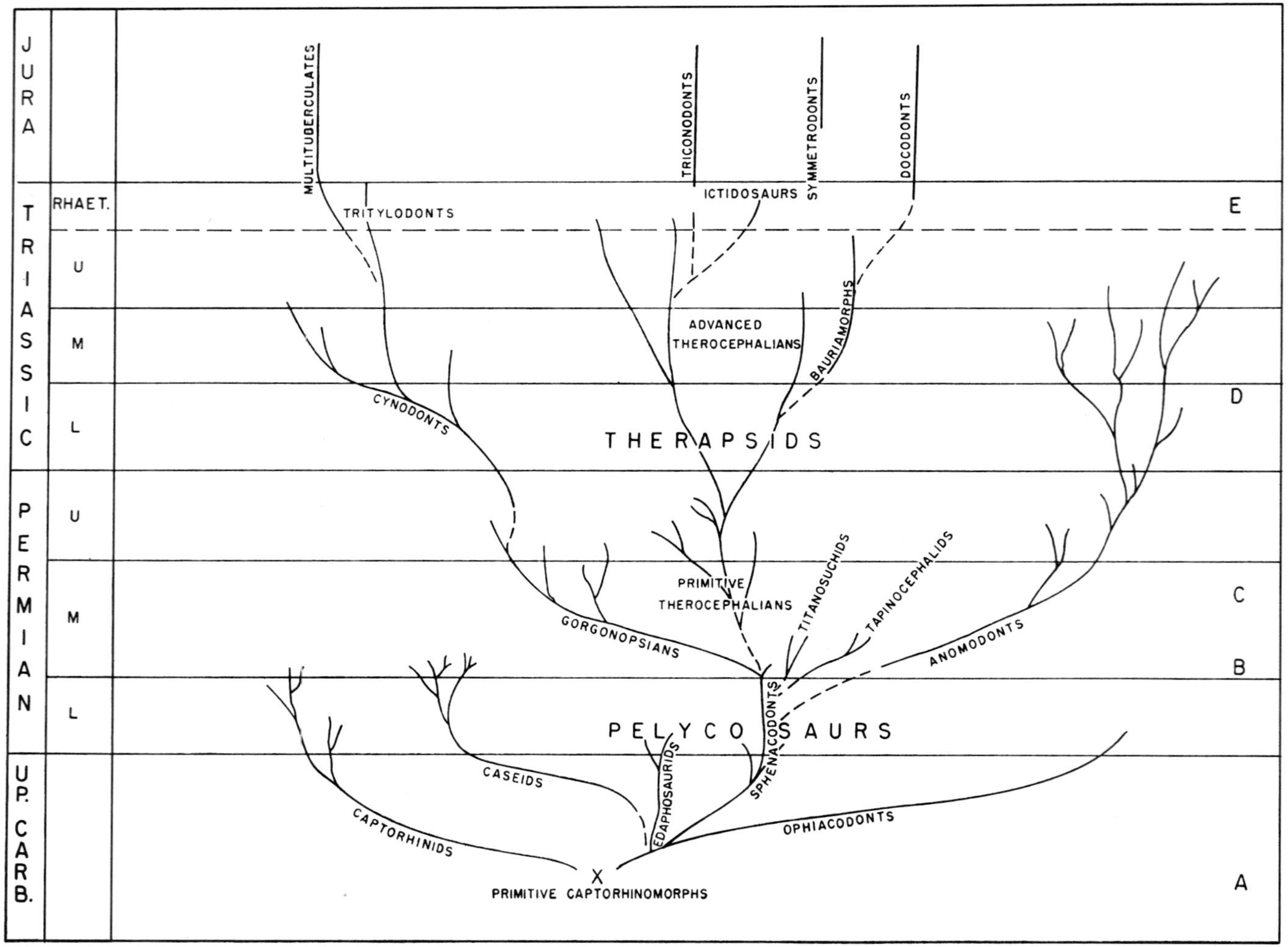
JURA
TRIASSIC
PERMIAN
UP. CARB.
RHAET.
U
M
L
U
M
L
MULTITUBERCULATES
TRICONODONTS
SYMMETRODONTS
DOCODONTS
TRITYLODONTS
ICTIDOSAURS
ADVANCED THEROCEPHALIANS
BAURIAMORPHS
CYNODONTS
THERAPSIDS
PRIMITIVE THEROCEPHALIANS
TITANOSUCHIDS
TAPINOCEPHALIDS
GORGONOPSIANS
ANOMODONTS
PELYCOSAURS
SPHENACODONTS
EDAPHOSAURIDS
CASEIDS
CAPTORHINIDS
OPHIACODONTS
X
PRIMITIVE CAPTORHINOMORPHS
E
D
C
B
A

It is primarily late Carboniferous and early Permian in time and, where it extends into the middle Permian, its elements are, for the most part, found only in persistent deltaic deposits. The second item of importance is that in the course of this radiation there was a great deal of adaptive divergence but little consistent tendency in the various lines to develop increasingly mammal-like characters. The sphenacodonts do become somewhat more mammal-like in the course of their evolution but even here we find but slight evidence of the phenomenon of independent acquisition of mammal-like features in the different lines.

The events marked as "B" represent the transition from sphenacodont pelycosaurs, to therapsids. This is a gradual change and the placement of transitional genera in one group or the other is a matter controlled more by geography and stratigraphy than by morphology. Such elements are known both in Russia, in zones 1 and 2, and in North America in the San Angelo. Most details of the transition appear to be lost as a result of lack of suitable non-deltaic environments in the waning stages of the lower Permian.

The events marked "C" represent the earliest phases of therapsid radiation. As in the pelycosaur radiation, both carnivorous and herbivorous forms developed, for there was a strong and diverse adaptive evolution. In these various lines, the tapinocephalids, the titanosuchids, the gorgonopsians, the therocephalians, and the anomodonts, however, there appeared, independently, incipient features, which in their fruition and integration come to characterize the state we may call "mammalness." Stage "D" represents the advanced therapsid radiation. In the various lines, now widely separated, there is a continuing acquisition of mammal-like characters, and "perfection" of those mammal-like features derived from more primitive representatives.

Finally, "E" represents the transition from reptiles to mammals. This is shown as taking place in several lines along the pattern proposed by the writer in 1944 (Olson, 1944). The concept of multiple origin of mammals as more or less formalized in that report was not, of course, new. Since that date, it would appear, however, that the great majority of students of this segment of evolution, with a few notable exceptions, have considered the implications of this representation to be a fair approximation of the events that lead to mammals.

INTERPRETATION OF THE EVOLUTIONARY PATTERNS

If the sequence of events suggested in Figure 63.1 can be considered a proper presentation of the broad pattern of mammalian evolution, we have, I believe, made significant progress in arraying the facts gleaned from the record. To me, at least, a most important aspect of our task of elucidation falls in the area of interpretation of the factors that have causal relationship to the patterns that are observed. The most striking feature of the history of the mammal-like reptiles is the independent acquisition of mammal-like characters by the various therapsid lines. . . . It is upon this feature that I will focus attention in the rest of this paper.

FIGURE 63.1
Evolution of mammalian predecessors. [The phylogenetic relationships shown in this figure, drawn in 1959, do not completely agree with current (1969) thinking. Stages *A*, *B*, *C*, and, for the most part, *D* need little modification; but much additional information about advanced therapsids and primitive mammals has prompted rethinking on the probable relationships between the two groups. Triconodonts quite certainly arose from cynodonts, and it is probable that docodonts and perhaps symmetrodonts had a similar origin. Ictidosaurs, which are reptilian but with many mammalian features, may also be closer to cynodonts than indicated. The origin of multituberculates is not certain, but possibly they arose from one of the mammalian stocks. 8he prevailing view as this book goes to press is that the mammals as a whole may have arisen from the highly diverse cynodonts. The position of monotremes remains uncertain. Thus, although the general principles illustrated in the diagram and discussed in the paper remain little changed—because mammal-like structures clearly did arise in parallel fashion in a number of adaptively divergent lines of therapsids—it is now felt that the probability is extremely small that more than one evolutionary line gave rise to the *full* array of features necessary for animals to be defined as mammals.—E.C.O., 1969]

In essence, this pattern of evolution represents a case of multiple directional evolution within a coherent taxonomic group at an ordinal level. Examples of directional evolution are plentiful in the fossil record. Cases of multiple lines at a familial or higher level, are less common and often difficult to recognize because of the confusion that similarities introduce into taxonomic determination. The amphibians and the holostean fish show evidence of this pattern, and there are probably a number of other valid cases. At present, however, the therapsid case is probably the most precisely documented.

This has posed a number of interesting problems. To set these more precisely, I will depart for the moment from direct consideration of interpretation to summarize what seems to be involved. First, the various evolving lines of therapsids existed in the same general environment at the same time. Second, each line had its own adaptive evolution. Third, there are, in the same beds and presumably in the same general environment, other reptilian groups which show both similar and different adaptive modifications. Fourth, there appear in each of the lines of therapsids, irrespective of their adaptation to one or another facet of the environment, common characters, which are usually more fully expressed sometime after their origin than when they first appear. To some extent, some of these characters show an impact of the adaptive modifications in a particular line, but this is the exception rather than the rule. Few of the characters and none of the suites of characters under consideration appear in other reptilian groups.

The various features show no evidence of sudden acquisition, but rather appear as minor modifications which gradually become better expressed. . . .

Some of these characters seem specifically adaptive. Most, however, are adaptive in a somewhat modified use of the term, in that they have "general" rather than "particular" adaptive significance. They are for the most part rather different from the strictly adaptive features found in lines as they diverge into various subzones of the environment and become better suited to exploitations of particular conditions.

Since phenomena of directional evolution are seen primarily in the fossil record the majority of speculations about them have been by paleontologists. Some have proposed one or another form of vitalistic causation, whereas others have approached the problems from the point of view of genetics and selection. There are interesting problems where but a single line is involved, but these are considerably compounded when we have multiple lines and where the trends flourish in the face of highly varied adaptive patterns.

Various explanations can be and have been proposed. One involves the idea that the complex genotype was strongly predisposed to certain changes and sequences of changes that are reflected through time by the phenotype. Or it can be thought that the characters expressed were latent in the common inherited genotype, and not expressed phenotypically until some time after divergence had occurred. The action of suppressive elements in the genotype may be invoked to augment this concept. Frequently, where there is no evident adaptive aspect of a character or where it seems actually deleterious, the concept of linkage to important features is cited. A special case is where a character as initiated has no apparent value but later assumes some important role. Probably all of these suggestions plus others have some element of truth in them, but none seems sufficient or entirely satisfactory to me in the present case.

Consideration of characters of the sort we have noted, their way of appearance and development, plus various similar considerations, have at times in my own mind and I am sure in the minds of others, given rise to an uneasiness with regard to the current genetic-selective concepts of evolution. This has been expressed in particular by some invertebrate paleontologists, who have either proposed contrary approaches, for example, Schindewolf (1954), or have merely abandoned efforts of interpretation and thus have left their opinions unvoiced in the literature. There has also, however, appeared an increasing, although specifically unexpressed, tendency of vertebrate paleontologists, especially in England, to "leave well enough alone" the problems of causation of evolution and to restrict their work to description of the record. In part this appears to stem from difficulties of reconciliation of results from recent materials and those of the fossil record.

Where then do we stand, especially with respect to the apparent dualism in the therapsids? Are we dealing with two kinds of systems, one for now and one for the future? Are we seeing in the fossil record something that does not come to light in laboratory and field studies of evolution? Is there a gap in the current theory, which while it may be correct, is not sufficient? Or are we being deluded by a faulty record which gives false interpretation of the events we believe it records?

I believe that the answer to each of these questions is in the negative. Also I deplore the tendency toward abandonment of efforts to seek solutions, even though answers must remain tentative. Rather, I think that whatever fault there may be lies in part in the way that some of us at least, myself included, have tended to look at the evidence. I will not dwell upon the need of a population concept for I am sure that we all recognize it whether or not we use it in practice. It may merely be noted that I consider it essential to think about the therapsids in terms of temporally successive populations and population complexes modifying through the process of speciation. What I should like to discuss, however, is the predilection to look too restrictively at just what is provided for examination by the record, that is preoccupation with preserved characters, singly or in small numbers, *per se*.

A great many of the features that we observe in our fossil materials may best be considered as "symptomatic" of adaptation rather than, of themselves, primarily adaptively significant with respect to the external environment. They may point a way to understanding, but cannot in themselves best be considered solely or primarily in their relationship to external environment. Perhaps we do not think this way, but from what I read and hear, I cannot avoid the feeling that in general we do. Perhaps I can clarify my point by suggesting that it seems more profitable to think of many characters as basically adapted to the organism and secondarily, if at all, adapted to the external environment. Understand, I am not attempting to establish a rule that I believe must be followed for all characters. Rather, there may be conceived some characters that are about equal in their adaptive relationship to external and internal environmental situations, and, spread about such "mean" characters, a distribution that extends to near complete dependency in both directions. It is primarily the characters that emphasize relationship to internal features with which I am concerned and which, I feel, have posed the elements of confusion.

Viability, it seems safe to assume, is primarily related to physiological processes. Many ostensive characters of the phenotype, whose adaptive significance we may seek, whether or not they provide for a reasonable interpretation, probably have little or nothing to do with the success of the particular organism in reaching reproductive maturity. To have selective advantage, they must operate to increase the probabilities of such viability or in some other way promote the chances of reproduction. Certainly some of the characters observable in fossils act in this way, but in many, or perhaps, most cases, it seems extremely risky to infer primary selective value merely on the basis of after the fact evidence of persistence or interpretation with respect to a single specific function. Not the least of the danger is the fixation of attention on the single item, which obscures the part that it may play in the total complex of the organism, which is the primary unit upon which selective action operates from the time of conception.

In the framework which recognizes physiological processes as dominant in the success of an organism, the patterns of evolution seen in the therapsids find ready explanation and it may well be that other cases can be clarified as well. In fact, the solution of the problems of acquisition of suites of similar characters in a series of distinct but related multiple lines yields so readily to such an interpretation that I cannot but feel that others will say, "Of course, that's what I have been saying all along." Somehow, if this is true, I have missed the boat, for until recently this problem has been very puzzling to me.

As has frequently been stated, the key to evolution of the mammals, relates to increasing activity. But, of course, other groups of reptiles also became very active and showed no approaches toward what we call "mammalness." From one such line came the birds. We know that a result of therapsid-evolution was homoeothermy. So was a result in the evolution of birds, but the structural modifications were in most respects very different. There is some evidence that there were "experiments" with blood temperature control in some of the pelycosaurs, e.g. in the long spines of such forms as *Dimetrodon*. It appears that the therapsids arose from the most active of the known pelycosaurs, the sphenacodonts. It is evident that in the pelycosaur evolution, there are very few cases of independent acquisition of similar characters in different lines and none of acquisition of similar suites of characters. Only with the development of the therapsids did this take place. Thus there appears to have developed, late in sphenacodont history, a threshold which cast subsequent evolution into a new framework. I suggest, from the remarks on homoeothermy above, and from the nature of many of the independently acquired characters, that this threshold represents the inception of a basic physiological change, and that this change is the development of incipient homoeothermy.

Several interacting phenomena are called into play in a rational explanation. The genotype inherited by all therapsids had a common building plan and presumably this organization was to some extent expressed in the physiology and soft anatomy of the late sphenacodonts. Clearly, within the physical environments into which most therapsids radiated, uplands away from deltaic lands, there would be a strong selective value in increase of homoeothermy, in large part irrespective of the particular ecological zone or subzone which a particular stock came to occupy. Any change or series of changes in structural components that were advantageous to the perfection of homoeothermy, whether in relationship to external environment, internal environment, or both, would promote the selective advantage of the organism. It is this sort of character, as we see it in the preserved individual, that I feel should be looked at in terms of its adaptation to this common and vital physiological process.

In the therapsids, as in any taxonomic category, the genotype operating through the stages leading to adulthood imposed limitations upon the nature and degree of changes permissible for viability. Thus only limited types of changes were possible. With continuing selection favoring the physiological process of homoeothermy any feature which appeared and was favorable to this process would tend to have selective advantage. In view of the limitations imposed by heredity, the nature of the variability produced by the genotypic modifications would tend to be very similar in recently diverged populations and selection related to homoeothermy would tend to produce very similar results. These results, in turn, would themselves become restrictive and insure limitations of the possible selective avenues in successive populations.

This holds, of course, only if we consider the characters in question as primarily adapted to some underlying, continuously selected feature of the organism. Adaptation to particular external conditions, for example to a particular type of food, to mating patterns, to locomotion, could proceed through exploitation of variations in the same genotype in any direction for which variation provided the raw materials. Probably no changes can be considered totally independent, but the degree of interdependency clearly varies greatly. To the extent that adaptive changes primarily related to external environment were compatible with the changes concerned most intimately with physiological change, both the process of general improvement, that is increased effectiveness in many types of environment, and process of special adaptation could proceed together in harmony. If the latter attained ascendency, that is if the immediate adaptive advantage outweighed the advantage of physiological improvement, we should expect to see cessation of the acquisition of characters adapted to the physiological process. This is what may have happened in some of the anomodont lines where this cessation and even some retrogradation of some of the suites of characters occurs.

Through this type of approach a rational and basically simple explanation of the phenomenon with which we have been concerned is at hand. On analysis, a great many of the characters which appear in varying temporal order, but apparently inevitably, in the therapsid lines can be logically related to homoeothermy. . . . The relationships in some instances appear quite direct, such as those of the secondary palate and related masticatory functions. Others, such as modifications of neural structure inferred from the cranial changes are in part direct, but in part less direct and related to body functions. . . .

THE SOURCE OF MAMMALS

If this general approach is followed, with recognition that physiological factors are the primary ones under selection, the concept of multiple origins of mammals is established on a firmer basis. Selection in all lines of therapsids will tend toward the mammalian condition and in any line in which there is full attainment of the physiological characteristics of the primitive mammals, we may expect expression of the secondary characters at essentially a mammalian level. In cases in which characteristics not primarily related to the developing physiology take ascendency in the selective hierarchy there will not be fruition of the total suite of ostensive characters of the skeleton which we call mammalian. Such lines will not then reach the mammalian threshold. We can say nothing about the development of reproductive mechanisms from any direct evidence except that cited by Brink, which seems very tenuous. However, glandular development in the skin which clearly has a selective value to developing homoeothermy, could pave the way for development of mammary glands. This in turn could set the stage for development of live birth at an immature level of development. The various stages of viviparous reproduction observed in mammals could have developed through relationship to the chain of events inferred in the evolutionary sequences which have been outlined.

What is a mammal and what is not a mammal, in the transition witnessed in the Rhaetic or Liassic, is pretty much an academic question and an *answer to it* depends in large part upon the objectives and philosophy of the one who poses the question. It seems to me that a satisfactory answer lies basically in the taxonomic convenience which it provides. If some genus ties in most logically with developing lines which are generally recognized as mammalian, it should be placed with the mammals. If it ties in more readily with some group of reptiles, which appears to have lead up to it, it should be placed with the reptiles. If we are ever blessed with such complete knowledge of the transition that some genus ties in equally well with a reptilian line and mammalian line, I presume that the best answer, if one must be had, is to be found in a flip of a coin. An alternative lies in a drastic modification of class structure as now commonly used and recognized. I believe that this is generally undesirable at present and that it is of dubious value for the foreseeable future, since at best it can result in only a slightly more functional reconciliation of incommensurates. . . .

LITERATURE CITED

Brink, A. A., 1956, Speculation on some advanced mammalian characteristics in the higher mammal-like reptiles: Palaeontologia Africana, v. 6, p. 77–95.

Crompton, A. W., 1958, The cranial morphology of a new genus and species of Ictidosaurian: Zool. Soc. London Proc., v. 130, pt. 2, p. 183–216.

Crompton, A. W., and E. Ellenberger, 1957, On a new cynodont from the Molteno beds and the origin of tritylodonts: South African Mus. Ann., v. 44, p. 1–14.

Efremov, I. A., 1950, Taphonomy and the geological record (in Russian): Acad. Sci. USSR Inst. Palaeontology Trudy, v. 24, p. 1–176.

———, 1954, Fauna of terrestrial vertebrated in the Permian copper sandstones of the Western Pre-Urals (in Russian): Acad. Sci. USSR Inst. Palaeontology Trudy, v. 54, p. 1–416.

Efremov, I. A., and B. P. Vjuschkov, 1955, Catalogue of localities of Permian and Triassic vertebrates of the territories of the U.S.S.R. (in Russian): Acad. Sci. USSR Inst. Palaeontology Trudy, v. 46, p. 1–185.

Kermack, K. A., and F. Mussett, 1958, The jaw articulation in Mesozoic mammals: Internat. Zool. Cong. 15th Sess. Rept., sec. V, paper 8, p. 1–2.

Kühne, W. G., 1956, The liassic therapsid *Oliogokypus:* London, British Museum (Natural History), p. 1–149.

———, 1958, Rhaetische Triconodonten aus Glamorgan, ihre Stellung wischen den Klassen Reptilia und Mammalia und ihr Bedeutung für die Reichart'sche Theorie: Paläontol. Zeitschr., v. 32, p. 197–235.

Olson, E. C., 1944, Origin of mammals based upon the cranial morphology of therapsid sub-orders: Geol. Soc. America Spec. Paper 55, p. 1–136.

Olson, E. C., and J. R. Beerbower, 1953. San Angelo formation, Permian of Texas, and its vertebrates: Jour. Geology, v. 61, p. 389–423.

Patterson, B., 1956, Early Cretaceous mammals and the evolution of mammalian molar teeth: Feildiana Geology, v. 13, p. 3–101.

Schindewolf, O. H., 1954, Evolution im Lichte der Paläontologie: Internat. Geol. Cong. 19th Sess. Rept., v. 19, p. 93–107.

64

Evidence of Climatic Change in the Geologic Record of Plant Life

ELSO S. BARGHOORN
1953

Plant life has existed on the earth for more than a billion years. Although this extent of time is essentially inconceivable to the human mind as anything more than an arithmetic expression, it nevertheless provides a chronological framework within which the evolutionary picture may be visualized. The known fossil record of plants from which this picture emerges is a fragmentary, though decipherable, sequence of tangible organic forms, featured by a remarkable progression from simplicity to complexity.

The geologic record yields only the history of morphologic change and tells us nothing directly of the physiologic responses of organisms. These must be inferred or surmised through analogy with known relations of form and function in existing organisms. For example, the extremely thick leaf cuticles and other structural modification of many xerophytic plants can reasonably be interpreted as evidence of adaptations to resist water loss and hence adaptation to arid climate. By the same token, comparable structures in fossil forms may reasonably be interpreted as evidence of arid climate in the past, especially if the degree of taxonomic relation between the living and the extinct is known.

Because of the innumerable and frequently obscure relations between structure and function in higher plants I should like to raise the question whether the increasing morphologic complexity that features organic evolution has not also been associated with a physiologic evolution, the essence of which is an increased sensitivity or susceptibility on the part of the organism to react to physical factors of the environment. Such an assumption applied to plants would certainly aid in explaining the extraordinary cosmopolitan distribution of many ancient groups, over the surface of an earth, which throughout geologic time must have possessed climatic zones, regardless of how different these were from existing geographic zones. There exist today no truly cosmopolitan species of higher plants, and the study of ecology and distribution of living

From *Climatic Change: Evidence, Causes and Effects*, edited by Harlow Shapley, pp. 235–248. Harvard University Press, Copyright 1953 by the President and Fellows of Harvard College. Reprinted with permission of the author and the publishers.

plants is to a great extent concerned with relating geographic ranges to factors of the environment. We are able today to recognize the larger climatic zones, or types of climates, by characteristic flora and fauna. How far back in the geologic record this relation can be extended is certainly an open question. It is, however, basic to our concept that the history of climate may be read in the history of life. Certainly since the appearance of higher plants it seems reasonable to accept the idea that natural selection has been strongly influenced by physiologic demands imposed by the physical environment. Therefore environment participates in the direction of evolution and in the natural selection of anatomic features that we ordinarily think of as the physical evidence of evolution. If we accept these premises we have accepted the idea that climate and evolution are closely entwined, to the extent that knowledge of climate and its history are fundamental to the understanding and interpretation of the paleontologic record. As George Gaylord Simpson [1] has recently pointed out, "search for *the* cause of evolution has been abandoned." However, it seems evident to the writer, as to many others, that climatic change has been a most significant, if not *the most* significant factor in the migration and dispersal of the existing terrestrial flora and fauna, whatever the ultimate causes of initiating biological variation, that is, of evolution, may be.

It seems appropriate at this point, and before surveying the geologic record, to examine the fundamental basis for assuming that plants and their distribution are related to changes in climate. The land plant is a photosynthetic mechanism, thermodynamically concerned with trapping solar energy through the chemistry of photosynthesis. As such, its efficiency, as well as that of the vegetation as a whole, is confined within the physical ranges of protoplasmic activity, especially with respect to availability of water and of heat, to mention only two factors essential for life. Since these physical limitations are thrust upon the plant through the agency of the atmosphere, it necessarily follows that atmospheric conditions—the essence of climate in meteorologic terms—profoundly affect the vital processes of vegetation to such an extent that climate constitutes a major control over growth and survival. In this connection, it may be noted that higher plants as individuals cannot migrate to more favorable environments as most higher animals are able to do. Extreme conditions of temperature or of available moisture consequently serve to limit photosynthetic activity and, therefore, exert control on the maximal tolerance of land plants. Through the operation of natural selection on the inherently variable population there occurs a distribution of forms best suited to meet the limitations of a wide range of physical conditions. In this way climate (and physiography) are geographically correlated with vegetation, in a vague but nevertheless definable interrelation. The closeness of the relation between climate and vegetation is sufficiently well developed, as noted before, to allow the major climatic zones of the earth's surface to be defined by vegetational areas.

Extensions of the relation between climate and vegetation may be made in two directions. One of these lies in quantitative analysis of climatic factors which may operate in delimiting the geographic distribution of constituent members of the vegetation. The other line of inquiry lies in extending known correlations of climate with vegetation into the geologic past. Such extensions into the past records of vegetation comprise the nucleus of botanical paleoecology, though in its broadest terms paleoecology deals with the totality of physical as well as biological evidence of past environments. It is my intention here to present evidence that land plants are probably the most valid and widespread biological indicators of past physical conditions, especially of climate.

There are two basic assumptions for the paleobotanical interpretation of climatic history. The first of these is that plant groups of the past had environmental requirements similar to those which they possess today, the degree of similarity being a function of morphologic, taxonomic, and hence genetic affinity or relationship. The second assumption is that an environmental complex of definable climatic and other physical conditions supports a biotic population which is in general equilibrium with these conditions, and that this population will show no more than minor (specific) changes unless there is distinct alteration of the environmental conditions.

Acceptance of these two principles provides

us with an extremely valuable means for examining and interpreting the history of climate, though their bland acceptance by the unwary investigator may lead to erroneous and unfortunate conclusions. For example, morphologically similar but ecologically different forms of variable species may complicate or confuse the issue in that their presumed living equivalents exist today under different environmental conditions. In addition, certain species, and to a greater extent genera, of the living flora commonly exhibit such widespread distribution, and occur in such diverse habitats, that they provide little basis for evaluating environmental conditions.

A further possible objection to the logical basis of paleoecology may be found in the rather startling realization that its working concepts, if too rigidly adhered to, would deny the operation of organic evolution. Organic evolution demonstrates that organisms vary, disseminate, and adapt through natural selection to meet changing environmental conditions. To the botanist concerned with plant evolution, this aspect of the problem may raise a real obstacle to accepting the entire structure of paleoecology, and would necessitate a retreat to considerations dealing largely with extremes of the physical environment and their relation to limiting plant growth in general.

Students of plant distribution and biogeography are frequently skeptical, and justifiably so, about the interpretation of past ecology on the basis of fossil plants. The argument is sometimes advanced that adaptation, that is, evolution, is more rapid than climatic change and that therefore the stratigraphic sequence with which the paleoecologist deals is an evolutionary rather than an ecologic sequence. If this view be accepted, paleoecology becomes a grant delusion of circular reasoning, whereby climate is interpreted in terms of evolution, and evolution interpreted in terms of climate, with infinite concordance of the evidence.

Because of our limited understanding of the actual causes of evolution, certain weaknesses in the methods of paleoecology must be carefully weighed. Perhaps it would be reasonable to conclude that the paleoecologic method when applied to more than major details of climatic history is largely limited to the Cenozoic era in geologic time, during which period fossil representatives of many living groups are known and can be studied in terms of existing ecology and present environmental relations. Accuracy of the method in elucidating the history of climate seems to be inversely proportional to the geologic age of deposits from which the evidence is secured. Ecologic interpretation of ancient and extinct groups of plants will always be subject to uncertainties, and will always require confirming evidence from the physical geology and paleozoölogy.

The over-all geologic record of terrestrial plants seems to provide us with certain basic concepts. I should like to enumerate three.

(1) Higher plants can exist only within certain thermodynamic, physiologic limits imposed by climate. Their remains in richly fossiliferous sediments, or in the form of coal seams, therefore indicate that the climate at the time of deposition was neither too arid nor too cold for vigorous vegetative growth. In this connection, it should be noted that coal seams and other plant-bearing deposits such as are known from high latitudes on the Antarctic continent could not conceivably form today under existing climatic conditions [at that latitude].

(2) Species of plants, even though genetically variable and composed of numerous ecologically different forms, are geographically limited by environmental factors, among which climate is of prime importance. If this were not the case, it would be impossible to decipher any meaning whatsoever in the history of climate deduced from the paleontologic record.

(3) Associations or communities of plants, to an even greater extent than individuals, exist in a dynamic, though not easily definable, equilibrium with climate, in particular with extremes of temperature and moisture. Climatic change can alter the equilibrium and result in the migration of plant associations, through natural selection and population pressure, to areas resembling climatically their former habitats. Plant associations are not constant populations, but assemblages continually undergoing change by extinction of forms and by evolution of new types. The tendency for plant associations to retain their essential taxonomic identity through

extensive latitudinal and longitudinal migrations is one of the most impressive features of the Cenozoic history of vegetation, a fact which early engaged the attention of both Charles Darwin and Asa Gray.

With both the strengths and the weaknesses of paleoecology in mind, it is possible to review more objectively the paleontologic record of plants and its bearing on the history of climate and climatic change.

More than one-half the total chronologic record of plant life is restricted to marine sediments, and the bulk of this marine record is limited to calcareous algal deposits. Ecologic interpretation of these plant-bearing marine formations, some of great antiquity in pre-Cambrian rocks, is potentially of much significance, especially wherever correlation is possible wth associated faunas. Calcareous algae are world-wide in distribution at present, but their quantitative role in carbonate precipitation, owing to the chemistry of sea water, is strikingly greater in warm, shallow seas than in cold marine waters. Occurrence of extensive deposits of stromatolites, now generally agreed to be of calcareous algal origin, in the pre-Cambrian sediments of the Belt Series in Montana, in the Black Hills of South Dakota, and in the Northwest Territories of Canada [2] provide evidence of former widespread seas over areas that are now in cold temperate and even subarctic regions. In marine sediments of early Paleozoic age, algal reefs are fairly common over many areas of the continents, in both the Northern and Southern Hemispheres. These reefs provide a disconnected but widespread record of invasion of the Cambrian and Ordovician seas into large areas of the present continents. If viewed in terms of present-day ecology, the distribution of early Paleozoic marine algae would indicate extensive poleward spread of warm, shallow seas, a marked contrast to the cold-water floras of many middle-latitude regions today.

From paleobotanic evidence, the climatic history of the present continents begins in the late Silurian and early Devonian. Continental sediments of this time record the most striking transformation known in the paleontologic record of plant life, namely, the emergence of plants from the sea and the establishment of a true land flora. The significance of this step in the subsequent evolution of vascular plants and of animals is of paramount importance. The development of terrestrial animals, in particular the vertebrates, has been greatly influenced by developments in plant evolution, especially among the so-called herbivorous animals. One example suffices to illustrate the interrelation: the evolution and dispersal of grazing animals during Tertiary time are closely associated with the evolution and spread of grasses and grassland environments. It is perhaps reasonable to conclude that the origin of a land flora of vascular plants was a biologic prerequisite for the successful liberation of animal life from the sea, though, as R. J. Russell [3] has pointed out, marine vertebrate animals were certainly not evolving in premeditation of the event.

Early land plants show two outstanding features: first, extreme simplicity of structure and small size; and second, very widespread geographic distribution. Occurrence of abundant Devonian plant life from terrestrial sediments of such widely removed areas as the Falkland Islands, Spitzbergen, and the interior of Asia and North America, to name only a few localities, indicate either an enormous range of tolerance on the part of structurally similar plants, or the presence of far more uniform and milder climate than occurs today [or a different configuration of the continents]. The emergence of Devonian plant-bearing strata from beneath the melting glaciers of Ellesmere Land and Spitzbergen is impressive evidence of climatic change.

Unfortunately our knowledge of early Devonian plants from areas within the present tropics is extremely limited, and it is not possible to attempt a reconstruction of the climatic zones of the earth during Devonian time on the basis of plant distribution. The known distribution of Devonian plants, especially their diversification in high latitudes, suggests that glacial conditions did not exist at the poles. . . .

By the end of Devonian time land plants had evolved many complex types, some of which were true trees and constitute evidence of the earliest forests. One group of upper Devonian large trees, the genus *Callixylon*, was widespread in what are now such ecologically diverse environments as those of Oklahoma,

Indiana, New York State, and western Siberia. The paleobotanic record would indicate a nonglacial climate, with probably great expansions of humid warm temperate regions into higher latitudes during most of the Devonian. Establishment of the terrestrial flora probably in itself constituted a climatic factor, or at least a factor of local importance in climatic change. Covering of the former bare land surfaces of the earth with vegetation contributed influences that did not exist before, such as the accelerated loss of ground water from the soil, effected by absorption and transpiration from plants, and the acceleration of the oxygen–carbon dioxide interchange brought about by enormous new areas of photosynthetic activity. Geologic processes such as erosion and weathering would be very different on an earth devoid of vegetation from what they are on the present continental surfaces, where numerous interrelations exist between vegetation and erosion. Considerations such as these, however, quickly lead us into questions that are beyond the reach of paleontologic evidence and can be answered or thought of in terms of logic rather than discovery.

Despite the lapse of time that separates us from the floras of the Carboniferous, we probably possess today more knowledge of the plant life of that Paleozoic period than of any other period in geologic history until the Pleistocene and Recent. Sedimentary rocks of that time have been given an appropriate geologic memorial in the name Carboniferous, or carbon-bearing, because of the accumulations of plant residues which we recognize as coal. The mining of coal and associated sediments has yielded, as a by-product, great collections of fossil plants and a great variety of information on their structure, classification, and distribution, to such an extent, in fact, that a substantial part of our knowledge of extinct plants is limited to floras of the late Paleozoic, especially the Carboniferous.

A fairly extensive literature exists on the subject of presumed coal-swamp climates and the environmental conditions of coal deposition. Many of the earlier writers were strongly influenced by now outmoded ideas of the geologic history and the age of the earth. The concept of residual initial earth heat, and final cooling to the present glacial climate, was widely held for a surprisingly long period and much influenced thinking even into the twentieth century.

At present, there is no uniformly accepted theory of Carboniferous climate, nor an adequate explanation of the enormous accumulations of coal during this period geologic time. It is quite probable that the explanation is both physiographic and climatic and is related to the erosional history of the continents. Early Carboniferous floras exhibit a remarkable uniformity in composition with regard to major and minor groups of plants. The geologic record indicates that their migration and the establishment of larger groups was probably world-wide. The widespread dispersal of early Carboniferous (Mississippian) plants is well attested by deposits from both Northern and Southern Hemispheres.

From the paleontologic evidence available, it would appear that there was very slight climatic zonation between high and low latitudes during the major part of the Carboniferous. Very similar floras occur in regions that today show extreme climatic differences, for example, northeastern Europe and the eastern Mediterranean, or Nova Scotia and central Kansas. The earlier Carboniferous floras of the Southern Hemisphere contain many groups of plants also common to Holarctic regions. Even within the present-day tropics there can be found little indication of regional differentiation of the early Carboniferous vegetation. It is probably significant in connection with Carboniferous climates that the bulk of the world's Paleozoic coals occur in what are now temperate latitudes. The coal-swamp climate was quite likely one featured by excessive humidity rather than high temperatures. Peat formation, the first stage in coal deposition, is more favored in warm temperate than in tropical regions today, although peat deposits are by no means absent in equatorial regions. It should be noted that the major part of the Carboniferous coals are derived from woody plants, and the source vegetation and presumed environment bear no resemblance to the type of vegetation and conditions that characterize northern peat bogs; they were, rather, forest accumulations.

One impressive indicator of uniform climate over great areas of the Carboniferous continents is the great absence of annual growth rings in coal-swamp trees. The entire question of ring development in woody plants is one fraught with botanical variables as well as climatic variables. However, the consistent absence of any index of seasonal growth seems difficult to explain except on the assumption that winter cold and seasonality of rainfall were absent or at a minimum. In existing woody plants, annual ring development may occur under nearly uniform climatic conditions, as in equatorial rainforests. Nevertheless, in climates with distinct seasons, seasonal effect is almost invariably reflected in pronounced annual growth rings.

The picture of Paleozoic climate, developed from paleobotanic evidence, would scarcely be complete, or indeed fairly represented, if reference were not made to the climatologic anomaly recorded in plant-bearing beds of the late Carboniferous (Permo-Carboniferous) of the Southern Hemisphere. Here there is ample evidence of widespread continental glaciation of the austral continents including tropical Africa, and also peninsular India. Associated with geologic evidence of glaciation occur remains of a depauperate flora characteristically represented in the Lower Gondwana beds of India. This flora is featured by a small number of species and a pronounced difference, botanically, from the supposedly contemporaneous coal-swamp flora of the northern land masses. Remains of plants have recently been found even within the tillites of the Talchir boulder beds of India [4], indicating that a flora developed in a rigorous climate certainly in the near proximity of glacial conditions.

Fragments of wood from late Paleozoic austral deposits frequently show pronounced ring growth as further evidence of seasonal periodicity, probably winter cold. Contrast between the paleoecologic conditions of late Paleozoic climates in the Northern and Southern Hemispheres is so great as to evoke equivalently bizarre explanations. One of these is the often refuted but continually persistent concept of continental drift, a hypothesis that unfortunately creates more problems than it sets aside. Whatever explanation is finally made of the problem of late Paleozoic climate, the available geologic and paleobotanic evidence relating to the period now constitutes one of the great enigmas of paleoclimatology.

Although floras of the early Mesozoic, especially the Triassic period, are poorly known in comparison with those of the late Paleozoic, they provide evidence of a return to more uniform world-wide climate. This is indicated by an increasing cosmopolitanism of certain groups of plants which make their first appearance in the Mesozoic. The rapid development of coniferous trees and other groups of primitive seed plants, which show structural adaptation to arid or semiarid environment, support diverse geologic evidence pointing to well-developed dry or monsoonal climates in temperate latitudes during the early Mesozoic. Triassic coals are not common, but their existence indicates the prevalence of humid mesophytic forest climates in other parts of the temperate regions, for example, in the south central Atlantic states of the United States. Cosmopolitan dispersal of certain groups of plants and their extension into high latitudes appears to have reached its peak in the Mid-Mesozoic, probably in the early Jurassic.

Jurassic floras, botanically rich in varied types, are known from some of the most northerly land areas of the Arctic, such as northern Greenland and Franz Josef Land, north of the 80th parallel. The most remarkable evidence of the nonglacial climate of polar regions in Jurassic time, however, was discovered on the Third Byrd Expedition to Antarctica. Fossil plants and coal were collected on Mount Weaver, at an elevation of 10,000 feet at latitude 86°58′S. The plants themselves, interestingly enough, belong to genera known from Jurassic sediments of temperate and even arctic regions of the Northern Hemisphere. The development of coal-forming swamps close to the South Pole demands an explanation allowing for extraordinary climatic change [or latitudinal drift of Antarctica]. Botanically also, Jurassic floras present the curious anomaly of a well-differentiated vegetation developing under the physiologic conditions of the polar night.

With the close of the Mesozoic it becomes possible to refine greatly the paleoecologic interpretation of climate. By Upper Cretaceous time the Angiosperms, the ubiquitous group of flowering plants that now dominate the earth's vegetation, had attained great diversity. Many existing genera of trees and shrubs can be recognized in Upper Cretaceous rocks, and by the early Cenozoic a number of associations of genera, surprisingly similar to mid-latitude forest associations in the present living flora, have been described. With the appearance of extant forms providing possible ecologic indices of existing environments, the reconstruction of climatic history becomes far clearer. Because of the extent of detail known at present, it is desirable to present here only the major features of the extraordinary trends of Cenozoic climate which culminated in the last glaciation.

The luxuriant growth of broad-leaf hardwood forests in high Arctic latitudes persisted from the Cretaceous into the Eocene and probably the Oligocene, indicating a prolonged continuation of humid warm temperate, or at least temperate forest climate in polar regions. Evidence for this may be found in both Arctic and Antarctic regions. During the early Cenozoic the northern *mid-latitudes* were covered by a vegetation, the botanical equivalent of which is now largely confined to subtropical and even tropical climates. A striking example of this is the rich and varied flora of the Eocene London Clay, the present equivalent of which is now to be chiefly found in the Austro-Malaysian tropics, or in New England in the Brandon lignite flora of western Vermont, the major equivalent of which now exists in the Atlantic and Gulf coastal plain area. It seems quite unlikely that truly tropical conditions occurred in mid-latitudes during the Eocene. It is more probable that the absence of pronounced winter freezing allowed an unusual extension poleward of tropical plants. Thus the situation was featured by a gentle temperature gradient between high and low latitudes instead of the steep gradient which now exists. Hence the absence of cold, the lethal factor to tropical vegetation, rather than extreme warmth is indicated. Rainfall, however, would have to be far greater than is easily explainable for such high latitudes as 48° to 52°N, probably of the order of 70 to 80 inches per year.

A shift in vegetational belts initiated by gradual climatic change and manifested by migration of forest association apparently began in the late Eocene. By the mid-Tertiary, temperate forms begin to appear in increasing numbers in mid-latitude floras, and with them a sudden influx of herbaceous plants. The appearance and rapid evolution of herbs is primarily a phenomenon of the late Cenozoic and an evolutionary development of great importance to many mammalian groups, including man. Climatic deterioration probably went on at an accelerating rate during the late Tertiary and it is probable that glacial conditions began to develop at the poles in the mid-Pliocene. Later Pliocene floras are essentially modern, though indicative of somewhat warmer climates in terms of the present geographic range of many forms represented. Unfortunately, the total number of Pliocene floras known is regrettably small.

TABLE 64.1
List of floras plotted on graphs (Figures 64.1–64.3)

1. Woodbine	17. Weaverville
2. Tuscaloosa	18. Bridge Creek
3. Ripley	19. Alum Bluff
4. Vermejo	20. Latah
5. Laramie	21. Tehachapi
6. Medicine Bow	22. Calvert
7. Lance	23. Mascall
8. Raton	24. San Pablo
9. Wilcox	25. Weiser
10. Green River	26. Remington Hill
11. Claiborne	27. Esmeralda
12. Comstock	28. Black Hawk Ranch
13. Goshen	29. Mulholland
14. Jackson	30. Sonoma
15. LaPorte	31. Mt. Eden
16. Catahoula	32. Citronelle

In an attempt to reduce the large volume of paleobotanical data to a graphic representation of Cenozoic paleoecology, recourse has been made to botanical and geographic analyses of 32 of the larger Tertiary floras which have been described from North America (Table 64.1). The genera of flowering plants in each

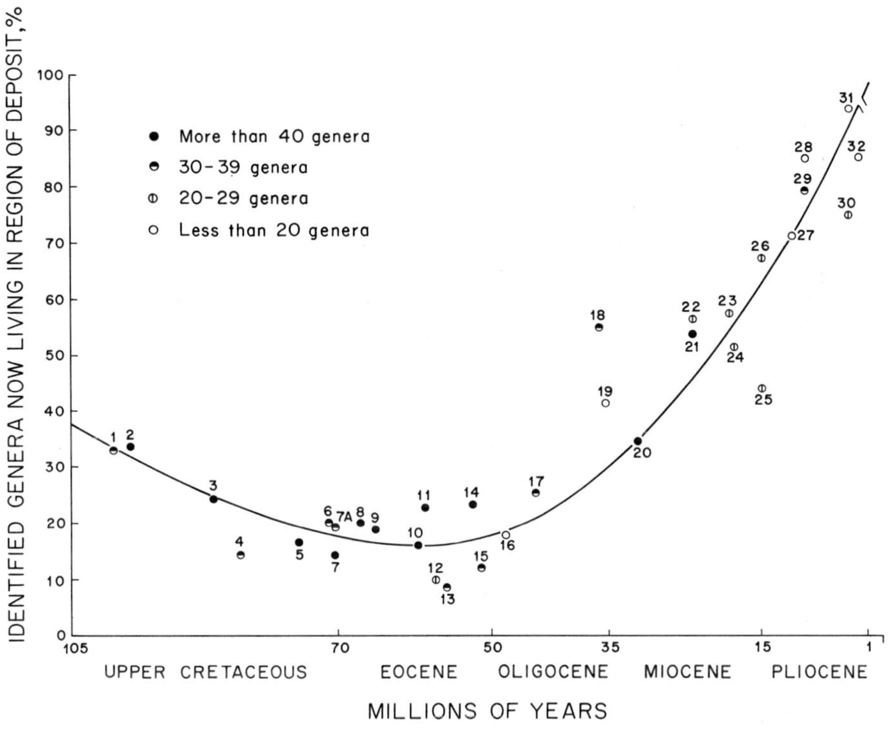

FIGURE 64.1
Relation between geologic time and the proportion of genera in fossil floras which also occur today in the geographic region of the respective deposits. The higher a point is on the curve the greater the similarity in generic composition to the existing flora. The slope of the curve from the middle Eocene to the Pleistocene indicates the rate of trend toward the modern flora and can be regarded as a curve of climatic change. The age of each flora is that proposed by the author. Data are restricted to higher plants. Numbers refer to floras listed in Table 64.1.

flora have been segregated statistically into three elements: (1) extant genera which at present occur in the bordering geographic areas of the fossil deposit and hence are designated "native" (Figure 64.1); (2) extant genera which are now exotic to the bordering geographic areas of the deposit (Figure 64.2); and (3) genera which are not assigned to a living group and which can be regarded as extinct or botanically unidentified (Figure 64.3). The percentage in each category has been computed with reference to the total number and plotted against geologic time. The increasing percentage of the "native" generic element in succeedingly younger Tertiary floras is quite striking. It should be emphasized that it is the "native" element in which accuracy of botanical identification is greatest.

From the relation shown it is apparent that American early Tertiary floras were consistently featured by a large exotic element and that this exotic element begins to decline in the late Eocene and Oligocene. By the later Tertiary, continuing to the Pleistocene, the influx of genera native at present to the respective geographic areas increases at an almost exponential rate [5].

The relation demonstrated here seems clearly to indicate climatic change and vegetational migration. The changing composition of successive floras is not due primarily to evolution of new types but rather to migration of associations of plants. The most significant feature of the Cenozoic migration of vegetation is the steady retreat of the temperate forest flora from Arctic regions and the concomitant retraction of the early Tertiary tropical elements of mid-latitude floras into the present marginal tropics. The curve of floristic change may therefore be translated into a curve of climatic change. If this interpretation be accepted, it appears that the great trend of Cenozoic climate which culminated in Pleistocene gaciation began in the mid-Tertiary, probably more than 20 million years ago. Pleistocene glaciation itself, of which present climate is in many respects an extension, may then be regarded as a geologic and climatologic event the antecedents of which extend over a fair segment of recent geologic time and is not to be viewed as a sudden change in the history of the earth's climate.

Evidence for interpreting climatic history from paleobotanic history is drawn from such wide and varied sources, both stratigraphic and geographic, that this survey is more an abstract than a detailed analysis of the geologic record of plants. However, certain conclusions emerge from the paleontologic record as a whole. Perhaps the most outstanding conclusion to be drawn is that, throughout the past several hundred million years of earth history, plant distribution demonstrates a far more uniform and less intensified latitudinal zonation of climate than now exists on the continents [a conclusion that is less obvious in 1970 than in 1953, before the recognition of plate tectonics and the rehabilitation of continental drift]. The greater part of climatic history, evidenced by extinct floras and their distribution, appears to have been characterized by more equable distribution of temperature and probably also

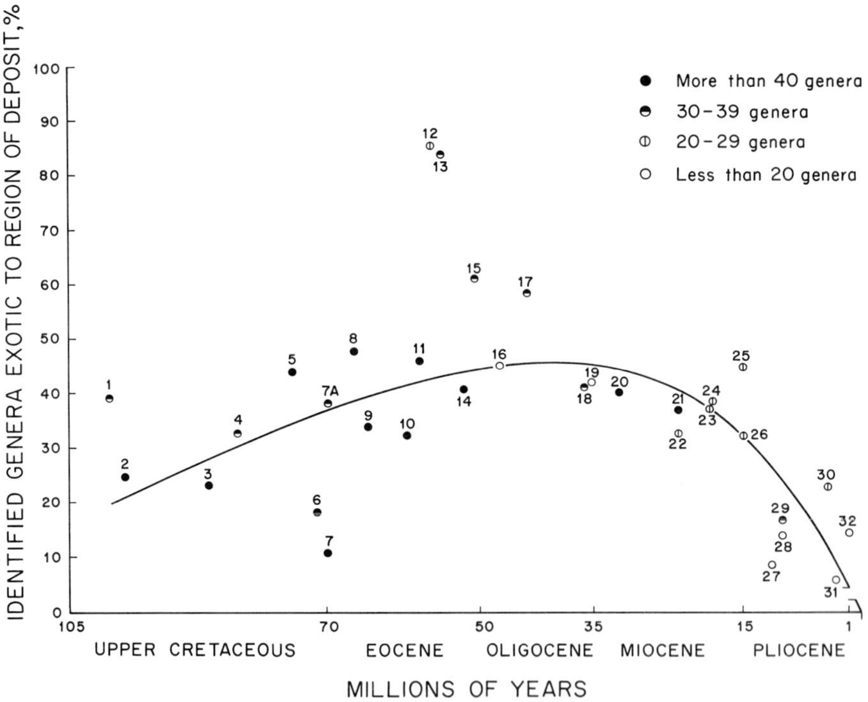

FIGURE 64.2
Relation between geologic time and the proportions of genera which occur in the respective deposits but are now exotic to the geographic regions of the deposits. The higher a point is on the curve, the greater the difference in generic composition from the existing flora. The exotic element is composed largely of genera now limited to warmer temperate or subtropical regions. The exotic genera rapidly decline in the later Tertiary owing to retreat southward of the warmer elements of the various floras. The data are not the direct inverse of Figure 64.1 because of the unidentified or extinct elements in the fossil floras. Numbers refer to floras listed in Table 64.1.

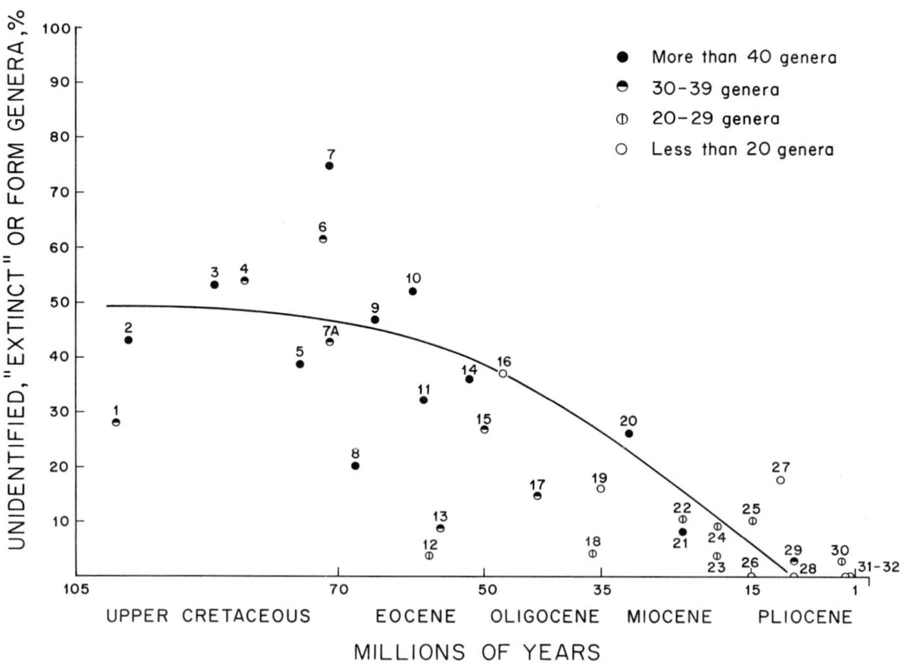

FIGURE 64.3
Graph comparable to Figures 64.1 and 64.2, but showing the changing percentages of unidentified or "extinct" genera. The percentage of this element in fossil floras is highly variable, owing to the uncertainty of assigning certain forms to recognized living genera. It is significant, however, that the percentage of unidentified forms drops sharply in post-Eocene deposits, a fact which emphasizes the rapid modernization of angiosperm floras, both geographically and biologically, in the later Tertiary. Numbers refer to floras listed in Table 64.1.

of rainfall. This geologically "normal" climate has been altered at long intervals by far briefer periods of polar ice and glaciation of the continents, even into middle and lower latitudes. In view of the geologic record of plant distribution in the past, especially in high latitudes of the Arctic and Antarctic, it is apparent that the present climate of the earth is not a logical point of departure for interpreting past ecologic conditions of the present land surfaces, nor probably in the shallower seas of the continental slopes. Detailed studies of the morphologic and taxonomic relations of fossil assemblages and additional information on the ecologic tolerance of living plants are greatly needed in further clarifying the paleoecologic record of climatic change.

REFERENCES

1. G. G. Simpson, "Periodicity in vertebrate evolution" (symposium on distribution of evolutionary explosions in geologic time), *Jour. Paleontology*, v. 26, p. 359–370 (1952).
2. C. L. Fenton, "Algae of the Pre-Cambrian and Early Paleozoic—symposium on paleobotanical taxonomy," *Am. Midland Naturalist*, v. 26, p. 259–264 (1946).
3. R. J. Russell, "Climatic change through the ages," in U.S. Department of Agriculture, *Climate and Man—Yearbook of Agriculture* (Washington, D.C.: U.S. Government Printing Office, 1941), p. 67–98.
4. M. N. Bose, "Microfossils from the Talchir Boulder Bed," *Indian Bot. Soc. Jour.*, v. 29, p. 1–46 (1950).
5. E. S. Barghoorn, "Age and environment—a survey of North American Tertiary floras in relation to paleoecology," *Jour. Paleontology*, v. 25, p. 736–744 (1951).

SECTION IX

EVOLUTION, EXTINCTION ENVIRONMENT, AND PALEOCLIMATOLOGY

The most universal quality is diversity.

Michel de Montaigne

Here we shall sample some writings on organic evolution, environmental influences on the biosphere, extinction, paleobiogeography, and paleoclimatology. Justice clearly cannot be done to these complexly interrelated subjects in the space available. The papers included here will provide perspective on the present state of the art, and those interested in further reading on any of the subjects here introduced will find a wealth of additional information in the Supplemental Reading.

Once again, the reader with no background in organic evolution is advised to consult an introductory paper by George Gaylord Simpson. The chapter titled "Theories of Evolution" from his book *Life of the Past* (1953c, pp. 140–150, see Supplemental Reading) is a clear and simple exposition of contemporary evolutionary theory, with suitable emphasis on the history of ideas. The motivated reader will certainly want to supplement such an introduction with readings of the more professionally oriented modern writings of Simpson and others, of Charles Darwin, and of Darwin's contemporary analysts Asa Gray and Louis Agassiz (see Supplemental Reading).

The introductory paper for this section, Reading Selection 65, "The Evolution of Living Systems," by Harvard University biologist Ernst Mayr, is a summary of modern views on that subject. Mayr emphasizes the enormous diversity of living systems, which he sees as the product of selective pressures to cope with the diversity of environmental conditions. The central problem of organic evolution, as Mayr sees it, is to explain how the descendants of common ancestors became different. Unfortunately, the comparative study of biological diversity has barely begun.

Reading Selection 66, "The Influence of the Environment," is by Yale University ecologist G. Evelyn Hutchinson. He sees the general nature and composition of the evolving biosphere as an inseparable aspect of the environment. He points out the dangers of becoming fascinated with details that contribute to, but do not of themselves compose (or supplant) the larger view.

Next we turn, all too briefly, to the problem of extinction. We begin with another essay by George Gaylord Simpson (Reading Selection 67), which surveys the growth of, and rationale for, various hypotheses that have purported to explain extinction. Simpson's central conclusion remains unmodified: "Our failure to be explicit about particular instances of extinction is not because such an event is . . . inexplicable in detail but . . . because there are so many possible detailed explanations that we cannot choose among them."

Interested readers will want to consult the three papers on extinction by N. D. Newell and the one by Van Valen and Sloan listed in the Supplemental Reading, as well as the extensive published record alluded to in those publications. Some of the seemingly catastrophic extinctions of record are also described in Reading Selection 56, by Newell; and, in Reading Selection 77, by Emiliani, who presents evidence to support the thesis that decreasing Late Cretaceous temperatures may have contributed to the decline of the dinosaurs. Here it must suffice to look at two well-documented examples of rather abrupt and extensive extinctions among two groups of marine organisms. The first of these is described in a paper written in 1922 by the late Carl Diener of the University of Vienna—the near extinction at the end of the Triassic of the coiled and complexly sutured cephalopods known as ammonites (Reading Selection 68). By latest Triassic time, the ammonites were reduced to a few species of the single genus *Phylloceras* (including the subgenus *Rhacophyllites*), from which they expanded again during the Jurassic, finally to vanish forever at the end of the Cretaceous.

In Reading Selection 69, professor emeritus M. N. Bramlette of the University of California deals with the abrupt extinction of a variety of minute floating plants (phytoplankton) at the very end of the Cretaceous Period in both North America and Europe. Because phytoplankton are the primary food producers in the sea, to explain their elimination is to explain a general collapse of the marine nutrient pyramid, with extinctions at all levels. Bramlette's suggested explanation is a reduced supply of mineral nutrients from erosionally reduced continents, combined with a low rate of turnover of nutrient-accumulating bottom waters because of reduced thermal gradients. This explanation was subsequently challenged and amplified in an exchange of views between Bramlette and Newell, but it remains as plausible an explanation as we have for a particular set of extinctions—those undergone by the marine biotas of latest Mesozoic time. The question, however, remains: Why did the dinosaurs become extinct at about the same time?

Next we introduce the discussion of paleoclimatology, beginning with the editor's paper "Paleobiogeography of the Marine Realm" (Reading Selection 70). This paper first considers the limitations of paleobiogeographic evidence and factors that affect the existence and distribution of marine organisms. Against this background, the interpretive basis of marine paleobiogeography is examined, and the identification of equatorial and polar positions in the geologic past is discussed. Brief consideration is then given to several marine biogeographical provinces, possible mechanisms for the distribution of marine organisms, and broad habitat conditions for different parts of the geologic column.

Linking naturally to the editor's paper is Reading Selection 71, "Paleoclimates," a thoughtful paper by paleontologist J. Wyatt Durham of the University of California. After briefly discussing the content, history, methods, and limitations of paleoclimatology, Durham reviews four examples from the published record. Separate consideration of biological evidence for the terrestrial and marine climates of the Tertiary of the northern hemisphere indicates approximate parallelism between the boundaries of the Tertiary and existing zones. Late Cretaceous climatic zonation based on oxygen isotopes points to similar parallelism of climatic boundaries and, as in the earlier Tertiary, a northward displacement of the tropical zone, reflecting generally milder climates in the northern hemisphere than now. A fourth example involves the complex problem of Pleistocene climatic zonation. Durham concludes with an objective discussion of generalities on paleoclimatology. It is widely believed that climate was more equable than now for most of Phanerozoic time; but our knowledge of ancient climates is still highly generalized and lacking in important detail.

The possible paleoclimatologic implications

of rock magnetism have been much discussed in recent years. Paths of magnetic polar migration through geologic time are consistent with both continental drift and major changes in the location of the earth's axis of rotation. One of the most persistent and effective critics of migration of the rotational poles has been paleontologist F. G. Stehli of Western Reserve University. For Reading Selection 72, therefore, we turn to his paper on "Permian Zoogeography and Its Bearing on Climate." There Stehli examines data on the distribution of several groups of Permian fossils that suggest a temperature zonation. He plots contours for the distribution, during Permian time in the northern hemisphere, of numbers of genera in two families of brachiopods. The zero points in the resulting diversity gradients are near the present north pole, with diversity increasing equatorward, as for living organisms. Interpreting his contours as conforming to the general trend of paleoisotherms, Stehli arrives at the conclusion that "large-scale latitudinal movements have not affected the northern continents since Permian time." Note that he does not rule out *longitudinal* drift of continents.

Against the background of Stehli's paper, Reading Selection 73 is especially interesting. It is a condensed study of Upper Paleozoic glacial deposits of the southern hemisphere, written by geologists Warren Hamilton of the U.S. Geological Survey and David Krinsley of the City University of New York. Hamilton and Krinsley review and illustrate the complex of criteria for glacial deposits, especially till fabrics, dropstones, and directionally striated pavements; and they introduce new evidence based on electron microscopy of the surface textures of sand grains from tills. Then they pull together the results of many previous workers to make a compelling case for Gondwana glaciation (which they much less convincingly squeeze into the Early Permian). During that glaciation, "ice flowed northwestward onto South America, southwestward onto South Africa, and northward onto India and Australia from directions in which there are now only tropical and temperate oceans and carried shield-type silicic plutonic rocks when it reached the continents." They reconstruct Gondwanaland—as they reason it might have been in Permian time—from whose position near the south pole, they infer, the constituent continents (except for Antarctica) drifted far across both longitude and latitude to their present southern-continent positions. They assert a similar drift for the northern continents, but do not develop evidence for such a conclusion.

Inasmuch as the evidence and conclusions of Stehli apply primarily to the northern hemisphere, and those of Hamilton and Kinsley primarily to the southern hemisphere, the possibility remains that neither view embodies the entire truth, or that neither view is wholly wrong. The strong contrast between the evidence for and against latitudinal displacement of continents as observed in different hemispheres has given rise to much (often heated) disagreement. Two of the more detached (and opposing) studies—both, unfortunately, too long to be included in this book—are those of Henno Martin (1961) and George Gaylord Simpson (1953a). Both are listed under Supplemental Reading. An excellent summary of the current state of knowledge bearing on continental drift is provided by Reading Selection 34, which might well be reviewed at this point. Southern hemisphere data indicating former continental connections are succinctly and fairly summarized by Woodford (1965, see Supplemental Reading).

Of particular interest from the historical viewpoint are those papers in the Supplemental Reading by Agassiz (1860) and Gray (1860), giving constrasting opinions on Darwin's ideas about the origin of species. Those publications may not be readily available, but they should be read by all those who have access to them. Similarly, Chamberlin's paper (1888) and one of the papers by Simpson (1953a) may be hard to come by, but the first offers an exceptional, early perspective on the characteristic traces of gravity-mass-movements, and the second is a clear and simple exposition of the principles of paleozoogeography.

Supplemental Reading

Agassiz, Louis, 1860, On the origin of species (*from* Contributions to the natural history of the United States, v. 3): Am. Jour. Sci., ser. 2, v. 30, p. 142–154.

Ager, D. V., 1967, Brachiopod paleoecology: Earth-Science Rev., v. 3, p. 157–179.

Brooks, C. E. P., 1949, Climate through the ages: New York, McGraw-Hill, 395 p.

Chamberlin, T. C., 1888, The rock-scorings of the great ice invasions: U.S. Geol. Survey 7th Ann. Rept., p. 155–248.

Cloud, P. E., Jr., 1959, Paleoecology—retrospect and prospect: Jour. Paleontology, v. 33, p. 926–962.

Cooper, G. A., and Alwyn Williams, 1952, Significance of the stratigraphic distribution of brachiopods: Jour. Paleontology, v. 26, p. 326–337.

Cox, Allan, and R. R. Doell, 1960, Review of paleomagnetism: Geol. Soc. America Bull., v. 71, p. 645–768.

Darwin, Charles, 1859, On the origin of species by natural selection, or the preservation of favored races in the struggle for life: John Murray, 502 p. (Recent paper back editions are available from Atheneum, Collier Books, Mentor Books, and Washington Square Press.)

Davis, A. G., and G. F. Elliott, 1957, The paleogeography of the London Clay sea: Geologists' Assoc. Proc., v. 68, pt. 4, p. 255–277.

DeBeer, Gavin, 1964, Atlas of evolution: Camden, N.J., Thomas Nelson and Sons, 202 p.

Doumani, G. A., and W. E. Long, 1962, The ancient life of the Antarctic: Scientific American Offprint 863, 13 p.

Edwards, W. N., 1955, The geographical distribution of past floras: Adv. Sci., v. 12, no. 46, p. 165–176.

Gray, Asa, 1860, Review of Darwin's theory on the origin of species by means of natural selection: Am. Jour. Sci., ser. 2, v. 29, p. 153–184.

Henderson, L. J., 1913, The fitness of the environment: New York, Macmillan, 317 p. (Reprinted by Beacon Press, 1958.)

Ladd, H. S., ed., 1957, Paleoecology (v. 2, Treatise on marine ecology and paleoecology): Geol. Soc. America Memoir 67, 1077 p.

Lewontin, R. C., ed., 1968, Population biology and evolution: Syracuse, N.Y., Syracuse University Press, 206 p.

Martin, Henno, 1961, The hypothesis of continental drift in the light of recent advances of geological knowledge in Brazil and in South West Africa (seventh A. L. du Toit Memorial Lecture): Geol. Soc. South Africa Quart. News Bull., v. 56, annexure, 47 p.

Moore, R. C., 1948, Evolution of the Crinoidea in relation to major paleogeographic changes in earth history: Internat. Geol. Cong. 18th Sess. Rept., pt. 12, p. 27–53.

Nairn, A. E. M., ed., 1961, Descriptive paleoclimatology: New York, John Wiley and Sons, Interscience Publications, 380 p.

———, ed., 1964, Problems in paleoclimatology: New York, John Wiley and Sons, Interscience Publications, 705 p.

Newell, N. D., 1962, Paleontological gaps and geochronology: Jour. Paleontology, v. 36, p. 592–610.

———, 1963, Crises in the history of life: Scientific American Offprint 867, 16 p.

———, 1966, Problems of geochronology: Acad. Nat. Sci. Philadelphia Proc., v. 118, p. 63–89.

Radforth, N. W., 1966, The ancient flora and continental drift: Royal Soc. Canada Spec. Pub. 9, p. 53–70.

Reid, E. M., and M. E. J. Chandler, 1933, The London clay flora: London, British Museum (Natural History), 561 p.

Schwarzbach, Martin, 1963, Climates of the past (translated by R. O. Muir): Princeton, N.J., D. Van Nostrand, 328 p. [From Martin Schwarzbach, 1961, Das Klima der Vorzeit (2d ed.): Stuttgart, Ferdinand Enke Verlag, 211 p.]

Shapley, Harlow, ed., 1953, Climatic change: Cambridge, Mass., Harvard University Press, 318 p.

Simpson, G. G., 1953a, Evolution and geography: Oregon State System of Higher Education, Condon Lectures, 64 p.

———, 1953b, The major features of evolution: New York, Columbia University Press, 434 p.

———, 1953c, Life of the past: New Haven, Conn., Yale University Press, 198 p.

Spjeldnaes, Nils, 1961, Ordovician climatic zones: Norsk geol. tidsskr., v. 41, pt. 1, p. 45–77.

Teichert, Curt, 1958, Cold- and deep-water coral banks: Am. Assoc. Petroleum Geologists Bull., v. 42, p. 1064–1082.

———, ed., 1952, Symposium sur les Séries de Gondwana: Internat. Geol. Cong. 19th Sess. Rept., 399 p.

Van Valen, Leigh, and R. E. Sloan, 1966, The extinction of the multituberculates: Systematic Zoology, v. 15, p. 261–277.

Woodford, A. O., 1965, Historical geology: San Francisco, W. H. Freeman and Company, 512 p. (p. 339– 366, Gondwanaland).

Woodring, W. P., 1957, Marine Pleistocene of California: Geol. Soc. America Mem. 67, v. 2, p. 589–597.

Wright, H. E., Jr., and D. G. Frey, eds., 1965, The Quaternary of the United States: Princeton, N.J., Princeton University Press, 922 p.

65

The Evolution of Living Systems

ERNST MAYR

1964

From *Proceedings of the National Academy of Sciences*, vol. 51, pp. 934–941, 1964. Reprinted with permission of the author and the National Academy of Sciences.

The number, kind, and diversity of living systems is overwhelmingly great, and each system, in its particular way, is unique. In the short time available to me, it would be quite futile to try to describe the evolution of viruses and fungi, whales and sequoias, or elephants and hummingbirds. Perhaps we can arrive at valid generalizations by approaching the process in a rather unorthodox way. Living systems evolve in order to meet the challenge of the environment. We can ask, therefore, what *are* the particular demands that organisms have to meet? . . .

The first challenge is to cope with a continuously changing and immensely diversified environment, the resources of which, however, are not inexhaustible. Mutation, the production of genetic variation, is the recognized means of coping with the diversity of the environment in space and time. Let us go back to the beginning of life. A primeval organism in need of a particular complex molecule in the primordial "soup" in which he lived, gained a special advantage by mutating in such a way that, after having exhausted this resource in his environment, he was able to synthesize the needed molecule from simpler molecules that were abundantly available. Simple organisms such as bacteria or viruses, with a new generation every 10 or 20 minutes and with enormous populations consisting of millions and billions of individuals, may well be able to adjust to the diversity and to the changes of the environment by mutation alone. In addition, they have numerous mechanisms of phenotypic adaptation. A capacity for mutation is perhaps the most important evolutionary characteristic of the simplest organisms.

More complex organisms, those with much longer generation times, much smaller population size, and particularly with a delicately balanced coadapted genotype, would find it hazardous to rely on mutation to cope with changes in the environment. The chances that the appropriate mutation would occur at the right time so that mutation alone could supply appropriate genetic variability for sudden changes in the environment of such organisms are virtually nil. What, then, is the prerequisite for the development of more complex living systems? It is the ability of different organisms to exchange "genetic information" with each other, the process the geneticist calls recombination, more popularly known as *sex*. The selective advantage of sex is so direct and so great that we can assume it arose at a very early stage in the history of life. Let us illustrate this advantage by a single example. A primitive organism able to synthesize amino acid *A*, but dependent on the primordial soup for amino acid *B*, and another organism able to synthesize amino acid *B*, but dependent on the primordial soup for amino acid A, by genetic recombination would be able to produce offspring with the ability to synthesize both amino acids and thus able to live in an environment deficient in both of them. Genetic recombination can speed up evolutionary change enormously and assist in emancipation from the environment.

Numerous mechanisms evolved in due time to make recombination increasingly precise in every respect. The result was the evolution of elaborately constructed chromosomes; of diploidy through two homologous chromosome sets, one derived from the father, the other from the mother; of an elaborate process of meiosis during which homologous chromosomes exchange pieces so that the chromosomes of father and mother are transmitted to the grandchildren not intact, but as newly reconstituted chromosomes with a novel assortment of genes. These mechanisms regulate genetic recombination among individuals, by far the major source of genotypic variability in higher organisms.

The amount of genetic diversity within a single interbreeding population is regulated by a balance of mechanisms that favor inbreeding and such that favor outbreeding. The extremes, in this respect, are much greater among plants and lower animals than among higher animals. Extreme inbreeding (self-fertilization) and extreme outbreeding (regular hybridization with other species) are rare in higher animals. Outbreeders and inbreeders are drastically different living systems in which numerous adaptations are correlated in a harmonious manner.

The result of sexuality is that ever-new combinations of genes can be tested by the environment in every generation. The enormous power of the process of genetic recombination by sexual reproduction becomes evident if we remember that in sexually reproducing species no two individuals are genetically identical. We must admit, sex is wonderful!

However, even sex has its drawbacks. To make this clear, let me set up for you the model of a universe consisting entirely of genetically different individuals that are *not* organized into species. Any individual may engage in genetic recombination with any other individual in this model. New gene complexes will be built up occasionally, as a result of chance, that have unique adaptive advantages. Yet, because in this particular evolutionary system there is no guarantee that such an exceptional individual will engage in genetic recombination *only* with individuals having a similarly adaptive genotype, it is inevitable that this exceptionally favorable genotype will eventually be destroyed by recombination during reproduction.

How can such a calamity be avoided? There are two possible means, and nature has adopted both. One method is to abandon sexual reproduction. Indeed we find all through the animal kingdom, and even more often among plants, a tendency to give up sexuality temporarily or permanently in order to give a successful genotype the opportunity to replicate itself unchanged, generation after generation, taking advantage of its unique superiority. The history of the organic world makes it clear, however, that such an evolutionary opportunist reaches the end of his rope sooner or later. Any sudden change of the environment will convert his genetic advantage into a handicap and, not having the ability to generate new genetic variability through recombination, he will inevitably become extinct.

The other solution is the "invention," if I may be pardoned for using this anthropomorphic term, of the biological species. The species is a protective system guaranteeing that only such individuals interbreed and exchange genes as have largely the same genotypes. In this system there is no danger that breakdown of genotypes will result from genetic recombination, because all the genes present in the gene pool of a species have been previously tested, through many generations, for their ability to recombine harmoniously. This does not preclude considerable variability within a species. Indeed, all our studies make us realize increasingly how vast is the genetic variability within even comparatively uniform species. Nevertheless, the basic developmental and homeostatic systems are the same, in principle, in all members of a species.

By simply explaining the biological meaning of species, I have deliberately avoided the tedious question of how to define a species. Let me add that the species can fulfill its function of protecting well-integrated, harmonious genotypes only by having some mechanisms (called "isolating mechanisms") by which interbreeding with individuals of other species is prevented.

In our design of a perfect living system, we have now arrived at a system that can cope with the diversity of its environment and that has the means to protect its coadapted, harmonious genotype. As described, this well-balanced system seems so conservative as to offer no opportunity for the origin of additional new systems. This conclusion, if true, would bring us into a real conflict with the evolutionary history of the world. The paleontologists tell us that the number of species has increased steadily during geological time and that the multiplication of species, in order to compensate for the extinction of species, must occur at a prodigious rate. If the species is as well-balanced, well-protected, and as delicate as we have described it, how can one species be divided into two? This serious problem stumped Darwin completely, and evolutionists have argued about it for more than one hundred years.

Eventually it was shown that there are two possible solutions, or perhaps I should say two normally occurring solutions. The first mode occurs very frequently in plants, but is rare in the animal kingdom. It consists in the doubling of the chromosome set so that the new individual is no longer a diploid with two sets of homologous chromosomes, but, let us say, a tetraploid with four sets of chromosomes, or if the process continues, a higher polyploid with an even higher chromosome number. The production of a polyploid constitutes instantaneous speciation; it produces in a single step an incompatibility between the parental and the daughter species.

The other mode of speciation is simplicity itself. Up to now, we have spoken of the species as something rigid, uniform, and monolithic. Actually, natural species, particularly those that are widespread, consist like the human species of numerous local populations and races, all of them differing more or less from each other in their genetic composition. Some of these populations, particularly those at the periphery of the species range, are completely isolated from each other and from the main body of the species. Let us assume that one of these populations is prevented for a long time from exchanging genes with the rest of the species, because the isolating barrier—be it a mountain range, a desert, or a waterway—is impassable. Through the normal processes of mutation, recombination, and selection, the gene pool of the isolated population becomes more and more different from that of the rest of the species, finally reaching a level of distinctness that normally characterizes a different species. This process, called "geographic speciation," is by far the most widespread mode of speciation in the animal kingdom and quite likely the major pathway of speciation also in plants.

Before such an incipient species qualifies as a genuine new species, it must have acquired two properties during its genetic rebuilding. First, it must have acquired isolating mechanisms that prevent it from interbreeding with the parental species when the two again come into contact. Secondly, it must also have changed sufficiently in its demands on the environment, in its niche utilization (as the ecologist would say), so that it can live side by side with mother and sister species without succumbing to competition.

KINDS OF LIVING SYSTEMS

In our discussion of the evolution of living systems, I have concentrated, up to now, on major unit processes or phenomena, such as the role of mutation, of genetic recombination and sex, of the biological species, and of the process of speciation. These processes give us the mechanisms that make diversification of the living world possible, but they do not explain why there should be such an enormous variety of life on earth. There are surely more than three million species of animals and plants living on this earth, perhaps more than five million. What principle permits the coexistence of such a wealth of different kinds? This question troubled Darwin, and he found an answer for it that has stood the test of time. Two species, in order to coexist, must differ in their utilization of the resources of the environment in a way that reduces competition. During speciation there is a strong selective premium on becoming different from pre-existing species by trying out new ecological niches. This experimentation in new adaptations and new specializations is the principal evolutionary significance of the process of speciation. Once in a long while one of these new species finds the door to a whole new adaptive kingdom. Such a species, for instance, was the original ancestor of the most successful of all groups of organisms, the insects, now counting more than a million species. The birds, the bony fishes, the flowering plants, and all other kinds of animals and plants, all originated ultimately from a single ancestral species. Once a species discovers an empty adaptive zone, it can speciate and radiate until this zone is filled by its descendants.

To avoid competition, organisms can diverge in numerous ways. Dr. Hutchinson has mentioned size. Not only has there been a trend toward large size in evolution, but also other species and genera, often in the same lines, have evolved toward decreased size. Small size is by no means always a primitive trait.

Specialization for a very narrow niche is perhaps the most common evolutionary trend. This is the characteristic approach of the parasites. Literally thousands of parasites are restricted to a single host, indeed restricted to a small part of the body of the host. There are, for instance, three species of mites that live on different parts of the honey bee. Such extreme specialization is rare if not absent in the higher plants, but is characteristic for insects and explains their prodigious rate of speciation. The deep sea, lightless caves, and the interstices between sand grains along the seashore are habitats leading to specialization.

The counterpart of the specialist is the generalist. Individuals of such species have a broad tolerance to all sorts of variations of climate, habitat, and food. It seems difficult to become a successful generalist, but the very few species that can be thus classified are widespread and abundant. Man is the generalist par excellence with his ability to live in all latitudes and altitudes, in deserts and in forest, and to subsist on the pure meat diet of the Eskimos or on an almost pure vegetable diet. There are indications that generalists have unusually diversified gene pools and, as a result, produce rather high numbers of inferior genotypes by genetic recombination. Widespread and successful species of *Drosophila* seem to have more lethals than rare or restricted species. It is not certain that this observation can be applied to man, but this much is certain, that populations of man display much genetic variation. In man we do not have the sharply contrasting types ("morphs") that occur in many polymorphic populations of animals and plants. Instead we find rather complete intergradation of mental, artistic, manual, and physical capacities (and their absence). Yet, whether continuous or discontinuous, genetic variation has long been recognized as a useful device by which a species can broaden its tolerance and enlarge its niche. That the same is true for man is frequently forgotten. Our educators, for instance, have tended far too long to ignore man's genetic diversity and have tried to force identical educational schedules on highly diverse talents. Only within recent years have we begun to realize that equal opportunity calls for differences in education. Genetically different individuals do not have equal opportunities unless the environment is diversified.

Every increase in the diversity of the environment during the history of the world has resulted in a veritable burst of speciation. This is particularly easily demonstrated for changes in the biotic environment. The rise of the vertebrates was followed by a spectacular development of trematodes, cestodes, and other vertebrate parasites. The insects, whose history goes back to the Paleozoic nearly 400 million years ago, did not really become a great success until the flowering plants (angiosperms) evolved some 150 million years ago. These plants provided such an abundance of new adaptive zones and niches that the insects entered a truly explosive stage in their evolution. By now three quarters of the known species of animals are insects, and their total number (including undiscovered species) is estimated to be as high as two or three million.

PARENTAL CARE

Let me discuss just one additional aspect of the diversity of living systems, care of the offspring. At one extreme we have the oysters that do nothing whatsoever for their offspring. They cast literally millions of eggs and male gametes into the sea, providing the opportunity for the eggs to be fertilized. Some of the fertilized eggs will settle in a favorable place and produce new oysters. The statistical probability that this will happen is small, owing to the adversity of the environment, and although a single full-grown oyster may produce more than 100 million eggs per breeding season, it will have on the average only one descendant. That numerous species of marine organisms practice this type of reproduction, many of them enormously abundant and many of them with an evolutionary history going back several hundred million years, indicates that this shotgun method of thrusting offspring into the world is surprisingly successful.

How different is reproduction in species with parental care! This always requires a drastic reduction in the number of offspring, and it usually means greatly enlarged yolk-rich eggs, it means the development of brood pouches, nests, or even internal placentae, and it often means the formation of a pair-bond to secure the participation of the male in the raising of the young. The ultimate development along this line of specialization is unquestionably man, with his enormous prolongation of childhood.

Behavioral characteristics are an important component of parental care, and our treatment of the evolution of living systems would be incomplete if we were to omit reference to behavior and to the central nervous system. The germ plasm of a fertilized egg contains in its DNA a coded genetic program that guides the development of the young organism and its reactions to the environment. However, there are drastic differences among species concerning the precision of the inherited information and the extent to which the individual can benefit from experience. The young in some species appear to be born with a genetic program containing an almost complete set of ready-made, predictable responses to the stimuli of the environment. We say of such an organism that his behavior is unlearned, innate, instinctive, that his behavior program is closed. The other extreme is provided by organisms that have a great capacity to benefit from experience, to learn how to react to the environment, to continue adding "information" to their behavior program, which consequently is an open program.

Let us look a little more closely at open and closed programs and their evolutionary potential. We are all familiar with the famous story of imprinting explored by Konrad Lorenz. Young geese or ducklings just hatched from the egg will adopt as parent any moving object (but preferably one making appropriate noises). If hatched in an incubator, they will follow their human caretaker and not only consider him their parent but consider themselves as belonging to the human species. For instance, upon reaching sexual maturity they may tend to display to and court a human individual rather than another goose. The reason for this seemingly absurd behavior is that the hatching gosling does not have an inborn knowledge of the Gestalt of its parent; all it has is readiness to fill in this Gestalt into its program. Its genetically coded program is open; it provides for a readiness to adopt as parent the first moving object seen after hatching. In nature, of course, this is invariably the parent.

Let us contrast this open program with the completely closed one of another bird, the parasitic cowbird. The mother cowbird, like the European cuckoo, lays her eggs in the nests of various kinds of songbirds such as yellow warblers, vireos, or song sparrows, then to abandon them completely. The young cowbird is raised by its foster parents, and yet, as soon as he is fledged, he seeks other young cowbirds and gathers into large flocks with them. For the rest of his life, he associates with members of his own species. The Gestalt of his own species is firmly imbedded in the genetic program with which the cowbird is endowed from the very beginning. It is—at least in respect to species recognition—a completely closed program. In other respects, much of the behavioral program of the cowbird is open, that is, ready to incorporate experiences by learning. Indeed, there is probably no species of animals, not even among the protozoans, that does not, at least to some extent, derive benefit from learning processes. On the whole, and certainly among the higher vertebrates, there has been a tendency to replace rigidly closed programs by open ones or, as the student of animal behavior would say, to replace rigidly instinctive behavior by learned behavior. This change is not a change in an isolated character. It is part of a whole chain reaction of biological changes. Since man is the culmination of this particular evolutionary trend, we naturally have a special interest in this trend. Capacity for learning can best be utilized if the young is associated with someone from whom to learn, most conveniently his parents. Consequently there is strong selection pressure in favor of extending the period of childhood. And since parents can take care of only a limited number of young, there is selection in favor of reducing the number of offspring. We have here the paradoxical situation that parents with a smaller number of young may nevertheless have a greater number of grandchildren, because mortality among well cared for and well-prepared young may be reduced even more drastically than the birth rate.

The sequence of events I have just outlined describes one of the dominating evolutionary trends in the primates, a trend that reaches its extreme in man. A broad capacity for learning is an indispensable prerequisite for the development of culture, of ethics, of religion. But the oyster proves that there are avenues to biological success other than parental care and the ability to learn.

One final point: how can we explain the harmony of living systems? Attributes of an organism are not independent variables but interdependent components of a single system. Large brain size, the ability to learn, long childhood, and many other attributes of man, all belong together; they are parts of a single harmoniously functioning system. And so it is with all animals and plants. The modern population geneticist stresses the same point. The genes of a gene pool have been brought together for harmonious cooperation, they are coadapted. This harmony and perfection of nature (to which the Greeks referred in the word *Cosmos*) has impressed philosophers from the very beginning. Yet there seems to be an unresolved conflict between this harmony of nature and the apparent randomness of evolutionary processes, beginning with mutation and comprising also much of reproduction and mortality. Opponents of the Darwinian theory of evolution have claimed that the conflict between the harmony of nature and the apparent haphazardness of evolutionary processes could *not* be resolved.

The evolutionist, however, points out that this objection is valid only if evolution is a one-step process. In reality, every evolutionary change involves two steps. The first is the production of new genetic diversity through mutation, recombination, and related processes. On this level randomness is indeed predominant. The second step, however—selection of those individuals that are to make up the breeding population of the next generation—is largely determined by genetically controlled adaptive properties. This is what natural selection means; only that which maintains or increases the harmony of the system will be selected for.

The concept of natural selection, the heart of the evolutionary theory, is still widely misunderstood. Natural selection says no more and no less than that certain genotypes have a greater than average statistical chance to survive and reproduce under given conditions. Two aspects of this concept need emphasis. The first is that selection is not a theory but a straightforward fact. Thousands of experiments have proved that the probability that an individual will survive and reproduce is not a matter of accident, but a consequence of its genetic endowment. The second point is that selective superiority gives only a statistical advantage. It increases the probability of survival and reproduction, other things being equal.

Natural selection is measured in terms of the contribution a genotype makes to the genetic composition of the next generation. Reproductive success of a wild organism is controlled by the sum of the adaptive properties possessed by the individual, including his resistance to weather, his ability to escape enemies, and to find food. General superiority in these and other properties permits an individual to reach the age of reproduction.

In civilized man these two components of selective value, adaptive superiority and reproductive success, no longer coincide. The individuals with above average genetic endowment do not necessarily make an above average contribution to the gene pool of the next generation. Indeed the shiftless, improvident individual who has a child every year is sure to add more genes to the gene pool of the next generation than those who carefully plan the size of their families. Natural selection has no answer to this predicament. The separation in the modern human society of mere reproductive success from genuine adaptedness poses an extremely serious problem for man's future.

In this brief discussion of the evolution of living systems, I have been unable to do more than outline basic problems. We are beginning to understand the role of mutation, of genetic recombination, and of natural selection. The comparative study of the overwhelming multitude of diverse living systems has only begun. Because much of our environment consists of living systems, their study is of great importance. Indeed it is a prerequisite for understanding ourselves, since man also is a living system.

66

The Influence of the Environment

G. EVELYN HUTCHINSON

1964

From *Proceedings of the National Academy of Sciences*, vol. 51, pp. 930–934, 1964. Reprinted with permission of the author and the National Academy of Sciences.

The biosphere, or part of the earth within which organisms live, is a region in which temperatures range not far from those at which water is liquid. It receives a radiation flux of wavelength >3200 A from the sun or has the products of photosynthesis made available by gravity as in the dark depths of the ocean. Numerous interfaces are present in most parts of the biosphere. It is geochemically characterized by atmophil elements in relative quantities such that both oxidized (Eh $\simeq$ 0.5 volt) and quite reduced (Eh $\simeq$ 0.0 volt) regions are both easily possible often within a few millimeters of each other as in lake sediments. Conditions for such a region on a planet are fairly critical, and would probably always involve loss of the initial gaseous phase with reformation of the atmosphere from frozen or chemically combined material.

Chemically, living organisms are mainly made of cosmically common, light, easily soluble atmophil and lithophil elements. The special properties of the several important elements, such as hydrogen bridge formation, the formation of long carbon chains, the possible existence of —COOH and of $—NH_2$ in the same molecule, the easily oxidized and reduced system —SH HS— $\rightleftarrows$ —S—S—, the high energy phosphate bond and various other less striking properties exhibited by common biophil elements (of which phosphorus, with an odd atomic number between Si and S, is the rarest) are obviously fundamental. Without these properties life as we know it would be impossible.

The reduction of magnesium concentration in the earth's crust, as compared with the mantle, and the consequent approximate equalization of the amounts of Na, K, Mg, and Ca provide a geochemical rather than a purely chemical example of the "fitness of the environment" to use Henderson's phrase. However, it is difficult to be sure we know we are talking sense in this field without comparative instances, or whether we are involved in problems like the insoluble metaphysical question of childhood, Why am I not someone else? The exploration of the surface of Mars may give, long before the National Academy is celebrating another centenary, some welcome contrasting information. Meanwhile it is reasonable to suppose that extreme rarity and extreme insolubility, leading to a very low concentration of some elements within living tissues, do limit their functional importance.

If we consider an average mammalian liver cell of diameter about 23.4 μ, of volume, assuming a spherical form, of about 6700 μ^3, and of mass, if a density rather more than unity be assumed, of about 7×10^{-9} gm, we can obtain from published analyses [1] a rough idea of the mean number of atoms per cell as follows.

$>10^{14}$	**H, O**	
10^{12}–10^{14}	**C, N**	
10^{10}–10^{12}	**S, P, Na, K, Mg, Cl, Ca, Fe,** Si	
10^{8}–10^{10}	**Zn,** Li, Rb, **Cu, Mn,** Al, Fe, Br	
10^{6}–10^{8}	Sn, Ti, Mo, **Co, I,** Pb, Ag, B, Sr, Ni, V, Sc, Cd, **?Cr, Se**	
10^{4}–10^{6}	U, Hg, Be . . .	40 additional reactive natural elements probably in these rows.
10^{2}–10^{4}	. . . .	
10^{0}–10^{2}	Ra	

The elements known to have a function in mammals, other than in maintaining the integrity of skeletal structures (as do F, and possibly [2] Sr and Ba), are given in boldface type. It is evident that the probability of an element having a function decreases with decreasing concentration. When such a table was published twenty years ago, there were 9 elements in the 10^6–10^8 atoms per cell category with only cobalt functional; now there are analytic data for 14 and a presumption that chromium and selenium, which with iodine are now known to be functional, fall here. Evidently about a quarter of the elements with 10^6–10^8 atoms per cell may have a function. In the next two rows we might guess probabilities of 0.1–0.01 of function. This may imply one or two surprises. What is interesting is that although cobalt is enriched relative to nickel in liver, as in nearly all tissues of higher animals, over its concentration in the lithosphere, or for that matter in plants, it is still little more abundant than lead and less so than molybdenum. To use an element such as cobalt the biochemistry of utilization must be reasonably specific. There are plenty of atoms of various kinds around in such concentrations that they could play a part as antimetabolites as well as significant functional roles in enzyme systems. It is possible that this sets the lower limits of concentration at which biochemically significant substances occur. There might be too many commoner accidental and potentially interfering materials around for any very important substance to work practically at 10^4 atoms or molecules per cell. The variety of elementary composition may thus set the standard of purity within which biochemical evolution has occurred.

We may roughly divide most of the biosphere into a purely liquid part, and solid-liquid and solid-gaseous parts, corresponding to (1) the open ocean, (2) the sea bottom, margin, and inland waters, and (3) the colonized land surfaces. In the first, it is possible that iron, which is almost insoluble under oxidizing conditions in inorganic aqueous systems, usually limits the amount of living matter, while in the last, water supply is the most important determinant. In the water-solid systems, including lakes and neritic marine environments, phosphorous, nitrogen, and other elements may be limiting.

The whole plant community can, since it is interconnected through the CO_2 and O_2 of the atmosphere, be regarded as an extremely inefficient (efficiency not much more than 0.1% in most cases in nature) photosynthetic machine. The details of the biochemistry of photosynthesis have been elucidated in recent years in most impressive studies by various investigators. We are, however, still rather ignorant of the quantitative details of the over-all biogeochemical process. It is evident that both the ocean [3] and the plant cover [4] of the continents play a major part in regulating the CO_2 content of the atmosphere, but this regulation is not sufficient to prevent a slow rise [5] due partly, but perhaps not entirely, to the production of the gas by combustion of fossil fuels.

The use of plant material by animals as food is ordinarily a much more efficient process than the photosynthetic capture of the radiation flux from the sun, and allows the existence of a considerable mass of and extraordinary diversity of animals. This diversity is however clearly in part due to the diversity and structural complexity of higher plants. A large part of contemporary ecological research is devoted to elucidation of the general principles that permit the coexistence of very large numbers of species together in a single locality.

The complexity of communities has fascinated naturalists from before Darwin, who described it classically. Only recently has it become apparent what a wealth of quantitative relationships can be seen in the complex structure. Remarkable and quite diverse types of theory, some of which have proved of considerable value in empirical studies, have been developed to deal with this sort of problem, though we still have an enormous amount to learn. While ordinarily the principle of competitive exclusion [6], which can be phrased in abstract geometrical terms as the statement that two coexisting species do not occupy the same niche, is a good point of departure so long as it is not applied in too naive a manner, the claim may be made that the principle is inapplicable in practice because there would never be a possibility of demonstrating that the niche requirements of two species were, or were not, exactly the same. Actually what is involved is the question as to whether in competition two species could be so nearly equivalent that one would not replace the other in any reasonable time, such as the lifetime of an observer, the period of existence of relevant scientific records, or the period during which the average state of the habitat remained unchanged. The possibility that two competing species might be exactly matched contradicts what has been called the axiom of inequality [6], that two natural bodies are never exactly the same. The possibility that in very large populations where the dynamics are essentially deterministic, they might be so nearly evenly matched that competition would proceed too slowly to detect, has been seriously suggested for phytoplankton associations, the multispecific nature of which seems otherwise paradoxical [7]. In this, as in other aspects of ecology, the role of time, or of the rates at which things can happen, has been inadequately studied.

In general the speed at which things happen in a very small organism will depend on physical processes of which ordinary diffusion is likely to be the most critical. In larger organisms the celestial mechanics of the solar system, giving days, tidal periods, lunar months, and years, can introduce apparently arbitrary rates into the life of an organism which will interact with rates set by small-scale physical processes. The extent of various kinds of biological clocks is one of the most important phenomena recently discovered in biology. The evidence from odd cases in which periodic processes occur pathologically [8] suggests that the full significance of the gearing of organisms, including ourselves, to the cycle of day and night is not even yet apparent. Moreover a case perhaps could be made for supposing that sometimes clocks can exist which, having evolved in relation to the environment, are no longer set to be synchronous with external periodicities. The human female reproductive cycle, shared by a number of primates, has long suggested a lunar month in spite of the lack of synchrony. Possibly it represents a lunar clock no longer set by the moon; an effect of moonlight on the reproductive cycle of some tropical mammals, including prosimians, has been noted [9].

Even more extraordinary are the clocks regulating the three species of seventeen-year and the three of thirteen-year cicadas [10]. Here apparently synchrony is adaptive, so that three species bear the brunt of predation, with the different broods emerging so irregularly that there is little chance of a permanent increase in predator population.

Individual cases of a striking kind can, as these, be given at least hypothetical, though very plausible, explanations. We still lack, however, a really clear understanding of the relationship of rates of living and of evolution to the rates of physical change in the universe.

There are two extreme possible ways of evolution in relation to time. Since natural selection will go faster when generations succeed each other faster, one way is the evolution of progressively smaller and more rapidly reproducing organisms. However, the smaller an organism the less it can do. An alternative path gives large, slower reproducing organisms in which, when a nervous system capable of learning is developed, a premium is put on experience. Even in organisms such as plants, which do not learn in the ordinary sense of the word, a perennial can wait about at least metaphorically for a favorable season for reproduction. In the first case the time scale is set by the physical processes of diffusion; in the other extreme case, presumably by some function of the rate at which various things, such as learning, can occur.

In a varying environment, the time taken to learn about a seasonal or otherwise infrequent event will partly depend on the incidence of that event. Some sea birds seem to need several years' experience to learn how to get food for their chick or chicks [11]. The advantage of this learning must be great enough to offset the extra prereproductive mortality, which inevitably accompanies a delay in breeding.

It has recently been suggested that the great intraspecific competition on the limited feeding grounds near nesting sites puts a premium on expertness during the reproductive season and, until this has been acquired, attempts at breeding are wasteful and, to some extent, dangerous. Where mortality is lowest, possibly of the order of 3 per cent per annum in the albatrosses, the period prior to reproduction may be nine years, even though these immense birds have reached maximum size in their first year. In a case like this, learning can obviously only take place during the special period of reproduction, and expertness takes several years to acquire. But it is not clear why human learning of perennial activities should take so long when most of the individual events in our sensory and nervous systems take times measured in milliseconds, rather than months, while on the motor side, a good pianist can play ten notes a second if he has real cause to do so.

In the present and most legitimate excitement over the reading of genetic codes, it is important to remember that lexicography and grammar are not literature, even though the fixing of meaning to symbols and the rules of their ordering make literature possible. The literature of living organisms is very varied, and is perhaps most exciting in the epic or evolutionary forms in which organisms are continually changing in response to selection by a changing environment. Deduction from the possible molecular states of organisms is hardly likely to be an efficient way of exploration; an empirical approach to events is equally needed. A real ecology of time, relating the rates at which things happen in organisms, whether rapid physiological changes or the very slow changes of phylogenesis to the rates of the outside world, is so far only approached at the short-time physiological end. In the immediate future, as argon-potassium dating develops, it will be possible to study evolutionary rates of certain well-known phyletic lines, notably in the Tertiary mammals, with greatly increased precision. Details of variation in evolutionary rates will become accessible and should add enormously to our knowledge of organic change under long time spans.

REFERENCES

1. G. E. Hutchinson, *Quart. Rev. Biology*, v. 18, p. 331 (1943); with additional data for Sc: G. Beck, *Mikrochemie ver. Mikrochim. Acta*, v. 34, p. 62 (1948); for Be, B, Co, Hg: R. M. Forbes, A. R. Cooper, and H. H. Mitchell, *Jour. Biol. Chemistry*, v. 209, p. 857 (1954); for Si: A. O. Gettler and C. J. Umberger, *Am. Jour. Clin. Pathol.*, Tech. Sec., v. 9, p. 1 (1945); for F: S. K. Gushchin, *Voprosy Pitaniya*, v. 19, p. 71 (1960); for I: M. J. Gustun, *Voprosy Pitaniya*, v. 18, p. 80 (1959); for As: M. A. Herman, T. J. Wiktor, and A. A. van Hee, *Bull. Agr. Congo Belge*, v. 51, p. 403 (1960); for Br: Giovanni Moruzzi, *Italiana Biologia Sperimentale Boll.*, v. 11, p. 725 (1936); and for Cd: A. O. Voinar, *Akad. Nauk SSSR Konf. Mikroelement Trudy*, v. 1950, p. 580 (1952).
2. O. Rygh, *Soc. Chimie biol. Bull.*, v. 31, p. 1052 (1949).
3. R. Revelle and H. E. Suess, *Tellus*, v. 9, p. 18 (1957); B. Bolin and E. Eriksson, in *The Atmosphere and the Sea in Motion* (Rochester, N.Y.: Rockefeller Institute Press, 1959), p. 130; E. Eriksson and P. Welander, *Tellus*, v. 8, p. 155 (1956).
4. H. Lieth, *Jour. Geophys. Research*, v. 68, p. 3887 (1963); B. Bolin and C. D. Keeling, *Jour. Geophys. Research*, v. 68, p. 3899 (1963).

5. G. S. Callendar, *Tellus*, v. 10, p. 243 (1958); B. Bolin and C. D. Keeling, *Jour. Geophys. Research*, v. 68, p. 3899 (1963).
6. G. Hardin, *Science*, v. 131, p. 1292 (1960).
7. G. A. Riley, in *Marine Biology 1* (Washington, D.C.: American Institute of Biological Sciences, 1963), p. 70; G. E. Hutchinson, *Am. Naturalist*, v. 95, p. 137 (1961).
8. Curt P. Richter, [U.S.] *Natl. Acad. Sci. Proc.*, v. 46, p. 1506 (1960).
9. U. M. Cowgill, A. Bishop, R. J. Andrew and G. E. Hutchinson, [U.S.] *Natl. Acad. Sci. Proc.*, v. 48, p. 238 (1962); J. L. Harrison, *Raffles Mus. Bull.*, v. 24, p. 109 (1952).
10. R. D. Alexander and T. E. Moore, *Univ. Michigan Mus. Zool. Misc. Publ.* 121, p. 1 (1962); H. S. Dybas, and M. Lloyd, *Ecology*, v. 43, p. 444 (1962).
11. N. P. Ashmole, *Ibis*, v. 103b, p. 458 (1963).

67

Extinction

GEORGE GAYLORD SIMPSON

1953

In the grand pattern of evolution nothing is more dramatic than the prevalence of extinction. The earth is a charnel house for species as for individuals. If this were not so, progressive evolution would have slowed or stopped long since. The total energy available for life is limited, and in the long run some groups must become extinct if others are to arise. Romer (1949a) remarks that "extinction is the common lot, survival the exception," and he estimates that perhaps not more than one per cent of middle Mesozoic tetrapods have living descendants. The problems of extinction are as pertinent to the whole course of evolution as the problems of origination. Extinction has repeatedly been discussed as it has affected given groups or in general, for instance recently by Colbert (1949a) and Arambourg (1950), whose reviews of the subject have been constantly useful in preparing this chapter. In spite of much attention to the subject, there is a lack of decisiveness and explicitness in most discussions of it. This treatment will not be an exception, but it will attempt to point out why we can seldom be decisive and explicit.

Four sorts of fully general theories of extinction stand out among more detailed suggestions. One sort maintains that extinction is a kind of momentum effect, that organisms evolve themselves out of existence. Another draws from the racial life cycle analogy the idea that races have a fixed span, as have individuals, and finally die of old age. The third sees the environment as executioner, slaughtering hapless populations. The fourth considers extinction as a derangement of coordination between organism and environment, a failure of adaptive response. The third sort of theory need not be discussed apart from the last, which, as well as the first two, will receive separate consideration. There are also some special topics which have aspects, at least, related to extinction and which will be briefly reviewed in this chapter, particularly relicts, blind alleys, and the irreversibility of evolution.

From *The Major Features of Evolution* by George Gaylord Simpson, pp. 281–303. Columbia University Press, 1953. Reprinted with permission of the author and the publisher.

HYPERTELY

Evolution has some characteristics that resemble inertia and momentum. A few students have gone so far as to take these indications literally, naively applying to evolutionary sequences the classical laws of mechanical motion. Abel (1928) did this rather elaborately and justified it by saying that organisms function, function is activity, activity is motion, therefore—! This is such obvious semantic double-talk that it need not detain us. Nevertheless, the thought that somehow evolutionary momentum carries trends to inadaptive lengths and causes extinction has been expressed so often and with such a wealth of supposed examples that it cannot be ignored. Such an effect produces hypertely, a term that literally means that change has been carried too far. It is noteworthy that critics of selectionist theory in general and of the modern synthetic theory in particular use hypertely as their crushing argument. Some leading proponents of this theory have also frankly admitted that hypertely is a major stumbling block. Thus Haldane (1932) despaired that such phenomena "are not obviously explicable on any theory of evolution whatever," Waddington (1939) emphasized that no explanation in terms of selection had been offered, and Huxley (1942) essentially repeated Waddington's observation. On the other hand, I (1944a) tried to show that the synthetic theory (which involves a great deal more than selection) can well account for claimed cases of hypertely, and I believe there is a growing consensus to this effect.

Almost any case in which size, structure, or habit (although this is less often mentioned) is carried to extremes may be cited as hypertely, especially if it is bizarre to our human eyes. (To a lemur, man must be strongly hypertelic.) The assumption is that in true hypertely, the extreme is inadaptive and did or will lead to extinction. Cuénot (1925, 1951) mentions as hypertelic the displays of male pheasants, peacocks, and birds of paradise, the horns of various beetles, peculiar appendages in Hemiptera, the hornlike canines of *Babirussa,* and numerous other oddities.

At the outset, the fact that the organisms bearing the hypertelic structures just mentioned are alive and doing well (except as molested by man) casts some doubt on the idea that hypertely is inherently inadaptive and is a or *the* cause of extinction. Moreover, most or all of these hypertelic structures do have definite uses to the organisms, whether we approve the uses (e.g., to stimulate females) or think them performed as well as possible (e.g., by the pseudo-horns of *Babirussa*). As to size, the most hypertelic of all organisms, whales, are also living and their size is apparently useful to them. As to habit, the courtship procedures of some birds or the social organizations of some insects seem about as hypertelic as possible and yet are clearly useful to those concerned. Such observations enjoin a certain caution in assuming that if extinct animals had some peculiar feature, it caused their extinction by hypertely.

Classic examples of hypertely in extinct animals, cited over and over again in almost all discussions either of hypertely, or of extinction, are the coiling of *Gryphaea,* the antlers of *Megaloceros,* the elongated dorsal spines of some pelycosaurs, and the canines of the sabertooths. The sabertooth example is fictitious, and the pelycosaur dorsal protuberance had a probable adaptive significance. Romer (1949a) also adds that the "spinescent" pelycosaurs were very flourishing in their time and became extinct no more rapidly than their spineless relatives. The cases of *Gryphaea* and *Megaloceros* are sufficiently interesting and well analyzed to treat them as key examples of hypertely and as evidence on its nature and causes.

Gryphaea was a Mesozoic pelecypod, a form-genus derived with iteration from a conservative oysterlike stock. In it, one valve became progressively more tightly coiled until "in some individuals the umbo of the left valve actually pressed against the outer surface of the right valve, so that this could be opened only slightly if at all. Such a state of affairs could only lead to the death of the individual and the extinction of the race" (Swinnerton, 1923; I do not find the statement in the last edition of that book). In a long series of studies, British students have analyzed this trend and the populations showing it in much detail (especially, Trueman, Maclennan and Trueman, Swinnerton, and Arkell, see references in Westoll, 1950) and Westoll (1950) has lately given a new interpretation. The complex trend involved shortening of the area of attachment, earlier onset of arching, increase in degree of arching or spiral angle, thickening of left valve, etc. The net effect (which in this case of "hypermorphosis" follows more or less the same sequence in ontogeny and phylogeny) is a series starting with a normal oyster, left valve broadly attached and shell aperture not far from parallel to the attachment (Figure 67.1). The attachment becomes progressively smaller and the aperture increasingly vertical until its center is straight up. Finally, the now heavy shell breaks loose from the small attachment and is anchored and oriented on the substrate by its own weight and shape.

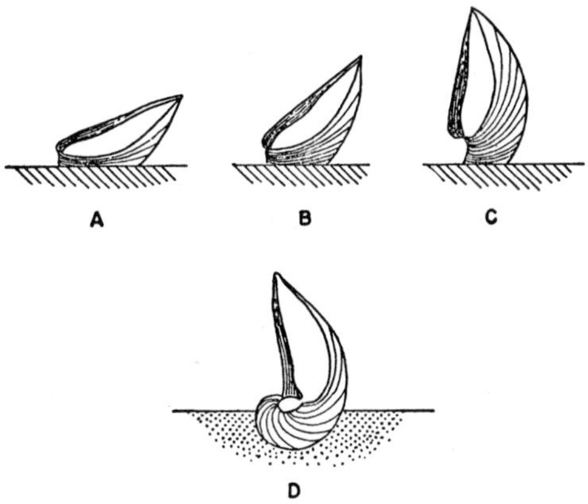

FIGURE 67.1
Evolution of *Gryphaea*. *A–C*, sections through progressive stages in a lineage of *Gryphaea*, growing on a solid substrate, showing effect of shortening of the area of attachment and increase in the spiral angle; *D*, section of an adult in the final stage of the *Gryphaea incurva* lineage: the shell is shown as broken free from its juvenile attachment and lying partly embedded in a soft substrate. (Slightly altered from Westoll, 1950.)

Westoll interprets the history in terms of two trends. One, rather steady, was toward larger size. The other, more rapid and accelerating, was toward tighter coiling (and associated characters). The latter trend can be represented by the size at which the coiling, if continued at the same rate, would cause closure of the two valves (Figure 67.2). In early forms with slight coiling, the size at closure would have been very large, about 50 centimeters, a size never reached or even approached in the actual populations. With increased coiling, however, this critical value fell rapidly. At the same time, size increased, and in a final stage, *Gryphaea incurva,* the two trend lines began to intersect so that the large members of the population did reach closure, which entailed their death.

Both of these trends were adaptive. Increase in size, as previously discussed, is a very common trend and in such a case as this is almost certainly favored by selection because of the advantages of larger size and of quicker growth for obtaining food. The trend toward coiling, which raised the aperture and later led to unattached life on the bottom, was adaptive for living on an unconsolidated or muddy bottom. It is, in fact, known from the sediments in which *Gryphaea* is found that it flourished in such environments. Nevertheless, the two adaptive trends have a limit imposed by intersection of the size trend and closure trend.

In the actual case, this limit was reached but not passed. Only the largest and hence, as a rule, oldest animals reached closure in the most advanced populations. For the population as a whole this was still not inadaptive. Death of nonsocial animals once they are past breeding age or even in late breeding age is not disadvantageous to the species, and it may be advantageous in increasing the space for younger, vigorously breeding individuals. Further selection on the two trends favorable to younger and younger animals, might, as Westoll suggests, have brought closure so early in the breeding period as really to interfere with reproduction of the population. This point does not seem to me to have been reached, but the somewhat delicate equilibrium would certainly make the population especially sensitive to competition or to environmental change. In either case, the whole phenomenon is most reasonably explained as occurring under the influence of selection and no mysterious momentum effect is required or really suggested.

The case of *Megaloceros,* the so-called Irish elk (which was a large stag and ranged over a wide territory in Europe), is more widely familiar. In a trend that can be followed approximately from the Pliocene through the Pleistocene, these animals became very large and the antlers of the males became proportionately still larger until they were truly enormous. Many students have considered them so large that they "must have been" disadvantageous. I can only feel awe for anyone who *knows* that structures were disadvantageous in animals that were very abundant for tens of thousands of years and more, but let us suppose that they were, or were becoming so at their largest. (They were certainly not lethally so before that stage, if ever.) There still are several possible explanations relying on known mechanisms and excluding an unknown momentum mechanism. One is selection for youth, mentioned in connection with *Ostrea* and previously suggested for this case by Haldane. Rapid antler growth would favor younger stags in reproduction and would not reduce population size and reproduction even if it produced disadvantageously large antlers in old stags. Only when the disadvantage reduced the total capacity of the whole group of stags, which would be quite late in a polygamous species, would the trend for accelerated growth really become disadvantageous to the population.

Another possibility, or indeed probability, is that this was an example of selection in correlated trends. Body size and antler size were probably allometric in *Megaloceros*, as they are known to be in its ally *Cervus elaphus* (Huxley, 1932), with $k > 1$ for antler on body regression. In early stages, selection was for both larger body and larger antlers, the allometric relation then accelerating the trend. When the point was reached where antler size ceased to be advantageous, selection against further increase in antlers was weaker than that for further increase in body size. The latter trend then continued, and therefore allometric increase in antler size continued, until the opposite selection pressures became equal. Body size was then somewhat under its optimum and antler size somewhat over its. That so specialized a creature might then be especially susceptible to extinction with environmental change is a different point, invoking no momentum effect.

This sort of balanced effect is probably very general in cases of correlated trends, which are themselves very frequent and could involve any of the sorts of correlation previously discussed with the possible exception of adaptive correlation. When changes are correlated in any way through the genetic system (which also determines allometry, of course), the net effect of selection will be the algebraic sum for *all* characters involved. In such a case the net effect may quite frequently be some change against selection for some one character. It is again the total situation and not an artificially isolated element that determines the outcome.

Many of the characters commonly designated as hypertelic are striking secondary sexual characters. These are in all analyzed cases either neutral secondary effects of sex or, especially in those called hypertelic, they are advantageous to the individual in sexual selection. They are then adaptive, not, to be sure,

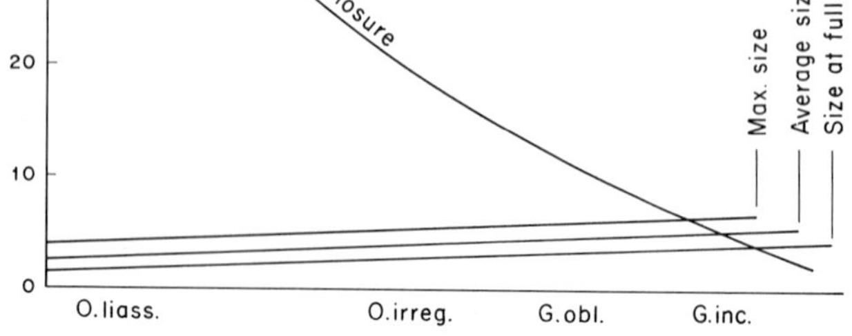

FIGURE 67.2
Trends of size and closure in a lineage of *Gryphaea*. The "closure" trend reflects tightness of coiling and shows the size at which the valves would have clamped shut if the animals had grown to that size. The three straight lines show maximum size, mean adult size, and size at sexual maturity in observed and (*to the right*) extrapolated populations. At the bottom are labeled stages in the sequence conventionalized as species, from *Ostrea liassica* to *Gryphaea incurva*. A population would necessarily become extinct from closure near the point where the bottom size line intersects the closure line. No known population reaches that point. (After Westoll, 1950.)

to some other environmental factors but to factors in the intrademe environment. Intrademe selection may be dysgenic for the species (although this is seldom clear), but it is adaptive if the total situation is kept in mind. The same may be said of "altruistic" selection (about which I also have misgivings): it may seem inadaptive for the individual but it is adaptive for the species and a balance is struck.

The nearest thing to a true momentum effect that is at all likely really to occur in nature would result if mutation overcame selection pressure and directed a change or trend. It has heretofore been pointed out that this is extremely improbable. Among the very few examples that might just possibly involve such an effect is that of the brachiopods described by Fenton (1935). He found that in *Atrypa* the most consistent trends were degenerative, mostly a loss of regularity in details of shell ornamentation. The adaptive significance, if any, of these details is unknown and can hardly have been very important. This may have been, in a manner of speaking, permissible nonadaptive change oriented by mutation. The fact (as I see it) that over-all control of evolutionary change is usually adaptive by no means rules out the possibility of a considerable amount of such permissible, nonadaptive change.

In a case like the progressive disruption of striations in *Atrypa*, calling changes "degenerative" may well be a human aesthetic judgment that has no real bearing. There are occasional instances, however, that do seem degenerative in a pathological sense. Fenton also noted a slowness in repair of lesions in late populations of *Atrypa*. More striking is the high incidence of bone diseases in the latest European cave bears (*Ursus spelaeus*) studied by Breuer, Ehrenberg, and others (see summary in Abel, 1935). It is a reasonable interpretation that the amount of disease was increased by life in damp, dark caves which were, nevertheless, advantageous as lairs. Again there was a balance of selection pressures on two different aspects of adaptation. One might say that the bears paid for their homes with a certain amount of disease. Again, too, this was a precarious balance, which in this case was upset by man. *Ursus spelaeus* was one of the earliest species to be helped to extinction by his destructive cave-mate *Homo sapiens*.

Nopcsa (1923) and others have noted that certain evolutionary changes characterizing whole populations and normal in that sense closely resemble the results of disease in other groups. Thus bone-thickening resembling pathological pachyostosis is common in early stages of aquatic adaptation. Pituitary enlargement and gigantism may be associated as in acromegaly (e.g., Edinger, 1942). Amynodont rhinoceroses have a short-legged, big-headed facies similar to that of achondroplasia (Wood, 1949). These and all the examples of what Nopcsa called "arrhostia" seem clearly to be adaptations definitely advantageous to the groups in which they were normal and they are not really either pathological or hypertelic in any special sense of the word. In some cases the resemblance to pathological conditions in other groups is merely a coincidence. In others, it may reflect the same mechanism (perhaps so in racial and pathological gigantism). This raises the interesting point that one group's pathology may be another's health. The growth mechanism is doubtless much the same in both, but it is normal and adaptive for some lizards to grow to one foot in length and for some dinosaurs to grow to fifty feet. It would be equally pathological for the same mechanism to produce a dinosaur a foot long or a lizard fifty feet long. "Arrhostia" involves no evidence for racial pathology or inadaptive momentum or hypertely.

Cases in which there really is an over-all inadaptive balance for the whole organism in the total environmental situation apparently usually have the same general cause: what was a favorable balance has become unfavorable because of environmental change more rapid than possible adaptive response by the populations affected. This lag (Darlington, 1939) is the usual cause of extinction and it is discussed as such below. It is mentioned here in order to point out that it has nothing to do with hypertely or momentum although it can be readily mistaken for the supposed effects of those dubious factors.

The following list summarizes various possible ways in which there may arise characters that *seem* to be extreme and inadaptive and that have been called hypertelic by some students.

1. The character in question is really adaptive (e.g., the pelycosaur "fin")
2. The character may be more or less inadaptive in degree, at least, but is linked with adaptive characters and involved in a balance the net effect of which is adaptive:
a. Allometry (e.g., antlers of *Megaloceros*)
b. Other forms of genetic correlation (this is a possible or probable factor in many cases, e.g., in *Atrypa*, but it cannot be clearly designated in examples known to me)
c. Altruistic and individual (e.g., juvenile, sexual) selection (probably a factor in *Gryphaea*, perhaps in *Megaloceros*)
d. Ecological, biochemical, etc., balance (e.g., cave bears)
3. The characters are actually inadaptive and not balanced with adaptive characters:
a. Drift (possible in many cases, but not clearly distinguishable from other possibilities in given examples)
b. Mutation pressure (improbable; possible in a few cases, e.g., *Atrypa*)
c. Lag (extremely common, the usual or universal cause of extinction)

Figure 67.3 symbolizes three general cases in which characters really inadaptive may occur. A fourth possible case, involving drift, is not shown as its bearing seems theoretically clear enough without symbolization.

The conclusion is that true momentum or hypertely defined as the result of momentum does not occur in evolution, except for the slight possibility of evolution dominated by mutation pressure, if that be considered momentum.

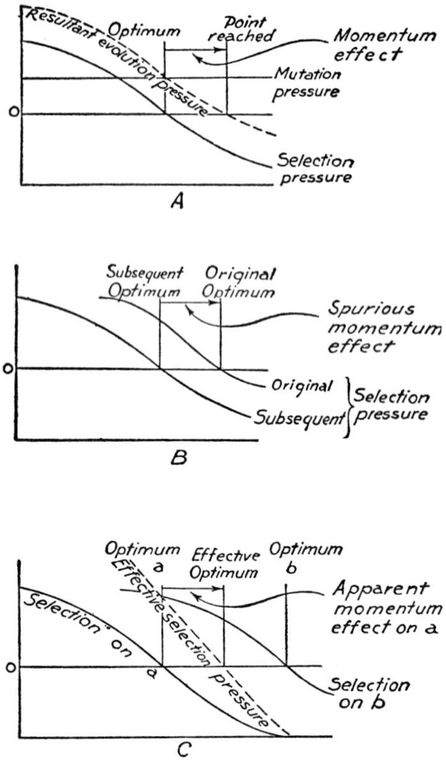

FIGURE 67.3
Analysis of some supposed momentum effects in evolution. The tendency of a given evolutionary factor is to carry the character to the point where the line graphing intensity of that factor intersects line O. A, constant mutation pressure plus selection pressure about the optimum produces a resultant evolution pressure that intersects O beyond the selective optimum; B, backward shift of optimum makes original optimum inadaptive and produces spurious aspect of momentum for group that had reached the original optimum; C, correlation of two characters with different optima makes effective selection pressure different from selection for either character alone and places the effective optimum beyond the optimum for one of the characters.

RACIAL SENILITY

The idea that groups of organisms become old and die of senile degeneration [has been] mentioned in connection with the theory of racial cycles. It has also been advanced as a general cause of extinction. Little space need here be devoted to this hypothesis, which merely seems absurd to me (e.g., 1949a) and to many other students (e.g., Arambourg, 1950; Romer, 1949a; Rensch, 1947; Carter, 1951—to mention only a few).

On the face of it, the term "senility" applied to evolving groups is a misused metaphor where not even analogy exists. Nothing in a continuously reproducing population does or can possibly correspond with the process of aging in an individual. Moreover, all lineages existing at any one time are of precisely the same age, so how can some be "young" and some "old"? Unless life has arisen in more than one period of earth history, which is extremely improbable, all must necessarily have undergone the same span of continuous reproduction. Why, too, should related lineages or groups even at the same taxonomic level have such very different spans? To reply that some are cut off before they reached old age is to deny what is claimed, i.e., that extinction is caused by old age. To reply that some lines age more rapidly than others is a circular argument that assumes what is to be proved.

Supposed evidence for racial senility is of two intergrading sorts: it is pointed out that the last members of a lineage are often extreme or hypertelic, and it is claimed that an outburst of variation (mainly intergroup), of degeneration, and of bizarre and inadaptive forms often precedes extinction. As to the first point, it is obvious that if a group is changing at all, its last members will have changed the most, regardless of when extinction occurs. That they have usually, or ever, changed too much at the time of extinction is either a statement of the obvious (they became extinct because something was wrong) or an assumption of evolutionary momentum, a concept that we have just seen reason to discard.

The second sort of argument for racial senility, which is at least more interesting than the first, dates especially from Hyatt in the 1890's. He pointed out that ammonites toward the end of their history developed remarkable complication and variety of sutures and ornamentation and that they took on numerous (to our eyes) bizarre forms, showing spiral rather than plane coiling, unrolling in various ways, and even becoming irregularly serpentine. This is still the standard example of racial senility. It has, however, repeatedly been pointed out that: (a) "senile" forms began to appear 100 million years and more before extinction of the ammonites; (b) particular groups in which "senile" forms are most common are among the longest-lived groups of ammonites; (c) "senile" forms were often very abundant and obviously successful over long periods of time; (d) progressively adaptive significance can be assigned to some supposedly degenerative "senile" trends; and (e) normal or "youthful" forms persisted to the very end of ammonite history and then became just as extinct as the "senile" forms.

Many or all of the same insuperable objections apply to every other supposed case of racial senility. Some of the hadrosaurian and ceratopsian dinosaurs developed grotesque skull characters toward the end of ther evolution, but lineages with normal skulls also persisted and it was the extinction of these that ended the history. Among dinosaurs in general, some of the last were as small and relatively unspecialized as the first.

Outbursts of peculiar forms that would certainly be considered senile if the group happened to be extinct occur among organisms that are now living and thriving. Many Recent beetles are as "hypertelic" and "senescent" as ever were the ammonites or any other extinct group, but beetles are obviously among the most successful forms of life in the world today and to consider them as on the verge of extinction would be ridiculous.

The appearance toward the end of a group's history of anything that could reasonably and even descriptively be called hypertely or senile degeneration is, moreover, the exception rather than the rule. I think any unbiased review would support Rensch's (1947) statement (in German) that, "In innumerable cases lineages become extinct without there being recognizable in the last forms any sort of morphological or pathological degenerative phenomena." For instance in the radiation of the notoungulates, all the groups became extinct one by one and in no case did the last forms look like anything but perfectly normal members of the group. They did not become senile; they merely became extinct.

Quite aside from the absurd idea of racial senility, it would be expected theoretically that a group on the verge of extinction would show increased variation and degeneration. As an adaptive zone is becoming untenable, which in broad terms is what happens in any case of extinction, centripetal selection relaxes and centrifugal selection comes into play. Survival depends on getting out of the zone and effective selection will finally all be away from the ancestral type. In dwindling populations dysgenic inbreeding and genetic drift are likely to occur. In some recent animals approaching extinction there is some evidence that such effects do indeed appear. There are some possible examples among fossils (Fenton's *Atrypa* could be one), but instances that can reasonably and clearly be so interpreted are remarkably rare in view of the theoretical expectation. The reason for their rarity is probably that by the time these effects begin to occur extinction is usually so near that it follows instantly, as far as the fossil record could show, and morphological degeneration does not have time to become really appreciable.

In a broader sense, something related to this expected phenomenon, but without clearly degenerative small population effects as far as the record usually shows, may be involved in groups with a multiplicity of phyla up to their extinction. Sometimes this multiplicity seems to represent, in a sense, a sort of exploration of possibilities in an environment that is degenerating with respect to ancestral adaptations (Figure 67.4 A). In that case it would be a more reasonable figure of speech to say that the group shows virility in the face of adversity rather than to call it senile. Sometimes one or more of the exploring lines do find a new and successful adaptation (Figure 67.4 B). This diagram quite closely resembles the history of late therapsid reptiles, which split into a large number of lines most of which became extinct but three or more of which became "mammals."

LOSS OF ADAPTATION

Adaptation is an extremely complex two-way fit between population and environment. Changes in environment are incessant; no environment is really and completely the same for two seconds in succession. In all cases adaptation necessarily includes a certain range of tolerance for environmental change. When, as *almost* always happens sooner or later, environmental change exceeds a former range of tolerance one of two things must happen. Populations involved may change so as to maintain

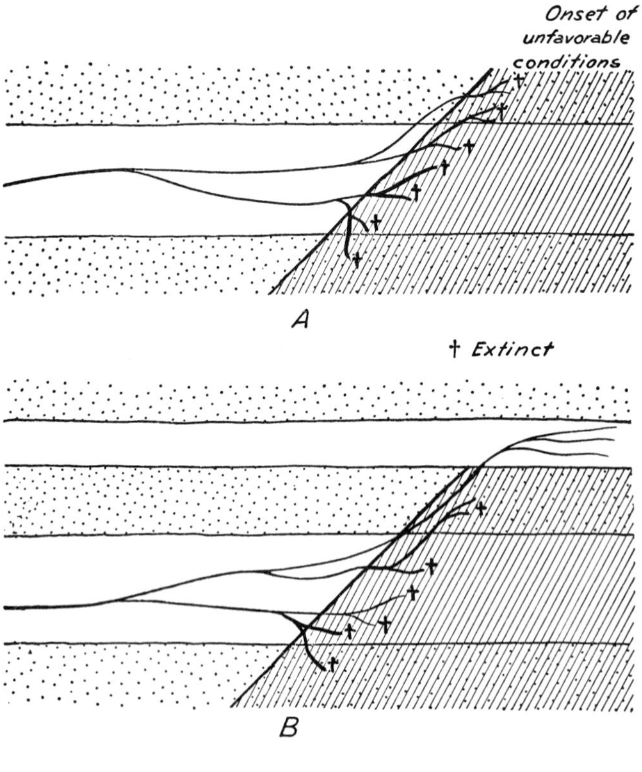

FIGURE 67.4
"Exploratory" lines in a degenerating adaptive zone. A, no other adaptive zone is reached and the whole group becomes extinct; B, another adaptive zone is reached by one (or more) lines, a new adaptive type arises, and the old type becomes extinct.

adaptation or to achieve new adaptation: that is the usual, but it would appear not universal, reason for evolutionary change. Or the populations involved may not change sufficiently and adaptation may be lost: that, quite simply, is the usual cause of extinction, the only other possible cause being loss of existing adaptation by genetic drift.

Since some degree of adaptation is, almost by definition, the requisite for continued existence, saying that loss of adaptation is the cause of extinction comes perilously near to saying that loss of existence causes extinction. The statement is not quite as trivial as that, however. By designating adaptation as the key to extinction, as well as the key to existence, an end can be put to the old, long, and futile argument about whether "internal" or "external" factors cause extinction. It becomes clear that the cause is neither in the organisms nor in their environment but in the relationship between the two.

The problem is thus broken down into two aspects. It seems to be true, as many students have said (e.g., Arambourg, 1950, with quite unnecessary apologies for being "Lamarckian" because he took the environment into consideration), that extinction rarely if ever occurs without change of environment. It is, however, equally true that extinction never occurs without a failure of response in the populations affected. The change in environment is not the "cause" of the characters of populations that make them fail and therefore is not, as often stated, the "cause" of extinction. Extinction is not the invariable or even the usual outcome of change in environment. Of two populations undergoing comparable changes of environment, one often fails while the other succeeds. To explain any particular case of extinction it is, then, necessary to specify two things: what pertinent change occurred in the environment, and what factors in the population prevented sufficient adaptive change.

Some environmental changes are so rapid and brutal that they are obviously beyond the capacity for adaptive change in any population. Then it is unnecessary to specify the population factors, not because they are any less involved, but because we know that the whole mechanism of population change is simply incapable of rising to such a rate of action. This is true of practically all cases of extinction that have had any study while they were actually occurring, most of which were due to man, either because his destructive power was itself the precipitating change in the environment or because he changed other aspects of the environment (see the interesting popular summary by Williams, 1951).

It has been seen that really marked changes in natural populations, even under strong selection pressure, commonly take on the order of 10^5 years and upward, even though relatively trivial changes as in frequencies of existing alleles or chromosome arrangements may be very rapid. Any environmental factor capable of killing off the whole population of a species in 10^5 years or less is more likely than not to cause extinction. Man obviously can do this for almost any species to which he devotes his attention. (Perhaps there are exceptions among organisms that take refuge in an environment man would prefer not to destroy, i.e., himself, and that are, moreover, capable of exceptionally rapid change: parasitic and pathogenic protistans.)

It is also evident that such events may occur without man. Volcanic eruptions have wiped out whole species in a day, but only insular forms or others very limited in distribution. Human introduction of competitors (e.g., rabbits in Australia) or predators (e.g., mongooses in the West Indies) have also led to extinction so rapid that adaptive response was simply out of the question, and such invasions have repeatedly occurred in the past without human aid. There is a possibility that a single extreme fluctuation in a normal environmental variant, in weather, for instance, would cause immediate extinction, and incidentally such a fluctuation would in almost all cases be absolutely impossible to observe in the stratigraphic record. We are, however, protected from the probability of being thus baffled by the fact that almost any group old enough to have a distinctive adaptive type must already have persisted through the whole possible range of weather and could only be seriously affected by slower change in climate.

The point about such intense, quick environmental changes is that they are beyond the capacity for change of the evolutionary mechanism as a whole. *Any* group subjected to them becomes extinct, so that there is no point in discussing differences that determine differential extinction. Rapid and nondifferential extinctions probably have been very common. For instance local (at least) extinctions of three of the four iterative lines of *Olenus* were probably of this sort: all trilobites disappeared from the area from one stratigraphic plane to the next. Nevertheless, slower extinction and clearly differential extinction are also common. The notoungulates took a long time to die out, even after the irruption of competitors from North America. Horses became extinct in North America while bison, living with the horses and with considerable adaptive similarity, did not.

The ultimate genetical causes for failure of adaptive response in a population are simple and clear, although more explicit analysis is often complex and obscure to the point of impossibility. Materials for change are expressed variation, pooled potential variability, and new mutations. Obviously, loss of adaptation will follow environmental change if expressed variation is not adequate or appropriate, if, further, appropriate potential variability either does not exist or cannot be released fast enough, and if, still further, appropriate new mutations do not occur or are not fixed or do not achieve phenotypic realization at a sufficient rate. Faced by a given degree of environmental change, groups with lower phenotypic variation, lower genetic variability, lower mutation rates, or any combination of these are more likely to become extinct.

For various reasons, small populations and panmictic populations of any size are more likely to become extinct than moderate to large populations and populations subdivided into partly isolated breeding groups or demes. Small populations have limited variability at any one time and low absolute incidence of mutation, and they may be subject to genetic drift. They are also likely to be narrowly localized and so more subject to rapid extinction by a regional catastrophe. Panmictic populations have relatively low expressed and potential variability. Other things being equal, the larger the population the more potential variability, at least, it is likely to have and the larger its absolute rate of mutation will be. Size for size, the more subdivided a population is, the higher will be both expressed and potential variability, and also the less likely is any temporary or local disturbance to upset the balance of the whole.*

Most organisms have optimal and minimal population sizes and densities (see review in Allee, Emerson, Park, Park, and Schmidt, 1949). Under normal conditions, the optimum is a stable equilibrium to which the population tends to return after fluctuations either above or below. The minimum (for a self-reproducing population) is, however, an unstable point. Fluctuation above the minimum tends to go on to the optimum and that below the minimum tends to go on to extinction. The unstable equilibrium point may be rather high, especially for social animals. Extinction of populations may thus ensue even though the unfavorable environmental factor ceases to operate or does not operate to eliminate all individuals but only to reduce size of population unusually far below the optimum.

That one population may have and another may lack the *sort* of variability required is also and clearly another factor in extinction, but a rather mysterious one in most cases. Horned rhinoceroses have survived and hornless rhinoceroses otherwise similar became extinct. Supposing that lack of horns was a factor in extinction of the latter, which is at least possible, we may say that they lost adaptation because they had no variation or mutation in the direction of horns. We certainly cannot say *why* they did not have such variation, when their relatives did have. In this and in the great number of similar cases, we can only clothe our ignorance in the words "mutation is random." (Incidentally, such cases have a bearing on the reactionary Lamarckian-Michurinist doctrine that organisms develop what they need.)

The clearest general relationship between characters of organisms and the chances of extinction and the one most often mentioned concerns their breadth of adaptation or special-

* An influence of lack of subdivision is dramatically illustrated by the rapidity of extinction of the passenger pigeon and near extinction of the plains bison by man. Both had enormous but little subdivided populations.

ization. Narrowness of adaptation means that the organisms range over a smaller variety of environmental conditions. The adaptation is therefore more likely to be affected by environmental change than in the case of organisms that tolerate or thrive in a wider environmental range. Under relatively constant conditions or with a general deterioration of the whole range of both, the more narrowly adapted animals have the advantage, but with more specific change the more widely adapted animals are less likely to become extinct. (This is, of course, survival of the more or the less specialized.) In this, as in so much of evolution, there is a balance, and neither broad nor narrow adaptation has become the general rule although the more usual tendency is for narrowing of adaptation.

It does not follow automatically that because a narrower adaptive zone is more liable to change the populations in it are more liable to extinction. Extinction ensues only if the populations fail to change adaptively. Many narrowly adapted organisms are still able to make extensive changes and thus to avoid extinction in a changing environment, but on an average narrowly adapted forms are also more specialized in another sense: they are, one might say, less plastic; the sorts of change they can undergo are more restricted. It is this combination of factors, of two different things both usually called "specialization," that makes such a situation likely to lead to extinction.

Specialization in the sense of limitation of further change may also occur without specialization in the sense of narrowed adaptation, although the two do tend to be associated. It is not at all clear that any one lineage of one-toed grazing horses has a narrower adaptive range than had a lineage of three-toed grazing horses. Indeed the adaptive range of the former may be wider and they did survive after the three-toed horses became extinct. But the one-toed horses do have less chance of further adaptive change and are more specialized in that sense of the word.

The word "specialization," one of many ambiguous and abused terms too loosely used in evolutionary studies, is also often applied in a relative way to comparatively large changes from an ancestral or modal condition. Thus man is "specialized" in being much bigger than most or than early primates, but a whale the size of a man would be considered "unspecialized" in size. It may even be considered that *Nannippus* is "specialized" because it is smaller than its immediate ancestors while a *Mesohippus* of the same size is "unspecialized" because it is smaller than its immediate descendants. Specialization in this sense has no necessary relationship with either of the other two sorts of specialization or with extinction.

Extinction in which specialization (of any sort) is involved is usually said to be due to overspecialization, but this way of putting things confuses the issue. It seems to imply that overspecialization is a definable extra degree of specialization or that it is something quite different, even moralistically so, "bad" as opposed to "good" specialization. Of course it is nothing of the sort. Overspecialization is just specialization that has become disadvantageous because the environment has changed. Precisely the same characters may be highly adaptive at one time or in one group and inadaptive at another time or in a different group. To call them now "specialization" and now "overspecialization" only obscures their real relationship to survival and to extinction.

The sorts of environmental changes that may be involved in extinction are legion. The environment is extremely complex and any sort of change in it may require changed adaptation which in turn may lead to extinction if organisms fail in adaptive change. Changes in biotic environment especially likely to lead to extinction include appearance of new competitors or predators, disappearance of types of animal or vegetable food, and appearance of new pathogenic organisms. (The "appearances" in question are more often by spread or migration than by immediate evolution *in situ*.) The changes in physical environment most often discussed are those of climate, heat or cold, aridity, etc., but other physical changes may have been equally or more important, such as withdrawal of the great epicontinental seas in times of high continents (like the present) or disappearance of high alpine environments in times of low continents. Many lists of such possibilities have been compiled, but an attempt to compile a complete list, even in general terms, would be futile.

TABLE 67.1
Variety of multituberculates and rodents in Early Cenozoic deposits of the Rocky Mountain region

Ages			Multituberculates		Rodents	
			Genera	Species	Genera	Species
Eocene	late		0	0	13	31
	mid		0	0	9	19
	early	B	0	0	3	8
		A	3	5	1	4
Paleocene	late		7	11	1	1
	mid		6	17	0	0
	early		5	7	0	0

Source: after Jepson, 1949.

Changes possibly concerned may be as varied and complex as the environment itself, which is so intricate and diverse as to defy adequate description.

Special interest attaches to competition as a factor in extinction both because it seems to have been common and because it more often can be specified in relation to the fossil record than can any other factor. It is quite common for two groups of similar adaptive type to be found together and for one to decrease to extinction while the other increases. In such cases the most likely hypothesis, at least, is that competition led to extinction of one group, although of course this may not really have been true in a given case. A particularly good example, as its compiler says "almost too perfect," is given by the replacement of multituberculates by rodents as discussed by Jepsen (1949). Table 67.1 (from Jepsen) indicates numbers of genera and species of the two groups known in the area (the Rocky Mountain region of North America) where the earliest known rodents and last known multituberculates occur. The two groups are markedly different in ancestry and many features of anatomy, but strikingly similar in rodentlike adaptation. The decline of the older group as rodents appeared and began to expand is evident in the table. Moreover, multituberculates are relatively abundant in all known late Paleocene local faunas but one (Bear Creek, Montana), where they are absent; precisely there is the only known occurrence of Paleocene rodents.

In such cases a complete explanation would also state why the succeeding competitor was superior. This can seldom be clearly stated, but some suggestion is often possible. In the example just given, Jepsen points out that rodent incisors are clearly more efficient mechanically than those of multituberculates. A frequent statement regarding broad competitive replacements is that the replacers are more "progressive" and the replaced more "primitive," which even if it means something, certainly explains nothing. In the case of South American—North American faunal interchange and ensuing competition, in which the North American forms were much more successful, I (1950b) have pointed out that the latter do not seem in any clear, objective way to be more progressive or efficient but that they were the winnowed products of a long series of intercontinental competitions while the South American forms had been isolated for 70 million years or so.

Replacement by competition is one aspect of what Arambourg (1950) calls "paleontological relays," that is, the successive occupation of the same broad adaptive zone by different taxonomic groups. In all, three cases may occur: (1) replacement by competition, (2) immediate replacement, and (3) delayed replacement. The second case involves extinction of one group immediately followed by spread of another, as if the presence of the first had inhibited and its extinction promoted the development of the second. Colbert (1949b) shows that following extinction of the phytosaurs the crocodilians, which had already arisen as a small upland group, invaded the lowlands and developed the phytosaurlike adaptations which they still have today. In such cases of immediate succession, the precision of the time scale is usually insufficient to rule out the possibility of competition or of delayed replacement. Recent examples show how rapid extinction by competition may be. In limited areas like islands, at least, it may ensue in a few years or even months. With such rapid replacement, chances would be against finding the competing forms together at the same stratigraphic level.*

The third possibility, which also has often occurred, is delayed replacement, such as that of ichthyosaurs by cetaceans. In such cases rise of the later group obviously had no effect on the earlier. Even when replacement or relay occurs, this does not always or necessarily involve competition.

Extinction, like origin of new groups, has been more common at some times than others and has several times reached peaks so high and has affected so many different groups that coincidence seems ruled out. One such time of mass extinction, affecting some terrestrial but more marine animals, was roughly localized at the Paleozoic-Mesozoic transition and another, affecting some marine but more terrestrial animals, roughly at the Mesozoic-Cenozoic transition. (It is no coincidence that these approximate the era boundaries; the boundaries were placed there in the geological time scale because of the extinctions.)

It should be emphasized that these mass extinctions are not instantaneous or even brief events. They extend over periods of tens of millions of years (see, e.g., discussion by Watson, Prenant, Westoll, Simpson, Cuénot, and Arambourg following Arambourg, 1950). This makes the phenomenon all the more mysterious, because we have to think of environmental changes that not only affected a great many different groups in different environments but also did so very slowly and persistently. The only general and true statement that can now be made about, say, the extinction of the dinosaurs is that they all lost adaptation in the course of some long environmental change the nature of which is entirely unknown. There have, of course, been many speculations, some of them very ingenious** but none of them probable.

Aside from cases of apparent competition and some extinctions that seem to have been secondary effects of extinction of a food supply, the sad fact is that explicit assignment of immediate causes to particular instances of extinction is almost always unconvincing. We may say with full assurance that all were failures of adaptation to changing environments, but in few cases can a candid paleontologist even attempt to say precisely what changed and exactly why adaptation failed. This is not surprising in view of the extreme complexity of possible changes and adaptive responses, the improbability that any one, clear-cut factor acted alone, and the fact that many of the factors can seldom or never be determined from the fossil record. We know, for instance, that viruses infecting a species biochemically unable to resist them could cause extinction, but we cannot now and probably can never say that this is what happened to any one extinct species. Our failure to be explicit about particular instances of extinction is not because such an event is esoteric and inexplicable in detail but, quite the contrary, because there are so many possible detailed explanations that we cannot choose among them.

* Extinction of dinosaurs and spread of Paleocene mammals cannot be explained in this way, because early Paleocene mammals seem certainly too different from any dinosaurs to have caused such rapid competitive extinction of the whole group.

** As an example of such ingenuity, Cowles (1945) has demonstrated that heat-sterilization can occur in recent reptiles and suggests that this happened to the dinosaurs. But further studies by Colbert (1946) make that application highly improbable, and most students think that if there was any climatic change at the end of the Cretaceous it was toward generally cooler climates.

WORKS CITED

Abel, O., 1928, Das biologische Trägheitsgesetz: Biol. Gen., v. 4, p. 1–102.

———, 1935, Vorzeitliche Lebensspuren: Jena, Fischer.

Allee, W. C., A. E. Emerson, O. Park, T. Park, and K. P. Schmidt, 1949, Principles of animal ecology: Philadelphia, W. B. Saunders.

Arambourg, C. 1950. Le problème de l'extinction des espèces et des groupes: Centre Nat. Recherche Sci. [Paris] Colloques Internat., v. 21, p. 89–111.

Carter, G. S., 1951, Animal evolution, a study of recent views of its causes: London, Sidgwick and Jackson.
Colbert, E. H., 1946, Temperature tolerances in the American alligator and their bearing on the habits, evolution, and extinction of dinosaurs: Am. Mus. Nat. Hist. Bull., v. 86, p. 327–374.
———, 1949, Some paleontological principles significant in human evolution: Studies Phys. Anthropology, v. 1, p. 103–149.
Cowles, R. B., 1945, Heat-induced sterility and its possible bearing on evolution: Am. Naturalist, v. 79, p. 160–175.
Cuénot, L., 1925, L'adaptation: Paris, G. Doin.
Cuénot, L. (with collaboration of A. Tétry), 1951, L'évolution biologique, les faits, les incertitudes: Paris, Masson.
Darlington, C. D., 1939, The evolution of genetic systems: London, Cambridge University Press.
Edinger, T., 1942, The pituitary body in giant animals fossil and living—a survey and a suggestion: Quart. Rev. Biology, v. 17, p. 31–45.
Fenton, C. L., 1935, Factors of evolution in fossil series: Am. Naturalist, v. 69, p. 139–173.
Haldane, J. B. S., 1932, The causes of evolution: New York and London, Harper.
Huxley, J. S., 1932, Problems of relative growth: London, Methuen.
———, 1942, Evolution, the modern synthesis: New York, Harper.
Jepsen, G. L., 1949. Selection, "orthogenesis," and the fossil record: Am. Phil. Soc. Proc., v. 93, p. 479–500.
Jepsen, G. L., E. Mayr, and G. G. Simpson, eds., 1949, Genetics, paleontology, and evolution: Princeton, N.J., Princeton University Press.
Nopcsa, F., 1923, Vorläufige Notiz über Pachyostose und Osteosklerose einiger marinen Wirbeltiere: Anat. Anz., v. 56, p. 353–359.
Rensch, B., 1947, Neuere Probleme der Abstammungslehre, die transspezifische Evolution: Stuttgart, F. Enke.
Romer, A. S., 1949, Time series and trends in animal evolution, *in* G. L. Jepson, Mayr, and G. G. Simpson, eds., Genetics, paleontology, and evolution: Princeton, N.J., Princeton University Press.
Simpson, G. G., 1944, Tempo and mode in evolution (1st ed.): New York, Columbia University Press.
———, 1949, The meaning of evolution: New Haven, Conn., Yale University Press.
———, 1950, History of the fauna of Latin America: Am. Scientist, v. 38, p. 361–389.
Swinnerton, H. H., 1923, Outlines of palaeontology: London, Arnold.
Waddington, C. H., 1939, An introduction to modern genetics: New York, Macmillan.
Westoll, T. S., 1950, Some aspects of growth studies in fossils: Royal Soc. [London] Proc., ser. B, v. 137, p. 490–509.
Williams, J., 1951, Fall of the sparrow: New York, Oxford University Press.
Wood, H. E., II, 1949, Evolutionary rates and trends in rhinoceroses, *in* G. L. Jepson, E. Mayr, and G. G. Simpson, eds., Genetics, paleontology, and evolution: Princeton, N.J., Princeton University Press.

68

A Critical Phase in the History of Ammonites

CARL DIENER
1922

From *American Journal of Science,* ser. 5, vol. 4, pp. 120–126, 1922. Reprinted with permission of the *American Journal of Science.*

The extinction of ammonites, those masters of the Mesozoic seas, near the close of the Cretaceous period is a fact well known to all students of palæontology. The number of their families and genera is diminishing gradually during the Senonian epoch. Five species only reach into the stage of the Mæstrichtian. Not one passes the fatal border of the Danian [basal Cenozoic].

It is, however, less known, that the existence of ammonites was threatened by a similar crisis at a considerably earlier period of the Mesozoic era. They passed through a very critical phase at the boundary of the Rhætic [uppermost Triassic] and Liassic [basal Jurassic] stages. All but one phylum of Triassic ammonites became extinct at the close of the Rhætic epoch. By the survival of this single phylum, which in the Lower Lias gave rise to the development of a new and rich fauna, the ammonites were saved from complete extermination.

E. v. Mojsisovics was the first to notice this remarkable crisis in the history of Triassic ammonites. For fuller details the reader is referred to J. F. Pompeckj, "Ammoniten des Rhæt" (Neues Jahrb. f. Mineral., etc., 1895/II, pp. 1–46) and to some of my own memoirs.

The Upper Triassic deposits of Tethys are divided generally into three subdivisions, the Carnic, Noric and Rhætic stages. E. v. Mojsisovics divided both the Carnic and Noric stages into three substages, thus imparting to the Rhætic stage a taxonomic value inferior to that of the two preceding ones. Many genera belonging to all the known families of Upper Triassic ammonites reach the acme of their development in the Carnic stage. Although a considerable number of older genera are found for the last time at this level, the ammonite fauna of the Noric stage is a continuation and evolution of the Carnic fauna in every branch of life. The last life phase of the Noric stage seems to be the first which is distinguished from the preceding by the apparent extinction of numerous wide-spread and important genera and by the absence of any new elements either of foreign origin or derived from endemic forms. Nevertheless it is doubtful whether a single family of lower Noric ammonites becomes really extinct.

This decay is completed in the Noric epoch. From this stage eleven forms of ammonites only have been enumerated by Pompeckj, all of them of decidedly Triassic affinities. Five belong to the Noric genus *Choristoceras* and its subgenus *Peripleurites*, a phylogerontic descendant of the Ceratitidæ, whose last whorl became gradually uncoiled. *Arcestes*, the true leading genus of the Hallstatt limestone, is still represented by two species. To these are added one species of *Monophyllites* (*Mojsvarites*), of *Megaphyllites*, and a specifically undeterminable representative of *Cladiscites*, all genera of considerable vertical range. A single newcomer is indicated by *Hesperites*, a genus still imperfectly known, which is probably allied to the family of Trachyceratidæ.

It is noteworthy that not a single ancestral representative of Liassic ammonites is recognized in this assemblage. The discovery of one other genus is to be expected with certainty, although it has as yet not been found in beds of Rhætic age. This is *Phylloceras* or, more exactly, *Rhacophyllites*, if this subgeneric designation is extended to all widely umbilicated species of *Phylloceras*. *Rhacophyllites debilis* Hau. and *R. neojurensis* Quenst. are among the most common leading fossils of the upper Noric substage. In the Lower Lias, *Phylloceras*, *Rhacophyllites* and *Euphyllites* are remarkable for their richness and variety. The apparent intermittence of *Phylloceras* in the Rhætic is therefore purely accidental. It is in reality the only genus surviving the general extermination of Triassic ammonites.

The importance of the gradual decline of Triassic ammonites during the Rhætic epoch is evident from a comparison with the number of genera in the Carnic and Noric faunæ. Those faunæ do not contain less that 146 genera and subgenera of ammonites, which were reduced to six in the Rhætic stage. Hyatt was certainly right in speaking of a "culmination of ammonites in the Upper Trias after a period of uninterrupted progressive evolution from the early Devonian." Both the Carnic and Noric ammonites were highly varied, including forms with long and short body-chambers, with few and simple clydonitic sutures (*Lobites*) and with a very large number of the most complicated sutural elements (*Pinacoceras*); smooth, globose shells with serial lobes (*Arcestes*) and extremely flattened shapes (*Pompeckjites*); shells exhausting almost every possible combination of sculpture from the most graceful ornamentation (*Acanthinites*) to stout ribs (*Heraclites*) and profusely tuberculated costations (*Trachyceras*).

The close of the Rhætic epoch is marked by the final disappearance of all Triassic types, excepting *Phylloceras*. Primitive and highly specialized forms were equally subjected to this general extermination.

In the eastern Alps the beds of the lowest Lias follow above those containing a Rhætic fauna without any unconformity. There is no trace of a hiatus nor of any diastrophic movement between the two groups. Nevertheless the ammonite fauna of the lowest zone of the Mediterranean Lias is entirely different from that of the Upper Trias. The first impression of this Liassic fauna is the sudden introduction of a large number of types which are only a little less manifold and diversified than those of the Upper Noric, but do not exhibit any phylogenetic affinities with them. We are indebted to F. Waehner for their careful and detailed examination.

There is little doubt that the extinction of the different phyla of Triassic ammonites prepared the way for the evolution of a new and vigorous stock, which originated from the genus *Phylloceras*, the only one which connects the faunæ of the Triassic and Liassic periods. *Phylloceras* is the ancestor of the two leading families of the lowest Lias, the Arietitidæ and Lytoceratidæ. Waehner and Pompeckj have demonstrated their intimate relationship with *Psiloceras*, the most primitive element of the Arietitidæ. Together with *Psiloceras*, more specialized types of the Arietitidæ: *Ægoceras*, *Schlotheimia*, *Arietites*, make their appearance in the deepest zone of the Lias. But they are comparatively rare, *Psiloceras* remaining the predominant genus in this and the following life-phase. All these genera are linked together most closely with the ancestral *Psiloceras*.

Of equal moment is the sudden appearance of the Lytoceratidæ in the Lower Lias, where they are represented by the genera *Lytoceras, Ectocentrites* and *Pleuracanthites*. Forms transitional between *Pleuracanthites* and *Psiloceras* have been described by Waehner. Thus *Phylloceras* was destined to give rise to all Lower Triassic ammonites by the intervention of *Psiloceras*.

Thus an aspect quite different from that of the Upper Trias is given to the ammonite fauna of the Lower Lias. Not one of the numerous and diversified genera of world-wide distribution, belonging to the families of Arcestidæ, Cladiscitidæ, Pinacoceratidæ, Haloritidæ, Tropitidæ, Didymitidæ, Ceratitidæ, Tirolitidæ, and Trachyceratidæ is represented in the latter. Their place has been taken by Arietitidæ and Lytoceratidæ. *Phylloceras*, which never played an important part in the fauna of the Upper Trias, was the only survival and was destined to become the ancestor of all Liassic ammonites.

In direct opposition to these facts, Steinmann denied the extermination of Triassic ammonites at the close of the Rhætic epoch. His reconstruction of a phyletic tree, in which *Macrocephalites* is branching off from *Juvavites, Sphœroceras* from *Halorites, Harpoceras* from *Discotropites, Desmoceras* from *Arcestes, Pachydiscus* from *Cladiscites*, need not be discussed here. It means toying with possibilities, the reality of which can never be proved. One of his critical arguments, however, deserves consideration. He believes the palæontological record not to be sufficiently perfect to prove a real decline of the Triassic ammonites during the Rhætic epoch. It is true that cephalopod-bearing strata of Rhætic age have scarcely been discovered up to now outside the north-eastern Alps. But here they are as rich in ammonites as many beds of the Ladinic or Noric stages. Our knowledge of Rhætic ammonites is certainly not more limited than that of Permian ammonites after the discovery of the Artinsk and Sosio fauna. There is, consequently, as much evidence of a decline of the group during the Rhætic, as there is of a decline of the trilobites during the Carboniferous and Permian.

Such are the facts. They show us a great dying-out of ammonites towards the close of the Triassic and a rebirth, as it were, of a new fauna in the early Liassic, giving rise to the great wealth of Jurassic ammonite evolution. In entering into a discussion of the probable causes of this remarkable event in the life history of ammonites, we have to face the grave problem of the repeated extinction of large and flourishing groups of organisms. That this extinction has been partial only, affecting all but one stock of Triassic ammonites, marks the special case of our problem.

If we reflect on the multitude, the variety, and the complexity of the facts to be explained, and the scantiness of our information regarding them, we shall be ready to acknowledge that a full and satisfactory solution of so profound a problem is hardly to be hoped for, and that the most we can do in the present state of our knowledge is to hazard a more or less plausible conjecture.

Massive Extinctions in Biota at the End of Mesozoic Time

M. N. BRAMLETTE

1965

From *Science*, vol. 148, pp. 1696–1699, 1965. Reprinted with permission of the author and the American Association for the Advancement of Science.

The profound and geologically abrupt changes in the earth's biota, particularly those marking the end of Paleozoic and of Mesozoic time, have been the subject of much speculative discussion. A review by Newell [1] is one of the more recent and comprehensive on this subject, but does not include the possible explanation suggested here. These great changes primarily reflect a geologically sudden extinction of many important elements of the earth's population—the extinction of some large populations thriving toward the end of Mesozoic time being more demonstrably abrupt than that at the end of the Paleozoic. However, the causes of these major events were not necessarily similar, since the physical condition of the earth and the populations of organisms most affected were not closely similar at these two times. The extinction at the end of the Mesozoic seems, in the fossil record, to be most obviously and strikingly reflected by the planktonic life (plant and animal) of the oceans and by the larger forms dependent on plankton, such as ammonites and belemnites, whose extinction at that time has long been recognized. That so much marine life became extinct solely from a lack of adequate nutrition seems an oversimplification, but evidence that such a lack may have been the critical factor under the probable environmental conditions of that time deserves some consideration.

Among previous explanations, the one suggestion that the extinction occurred as a result of excessive radiation from an exceptional cosmic event might seem intriguing because such radiation could have had widespread and nearly instantaneous effects on life. Loeblich and Tappan [2] suggest that such radiation might have induced mutations and more extinctions in the planktonic than in the more protected benthonic foraminifera at the end of the Mesozoic. However, even a thin layer of surface water would serve as an effective blanket, according to Urey [3], and, as mentioned by Newell [1], the radiation would have affected land plants much more than the record indicates. The suggestion of a climatic change with a reduction in temperature seems to have little support, and the effects of such a change should likewise be most apparent in the fossil land plants rather than in the marine life. Changes in sea level may have adversely affected nearshore marine life, as Newell and others have advocated, but such changes should not have affected the plankton populations to the unusual degree that is evident.

Life in the oceans may include an even greater number of individuals (although not of taxa) than that on land because of the much greater surface area and depth of the marine part of the biosphere. Evidence is here summarized that this vast planktonic life was drastically affected at the end of Mesozoic time, and that this effect might be expected from certain physical conditions of the earth at that time which resulted in a reduced supply of detritus, with the required nutrients, to the ocean.

There appears to have been a proliferation of population sizes, as well as of the taxa, among some of the plankton groups during late Mesozoic time. However, that limitation of the population according to Malthusian principle would culminate in wholesale destruction seems improbable without some superimposed adversity, such as a decrease in the supply of nutrients to the ocean waters. The volume of nutrients in the depths of the vast oceanic reservoir might appear nearly inexhaustible to the biologist, but it appears that the supply of nutrients from the ultimate source on land decreased over some millions of years. This condition, however, should not have considerably affected the much greater amount of major inorganic constituents, or salinity, of the oceans. Whether or not the amount of nutrients in the oceans could have decreased to a level below the threshold for support of much of the phytoplankton, as in some laboratory experiments, and thus have resulted in mass extinctions in a geologically brief episode, is a serious and difficult question. This question is considered below after a review of the record of distribution of the fossils and of the environmental conditions which seem significant to any interpretation.

Changes in the plant and animal life on land were at a more nearly normal rate during late Cretaceous time. Even the conspicuous example of the extinction of the dinosaurs is not demonstrably such a sudden and wholesale destruction of thriving populations. Perhaps, too, a degree of circular reasoning is involved in the case of the dinosaurs, as certain strata, for whose ages adequate supplementary paleontologic evidence is lacking, have been reassigned from Cenozoic to late Mesozoic when some dinosaur remains have been discovered in them. The dinosaur remains are sparse, and synchroneity of the enclosing strata is commonly not well established from other evidence.

RECORD OF THE FOSSIL PLANKTON

The succession shown in Figure 69.1 for the distribution of calcareous nannoplankton is evident from the direct superposition of strata in Alabama, and is similarly clear for the Danian

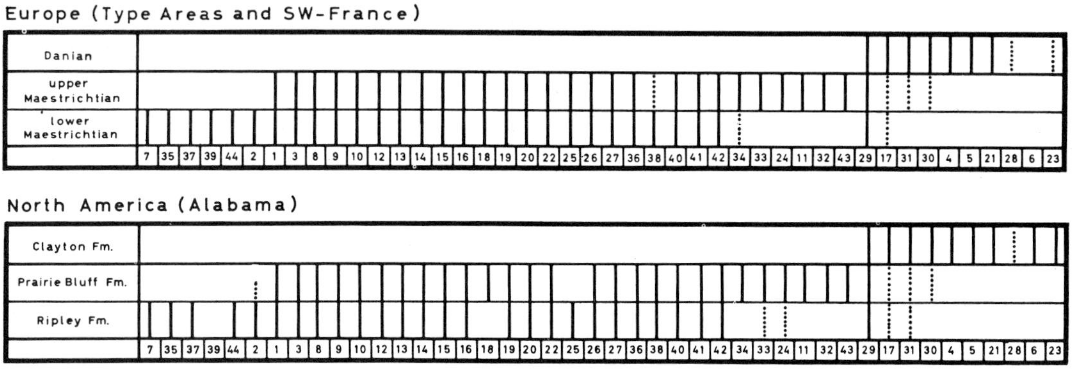

FIGURE 69.1
Distribution of calcareous nannoplankton in stratigraphic arrangement. Shows change at top of Maestrichtian, and equivalent in Alabama. Numerals correspond to names of taxa as given by Bramlette and Martini [9], where this illustration first appeared.

resting directly on the earlier strata in Denmark and France. The correlation and age assignments agree with those from most recent studies of the foraminifera and other groups of fossils. Samples containing vast numbers of nannoplankton (dominantly protophyta) from the indicated taxa were taken from within a few meters below and above the top of the Mesozoic strata (upper Maestrichtian and the equivalent in Alabama). The skeletal remains of the marine calcareous plankton (nannoplankton and planktonic foraminifera) constitute about one-half the total in these chalk formations—countless millions of the "nannofossils" (averaging less than 10 microns) occurring in a few cubic centimeters of the chalk. The distribution of the identified taxa of nannoplankton shown in Figure 69.1 is fairly representative of other known regions.

A surprisingly similar distribution, with a comparable number of extinctions at this same time, of the taxa of planktonic foraminifera is shown by unpublished results of several investigators of this group of fossils, and is indicated in part by Bolli, Loeblich, and Tappan [4] and by Berggren [5]. The sparsity of preserved fossils from other groups of plankton, such as the radiolarians, diatoms, and dinoflagellates or "hystrichospherids," in strata of these ages precludes an equally clear comparison, although the meager evidence does suggest that marked extinctions occurred at the end of the Mesozoic. Among the larger forms of marine life which have preservable hard parts and are dependent on the smaller plankton, the complete extinction at that time of the belemnites and of the large, diversified, and long-existent group of ammonites is well known.

The data on calcareous nannoplankton and planktonic foraminifera are now adequate to indicate this world-wide extinction of most of the distinctive taxa, and to show that the extinction of these large populations was so abrupt that the stratal record of transition still remains obscure. A record, even though an abbreviated one, will doubtless be found which shows diminished numbers of Cretaceous taxa and individuals associated with progenitors of the few early Cenozoic forms. Although some stratal discontinuity is commonly found at this horizon, much evidence indicates that the hiatus was not a long one in geological time, particularly because any large record of deposition missing in some areas should be represented by sedimentation elsewhere. The hiatus thus may involve many thousands of years but probably much less than a million; comparable changes in the fossil record normally require some millions of years. Such a long period of existence during Mesozoic time is indicated for many of the planktonic taxa which became extinct at the close of that era. It required several million years also for the meager assemblages of the nannoplankton and planktonic foraminifera surviving into the earliest Cenozoic to develop diversification comparable to that found in the late Mesozoic.

SIGNIFICANCE OF LAND CONDITIONS

There is no dispute with the principle of uniformitarianism in the view that the relative rate or intensity of the normal processes produced very different net restults over much of the earth for long periods of time. In late Mesozoic time it seems that there were environmental factors which should have greatly reduced the supply of nutrients to the oceans, nearly all of which must be derived from the land surface. The character of the near-shore sedimentary deposits of the late Mesozoic indicates an almost senile earth for that time—or better termed a "hibernating" earth, because of the return to unusual vigor during the late Tertiary to Recent time. Some of the evidence is summarized below which suggests that the earth was not stirring with the usual amount of orogeny, uplifts, and erosion with the resulting supply of detritus to the oceans. No complete change in these conditions is probable; only an appreciable diminution from normal need be assumed, because there now exist large oceanic areas, for instance in the central north Pacific, where nutrients are inadequate for a prolific microplankton.

No large regions of unusual aridity appear to have caused a reduction in the supply of detritus in the late Mesozoic—apparently there was at that time even less aridity indicated by the strata than is normal for the earth. With normal rainfall and stream-flow from topographically reduced land surfaces, the amount of eroded detritus would be reduced, and in time the resulting old soils would have been depleted of nutrients, including the "soil extracts" containing such organic compounds as thiamine and vitamin B_{12}.

There is evidence over large parts of the earth that erosion and supply of detritus (presumably including the unrecognizable "soil extracts" which are so valuable in plankton cultures) were abnormally low in late Mesozoic time, although a stratal record of that particular time is lacking or is covered by later deposits in yet larger areas.

Most of northern Europe has marine chalk deposits of late Mesozoic age, indicating relatively little supply of land-derived detritus into these marginal sea deposits, and the same is true for much of southern Europe and northern Africa. Chalk accumulation around much of the Gulf of Mexico at this time likewise implies that little detritus was derived from most of the central part of North America, and a similar condition is indicated for western Australia.

Some regions with marine deposits of this age have extensive accumulations of richly glauconitic sediments rather than chalk, and these, too, indicate that the supply of detritus was reduced, so that the slowly accumulating glauconite formed a large proportion of the sediments. Although occurring in strata of many places and ages, such highly glauconitic sediments are conspicuous in most of the strata of latest Mesozoic age along the east coast of the United States, and even in considerable areas of "never quiet" California. In the Crimea, W. A. Berggren reports [6], "The contact is characterized by abundant glauconite, immediately underlain by one to three meters of glauconitic sands with abundant oyster remains." In the major geosyncline of northern South America, Hedberg [7] reports glauconitic sediments only in the formation assigned to the latest Mesozoic and early Cenozoic, which suggests a reduced supply of sediment even in such a trough of generally rapid accumulation. Marine strata of this age in western Equatorial Africa are reported by Reyment [8] to be interbedded with extensive coal deposits, which may be evidence of some reduction of sedimentation.

Search of the literature for adequate descriptions of other areas in the latest Mesozoic and earliest Cenozoic remains to be done. Certainly there are some regions with deposits of this age, however, which indicate very active erosion and sedimentation, but, to repeat, only a subnormal supply from large areas of land should in time affect all the open oceans. One example of very active uplift and erosion during this period is known in the Rocky Mountain region, but most of the detritus accumulated in the same general region, much of it in non-marine basins, and presumably relatively little of that part supplied to the adjacent inland sea would have reached the open oceans.

Land conditions that evidently resulted in abnormally low supplies of detritus to many parts of the oceans should thus with time have affected the available nutrients of the entire volume of the ocean waters. The difficult problem is posed, however, as to whether a long period of decreasing supply could culminate in a sudden extinction of much of the protophyta which formed the base of important food chains throughout the oceans. The relation of the time factor of geological events to that of laboratory experiments is too commonly an imponderable one.

LABORATORY EXPERIMENTS AND GENERALITIES

Some laboratory experiments show that cultures of phytoplankton may thrive in normal growth and rate of proliferation as they consume unreplenished nutrients in the medium until threshold conditions are reached that cause a sudden death of all. This likewise occurs in some cultures which include populations of more than one group, because the requirements, or limiting ones, are similar for many forms. Whether such results could be meaningful for the vast expanse of oceans would certainly seem very doubtful, except that some thousands of years for extension of the results upon plankton life would appear almost as brief in the geological record as the time involved in the laboratory experiments.

Much evidence indicates that the oceans were more uniform, at least with respect to surface water temperatures, in the late Cretaceous than at present, probably with an associated decrease in intensity of upwelling and other currents, and thus the conditions were then somewhat more comparable to those of a laboratory culture. If the indicated conditions could have resulted in widespread threshold effects on most of the phytoplankton, the disastrous consequences for many higher forms of life in the food chain of the oceans would surely have followed in a geological time so brief as to appear synchronous.

Consideration of this problem obviously should include data on other groups of fossils, but information on the significant aspects seems inadequate, or needs analysis by specialists on these fossils. The interesting histograms of Newell [1], showing the changes with time in the number of families within larger groups, suggest the magnitude of the event at the end of the Mesozoic. Possible causes should be reflected better, however, by an analysis of such changes shown in populous groups of similar habitat within these higher phylogenetic groupings. For example, Newell's histograms show the extinction of all the many families of ammonites at the end of the Mesozoic, a phenomenon which appears to be of particular causal significance because all of these ammonites seem to have belonged to the marine nekton. In contrast, his histogram on families of foraminifera shows little change at this time because the very populous planktonic taxa which became extinct are classed in only a few of the many families considered. The families of crinoids plotted likewise include family groups of planktonic, benthonic, and deep- and shallow-water habitats, and separate consideration of these groups should prove interesting.

Among the benthonic "shallow-water" forms, the *Rudistae* are conspicuous as a large group which became extinct at the end of the Mesozoic. Perhaps it is significant that the sessile rudistids seem most commonly to have existed on a calcareous substrate, which suggests a water environment with detritus and nutrient supply more nearly comparable with the open ocean than with that of those near-shore organisms which lived on a substrate of clastic detritus. The latter environment should have had a more nearly adequate food supply near shore even if less food reached the open oceans. One test of this possibility might be whether those taxa of corals commonly associated with rudistids were comparably affected.

Certain geochemical tests could, perhaps, prove significant for this or some other explanation—possibly by revealing differences between critical minor elements in clays or in the phosphatic skeletal remains of fish of the latest Maestrichtian and the clays or skeletal remains from earlier Maestrichtian strata of the same area—if diagenetic changes have not obscured any original differences in these constituents. In any case, some aspects of this discussion seem to bear on the ultimate solution of this intriguing and important problem in earth history.

APPENDIX

An explanation should be added on the usage of certain terms involved in the rules of stratigraphic nomenclature. The abrupt extinctions of a surprisingly large part of Mesozoic marine life took place prior to deposition of the strata of the Danian Stage and are commonly interpreted as occurring at the end of Mesozoic time. Others, however, place the Danian in the latest Mesozoic—in which case this marked change would have occurred within latest Mesozoic time. Paleontologic aspects of this problem have received extensive review recently by Berggren [11].

The Danian was originally assigned by Desor (1846) to the Mesozoic [12]. Rules of priority in nomenclature are essential, and Desor's name for the Danian Stage should remain fixed. Such rules are not applicable, however, to Desor's placement of these Danian strata in the Cretaceous (upper Mesozoic). Precise limits at a type locality were not indicated by d'Halloy (1822) in his original designation of the Cretaceous [13], but the indicated Cretaceous strata in France have been generally accepted as including equivalents of the strata of the type Maestrichtian, which therefore was included as an upper stage of the Cretaceous. Priority would place the Danian Stage as an uppermost stage of the Cretaceous only if evidence indicated that the type Danian strata were equivalent in age to part of the chalk of the originally designated Cretaceous in France—and there seems little or no evidence for this. The Cretaceous System and other time-stratigraphic units would have little meaning as such if strata placed in them by correlations extended to the type locality from elsewhere were not subject to necessary adjustments, when and if justified by additional evidence (which, it is hoped, will eventually include consistent radiometric evidence).

REFERENCES AND NOTES

1. N. D. Newell, *Jour. Paleontology*, v. 55, p. 592 (1962).
2. A. R. Loeblich and H. Tappan, *Geol. Soc. America Bull.*, v. 75, p. 386 (1964).
3. H. C. Urey, personal communication.
4. H. M. Bolli, A. R. Loeblich, Jr., H. Tappan, *U.S. Nat. Mus. Bull.*, v. 215, p. 22 (1957).
5. W. A. Berggren, *Internat. Geol. Cong. 21st Sess. Rept.*, pt. 5, p. 181 (1960).
6. W. A. Berggren, personal communication.
7. H. D. Hedberg, *Geol. Soc. America Bull.*, 48, p. 1995 (1937).
8. R. A. Reyment, personal communication.
9. M. N. Bramlette and E. Martini, *Micropaleontology*, v. 10, p. 295 (1964).

10. I thank my colleagues, W. R. Riedel and F. L. Parker, for valued criticisms and suggestions.

11. W. A. Berggren, *Stockholm Contrib. Geology*, v. 11, no. 5, p. 103 (1964).
12. E. Desor, *Soc. géol. France Bull.*, ser. 2, v. 4, p. 179 (1846).
13. J. J. O. d'Halloy, *Annales Mines*, v. 7, p. 373 (1822).

70

Paleobiogeography of the Marine Realm

PRESTON CLOUD
1961

From *Oceanography* (AAAS Publication 67), edited by Mary Sears, pp. 151–200. American Association for the Advancement of Science, 1961. Reprinted with permission of the publisher.

The ultimate aim of biogeography is to express and interpret the dispersal of the individual components of the biosphere through the filter systems of physical geography and environment and their organization into distinctive, areally limited communities, provinces, and realms.

It is self-evident that, in order to survive as more than an ecologic or evolutionary curiosity, a species must be able to migrate, to install itself in new locations, to mature and reproduce there, and to adapt itself to local conditions of existence over a sustained interval of time. The degree to which different organisms do this summarizes the ecologic vitality of the species and is the best measure of success in the basic competition of all life for a larger measure of the total energy supply. The patterns created in the struggle for perpetuity are the essence of descriptive biogeography and paleobiogeography, which necessarily precede all useful efforts toward interpretation.

These static patterns, moreover, have dynamic and historic causes of such complexity that only the boldest have dared confront them, and they too commonly with extraneous and weakly documented hypotheses—frequently repeated in substantiation of themselves after cycling through other and unfamiliar disciplines. The results of such circular reasoning are well illustrated by various ad hoc land bridges, whose unbridled rising and sinking in the late nineteenth and early twentieth centuries explained alike the similarities of geographically distant biotas, and the dissimilarities of neighboring ones, both at sea and on land. Handlirsch (1937) and Schmidt (1955) have effectively demolished the general application of this now diminishingly popular mechanism (see Croizat, 1958, for the opposite view), which, for the moment, merely illustrates the need for verifiable interpretive principles and generalizations.

Modern marine biogeography at least has the advantage of recognized ancestry (Forbes, 1844; Schmarda, 1853; Forbes and Godwin-

Austen, 1859; Regnard, 1891; Ortmann, 1896; Petersen, 1914, 1915a, 1915b; Ekman, 1953; Pérès and Picard, 1955; Pérès, 1957; Hedgpeth, 1957b, 1957c, 1957d). Even the parentage of paleobiogeography is obscure, however.

D'Orbigny, who was more sensitive to the qualities of his legitimate scientific children (Heron-Allen, 1917), devoted two pages of his famous *Cours élémentaire*, etc. (1849, Pt. 1, pp. 6–7) to stressing the importance of knowing all about the conditions of existence, only to conclude (op. cit., 1851, Pt. 2, [1] p. 241) that "Depuis le commencement du monde animé jusqu'aux derniers étages des terrains tertiaires (sic), on voit . . . une répartition uniforme des êtres tout à fait indépendante des lignes isothermes actuelles, et . . . toujours la faune tropicale"—a paleontological part truth that to some degree still encumbers paleobiogeographical inquiry.

Neumayr (1883, 1885) subsequently reached a contrary conclusion from his global analysis of the Jurassic faunas, delineating climatic zones comparable to those of the present day. Although Neumayr's zonation has since been discredited in detail by Uhlig (1911) and Arkell (1956, pp. 615–618), these authors agree that there was at least a broad climatic zonation roughly parallel to present latitudinal belts in Middle and Late Jurassic time; and fluctuating climatic zonation parallel to the present equator is now widely accepted for the Cenozoic and late Mesozoic (see Durham, 1959, for a recent summary). For Paleozoic time in general the question is still moot, and much additional work will be needed to resolve it.

Johannes Walther laid the basis for subsequent expansion of marine paleobiogeography as a distinct empirical discipline with his *Einleitung in die Geologie als historische Wissenschaft* in 1893–1894, and many paleontologists and geologists since Neumayr and Walther have constructed paleogeographic, or, more accurately, shoreline maps, utilizing various combinations of geologic and paleobiologic evidence. Recent activities in marine paleobiogeography are exemplified in stimulating papers by Caster (1952), George (1958), Minato (1953), Ager (1956), and Davis and Elliott (1957)—named in stratigraphic sequence. The summary account by Davis and Elliott on the early Eocene London clay sea deserves special notice, both because of the wealth of information available and for the skill and balance with which these authors utilized it to reconstruct the living conditions and biogeographic affinities of this classic sequence.

Growing interest in the fundamental aspects of paleobiogeography is reflected by the synthetic works of the Termiers (1952, 1957, 1959; Wells, 1953) and by the fact that the first session of the Soviet Union's All-State Paleontological Society in 1955 was devoted to "Problems of paleobiogeography and biostratigraphy" (Stepanov, 1957). On the western side of the Atlantic, the paleobiogeographic data are one of many ingredients of the U.S. Geological Survey's program to produce a series of paleotectonic maps, which will summarize the historical development from Cambrian onward of sedimentation, biotal migration, and crustal movement within the continental United States (McKee et al., 1956, 1959).

The pressing need, as in most empirical disciplines today, is for a clear sequence of integrative principles that will strike more directly and surely through the growing clutter of facts to the yet distant treasures beyond. The cycle is a vicious one for, generally speaking, large masses of data must still be assimilated, organized, and correctly interpreted on regional or worldwide scales before the essential principles can be confidently formulated or the unique explanation deduced for any given set of local or temporary conditions. This should not deter us, however, from formulating, as best we can, such working principles as will give structure to existing knowledge and direction to new research.

GENERAL LIMITATIONS OF PALEOBIOGEOGRAPHIC EVIDENCE

Paleobiogeography is no exception to the rule that all constructions of the mind are beset by two groups of limiting factors, human and objective.

Because thought processes are complex and language is linear, the mental image of one mind cannot be conveyed instantaneously and unerringly to another except in some forms of mathematical expression, which do not apply generally to the complexities of the biosphere. An imperfect means of communication at best, language may become perversely irrational in relation to facts or concepts with which one is emotionally involved. Weak arguments may then be bolstered with unwarrantedly strong statements, and, by way of compensation, strong probabilities may be stated with uncalled for reserve. This is the involvement paradox (Figure 70.1) manifestations of which include the dubious use of expressions such as *must be, doubtless,* and *obviously*—warning flags that invite both reader and writer to reconsideration of the evidence. The more interpretive the subject the more prevalent the effects of the involvement paradox, and the focal problem of paleobiogeography (and paleomagnetism) is the highly interpretive subject of the former arrangement and orientation of the earth.

Objective factors affecting the application of paleobiologic evidence to paleobiogeographic problems are both external and internal, but all are expressed and controlled by the broad external conditions of geographic range, habitat variation, and time. The general effect of these conditioning factors on the applications of the evidence is roughly indicated in Figure 70.2, where paleobiogeography stands, within the matrix of evolution, as the intermediate keystone of the pyramid described by the long- and wide-ranged, ecologically restricted biotic elements that make the best paleoecologic indicators, and the wide-ranged, facies-crossing forms of short time span that are favored for stratigraphic markers. Paleontology in practice is not so simple as that, but it is a fact that a wide range of intermediate geographic and habitat characteristics is of interest for paleobiogeography, provided the species are not too ubiquitous; and provided the ecology, evolutionary sequence, and time dimension can be supplied by other forms.

No biogeographic or paleobiogeographic conclusions are any better than the data and interpretive principles on which they are based, so an accurate and refined systematics and a knowledge of the geographical distribution of modern organisms are at the base of the pyramid. Without this foundation the structure floats in thin air. To assume, for instance, as some have done, that wide geographic separation excludes the prospect of systematic identity is to bias the data. It is only by critical analysis of objective similarities and differences between biotas, in context with the inferred relations of land and sea and the paleoecologic implications of the enclosing sediments, that useful concepts of migration

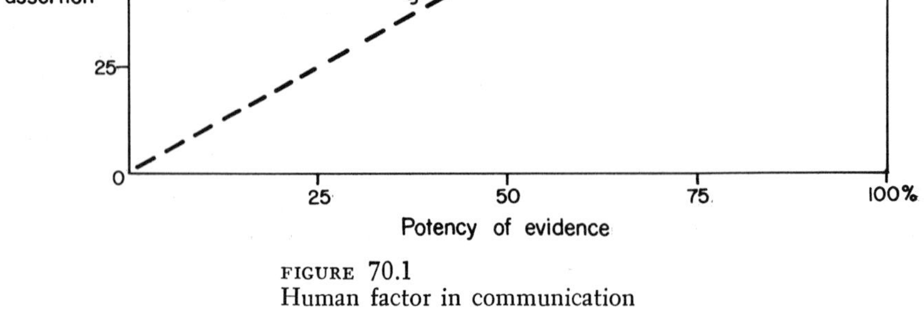

FIGURE 70.1
Human factor in communication

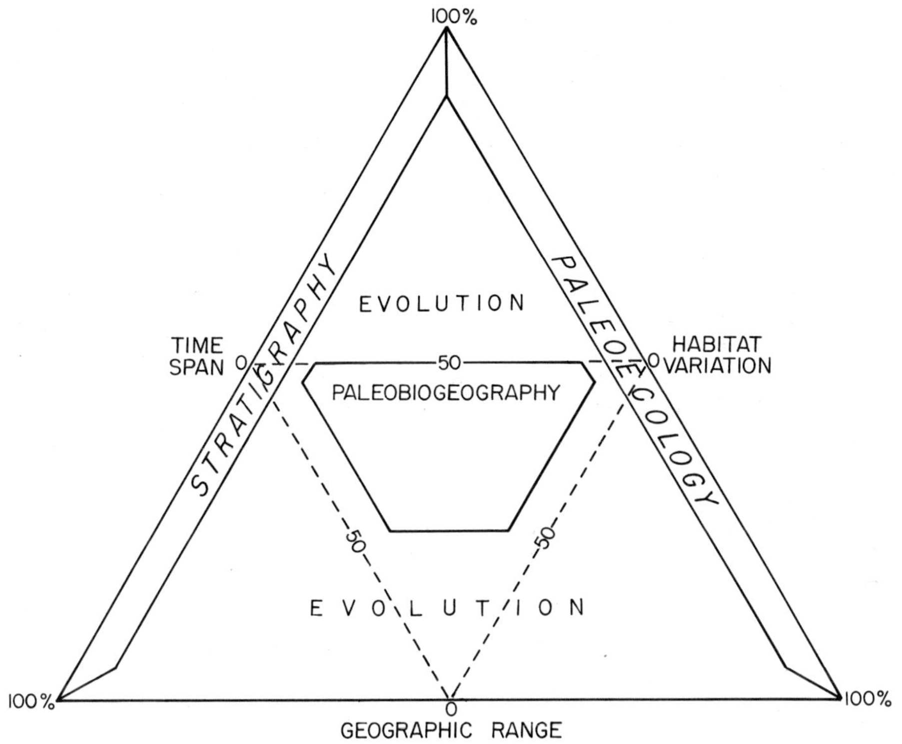

FIGURE 70.2
External conditions affecting the application of paleobiological data

routes and dispersal mechanisms can be evolved for comparison with the land connections, current systems, and regional climatologic variation demanded by given earth models.

DISTRIBUTION OF MARINE ORGANISMS

According to the basic geological principle of uniformitarianism, which uses observable and testable processes and dynamic relations as the keys to past events, the interpretation of marine paleobiogeographic data is based on analysis of the mechanisms that affect the survival and dispersal of organisms and organic remains in the present seas (Figure 70.3). Given a particular set of geographic, climatologic, and historic conditions, the variables involved are of three kinds: external, internal, and cobiotic. External factors are those of the physical and chemical environment; internal factors are those that exist within, and are an integral part of, the organism itself; and cobiotic factors are those introduced by the rest of the contiguous biosphere, including that part of the biosphere which may live within, consume, or destroy the dead remains of the organism in question. The response of the organism to these variables is expressed in its adaptive and competitive characteristics and ultimately in its range in environment, space, and time. The biotal composition of a given area or habitat at a given time is a composite function of metabolic intensity and rate of evolution (e.g., Bray and White, 1954, pp. 83–84), duration of biota and environment (e.g., Fischer, 1960, p. 80), and intrinsic characteristics of environments and organisms. The limiting conditions of existence for a particular species at a given place may involve any of those obtaining at the time of, or before, its existence. The principal influences that affect the biogeographical characteristics of the organic community or biome, however, are those major external variables that undergo the maximum fluctuation (e.g., Jones, 1950, p. 299).

EXTERNAL FACTORS OF EXISTENCE

External factors influencing the geographic distribution of the marine biotas are, of course, vastly different from those at work above sea level. Water is heavier, more viscous, a much poorer heat conductor, a far superior heat reservoir and transfer system, and has a far lower gaseous oxygen content and higher freezing point than air. Ocean water is richer in most kinds of dissolved solids and has a far more uniform composition than fresh water. Migration routes for land animals are likely to be barriers and isolating mechanisms for marine ones.

Let us look at the principal external variables that influence the distribution of marine biotas under given geographic, climatologic, and historic configuration. In Figure 70.3 the systematic variables define major biogeographical provinces or zones; local variables are shown at the top. Forbes and Godwin-Austen (1859, p. 17) recognized these same variables a century ago when they stated: "The distribution of marine animals is primarily determined by the influence of climate or temperature, sea-composition and depth, in which pressure, and the diminution of light are doubtless important elements." Plants do not fit the same detailed scheme, but they are equally subject to the three basic variables, sunlight, temperature, and salinity.

Sunlight, of course, is the primary source of radiant energy that impels the whole earthly biosphere and is responsible for all but a minute fraction of its available heat budget. Together with the earth's trajectory and rotation, and the pull of the sun on its equatorial bulge, sunlight determines the latitudinal climatic zones, which designate by other words the amount of local available energy. It determines the vertical division of the hydrosphere into photic, dysphotic, and aphotic zones, which can also be expressed in terms of photosynthesis, oxygenation, and temperature.

Temperature, which is effectively one expression of light, provides us with the most concrete basis of biogeographic subdivision

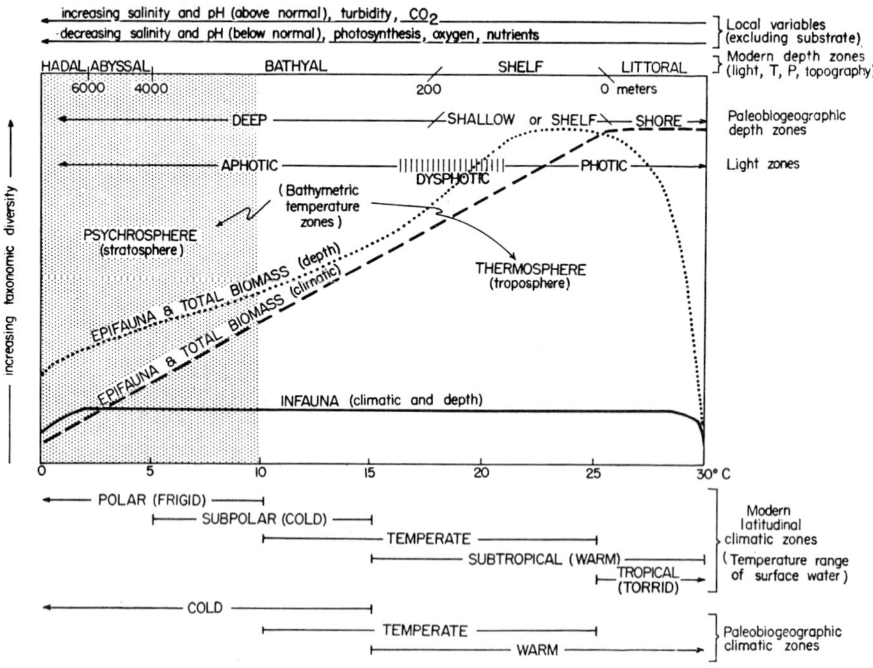

FIGURE 70.3
Principal external variables affecting the distribution of marine biotas

and the most convenient circumglobal terms. Global temperature and temperature zonation has, of course, varied in the past, from causes both terrestrial (e.g., Plass, 1956) and extraterrestrial (e.g., Brooks, 1951, pp. 1016–1017); and, for the paleobiogeographer, it is essential not to confuse temperature subdivisions with geodetic terms such as tropical, polar, or equatorial. The sequence warm, temperate, and cold, with the temperature ranges indicated (Figure 70.3), describes the local conditions and biotal affinities as closely as the paleobiogeographer can usually recognize them, and without commitment as to orientation, subsequent movement, and geodesy. In paleobiogeography also it is rarely meaningful to attempt to approximate depth zones more closely than intertidal, shallow, and deep, with *deep* as here used including everything below the photic zone (or "wave base"). Quantitative depth and temperature limits naturally should be estimated wherever the evidence permits, but the usual kinds of paleontological and sedimentological evidence are apt to limit depth evaluation of ancient seas to more ambiguous terms such as shelf, shallow shelf, deep shelf, shallow slope, deep slope, basin, or shore zone. The limiting effects of temperature and other variables may affect the organism differently at different stages of existence; Hutchins (1947) showed how upper and lower seasonal temperature limits on installation and survival produce four basic types of latitudinal zonation of interest to zoogeographers.

Salinity affects the inhabitants of the hydrosphere through osmosis and secondarily through density, light penetration, pH, and the distribution of mineral nutrients.

The distribution of life in the marine realm under conditions existing at any given time is a reflection of the variables mentioned, plus depth, pressure, gas content, and turbidity of the water and substrate conditions. The paleobiogeographer has only the fossils and the enclosing sediments, which may or may not have been associated in life. He must deduce the rest from the biological characteristics, regional distribution, and evolution of his fossils, and from the geochemical, mineralogical, textural, and structural characteristics of his sediments.

It is gratifying to know, therefore, from contemporaneous biogeographic and ecologic research that there are distinctive patterns in the variety, numerical abundance, sizes, and even shapes of organisms that denote trends, if not specific points, in the external environment of the life assemblages concerned (Clements and Shelford, 1939; MacGinitie and MacGinitie, 1949; Allee et al., 1949; Jones, 1950; Ekman, 1953; Hedgpeth, 1957a; Fischer, 1960). The curves shown in Figure 70.3, to be sure, are only a caricature of the changes in relative taxonomic variety (including variety but *not* bulk of total biomass) that accompany changes in the external variables, but they do suggest their general shape. We owe to Petersen (1914, 1915a, 1915b) and Thorson (e.g., 1957) the emphasis on the great variation displayed by the epifauna, and to some extent by the nekton and plankton, as contrasted to the intrinsically less varied infauna (*in* the substrate, not the endofauna, which includes internal symbionts). This difference reflects the closer interrelations of the epifauna with external climate and associated plant and animal communities. If it were not known, it would have been logical to deduce that the infauna occupies the ecologic realm of least variation and greatest stability.

I have summarized elsewhere (Cloud, 1959b, p. 931) the paleobiogeographically useful and well-known gradients in variety, abundance, and size with temperature, salinity, and depth, and these are discussed in articles by several authors in Hedgpeth (1957a) and by Jones (1950). It will suffice here to underscore that these gradients are broadly similar in kind and are to be distinguished primarily on the basis of abruptness of variation, associated changes in morphology and composition of the biotas, and sedimentological evidence, including that from isotopic and geochemical methods.

In general, however, the paleobiogeographer is safe in concluding (Figure 70.3) that great biotal variation is presumptive evidence of warm, shallow seas of normal salinity and that widespread faunas of limited variety and relatively persistent composition (and commonly large numbers of individuals) are likely to represent waters that were cold or deep, or both. Limited variety and abruptly changing composition of biotas implies local salinity deviations, especially if the biotas include a relatively large proportion of internally stable or homoiosmotic organisms such as fishes and some crustaceans, and exclude internally variable or poikilosmotic forms, such as echinoderms, cephalopods, brachiopods, bryozoans, and corals.*

INTERNAL AND COBIOTIC FACTORS OF EXISTENCE

Internal variables affecting the geographic distribution of marine organisms include their individual metabolism and mobility, frequency and range of movement, manner of and adaptations for movement or fixation, sensory responses, size and specific gravity, mode and time of reproduction, and length of larval life. To these should be added their adaptability to variations in the physical, chemical, and gaseous conditions of the external environment; their reproductive lability; and their evolutionary intensity, which is a function of metabolism, rate of change, and time.

The cobiotic factors include all facets of competition for the available energy resources —light and mineral nutrient absorption by the photosynthesizers, nature of and availability to the organic nutrient supply by the heterotrophs, predation, symbiosis, and degree of occupancy of available ecologic niches.

The internal and cobiotic factors have important effects on the numbers and individual survival prospects of the various categories of organisms, as roughly indicated in Figure 70.4, a scheme inspired by the work of Blegvad (1915) and Imbrie (1959). Size, reproductive characteristics, and competition are not specifically included in this diagram. Number of offspring, however, decreases, and size of individual, length of parental dependency, and degree of parental care in general increase toward the left, with decreasing size of the breeding population. Competitive factors are involved throughout. Moreover, an important paleobiogeographical exception to the direction of size increase is provided in the case of the shelled invertebrates. Other factors being equal, they grow larger in the presence of an abundant and regular supply of calcium carbonate, or in the warmer, normally salty seas of any given plane in time.

There is, in any event, a relationship between mode of life, size of breeding population, number of offspring, and individual survival prospects which is important to the paleobiogeographer. But survival of the individual is only one of the factors that controls survival of the species, and there is probably an optimum size to breeding populations which varies in the same direction as numbers of offspring and is related in some way to mutation incidence. The paleobiogeographical evidence, moreover, is seriously affected by the ability of a species to survive in the rocks as well as in time. Because of this, paleontologists concentrate on organisms with preservable hard parts, on special types of deposits where the imprints or remains of soft-bodied organisms may be preserved, and on sedimentological evidence that bears on the nature of burial and amount of movement after death.

DISPERSAL

The factors already discussed define the conditions of existence. Whether a given species, community, or biota actually exists at the various places where it might, if it could gain a foothold and displace competitors, depends also on its ability to be dispersed, on the migration routes available for dispersal, and on the barriers and natural filters that block dispersal or permit the passage only of particular biotic elements, in a particular direction, or by chance. This, in turn, depends in large degree on the global wind and water circulation, and on the geographic configuration of the earth, which varied in the past. The factors involved are well illustrated by the phenomenon of bipolarity (e.g., Wimpenny, 1941); by differences and similarities between the Recent and

* By convention, the widely employed prefixes *poikilo* and *homoio* designate marked *internal* variation vs. little or no variation, whereas *eury* and *steno* refer to *external* tolerance. A homoiosmotic organism is also euryhaline because its ability to regulate the salinity of its body fluids permits it to survive a wide range of external salinities. A poikilothermal animal is characteristically stenothermal in habitat tolerance, because its inability to regulate body temperature is deleterious under wide external temperature variation.

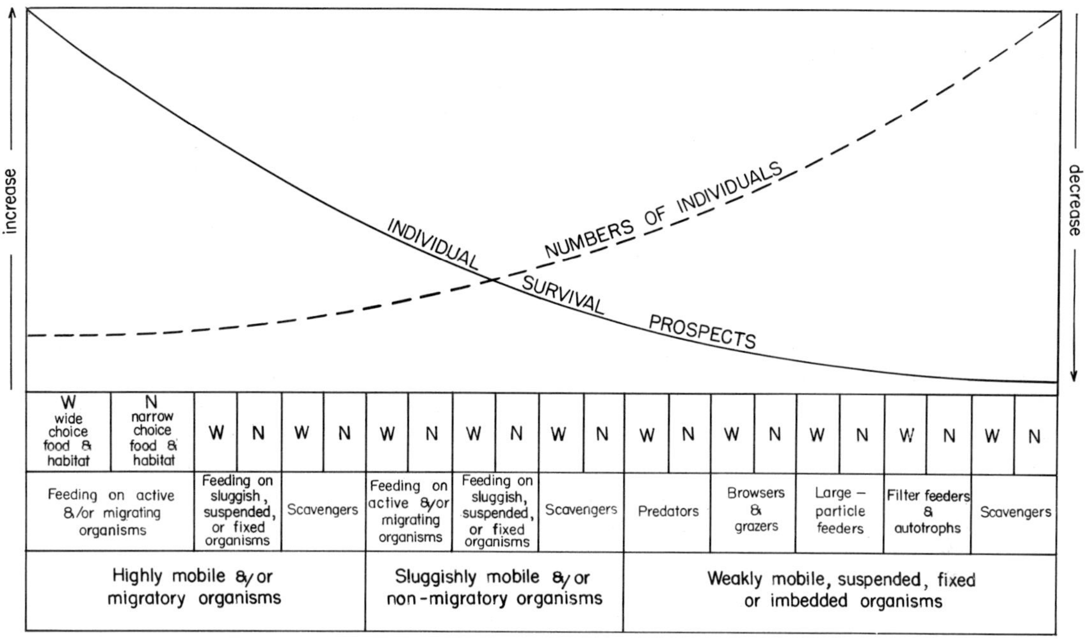

FIGURE 70.4
Numbers and individual survival prospects of marine organisms regulated by different internal and cobiotic factors

Tertiary marine faunas on opposite sides of the Isthmus of Panama (Woodring, 1954, 1959); by the now classic differences between the Tertiary mammalian faunas of North and South America (e.g., Simpson, 1953, pp. 21, 55); by recent Mediterranean faunal changes (Pérès and Picard, 1959); and by the well-known marsupial faunas of Australia and the success with which later introduced placental mammals were able to establish themselves there. Some of the variables are illustrated in Figure 70.5, and others will be discussed.

The reproductive cycle is the internal control. All vertebrates and ovoviviparous invertebrates disperse by moving themselves, or by transport on other moving objects. Most marine invertebrates and plants, however, broadcast numbers of fertilized eggs, larvae, spores, or seeds which are carried about by currents, wind, or more esoteric mechanisms. High mortality is balanced by larger numbers of offspring (Figure 70.4), and is reduced in some bottom-dwelling invertebrates by a limited ability of the individual larva to select its substrate (Thorson, 1946, pp. 463–466).

Other factors being equal, highest probabilities for dispersal are naturally enjoyed by species with large breeding populations that live at times of the maximum extent of favorable climatic and ecologic conditions and optimum geography, as Axelrod (1952) showed for the terrestrial angiosperms. On the other hand, the more widely spaced the sites of habitable environment, the more ingenious are the devices through which the successful migrant attains dispersal. This is particularly true of certain euryhaline estuarine species which may go through resting stages like those of the nonmarine mollusks, during which they can be transported on floating objects or blown about by the wind; of the cold-water diatoms, whose resting spores may be carried across the inhospitable equatorial regions by way of the upper atmosphere; and of the polychaete annelids. The polychaetes, indeed, have the largest number of cosmopolitan species among the marine benthos (Thorson, 1950, pp. 30–33, 38; Cloud, 1959a, pp. 395–396) simply because those species, like some of the actinians and sponges, are able to undergo different forms of reproduction and larval development according to local conditions (Thorson, 1946, pp. 427–429, 476; 1950). Otherwise widespread living organisms, some narrowly restricted in their adult choice of habitable conditions, are characterized as a rule by easily dispersed, long-lasting early stages, and it is a proper working hypothesis to consider that the same was probably true in the past.

The most widely distributed types of marine organisms in modern times are as follows.

1. Actively nektonic organisms such as fish, cetaceans, and some cephalopods.
2. Planktonic organisms, and those which at some stage in their lives may attach themselves to, or be carried naturally within, members of the migrating nekton or floating objects such as driftwood or pumice. (The paleogeographer does not bother about ships except in choosing analogies, or before Jurassic time about birds.)
3. Brackish-water mollusks, plants, and insects characterized by viviparous or parthenogenetic reproduction; or by spores and resting stages which may be transported by wind (and birds), or on floating or swimming objects, and which may undergo long periods of estivation.
4. Organisms such as marine annelids which have great larval and reproductive lability.
5. Species of shallow, warm, or temperate marine waters with long-lasting planktonic larval stages.
6. Deep-water and cold-water species having abbreviated larval life or viviparous (including ovoviviparous) reproduction and able to move or drift with deep currents (Bruun, 1957, p. 663).

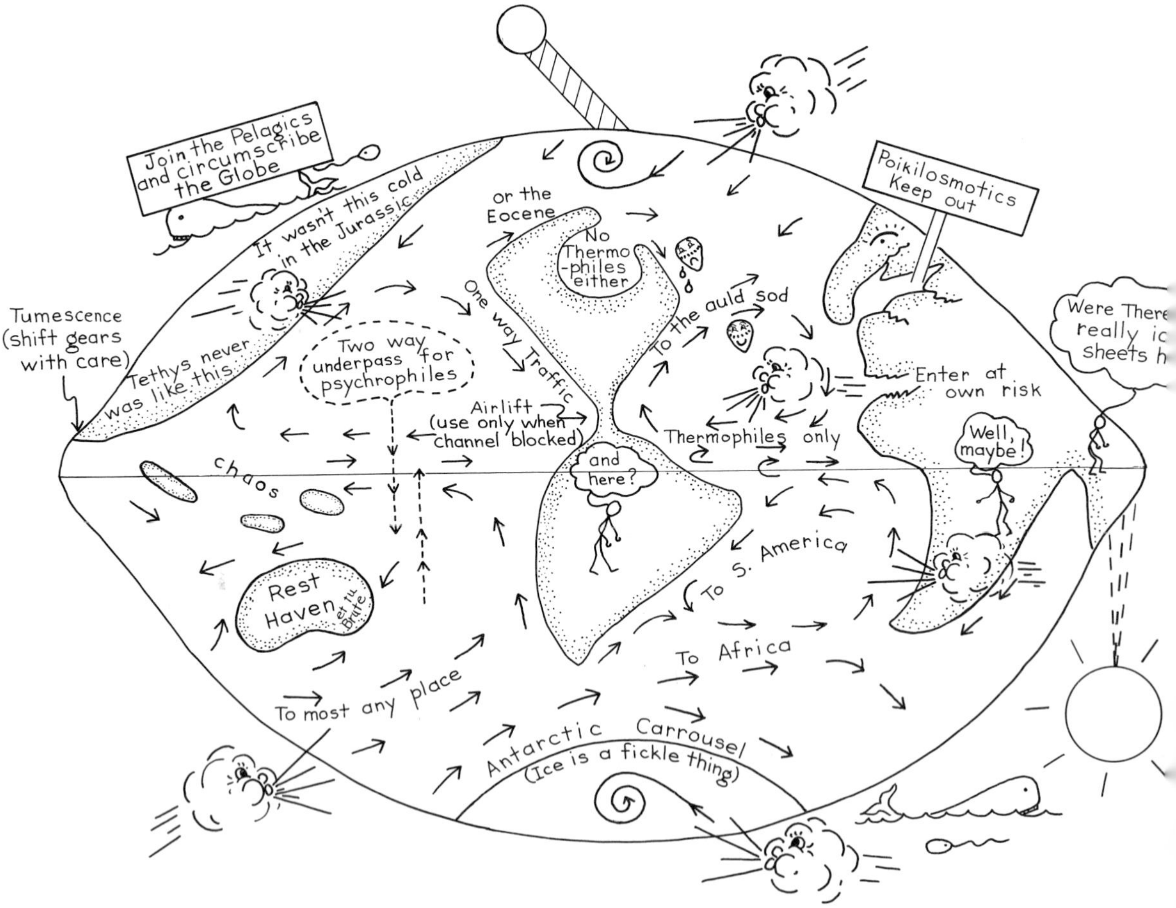

FIGURE 70.5
Life at sea as the paleobiogeographer sees it and as it might have been

The paleobiogeographer should have good reason for eliminating the above categories, as well as the peculiarly geologic uncertainties and the statistical probability of viable freak transport, before concluding either that geographic factors require otherwise similar fossil populations to belong to nomenclaturally different species, or that drastic paleogeographic changes are in order.

Wind transport deserves emphasis beyond the mere notation that dispersal of spore-forming organisms can be so achieved. Since the volume and weight of an object varies as the cube of its median diameter and the surface area only as the square, it is obvious that the likelihood of movement by wind increases with decrease in size, assuming similar specific gravity and, on the part of aquatic organisms, proximity to air-water boundary. As early as 1830, Ehrenberg described a variety of microorganisms from atmospheric dust, but Charles Lindbergh made the first *in situ* collections of high-altitude aerial plankton on his flight over the Greenland ice cap in 1933 (Meier, 1935). Gislén (1948, pp. 124–125) reports that it is common for animals up to a few millimeters long (especially fish) to be transported by winds, and he records aerial transport of animals as much as 10 cm long. If inferred prevailing or seasonal wind tracks fall in the right places and directions for the times involved, they could provide sweepstakes routes (Simpson, 1940a, pp. 152–157; 1953, pp. 23–25) whereby very rare but significant successful passages might account for the transport of exotic marine biotal elements that otherwise appear to demand the movement of established land barriers or the emplacement of temporary shoals across historic deeps.

With regard to the more orthodox forms of transport by water currents, various limiting factors are involved. Most important are the characteristic sites of adult and larval existence and the presence of tropisms with regard to light, current, or bottom; the direction, orientation, temperature, and depth of the current or passage along which movement may take place; and the nature and orientation of natural barriers and filters.

Planktonic eggs and larvae are more easily dispersed, but those that stay on or near the bottom are less likely to be eaten or to drift into unfavorable areas. The advantage varies according to the conditions and degree of continuity of tolerable adult and breeding habitat. The dispersal and persistence of species that inhabit warm and shallow waters is favored by larvae that drift near the surface in the mild equatorial currents, provided larval existence is not so long as to carry them beyond contiguous favorable bottom, or is long enough to ensure dispersal across surrounding deeps and near-continuous occupancy of more remote shoals. A similar degree of drifting for the stenothermal benthos of cold and deep waters presents greater hazard of introduction to inclement biogeographic realms. Natural selection, therefore, accounts for the abbreviated larval life or viviparity that characterizes cold-loving (psychrophilic) species and those of narrow depth range (stenobathyal). In the cold-temperate waters around Denmark, Thorson (1946, pp. 472–479) found that about one-third of the bottom invertebrates have a short or no pelagic life, whereas two-thirds have a larval life little exceeding three weeks on an average (longer in the same species in wintertime, presumably because of metabolic retardation). It would be interesting to have a similar study of the reproduction and larval development of warm water species. This should show lengths of planktonic larval life corresponding to the spacing of deeps and shoals, and degree of endemism.

Consider the implications of larval life and currents for dispersal. In an ordinary half-knot current a floating object could travel 170 km in a week or 500 km in three weeks; a two- to four-knot current like the Gulf Stream, if it were persistent, could travel 700 to 4000 km over the same time. Conceivably, therefore, a species with long-lived larvae and luck could cross the narrower parts of the Atlantic in one jump! If the larvae are attracted to light (phototropic) and currents (rheotactic), they are more likely to stay near the surface and in the main drift, and long larval life with a range of substrate selectivity (Thorson, 1946, p. 479) accordingly increases the possible distance of individual dispersal and the prospects of continued existence of the species, assuming favorable current patterns.

If, on the other hand, planktonic larvae or adults habitually live at depths greater than those of available transport channels, they can be moved through such channels only as a result of upwelling movements at the right time and place. Thus many pelagic microorganisms are rare in shallow-water deposits because they live suspended at some favored range of depth well below the surface, perhaps most commonly near the bottom of the photic zone where the phytoplankton have the first chance at upwelling mineral nutrients and the zooplankton the richest grazing grounds. An illustration of the possible paleobiogeographic significance of this is provided by the Tertiary Panamanian passage, which at times may have retarded the movement from Atlantic to Pacific (and the reverse) of deep-floating plankton, while facilitating the passage of near-surface plankton, including the pelagic larvae of benthonic species. The mere fact of a pelagic existence does not assure wide or instantaneous dispersal, nor does a benthonic adult life exclude geologically rapid and wide distribution.

Clearly, also, the intrinsic characteristics of migration routes and obstacles to migration are highly significant. Simpson (1940a, 1940b, 1952, 1953), who has discussed this question philosophically, with special regard to terrestrial mammals, aptly describes the paths of interchange as corridors, filters, and sweepstakes routes. Most migration routes in the sea are to some degree filters. Currents provide easy downstream transport but retard upstream movement. East-west currents are likely to be temperature barriers to shelf and littoral biotas, and north-south currents, like the American limb of the Gulf Stream, may abandon the hapless larva (or adult) beyond the limits of its temperature tolerance or reproductive range. Passes between land areas or into epicontinental seas may be subject to fluctuations of salinity and turbidity that will exclude organisms sensitive to these variables.

Land masses that trend from north to south are likely to deflect currents into areas where they would not otherwise flow, as the north equatorial current of the Atlantic Ocean is turned northward under the influence of the Coriolis effect to become the Gulf Stream. Sharp faunal distinction is common from eastern to western sides of such lands. Wide oceanic depths, like those of the eastern North Pacific, are barriers or sweepstakes routes to benthonic biotas in the absence of strong (steady or episodic) transverse surface currents. Given continued accretion of the hydrosphere (Rubey, 1952) or subsidence of ocean basins through geologic time, however, combined with long duration of present or antecedent oceanic rises, even transoceanic "bridges" become possible at some places and times (Axelrod, 1960, Figs. 6, 8, and 9). For the broadly cosmopolitan abyssal communities that cover half the globe (Bruun, 1957) and for the cold-loving bipolar benthos, the depths themselves are corridors beneath the equatorial surface waters and staging areas for invasions of the hadal depths (Bruun, 1957, pp. 654–661; Wolff, 1960).

INTERPRETIVE BASIS OF MARINE PALEOBIOGEOGRAPHY

GENERAL PROBABILITIES

Those familiar with the geographic distribution, sedimentary associations, and nature of the fossil marine biotas recognize that parallels can be drawn with the distribution of modern marine organisms. Some paleobiogeographic generalizations that appear to apply over a wide range or all of fossiliferous time are listed on Table 70.1. With the exception of No. 14, these categories are not considered further. The citation of case histories would only document associations that follow from distribution characteristics already discussed, and I have reviewed the more specifically ecologic principles and methods elsewhere (Cloud, 1959b). It is of more interest in the present context to get on to subjects involving latitudinal zonation and orientation, for which a brief review of paleoclimatology is prerequisite.

PALEOCLIMATOLOGIC ESSENTIALS

Paleobiogeography, in fact, may be characterized as the mirror of paleoclimatology, in which the blemishes that make it interesting are due to geographic or physiographic (including geomorphologic, bathymetric, and substratal or faciological) isolation, the filtering properties of migration routes, and the intrinsic properties of biologic systems—giving rise to the provincial categories recognized by the

TABLE 70.1
Some recurrent broad categories of marine communities and biotas, and their general paleobiogeographic implications*

Distribution	Variety	Special systematic features**	Endemism	Probable general paleobiogeography	Termier provinces
Wide	Small	Shells thin or absent, poikilosmotics present	Slight to moderate	Circumpolar or deep water	Climatologic or Physiographic
Local	Small and consistent	Shells thin or absent, poikilosmotics present	Marked	Isolated cold	Relict-Physiographic
Local	Small and consistent	Shells thin or absent, poikilosmotics rare or missing	Marked	Isolated hypersaline	Relict-Physiographic
Local	Small and sharply gradient	Thin shelled mollusks, fish, and crustaceans; poikilosmotics rare or missing	Marked	Estuarine	Relict-Physiographic
Wide	Large	Abundant calcareous shells	Slight to moderate	Temperate, shallow, and essentially continuous	Climatologic
Wide	Maximum	Abundant and commonly thick calcareous shells or tests	Slight to moderate	Warm, shallow, and essentially continuous	Climatologic
Wide	Large	Abundant and commonly thick calcareous shells or tests	Moderate	Warm, shallow, and discontinuous	Climatologic-Stepwise
Local	Moderate	Abundant and commonly thick calcareous shells or tests	Marked	Warm, shallow, and isolated	Relict-Physiographic
Wide	Moderate to large	Microscopic and non-calcareous, with filaments or floating devices	Slight	Circumglobal cold pelagic	Climatologic-Expansive
Wide	Moderate to small	Microscopic and calcareous with filaments or floating-devices	Slight	Circumglobal warm pelagic	Climatologic-Expansive
Wide	Small	Aquatic vertebrates	Very slight to none	Circumglobal to world-wide, nektonic	Expansive
Wide	Small	Aquatic angiosperms	Slight to marked	Shelf	Physiographic
Wide	Small	Dasycladacean or codiacean algae	Slight to moderate	Warm, photic	Climatologic-Physiographic
Wide	Small to moderate	Mainly tracks and burrows of regular pattern in flysch facies sediments	Broad similarity through time and space	Deep, infauna preponderant	Physiographic-Stepwise

* Exclusive of many significant components of special and overlapping application such as corals and small benthonic Foraminifera.
** Invertebrate unless specified.

Termiers (1957, 1959, pp. 81–98) and listed at the right side of Table 70.1.

Climate itself depends on the circulation of the atmosphere (Figure 70.6) and the sea (Figure 70.5), the distribution of land and water, the position and inclination of the earth's rotational axis, the composition of the atmosphere, the path of the earth about the sun, and on strictly solar manifestations. Wexler (1957) has summarized modern concepts of atmospheric circulation; Trewartha (1954) has discussed the elements of modern climate; Landsberg (1958) has reviewed recent climatic trends; and Brooks (1949), Schwarzbach (1950), and Lasareff (1929) have suggested physical methods for deducing ancient climates. Shapley et al. (1953) have reviewed possible causes, effects, and evidences of climatic change; and Rukhin (1957) and Durham (1959) have summarized paleoclimatic indicators and manifestations. The slender classic by Dubois (1895) is as nice an illustration as we have of the nature of the geologic evidence and reasoning, despite the 65 years that have elapsed since it was published. And, for the future, the way to more rigorous analysis of paleooceanographic data and reproduction of ancient marine currents has been outlined by Stommel (1957) and von Arx (1957).

From these and other works we know that the rotation and frictional effects of the earth, the position of the polar axis, the pull of the sun on the equatorial bulge, secular variations of the solar heat budget, and thermal variations of the atmosphere are responsible for the major wind fields—their location, orientation, breadth, and strength—and that wind patterns and size and orientation of land masses are the principal determinants of ocean currents. If, to these, we add the Coriolis deflection, the monsoon effect, the thermal influence on oceanic circulation, and the general relief and land connections, we have named the paleoclimatic and paleocurrent factors that can profitably be considered, and which give rise to the broad biogeographical subdivisions of land and sea, best reflected on a worldwide basis by the distribution of marine plankton (Figure 70.7).

Employing a rotating tank apparatus similar to that of von Arx (1957) to create patterns of oceanic circulation for various paleogeographic models for the same time interval, and allowing for effects on the planetary wind and current system of secular variations in the latitudinal distribution of heat (Brooks, 1949, pp. 50–53), the paleobiogeographer could experimentally determine which circulation pattern best satisfies known biotal distributions and his climatic inferences. He can, of course, do the same thing with a crayon on a globe, or with pencil and paper, but in any case it is of value to check the dynamic details on experimental models. Such an approach could greatly improve the basis of paleoclimatology and more effectively test the relative probability of appar-

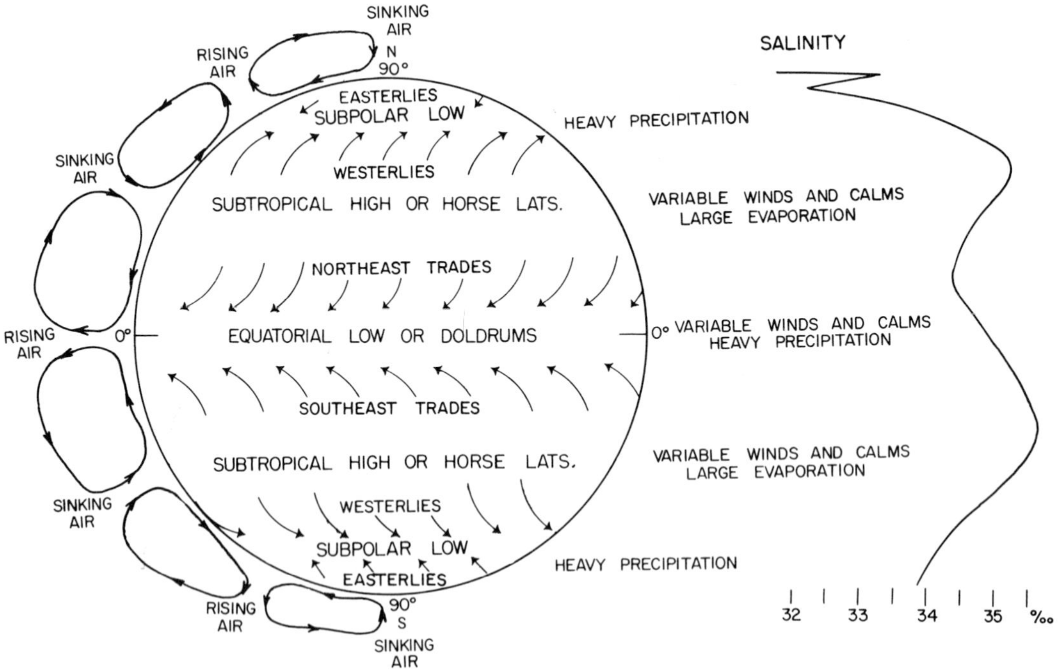

FIGURE 70.6
Schematic tropospheric wind system. For a hypothetical water-covered earth with strong latitudinal temperature gradient and mean annual salinities of present surface waters. (Slightly modified after Fleming *in* Hedgpeth, 1957, pp. 90–91.)

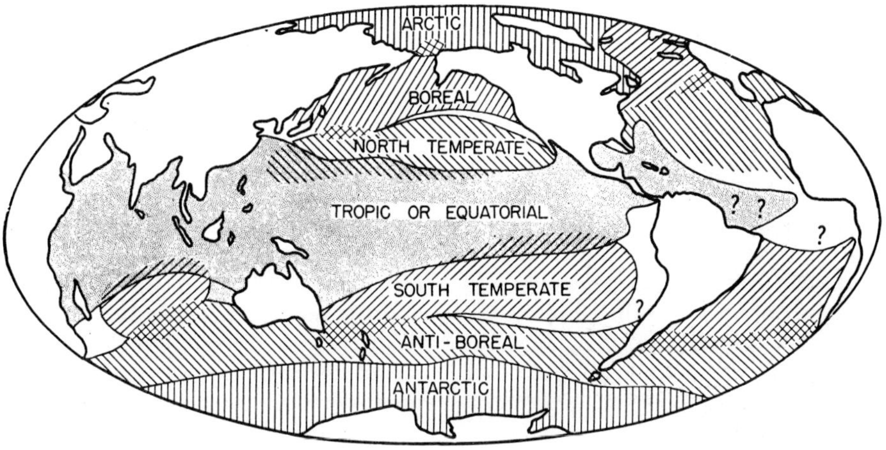

FIGURE 70.7
Circumglobal biogeographical belts as defined by marine plankton. (Mainly according to Steur, 1933, as modified by Hedgpeth, 1957, p. 367.)

ent polar wandering, continental drift, or stability of the outer crust and continents at various times in the past.

IDENTIFICATION OF EQUATORIAL AND POLAR POSITIONS

Given a particular distribution at the present surface of the earth of reliably determined fossil organisms, communities, and biotas whose ecologic significance is believed understood, the special job of the paleobiogeographer is to relate these variables consistently. Factors complicating this task include the parallelism between the latitudinal and the vertical distribution of life, heat transport by water currents, parallel origins of similar associated phenomena, and the poleward migration and blending of paleobiogeographic temperature indicators at times of less-marked latitudinal temperature zonation.

Brooks (1949, pp. 50–53, 189, 192–197) illustrated the dependence of the present wind scheme on the pressure balance between poleward temperature decrease in the lower 8 km of the atmosphere (troposphere) and the poleward *increase* of temperature in the stratosphere. He discounts the significance of the glacial anticyclone per se. Lessening of the tropospheric temperature gradient poleward would reduce polar air pressures and result in repression of the polar easterlies and expansion poleward of the westerly wind systems and the low-latitude trade winds. The global system of ocean currents would necessarily undergo parallel changes, with the result that all their boundaries would be moved poleward (Figures 70.5–70.7) and eventually eliminate the easterly polar currents. This would accelerate the warming effect at the poles and further reduce the actual temperature gradient between poles and equator, as (Dubois, 1895, pp. 72–99) would also be the case in the event of greater general input of solar heat.

The accepted technique for the paleobiogeographical location of equator and poles for a given time interval is to draw a line through the middle of an areal distribution pattern of biological indicators of warm water, and then to find the locus of points that would have been about 90 degrees from such a line by moving poles or continents until the best fit is found. If the paleobiogeographer is to contribute critically to hypotheses of polar migration and continental drift, he should also be constantly on the lookout for the most reasonable interpretations of his evidence in the light of climatologic and ecologic variables, without too much regard for what anyone else thinks may have happened to the crust, but with a healthy awareness of its physical properties.

It is, of course, important not only to arrive at correct conclusions, but to do so for the right reasons—to analyze in terms of processes, energy relations, reaction rates (intensity and time), phases, and components, and not merely of empirical analogy. For example, abundance of calcium carbonate (as coral and other organic reefs, as beds of thick-shelled mollusks and Foraminifera, or simply as limestones and dolomites without regard to skeletal composition) is commonly interpreted as evidence of former tropical conditions. Such abundance of itself does not demany any specific temperature conditions or latitudinal restriction. Rather it demands persistent saturation, which can happen at any temperature or latitude if enough calcium and carbonate ions are present in proportion to other ions in the solution. Because temperature is an important factor with regard to the carbonate ion, other factors being equal, the prospects of calcium carbonate precipitation *will* increase with increasing temperature. No matter how cold or warm the oceans were at any particular time, however, they can hold only a finite number of calcium (or magnesium) and carbonate ions before precipitation begins. Thus, assuming the generally constant composition of sea water, the proportion of carbonate sediments and shells at any given time should vary with latitudinal or local temperature, and the total amount of calcium carbonate precipitated should be a general function of world climate. The general interpretation, it seems, is probably justified, but not for the reasons usually given; and the reasons are important because their misapprehension can lead to unwarranted narrowing of objective alternatives. Thus, an abundance of either organic or inorganic calcium carbonate of great age at currently high latitudes may mean, for the time of deposition, either a greater general uniformity of climate, the deflection of warm currents poleward as a result of special terrestrial configuration, a preceding climatic shift from *relatively* cooler to *relatively* warmer, changes in carbon dioxide tension or ionic composition of the sea, or shifting of the poles or crust. Here also Brooks (1949, pp. 133, 150–151, 204, 206; 1951, p. 1017) has provided useful reference data in the form of paleotemperature equations, as well as his own estimated and calculated mean temperatures for various intervals from the pre-Paleozoic onward—computations soon to be outmoded, we may hope, by isotopic paleotemperature data.

Although the subject is not exactly marine or biogeographic, physical evidence taken as indicative of pre-Pleistocene ice sheets is also fundamental to the problem of polar location. This is too important to be left to the experts and too prevalent at low latitudes to be accepted as representing latitudinal changes without seeking other explanations both for the deposits and for how those demonstrably glacial came to be so. Crowell (1957) has aptly underscored the similarities between tillites and pebbly mudstones due to other forms of gravity mass movement, specifically marine, and the point needs no repetition to one who has seen both. Even striated pavements are not sacred; they also can be produced by other and more rapid gravity movements than the creep of frozen water (e.g., rock or gravel slides, nuées ardentes). Paleoglacial events that survive the called-for critical reexamination and are too big to be the product of mountain glaciers may still be explained by the same adiabatic cooling of rising moist winds that explains the mountain glaciers, but on a larger scale, as Brooks (1949, pp. 252–257) suggested may be the case for inferred Gondwana glaciation.

Finally, we have to consider an ingenious and purely biologic scheme elaborated by Ma (1952, and series of papers there cited) for determining paleolatitudes on the basis of interrupted growth in corals, and his interpretations in support of theories invoking a blend of polar and crustal drift. Ma's data themselves, however, are open to other interpretations. The formation of growth zones in a coral (or a mollusk) are a function of metabolic variations that could be and probably are related to a number of environmental factors other than temperature. They are not really comparable, for instance, to those of deciduous woods, which annually pass through a temperature-controlled interval during which growth can proceed only from already stored nutrients, an effect that overshadows all other growth variations of the individual tree.

SAMPLES AND PROBLEMS FROM MARINE PALEOBIOGEOGRAPHIC RECORD

In the immense ranges of geologic time it is inevitable not only that a great range of individual paleobiogeographic patterns should

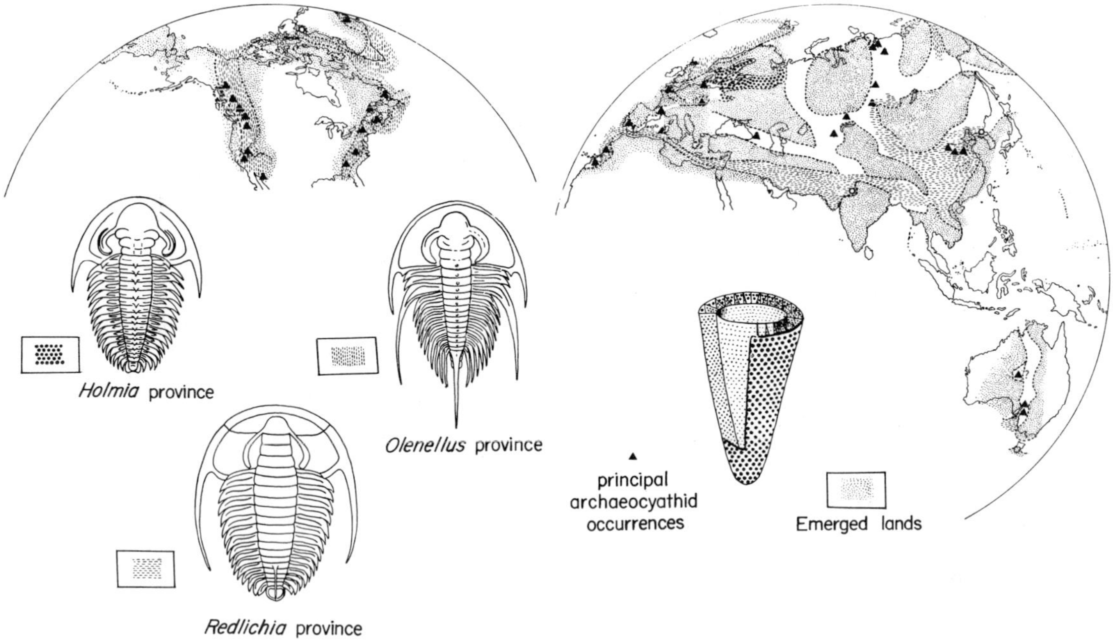

FIGURE 70.8
Marine paleobiogeographic provinces of the Early Cambrian. (Modified after Termier and Termier, 1959, pp. 28–29.)

occur but also that certain broadly overriding combinations will repeat themselves. The most familiar of these overriding patterns to the marine paleobiogeographer are the Tethyan and Antarctic transport routes and the Panamanian and Gondwana barriers (or filters).

By way of illustrating both that reasonable biogeographic interpretations can be made over a wide range of past time and that great problems remain unsolved, a few lines will now be devoted to these and other reconstructions from different parts of the geologic record.

EARLY CAMBRIAN BIOTAL PROVINCES

Near the dawn of recognized metazoan life, in the opening scenes of the Paleozoic era, an expansive paleobiogeographic realm is represented by the broad-headed olenellid trilobites (Order Redlichiida) of Early Cambrian and earliest Middle Cambrian age, with three provinces defined by distinctive genera or generic groups. Figure 70.8 illustrates the known global distribution of these provinces, compiled by the Termiers from the labors of generations of Cambrian specialists. Although the distinctive "genera" are now sometimes finely subdivided, and are not strictly contemporaneous (Öpik, 1958), their paleobiogeographic distinction is a fact. In a general way *Olenellus* represents a North American province, *Redlichia* a combined Tethyan and Cathaysian province, and *Holmia* a North Eurasiatic province. The generic names are simply by-names for the larger faunal (mainly trilobitan) assemblages they characterize, like Petersen's communities and d'Orbigny's zones. These assemblages are primarily associated with argillaceous detrital deposits near the continental margins of their time; and, as for the olenellids themselves, their broad, flat shapes, their inability to enroll in adult stages, and the tracks they have left in the sediments suggest that they were members of a mud-grubbing benthonic fauna whose early broad differentiation into endemic genera and faunal provinces reflects the gradual dispersal through relatively brief larval stages more than it does provincial environmental differences.

In the photic zone of the shelf and bank

seas adjacent to or within these olenellid provinces, calcereous spongelike archaeocyathids joined with a variety of lime-fixing algae to create reef-like organic buildups from the mouth of the Khatanga River in Siberia to central East Greenland and to the Beardmore Glacier area of Antarctica. The presence of a variety of filamentous and botryoidal algal structures associated with the archaeocyathids confirms their preference for the shallower and probably warmer parts of the Cambrian seas.

Conversely, the detrital and weakly calcereous deposits of the adjacent olenellid assemblages imply deeper, cooler waters for them, which is consistent with the generally modest endemism and smaller biotal variety of the olenellid provinces. Moreover, although the archaeocyathids were locally able to establish themselves in the shallower parts of the olenellid provinces, the olenellids were seemingly not able to migrate across the broad epicontinental reaches of the shallower and more extensive archaeocyathid seas, as in Siberia. Around the central core of North America, the olenellids generally occur inside the belt of archaeocyathids, which may mean either that the latter occupied narrow shelf seas adjacent to offshore lands and defining the outer edge of geosynclinal olenellid seas, or that deeper shelf seas with olenellids were separated by shelf-edge archaeocyathid reefs from the yet unknown geosyncline proper further offshore. More evidence is needed to resolve this problem.

Regardless of its more specific details, the described fourfold biogeographic classification of the Early Cambrian biotas is fairly interpreted as implying a regional sedimentological and bathymetric subdivision within a generally warm global climate of little or yet undeciphered, latitudinal variation. Information so far synthesized neither demands nor opposes a different latitudinal orientation from the present one.

GONDWANA

Intermittently from middle Paleozoic (Devonian) through at least early Mesozoic (Triassic) time, significant fractions of the marine and terrestrial biotas of the southern hemisphere were enabled to encircle it, but were retarded as to movement in a northward direction, or receipt of northern admixtures, by something geologists like to call Gondwana [Land of the Gonds (Caster, 1952, p. 126)]. Gondwana, or Gondwanaland, has commonly been interpreted as a more or less east-west, transoceanic land mass whose composition varies with author and time but which generally includes a large part of Africa, usually parts or all of South America and India, and commonly Australia and Antarctica (for recent summaries see Teichert, 1958; King, 1958).

Similarities in the Early Devonian marine faunas of South America and South Africa have long attracted attention, and recently have been extended to include Tasmania (Boucot and Gill, 1956). These similarities played a prominent part in a recent symposium on the problem of land connections across the South Atlantic (Mayr et al., 1952) and were one of the key factors leading to the principal conclusion drawn by some participants of that symposium that a "faunal connection" and presumably a land connection "seems to have existed until at least 180 million years ago, but was no longer in existence 130 million years ago" (Mayr, 1952, p. 257). Indeed, the evidence for continuity of Devonian land between Africa and South America was so vigorously and persuasively presented by Caster (1952) as to stimulate review and search for an alternative.

Figure 70.9 compares Early Devonian faunal relations from South Africa to South America, with different patterns of distribution found among the living shelly benthos and an Oligocene Tethyan example. These data, to be sure, are of very unequal value, and some are badly in need of revision and refinement. They do, however, give a rough order of relations which may be interpreted as implying either (1) a similarity of biogeographic relations between the southern hemisphere marine Devonian and the Oligocene Tethyan and Recent Indopacific, or (2) a tendency toward a higher proportion of nomenclatural identities between contemporaneous smaller faunas of like ecology regardless of other factors.

I am not merely quibbling, therefore, when I urge, as Dunbar (1952) urged, that other factors be considered in interpreting the impressive degree of nomenclatural identity be-

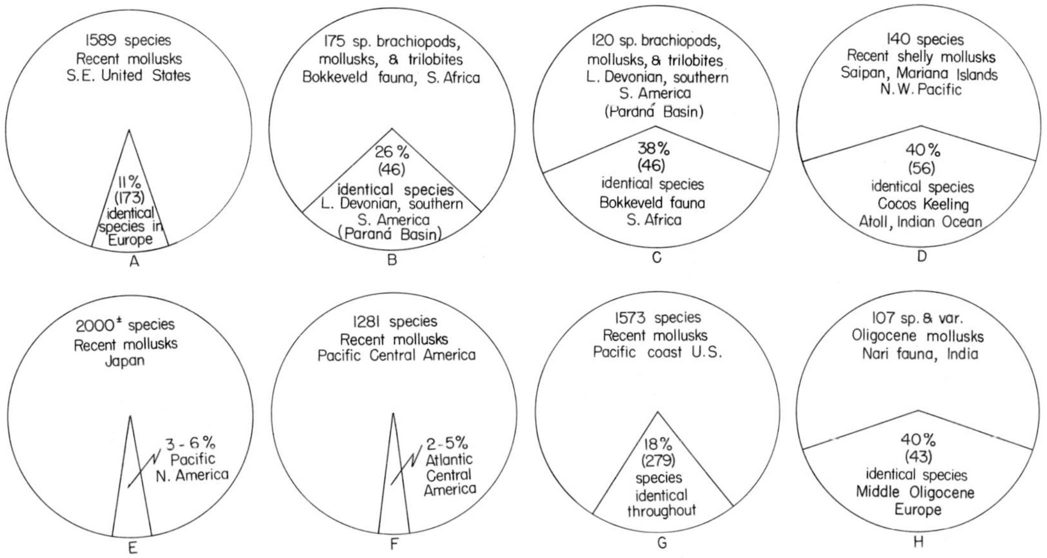

FIGURE 70.9
Nomenclatural identities among described shelly marine benthos in the Early Devonian of the Southern Hemisphere compared with living shelly benthos and an Oligocene pattern. A (Dall, 1889; Durham, 1952) and *E* (Keen, 1937; Durham, 1952), transoceanic, subtropical to temperate; *B* and *C* (Caster, 1952, pp. 114–16), Devonian faunas in question; *D* (Cloud, 1959a, p. 395), transoceanic, tropical with island stepping stones; *F* (Durham, 1952), across north-south isthmian barrier, tropical; *G* (Durham, 1952), north-south shoreline, temperate; *H* (Durham, 1952), middle Cenozoic (Oligocene) east-west Tethyan shoreline.

tween southern hemisphere Devonian marine faunas. Not only are the described faunas small but also, being from similar Paleozoic rocks and relatively inactive areas paleontologically, they are likely to be conservatively identified and biased in the direction of the more conspicuous, more readily identifiable species, and the brachiopods. Perhaps more nearly comparable data would be obtained if, for instance, among the modern Indopacific faunas one were to identify only the cypraeids and cones. The identities from Saipan to Cocos-Keeling (Figure 70.9 D) would then rise from 40% to 70%, across more than 3000 miles of ocean and three opposing east-west current systems—a degree of similarity fully as remarkable as that of the southern hemisphere Devonian, even allowing for the shoalwater stepping stones between.

Assuming no crustal drift or foundering, we might expect to find analogies between the Devonian couple and the Recent North Atlantic faunas, which involve distances and potential intermediate stepping stones of about the same order of magnitude. Although such a comparison is hindered by the fact that mainly subtropical west Atlantic species are compared with temperate east Atlantic species (Figure 70.9 A), it is nevertheless impressive to find an 11% transoceanic nomenclatural identity between faunas of about 1600 species from different latitudinal zones. The same check list (Dall, 1889), incidentally, shows 6 out of 21 morphological species and varieties of living brachiopods native to the southeastern United States as occurring in Europe: a 29% identity that compares more favorably with that between members of the Devonian couple (Figure 70.9 B, C).

If, as it seems, similarities in the Early Devonian faunas of the southern hemisphere are not a compelling argument for former continental connection, how else may they be explained? These similarities could be explained without catastrophic geographic changes if eastward and northeastward flowing currents such as now encircle Antarctica as the great West Wind Drift (Figure 70.5) existed in Devonian time and dispersed floating larvae from a circum-Antarctic shelf-sea to the shores of southern hemisphere land masses having similar marine faunas, and provided that such dispersal were repeated at frequent enough intervals to retard local endemism. That Devonian Antarctica was ice-free is implied by the presence of Late Devonian fish well up in the thick and apparently uninterrupted later Paleozoic terrestrial deposits of eastern Antarctica (Adie, 1952), and by the occurrence . . . of Early Devonian brachiopods which came to my attention through the courtesy of W. E. Long. The probable intermittent presence of isthmian linkage between Antarctica and other southern hemisphere lands (e.g., Axelrod, 1960, Figs. 6, 8, and 9) provides a contributory or alternative explanation, but probably it is not necessary to explain the paleobiogeographical facts.

The answer may be found in more and larger collections of Antarctic and other southern hemisphere fossils. . . . Meanwhile available evidence for the Devonian seems at least as well explained by mechanisms that do not demand the former existence of a cratonic link or links as by those that do (see also Gill, 1958, p. 115).

But what of other evidence for Gondwana? The late Paleozoic *Glossopteris-Gangamopteris* flora, which Gondwana was invented to explain in the first place (Teichert, 1958, p. 563), has lost ground as proof of continental linkage with the discovery of associated winged sporelike bodies in the Permian of India, Australia, Antarctica, and perhaps South Africa (Virkki, 1937; Sahni, 1938, pp. 14–15, 20–21). Simpson (1953, pp. 61–62) concluded, "All the biogeographic features in the known history of mammals are best accounted for on the theory that the continents have had their present identities and positions." The fresh water galaxid fishes of southern South America, Africa, Australia, and New Zealand are widely euryhaline, and Myers (1949) suggested that they could probably cross the present ocean basins. Teichert (1958) finds present paleobiogeographic evidence to indicate the existence of open ocean west of Australia since early Paleozoic and isolation of Australia since Permian or earlier.

Gondwana as a transoceanic land mass, therefore, remains an as yet unsatisfactorily documented and biogeographically unnecessary hypothesis. Insofar as its biogeographic basis is concerned, the linking elements could just as well have been dispersed from an ice-free Antarctic center under the influence of the circum-Antarctic West Wind Drift or the wind itself, aided by the northward deflection resulting from the Coriolis effect; or, in the case of the terrestrial vertebrates, through demonstrable northern hemisphere routes.*. . .

TETHYS AND OTHER MESOZOIC SEAWAYS

Repeatedly, from the beginning of latest Paleozoic time, the thick-shelled benthos and nekton of the world ocean encircled it over a route through the present Mediterranean depression and Middle Eastern and central Indian lowlands, except as hindered by transverse obstacles, mainly in the region of Central America. This meridional seaway is called Tethys, and it would function anew with moderate rise of the sea or subsidence of the land.

Tethys reached its peak after an interval of temporary blockage coincident with the desiccation transitional from Paleozoic to Mesozoic times. The rich warm-water shelly faunas and reef biotas of later Mesozoic time spread from India to western North America (e.g., Smith, 1910, p. 482) and reached northward along more temporary routes to high latitudes, and even beyond the Arctic and Antarctic circles. Dasycladacean algae, denoting warm water in the upper photic zone, are common associates of some faunal facies.

The Jurassic (middle Mesozoic) has the best-documented record of the systems with intimate Tethyan connections. Uhlig (1911) showed that Neymayr's (1883, 1885) pioneer efforts toward a worldwide zonation of the Jurassic marine faunas were based on faulty analogy, but he sustained the idea of broad latitudinal zonation parallel to the present one.

* [This is not inconsistent, however, with a Gondwana model like the one suggested by J. T. Wilson (1963, Supplemental Reading, Section V) in which there is a clustering of the continents, the continents are of their present dimensions, drift is primarily longitudinal, and significant latitudinal movement occurs only for India, Australia, Antarctica and Arabia.—P.C.]

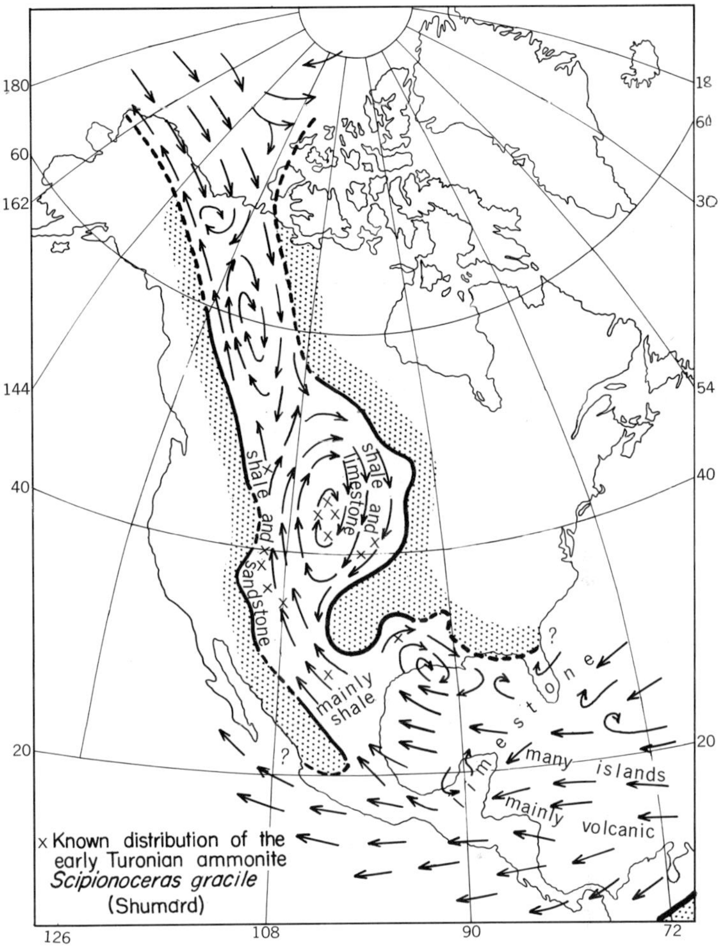

FIGURE 70.10
Early Late Cretaceous (Turonian) seaway through Rocky Mountain geosyncline. With inferred current patterns assuming no latitudinal change. (Shorelines adapted from Schuchert, 1955, map 73, and Woodring, 1954, Fig. 1.)

He extended the warm and temperate climatic zones northward and dispensed with Neumayr's cold zones. He also recognized nine separate marine provinces in the Jurassic, all with channels to the Tethyan seaway. Uhlig's scheme in turn has undergone revision by Arkell (1956, pp. 606–618), who reduced the provinces to three, Tethyan, Pacific, and Boreal. On the basis of his master work on the Jurassic geology of the world, Arkell concluded that the Early Jurassic (Lias) fauna was essentially universal and Tethyan; the divisions evolved later, with much shifting of boundary zones. Limestone is rare or lacking in high latitudes, but a conspicuously shelly fauna is recognized as far north as Greenland. Arkell (1956, p. 616) logically concludes that even the subpolar waters of Liassic time "were at least as warm as those of the present temperate zone." From the distributional data it would have been pardonable to call them temperate without qualification.

General Cretaceous (late Mesozoic) paleoclimatology runs in much the same vein as that of the Late Jurassic. The very widespread Cretaceous deposits and rich shelly faunas, however, offer enticing prospects of doing something more refined about the paleobiogeography. In the hope of spurring more interest in this, I have tried reconstructing a current system for the well-documented early Late Cretaceous seaway through North America (Figure 70.10), connecting with the Tethyan seaway at the south.

The evidence of the ammonites and inoceramids from Greenland and northern Alaska

(Imlay and Reeside, 1954, pp. 226, 242, and references there cited) and of the rich Cretaceous flora of west Greenland (Dubois, 1895, p. 13) confirms the warm-temperate nature of the Turonian climate of present Arctic regions. Hence (assuming no latitudinal change, and for reasons given) we may eliminate the polar easterly winds as an effective force and introduce a preponderant eastward current drift at high latitudes, driven by the west winds of a subpolar whirl. Such a current, presumably, would enter the northern end of the Rocky Mountain geosyncline, turn right under the influence of the Coriolis effect, and execute a clockwise gyral. Opposing this at the south, would be another clockwise gyral introduced by the Tethyan trade wind drift from the southeast in a similar way. Of course, numerous local irregularities would develop, but the two principal gyrals should impinge obliquely about at the present international boundary, and broadly separate different faunal provinces. The fact that the Turonian faunas of northern Alaska have Atlantic aspects (W. A. Cobban, oral communication) is not at odds with this. It is to be expected that entrainment of southern waters along the western side of the northern gyral, or even a narrow long-shore current from the south would filter some southern elements northward, and that the reverse might happen along the eastern side. There should, moreover, be a general coincidence of pelagic and shallow benthonic differences with the two suggested gyrals, as is hinted by the known distribution of the Turonian guide ammonite *Scipionoceras gracile* (Shumard), supplied by W. A. Cobban after the current system suggested in Figure 70.10 was plotted.

It would be of interest also to analyze the history of the Panamanian link and its effect on current movement and evaporite-carbonate sequences of the northern Gulf Coast over a range of Cretaceous time, but that is another job.

A PASSING REFERENCE TO THE TERTIARY

The Tertiary is replete with paleobiogeographical data of such a variety and degree of refinement as to offer a surfeit of choices for analysis. . . . Tertiary paleoclimates have been reviewed by MacGinitie (1958) and selected evidence from the marine realm bearing on Tertiary latitudinal zonation and progressive climatic deterioration has been condensed in papers by Durham (1950, 1952, 1959).

I could not bear to pass the Tertiary treasure box without at least mentioning the magnificent works of Ostwald Heer (1868–1883) and of Reid and Chandler (1933) on the older Tertiary angiosperms. Even though they are not marine paleobiogeography (and Heer's Arctic "tropical Miocene" is warm-temperate to subtropical Eocene and Paleocene) they establish the basis for paleoclimatologic conclusions that profoundly affect the marine realm. The already cited paleobiogeographic classic by Davis and Elliott (1957) on the London clay sea makes ample use of this data.

FLYSCH FACIES

The flysch facies, a generally early syntectonic basinal sediment characterized by intercalated coarse redeposited clastics and fine-grained pelagic sediments (e.g., Ksiazkiewicz, 1958, 1959) is a subject of timely and growing interest. I venture to add my own interpretation of the flysch facies as representing a recurrent or time-transgressive paleobiogeographic realm of major significance.*

It is well known that aside from redeposited shelf assemblages, occasional pelagic species, and the rare occurrence of unusual and impoverished benthonic associations, the flysch biota is represented almost exclusively by a relatively small variety of tracks and feeding burrows of

* For purposes of this discussion I adopt an objective definition of flysch facies which demands that the coarse layers possess four critical descriptive features suggested to me by Prof. Ksiazkiewicz: (1) pronounced lateral continuity; (2) sharp bottom contacts and commonly gradational tops; (3) generally well-defined internal structure; (4) plentiful sole markings showing directional characteristics. It is only fair to remark that Professor Ksiazkiewicz does not himself insist on so restrictive a definition.

For further discussion of the problem see also R. Trümpy, *Geol. Soc. America Bull.*, v. 71, no. 6, p. 873–880 (1960) or the comprehensive monograph of N. B. Vassoevich, *The Flysch and the Methods of Its Study* (in Russian) (Leningrad: Gostoptekhizdat, 1948).

unusual regularity and distinctive form (e.g., Seilacher, 1954, Fig. 2; Cloud, 1959b, Fig. 6). Two things besides their regularity stand out about these *Lebensspüren* or trace fossils. First, they are pretty much the same all over the world and from middle Paleozoic, or earlier, to late Cenozoic. Second, they commonly cut across physical markings made by gravity emplaced sediments that were moved rapidly across and dumped upon the surface on which the organic markings were made later.

We know, therefore, that the mobile benthonic fauna responsible for the distinctive organic trackways and burrows of the flysch facies lived largely within the sediments—that it was primarily an *infauna*. It is evident, too, although we have never knowingly observed the makers of these particular markings, that the organisms responsible for them maintained or adopted broadly similar distinctive habits of feeding and movement, did not vary widely in size, and had functionally similar locomotor, digging, and feeding equipment through a remarkably wide range of space and time, and despite the relative geographic isolation of many flysch basins. If we assume that the animals as well as the tracks were similar, we have in effect drawn a very close parallel between the fauna of the flysch facies and the modern infauna of the cold aphotic depths as described by Thorson (1957, pp. 463–466) and indicated in Figure 70.3. Even those species which worked at the sediment-water interface of the flysch seas commonly produced a regular pattern of searching and feeding tracks in the manner of many organisms that work in darkness, and some deep-sea photographs show remarkably flyschlike organic markings.

I have previously approached this conclusion with more reservation (Cloud, 1959b, p. 944) simply because there has been so widespread a trend, uncritically following Ph. H. Kuenen's inspired lead and on what I consider less satisfactory evidence, to interpret all flyschlike sediments as deep-water deposits and too wide a range of sediments as flysch. However, the evidence so briefly reviewed above does strongly suggest that the known benthonic megafauna of the flysch facies as here defined represents an infauna of relatively deep water: probably mainly bathyal (below 200 m) and perhaps locally even abyssal. Evaluation of the microfaunal assemblages of the younger flysch facies deposits earlier led Ksiazkiewicz (1958, p. 419) and before him Grzybowski (Ksiazkiewicz, 1956, p. 387) to a similar induction. As defined by the markings left by its benthonic megafauna, moreover, the flysch facies can be considered to represent the farthest ranged and longest lasting paleobiogeographic realm (if it may be so called) in the recorded history of the earth. This, to be sure, opposes both the dictum that little is represented in the fossil record beyond shelf elements, and the suggestion sometimes made that the existing deep-sea fauna has evolved in younger geologic times from invasion of basins that were stagnant through a preceding epoch of little climatic differentiation. The idea of general deep-sea stagnation in the nonglacial geologic past is opposed not only by the probable persistence of a long-ranged flysch facies fauna but also by the antiquity of deep-sea elements such as the Monoplacophora, by hadal endemism in general (Wolff, 1960, pp. 100–102, 104), by the importance of oxygen-bearing turbidity current sedimentation and oxidized sediments in the deep sea basins, and by the certainty that there always was some temperature gradient between equator and poles and some frictional turnover of the water masses related to the opposing wind systems which must exist in order to maintain the circulatory balance of the atmosphere.

The rarity or absence of recognized contiguous shelf facies and intermediate equivalents is a principal difficulty with acceptance of the flysch facies as everywhere deep. Obviously there were contiguous shallow waters, and, although it is a stock suggestion that the flysch facies sediments have invariably been disconnected during compressive deformation, it seems certain that some of the equivocal flyschlike sediments will prove to be of an intermediate nature. A comprehensive survey of an undeformed flysch basin is badly needed.

REFERENCES

Adie, R. J., 1952, Representatives of the Gondwana system in Antarctica, *in* Symposium sur les séries de Gondwana: Internat. Geol. Cong. 19th Sess. Rept., p. 393–399.

Ager, D. V., 1956, The geographical distribution of

brachiopods in the British Middle Lias: Geol. Soc. London Quart. Jour., v. 112, pt. 2, no. 446, p. 158–187.

Allee, W. C., A. E. Emerson, O. Park, T. Park, and K. Schmidt, 1949, Principles of animal ecology: Philadelphia, W. B. Saunders.

Arkell, W. J., 1956, Jurassic Geology of the World: New York, Hafner.

Axelrod, D. I., 1952, Variables affecting the probabilities of dispersal in geologic time: Am. Mus. Nat. Hist. Bull., v. 99, p. 177–178.

———, 1960, The evolution of flowering plants, *in* Sol. Tax, ed., Evolution after Darwin, v. 1: Chicago, University of Chicago Press, p. 227–305.

Blegvad, H., 1915, Food and condition as nourishment among the communities of invertebrate animals found on or in the sea bottom in Danish waters: Danish Biol. Sta. Rept. 22, p. 41–78.

Boucot, A. J., and E. D. Gill, 1956, *Australocoelia*, a new Lower Devonian brachipod from South Africa, South America, and Australia: Jour. Paleontology, v. 30, no. 5, p. 1173–1178.

Bray, H. G., and K. White, 1954, Organisms as physio-chemical mechanisms, *in* New biology, v. 16: London, Penguin Books, p. 70–85.

Brooks, C. E. P., 1949, Climate through the ages—a study of the climatic factors and their variations (rev. ed.): New York, McGraw-Hill.

———, 1951, Geological and historical aspects of climate change, *in* T. F. Malone, ed., Compendium of meteorology: Boston, American Meteorological Society, p. 1004–1018.

Bruun, A. F., 1957, Deep sea and abyssal depths, *in* J. W. Hedgpeth, ed., Treatise on marine ecology and paleoecology, v. 1. Ecology: Geol. Soc. America Mem. 67, p. 641 –672.

Caster, K. E., 1952, Stratigraphic and paleontologic dara relevant to the problem of Afro-American ligation during the Paleozoic and Mesozoic: Am. Mus. Nat. Hist. Bull., v. 99, p. 105–152.

Clements, F. E., and V. E. Shelford, 1939, Bioecology: New York, John Wiley and Sons.

Cloud, P. E., Jr., 1959a, Geology of Saipan, Mariana Islands, IV. Submarine topography and shoal-water ecology: U.S. Geol. Survey Prof. Paper 280K, p. 361–445.

———, 1959b, Paleoecology—retrospect and prospect: Jour. Paleontology, v. 33, no. 5, p. 926–962.

Croizat, Leon, 1958, Panbiogeography: Caracas; distributed by Wheldon and Wesley, Ltd., Codicote, England.

Crowell, J. C., 1947, Origin of pebbly mudtones: Geol. Soc. America Bull., v. 68, p. 993–1010.

Dall, W. H., 1889, A preliminary catalogue of the shell-bearing marine mollusks and brachiopods of the south-eastern coast of the United States: U.S. Natl. Mus. Bull., v. 37.

Davis, G., and G. F. Elliott, 1957, The paleogeography of the London clay sea: Geologists' Assoc. [England] Proc., v. 68, pt. 4, p. 255–277.

Dubois, Eugene, 1895, The climates of the geological past, and their relation to the evolution of the sun: London, Swan Sonnenschein.

Dunbar, C. O., 1952, Discussion (of Caster, 1952): Am. Mus. Nat. Hist. Bull., v. 99, p. 153–158.

Durham, J. W., 1950, Cenozoic marine climates of the Pacific coast: Geol. Soc. America Bull., v. 61, p. 1243–1264.

———, 1952, Early Tertiary marine faunas and continental drift: Am. Jour. Sci., v. 250, p. 321–343.

———, 1959, Palaeoclimates, *in* L. H. Ahrens, ed., Physics and chemistry of the earth: New York, Pergamon Press, v. 3, p. 1–16.

Ehrenberg, C. G., 1830, New observations on the blood-like phenomena observed in Egypt, Arabia, and Siberia, with a view and critique of the early accounts of similar appearances: Edinburgh New Philos. Jour., 1830–31, p. 122–136, 341–352.

Ekman, Sven, 1953, Zoogeography of the sea: London, Sidgwick and Jackson. (English ed. of original Swedish ed., 1935.)

Fischer, A. G., 1960, Latitudinal variations in organic diversity: Evolution, v. 14, p. 64–81.

Forbes, Edward, 1844, Report on the Mollusca and Radiata of the Aegean Sea, and on their distribution, considered as bearing on geology: British Assoc. Adv. Sci. 13th Mtg. Rept., p. 130–193.

George, T. N., 1958, Lower Carboniferous paleogeography of the British Isles: Yorkshire Geol. Soc. Proc., v. 31, p. 227–318.

Gill, E. D., 1958, Australian Lower Devonian Paleobiology in relation to the concept of continental drift, *in* Continental drift—a symposium: Hobart, University of Tasmania Department of Geology, p. 103–122.

Gislen, Torsten, 1948, Aerial plankton and its condition of life: Cambridge Philos. Soc. Biol. Rev., v. 23, p. 109–126.

Handlirsch, Anton, 1937, Neue Untersuchungen über die fossilen Insekten; mit Ergänsungen und Nachträgen sowie Ausblicken auf phylogenetische, palaeogeographische und allgemein biologische Probleme. I: Naturh. Mus. Wien Annalen, v. 48.

Hedgpeth, J. W., ed., 1957a, Treatise on marine ecology and paleoecology, v. 1. Ecology: Geol. Soc. America Mem. 67.

———, 1957b, Classification of marine environments, *in* J. W. Hedgpeth, ed., Treatise on marine ecology and paleoecology, v. 1. Ecology: Geol. Soc. America Mem. 67, p. 17–27.

———, 1957c, Concepts of marine ecology, *in* J. W. Hedgpeth, ed., Treatise on marine ecology and paleoecology, v. 1. Ecology: Geol. Soc. America Mem. 67, p. 29–52.

———, 1957d, Marine biogeography, *in* J. W. Hedgpeth, ed., Treatise on marine ecology and paleoecology, v. 1. Ecology: Geol. Soc. America Mem. 67, p. 359–382.

Heer, Oswald, 1868–1883, Flora fossilis arctica, v. I (1868): Zurich, F. Schulthess; v. II (1871):

Winterthur, J. Wurster & Co.; v. III (1875), v. IV (1877), v. V (1878), v. VI (1880), v. VII (1883): Zurich, J. Wurster & Co.

Heron-Allen, Edward, 1917, Alcide d'Orbigny, his life and work: Royal Microscop. Soc. Jour., 1917.

Hutchins, L. W., 1947, The bases for temperature zonation in geographical distribution: Ecol. Mon., v. 17, no. 3, p. 325–335.

Imbrie, John, 1959, Classification and evolution of major adaptive invertebrate types, *in* Preprints International Oceanographic Congress: Washington, D.C., American Association for the Advancement of Science, p. 278.

Imlay, R. W., and J. B. Reeside, Jr., 1954, Correlation of the Cretaceous formations of Greenland and Alaska: Geol. Soc. America Bull., v. 65, p. 223–246.

Jones, N. S., 1950, Marine bottom communities: Cambridge Philos. Soc. Biol. Rev., v. 25, p. 283–313.

Keen, A. M., 1937, An abridged check list and bibliography of west North American marine Mollusca: Stanford, Calif., Stanford University Press.

King, L. C., 1958, Basic palaeogeography of Gondwanaland during the late Paleozoic and Mesozoic eras: Geol. Soc. London Quart. Jour., v. 114, pt. 1, p. 47–77.

Ksiazkiewicz, Marian, 1956, Geology of the northern Carpathians: Geol. Rundschau, v. 45, p. 369–411.

———, 1958, Sedimentation in the Carpathian flysch sea: Geol. Rundschau, v. 47, p. 418–425.

———, 1959, Life conditions in flysch basins, *in* Preprints International Oceanographic Congress: Washington, D.C. American Association for the Advancement of Science, p. 280.

Landsberg, H. E., 1958, Trends in climatology: Science, v. 128, p. 749–758.

Lasareff, P., 1929, Sur un méthode permettant de démontrer la dépendance des courants océaniques des vents alizés et sure le rôle des courant océaniques dans le changement du climat aux époques géolgiques: Beitr. Geophys., v. 21, p. 215.

Ma, Ting Ying H., 1952, Research on the past climate and continental drift, v. 5: Taipei, World Book Co.

MacGinitie, H. D., 1958, Climate since the Late Cretaceous, *in* Carl L. Hubbs, ed., Zoogeography: Washington, D.C. American Association for the Advancement of Science, p. 61–79.

MacGinitie, G. E., and Nettie MacGinitie, 1949, Natural history of marine animals: New York, McGraw-Hill.

McKee, E. D., et al., 1956, Paleotectonic maps—Jurassic System: U.S. Geol. Survey Misc. Geol. Inv. Map I-175.

———, 1959, Paleotectonic maps—Triassic System: U.S. Geol. Survey Misc. Geol. Inv. Map I-300.

Mayr, Ernst, ed., 1952, The problem of land connections across the South Atlantic, with special reference to the Mesozoic: Am. Mus. Nat. Hist. Bull., v. 99, 79–258.

Meier, F. C., 1935, Collecting micro-orgainisms from the Arctic atmosphere (with field notes and material by C. A. Lindbergh): Sci. Monthly, v. 40, p. 5–20.

Minato, Masao, 1953, Palaeogeography des Karbons in Ostasien: Japan Acad. Proc., v. 29, no. 6, p. 246–253.

Myers, G. S., 1949, Salt-tolerance of fresh-water fish groups in relation to zoogeographical problems: Koninkl. Zool. Genoot. Amsterdam Bijdragen tot de Dierkunde, v. 28, p. 315–322.

Neumayr, Melchoir, 1883, Über klimatische Zonen wahrend der Jura- und Kreidezeit: Akad. Wiss. Wien Math.-naturw. Kl. Denkschr., v. 47, p. 277–310.

———, 1885, Die geographische Verbreitung der Juraformation: Akad. Wiss. Wien Math.-naturw. Kl. Denkschr., v. 50, p. 57–144.

Öpik, A. A., 1958, The Cambrian trilobite *Redlichia* —organization and generic concept: Australian Bur. Mineral Resources Geol. Geophys. Bull. 42.

d'Orbigny, Alcide, 1849–52, Cours élémentaire de Paléontologie et de Géologie stratigraphiques, v. I (1849), v. II, pt. 1 (1851): Paris, V. Masson.

Ortmann, A. E., 1896, Grundzüge der marinen Tiergeographie: Jena, Gustav Fischer.

Pérès, J. M., 1957, Essai de classement des communautés benthiques marines du globe: Station Marine d'Endoume Rec. trav., pt. 22, p. 23–53.

Pérès, J. M., and J. Picard, 1955, Biotopes et biocoenoses de la Méditerranée Occidentale comparés à ceux de la Manche et de l'Atlantique Nord-Oriental: Arch. zool. exp. gén., v. 92.

———, 1959, Origin, distribution and alterations of the Mediterranean benthic fauna, *in* Preprints International Oceanographic Congress: Washington, D.C., American Association for the Advancement of Science, p. 228.

Petersen, C. G. J., 1914, Valuation of the sea, II. The animal communities of the sea bottom and their importance for marine zoogeography: Danish Biol. Sta. Rept. 21.

———, 1915a, On the animal communities of the sea bottom in the Skagerak, the Christiania Fjord and the Danish waters: Danish Biol. Sta. Rept. 23.

———, 1915b, Notes to Charts I and II, Appendix to Rept. 21: Danish Biol. Sta. Rept. 22.

Plass, G. N., 1956, Carbon dioxide and the climate: Am. Scientist, v. 44, p. 302–316.

Regnard, Paul, 1891, Recherches experimentales sur les conditions physiques de la vie dans les eaux: Paris, G. Masson.

Reid, E. M., and M. E. J. Chandler, 1933, The London Clay flora: London, British Museum [Natural History].

Rubey, W. W., 1951, Geological history of sea

water: Geol. Soc. America Bull., v. 62, p. 1111–1147.
Rukhin, L. B., 1957, Paleoclimatology and biostratigraphy (in Russian), *in* Problems of paleobiogeography and biostratigraphy: All-State Paleontol. Soc. Trans., 1st Sess. (1955), p. 25–41.
Sahni, Birbal, 1938, Recent advances in Indian paleobotany: Univ. Lucknow Fac. Sci. Studies, no. 2.
Schmarda, Ludwig K., 1853, Die geographische Verbreitung der Thiere: Vienna, C. Gerold and Son.
Schmidt, K. P., 1955, Animal geography, *in* A century of progress in the natural sciences, 1853–1953: San Francisco, California Academy of Sciences, p. 767–794.
Schuchert, Charles, 1955, Atlas of paleogeographic maps of North America: New York, John Wiley and Sons.
Schwarzbach, Martin, 1950, Das Klima der Vorzeit —eine Einführung in die Paläoklimatologie: Stuttgart, F. Enke.
Seilacher, Adolf, 1954, Die geologische Bedeutung fossiler Lebensspüren: Deutschen geol. Gesell. Zeitschr., v. 105, p. 214–227.
Shapley, Harlow, ed., 1953, Climatic change: Cambridge, Mass., Harvard University Press.
Simpson, G. G., 1940a, Mammals and land bridges: Washington Acad. Sci. Jour., v. 30, p. 137–163.
———, 1940b, Antarctica as a faunal migration route: Pacific Sci. Cong. 6th Sess. Proc., v. 2, p. 755–768.
———, 1952, Probabilities of dispersal in geologic time: Am. Mus. Nat. Hist. Bull., v. 99, p. 163–176.
———, 1953, Evolution and Geography: Oregon State System of Higher Education, Condon Lectures.
Smith, J. P., 1910, Ancient climates of the West Coast: Pop. Sci. Monthly, v. 76, p. 478–486.
Stepanov, D. L., ed., 1957, Problems of paleobiogeography and biostratigraphy (in Russian): All-State Paleontol. Soc. Trans., 1st Sess. (1955).
Steuer, A., 1933, Zur planmässigen Erforschung der geographischen Verbreitung des Hal. planktons, besonders der Copepoden: Zoogeographica, v. 1, p. 269–302.
Stommel, Henry, 1957, A survey of ocean current theory: Deep-Sea Research, v. 4, p. 149.
Teichert, Curt, 1958, Australia and Gondwanaland: Geol. Rundschau, v. 47, p. 562–590.
Termier, Henri, and Genevieve Termier, 1952, Histoire géologique de la biosphere: Paris, Masson.
———, 1957, Les provinces paléobiogéographiques: Soc. géol. Belgique Annales, v. 81, p. B75–B93.
———, 1959, Evolution et paleogeographie: Paris, Albin Michel.
Thorson, Gunnar, 1946, Reproduction and larval development of Danish marine bottom invertebrates: Komm. Danmarks fiskeri-og havundersgelser Medd., ser. Plankton, v. 4, no. 2.
———, 1950, Reproductive and larval ecology of marine bottom invertebrates: Cambridge Philos. Soc. Biol. Rev., v. 25, p. 1–45.
———, 1957, Bottom communities, *in* J. W. Hedgpeth, ed., Treatise on marine ecology and paleoecology, v. 1. Ecology: Geol. Soc. America Mem. 67, p. 461–534.
Trewartha, G. T., 1954, An introduction to climate (3d ed.): New York, McGraw-Hill.
Uhlig, Victor, 1911, Die marinen Reiche des Jura- und der Unterkreide: Geol. Ges. Wien Mitt., v. 4, no. 3, p. 329–448.
Virkki, Chinna, 1937, On the occurrence of winged pollen grains in the Permo-Carboniferous rocks of India and Australia: India Acad. Sci. Proc., v. B6, no. 6, p. 428–431.
von Arx, W. S., 1957, An experimental approach to problems in physical oceanography, *in* L. H. Ahrens, ed., Physics and chemistry of the earth: New York, Pergamon Press, v. 2, p. 1–29.
Walther, Johannes, 1893–94, Einleitung in die Geologie als historische Wissenschaft, v. 1. Bionomie des Meeres; v. II. Lebensweise der Meerestiere: Jena, Gustav Fischer.
Wells, J. W., 1953, A synthesis of paleobiogeography (Termier): Ecology, v. 34, p. 811–813.
Wexler, Harry, 1957, The circulation of the atmosphere, *in* The planet earth: New York, Simon and Schuster, p. 113–121.
Wimpenny, R. W., 1941, Organic polarity, some ecological and physiological aspects: Cambridge Philos. Soc. Biol. Rev., v. 16, no. 4, p. 389–425.
Wolff, Torben, 1960, The hadal community—an introduction: Deep-Sea Research, v. 6, p. 95–124.
Woodring, W. P., 1954, Caribbean land and sea through the ages: Geol. Soc. American Bull., v. 65, p. 719–732.
———, 1959, Tertiary Caribbean molluscan faunal province, *in* Preprints International Oceanographic Congress: Washington, D.C., American Association for the Advancement of Science, p. 299.

Paleoclimates

J. WYATT DURHAM
1959

Shortly after it became accepted that fossils (in the modern sense) were the remains of organisms, speculation on climates formerly present in certain areas began. Lyell (1830, pp. 92–143), in the first edition of his classic *Principles of Geology*, devotes three chapters to this general subject. He (op. cit., p. 33) likewise notes, for instance, that Robert Hooke (in a posthumous work published in 1705) had concluded "it is necessary to suppose that England once lay under the sea within the torrid zone!"

The occurrence of palms and other types of tropical vegetation in northern latitudes where temperate or frigid climates now hold sway; the finding of elephants and rhinoceroses frozen in the ice of Siberia; and the occurrence of tropical types of shells and corals in Europe: these were the kinds of fossils that caused speculation as to the conditions under which they had lived and that usually led to the conclusion that a tropical or "warmer" climate had existed where they were found.

Much variation has existed in the terms used to denote climates of the past: milder, more benign, more equable, temperate, moderate, tropical, more tropical, warmer, colder, boreal, arctic, glacial and more uniform are qualifying words often used. In rare instances only, until the advent of modern geochemical techniques, has a more precise terminology been attempted. In many cases there has been a deliberate lack of precision, probably because it was felt that the available data did not justify any refinement. At the present time, *tropical* (in a climatic sense) usually indicates average temperatures above 20°C in considering terrestrial climates, but in the sea (Vaughan, 1940, p. 444) *tropical* has been defined as having temperatures above 25°C, and *subtropical* as having minimum temperatures between 15° and 25°C. However Ekman (1953, p. 3) has defined *tropical* as having temperatures above 20°C in the coldest month of the year. At times *tropical* has been considered to include *subtropical*.

Within the marine environment Vaughan

From *Physics and Chemistry of the Earth: Vol. 3*, edited by L. H. Ahrens and others, pp. 1–16. Pergamon Press, Inc., 1959. Reprinted with permission of the author and the publisher.

(1940) has proposed an additional six zones (three in each hemisphere) based on temperature. These are: two *polar zones*, temperature limits − 1.9° to + 5°C; two *subpolar zones*, temperature limits + 5° to + 10°C; two *temperate zones*, minimum temperatures + 10° to + 15°C. On land the usage of temperature and climatic zones has been more confused with these zones being based on varying definitions and often being confused with "life zones." At times the terms temperate, boreal, arctic, and so forth, have had a purely geographic significance, at other times they have been based on temperatures or other climatic factors. In the *Encyclopædia Britannica* (1952 ed.), under *climate*, the terms *torrid*, *temperate* and *frigid* are applied to the three principal geographic climatic zones, while *tropical* (+ 20°C mean annual temperateure), *temperate* (with minimum temperature 10°C in warmest month), and *cold* (warmest month colder than 10°C) are the three principal temperature zones.

METHODS

In the broad sense palæoclimatology should be concerned with the occurrence in past geological time of all the factors (temperature, precipitation, winds, etc. and their seasonal distribution and variation) considered by the climatologists, but to those concerned with the evidence from the marine record, it has often been limited to palæotemperatures only. The methods used to arrive at these conclusions are many. Most of the interpretations of past years have been based on the palæogeographic distribution of organisms that are either still living or closely related to living taxa of supposed thermophilic (warm-limited) or frigophilic (cold-limited) character, or on supposedly significant associations of organisms. At other times, lithological features of the rocks, such as the occurrence of arkoses, salt deposits, gypsum, redbeds and coal, have been used. In recent years, with the rise of geochemistry, the relative abundance of certain isotopes (such as ^{16}O and ^{18}O), the crystalline form (aragonite-calcite ratio), the presence and relative abundance of certain elements or compounds (magnesium, strontium, amino acids, etc.), and other chemical means have been used, often with a degree of precision seemingly much greater than that obtained by the more long-standing methods. However additional work (Lowenstam and Epstein, 1954; Lowenstam, 1954; Chave, 1954) has shown the need for more data regarding the biological processes involved before the results obtained by chemical means can be properly evaluated.

Lowenstam and Epstein (1954, pp. 207–209) have pointed out that many organisms secrete their skeletal material only during a part of the temperature range at a given locality, and that this threshold varies for different organisms. Thus analysis of the shells of the various components of a fossil assemblage may indicate different temperatures at the time of deposition even though they all lived together. After fossilization, various geological processes may modify the chemical composition of the remains of an organism: percolating waters may change the chemical composition; pressure and heat can alter the mineralogical composition. In using isotopic and other chemical analysis, care must be exercised to obtain a fair sample of the original population and to make sure that no significant alteration has occurred subsequent to death or burial.

The utilization of the presence (or absence) of different kinds of organisms for recognition of past climates is founded on "the basic assumption of uniformitarianism—namely, that the animals and plants of the past lived under essentially the same environmental conditions as do their living relatives . . ." (Ladd, 1957a, p. 1). Some of the various organisms that have been used in this manner are listed by Durham (1950, pp. 1247–1249).

In using "uniformitarianism" in interpreting the presence (or absence) of certain organisms or assemblages of organisms much care must be exercised. Kirk (1928) has drawn attention to many of the false assumptions and hindrances. Woodring and Bramlette (1950, p. 99) have concluded that the range of living species closely related to, or identical with fossils cannot be used as "a close guide"' to reconstruct past environments because the physiological requirement of the organism may have changed. It does not seem probable that the extreme conservatism of Woodring and Bramlette is justified, and even they were inconsistent in its application. They were impressed by the incongruous association in the fossil record of species whose present day ranges are in some cases separated by hundreds of miles. Perhaps the most common anomaly of this sort occurs with respect to the distribution of "northern" (or supposed "cold water" limited) and "tropical" (or supposed "warm water" limited) organisms. Some of the incongruities are due to "upwelling," a phenomenon whose effects on distribution have only recently been recognized (Dawson, 1951; Emerson, 1956b; Valentine, 1955). In association with "upwelling" Emerson found "northern" species that were several hundred miles south of their "normal" range. In short distances laterally the faunas consist of typical "southern" species only, so that it is easy to obtain anomalous associations of dead shells. It is a well known fact that shells or remains of dead organisms may be transported considerable distances from their life habitat (Ladd, 1957b, pp. 31, 37–40, 49–50, 53).

Other apparent incongruities may be due to inadequate understanding of the factors controlling distribution of "northern" types. The pelecypod genus *Patinopecten* lives along the Pacific Coast of North America only north of San Francisco Bay. In consequence it has often been cited (e.g. Smith, 1919, pp. 130–131) as indicating a "northern" or cool temperature. However this same genus occurs (Durham, 1950, p. 1244) in the Plio-Pleistocene of the Gulf of California in the same beds as, and in close proximity to reef type corals and other tropical elements. It is obvious in this case that the environment was tropical. Other similar cases could be cited.

In general it seems that many more members of cold water faunas are euryopic than members of warm water faunas. Perhaps their euryopic nature indicates that they are less specialized, and therefore less well suited to particular environments in the warmer seas, and in consequence they will invade these areas only if a niche becomes available. When a more efficient occupant of the niche appears, the invader has to retreat to the cooler (and less favorable?) habitats. This general hypothesis seems to be borne out by the much greater diversity of organisms in the tropics as contrasted to the polar regions. MacGinitie (1955, p. 171) notes that only thirty pelecypods and eighty-nine gastropods were found in the extensive recent studies of the marine fauna of the Point Barrow, Alaska, region. This is in marked contrast to the size of the shelled molluscan fauna of marine tropical areas like the Panamic where the total number of species is estimated to be around 2500. In both areas by far the major portion of the fauna lives in "shallow" water, thus seemingly indicating that warmer temperatures (in contrast to variations in depth, light penetration, and type of substrate) are responsible for the greater diversity of the tropics.

In a study (Durham, unpublished) of the distribution of 964 gastropod genera (11,580 records from 2062 localities); twenty-six of 108 genera recorded from the "polar" (below 5°C surface temperature) zones were restricted to that region; 211 of 532 genera were restricted to the temperate (surface temperature range 5° to 20°C) zones; and 384 of 671 genera were restricted to the tropical (surface temperature above 20°C) zone. Only forty-eight genera were found in all three zones, and over half of the tropical genera were restricted to the tropics (as defined by surface oceanic temperatures). On a species level the restriction to the tropical areas is still greater. In this study, some of the genera were represented by only one or two records, and thus their restriction to a zone may not be significant. Of the genera restricted to the polar zone, in only one case (*Valvatella*) was the restriction supported by more than ten records. Within the tropical zone, however, fourteen genera, with more than twenty-five records each, were restricted, and an additional twenty-one genera with more than twenty-five records were largely restricted. The distribution of the gastropod genera would strongly support the hypothesis that the tropical elements are more significant than cool water elements. If this hypothesis is true, then many interpretations of the presence of "cold water elements" in faunas (e.g. Davies, 1934, pp. 69, 76; Smith, 1919, pp. 131, 145, etc.) are not significant in terms of climate.

As indicated above the presence of thermophilic organisms seems to be much more important than the presence of "cool water" elements, but their significance must be supported by evidence (such as growth stages) that they lived (in the sense of completing a life cycle) where found. It is well known (e.g. Sverdrup et al., 1942, pp. 862–863) that organisms, particularly planktonic ones, may be carried out of their normal warm water environment and live there for considerable periods but not be able to reproduce. Within the marine environment frigophilic organisms can usually find suitable temperatures in deeper water within the same region, and they are thus not significant in terms of the regional climate. The gastropod *Fusitriton oregonensis*, common in intertidal areas from Puget Sound to Alaska is found only in deeper water off southern California (see Woodring, 1938, p. 24; Woodring et al., 1946, p. 72), but characteristic shallow water tropical genera such as *Cypraea* have no such alternative.

LIMITATIONS

Inferences about past climates are based on certain assumptions and limitations. The first and most significant of these assumptions is of course the "Principle of Uniformitarianism," that is that the principles and processes operating in the past are the same as those of today. This is one of the basic tenets of geology and its related sciences.

In the present paper it is also assumed that there has been no "Continental Drift" and/or "Polar Wandering" (at least with respect to the earth's rotational axis). If this assumption is not made, the inferences for particular localities are still valid, but regional or world-wide syntheses of the data cannot be made until the relative geographic positions of the individual localities can be fixed by means of other data. The reasons for making this assumption during the Tertiary have been discussed elsewhere (Durham, 1952). In essence, these reasons are.

(1) All known marine faunas of Early Tertiary age in the present tropical belt are of tropical character.
(2) The character of marine Early Tertiary faunas outside of the present tropical belt indicates that at this time the boundaries of the tropics were much farther poleward, but still essentially parallel to those now existing and not compatible with some other position of the rotational pole.

This interpretation, based on the marine faunas is fully supported by the evidence from the Early Tertiary floras of the northern hemisphere (Chaney, 1940).

In arriving at conclusions about past climates, the distribution, abundance, and mode of preservation of fossils and sediments of the particular age concerned impose obvious limitations. As yet no means of arriving at an interpretation of climate from igneous rocks has been proposed. If there are no fossils or sediments of a particular age in an area, no direct conclusions can be made about that area at that time. A secondary, but nevertheless important qualification is the magnitude of the time interval under study and the degree of

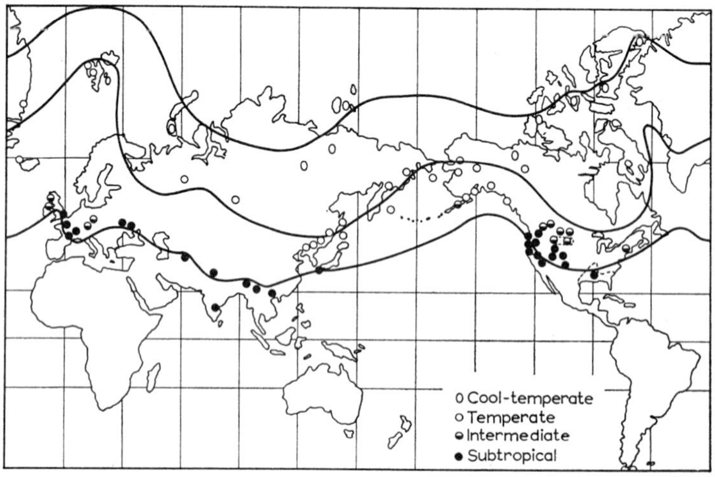

FIGURE 71.1 Distribution of Eocene isoflors in the Northern Hemisphere. (After Chaney, 1940, Fig. 2.)

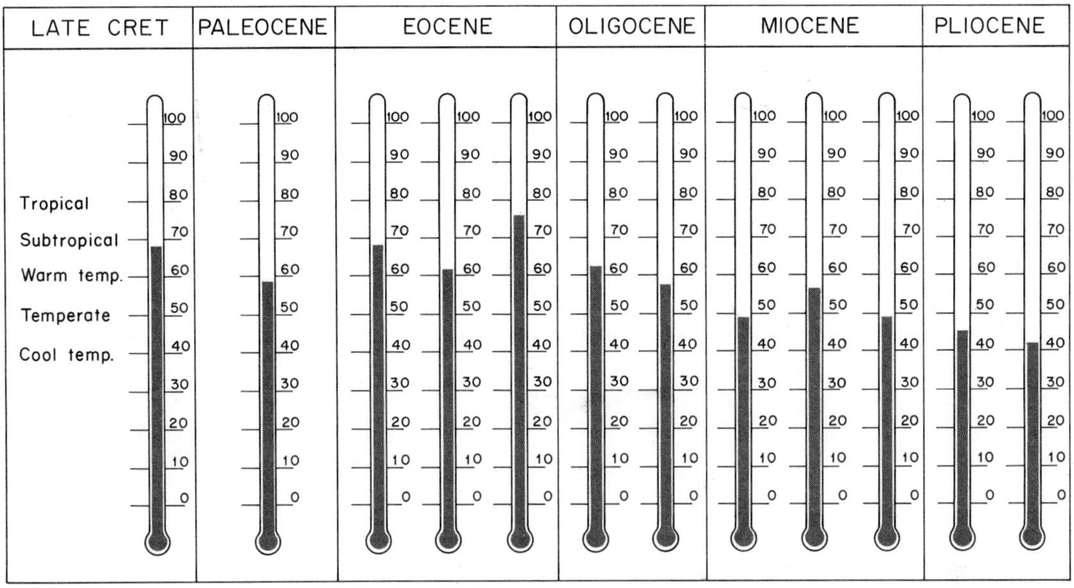

FIGURE 71.2
"Thermometers of the Ages." Generalized climatic regime of Late Cretaceous and Tertiary in middle latitudes (Lat. 40° to 50° N) of western United States. Figures indicate approximate mean annual temperatures. (After Dorf, 1955, p. 587, Fig. 3.)

precision with which assignments to the interval can be made. Within the Pleistocene there are numerous instances of climatic changes documented by fossil occurrences, but which as yet cannot be integrated into a coherent scheme because their age relationships are uncertain. The development of carbon isotope dating techniques has helped greatly in the latest Pleistocene, but since this technique at present is not valid for ages greater than about 35,000 years, other similarly precise dating techniques must be (and are) developed for the remaining 950,000 years (more or less) of the epoch.

The extent to which remains of organisms are preserved as fossils in the rocks, and subsequent to that, the extent to which the fossil biotas have been studied control the significance of conclusions based upon them. Nevertheless, even in limited assemblages the presence of stenopic organisms such as reef corals may outweigh limited knowledge of the associated organisms. The modes and possibilities of preservation in the fossil record have been generally discussed by Ladd (1957a, pp. 9–25). However as a measure of the adequacy (or inadequacy) of the fossil record it should be pointed out that whereas living tropical shelled molluscan faunas (from all habitats) are estimated to number between 2000 and 2500 species in any one region (e.g. Caribbean or Panamic Regions), fossil molluscan faunas reputedly well studied usually number far fewer species. For example only 352 molluscs are recorded from the upper Eocene Jackson fauna (of tropical character) of the Gulf Coast of the United States (Durham, 1952, p. 330). In all fairness however it should be pointed out that the known fauna in this case does not include a deep water facies and rocky coast habitats are largely unrepresented. By far the best known fossil molluscan fauna is that of the Paris Basin Eocene. About 3600 species and varieties have been recorded from the Palæocene and Eocene of this area. This interval probably includes over a third of the 60 million years of the Tertiary and in many lineages much evolution took place. Probably a large percentage of the fauna was replaced several times because of this evolution and the actual known fauna of each moment of time is much smaller. The hazards of burial and fossilization may reduce the apparent size of faunas greatly. Wave action, scouring by currents, the action

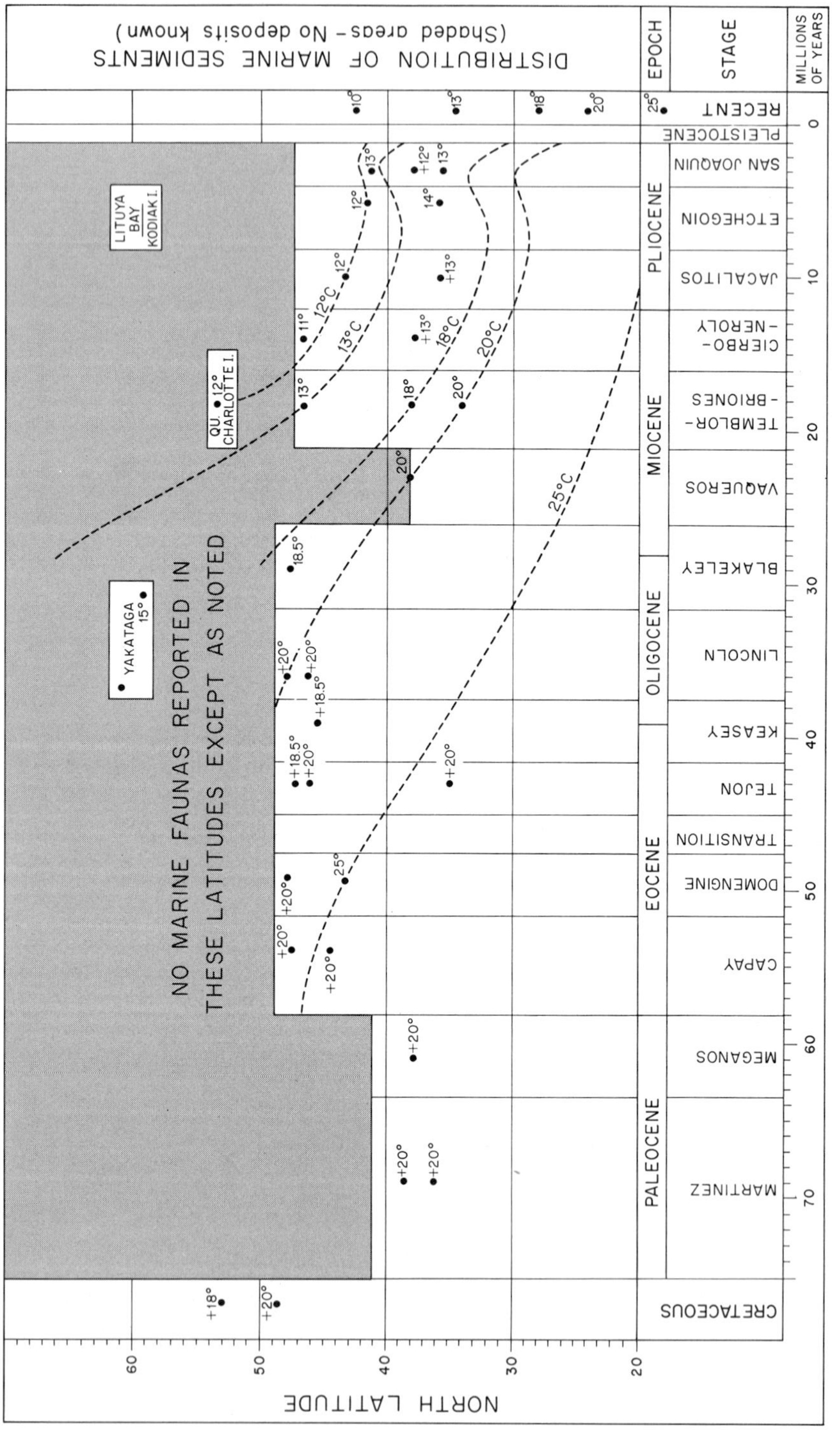

FIGURE 71.3
Past positions of February marine isotherms along the Pacific Coast
(After Durham, 1950, p. 1259, Fig. 3.)

of scavengers in comminuting hard parts, the hazards of collection, and other less well known factors tend to reduce the apparent size of fossilized biotas.

The quality of the systematics involved in the comparison of faunas needs to be carefully considered. The differences between the systematics of present day "lumpers" and "splitters" may be of the same magnitude as between those of today and those of Linnaeus. Thus faunal lists cannot be directly compared until the level of the systematics has been evaluated.

Conclusions based on physical and chemical analyses are limited: first by the extent to which the materials used for analysis have been modified subsequent to their formation or burial in the rocks, and second by the extent to which the processes controlling their formation are understood.

INTERPRETATIONS OF PAST CLIMATES

During the past twenty years there has been considerable work in the field of palæoclimatology, much of it using the newer techniques. In the "Bibliography and index of geology exclusive of North America" for 1954, thirty-five titles appear under this subject heading. In the "Bibliography of North American geology" for 1952 and 1953 there are thirty-eight titles on the same subject. Of these seventy-three titles, thirty-six are concerned only with the Pleistocene and post-Pleistocene. The results obtained in these various studies are for the major part in general agreement, but a few are markedly at variance with one another. Obviously it is impossible to review all these papers within the limits of the present article, so some of the conclusions dealing with four different aspects and methods have been selected for presentation. These are followed by a general discussion of past climate.

TERTIARY TERRESTRIAL CLIMATES OF NORTH AMERICA

Plants in general seem to be much more sensitive to the different facets of climate than animals, and as a result palæobotany, when there are adequate floras available, gives much detailed information about the different aspects of past terrestrial climates. Fossil floras of Tertiary age in the northern hemisphere are widespread, in both time and space, and many of them have been well studied. Chaney (1940) discussed these northern floras in general, and emphasizing those around the rim of the North Pacific, compared them with modern floras and gave his conclusions regarding Tertiary climates. Some of his conclusions have been modified in detail by work such as that of Axelrod (1956), and Dorf (1955) but the general results presented are still valid.

Chaney (op. cit.) concluded first of all, on the basis of the floral distribution, that the geographic positions of the continents during all the Tertiary was the same as that now existing. Second, he showed (op. cit., pp. 474–475) that floras of a "subtropical" type extended much further poleward in the northern hemisphere during the early Tertiary than at present (Figure 71.1), and that during the later Tertiary they gradually retreated towards the tropics until the present distribution pattern was attained. He likewise concluded that the climatic zones of the early Tertiary had distribution patterns similar to those now existing, but that their boundaries were more poleward. He notes (op. cit., p. 484) ". . . in both North America and Eurasia, older Tertiary floral units ranged somewhat farther north on the windward than on the leeward coasts," a distribution pattern essentially like that of today.

The evidence presented by Chaney also indicates, for instance, that lowlands extended eastward across California, Washington and Oregon until near the end of the Miocene—until that time there were no Cascade Mountains or Sierra Nevada-Coast Ranges to separate a humid coastal belt from an interior arid one.

Chaney did not define his terms "subtropical," "temperate," etc. but Dorf (1955, p. 587, Fig. 3) in considering the same part of the western United States concluded that the mean annual temperatures at latitudes between 40° and 50°N, varied (Figure 71.2) from a maximum of about 23.9°C in the upper Eocene to about 5.5°C in the late Pliocene. Dorf (op. cit., pp. 588–589) also points out that Tertiary climates in the southeastern United States and northwestern Europe followed the same trends as in western United States. Colbert (in Shapley et al., 1953, pp. 266–269) concludes that the terrestrial vertebrates show the same climatic trends as plants during the Tertiary.

TERTIARY MARINE CLIMATES

The writer (Durham, 1950, 1952) has discussed the Tertiary marine climates of the Pacific Coast of the United States and the Eocene marine climates of the world. Such additional evidence as has become available since then has caused only minor changes in the conclusions presented in those two papers. "Climate" as used in those papers was largely restricted to temperature, although of necessity inferences as to depth of deposition (corresponding to elevation in terrestrial environment) were also made. Thermal conclusions were made in terms of average water temperatures prevailing at the surface of the oceans during the coldest month of the year (February in the northern hemisphere).

It was concluded first of all (Durham, 1950, pp. 1244–1247; 1952) that the evidence from the early Tertiary marine faunas militates against any shifting of the continents ("continental drift") since the Mesozoic, and as a corollary to this, that the north pole had also occupied the same position as at present. Secondly, on the Pacific Coast (Durham, 1950, pp. 1251–1260) the tropical zone on the oceans extended north of 50°N latitude in the Eocene (Figure 71.3) and gradually retreated southward during the Tertiary, with recognizable oscillations in the late Pliocene and Pleistocene. This climatic pattern is in accord with that presented by Chaney (1940) for the terrestrial climate of the same region. Thirdly, it was shown (Durham, 1952, pp. 332–339) that

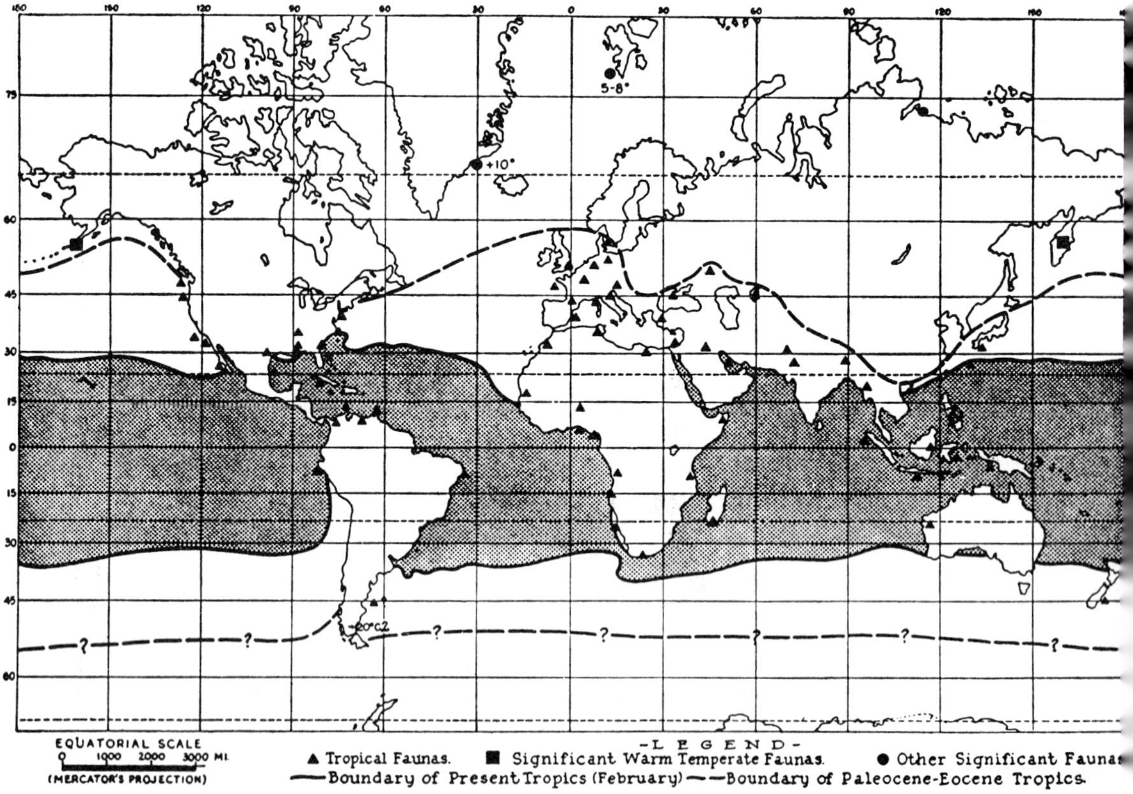

FIGURE 71.4
Paleocene-Eocene tropical zone. (After Durham, 1952, p. 338, Fig. 1.)

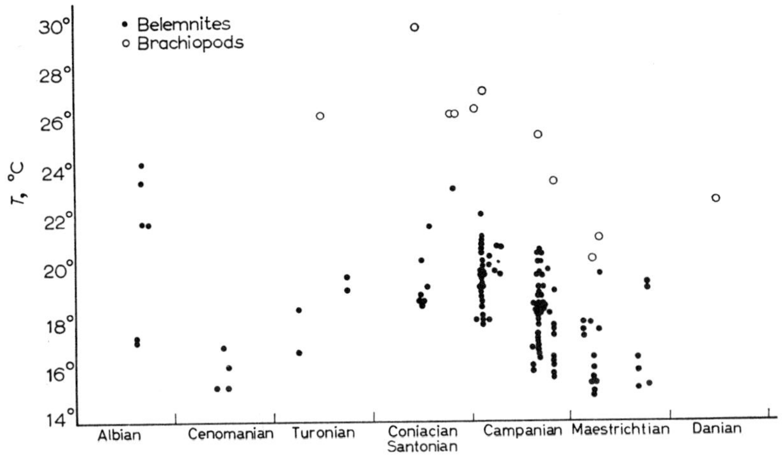

FIGURE 71.5
Mean-temperature distribution of belemnites and brachiopods from Albian to Danian in western Europe. (After Lowenstam and Epstein, 1954, p. 226, Fig. 10.)

the same poleward extension of the tropical zone (Figure 71.4 occurred on a world-wide basis during the Early Tertiary. When faunal lists of the later Tertiary are examined on a world-wide basis and using the same criteria, a gradual retreat, in time, of the isotherms towards the Equator, as on the Pacific Coast, is apparent. Again these conclusions are in accord with those of Chaney (1940), Colbert (in Shapley et al., 1953), and Dorf (1955) for the terrestrial climates.

UPPER CRETACEOUS MARINE TEMPERATURES BASED ON OXYGEN ISOTOPES

The recognition of a temperature factor in control of the $^{18}O/^{16}O$ depositional ratio of calcium carbonate prompted a series of determinations of palæotemperatures by means of this ratio. Lowenstam and Epstein (1954) summed up the results of their investigations to that date. The usefulness of this method depends upon the unaltered condition of fossilized shells and they found that among the common Cretaceous fossils, belemnite guards were usually not altered and thus the most useful. They also found that in general the shells of other invertebrates, such as brachiopods, Ostreidæ, and *Inoceramus*, recorded a higher temperature than the associated belemnites. This is in accord with their investigation into the deposition of carbonate in the shells of living organisms in Bermuda where they found that different species had characteristic temperature ranges in which the shell was deposited and that most species did not record the total temperature range of their environment.

Lowenstam and Epstein (op. cit., p. 247) caution that the ". . . study is solely an exploratory investigation of the potential application of the paleotemperature method, and hence the interpretations must be regarded as probable rather than definite." Their general findings on the basis of belemnites and brachiopods for the Upper Cretaceous of western Europe show (Figure 71.5) a high in late Albian, a low (about 16°C on basis of belemnites) in the Cenomanian followed by a gradual increase until the Coniacian-Santonian (about 20°C on basis of belemnites), followed by a decline (to nearly 16°C) in the lower Maestrichtian, and finally a rise again in the later Maestrichtian. Whatever the significance of these mean temperatures in terms of the life habitat of the belemnites (the brachiopods consistently indicate higher temperatures), it is worthy of note that these temperatures are between 6° and 10°C higher than the mean annual temperatures of the adjacent seas at the present time and that they indicate subtropical to tropical surface marine temperatures for

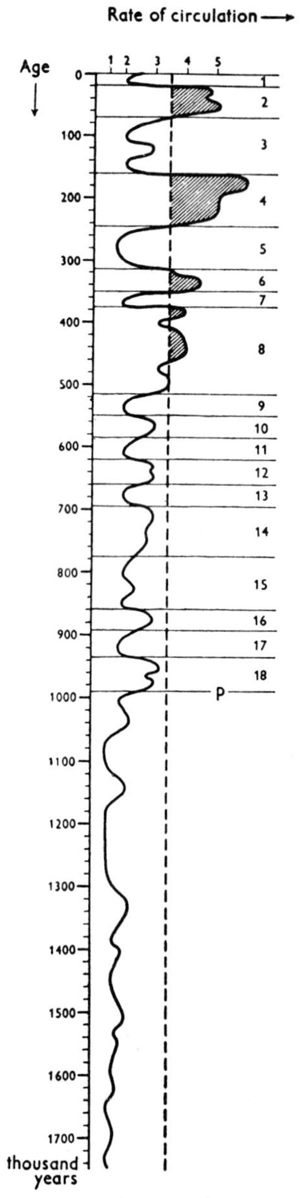

FIGURE 71.6
Rate of low latitude atmospheric circulation as a function of time. The abscissa scale is arbitrary and the relative amplitudes of the circulation changes are inferred mainly from the quantitatively measured rate of accumulation of calcium carbonate, the qualitatively estimated rate of dissolution of calcium carbonate, and the quantitatively determined microfossil distribution. *Dashed line,* the inferred minimum rate of circulation occurring in connection with extensive glaciations; *P,* the climatic Pliocene-Pleistocene boundary. The Pleistocene main stages (*1–18*) are indicated and their approximate boundaries drawn in the diagram. (After Arrhenius, 1952, p. 199, Fig. 3.4.2.)

western Europe during the Upper Cretaceous. This poleward extension of the tropical zone is in accord with the conclusions of Durham (1950, p. 1252) and Dorf (1955, pp. 587–588) for the Cretaceous of the Pacific Coast of North America from different lines of evidence, and of Colbert (in Shapley et al., 1953, pp. 264–266) for the Cretaceous as a whole from the evidence of fossil vertebrates.

As in the Early Tertiary, the evidence from several different lines of reasoning points to much more widespread [latitudinally broader] tropical climatic zones than at present. The detailed evidence from oxygen isotope analyses suggest that there were expansions and contractions in the geographic expanse of the tropical zone.

PLEISTOCENE OCEANIC TEMPERATURES

As noted earlier the difficulties attendant upon making refined correlations of small time intervals in the Pleistocene has hindered a synthesis of much available climatic data. However the

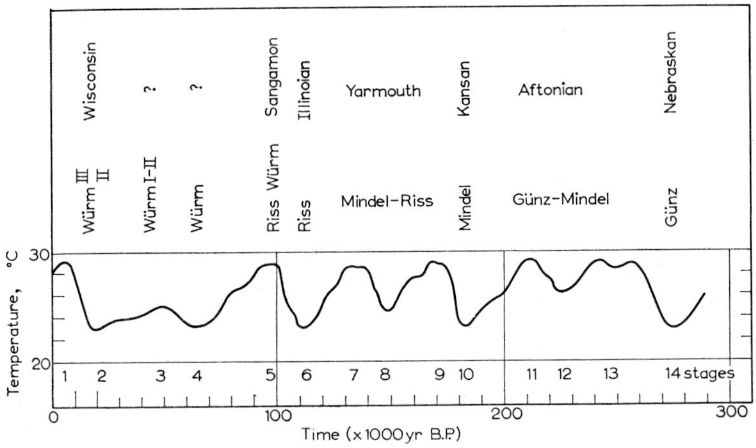

FIGURE 71.7
Generalized low latitude oceanic temperature variations. Correlated with terrestrial glaciations for part of Pleistocene. (After Emiliani, 1955, p. 569, Fig. 15.)

recent development of long coring devices has made long cores, in many instances apparently representing continuous sedimentation, of oceanic sediments available. Some cores of this type have been interpreted as containing a complete representation of the Pleistocene (Arrhenius, 1952, p. 192, Fig. 3.3.1; Emiliani, 1955, p. 547). Various methods and combinations of methods (see Arrhenius, 1952; Emiliani, 1955, 1957; and Ericson et al., 1956), including oxygen isotope ratios, carbonate ratios, distribution of thermophilic species of foraminifera, radiocarbon dating, titanium content as a function of age, percentage of biogenous silica, amount of nitrogen and amount of phosphorus are being used to arrive at a detailed history of the marine Pleistocene.

Nine warm stages alternating with nine cold stages were recognized in the eastern Pacific by Arrhenius (1952, pp. 18, 199) in the interval he assigned to the Pleistocene. Arrhenius summarized his results in a graph (Figure 71.6) expressing rate of atmospheric circulation, with maximum circulation corresponding to periods of extensive glaciation, and minimum circulation to warm interglacial periods. Thus instead of the usual four or five major cold intervals commonly recognized in the Pleistocene, Arrhenius' data would indicate nine. Emiliani (1955) in summarizing the data from deep-sea cores has apparently accepted Arrhenius' interpretations from the Pacific, and integrating them with other work from the Atlantic, has correlated the results with the standard American and European glacial chronologies (Figure 71.7). The general results indicate that mean annual surface oceanic temperatures in the low latitudes fluctuated by about 6°C during the Pleistocene.

The results arrived at by Arrhenius, Emiliani, and Ericson et al., are in strong contrast to those of Crickmay (1929) who recognized seven climatic zones in a lower Pleistocene near shore marine section near Los Angeles, California, slightly under seventy-five feet thick. His interpretations were based on fossil associations, with the incongruities ascribed to the presence of derived fossils. Most workers in the same area do not at present accept his conclusions.

PAST CLIMATES—GENERALITIES

If the conclusions presented above for Cretaceous and later climates are valid—and there seems no escaping their general validity if the principle of uniformitarianism is accepted—one conclusion seems inescapable. This is that the present restriction of tropical climates to a relatively narrow belt (and in periods of glaciation to an even narrower belt) of the earth's surface is an unusual situation (Figure 71.8). The evidence for the Cretaceous and Tertiary indicates that for most of the time prior to the Pliocene the tropical zone was more widespread than now, and that during certain inter-

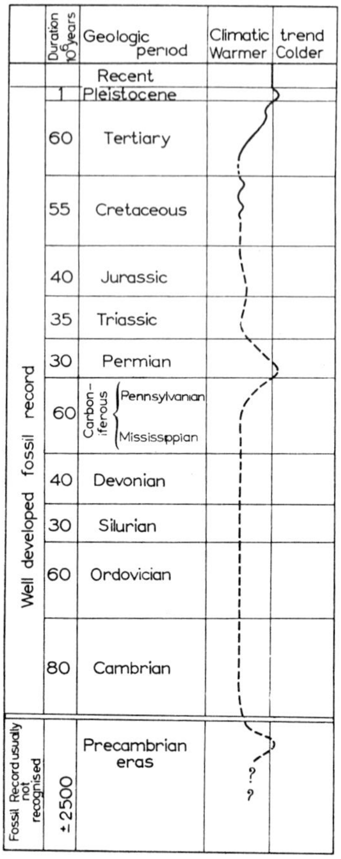

FIGURE 71.8
Generalized climatic trends in middle latitudes

vals at least, the boundary of the tropics was at some point between 50° and 60°N latitude in the northern hemisphere and occupied a similar position in the southern hemisphere. The evidence becomes more difficult to interpret in pre-Cretaceous times because there are no close living relatives for most organisms and the fossils are more often poorly preserved or are chemically altered. Nevertheless the conclusions of various workers, such as Barghoorn (in Shapley et al., 1953, pp. 239–243) on the palæobotanical evidence, Colbert (in Shapley et al., 1953, pp. 249–264) on the evidence from fossil vertebrates, Lochman (1957, pp. 154–157) on the Cambrian and Lower Ordovician of Montana, Cloud and Barnes (1957, pp. 195–196) on the Early Ordovician of Texas, Brooks (1949, pp. 21–27, 382) in his discussion of "Climate through the ages" and Schwarzbach (1950, p. 160) in his summary of past climates in central Europe, indicate that a more widespread tropical or "warm" climate prevailed over much of the Palæozoic, Mesozoic and Tertiary. Major episodes of glaciation prior to the Pleistocene are also recognized, indicating that there have been major fluctuations in world-wide climate.

Ting Ying H. Ma in his detailed studies on corals (1937a, 1937b) has presented much valuable information showing how variations in temperature affect the growth of corals, and how this variation may be recognized in fossils. Ma has also published several thick volumes (especially his series *Research on Past Climate and Continental Drift*) attempting to synthesize his data but his compilations reflect his lack of access to the world-wide literature.

There seems to be no general agreement as to the causes of climatic variation. Alternating intervals of high and low topographic relief of the earth's surface, variation in heat due to internal radioactivity of the earth, changes in the composition of the atmosphere, variation in radiation from the sun, astronomical and cosmical changes, presence of large amounts of volcanic dust in the earth's atmosphere and variations in circulation patterns are some of the causes that have been evoked to explain the changes.

In summary it seems highly probable that as our techniques are refined and as new methods are developed that our knowledge of the climates of older geological intervals will be much increased in detail and precision.

REFERENCES

Arrhenius, G., 1952, Sediment cores from the east Pacific: Swedish Deep-Sea Exped. 1947–48 Rept., v. 5, pt. 1, p. 1–227.

Axelrod, D. I., 1956, Mio-Pliocene floras from west central Nevada: Univ. California Geol. Sci. Pub., v. 33, p. 1–322, pls. 1–32.

Beaufort, L. F. de, 1951, Zoogeography of the land and inland waters: London, Sidgwick and Jackson.

Brooks, C. E. P., 1949, Climate through the ages (rev. ed.): New York, McGraw-Hill.

Casanova, R. L., 1955, Palaeoecologic analysis of some Tertiary echinoids of the Caribbean and South America: Paleontol. Res. Lab. Spec. Invest. Rept. v. 2, p. 1–8.

Chaney, R. W., 1940, Tertiary forests and continental history: Geol. Soc. America Bull., v. 51, p. 469–488, pls. 1–2.

Chavan, A., 1950, Remarques sur la signification climatique des mollusques marins fossiles: Soc. géol. France Bull., ser. 5, v. 19, p. 507–512.

Chave, K. E., 1954, Aspects of the biogeochemistry of magnesium, 1. Calcareous marine organisms: Jour. Geology, v. 62, p. 266–283.

Cloud, P. E., Jr., and V. E. Barnes, 1957, Early Ordovician sea in central Texas, *in* H. Ladd, ed., Treatise on marine ecology and paleoecology: Geol. Soc. America Mem. 67, p. 163–214.

Crickmay, C. H., 1929, The anomalous stratigraphy of Deadman's Island, California: Jour. Geology, v. 37, p. 617–638.

Davies, A. M., 1934, Tertiary faunas, v. 2. The sequence of Tertiary faunas: London, Thomas Murby.

Dawson, E. Y., 1951, A further study of upwelling and associated vegetation along Pacific Baja California, Mexico: Jour. Marine Research, v. 10, p. 39–58.

Diener, C., 1925, Grundzüge der Biostratigraphie: Leipzig and Wein, Franz Deuticke.

Dorf, E., 1955, Plants and the geologic time scale, *in* A. Poldervaart, ed., Crust of the earth: Geol. Soc. America Spec. Paper 62, p. 575–592.

Durham, J. W., 1950, Cenozoic marine climates of the Pacific Coast: Geol. Soc. America Bull., v. 61, p. 1243–1264.

———, 1952, Early Tertiary marine faunas and continental drift: Am. Jour. Sci., v. 250, p. 321–343.

Ekman, S., 1953, Zoogeography of the sea (trans. Elizabeth Palmer): London, Sidgwick and Jackson.

Emerson, W. K., 1956a, Pleistocene invertebrates from Punta China, Baja California, Mexico, with remarks on the composition of the Pacific Coast Quaternary faunas: Am. Mus. Nat. Hist. Bull., v. 3, p. 313–342, pls. 22–23.

———, 1956b, Upwelling and associated marine life along Pacific Baja California, Mexico: Jour. Paleontology, v. 30, p. 393–397.

Emiliani, C., 1955, Pleistocene temperatures: Jour. Geol., v. 63, p. 538–578.

———, 1957, Temperature and age analysis of deep-sea cores: Science, v. 125, no. 3244, p. 383–387.

Ericson, D. B., et al., 1956, Late-Pleistocene climates and deep-sea sediments: Science, v. 124, no. 3218, p. 385–389.

Fell, H. B., 1956, Tertiary sea temperatures in Australia and New Zealand, from the evidence of fossil Echinoderms: Internat. Zool. Cong. 14th Sess. Proc., 1953, p. 103–104.

Joleaud, L., 1939, Atlas de Paléobiogéographie: Paris, Paul Lechevalier.

Kirk, E., 1928, Fossil marine faunas as indicators of climatic conditions: Smithsonian Inst. Ann. Rept., 1927, p. 299–307.

Kulp, J. L., K. Turekian, and W. D. Boyd, 1952, Strontium content of limestone and fossils: Geol. Soc. America Bull., v. 63, p. 701–716.

Ladd, H. S., 1957a, Introduction, *in* H. Ladd, ed., Treatise on marine ecology and paleoecology: Geol. Soc. America Mem. 67, p. 1–29.

———, 1957b, Paleoecological evidence, *in* H. Ladd, ed., Treatise on marine ecology and paleoecology: Geol. Soc. America Mem. 67, p. 31–66, pls. 1–9.

Ladd, H. S., and G. Gunter, 1957, Development of marine paleoecology, *in* H. Ladd, ed., Treatise on marine ecology and paleoecology: Geol. Soc. America Mem. 67, p. 67–74.

Lochman, C., 1957, Paleoecology of the Cambrian in Montana and Wyoming, *in* H. Ladd, ed., Treatise on marine ecology and paleoecology: Geol. Soc. America Mem. 67, p. 117–162.

Lowenstam, H. A., 1954, Factors affecting the aragonite-calcite ratios in carbonate-secreting marine organisms: Jour. Geology, v. 62, p. 284–322.

Lowenstam, H. A., and S. Epstein, 1954, Paleotemperatures of the post-Aptian Cretaceous as determined by the oxygen isotope method: Jour. Geology, v. 62, p. 207–248.

Lyell, C., 1830, Principles of geology (1st ed.) v. 1: London, John Murray.

Ma, Ting Ying H., 1937a, On the seasonal growth in Palaeozoic tetracorals and the climate during the Devonian Period: Palaeontologica Sinica, ser. B, v. 2, pt. 3, p. 1–96, pls. 1–22.

———, 1937b, On the growth rate of reef corals

and its relation to sea water temperature: Palaeontologica Sinica, ser. B, v. 16, pt. 1, p. 1–426, pls. 1–100.

———, 1955, Climate and the relative positions of the continents during the Lower Carboniferous Period: Research on Past Climate and Continental Drift, v. 7, p. 1–99, pls. 1–50.

MacGinitie, G. E., 1955, Distribution and ecology of the marine invertebrates of Point Barrow, Alaska: Smithsonian Misc. Colln., v. 128, no. 9, p. 1–201.

Murakoshi, T., and K. Hashimoto, eds., 1956, Geology and mineral resources of Japan: Kawasaki, Geological Survey of Japan.

Schwarzbach, M., 1946, Klima und Klimagürtel im Alttertiär: Naturwissenschaften, v. 12, p. 355–361.

———, 1950, Das Klima der Vorzeit: Stuttgart, F. Enke.

Shapley, H., et al., 1953, Climatic change—evidence, causes, and effects: Cambridge, Mass., Harvard University Press.

Smith, J. P., 1919, Climatic relations of the Tertiary and Quaternary faunas of the California region: California Acad. Sci. Proc., ser. 4, v. 9, p. 123–173, pl. 9.

Sverdrup, H. U., M. W. Johnson, and R. H. Fleming, 1942, The oceans: New York, Prentice-Hall.

Valentine, J. W., 1955, Upwelling and thermally anomalous Pacific Coast Pleistocene molluscan faunas: Am. Jour. Sci., v. 253, p. 462–474.

Vaughan, T. W., 1940, Ecology of modern marine organisms with reference to paleogeography: Geol. Soc. America Bull., v. 51, p. 433–468.

Woodring, W. P., 1938, Lower Pliocene molluscs and echinoids from the Los Angeles basin, California, and their inferred environment: U.S. Geol. Survey Prof. Paper 190, p. 1–67, pls. 1–9.

Woodring, W. P. and M. N. Bramlette, 1950, Geology and paleontology of the Santa Maria district, California: U.S. Geol. Survey Prof. Paper 222, p. 1–185, pls. 1–23.

Woodring, W. P., M. N. Bramlette, and W. S. W. Kew, 1946, Geology and paleontology of Palos Verdes Hills, California: U.S. Geol. Survey Prof. Paper 207, p. 1–145, pls. 1–37.

Permian Zoogeography and Its Bearing on Climate

F. G. STEHLI
1964

This paper considers the possible relationships between the observed distribution of several groups of Permian fossils and the climate of the Permian Period. The methods used and the data employed are, in part, those previously presented (Stehli, 1957). The entire problem is re-evaluated in the light of data which have accumulated since 1957. An attempt is also made to determine the nature of Permian diversity gradients and to apply them to climatic interpretation.

FAUNAL DISTRIBUTION AS A TEMPERATURE INDICATOR

The distribution of modern organisms is strongly affected by temperature. The effects are many. First, organisms or assemblages of organisms which can exist only within a certain temperature range are restricted by the geographic limits of that range. Such an effect can be seen in the distribution of coral reefs of the present day (Figure 72.1). Secondly, diversity within any major group tends to decrease from low to high latitudes, so that a diversity gradient parallel to the latitudinal temperature gradient exists (see Figure 72.7). Thirdly, both altitude on land and water depth in the sea affect distribution, since there is a gradient of decreasing temperature as departure is made from sea level in either direction. The latter effect, at least as it affects the decrease of temperature with depth in the sea, may result largely from our present harsh climate and may not be typical of the Earth's history.

If one would seek temperature effects among populations of fossil organisms, means would seem to be available through the application of the above-noted principles; yet at the same time, certain limitations are apparent. Some of the possibilities and limitations should be considered before an attempt to apply palaeozoogeography to problems of ancient climate is made.

The range of a temperature-restricted form can be plotted to provide information on the

From *Problems in Palaeoclimatology,* edited by A. E. M. Nairn, pp. 537–549. John Wiley and Sons, Inc. (Interscience Publications), 1964. Reprinted with permission of the author and the publisher.

distribution of the temperature zone to which it is restricted. The temperature restriction of present-day coral reefs has been shown in Figure 72.1. To use such a method with fossil organisms, it is necessary either to determine in advance which organisms will be temperature-sensitive or to simply make plots empirically and then try to assess the possibility that restricted distributions which may be found are due to temperature. In the case of forms having living relatives, it is sometimes possible to use the first course. Permian reptiles, whose distribution is plotted below, are an example, since all modern reptiles control their temperatures behaviourally rather than physiologically. Any reptile too large to escape the surface environment by burrowing is thus restricted to warm areas. The same limitations should have applied to Permian reptiles, and plots based on such groups would seem to be quite reasonably interpreted as temperature related.

When restricted distributions are found by plotting ranges for organisms whose temperature requirements are not known, as must often be the case in dealing with extinct fossil groups, possibilities of error are numerous. There is always, for instance, the possibility that, though temperature is by far the most important cause of restricted ranges, some other environmental factor may have been operating, at least locally, in any particular group. A temperature control may be inferred, however, if the pattern found for little-known groups is generally coincident with those found for temperature-controlled forms or if the ranges of many groups tend to be coincident.

Problems which affect the use of all distribution plots are those involved in sampling. These problems include variable accessibility of sampling areas, variation in facies and variation in the thoroughness of collecting and study. Such problems make it very difficult to be sure that areas of apparent non-occurrence are not actually areas of non-discovery or non-recognition. Once more the best available evidence for the reality of the patterns observed

FIGURE 72.1
Generalized winter 15°C isotherms for both hemispheres and generalized distribution of present coral reefs. (After Sverdrup et al., 1946, and Ekman, 1953.)

FIGURE 72.2
Distribution of brachiopods belonging to the Enteletinae, Oldhaminidae and Richthofenidae during Permian time

comes from the coincidence of ranges in several groups of organisms. The existence of competent modern studies of large collections also greatly enhances the reliability of the basic data, the quality of which can thus be expected to steadily improve. A final general problem of considerable significance is the actual location of a range boundary, since control is seldom sufficient to completely define it. Range boundaries for distribution plots need not necessarily be drawn from one limiting occurrence to another. The boundary can only be said to lie between a control point falling in the zone of occurrence and the nearest one falling outside of it, and then only with certainty if sampling at the negative control point has been extensive and in appropriate facies. An example can be seen in Figure 72.1, where coral reefs are seen to be absent from the west coasts of continents because of improper facies development due to upwelling currents.

SUMMARY OF PREVIOUS WORK

Newell (1955) made the observation that Permian faunas of Zechstein type appeared to be geographically separated from those typical of Tethyan type. He suggested that climate exercised a major control over the distribution of these two faunal facies and that the Zechstein type was a cold-water and the Tethyan type a warm-water fauna. Newell specifically suggested (op. cit., p. 8) that some distinctive brachiopods (Richthofenids and *Leptodus*) were characteristic of the Tethyan facies and that the fusulinids, abundant in the Tethyan facies, were excluded from Zechstein facies.

An attempt was made to plot the apparent distribution of several groups of distinctive brachiopods and of some groups of fusulinids by Stehli (1957). He concluded that the resulting plots suggested temperature control of distribution for these organisms with range boundaries seeming to occur between 50° and 60° latitude in the northern hemisphere, while in the southern hemisphere data were too sparse to interpret (Figure 72.2). This view was subsequently criticized by Bain (1958), on the grounds that lack of control in areas devoid of marine Permian rocks permitted him to draw what is roughly a double sine curve bounding the distribution plotted. Stehli (1958) showed that the model presented by Bain (1958) was difficult to support if data on reptilian distributions were added to improve control in areas devoid of marine rocks. Runcorn (1959) also disagreed with the view presented by Stehli (1957), and suggested that the apparent distributions better fitted an Earth model, based on palaeomagnetic evidence, which differed from the present Earth model. Stehli (1959) plotted distribution patterns on the Earth model proposed by Runcorn (1959), but was not convinced that the fit was improved.

It was noted by Stehli (1957, 1958, 1959) that the plots he used relied partly on negative evidence and that additional data could thus alter them. To evaluate the possibility that the apparent distributions were due to chance, an attempt was made to determine the probabilities of obtaining the observed patterns by random sampling of a homogeneous population. The probabilities were low to very low, but there appears to be considerable doubt as to the validity of the statistical model, since it can never be known with absolute certainty that an organism does not occur simply because it has not been found.

RE-EXAMINATION AND UPDATING OF INFORMATION

It appears desirable to consider the distribution data in the light of information accumulated since 1957 and to reassess the significance of any patterns that may be shown to exist.

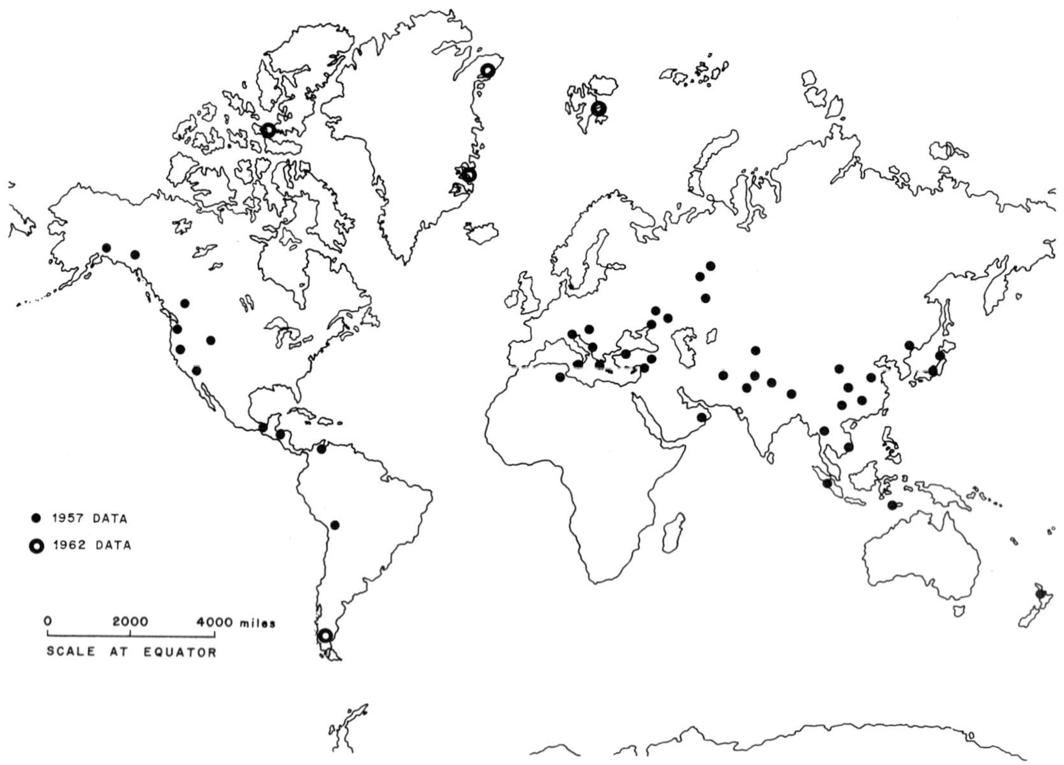

FIGURE 72.3
Permian fusulinid distribution

FIGURE 72.4
Distribution of *Aviculopinna* and "*Pinna*" during the Permian. (After Branson, 1948.)

Fusulinid data. It was known in 1957 that a few genera of fusulinids did, in fact, occur in high northern latitudes, but many genera and subfamilies belonging to the group had not been reported from such areas. The distribution of a number of groups of fusulinids was plotted by Stehli (1957), who presented the information shown here as Figure 72.3. In recent years the increasing tempo of exploration in the Arctic has resulted in new collections and in intensified study, and it is apparent that previous sampling for these small fossils had been inadequate. Their presence has now been reported from north-east Greenland (Ross and Dunbar, 1962), the Grinnell Peninsula of Devon Island (Harker and Thorsteinsson, 1960), and Spitsbergen (Forbes, Harland and Hughes, 1958). Further, so many identifications have been changed and new genera proposed that taxonomic problems presently make it impossible to adequately and consistently plot distributions. It must be said that, at the subfamily level at least, fusulinids now appear to have been world-wide during the Permian and that no temperature control can, at our present level of understanding, be seen in their distribution.*

Brachiopod data. The distribution patterns found for several Permian brachiopod groups, including the Richthofenidae, Oldhaminidae, Enteletinae, and a number of small families and groups of genera were presented by Stehli (1957). As with the fusulinids, additional collections of brachiopods have been made at high latitudes since 1957 (Dunbar, 1962; Harker and Thorsteinsson, 1960; Forbes, Harland and Hughes, 1958). Unlike the fusulinids, however, the additional collecting and study of brachiopods has not revealed the presence of any of the groups used for distribution studies outside the belt of occurrence as previously

* To my knowledge, fusulinids have still not been found in Australia, though it appears probable that they will be.

given. Additional collecting within this belt has produced additional occurrences in some groups. Figure 72.2 shows the presently known distribution of the Richthofenidae, Oldhaminidae and Enteletinae which summarize the ranges for all the brachiopod groups previously used.

It is concluded, in view of the large size and distinctive nature of many of the Permian brachiopods used here, that the failure of detailed studies to detect them enhances the probability that these forms are truly absent from high latitudes. Temperature control still appears to be the most probable explanation for the observed distribution of these forms, and their zonation, within the limits of the control, can be interpreted as parallel to the present Equator.

Pelecypod data. Consideration has been given to the possibility of finding among Permian marine invertebrates any group with closely related living descendants which are restricted to warm waters. The pelecypods, which have been in many respects a slowly evolving but persistent group, seemed to offer some possibilities. *Aviculopinna* of the Permian seems very close to modern members of the Pinnacea, and the latter are restricted to very warm temperate or warmer waters. Since the Pinnacea would seem to have evolved at bradytelic rates since Devonian time, it appears very likely that they have occupied the same environment at least since the Permian. Using Branson (1948) as a source, the known occurrences of *Aviculopinna* were plotted (Figure 72.4). It is true that this animal has not been widely encountered in Permian rocks, but all known occurrences do coincide with the zone deduced, from brachiopod distributions, to have been characterized by warm-water conditions.

Reptile data. During Permian time considerable areas now above sea level and available for study seem to have been sites of terrestrial

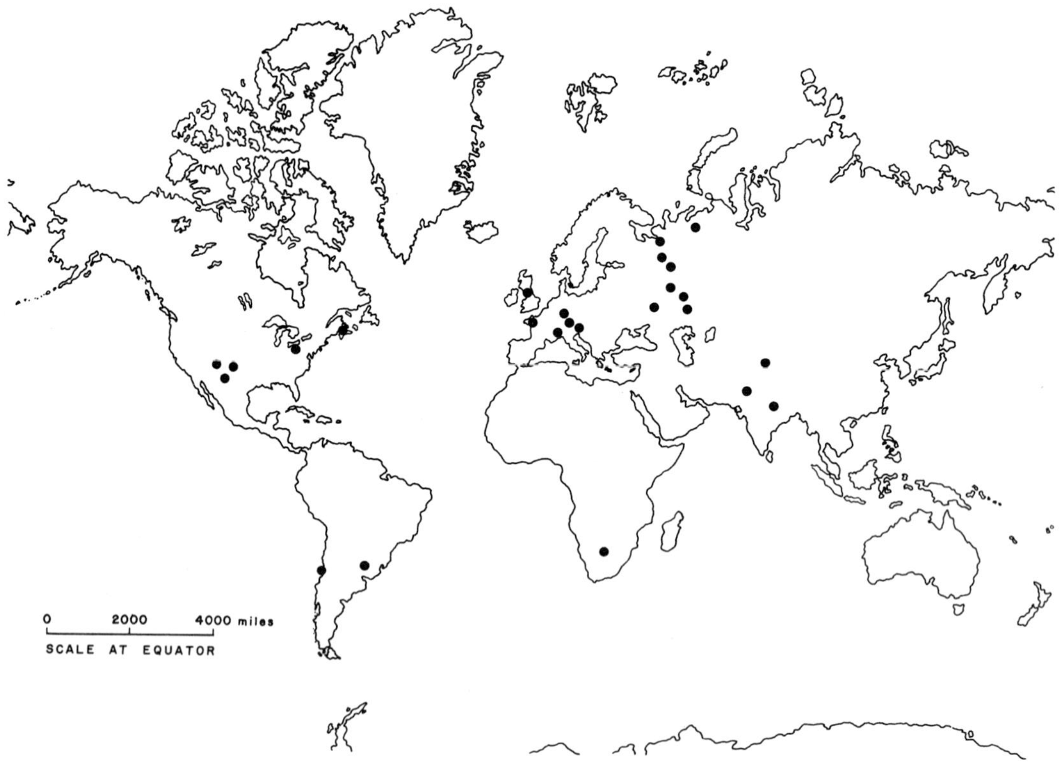

FIGURE 72.5
Distribution of large Permian reptiles. (Largely after Olson, 1962.)

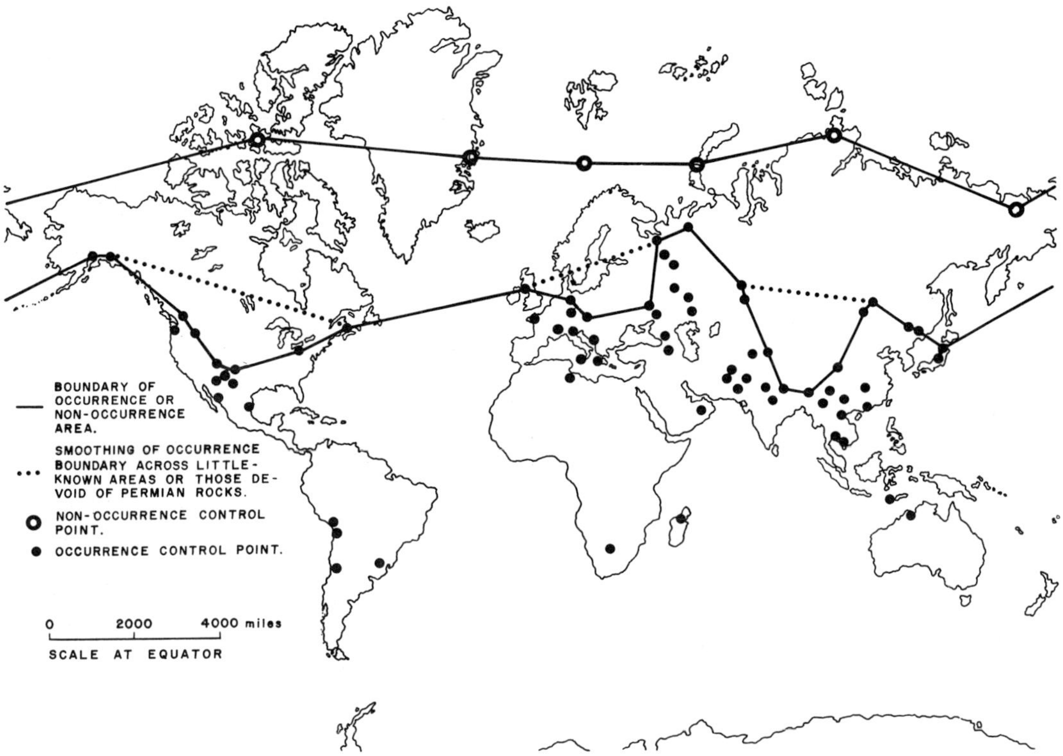

FIGURE 72.6
Generalized occurrence data for large Permian reptiles; oldhaminid, richthofenid, and enteletinid brachiopods; and *Aviculopinna* and "*Pinna*." With lines defining the limits of the region that may have contained the subtropical-temperate boundary.

deposition. In these rather extensive regions marine invertebrates are absent and cannot help us delineate temperature zones. Many of these regions of terrestrial Permian rocks have yielded the remains of a considerable fauna of large reptiles. It appears probable, since reptiles are poikilothermic, that areas yielding the remains of large Permian forms must have been warm during Permian time. It is true that some of these reptiles belong to phyla which, near the end of the Triassic, appear to have been approaching a mammalian condition, but the probability seems good that during the Permian they were cold blooded.

The known distribution of Permian reptiles, as adduced from the literature and especially from the recent excellent paper of Olson (1962), is given in Figure 72.5. It can be seen that several significant points are added in eastern North America, an area which is almost completely devoid of marine Permian rocks. Points are also added in European Russia, as far north as about 65°, and in western Europe. The points in western Europe are of particular interest, since they suggest that the absence of brachiopod faunas to be expected in the area may be due to some unfavourable marine conditions other than temperature (possibly salinity). Though the southern hemisphere has been largely excluded from this study because of poor control, it is of interest to note that Permian reptiles occur in South Africa and South America in the vicinity of 30° south.

If the general temperature requirements of large Permian reptiles are granted to be essentially the same as those of modern reptiles of similar size, severe limitations are thrown in the path of a temperature distribution such as that proposed by Bain (1958). In Figure 72.6 the reptilian distribution pattern is added to that for brachiopods and pelecypods. Within the limits of the control it would appear that a northern limit to the distributions might be as far north as 65°. The absence of control in eastern North America and especially in eastern Asia at this latitude results in considerable uncertainty as to the position of the boundary in these areas.

If one follows the procedure of connecting the nearest occurrence control points with a line and the nearest non-occurrence control points with another, it is likely that the true boundary occurs somewhere between these lines. A more realistic procedure, also shown in Figure 72.6, is to connect control points across areas devoid of control.

Summary of distribution data.

(1) Until the taxonomy of fusulinids is stabilized and further search is made for these small fossils, their distribution should be used in palaeoclimatic problems.

(2) Both Permian reptiles and the Permian clam *Aviculopinna* can probably be considered as warm-climate forms on the basis of distribution of related living forms. Their distribution is consistent with, but does not prove, the conclusion that a zone of warm conditions ran parallel to the present Equator during Permian time.

(3) Brachiopod distributions have remained unchanged by additional collecting in the non-occurrence zone in present high latitudes and, since they roughly coincide with probable warm climate forms, are useful for palaeoclimatic interpretations.

(4) The limit of warm climate for the northern hemisphere during the Permian probably lay between the extreme limits shown in Figure 72.6.

DIVERSITY GRADIENTS

INTRODUCTION

In view of the relatively poor definition of the range boundary in areas lacking closely spaced control, it appears desirable to obtain additional evidence which might aid in its location. As noted previously, diversity gradients in organisms might be applied to the present problem.

At least since 1878, when A. R. Wallace contrasted the great diversity of tropical biotas

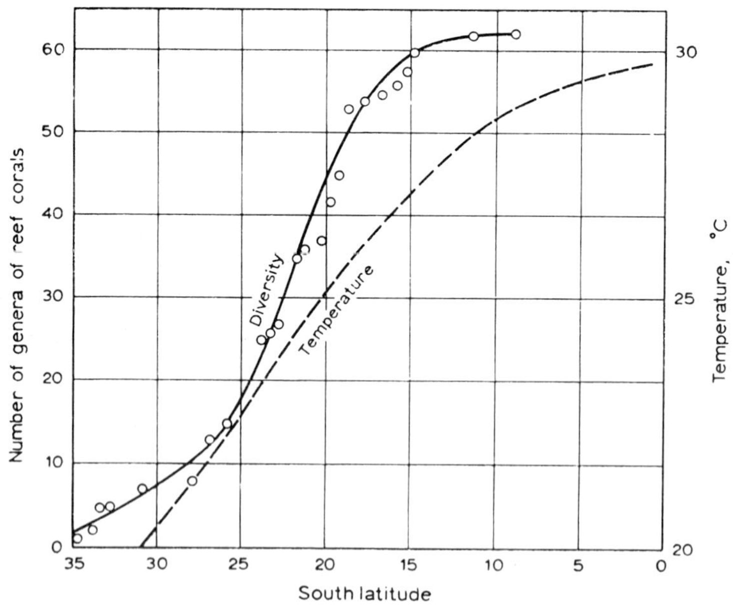

FIGURE 72.7
Diversity gradient in genera of reef corals along the Great Barrier Reef. (Data replotted from Wells, 1956.)

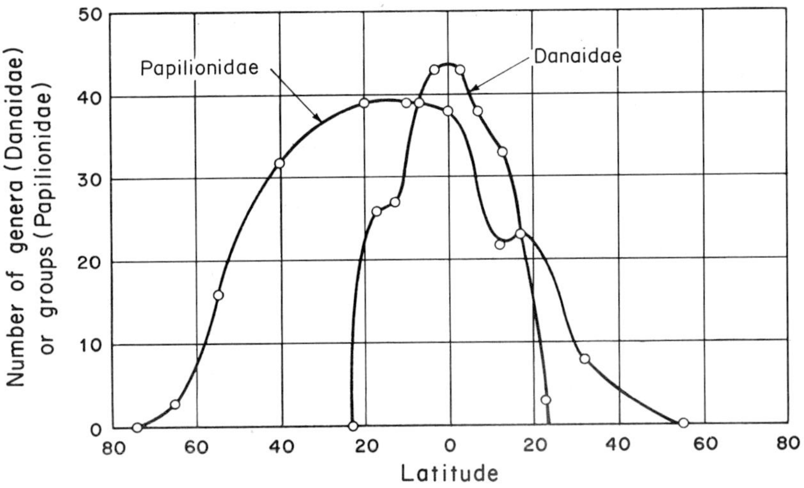

FIGURE 72.8
Diversity gradients in butterflies. (Data from Hovanitz, 1958.)

with the relative impoverishment of temperate ones, it has been clear that there exists a gradient in organic diversity between the Equator and the poles. Many investigators (e.g. Hutchins, 1947; Hedgepeth, 1957) have indicated that the principal role in limiting the distribution of organisms must be assigned to temperature. It would thus appear that diversity gradients should result from the ever more stringent restriction of ranges imposed by the increasingly unfavourable temperatures encountered as polar regions are approached. Fischer (1960), in a recent review and analysis, has brought together much information on diversity gradients in both marine and terrestrial organisms, and concludes that tempera-

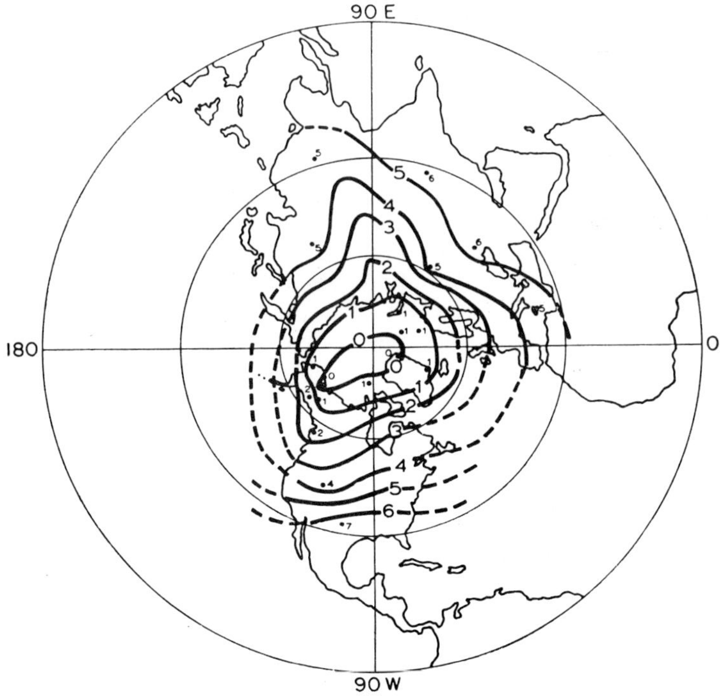

FIGURE 72.9
Diversity gradient in Permian terebratuloid brachiopods. (Stereographic projection.)

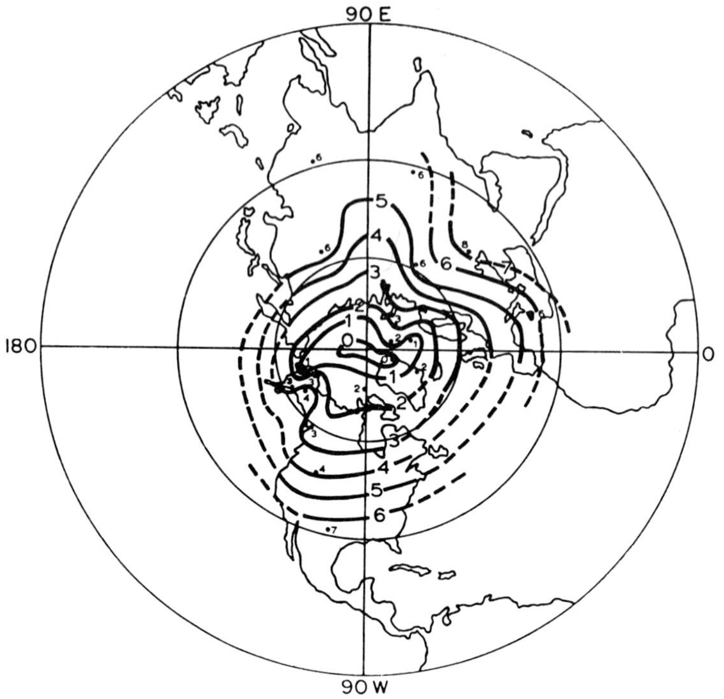

FIGURE 72.10
Diversity gradient in Permian orthotetaceid brachiopods. (Stereographic projection.)

ture is the major underlying cause of the observed gradients. The diversity gradients are so strong and so closely related to temperature gradients that there can be little doubt that temperature is the controlling factor. In Figure 72.7 data taken from a study of the corals of the Australian Great Barrier Reef by Wells (1955) are plotted to show the number of genera present as a function of latitude. For comparison, a generalized temperature curve is also plotted from data obtained from maps in Sverdrup, Johnson and Fleming (1942). An interesting example is also furnished by data from Hovanitz (1958) on the diversity gradient in several groups of butterflies. Figure 72.8 shows a surprisingly symmetrical gradient centred on the Equator for the strictly tropical family Danaidae. A gradient strongly skewed towards the northern hemisphere is shown for the widespread family Papilionidae. To the writer's knowledge, diversity gradients in modern biotas have not yet been plotted in map form. This is certainly necessary if present distribution is to be used as a model for the interpretation of past distributions, and is in progress in the writer's laboratory. Even in the absence of diversity maps for recent organisms, it is of interest to test the technique on Permian faunas.

PROBLEMS IN DATA ACCUMULATION

The marked nature of diversity gradients and their close relationship to temperature lead Stehli (1957, p. 615) to suggest their use in determining the nature and direction of ancient temperature gradients. He noted, however, that sampling of the fossil record was often poor and the information necessary for an adequate test of ancient diversity gradients difficult to accumulate. Since it appears desirable to test the supposed temperature control indicated in the range data with some other line of evidence, an attempt has been made to determine the nature of Permian diversity gradients.

In accumulating the required data, every attempt has been made to be as objective as possible, but many subjective judgements have of necessity been made. It need hardly be pointed out that valid quantitative data bear-

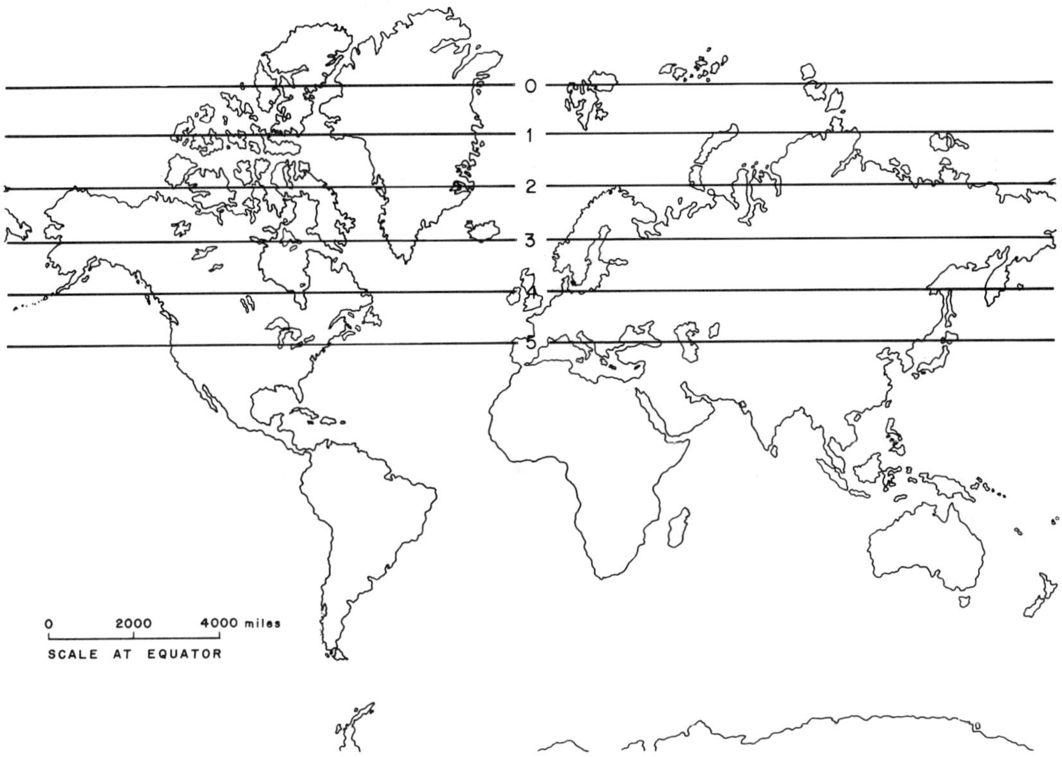

FIGURE 72.11
Linear surface fitted to terebratuloid diversity gradient data

ing on fossil diversity gradients are far more difficult to obtain than the simple presence or absence data needed to determine distributions. Problems which affect the data involve (1) the limited number of outcrop areas, (2) variations in facies, (3) inequalities in sampling due to inaccessibility, (4) inequalities in sampling due to the nature of exposures, (5) inequalities in the nature of study accorded collections, and (6) the subjectivity involved in taxonomy. Little could be done about items (1) and (3). An attempt was made to reduce the difficulties occasioned by items (2) and (4) through the choice of areas containing numerous exposures and by integrating studies within a region where possible. Item (5) introduced much subjectivity, since it was impossible to compare the thorough studies of a competent specialist with the incomplete, and often inaccurate, field determinations frequently reported. For this reason only those studies which were monographic in nature, those which represented considered determinations made by specialists or studies of limited nature which could be integrated to provide comparable data were included in the tabulations of diversity. It is hoped that this unavoidable procedure did not unduly prejudice the data. Item (6) was minimized by selecting groups that have received considerable study. In the case of the Orthotetaceids, the group has long been recognized and, at the generic level used in this study, taxonomic distinctions are quite easily made and are relatively objective. The terebratuloids were selected because the writer has recently completed a revision of the group for the *Treatise on Invertebrate Paleontology* and has examined material from most major areas of Permian rocks and has reviewed practically all the literature.

RESULTS

Data believed to be of roughly comparable quality were obtained for terebratuloid brachiopods from 18 stations in the northern hemisphere. The terebratuloid genera used in the compilations were *Cryptacanthia, Dielasma, Gefonia, Dielasmina, Hemiptychina, Heterelasma, Jisuina, Pseudodielasma,* and *Rostranteris.* Occurrences found for these genera ranged from 0 in northeast Greenland to 7 in west Texas. When the sampling areas are plotted on a map and contoured, the pattern which emerges is a clear-cut, though somewhat irregular, diversity gradient from low to high latitudes (Figure 72.9).

Data have been obtained for the orthotetaceids from the same 18 stations. The orthotetaceid genera used were *Derbyella, Derbyaeconcha, Derbyia, Geyerella, Kiangsiella, Meekella, Orthotetes, Orthotetella, Orthotetina, Plicatoderbyia, Pseudoderbyia, Schellweinella, Schuchertella,* and *Streptorhynchus.* Among these 14 genera, abundance at various stations ranged from 0 in northeast Greenland to 8 in the Caucasus region. When the abundances are plotted at their stations and the data contoured, a clear-cut, but irregular, diversity gradient once again emerges (Figure 72.10) which is similar to that found for the terebratuloids.

SURFACE FITTING

Due to difficulties in sampling and other sources of "noise," it is unavoidable that there should be considerable unevenness in the palaeontological data. Much of this unevenness is evident in the contoured data, despite the strong gradient which is revealed. In order to see the true form of the gradient without the overlay of minor complications, a simple surface was fitted. Since no programme was readily available to us which would permit our computer to handle a spherical surface, the data were plotted on a mercator projection. The computer developed best-fitting linear, quadratic and cubic surfaces to both sets of data. The linear surface shows a fraction fit of 80% for the Orthotetaceids and of 88% for the Terebratuloids. An "F" test showed that, in both cases, the linear surface fitted the data with a confidence in excess of 99%.

The linear surface should very closely approximate the overall diversity gradient and, thus, Permian temperature and latitude. Figures 72.11 and 72.12 show in contour form the

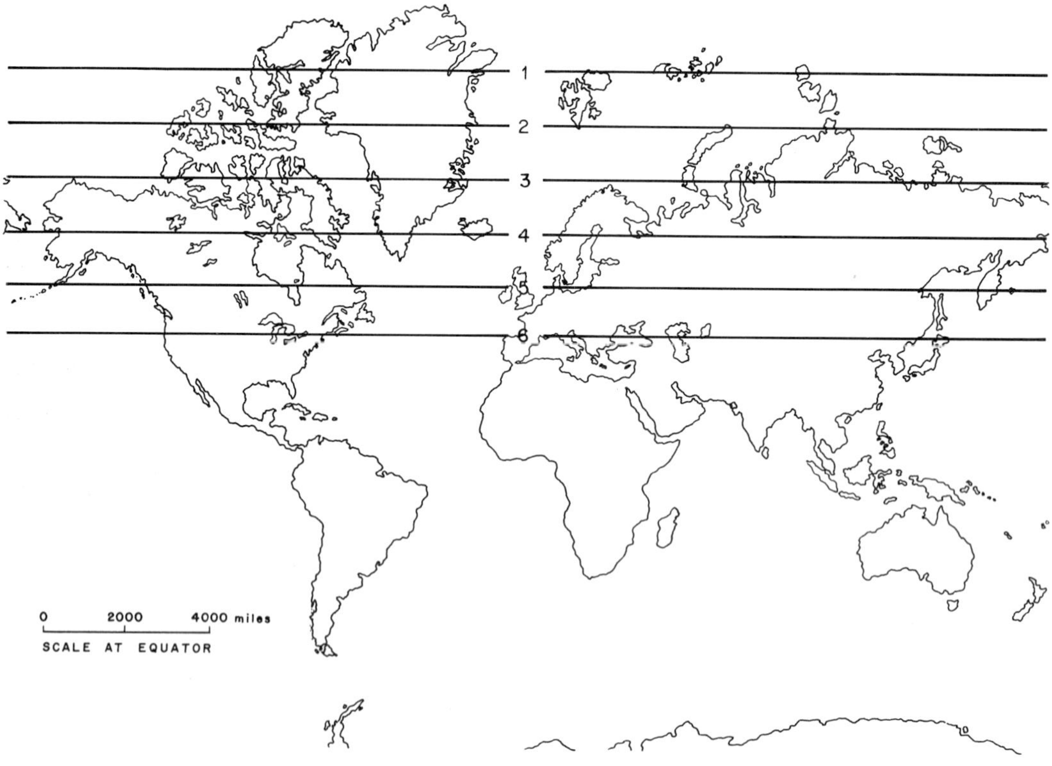

FIGURE 72.12
Linear surface fitted to orthotetaceid diversity gradient data

linear surfaces fitted to the diversity gradients. Clearly, the contours are nearly parallel to lines of latitude. Using a present Earth model, the pole as located from the terebratuloid data is coincident with the present North Pole. The pole position determined from the orthotetaceid data is found to lie at 88.5°N, 90°E. Because of the high-latitude distortion of the mercator projection, the data were also hand-contoured on a sphere and on a stereographic projection, and the close agreement obtained from the various plots suggests that the use of the mercator projection did not introduce any severe source of error.

It would appear that the technique of fitting simple surfaces to diversity gradients as reconstructed from quantitative palaeontological data may provide a high-resolution means of determining ancient pole positions. The data presented here are strictly preliminary and the method requires further testing and refinement. A really definitive test must be made for an interval of geologic time which does not suffer from the paucity of data which affects the Permian. Such a test using Cretaceous rocks is now being made by Dr. Charles Helsley and myself.

DISCUSSION

If it is granted that the diversity gradients establish the form and slope of a temperature surface for the northern hemisphere in Permian time, then comparisons can be made with the range data also believed to reflect temperature control. When this is done, it is found that the northern edge of the general boundary of the supposed warm-water conditions is grossly parallel to the contours expressing the form of the diversity and temperature gradient.

The palaeontologic data here employed to obtain palaeoclimatic information appear to give the general trend of palaeoisotherms. While the control available is not sufficient to eliminate the possibility of minor continental movements, none is required to explain the data. Control is sufficient to suggest that large-scale latitudinal movements have not affected the northern continents since Permian time and to place decided limitations on acceptable positions for the north rotational pole.

BIBLIOGRAPHY

Bain, G. W., 1958, Discussion—possible Permian climatic zonation and its implications: Am. Jour. Sci., v. 256, p. 596.

Branson, C. C., 1948, Bibliographic index of Permian invertebrates: Geol. Soc. America Mem. 26.

Dunbar, C. O., 1962, Faunas and correlation of the Late Paleozoic rocks of Northeast Greenland, pt. III: Medd. Grønland, v. 167, no. 6.

Fischer, A. G., 1960, Latitudinal variations in organic diversity: Evolution, v. 14, p. 64.

Forbes, C. L., W. B. Harland, and N. F. Hughes, 1958, Paleontological evidence for the age of the Carboniferous und Permian rocks of central Spitzbergen: Geol. Mag. [Great Britain], v. 95, p. 465.

Harker, P., and R. Thorsteinsson, 1960, Permian rocks and faunas of Grinnell Peninsula, Arctic Archipelago: Geol. Survey Canada Mem. 309.

Hedgepeth, J. W., 1957, Marine biogeography, *in* H. Ladd., ed., Treatise on marine ecology and paleoecology: Geol. Soc. America Mem. 67, p. 359.

Hovanitz, W., 1958, Distribution of butterflies in the new world, *in* C. L. Hubbs, ed., zoogeography: Am. Assoc. Adv. Sci. Pub. 51, p. 321.

Hutchins, L. W., 1947, The bases for temperature zonation in geographical distributions: Ecol. Mon., v. 17, p. 325.

Newell, N. D., 1955, Permian pelecypods of East Greenland: Medd. Grønland, v. 110, p. 1.

Olson, E. C., 1962, Late Permian terrestrial vertebrates, U.S.A. and U.S.S.R.: Am. Philos. Soc. trans., v. 52, p. 1.

Ross, C. A., and C. O. Dunbar, 1962, Faunas and correlation of the late Paleozoic rocks of Northeast Greenland, pt. II: Medd. Grønland, v. 167, no. 5.

Runcorn, S. K., 1959, Discussion—on the Permian climatic zonation and paleomagnetism: Am. Jour. Sci., v. 257, p. 235.

Stehli, F. G., 1957, Possible Permian climatic zonation and its implications: Am. Jour. Sci., v. 255, p. 607.

———, 1958, Reply [to Bain, 1958]: Am. Jour. Sci., v. 256, p. 600.

———, 1959, Reply [to Runcorn, 1959]: Am. Jour. Sci., v. 257, p. 239.

Sverdrup, H. V., M. W. Johnson, and R. H. Fleming, 1942, The oceans: New York, Prentice-Hall.

Wells, J. W., 1955, A survey of the distribution of reef coral genera in the Great Barrier Reef region: Great Barrier Reef Comm. Rept., v. 4, pt. 2, p. 21–29.

Upper Paleozoic Glacial Deposits

of South Africa and Southern Australia

WARREN HAMILTON

DAVID KRINSLEY

1967

From *Geological Society of America Bulletin,* vol. 78, pp. 783–800, 1967. Reprinted with permission of the authors and the Geological Society of America. [Fourteen of original thirty photographs deleted.]

Late Paleozoic glacial deposits have long been recognized throughout broad areas of the "Gondwana" continental masses of southern and central Africa, Australia and Tasmania, peninsular India, and southeastern South America and the Falkland Islands, and similar deposits have been found recently in Arabia and Antarctica. Despite the importance of these materials . . . there has been little study of them by modern methods. (Among the notable exceptions are the studies by Hübner [1966] in equatorial Africa, and by Frakes and Crowell [1967] in the Falkland Islands.) We present here brief field and laboratory descriptions of typical glacial sediments in the Republic of South Africa and southern Australia. The sampled localities and their significance are known to local geologists, but many of the observations summarized here have no analogues in the Gondwana literature. We also review published information on Late Paleozoic glaciation and comment on the significance of the glacial deposits for continental drift. Krinsley is responsible for the electron-microscopy section of the paper, and Hamilton for the remainder.

PALEOZOIC GLACIAL DEPOSITS

RECOGNITION OF GLACIAL MATERIALS

Some nonglacial processes form deposits that contain large clasts in fine matrixes and resemble tillites superficially. The pebbly mudstones described by Crowell (1957) are an example. An analysis of the features of such nonglacial sediments on the one hand and of Quaternary glacial drift on the other demonstrates that the following features in combination prove glaciation: (1) polished and striated pavements and roches moutonnées showing friction-cracking, plucking, *etc.*, underlying (2) massive, nonsorted debris, containing abundant rock flour, silt, and fine sand of multimodal grain size and including abundant fresh grains of easily weathered minerals, and stones

FIGURE 73.1
Exhumed roche moutonnée of Precambrian basalt. Ice moved toward upper left. Nooitgedacht Farm, Kimberley, Cape Province, South Africa.

—including faceted and striated blocks—to boulder size from both local and distant sources; and (3) laminated, fine-grained sediments enclosing numerous dropstones, some of them with striated facets. These and other criteria for glaciation are abundantly met in the upper Paleozoic deposits of the continental, low-relief, nonvolcanic regions of Africa, Australia, and the other Gondwana continents.

No detailed facies studies of Paleozoic continental glacial deposits have yet been published. (Some are underway by J. C. Crowell, L. A. Frakes, and their associates.) The lithologies and local relationships are nevertheless easily visualized by analogy with Quaternary glacial materials. Lee (1955, p. 5) described in idealized fashion the products of a single stand of a late Pleistocene ice front:

> The deposits near the margin [of the ice] would consist of till in the form of end moraine; gravel, sand, and till as kame moraine; and gravel and sand as moulin kames and some kame terraces. Beyond the margin would be gravel and sand as outwash apron and valley train. Behind the margin, although partly formed during its retreat, would be till as both ground moraine and ablation moraine, their relative abundance depending on how the ice-sheet wasted. Resting on this till would be gravel and sand as eskers, kames, kame terraces, and outwash, and over these in turn clay and silt deposited in local lakes formed by drift [and ice] dams.

GLACIAL PAVEMENT

The evidence for Late Paleozoic glaciation most impressive to the majority of geologists is probably the widespread occurrence of polished and striated pavements at the base of the tillites. Several hundred small exposures of pavements are known in South Africa and South-West Africa. Du Toit (1922, Fig. 1) noted 70 exposures, and more have been found since, in a region of only 5000 square miles in Natal. Many large areas of exposed roches moutonnées, reaching a maximum size of many acres, are known also. Among those who have described and illustrated these pavements are du Toit (1953, p. 270–280) and Martin (1961). In Australia, pavements have been found at perhaps 100 localities scattered widely across the southern half and northwestern part of the continent (e.g., David, 1950, p. 301–350). Most of these pavements occur on old hard rocks at the base of glacial sections, but many have been found also within tillites or on sedimentary rocks beneath tillites higher in the sections. Directions of ice motion shown by the pavements are typically subparallel over large regions. All common features of late Pleistocene glacial pavements (Chamberlin, 1888; Harris, 1943) are widespread also on these Paleozoic pavements.

Well-exposed glacial pavements were visited at two localities in South Africa and three in southern Australia. At Nooitgedacht Farm, near Kimberley in Cape Province, South Africa, roches moutonnées (Figures 73.1 and 73.2) have been exhumed discontinuously in dozens of large and small exposures over a tract of about 10 acres. The roches are carved from hard Precambrian basalt and preserve a brilliant glacial polish marked by striae. That the ice flowed south-southwest is shown by the striae, friction cracks, stoss smoothing, lee plucking, and the shapes of the roches. The pavement is overlain discontinuously by tillite, and both are overlain by shale containing rafted erratic materials.

One of the many small exposures of pavement in Natal (Figure 73.3) was examined. The striated surface of this pavement, like that of others nearby (du Toit, 1922, Fig. 1; King and Maud, 1964, p. 10), shows that the ice moved inland, to the southwest—although the shore of the Indian Ocean lies only 5 miles to the northeast. Overlying the pavement is thick massive tillite whose large erratic rocks include abundant granitic and gneissic rocks (Figure 73.4).

The best of the Australian glacial pavements visited is that polished brightly upon hard quartzite and exposed discontinuously for a quarter of a mile along the top of the sea cliff extending north from Hallett Cove, south of Adelaide in South Australia. The exhumed pavement shows almost no modification of its original features. Stoss and lee effects (Figure 73.5) are shown superbly along the entire exposure. Most friction cracks deepen northward in the direction of ice flow and are sharp and rough sided, but the many friction cracks and conchoidal spalls deepening against the flow are scooped and polished smooth. Small roches moutonnées show the same features on their sides, and in an extreme case, a low roche has an overhanging side that is polished and striated like the rest. The ice flowed northward

FIGURE 73.2
Boulder tillite lying on roche moutonnée of Figure 73.1 Glacial striae are parallel to hammer handle.

FIGURE 73.3
Glacial pavement on hard Table Mountain sandstone (Silurian?). Ice moved toward upper right (southwest). Block of overlying tillite is at upper left. South of Umgeni River in northwestern suburbs of Durban, Natal.

FIGURE 73.4
Massive tillite near Durban, Natal, above the glacial pavement of Figure 73.3. Clasts of light granitic rock are abundant. Dark clasts (*as below and right of penny*) of altered volcanic rocks blend with fine-grained matrix.

from the direction of the present deep Southern Ocean. Overlying the pavement are unconsolidated tillite and aqueoglacial sediments, the latter containing abundant dropstones, some of which bear striated facets (Figure 73.6).

Many of the other exposures of glacial pavements in South Australia are in the Inman River Valley, also south of Adelaide, where topography with a relief of 1800 feet was overridden by ice moving northwestward (David, 1950, p. 304–305). The largest of the Inman pavements, appropriately named Glacier Rock, was visited. This pavement consists of polished metasiltstone which forms a broad, gently sloping surface flanked by the exhumed steep side of a roche moutonnée, and both surface and roche are polished, striated, broadly grooved (the rock is softer than that at the localities noted previously), and friction-cracked. Cracks, and stoss and lee features, show that the ice moved northwestward toward the continental interior. The pavement is overlain by unconsolidated tillite and aqueoglacial sediments.

The third Australian pavement seen is a small exposure of polished and northward-striated metasandstone underlying poorly consolidated tillite near Bacchus Marsh, about 30 miles west of Melbourne in Victoria. This is one of many small exposures of pavement in this part of Victoria (Kenley, 1952, p. 57).

TILLITE

Upper Paleozoic tillite has been found over broad regions of South Africa and Australia. During the sampling for the present work, these tillites were visited at from one to five localities near each of the following places: Vereeniging, Transvaal; Durban and Pietermaritzburg, Natal; Kimberley and Matjesfontein, Cape Province; Hallett Cove and Inman River, South Australia; Bacchus Marsh and Ballan, Victoria; and Derwent Bridge, Wynyard, and Zeehan, Tasmania. This permitted a broad sampling of the continental deposits. The glacial materials seen vary in compactness and color from unconsolidated buff or light-gray deposits easily dug with a shovel to solidly lithified bluish- or greenish-gray tillites suitable for road metal. The materials are mostly massive unsorted deposits consisting of pebbles and boulders in a matrix of granules, sand, silt, and rock flour. Some directly overlie glacial pavements, and others are interbedded with standing-water and stream deposits. None are metamorphosed. All but that near Zeehan are in or near paleontologically dated sections.

The tillites range from discontinuous beds a few feet thick to uniform sections hundreds of feet thick. Three examples are noted here. The Dwyka Tillite exposed in the underground workings of the Bultfontein diamond mine at Kimberley forms discontinuous lenses up to 8 feet thick lying on a glacial pavement and overlain by glacial dropstone shale. At the other extreme, Dwyka Tillite at Durban is 750 feet thick, and large quarries in it show only faint stratigraphic breaks 100 feet or more apart. Tillites occur at many levels in the thick section near Bacchus Marsh; the lowest tillite lies directly on a glacial pavement, and the others are interbedded in units up to 100 feet

FIGURE 73.5
Polished pavement on quartzite, at Halibut Cove, South Australia. Ice flowed northward—toward upper right. Note stoss-and-lee effects: friction cracks deepening in direction of flow are sharp-edged but cracks deepening against flow are gouged and polished smooth.

FIGURE 73.6
Laminated siltstone and sandstone containing pebbles dropped from floating ice. Hallett Cove, South Australia. Arrows point to dropped pebbles.

thick with water-laid deposits. Some tillite shows rude internal bedding, but its glacial origin is indicated by the subhorizontal, nonimbricated clasts, striated stones, silt and rock-flour matrix, occurrence with glacial pavements, and interbedding with massive tillite.

The tillites examined rest on varied Paleozoic sedimentary and low-grade metasedimentary rocks, Precambrian low-grade metasedimentary and metavolcanic rocks, and Precambrian plutonic rocks (other tillites of Australia overlie Paleozoic granitic rocks). Rocks like those of the underlying material commonly comprise most of the coarse clasts of the tillites, but widely varying foreign rock types are invariably present. Fragments of gneissic and granitic rocks are common to abundant in all exposures seen. Thus, tillite near Kimberley overlies altered Precambrian volcanic rocks but includes abundant blocks of granitic (Figure 73.2), gneissic, and metamorphic rocks which have no possible nearby source; du Toit (1953, p. 276) noted that clasts of distinctive Bushveld granite, 800 miles southwest of its outcrop region, are common in tillite in this part of South Africa. Tillite near Durban lies upon older Paleozoic quartzite but contains abundant blocks of granitic and gneissic rocks (Figure 73.4), and metavolcanic rocks, as well as quartzite; and yet, the ice flowed from the northeast, in which direction, only a few miles distant, the tropical Indian Ocean now lies. Each of the other African tillites examined is similarly polymict.

Varied granites and gneisses are common also in all the Australian tillites examined. Local geologists recognize many rock types of known source area, but some clasts have no known source region within Australia (e.g., Kenley, 1952). A 12-foot-long erratic of granite, whose outcrop belt is at closest about 10 miles from this locality, was seen above a large exposure of glacial pavement by the Inman River in South Australia; erratics twice this size have been reported elsewhere in the area.

The size and proportion of pebbles and boulders vary widely. In most outcrops visited, blocks as much as 1 foot in diameter are abundant, and in many places blocks several feet across were seen; in others, nearly all are smaller than a few inches. Rounding is variable and large clasts vary from angular to well rounded within many outcrops although subrounded shapes are most common. Large clasts tend to be more rounded than small ones. At some localities, elongate clasts have a preferred

FIGURE 73.7
Striated facet on stone in bouldery tillite. Doctors Rock, Wynyard, Tasmania

orientation, their long axes tending to lie subparallel to pavement striae. Such an orientation, parallel to the direction of flow of the ice, characterizes modern subglacial till plastered out beneath moving ice (Holmes, 1941).

Striated and faceted pebbles and boulders are common enough at many localities so that a search of a few minutes is enough to locate several or many of them (Figure 73.7). A single striated facet is commonly present on such blocks. Uncommon blocks show one set of striae superimposed at an angle across an older set. In such features and in their general shapes, the striated and faceted stones resemble those of Pleistocene glacial deposits (see von Engeln, 1930).

FIGURE 73.8
Angular quartz and feldspar in a rock-flour matrix. Some of the larger grains are thin splinters. Dwyka Tillite, Matjesfontein, Cape Province, South Africa. Ordinary light.

The tillites are seen in thin section to contain angular grains and even splinters of easily weathered rocks and minerals in great abundance and variety (Figure 73.8). Fresh grains of plagioclase, potassic feldspar, and varied ferromagnesian minerals are invariably present, and in each thin section display characteristics indicating derivation from widely differing rock types. Euhedral grains of plagioclase occur wherever volcanic source rocks are available, and even saussuritized grains from altered rocks show no weathering effects. Sand-sized grains of fine-grained clastic sedimentary and metasedimentary rocks, high-grade metamorphic rocks, and altered volcanic rocks are present in widely varying proportions. Granitic and high-grade metamorphic rocks are represented by quartz, plagioclase, perthite, orthoclase, and minor biotite and hornblende. Silt-sized grains also are highly varied in mineralogy, and even easily weathered minerals form fresh and sharply angular silt in many specimens.

The sand-and-silt-sized lithic microclasts and mineral grains whose source is apparent can be assigned to three major types of rock terranes—sedimentary and low-grade metasedimentary, low-grade metavolcanic, and granitic and high-grade metamorphic suites. The source rocks shown by these grains, as by the accompanying pebbles and boulders, generally are dominated by rock such as that of the regional bedrock but also include rock with no nearby basement source. Many samples display a single dominant source type; even these display a subordinate source in at least one of the two other main types of source assemblages. Thus, tillite near Bacchus Marsh and Wynyard, where the basement rocks are low-grade metasediments, is dominated by grains from sandstone and low-grade metashale, but contains subordinate plutonic debris. Altered volcanic rocks dominate the microclasts in tillite near Kimberley, where such rocks also form the basement, but high-grade metamorphic microclasts and plutonic mineral grains are abundant. Plutonic sources dominate tillite near Matjesfontein. At Durban, sedimentary, metavolcanic, and plutonic rocks jointly supplied the sand and silt, as they did the pebbles and boulders.

The fine fraction of the matrixes of the apparently unaltered tillites is virtually isotropic when viewed in thin section with crossed nicols. Clay and fine-grained mica is obvious petrographically only in those tillites which contain also abundant clasts of slightly metamorphosed shales; these clays appear to be shredded clastic grains from such older rocks.

The near lack of clay was confirmed by X-ray diffractometer analyses, made and interpreted by Leonard G. Schultz (1965 and 1966, written communication), of three unweathered tillites from South Africa. An unaltered tillite sample from the 300-foot level of the Bultfontein Mine, Kimberley, was disaggregated, and the finer-than-0.06-mm fraction analyzed. This fraction comprises 61 per cent of the finer-than-2-mm matrix of the specimen and contains about 50 per cent quartz, 20 per cent sodic plagioclase, 5 per cent muscovite, and no detectable clay. This fine material is thus rock flour. Two samples of tillite lithified too solidly for disaggregation were broken into granules, of which those with the highest proportion of matrix materials were selected for X-ray powder analysis. One of these samples is from an Umgeni River quarry, Durban (near that illustrated by Figure 73.4), the other from near Matjesfontein (Figure 73.8). The samples are very similar in X-ray mineralogy and contain about 30 and 35 per cent, respectively, of quartz, 25 per cent each of oligoclase, 5 and 10 per cent potassic feldspar, 25 and 15 per cent of chlorite, and approximately 3 and 7 per cent illite. Neither contains recognizable non-illitic clay.

The chlorite and illite presumably represent both clastic and secondary grains. In unweathered Fennoscandian Pleistocene glacial materials, illite is the only clay present in drift derived from crystalline rocks, and formed either *in situ* or during glacial or cold-water transport by hydrolysis of mica and feldspar, and not by preglacial weathering, whereas chlorite in the tills represents both grains derived directly from the basement rocks and hydrated rock flour of ferromagnesian minerals (McNamara, 1966). Cummins (1962) and Roberts (1966) argued convincingly that the "argillaceous" matrix of most graywackes probably has formed *in situ* by postdepositional alteration of unstable silicate minerals in the fine-sand fraction of initially well-sorted sandstones (despite the long accepted assumption that the initial sediments were "muddy"). The two solidly lithified tillite samples analyzed by X rays contain abundant chlorite, probably derived in considerable part by similar alteration of tiny ferromagnesian grains. Alteration of tillite must destroy the unstable-mineral rock flour, silt, and fine sand, so altered tillite should resemble graywacke—and the hard, gray tillite seen at Durban and Matjesfontein is indeed intermediate in petrographic character between unaltered tillite and graywacke. Alteration sufficient to destroy the silt and sand is to be expected where Paleozoic tillites have been metamorphosed.

L. G. Schultz and Philip G. Hanna (1965, written communication) also analyzed by X-ray diffractometer the finer-than-0.66-mm fractions of four partly weathered samples of tillite, two from near Vereeniging, South Africa, and two from near Bacchus Marsh, Victoria. Each of these fine fractions contains quartz as its dominant component (50–70 per cent) and contains about 10 per cent of clastic muscovite. Kaolinite makes up 10 or 15 per cent of each of the two Australian samples, which contain 5 or 10 per cent of potassic feldspar but no plagioclase, and 30 or 40 per cent of the two African samples, in which no feldspar is detectable; chlorite is lacking in all of them. No mixed-layer clays were noted. The kaolinite is a weathering product; apparently plagioclase silt and rock flour and chlorite disappear on weathering before the potassic feldspar has been completely destroyed. Sand grains of both plagioclase and potassic feldspar in these samples show no weathering in thin section.

Mechanical analyses of five specimens of tillite soft enough to be disaggregated were made by Hanna (1965, written commun.). Three samples are from South Africa and two from Victoria. Grain-size distributions, as in modern tills, are irregularly bimodal or multimodal. Material of clay and silt sizes is abundant: despite the pebbly to bouldery character of the deposits, between 37 and 83 per cent of the matrix material finer than 2 mm is finer than 0.06 mm. The Vereeniging sample has minor grain-size peaks in the intervals 0.03–0.06, 0.125–0.175, and 1–2 mm and has 58 per cent of its total finer-than-2-mm material finer than 0.06 mm, 40 per cent finer than 0.03 mm, and 11 per cent finer than 0.004 mm. Another tillite sample from near Vereeniging has three conspicuous sand peaks (0.25–0.35, 0.5–0.7, and 1–2 mm) and yet has 31 per cent of the finer-than-2-mm material finer than 0.03 mm. Tillite from the Bultfontein mine at Kimberley has a major grain-size peak in the interval 0.03–0.06 mm, and has minor peaks in the ranges 0.175–0.25 and 0.5–0.7 mm, and has 36 per cent of its finer-than-2-mm material finer than 0.03 mm. All these samples save the one from the Bultfontein mine are a little weathered, and alteration to clay of their fine components must have resulted in grain-size distributions somewhat different from the initial distributions.

GLACIOLACUSTRINE SEDIMENT

Fine-grained, quiet-water, clastic rocks containing ice-rafted dropstones, some of the larger ones faceted and striated, are common in the glacial sections. Such rocks were examined near Vereeniging and Kimberley, South Africa, and Hallett Cove, Bacchus Marsh, and Wynyard, Australia. These deposits vary from sandstone and siltstone to varved shale.

In the Bultfontein mine at Kimberley, soft, laminated, nonfissile, light-gray shale lies upon discontinuous tillite and the underlying glaciated pavement. The shale contains sparse erratic pebbles and blocks, and is seen in thin section to consist of silt-sized (mostly smaller than 0.05 mm) angular grains and splinters of quartz, feldspars, ferromagnesian minerals, and calcite in a nearly isotropic rock-flour groundmass. Laminae are 0.3–2 mm thick, differ primarily in grain size, and are not graded. There is very little visible clay. An X-ray diffractometer analysis of this shale was made by L. G. Schultz (1966, written communication), who found its most abundant mineral to be quartz. Chlorite and sodic plagioclase each make up about 20 per cent of the sample, and illite no more than 20 per cent. No other clays are present in detectable amounts, and the abundance of chlorite demonstrates the sample to be unweathered.

The best varves seen are those of several exposures near Seabrook Creek south of Wynyard (described by Banks and others 1955). The rocks are laminated shales and siltstones containing abundant dropped sand, granules, and pebbles. Graded varves in the illustrated specimen (Figure 73.9) are 0.3–3 mm thick. Each varve begins with quartz silt, which is overlain by finer quartz silt and bedding-parallel flakes of white mica or highly birefringent clay; the ratio of quartz to mica, and the grain size of each, decrease upwards in each varve. There are many dropped grains, granules, and pebbles of fine-grained, slightly metamorphosed, sedimentary rocks, and sparser dropped grains from plutonic sources. The mica of the varved shale is similar to that of the sedimentary rock clasts and presumably was derived by the shredding of such rocks. Interbedded nonvarved shale similarly is composed mostly of very fine quartz and mica, but in nongraded laminae generally thicker than 0.5 mm, and also contains abundant dropstones.

At Hallett Cove, above the glacial pavement of Figure 73.5, laminated to obscurely layered poorly consolidated silt and fine sand are interbedded with layered to cross-bedded sand. Even the most finely laminated sediments con-

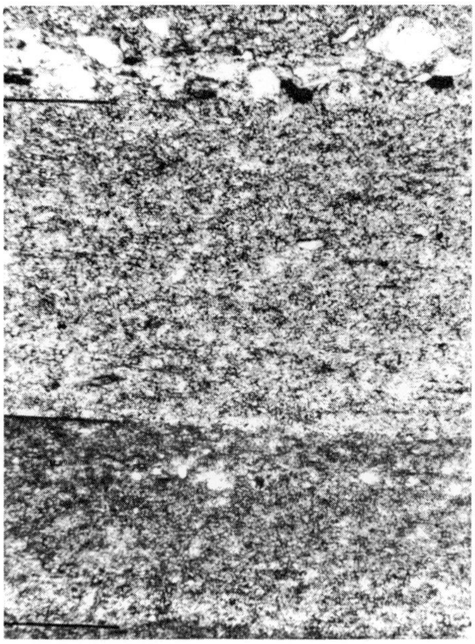

FIGURE 73.9
Varved shale. Bases of three varves are marked by lines at left. Seabrook Creek, Tasmania. Ordinary light.

tain numerous dropstones; the largest seen is 5 feet in diameter. A few large dropstones have striated facets. The concentration of dropstones varies from scattered (Figure 73.6) to abundant (Figure 73.10). The water-worked matrix was observed in thin section to consist of sharply angular to subrounded sand, mostly quartz but including much feldspar, cemented loosely by large poikilitic crystals of calcite. A mechanical analysis of this sand by P. G. Hanna (1965, written communication) showed the expected single gain-size peak and good sorting.

These descriptions typify the glaciolacustrine materials seen. Such deposits are widespread about southern Africa (e.g., du Toit, 1953, p. 273) and Australia (e.g., Banks, 1952). True varves are probably much less abundant than the use of the term would suggest, but some are certainly present; and dropstones, some of them faceted and striated, are widespread. Deposition in standing water, across which floating ice rafted detritus, is indicated, and may have been largely in lakes in the isostatically depressed belts along the fronts of retreating ice sheets.

OTHER GLACIAL MATERIALS

Fluvial sandstone and conglomerate are interbedded with glacial sediments at about half the localities visited although at none are they the dominant materials. Lenses and sheets of polymict imbricate-cobble conglomerate and of sand are common types. The association of these deposits with tillite in low-relief environments makes it probable that they are mostly of fluvioglacial origin, and their detritus must have been derived from glacial debris, whether during glacial or interglacial intervals. Fluvioglacial sediments in the glacial sections have been referred to by many geologists (e.g., du Toit, 1953, p. 273; David, 1950, p. 301–307), but little attempt appears to have been made to prove a fluvioglacial origin for them or to interpret them by analogy with specific equivalents in modern glacial drift.

Layered sediments interbedded with tillite and deformed plastically by overriding ice have been described from some Gondwana areas (as by Martin, 1961, 1964). In the course of the present work, tightly deformed lenses of sandstone were seen in tillites near Wynyard and near Bacchus Marsh. The lack of slump and flow structures at these localities shows that subaqueous sliding was not the cause of the deformation, which presumably was due to overriding by ice.

RECOGNITION OF GLACIAL MATERIALS BY ELECTRON MICROSCOPY

CRITERIA

Krinsley and Takahashi (1962a, 1962b, 1962c) found that quartz sand transported and deposited in different modern sedimentary environments shows by electron microscopy surface textures diagnostic of the various known sedimentary processes involved. They found also that the textures could be produced in the laboratory by simulating the transportation mechanisms. Many Recent and Pleistocene glacial sands have been studied, and 99 per cent of the grains examined display at least four of the following nine surface textural features (Krinsley and Funnell, 1965): (1) conchoidal fractures varying greatly in size, caused probably by variations in size of particles ground together; (2) very high relief, as compared with grains from nonglacial deposits, due to the large particle sizes present and to the great amount of energy available for grinding; (3) semiparallel steps, probably caused by shearing; (4) arcuate steps, probably percussion fractures; (5) parallel striations of varying length caused by scratching of other grains; (6) patterns of long prisms, possibly produced by cleavage or by recrystallization; (7) imbricate breakage blocks, which resemble hogbacks of steeply dipping strata; (8) polygonal breakage blocks; (9) indentations, due to small-scale grinding, superimposed on the other diagnostic features.

Quartz grains from upper Paleozoic tillites and aqueoglacial sediments of South Africa, Australia, and Antarctica were examined for this study and were found to have these same surface textures that are diagnostic of glacial origin in modern sediments.

METHOD

Objects studied by the electron microscope must be thinner than about 200 Å (0.00002 mm). Sand cannot be viewed directly: ultra-thin replicas of the surfaces must first be prepared. The process of replication and examination has been described by Krinsley and Takahashi (1964). A mold of a cleaned grain of quartz is made in acetate plastic. The mold is shadowed by evaporating a heavy metal such as chromium upon it at an angle of about 45 degrees, so that the density of the metal film varies with the orientation and slope of the surface topography. Carbon is next evaporated directly down on the mold to add density and strength to the film. The acetate is then dissolved away, and in the process, the film of metal and carbon flattens. Photographs are taken with a beam of electrons transmitted through the film. The thin parts of the film appear dark on the photographic negatives and light on the positive prints; the final photographs show the surface texture of the sand grains as though in shaded relief. The illusory direction of light source in the photographs is the direction opposite to that of shadowing by the metal.

RESULTS

Sand from upper Paleozoic deposits from two localities in South Africa, three in Australia, and one in Antarctica was studied with the

FIGURE 73.10
Probable subaqueous tillite. Hallett Cove, South Australia. Dropped pebbles and boulders are strewn liberally throughout bedded sandstone and siltstone; abundant debris from floating ice may be mixed with waterborne sediment.

FIGURE 73.11
Electron photomicrograph of conchoidal fractures on quartz grain. Bultfontein mine, Kimberley, South Africa.

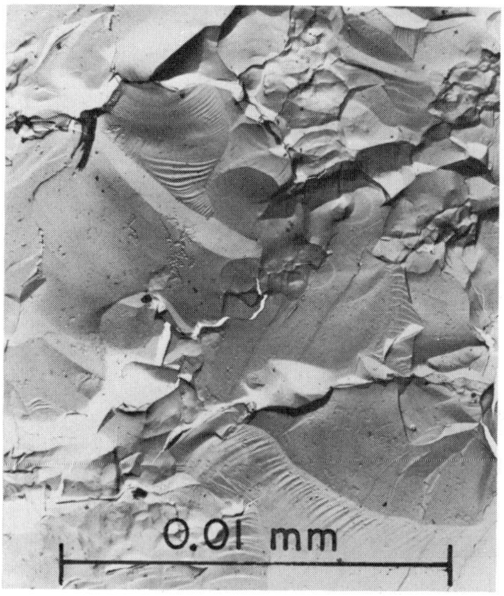

FIGURE 73.12
Electron photomicrograph of polygonal breakage blocks and small grinding indentations on quartz grain. Bultfontein mine, Kimberley, South Africa.

electron microscope. The entire replica for each of at least 12 grains per specimen was scanned. These Paleozoic glacial sediments display the same features in similar combination as do modern glacial deposits although the proportion of Paleozoic grains showing them is only about 50 per cent because of postdepositional solution. Only deposits soft enough to be disaggregated into original grains can be used, and among the Paleozoic materials, such deposits are generally somewhat weathered and have undergone at least slight diagenetic changes. The smallest diagnostic glacial texture, number 9 in the list, has been obliterated by solution in most of the Paleozoic samples studied. Compound sedimentary processes are distinguishable in modern sediments of known origin because of the superposition of textures they produce; thus, glacial sand carried by streams or reworked along beaches shows rounding and obliteration of glacial textures. Paleozoic glacial materials redeposited by running water display similar compound textures.

Descriptions of the diagnostic glacial textures of sand in the Paleozoic deposits follow. The electron photomicrographs (Figures 73.11–73.16) of these materials can be compared with those of Quaternary glacial sands presented by Krinsley and Takahashi (1962a, 1962c) and by Krinsley and Funnell (1965).

Dwyka Tillite, Kimberley, Cape Province, South Africa. The sample studied was collected from discontinuous massive pebbly tillite, 0–8 feet thick, lying upon a rolling glaciated surface of altered Precambrian volcanic rocks, in the 300-foot level of De Beers' Bultfontein diamond mine. The tillite matrix is soft greenish-gray rock composed of quartz and feldspar sand from plutonic rocks and sand- and granule-sized fragments of altered volcanic rocks in a matrix of silt and rock flour.

Quartz grains display a convincing array of glacial surface textures. Grains show conchoidal fractures varying greatly in size (Figure 73.11), very high surface relief, semiparallel steps, arcuate steps, and polygonal breakage blocks and small grinding indentations (Figure 73.12). Some grains show larger glacial markings worn down and partly obliterated by smaller, later ones. About half the grains studied have fresh surface textures, whereas those of the other half are variably rounded by solution.

Dwyka Tillite, Vereeniging, Transvaal, South Africa. The sand examined came from a massive tillite 10–15 feet thick exposed in a quarry 4 miles east of Vereeniging. The tillite is a weathered, loosely consolidated, yellowish-gray rock consisting of quartz and feldspar sand, and sand of granules of various fine-grained rocks in a matrix of silt and clay-sized material. There are abundant pebbles, mostly smaller than 1 inch in diameter, and sparse erratic boulders; one block 4 feet in diameter shows glacial striae all across a flat side.

Sand-surface textures have been considerably modified by solution, but of the nine textural criteria listed previously for glacial origin, all but numbers 6 and 8 were observed in the Vereeniging samples. The diagnostic features include parallel striations (Figure 73.13), and small breakage blocks produced by grinding, superimposed on large and partially worn breakage blocks (Figure 73.14).

Tillite, Bacchus Marsh, Victoria, Australia. Tillites and fluvioglacial sediments form a section hundreds of feet thick lying upon a striated and polished surface of deformed earlier Paleozoic rocks west of Melbourne. The samples studied are of yellowish-gray, poorly consolidated, silt-rich massive tillite which contains rare striated pebbles from a road cut 3 miles northwest of the town of Bacchus Marsh.

The electron microscope revealed all but one (parallel striations) of the textures of modern glacial deposits on the quartz grains examined. The abundance of these features here is as great as that in any sample of modern glacial sediments yet studied. There are the usual high surface relief, great variations of breakage patterns, features due to fine grinding, and so on. Closely spaced parallel steps and prismatic fractures are illustrated by Figure 73.15. The textures are almost unmodified by postdepositional processes.

Zeehan Tillite, Tasmania, Australia. The sample was collected from a highway cut 3 miles north-northwest of Zeehan, western Tasmania, from a nearly unconsolidated, very-light-gray, silt-rich, massive, pebbly tillite. This

FIGURE 73.13
Electron photomicrograph of parallel striations superimposed on rounded, parallel breakage blocks. Quarry 4 miles east of Vereeniging, South Africa.

FIGURE 73.14
Electron photomicrograph of small breakage blocks superimposed on large, worn ones. Quarry 4 miles east of Vereeniging, South Africa.

FIGURE 73.15
Electron photomicrograph of closely spaced parallel steps and prismatic fractures. Bacchus Marsh, Australia.

deposit, alone among those studied here by electron microscopy, has not been dated by fossils in the outcrop region; it could be early Pleistocene although it is similar to deposits of proven late Paleozoic age which are widespread in Tasmania.

Half of the grains examined with the electron microscope display the usual array of unmodified, diagnostic, glacial, surface textures —large variation in size of conchoidal breaks, semiparallel steps, high relief, grinding phenomena, *etc.* The other half of the grains show variable modification by postdepositional solution.

Kame Sand, Inman River, South Australia. Lying upon the large exposure of glacial pavement of Glacier Rock, south of Adelaide, is pebbly tillite and—the material studied by electron microscopy—yellowish-gray, unconsolidated, fine- to medium-grained, quartz-rich sand. The sand is well sorted, and has a single grain-size mode; it forms poorly defined beds whose depositional dip is 30 degrees away from the steep glacially scoured wall of the roche moutonnée against which they rest. The sand surrounds a 12-foot erratic block of granite from a source at least 10 miles away. The sand is interpreted to be a kame deposit and the erratic stone to have tumbled into it from adjacent ice, but it is possible that the sand has been reworked by postglacial —Permian or later—stream processes.

The sand exhibits a compound glacial-and-fluvial surface texture. Glacial textures—blocky, parallel, and conchoidal breaks, parallel scratches narrower than 1 micron, etc.—show varying but generally minor smoothing by stream erosion. The sand was clearly derived from glacial ice.

Buckeye Tillite, Horlick *Mountains, Antarctica.* Late Paleozoic tillites and aqueoglacial sediments have been found in several regions in Antarctica. The best known glacial section is that of the Horlick Mountains (Long, 1965), from which Robin L. Oliver of the University of Adelaide collected the specimen studied here. The sample is from low in the tillite on the ridge north of Mt. Glossopteris, and is of pebbly and coarsely sandy, massive, greenish-gray tillite which contains granitic, metamorphic, and sedimentary clasts to about 6 inches in diameter.

Despite considerable modification by postdepositional solution, most quartz grains studied show a suite of diagnostic glacial surface textures. The parallel steps and the large-scale evidence of percussion (Figure 73.16) are similar to those of many Quaternary glacial grains. At high magnification, the conchoidal breakage pattern shows considerable solution rounding. Most other textures diagnostic of glacial origin in young sediments were seen also in this old tillite.

CONCLUSIONS FROM ELECTRON MICROSCOPY

The sand grains studied from late Paleozoic glacial deposits of South Africa, Australia, and Antarctica display all the surface textures which are diagnostic of glacial origin in late Quaternary deposits. The ancient tillites cannot be distinguished by electron microscopy from modern ones except by the generally greater modification of the old materials by postdepositional solution.

LATE PALEOZOIC GLACIATION

GEOGRAPHIC DISTRIBUTION

Upper Paleozoic glacial deposits of the sort described here are widespread in the Gondwana continental masses of central and southern Africa, southern Arabia(?), most of Australia, India, southeastern South America and the Falkland Islands, and Antarctica. The total land area glaciated was comparable to that of the Northern Hemisphere continents covered by Quaternary ice sheets, but the Paleozoic glaciated terrane is now scattered from South Pole to tropics over half the earth's total surface.

The African glacial materials described briefly in the preceding pages are from widely separated areas of the Republic of South Africa. Other descriptions of South African glacial deposits have been given by du Toit (1922, 1953), Hälbich (1962), King and Maud (1964), and many others. The glacial deposits form the Dwyka Tillite at or near the base of the continental Karroo System. The Dwyka is thin and discontinuous in the north, but thickens southward across the continental platform to a thickness of several thousand feet in the geosynclinal southern Karroo, where the ice front discharged into deep water (du Toit, 1953, p. 270, 274). Pavement striae show ice flow to have been, in general, southward and southwestward, from major centers within the continent as well as east of it, toward the geosyncline (du Toit, 1953, Fig. 41). Particularly significant is the westward flow shown clearly at many localities in Natal, on the east coast: ice sheets carrying enough debris to form tillite a thousand feet thick even in coastal Natal (King and Maud, 1964, p. 9) came from the direction of the present Indian Ocean, and carried continental-shield rock debris. Local relief at the time of glaciation was generally low (du Toit, 1953, p. 276). Distinct tillites in many sections are separated by dropstone shales, fluvioglacial sediments, and inter-tillite glacial pavements, but tillite is the dominant material.

In northwestern South-West Africa, "Beautifully preserved striated floors, walls, and roches moutonnées show that the ice was moving westward . . ." through deep glacial valleys (Martin, 1961, p. 15). Relic glacial valleys have been reported also in the eastern Congo, where roches moutonnées and striae show northward ice flow; above the pavements are tillites containing striated stones, and varved shales with abundant dropstones (Boutakoff, 1948; Veatch, 1935, p. 151–153). The unequivocal tillite and varved dropstone shale that form a thick section in the lowlands of the Congo Basin were described in an excellent paper by Hübner (1966). No glacial pavements have yet been found in Rhodesia, Zambia, or southern Tanganyika, in each of which, however, thin, discontinuous tillite, locally containing striated stones, and laminated siltstone, locally containing dropstones, are present in the basal Karroo (Bond, 1952; Gair, 1959, p. 20–22; McKinlay, 1956, p. 89–93; Tavener-Smith, 1962).

Probable tillite, containing erratics up to 10 feet in diameter, occurs in an undated clastic section conformably underlying Upper (?) Permian limestone and sandstone on the stable platform of southern Arabia (Helal, 1965).

The basal Permian section of many areas in all states of Australia contains the diagnostic

FIGURE 73.16
Electron photomicrograph of parallel steps (*below*) and large percussion face (*above*). Modified by glaciofluvial action or by postdepositional solution. Horlick Mountains, Antarctica.

glacial assemblage of pavement, tillite with striated stones, and dropstone shale. David (1950, p. 301–371) described briefly many of these materials and referred to publications then available. Newer reports include Banks (1952; 1962), Banks and Ahmad (1962), Banks and others (1955), Banks and Read (1962), Clarke and others (1951), Glaessner and Parkin (1958), Kenley (1952), McWhae and others (1956, p. 51–75), Playford (1959), and Veevers and Wells (1961, p. 62–109). Whetten (1965) described glaciomarine sediments which he considered to be Upper Carboniferous. The tillites and subordinate other glacial deposits are thin and discontinuous across the low-relief stable platform of southern and central Australia, but thicken and interfinger with and are overlain by marine sediments around the western, northwestern, and eastern margin of the continent. The general direction of ice flow was northwestward in southern and northwestern Australia, but northeastward in Tasmania, hence toward open water in each case. Ice flowed on to southern Australia from the direction of the present Southern Ocean and carried continental debris when it reached the continent.

Upper Paleozoic glacial sediments occur in the basal part of the continental Gondwana System which discontinuously covers the central and northeastern Precambrian shield of peninsular India. The two known exposures of glacial pavement beneath tillite show northward ice flow (Smith, 1963a, 1963b). Tillite occurs at or near the base of a section of sandstone and shale, is generally no thicker than 100 feet, and contains abundant striated and faceted stones (Jowett, 1929; Murthy, 1957; Pascoe and Oldham, 1959, p. 927–928). In some areas, tillite is lacking and fluvial conglomerates, presumably derived from till, occur in the same part of the section (Ganju and Srivastava, 1959; Gee, 1932). Two thin varvites overlie separate tillites in one section (Ghosh, 1962).

Glacial sediments occur also in the highest Carboniferous or basal Permian of the Salt Range of West Pakistan, north of the Indo-Gangetic Plain but south of the Himalayas. A thin, discontinuous water-laid tillite contains blocks, many of them faceted, of rock types foreign to the region but similar to those of the shield far to the south (Pascoe and Oldham, 1959, p. 746–747; Reed and others,

1930). The overlying sandstone contains abundant dropstones in its lower part. The "Agglomeratic Slate" of Kashmir is of approximately the same age and might also be water-laid tillite; descriptions of it (for example, Pascoe and Oldham, 1959, p. 780) are sufficient to indicate that the rock is neither agglomerate nor slate, but are inadequate to permit distinction between tillitic and debris-flow origins.

In southern Brazil, Paraguay, Uruguay, and Argentina, tillites containing abundant striated stones are interbedded with and overlain by fine-grained sediments containing dropstones (du Toit, 1927; Harrington, 1956a; Woodworth, 1912, p. 52–91). The ubiquitous ice-deformation structures, like the five known exposures of striated pavement and roches moutonnées, show generally northwestward motion of ice: the ice sheets came from the direction of the present Atlantic Ocean (Martin, 1961, 1964). Glacial sediments derived from east of South America have an average thickness of about 2000 feet over an area of nearly half a million square miles (Martin, 1964). Many of the rock types in the tillites have no known South American source, but strongly resemble clasts in the correlative tillites of South-West Africa; and the great volume of glacial sediments requires a source region extending far eastward from present South America (Martin, 1961, 1964). Harrington (1965) puts at 70 per cent the proportion of the clasts in the tillites which have no possible known source in South America.

The tillite of the Falkland Islands is as thick as 2800 feet and probably was produced mostly by submarine deposition from an ice shelf (Frakes and Crowell, 1967; Halle, 1912). Many of the clasts have no possible local source. Because the general direction of transport was eastward, as indicated by cross-bedding, current indicators, channel trends, tillite fabric, and clast size, Frakes and Crowell (1967) suggested that the ice sheet came from South America. This, however, is difficult to reconcile with the known northwestward direction of flow on to South America, and tectonic rotation of the Falklands, and perhaps drift from a different position relative to South America may be indicated instead.

The basal upper Paleozoic part of the continental Beacon Sandstone of East Antarctica consists of glacial deposits in a number of regions scattered along the Transantarctic Mountains system. The best-described rocks are those of the Horlick Mountains where a section of 900 feet of tillite contains interbedded dropstone shales and internal glacial pavements and lies upon a basement pavement (Frakes and others, 1966; Long, 1965). Ice flowed west-southwestward, along the present trend of the mountain system. Barrett (1966) and Grindley (1963) are among those who have presented briefer descriptions of similar materials elsewhere in the Transantarctic Mountains. A thick marine conglomerate in the geosynclinal section of the Ellsworth Mountains of West Antarctica may be correlative ice-rafted tillite (Craddock and others, 1965).

Wanless and Cannon (1966) refer to other papers giving information on distribution of the glacial deposits.

AGE

Fossiliferous marine beds within or directly above the Gondwana glacial sections are nearly all of very early Permian age insofar as they can be correlated with European and Tethyan epochs. The high endemism of even the marine Gondwana fossils makes many correlations difficult, however; and marine interbeds are areally limited, so that most correlations depend on fossil land plants within or above the glacial sections, and are subject to still greater uncertainties of correlation. The most reliable dates are noted here. Many writers have assumed that there was widespread glaciation within the Late Carboniferous. Ambiguities in dating permit this interpretation, but only local Carboniferous glaciation should be regarded as proven. Glaciation within the later Early Permian was of local extent and was limited to Australia.

Repeated glaciation within the Late Paleozoic glacial period is shown by the alternation of tillite and water-laid sediment in many sections. There are, for example, 11 distinct tillites in the section west of Melbourne in Australia (David, 1950, p. 301–302) and five near Laingsburg in South Africa (du Toit, 1953, p.

274). Most sections elsewhere similarly show several or numerous tillites. No interregional correlations can yet be made between specific tillites.

Well-dated Australian tillites are mostly very Early Permian although some in the southeast are later Early Permian and some may be Late Carboniferous. Marine megafossils in interbeds at all levels in the glacial section of the Carnarvon Basin of northwestern Australia are certainly lower Lower Permian (Dickins and Thomas, 1959; McWhae and others, 1956, p. 64). Arenaceous foraminifera in interbeds in tillite in South Australia are also lower Lower Permian (Crawford, 1965). In Victoria, leaves of *Gangamopteris* (more likely Lower Permian than uppermost Carboniferous) occur in water-laid sediments interbedded high in the glacial section (Pant and Mehra, 1963). Tillites occur at two major levels in the Lower Permian of Tasmania, as dated by both land plants and abundant marine fossils, although erratics occur in all Lower Permian units (Banks, 1952; Banks and Ahmad, 1962). Tillite in New South Wales includes interbeds with a *Rhacopteris* flora, probably Upper Carboniferous (David, 1950, p. 293).

The Dwyka Tillite of southern Africa contains leaves of *Gangamopteris* and *Glossopteris* in a rare Transvaal find between pavement and basal tillite, and spores from the same flora have been found elsewhere in the Dwyka (du Toit, 1953, p. 279), so all of the glacial section may be Early Permian. A marine interbed in South-West Africa contains an earliest Permian *Eurydesma* fauna (Martin, 1961, p. 13).

A few interbeds of marine strata high in the Talchir Tillite of peninsular India contain very Early Permian invertebrates (Ahmad, 1957; Dickins and Thomas, 1959; Sahni and Dutt, 1962). Plants including *Gangamopteris* also occur high in the formation (Krishnan, 1956, p. 259).

An Early Permian age for much of the glacial material of Argentina is indicated by marine fossils; tillite in Brazil is more loosely dated, and may be either Late Carboniferous or Early Permian (Harrington, 1955; Martin, 1961, p. 13) [King's (1962, p. 36–53) argument for progression in time of glaciation from South America to Australia is based on the assumption that all of the South American tillite is Carboniferous, and this is not indicated by the marine invertebrate data].

Tillite in the Horlick Mountains of Antarctica contains Permian spores in shale interbeds high in the section (Long, 1965). Possible aqueoglacial deposits elsewhere in Antarctica contain Permian plants (J. M. Schopf, as cited by Craddock and others, 1965).

CONTINENTAL DRIFT

Both glacial and tropical desposits of the very Early Permian are now strewn about the earth from Antarctica through southern temperate and tropical latitudes to the northern tropics. Pleistocene ice sheets reached the sea only at latitudes above 40 degrees—but the Permian continental glaciers reached the sea even in now-tropical parts of South America, Africa, Australia, and India.

The low-latitude occurrences of Permian glacial deposits cannot be explained as products of glaciation of Tibet-like plateaus. Highlands were certainly present, as in South-West Africa and the eastern Congo, but most of the glaciated terrane had both low altitude and low relief. Ice flowed northwestward onto South America, southwestward onto South Africa, and northward onto India and Australia from directions in which there are now only tropical and temperate oceans and carried shield-type silicic plutonic rocks when it reached the continents. No geophysical evidence supports the possible conjecture that high-standing continents then existed in these oceans but have since sunk several miles beneath the sea. Only high-latitude juxtaposition of continents since scattered appears to provide an explanation for the glaciation and the ice flow.

The marine and continental deposits within or directly above the tillites are sparsely fossiliferous with assemblages not found elsewhere in the world. The obvious inference that these assemblages indicate cold climates has been made by many paleontologists. All marine faunas of the glacial sections are poor in species and most are characterized by the odd lamellibranch *Eurydesma*. The land floras of the glacial sections are characterized by deciduous(?) *Gangamopteris* and *Glossopteris*. Deposits of temperate climates—light- and dull-colored water-laid clastic sediments containing the *Glossopteris* flora and undistinguished brachiopod-lamellibranch marine faunas—succeed glacial deposits in the higher Lower Permian.

Tropical and subtropical Lower Permian deposits characterize another large part of the world. In northwestern South America, middle North America, the Atlantic sector of the Arctic (including Ellesmere Island, Greenland, and Spitzbergen), Europe, northern Africa, the Himalayan region, and eastern Asia, the Lower Permian contains indicators of warm marine waters and warm continental climates. Marine deposits of all these regions have thick biochemical limestones, bioherms and reefs of corals and other organisms, large foraminifers, and many other invertebrates indicating tropical or subtropical waters. Continental deposits include widespread red beds and evaporites and bear the distinctive tropical to xerophytic Euramerican flora.

It is thus not possible to postulate worldwide cooling as a cause of low-latitude Early Permian glaciation any more than it is possible to suggest worldwide warming as a cause of high-latitude Early Permian tropics. Like the glacial deposits, the Permian tropical materials are now scattered from the Equator almost to a pole.

Temperate conditions are shown by the Lower Permian of most of Siberia and much of the Alaskan region. Sediments are light-colored or drab clastics. Marine faunas are mostly assemblages of brachiopods and lamellibranchs that lack indications of warm water in either form or variety. The Siberian land flora is morphologically like the *Glossopteris* assemblage but is taxonomically quite different.

There is an obvious symmetry to the three great povinces indicated by these features, for the warm-climate province lies between the temperate Siberian-Alaskan one and the temperate-to-frigid Gondwana one. Paleomagnetic latitudes indicated by many published studies generally are low in the warm-climate terrane, moderate in the Siberian one, and moderate to high in the Gondwana lands (e.g., Briden and Irving, 1964; Irving, 1966). It is an obvious conclusion that the warm-climate assemblage represents the Early Permian tropics and subtropics, the Siberian represents the north-temperate zone, and the Gondwana represents south-temperate and antarctic zones.

Assumption of stability of the continents since the Permian must invoke sea-level continental glaciation in the tropics synchronously with the building of reefs in warm water near the North Pole; such a pattern is impossible on a spherical earth heated by the sun, and no reasonable explanation for it has ever been given by a proponent of continental stability. Shifting the earth's crust relative to its axis also provides no explanation for the distribution of climatic and magnetic latitude indicators of the Early Permian, for glacial and tropical materials both remain scattered from pole to equator no matter where the axis be postulated. Great expansion of the earth since the Permian as a means of separating the continents also fails as a hypothesis because the glacial and tropical indicators cannot in such a model be restricted to high and low latitudes, respectively, but rather must be strewn across all latitudes.

Only a drastic rearrangement of the continental masses can account for the present distribution of Lower Permian materials. Proponents of continental drift have long used evidence such as that noted here to argue that the regions glaciated during the Early Permian were then parts of a larger continent of Gondwanaland and lay at middle and high southern latitudes. Figure 73.17 is a reconstruction of Gondwanaland modified from du Toit (1937, Fig. 7) to account for new data from Antarctica and other regions, and provide a high minimum latitude for glacial deposits. All glacial deposits are at initial latitudes comparable to those of Pleistocene glaciation. All low-latitude regions appropriately show tropical characteristics throughout their sedimentary and paleontologic Lower Permian records. Published paleomagnetic pole positions yield latitudes compatible with this reconstruction. The reassembly brings together Paleozoic and early Mesozoic terranes, now separated by oceans, of closely similar petrology, stratigraphy, history, and paleontology. The best-known ties are those across the South Atlantic (e.g., du Toit, 1927, 1937; Caster, 1952; Maack, 1952; Martin, 1961) but the geology of the other continents also is appropriate for the positions shown.

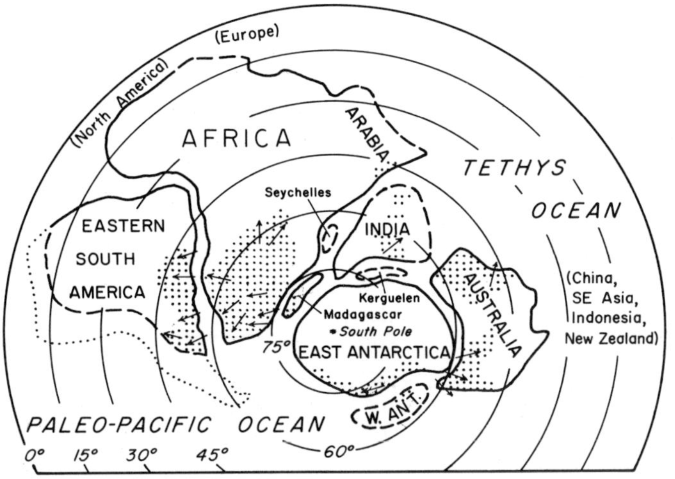

FIGURE 73.17
Reconstruction of Gondwanaland at beginning of Permian time, showing paleolatitudes. *Stipple,* regions of known tillite; *arrows,* directions of ice flow determined from glacial pavements; *solid lines,* margins of present continental masses changed little in internal shape since Permian time; *dashed lines,* margins of continental masses much deformed since the Permian (South America, Africa, India) and possible Permian positions of continental blocks now very different in shape (Seychelles and Kerguelen ridges, West Antarctica); *dotted line,* outer margin of present South America, shown for reference (but the entire Andean belt may have been at low latitude in the Early Permian).

GLACIATION AND SEDIMENTARY BASINS

The glacial deposits on each of the Gondwana continents typically lie unconformably upon older complexes, and throughout broad regions occur at the bases of sections of continental clastic rocks which extend upwards into the Mesozoic—the Karroo of Africa, Gondwana of India, Beacon of Antarctica, etc. Some sedimentary basins came into existence with glaciation and persisted for something like 100 million years afterwards.

A causal connection between glaciation and basining is likely. Isostatic depression and rebound accompanying glaciation apparently are not wholly reversible. Presumably depression and rebound are produced partly by density-phase changes and partly by lateral flow within a low-viscosity layer, and permanent changes in distribution of material accompany the flow.

Isostatic rebound is very rapid, being largely completed before a region is wholly free of ice and having a half-life of a mere 800 years or so (e.g., Matthews, 1966; Washburn and Stuiver, 1962). Rebound since Pleistocene and early Recent continental glaciation is probably virtually complete now: nonrebound processes account for most presently observable elevation changes. The present sedimentary basin that rims the Canadian Shield from the Mackenzie Delta to the Great Lakes, and the northward tilting of the Coastal Plain through the Middle Atlantic States, may represent permanent crust and mantle deformation produced by glaciation. The new Mackenzie-Great Lakes basin may ultimately contain a Gondwana-type sedimentary section.

SUMMARY

Glacial deposits of Late Carboniferous and Early Permian age have long been recognized throughout broad areas of the "Gondwana" continental masses. This paper describes some of these deposits in South Africa and southern Australia, and summarizes information from the literature on deposits of these and other regions.

The following features in combination are widespread in the Paleozoic deposits and prove continental glaciation: polished and striated pavements and roches moutonnées; massive, nonsorted debris (tillite) containing abundant clay-free rock flour, abundant fresh grains of easily weathered minerals, and stones including faceted and striated blocks from both local and distant sources; and laminated, fine-grained sediments enclosing numerous dropstones.

Electron-microscopy studies have shown that surface textures of sand grains in modern sediments vary diagnostically from one environment to another. The large suite of surface textures that uniquely characterizes Quaternary glacial grains also characterizes Paleozoic ones. X-ray study shows that the clay-sized fraction of unweathered tillites and glacial shales is largely devoid of clay.

Most of the well-dated Gondwana glacial deposits are of very Early Permian age. At least local glaciation occurred during the Late Carboniferous and also during the later Early Permian. Glacial stages alternated with interglacial ones.

The continental glaciers of even the now-tropical Gondwana continents reached sea level for marine deposits occur with glacial drift. Ice sheets bearing continental-shield debris flowed onto each continent from the direction of present oceans. The distribution of warm-climate Early Permian deposits is as aberrant as that of glacial deposits; red beds, evaporites, thick biochemical limestones, diverse-fauna coral bioherms, and large foraminifera occur, for example, in the northernmost lands of the Atlantic sector of the Arctic. Only continental drift offers a rational solution to the problems of distribution of paleoclimatic indicators. All the glaciated lands lay in latitudes between 45° and 90° S. in the since-fragmented continent of Gondwanaland.

Long-lasting sedimentary basins were produced by permanent changes in crust and mantle configuration resulting from glacial loading.

REFERENCES CITED

Ahmad, F., 1957, Observations on the Umaria marine bed: Geol. Survey India Rec., v. 84, p. 469–476.

Banks, M. R., 1952, Permian, Triassic, and Jurassic rocks in Tasmania, *in* Symposium sur les séries de Gondwana: Internat. Geol. Cong. 19th Sess. Rept., p. 63–88.

———, 1962, Permian: Geol. Soc. Australia Jour., v. 9, p. 189–215.

Banks, M. R., and N. Ahmad, 1962, The Permian System in western Tasmania: Royal Soc. Tasmania Papers and Proc., v. 96, p. 1–18.

Banks, M. R., and D. E. Read, 1962, The Malbina siltstone and sandstone: Royal Soc. Tasmania Papers and Proc., v. 96, p. 19–31.

Banks, M. R., G. E. A. Hale, and M. L. Yaxley, 1955, The Permain rocks of Woody Island, Tasmania: Royal Soc. Tasmania Papers and Proc., v. 89, p. 219–229.

Banks, M. R., J. L. Loveday, and D. L. Scott, 1955, Permian varves from Wynyard, Tasmania: Royal Soc. Tasmania Papers and Proc., v. 89, p. 203–218.

Barrett, P. J., 1966, Petrology of some Beacon rocks between the Axel Heiberg and Shackleton glaciers, Antarctica: Jour. Sed. Petrology, v. 36, p. 794–805.

Bond, Geoffrey, 1952, Evidence of glaciation in the lower part of the Karroo System in Southern Rhodesia: Geol. Soc. South Africa Trans., v. 55, p. 1–11.

Boutakoff, N., 1948, Les formations glaciaires et post-glaciaires fossilifères, d'age permo-carbonifère (Karroo inférieur) de la région de Walikale (Kivu, Congo belge); Univ. Louvain Inst. Géol. Mém. 9, 124 p.

Briden, J. C., and E. Irving, 1964, Palaeolatitude spectra of sedimentary palaeoclimatic indicators, *in* A. E. M. Nairn, ed., Problems in palaeoclimatology: London, Interscience, p. 199–224, 249–250.

Caster, K. E., 1952, Stratigraphic and paleontologic data relevant to the problem of Afro-American ligation during the Paleozoic and Mesozoic: Am. Mus. Nat. Hist. Bull., v. 99, p. 105–152.

Chamberlin, T. C., 1888, The rock-scorings of the great ice invasions: U.S. Geol. Survey Ann. Rept. 7, p. 147–248.

Clarke, E. de C., K. L. Prendergast, C. Teichert, and R. W. Fairbridge, 1951, Permian succession and structure in the northern part of the Irwin Basin, Western Australia: Royal Soc. Western Australia Jour., v. 35, p. 31–84.

Craddock, Campbell, T. W. Bastien, and R. H. Rutford, 1965, *Glossopteris* discovered in West Antarctica: Science, v. 148, p. 634–637.

Crawford, A. R., 1965, The geology of Yorke Peninsula: Geol. Survey South Australia Bull. 39, 96 p.

Crowell, J. C., 1957, Origin of pebbly mudstones: Geol. Soc. America Bull., v. 68, p. 993–1010.

Cummins, W. A., 1962, The greywacke problem: Liverpool Manchester Geol. Jour., v. 3, p. 51–72.

David, T. W. E., 1950, The geology of the Commonwealth of Australia, v. 1: London, E. Arnold, 747 p.

Dickins, J. M., and G. A. Thomas, 1959, The marine fauna of the Lyons Group and the Carrandibby Formation of the Carnarvon Basin, Western Australia: Australia Bur. Min. Res. Geol. Geophys. Rept. 38, p. 65–96.
Du Toit, A. L., 1922, The Carboniferous glaciation of South Africa: Geol. Soc. South Africa Trans., v. 24, p. 188–227.
———, 1927, A geological comparison of South America with South Africa: Washington, D.C., Carnegie Institution of Washington, 158 p.
———, 1937, Our wandering continents: Edinburgh, Oliver and Boyd, 366 p.
———, 1953, The geology of South Africa: New York, Hafner, 611 p.
Frakes, L. A., and J. C. Crowell, 1967, Facies and paleogeography of Late Paleozoic diamictite, Falkland Islands: Geol. Soc. America Bull., v. 78, p. 37–58.
Frakes, L. A., J. L. Matthews, I. R. Neder, and J. C. Crowell, 1966, Movement directions in late Paleozoic glacial rocks of the Horlick and Pensacola Mountains, Antarctica: Science, v. 153, p. 746–748.
Gair, H. S., 1959, The Karroo System and coal resources of the Gwebe district, northeast section: Northern Rhodesia Geol. Survey Bull. 1, 88 p.
Ganju, P. N., and V. K. Srivastava, 1959, Pebble fabric analysis of the Talchir boulder bed in the Jharia Coalfield, Bihar: Geol. Soc. India Jour., v. 1, p. 105–115.
Gee, E. R., 1932, The geology and coal resources of the Raniganj Coalfield: Geol. Survey India Mem. 61, 343 p.
Ghosh, P. K., 1962, Recurrence of glaciation in the Talchir Series, North Karanpura Coalfield, Bihar: Geol. Survey India Rec., v. 87, p. 751–756.
Glaessner, M. F., and L. W. Parkin, eds., 1958, The geology of South Australia: Geol. Soc. Australia Jour., v. 5, pt. 2, 163 p.
Grindley, G. W., 1963, The geology of the Queen Alexandra Range, Beardmore Glacier, Ross Dependency, Antarctica; with notes on the correlation of Gondwana sequences: New Zealand Jour. Geol. Geophys., v. 6, p. 307–347.
Hälbich, I. W., 1962, On the morphology of the Dwyka Series in the vicinity of Loeriesfontein, Cape Province: Univ. Stellenbosch Ann., ser. A, v. 37, p. 43–163.
Halle, T. G., 1912, On the geological structure and history of the Falkland Islands: Geol. Inst. Upsala Bull., v. 11, p. 115–229.
Harrington, H. J., 1955, The Permian *Eurydesma* fauna of eastern Argentina: Jour. Paleontology, v. 29, p. 112–128.
———, 1956a, Paraguay, *in* W. F. Jenks, ed., Handbook of South American geology: Geol. Soc. America Mem. 65, p. 99–114.
———, 1956b, Uruguay, *in* W. F. Jenks, ed., Handbook of South American geology: Geol. Soc. America Mem. 65, p. 115–128.
———, 1956c, Argentina, *in* W. F. Jenks, ed., Handbook of South American geology: Geol. Soc. America Mem. 65, p. 129–165.
———, 1965, Names and drift: Geotimes, v. 9, no. 9, p. 6.
Harris, S. E., 1943, Friction cracks and the direction of glacial movement: Jour. Geology, v. 51, p. 244–258.
Helal, A. H., 1965, On the occurrence and stratigraphic position of Permo-Carboniferous tillites from Saudi Arabia: Geol. Rundschau, v. 54, p. 193–207.
Holmes, C. D., 1941, Till fabric: Geol. Soc. America Bull., v. 52, p. 1299–1354.
Hübner, Helmut, 1966, Permokarbonische glazigene und periglaziale Ablagerungen aus dem zentralen Teil des Kongobeckens: Stockholm Contr. Geol., v. 13, p. 41–61.
Irving, E., 1966, Paleomagnetism of some Carboniferous rocks from New South Wales and its relation to geological events: Jour. Geophys. Research, v. 71, p. 6025–6051.
Jowett, Albert, 1929, On the geological structure of the Karanpura coalfields, Bihar and Orissa: Geol. Survey India Mem. 52, p. 1–144.
Kenley, P. R., 1952, The upper Palaeozoic glacial deposits of Victoria, *in* Symposium sur les séries de Gondwana: Internat. Geol. Cong. 19th Sess. Rept., p. 56–62.
King, L. C., 1962, The morphology of the earth: New York, Hafner, 699 p.
King, L. C., and R. M. Maud, 1964, Geology of Durban and environs: Geol. Survey South Africa Bull., v. 42, 54 p.
Krinsley, David, and B. M. Funnell, 1965, Environmental history of sand grains from the lower and middle Pleistocene of Norfolk, England: Geol. Soc. London Quart. Jour., v. 121, p. 435–461.
Krinsley, David, and Taro Takahashi, 1962a, Applications of electron microscopy to geology: New York Acad. Sci. Trans., ser. 2, v. 25, p. 3–22.
———, 1962b, Surface textures of sand grains—an application of electron microscopy: Science, v. 135, p. 923–925.
———, 1962c, Surface textures of sand grains—an application of electron microscopy—glaciation: Science, v. 138, p. 1262–1264.
———, 1964, A technique for the study of surface textures of sand grains with electron microscopy: Jour. Sed. Petrology, v. 34, p. 423–426.
Krishnan, M. S., 1956, Geology of India and Burma: Madras, Higginbothams, 555 p.
Lee, H. A., 1955, Surficial geology of Edmundston, Madawaska and Temiscouata counties, New Brunswick and Quebec: Geol. Survey Canada Paper 55-15, 14 p.
Long, W. E., 1965, Stratigraphy of the Ohio Range, Antarctica: Am. Geophys. Union Antarctic Research Ser., v. 6, p. 71–116.
Maack, Reinhard, 1952, Die Entwicklung der Gondwana-Schichten suedbrasiliens und ihre beziehungen zur Karru-Formation suedafrikas,

in Symposium sur les séries de Gondwana: Internat. Geol. Cong. 19th Sess. Rept., p. 339–372.

Martin, H., 1961, The hypothesis of continental drift in the light of recent advances of geological knowledge in Brazil and in South West Africa: Geol. Soc. South Africa Trans., v. 64, 47 p.

———, 1964, The directions of flow of the Itararé ice sheets in the Paraná Basin, Brazil: Bol. Paranaense Geog., no. 10–15, p. 25–77.

Matthews, Barry, 1966, Radiocarbon dated postglacial uplift in northern Ungava, Canada: Nature, v. 211, p. 1164–1166.

McKinlay, A. C. M., 1956, The Karroo System: Tanganyika Geol. Survey Dept. Mem. 1, p. 79–151.

McNamara, M. J., 1966, The paragenesis of Swedish glacial clays: Geol. Fóren. Stockholm Förhand., v. 87, p. 441–457.

McWhae, J. R. H., P. E. Playford, A. W. Lindner, B. F. Glenister, and B. E. Balme, 1956, The stratigraphy of Western Australia: Geol. Soc. Australia Jour., v. 4, pt. 2, 161 p.

Murthy, M. V. N., 1917, Some pebbles and boulders in the Talchir basal conglomerates, Dudhi tahsil, Mirzapur District, Uttar Pradesh: Geol. Survey India Rec., v. 84, p. 459–468.

Pant, D. D., and Bharati Mehra, 1963, On the occurrence of glossopterid spores in the Bacchus Marsh tillite, Victoria, Australia: Grana Palynologica, v. 4, p. 111–120.

Pascoe, E. H., and R. D. Oldham, 1959, A manual of the geology of India and Burma (3d ed.), v. 2: Calcutta, Govt. India Press, p. 485–1343.

Playford, G., 1959, Permian stratigraphy of the Woolaga Creek area, Mingenew district, Western Australia: Royal Soc. Western Australia Jour., v. 42, p. 7–28.

Reed, F. R. C., G. de P. Cotter, and H. M. Lahiri, 1930, The Permo-Carboniferous succession in the Warcha Valley, western Salt Range, Punjab: Geol. Survey India Rec., v. 62, p. 412–443.

Roberts, J. L., 1966, Sedimentary affiliations and stratigraphic correlation of the Dalradian rocks in the south-west highlands of Scotland: Scottish Jour. Geol., v. 2, p. 200–223.

Sahni, M. R., and D. K. Dutt, 1962, Argentine and Australian affinities in a Lower Permian fauna from Manendragarh, central India: Geol. Survey India Rec., v. 87, p. 655–670.

Smith, A. J., 1963a, Evidence for a Talchir (lower Gondwana) glaciation; striated pavement and boulder bed at Irai, central India: Jour. Sed. Petrology, v. 33, p. 739–750.

———, 1963b, A striated pavement beneath the basal Gondwana sediments on the Ajay River, Bihar, India: Nature, v. 198, p. 880.

Tavener-Smith, R., 1962, Karroo sedimentation in the mid-Zambesi Valley: Geol. Soc. South Africa Trans. and Proc., v. 65, p. 43–74.

Veatch, A. C., 1935, Evolution of the Congo Basin: Geol. Soc. America Mem. 3, 183 p.

Veevers, J. J., and A. T. Wells, 1961, The geology of the Canning Basin, Western Australia: Australia Bur. Mineral Resources Geol. Geophys. Bull. 60, 323 p.

von Engeln, O. D., 1930, Type form of faceted and striated glacial pebbles: Am. Jour. Sci., ser. 5, v. 19, p. 9–16.

Wanless, H. R., and J. R. Cannon, 1966, Late Paleozoic glaciation: Earth-Science Rec., v. 1, p. 247–286.

Washburn, A. L., and Minze Stuiver, 1962, Radiocarbon-dated postglacial delevelling in Northeast Greenland and its implications: Arctic, v. 15, p. 66–73.

Washburne, C. W., 1930, Petroleum geology of the State of São Paulo, Brazil: São Paulo Comm. Geog. Geol. Bol. 22, 282 p.

Whetten, J. T., 1965, Carboniferous glacial rocks from the Werrie Basin, New South Wales, Australia: Geol. Soc. America Bull., v. 76, p. 43–56.

Woodworth, J. B., 1912, Geological expedition to Brazil and Chile, 1908–1909: Mus. Comp. Zoology Harvard Coll. Bull. 46, p. 1–137.

SECTION X

THE RISE OF MAN, THE PRESENT, AND THE FUTURE

It is the capacity to predict the outcome of our own actions that makes us responsible for them and that therefore makes ethical judgment of them both possible and necessary.

George Gaylord Simpson

Section X, the last of this book, deals with the Quaternary, the most recent 3 million years or so of geologic time. This section focuses on the Pleistocene, particularly on the ice ages and the concurrent evolution and dispersal of man. It concludes with discussions of the nature of man and of his outlook for the future.

Space does not permit a detailed consideration of the possible causes of glaciation, important though that subject may be for Quaternary history. The section begins instead with a paper that states the main features to be explained by an acceptable theory of glaciation and presents one perennially popular hypothesis: Reading Selection 74—"The Ice Ages," by the distinguished astronomer E. J. Öpik of the Armagh Observatory, argues that the glacial epochs were intervals of generally cooler climate over the entire earth, taking exception to the view that increased precipitation alone could account for glaciation. More important, in Öpik's view, is average global temperature, especially low summer temperatures during ice advances. As knowledge has become more complete, it has become apparent that Pleistocene glaciation was both more extensive (Siberia, for instance was *not* ice-free—see Flint, 1957, in the Supplemental Reading) and more nearly synchronous over the earth as a whole than was formerly supposed. Glaciation, therefore, seems to require a world-wide decrease in absorbed solar radiation, which would in turn require either an increase in the solar reflectivity (albedo) of the earth, or a decrease in solar radiation. Öpik considers various ways to satisfy such requirements. The likely effects of variations in the earth's axis of rotation and the eccentricity of its orbit (as suggested by Croll, Milankovitch, and others) he finds too small. He finds cloudiness also unlikely to have been a very important factor—cloudiness is now near fifty percent and has probably been so throughout most of geologic time, because of the requirement that ascending and descending air be balanced. Nor do variations in the CO_2 content of the atmosphere appeal to Öpik. He supposes they would be completely swamped by the effects of water vapor. By elimination, then, he concludes that the most probable explanation for ice ages is variability in solar radiation, as suggested by Dubois in 1893. Such variability is a general property of dwarf stars like our sun.

Öpik's work at the Armagh Observatory between 1938 and 1952 implies a pulsation in luminosity of the dwarf stars, as a consequence of hydrogen diffusion and the convective instability involved in the conversion of hydrogen to helium. An increase in the generation of atomic energy deep within a star leads to an equivalent decrease in outward radiation, which could be reflected in an ice age on a suitably related planet such as the earth. Öpik's estimates of variation in solar luminosity, taking the present luminosity of the sun as unity, suggest 0.87 as the Pleistocene minimum, 1.02 as a probable interglacial value, and 1.09 as "normal" for the Tertiary. If solar luminosity were to drop below a value of 0.88 and ice were to spread below an average northern latitude of about 50°, the ice caps would become unstable; and, if such an unstable condition were prolonged for as much as 3000 years, glaciation could affect the entire earth. Major glaciations may have recurred cyclically throughout geologic time, Öpik supposes, with a frequency that "cannot be exactly calculated," but which he infers (from dubious geologic evidence) to be near 250 million years.

Of course the causes of continental glaciation are much disputed, and they will continue to be disputed until the evidence is clearer. Papers in the Supplemental Reading by Stokes (1955), Ewing and Donn (1956), and Livingstone, Ewing, and Donn (1959), present views different from those of Öpik, as does Reading Selection 77. Öpik's own views are much more fully developed in his 1953 monograph (see Supplemental Reading). Chapter 27 of Flint's well-known *Glacial and Pleistocene Geology* (see Supplemental Reading) gives a balanced consideration to the various hypotheses advanced prior to the time of its publication. Flint himself favored variation of solar luminosity, as Öpik did, but combined with the effects of late Pliocene and Pleistocene uplift. In 1970, a new, eclectic theory of glaciation was presented by J. C. Crowell and L. A. Frakes of the University of California (see Supplemental Reading). They accept Öpik's chief conclusion "that the ice ages can be explained only by a decrease in the amount of solar radiation as a whole," but prefer to relate this to changes in the average albedo of the earth rather than to variations in solar luminosity. Factors that influence the earth's albedo, in combination with continental drift (to explain shifting centers of glaciation) could, they maintain, account for the ice ages of record. It appears also—from the work of Crowell, Frakes, and others—that pre-Pleistocene glaciation may have been both less unusual and less periodic than has commonly been supposed.

Regardless of how opinion may vary about the fundamental causes of glaciation, there is little doubt about the effect of the related changes in temperature, rainfall, and sea level on the migrations of organisms and on the composition of biotic communities within a given geographical area. Ecologist and limnologist E. S. Deevey, Jr., of Dalhousie University, discusses such changes in a lively essay titled "Living Records of the Ice Age" (Reading Selection 75). Similarities and differences between the endemic faunas of Ireland, Great Britain, and the European mainland, and those between the faunas of various groups of islands in the Philippines, have long interested biogeographers. They imply a history of former land bridges connecting the various land masses in question. At the end of the last glacial episode, the melting of glacial ice gradually raised the sea to its present level—about 100 meters higher than at the peak of that glaciation—thereby separating previously connected land masses. Biogeographical evidence indicates that there were a number of such connections and separations in the near geologic past. Deevey also points out that the distribution of fresh-water fishes in the mainly arid Great Basin of the western United States, together with geological evidence, indicates that the area was once well-watered and filled with lakes. Those parts of Africa and the Near East that are now deserts have had a similar history. As we shall see, such changes surely had an important effect on the early distribution of the races of man.

Quaternary geology is, in fact, of central interest in man's efforts to understand the origin, diversification, and dispersal of his immediate ancestors. For it is in the Quaternary that we find the framework of ecological and paleoclimatological data that makes such interpretation both possible and meaningful, and those same data must also be taken into consideration in reflections about the future of man. No paper gives as good a sense of the complexity and relevance of the subject in as short a space as Reading Selection 76, "Quaternary Geology Reviewed," by Charles B. Hunt, a geologist at the Johns Hopkins University. In his characteristically perceptive, literate, and whimsical style, Hunt reviews three recent major compendiums of Quaternary geology, launching into a far-reaching evaluation of what is good and bad about the present state of the art. No introduction to the important problems and recent literature in the field of Quaternary geology is more succinct.

Much of the discussion of glaciation, and of human evolution and migration, has dealt with environmental temperature variation; but, until recently, we had no independent check on estimates based on traditional geological and paleontological criteria. Since the early fifties, however, the distribution of oxygen isotopes has been used as a kind of geologic thermometer to calibrate the climatologic record. The invention and use of this method is described in Reading Selection 77, "Ancient Temperatures," by marine geologist and geochemist Cesare Emiliani of the University of Miami. The growth of the idea and development of the method dramatically show how the right combination of scientific minds can work to produce results that none of them would have been likely to have produced individually. Fortunately, the right combination for this problem was brought about during the late forties and early fifties through the genius and energy of Harold Urey, and a workable, sufficiently sensitive tecnique was devised. After some preliminary work, Emiliani applied the method to the problem of working out a Quaternary temperature scale in deep-sea sediments. The temperature scale was related to time in the upper part of the sediment by radiocarbon dating, and in the part below, by extrapolation—assuming, on the one hand, a nearly uniform rate of sedimentation in a given core, and on the other, a correlation of the swings in the temperature curve with the postulated Croll-Milankovitch scale of glacial and nonglacial episodes. Although studies by others (Pecora and Rubin, 1967, see Reading Selection 78; Hay, 1967, and Ericson and others, 1964, see Supplemental Reading) indicate much older dates for the first glaciation and the beginning of the Pleistocene, Emiliani still considered it likely, as late as 1967 (see Reading Selection 78), that Pleistocene glaciation began only about 300,000 years ago. On such a time scale, Emiliani's paleotemperature curves based on oxygen isotopes seem to support the Milankovitch hypothesis, wherein Pleistocene glaciation is attributed to fluctuations in the earth's orbit and axis of rotation. Like Öpik, however, Milankovitch and Emiliani stress the importance of cool summers. According to their model, another glacial advance is to be expected about 10,000 years hence. Thus, in effect, Emiliani uses the oxygen-isotope method as a means of measuring both temperature and time for the Quaternary and, therefore, for the evolution of man. Even if Emiliani's time scale needs to be multiplied by a factor of five to ten, this will affect only the validity of the Milankovitch hypothesis, not the utility of the oxygen-isotope geologic thermometer, or the relative sequence of cold and warm episodes within which later hominid evolution occurred.

Before turning to man himself, it will be useful to seek a wider perspective on the question of the ages of Quaternary deposits. W. T. Pecora, Director of the United States Geological Survey, and Meyer Rubin, a geochemist with the Survey, give us that perspective in Reading Selection 78, a paper titled "Absolute Dating and the History of Man." There, Pecora and Rubin consider the experimental, geochemical, and geological requirements that limit the reliability of dating methods. Allowing for minor difficulties with the flux rate and half-life of radiocarbon, and for limitations in resolution by other methods, they find that experimental precision can generally be assumed. Considerable difficulty is experienced in establishing the geochemical validity of a sample, however. The systems most used are susceptible to both the addition and the loss of end products by natural processes that precede sampling. The greatest controversy arises over geologic validity. Many different systems of geochronology have been applied to the Quaternary, and the problem is somehow to integrate those systems: nuclear, glacial, paleomagnetic, geomorphic, eustatic, climatologic, palynological, marine invertebrate, nonmarine invertebrate, and vertebrate time scales must all be made to mesh. The main hope of introducing order to this complexity is that proper employment of nuclear methods may arbitrate among and systematize the others to that end. Unfortunately, the results obtained so for give ages for the beginning of the Pleistocene that range from 400,000 years to more than 3 million years (because of geochemical and geological uncertainties). The problem is best described as actively debated and unresolved. Work on a time scale involving the nuclear dating of magnetic polarity reversals, however, offers fresh promise for a solution. Recent studies suggest that when an age for the beginning of the Pleistocene is agreed upon it will be as much as 3–3.5 million years or more.

Against that background we are finally in a position to consider the genealogy and future of man, beginning with a review of known fossil primates by paleontologist Elwyn L. Simons of Yale University (Reading Selection 79). Now that paleontologists, anthropologists, geomorphologists, stratigraphers, and geochemists have begun to pool their efforts, more and better finds are being made of the fossil remains of man's ancestors, and those finds are being more meaningfully interpreted. Simons deals with the paleontological aspects of that exciting new interdisciplinary study. He identifies nine central questions, but he prefers to treat the subject chronologically.

The morphology of early primates from the Paleocene and Eocene of Europe and North America implies that the primates were derived from the insectivores. The higher primates (Anthropoidea) were already diversified by Oligocene time, although specimens of that age are rare and are known mainly from the early Oligocene Fayum beds of Egypt. It is the Miocene of East Africa and India, however, that provides the first good record of the superfamily Hominoidea. This record includes, in addition to the true apes (Pongidae), fragmental remains of *Ramapithecus punjabicus*, "the earliest probable hominid species" (see Lewis, 1934, in the Supplemental Reading). The fossil remains of *Oreopithecus*, an animal with aberrant hominid characteristics, were found in the Grosseto lignites of Tuscany. *Oreopithecus*, alive about 11 or 12 million years ago at the beginning of the Pliocene, is interesting as evidence of early diversification of the hominid stock, although it was probably not very close to the ancestral line of *Homo sapiens*.

The Pleistocene record of fossil primates, in contrast to that of the older Cenozoic, is so extensive as to leave little doubt about the broad evolutionary development of man during most of that epoch. Man, in the form of *Australopithecus* (including *Zinjanthropus*), had already branched off from the apes fairly early in the Pleistocene—as shown by the famous discoveries, by L. S. B. and Mary Leakey, of "*Zinjanthropus*," associated with Paleolithic artifacts, in "Bed I" at Olduvai Gorge in northen Tanzania, and of a species of *Homo* (probably *H. erectus*) in the overlying strata of "Bed II."

At the end of his discussion, Simons turns to the inevitable question: Where did man originate? His conclusion is that ". . . more evidence will have to be recovered before theories as to which continent was the cradle of mankind gain a sound foundation."

The distribution of man during late glacial and post-glacial times and the genealogy of the races of man are discussed in Reading Selection 80 by Harvard University anthropologist William W. Howells. Remains of essentially modern man dating from the end of the last interglacial are known from several different places, and *Homo sapiens* may already have existed as a distinct species by the end of the preceding (Riss or Illinoian) glacial episode—about 150,000 years ago in the time scale used by Howells, or 350,000 years ago on the time scale of Figure 78.3 (which may yet have to be doubled!). Racial differences can be established as "definitely older than 35,000 years." Man may have emerged from geographically distinct populations and begun to differentiate into races at the same time. There follows an inconclusive analysis of the causes of race and the dispersal of modern man over the globe. Howells discusses both the polyphyletic model, involving the parallel evolution of races from different ancestors, and the now more widely accepted monophyletic model, which supposes that the modern races diverged from a common ancestor, *Homo erectus* (earlier called *Pithecanthropus*). After the last glaciation, about 10,000 years ago, some men discovered that they could live more securely by cultivating the land or by herding stock than they could as nomadic hunters. New stone tools were invented, thus marking the beginning of the Neolithic period. The development of agriculture led to larger populations and permanent settlements, and from that evolved government, trade, standardization of exchange media, organized warfare, and, eventually, modern societies. Man is now at a crossroads, Howells believes. European domination of the world is ending and a new nationalism is emerging that makes it probable " . . . that racial lines and territories will again be more sharply drawn than they have been for centuries." What man will next make of himself is a subject on which Howells declines to speculate.

If man is to have a conscious influence on his own continuing evolution he should understand what it is that evolution might make of him. That question is explored in George Gaylord Simpson's essay "The Biological Nature of Man" (Reading Selection 81). Simpson emphasizes two points, made a century earlier by Charles Darwin: first, that man is a product of evolution involving natural selection; and second, that man is the descendant of creatures which would have to be called apes or monkeys. Meaningful inquiry into the nature of man begins with the recognition of his biological origins as the only fixed point of departure based on facts that we can verify for ourselves. Simpson doesn't exclude nonbiological approaches to understanding the nature of man, but he asserts that such approaches are meaningless unless they start with a recognition of man's biological nature. After reviewing some steps in humanoid phylogeny, Simpson points out that the large braincase, which we often regard as the most distinctive human characteristic, evolved only after the appearance of other skeletal features that clearly represent the genus *Homo*. He then takes up the systematics of *Homo sapiens*. Since all contiguous human populations interbreed to produce fertile offspring, and since none of them is connected to any other species by interbreeding, it is a biological fact that all races of man constitute a single species. There is no real doubt about the existence of racial types, but all races grade into others without definite boundaries, and there is no agreement even about how many races should be recognized. "Regardless of the diversity," Simpson states, "it is obvious that all men resemble one another much more than any of them differ from each other." He then tabulates twelve anatomical traits that characterize *H. sapiens* and differentiate him from all other species.

Even so, human anatomy reflects the true nature of man only to the extent that it is related to human behavior. Simpson suggests ten traits, already recognized by Darwin, that distinguish the behavior of man. Perhaps most important is man's elaboration of unique and complex cultures. Although, moreover, all aspects of human behavior interrelate with one another and with man's anatomical characteristics, Simpson singles out upright posture, tool-making, and language as the most distinctive attributes of man. (Jane Goodall's work with chimpanzees, however, has since shown tool-making not to be an exclusively human trait.) Language is the most human characteristic, but its origins are obscure. Through language, our mental processes achieve a conceptual scope and quality far beyond those of other animals. Those processes include foresight, which is the ability to predict the consequences of our own actions, and which, therefore, makes us responsible for those actions. With foresight, ethical judgement becomes both possible and necessary.

And now we ask how man might use his giant brain and his sense of ethics to solve the frightening problems epitomized by the population explosion—a phenomenon that exists, ironically, as a result of man's great success as a solver of problems. Leading demographer Kingsley Davis of the University of California reveals the dimensions of the current crisis in his essay "Population Policy: Will Current Programs Succeed?" (Reading Selection 82). Growing populations, once identified with prosperity and strength, are now a source of alarm. Davis questions the effectiveness of current "family planning" programs in coping with the problem. He finds that existing programs have ill-defined or undefined goals, and that it is not enough to aim only at reduction of the birth rate. When such a reduction is achieved, programs are hailed as successful, even though the reduced rate usually still permits rapid population growth. Even the "developed" nations suffer acutely from rapid growth of population. The supposedly high standard of living of a wealthy nation consists of a race to produce more and more goods by more and more people for an undefined goal which thus becomes, operationally, more goods, more people, and more pollution. The only rational goal is zero (or negative) population growth, " . . . because *any* growth rate [greater than zero], if continued, will eventually use up the earth."

The universal availability of free contraceptives, free legal abortion, and information on family planning could, at best, eliminate unwanted births. The evidence presented by Davis indicates that even *after* eliminating all unwanted births, the rate of population increase would still be alarmingly high all over the world. Real population control can probably be achieved only by changing the structure, motivations, economic philosophy, or laws of a society, and not simply by making better contraceptives available.

Davis analyzes the situation in Taiwan, acclaimed as a showpiece of response to a family planning program. He points out that most of the observed decline in the birth rate had actually taken place before family planning had received official emphasis; and that the decline correlates with trends in industrialization and urbanization which have traditionally been accompanied by decreasing birth rates. Moreover, for Taiwan as a whole, the rate of population increase is still close to an appalling three percent per year.

Why is it, therefore, Davis asks, that many of those—conservatives and liberals alike—who favor societal limitation of individual conduct in other respects are opposed to collective determination of a society's birth rate? He discusses the kinds of socio-economic measures that could be effective in controlling populations; and he points out that, above all, family planning must be supplemented with equivalent attention to research and experimentation, to determine and to implement the swiftest possible attainment of zero population growth. For unless man gives up the freedom to have as many children as he pleases, he must eventually lose all other freedoms.

"The Human Environment" (Reading Selection 83), the last selection in this book, was written by the zoologist and humanist Marston Bates of the University of Michigan. He discusses the concepts of total environment, effective environment, and perceptual or conceptual environment. Behavior turns on perception, so we can't understand behavior without knowing what the perceptual stimuli are. The conceptual environment, therefore, is critical, whether the concepts be rational or not. Culture, a characteristic human phenomenon, is a major expression of the conceptual environment. And culture has created the man-altered landscape in which people live. Our environment is both a consequence and a determinant of our activities. The results of that situation have not been altogether pretty.

But are we really trapped in some kind of irreversible degradation, or can we master ourselves and the system we have created? Francis Bacon once observed that you cannot command nature except by obeying her. How can we reintroduce that truism to a central place in man's conceptual environment? Because we made our conceptual environment, Bates adds hopefully, we can alter it if we will. But that is a task that cannot be left to a dedicated few, however impressive their credentials may be. It may happen that a dedicated few will define the goals and even the methods, but, until most men recognize that it is not only the abstract "mankind," but they and their children personally who are in trouble, there will never be the massive number of individual responses necessary to effect a significant change. Time is running out. The next thirty years will probably determine whether or not man can preserve a culture in which there is room for such things as poetry, or, for that matter, the study of earth history.

Once again, and for the last time, we turn to the provocative and thoughtful selections listed as Supplemental Reading. Of particular interest are the articles by E. G. Mesthene (1968), K. E. Boulding (1966), and the late President John F. Kennedy (1965). In his paper "How Technology Will Shape the Future," Mesthene stresses that all technology can do by itself is to revise our spectrum of options. It adds new choices; but the *decision* to apply technology to the realization of particular options often has the unforeseen effect of foreclosing other options. If one equates the quality of life with the variety and quality of options available, then one can say that the goal of society should be to avoid the thoughtless foreclosure of options. Thus, technology creates the choices, but whether we choose to use it—and where, and how, and to what extent—is what determines the outcome. Whether to apply or to reject available technologies, then, should be a matter of thoughtful judgment, based on the kind of informed foresight that attempts to take into account all possible effects and feedback, both advantageous and disadvantageous, on a global habitat in which all parts interact.

K. E. Boulding, representing a small minority of modern economists, thoughtfully argues the folly of planned obsolescence and turnover as measures of the success of the economy. What is important, rather, is the nature, the quality, and the extent of the total stock of facilities and resources, including the human resource.

The late President Kennedy, in one of his last public addresses, reminds us of the enormous potentialities of science, as well as the large and unavoidable time lag that occurs between the initiation of any research and the emergence of its benefits to society. He stresses the urgency of getting on with the business of science, particularly when it affects the sufficiency and integrity of man's future environment. In carrying out this task, all sciences interact, but the environmental and social sciences take on a special relevance and responsibility. Among these, none has more to contribute to determining the quality of man's future than the study of the earth itself.

Supplemental Reading

Axelrod, D. I., 1962, Post-Pliocene uplift of the Sierra Nevada, California: Geol. Soc. America Bull., v. 73, p. 183–198.

Beck, W. S., 1961, Modern science and the nature of life: New York, Doubleday, Anchor Books, 334 p. (p. 155–175, The latest revolution).

Berelson, Bernard, 1969, Beyond family planning: Science, v. 163, p. 553–543.

Bishop, W. W., and J. D. Clark, eds., 1967, Background to evolution in Africa: Chicago, University of Chicago Press, 935 p.

Boulding, K. E., 1966, The economics of the coming Spaceship Earth, *in* Henry Jarrett, ed., Environmental quality in a growing economy: Baltimore, Md., The Johns Hopkins Press, p. 3–14.

Brew, J. O., 1968, One hundred years of anthropology: Harvard University Press, 276 p.

Clark, J. D., 1965, The later Pleistocene cultures of Africa: Science, v. 150, p. 833–847.

Clark, W. E. LeGros, 1966, History of the primates (5th ed.): Chicago, University of Chicago Press, 127 p. (Revision of 1949 edition.)

Crowell, J. C., and L. A. Frakes, 1970, Phanerozoic glaciation and the causes of ice ages: Am. Jour. Sci., v. 268, no. 3, p. 193–224.

Dobzhansky, Theodosius, 1960, The present evolution of man: Scientific American Offprint 609, 7 p.

Ericson, D. B., Maurice Ewing, and Goesta Wollin, 1964, The Pleistocene epoch in deep-sea sediments: Science, v. 146, p. 723–732.

Ewing, Maurice, and W. L. Donn, 1956, A theory of ice ages: Science, v. 123, p. 1061–1066.

———, 1958, A theory of ice ages II: Science, v. 127, p. 1159–1162.

———, 1966, A theory of ice ages III: Science, v. 132, p. 1706–1712.

Flint, R. F., 1957, Glacial and Pleistocene geology: New York, John Wiley and Sons, 553 p.

Frye, J. C., 1961, Fluvial deposition and the glacial cycle: Jour. Geology, v. 69, p. 600–603.

Goldsmith, Maurice, 1967, The autonomy of science—some thoughts for discussion: Political Quart., v. 38, no. 1, p. 81–89.

Hay, R. L., 1967, Hominid-bearing deposits of Olduvai Gorge: [U.S.] Natl. Acad. Sci. Natl. Research Council Pub. 1469, p. 30–42.

Howell, F. C., 1959, The Villafranchian and human origins: Science, v. 130, p. 831–844.

Hubbs, C. L., 1957, Recent climatic history in California and adjacent areas, *in* The Committee on Research in water Resources of the University of California, Proceedings of the conference on recent research in climatology: Berkeley, The Committee, p. 10–22.

Hunt, C. B., 1953, Pleistocene-Recent boundary in the Rocky Mountain region: U.S. Geol. Survey Bull. 996-A, 25 p.

———, 1955, Recent geology of Cane Wash, Monument Valley, Arizona: Science, v. 122, p. 583–585.

Kennedy, J. F., 1965, A century of scientific conquest, *in* National Academy of Sciences–National Research Council, The scientific endeavor: New York, Rockefeller University Press, p. 312–319.

Leakey, L. S. B., 1962, Man's African origin: New York Acad. Sci. Annals, v. 96, art. 2, p. 495–503.

Lewis, G. E., 1934, Preliminary notice of new man-like apes from India: Am. Jour. Sci., v. 27, p. 161–181.

Livingston, D. D., Maurice Ewing, and W. L. Donn, 1959, Theory of ice ages (a discussion): Science, v. 129, p. 463–465.

Mesthene, E. G., 1968, How technology will shape the future: Science, v. 161, p. 135–143.

Öpik, E. J., 1953, A climatological and astronomical interpretation of the ice ages and of the past variations of terrestrial climate: Armagh Observatory Contrib. 9, 79 p.

Russell, I. C., 1885, Geological history of Lake Lahontan: U.S. Geol. Survey Mon. 11, 288 p.

Seaborg, G. T., 1967, Time, leisure, and the computer—the crisis of modern technology: Key Reporter Spring 1967, p. 2–4.

Simons, E. L., 1962, Fossil evidence relating to the early evolution of primate behavior: New York Acad. Sci. Annals, v. 102, art. 2, p. 282–294.

———, 1964, The early relatives of man: Scientific American Offprint 622, 14 p.

Strokes, W. L., 1955, Another look at the ice age: Science, v. 122, p. 815–821.

Straus, W. L., Jr., 1967, Nature of the problem of human origins and the evidence: Natl. Acad. Sci.–Natl. Research Council Pub. 1469, p. 1–17.

Tax, Sol, ed., 1960, The evolution of man: Chicago, University of Chicago Press, 473 p.

Tobias, P. V., 1965, Early man in east Africa: Science, v. 149, p. 23–33.

Washburn, S. L., 1968, The study of human evolution: Oregon State System of Higher Education, Condon Lectures, 45 p.

Washburn, S. L., and Phyllis Jay, eds., 1968, Perspectives on human evolution: New York, Holt, Rinehart and Winston, 287 p.

Wright, H. E., Jr., 1964a, Aspects of the early postglacial forest succession in the Great Lakes region: Ecology, v. 45, no. 3, p. 439–448.

———, 1964b, The classification of the Wisconsin glacial stage: Jour. Geology, v. 72, p. 628–637.

The Ice Ages

E. J. ÖPIK
1952

It is known that at certain epochs, not very remote as compared with the geological time scale, ice sheets similar to those of present Greenland repeatedly covered the northern portions of the continents of Europe, North America and Asia, and repeatedly disappeared again. These epochs were the so-called ice ages. According to modern methods of radioactive dating (ratio-carbon method of Libby [see Reading Selection 17]), the last advance of continental glaciation happened quite recently, only 11,000 years ago (Mankato-Wisconsin); the enormous ice sheet melted away in a few thousand years, being succeeded by a climate which was at first even slightly warmer than now. Altogether, at least four cases of glaciation advancing to moderate latitudes are known; simultaneously the glaciers and the snow line in the Alps and other mountains descended to a lower level, and from Alpine localities where traces of former glaciation were recorded, the four successive glacial periods were given the names Günz, Mindel, Riss, and Würm. The intervals between the glacial periods, or the interglacial periods, were relatively warm; for the most part slightly warmer than now. All this happened during the recent, "Quaternary" geological era. The duration of the Quarternary is not exactly known, but it was relatively short as compared with the total span of geological time: from 400,000 to 2 million years may be assigned approximately to the time interval elapsed since the start of the first glaciation (Günz).

Of course, an elaborate chronology of the Quaternary has been worked out on the basis of the so-called "astronomical theory" of the ice ages, which pretended to account for these climatic changes by variations in the elements of the earth's orbit (obliquity and eccentricity); and . . . textbooks have accepted this chronology. Unfortunately, the basis of it is unsound, as it amounts to making small causes responsible for consequences, large out of any proportion to the causes; hence, also, the contradictory conclusions with respect to the dating of Quaternary glaciation, arrived at by

From *The Irish Astronomical Journal,* vol. 2, no. 3, pp. 71–84, 1952. Reprinted with permission of the author and *The Irish Astronomical Journal.*

different authors. In brief, the "astronomical" chronology of the ice ages must be stamped as illusory and rejected *en bloc* [for a different conclusion, see Reading Selection 77]; the rather modest role which the variation of the orbital elements plays in climatic changes has been thoroughly analyzed by the present writer, to whose latest works the reader may be referred for details. Here it will suffice to mention one eloquent fact. The only definite dating of a glacial period is that of the Mankato (Wisconsin) forest, which was overcome by an *advancing* glacier of the last glaciation; the radiocarbon method . . . indicates that this happened 11,000 years ago; yet the "astronomical" theory assigns to that date a warm period, whereas the glaciation, according to the theory, should have happened much earlier. Thus, in the first test, the "astronomical" theory fails completely. Evidently, in this case the minute effects of obliquity and eccentricity of the earth's orbit which favoured a somewhat milder climate were entirely overcome and reversed by another, much more powerful factor, which led to a colder climate and an ice sheet that advanced to 38° latitude in North America. Elsewhere the ice did not reach as far south as this; in Europe, the limit was at 52–55°, in Siberia at 60° latitude. A surprising circumstance is that the Quaternary glaciation in Siberia has become known only recently; in most textbooks Siberia is referred to as having been free from ice. This is an example of how imperfect our knowledge of past glaciations may be, and summons us to caution, especially with respect to former ice ages which happened hundreds of millions of years ago, and of which fewer traces must have been preserved than of the recent Quaternary, which is an event so-to-speak of yesterday—nay, of to-day, as we are still *in* it.

Effects of Quaternary glaciation are recorded in the southern hemisphere, too, and even in the equatorial belt, where mountain glaciers showed a fluctuation of level similar to that in the Alps. There have been attempts to deny the simultaneousness of these changes of climate, and to ascribe them to different epochs, thus assuming an interglacial period in the southern hemisphere to be coincident with a glacial in the northern, or, generally, assuming a different succession of these events in the two hemispheres. This was done to force the facts into the strait-jacket of the "astronomical" theory. This theory requires the average temperature of our globe to remain unaltered, because the variations in obliquity and eccentricity of the orbit do not affect the average amount of heat received by the earth during the year; if one part of the earth grows colder, due to these variations, another must become hotter, in order that the average would remain unchanged. The average temperature at the equator should not alter much, according to the "astronomical" theory, and the lowering of the snow-line in the Andes and elsewhere had to be explained away by increased moisture and precipitation during the ice ages. Present geological data are definitely against such an explanation; everything points to plain, *dry* cold accompanying the glaciation. It was not so much the amount of moisture and snowfall, but primarily the average temperature, especially that of summer, which decided the formation of the glaciers and their retreat. As to the "astronomical" theory, it must be dismissed, anyway, because of the smallness of its effects.

At present there is little doubt that all the phenomena of Quaternary glaciation happened simultaneously all over the surface of our globe. The lowering of the glacier level in the Andes during the ice ages was caused by the equatorial regions becoming colder, in the same manner as in the rest of the earth. This is strongly supported by some preliminary results of the Swedish Deep-Sea Expedition; ocean deposits taken from the bottom of the Atlantic near the coast of Guinea and from the Caribbean Sea indicate for the ice age a microfauna of Foraminifera characteristic of *subpolar* climatic conditions at the sea surface. The ice ages reflected a general decrease of the average temperature of the earth, with the relative climatic zones being maintained, but all becoming colder simultaneously. In the British Isles, the temperature dropped to about that of present Greenland, and an ice sheet 1—1½ miles thick stretched from Scandinavia over the North Sea, completely covering Ireland, Scotland and most of England, of which only the southernmost part remained free. Reindeer, polar bear and other animals now restricted to polar regions roamed the outskirts of the ice in England and middle Europe, and primitive man established for the first time his primacy in the subpolar conditions of a cave-dweller and hunter, being forced to exercise his wits in these stern surroundings. During the last advance of the glaciers man learned a lesson from which he profited much in later ages, and still continues to do so: the true cradle of our civilization lies in the ice ages.

It seems that the duration of each glaciation was not very long, perhaps a few thousand years; the interglacial periods were probably longer, 100,000 years or more. . . . [Methods utilized in dating the Quaternary and their range of applicability are listed in Table 78.1 and discussed in Reading Selection 78.]

From all we know now, the Quaternary represents an exceptional period in the history of our globe. The repeated advance and retreat of glaciation is a phenomenon specifically restricted to this period; before that, for a time interval of about 200 million years, there was almost no permanent ice on the earth's surface; even the poles were free and enjoyed a temperate or cold-temperate climate. Again, attempts were made, by the advocates of the "astronomical" theory, to explain this away by assuming displacements of the continents and the poles on the earth's surface, in order that those places where geologists or palaeo-botanists recorded a warmer climate could be displaced nearer to the equator. At present we know that this definitely did not happen during the last 100–200 million years of the earth's history [but see Reading Selections 34 and 73]. Not only do astronomical observations of latitude and longitude disprove the existence of horizontal displacements of sufficient size along the earth's surface, but geological data are now complete enough to reconstruct the climatic zones (from fossil vegetation) during the Tertiary and Cretaceous, 50–100 million years ago [see Reading Selection 71]. The distribution of the climatic zones, including the warm anomaly caused by the Gulfstream, turns out to be practically the same as it is now, except that it was then generally warmer by 10–15°F; the position of the pole was the same, and the distribution of the continents essentially the same as at present, except that some low-lying continental plains were more often submerged, being covered by shallow seas. There is nothing mysterious in this latter circumstance, the level of the continents continually but slowly fluctuating up and down under the action of subcrustal forces; and especially because there was no ice in Greenland and the Antarctic, thus more water in the oceans: at the expense of the molten ice sheets, the sea all over the earth must have exceeded its present level by about 200 feet. When this happens again—and the polar ices will surely melt in the not-too-distant future, as they did several times before—most of Ireland and of many countries in the North of Europe and elsewhere will go under water. This negative blessing of a warmer climate may take place after hundreds of thousands, or millions of years; soon enough from a geological, but not from a human standpoint: there will be plenty of time for warning and adjustment. In any case, for the preceding long warm period the conclusion is the same as for the Quaternary: the climatic changes took place simultaneously all over the surface of the earth, and were not produced by local conditions. The Tertiary, Cretaceous and earlier were warm epochs; most of the geological history falls within such warm periods, at least for the 500 million years since the Cambrian. . . . From time to time this warm climate was interrupted by colder epochs, or ice ages, of which the present, Quaternary, still lasts. The preceding, Carbo-Permian, took place about 230 million years ago; it lasted for about 25 million years, leaving traces chiefly in the southern hemisphere, often near the equator; also, a succession of glacial and interglacial periods is recorded, similar to those of the Quaternary. Before this, a major ice age, the Eocambrian, happened 480 [650] million years ago, leaving traces in both hemispheres, also with an indication of alternating glacial and interglacial epochs. An intense Huronian glaciation is recorded 1,000 [>2150] million years ago, and between this and the Eocambrian, at least one [other] ice age must have happened [?]. Minor traces of ice are recorded between these major ice ages, but they are probably rightly dismissed as ordinary "mountain glaciation" (Umbgrove).

It seems thus that a normal, warm climate of the earth was repeatedly interrupted by ice ages, or periods of a colder climate; the succession of the ice ages was almost periodical, with a period of about 250 million years. The duration of the cold periods was relatively short, not more than 10 per cent of the total.

It may also be pointed out that the identification of the major ice ages depends little upon whether we consider the continents as fixed in their present positions, or as wandering around and changing their place with respect to equator and pole. The climatic difference was so large that, during the normal warm periods, permanent ice was absent altogether (except perhaps on some of the highest mountains), even the poles being free from ice during these periods. Whenever continental ice sheets were recorded by the geologist, even if these corresponded to polar regions, this meant a climate for the whole earth cooler than normal. . . .

In any case, it is now clear that the ice ages represent cases of a general deterioration of the climate of our globe. The present writer has made a detailed analysis of the conditions leading to glaciation in various latitudes, taking into account the amount of heat received from the sun, that radiated to space, and that transported by convection from, or to other parts of the globe (i.e., by atmospheric and oceanic circulation—winds, currents). The evaluation of the part played by convection has made possible for the first time a quantitative solution of various climatic problems, that of glaciation in particular. The new climatic method gave a definite answer to the part played by the variations in the obliquity and eccentricity of the earth's orbit, indicating a very modest, if not negligible role, unable to account for the actual phenomena of the ice ages.

The chief conclusion reached by the climatic analysis is that the ice ages can be explained only by a decrease in the amount of solar radiation absorbed by the earth as a whole; no redistribution of a fixed amount of heat between various parts of the globe would produce such an effect. The decrease of absorbed solar radiation can be attained in one of the two following ways (or both): either by an increase of the reflecting power of the earth, chiefly from increased cloudiness; or by a decrease in the amount of radiation emitted by the sun.

Clouds reflect most of the incident solar radiation back to space. There is some compensation from the "blanketing" effect of the clouds, which consists in decreasing the radiation to space; however, this is insignificant as compared with the loss of sunlight by reflection, and the net result from increased cloudiness is a lowering of the global temperature. From our analysis the influence of cloudiness on global temperature is found, as given in Table 74.1. In this table, additional reflection from snow-covered areas (which increase with decreasing temperature, or increasing cloudiness), as well as the departure from Stefan's law of radiation to space, caused chiefly by water-vapour absorption in our atmosphere, are taken into account.

TABLE 74.1
Mean temperature of the earth and mean cloudiness for present intensity of solar radiation

Cloudiness, %	Mean temp., °F
30	79
40	71
50	60
52*	58
60	48
70	36

* Present value of cloudiness

If cloudiness alone is made responsible for the climatic variations, the Tertiary, with a mean temperature of 72°F, would require 39%, and the coldest ice age perhaps 70% cloudiness, as compared with the present value of 52%. The range in itself does not appear excessive. However, it is more difficult to find a cause for such a variation. Clouds on earth are chiefly produced by ascending air currents, in which the rising air cools from expansion and leads to condensation of water vapour; this happens in the *Cumulus*, or "fair weather" daytime clouds, and in cyclonic areas of barometric lows. A descending current coincides, as a rule, with clear weather. Evidently, in our atmosphere the ascending and descending air masses, if summed up over the whole surface of our globe, must be exactly equal, because the total amount of air remains unchanged. Therefore, it may be expected that the cloud-covered and clear-sky areas should be nearly equal, and that 50 per cent cloudiness should be considered as a normal value for a planet like our earth. Remarkably enough, the actual value is very close to this. This present value of cloudiness having thus a kind of "theoretical" foundation, assumptions of widely-differing values in the past should be received with great caution.

Nevertheless, the "50 per cent rule" cannot be rigid. The formation of clouds requires the presence of sufficient moisture, and of certain "condensation nuclei," or hygroscopic salt particles, mostly produced by seawater spray drying in the air and being carried away by the winds. Both ingredients are more abundant over sea areas than over land. Hence ascending currents over continental areas may not always lead to cloud formation, as actually happens over large areas of south-eastern and southern Asia in summer. On the other hand, particularly in high latitudes, the cooling and condensation required for cloud formation may be caused by radiation to space, without the intervention of ascending currents; in such a case clouds may be present even over areas where there is a descending current. For these reasons, deviations on both sides of the ideal 50 per cent are possible. The relative areas and distribution of land and sea may therefore influence the average cloudiness, continents in tropical and moderate latitudes having a clearer sky than the oceans. This is illustrated by Table 74.2, in which the polar regions are omitted as being of minor importance in the absorption of solar radiation.

TABLE 74.2
Variation with latitude in average cloudiness of continental and oceanic areas

Latitude	Average cloudiness, % Continents	Sea	Total	Area, % continents
0° to 50° north	37.7	52.5	47.3	35.2
0° to 50° south	44.3	55.0	53.1	18.0

Not only do the land areas enjoy a clearer sky, but the larger continents of the northern hemisphere show the effect in a more pronounced degree than the smaller southern continents, swept by ocean winds. The figures of the table suggest, indeed, that variations in the relative areas of land and sea, by affecting the cloudiness, might have caused considerable changes in the mean temperature of the earth. If the present difference between the northern and southern hemispheres is considered as typical, changes in the mean cloudiness of up to 6 per cent, corresponding to variations in the mean temperature of about 6°F (cf. Table 74.1) might have occurred. The concentration of continents in the tropical and equatorial regions would lead to a warmer, of sea areas to a colder, general climate. . . . Even during the Tertiary, the general distribution of the continents was more or less the same as at present, and if there was a difference, it was in the sense of a somewhat increased sea area, which would mean a greater cloudiness, and a lower temperature, contrary to what actually did happen. . . . Evidently, variations in the land-sea ratio cannot account for the large climatic changes during the last 100 million years, from Cretaceous and Tertiary to Quaternary. For earlier epochs, this cause may have been of a somewhat greater importance, but still insufficient to explain the actual changes. A major cause must have been active, upon which other minor causes, such as the distribution of land and sea, the variation of the orbital elements, etc., were superimposed without much changing the effects of the major cause. The major cause is most likely to be identified with *true variations of solar radiation*; but, before turning to this topic, which occupies a central place in our investigations, we still have to consider some possible loopholes in the problem of cloudiness.

As mentioned above, cloud formation depends, among other things, on the presence of condensation nuclei in sufficient numbers; these are supposed to be provided chiefly by sea spray and, as such, their effect would be undistinguishable from the general effect of the distribution of land and sea. But it is not impossible that other sources of condensation nuclei exist, such as meteoric and volcanic dust. Particles of another kind, called sublimation nuclei, will have a direct effect on rain formation; these are solid minute particles, the origin of which is not yet clear; but their presence, in sponsoring precipitation from existing clouds and relieving the atmosphere from extra moisture, should decrease the average cloudiness and, thus, act in an opposite direction to the condensation nuclei. All these active nuclei may be produced by volcanic or meteoric sources, which may thus influence the climate in an indirect and unpredictable way. At present our knowledge of this possible cause of climatic fluctuations is practically nil, which makes it easy to advocate it as a . . . formula that solves all difficulties, without being itself understood. Minute quantities of active material are sufficient. On the other hand, the direct action of volcanic or meteoric dust in screening off solar radiation is too small and cannot be accepted for quantitative reasons. . . .

Variation in the amount of carbon dioxide in the atmosphere, a favourite topic in former speculations on climatic changes, need not be considered at all: absorption by water vapour practically covers all the absorption bands of carbon dioxide, and, in the presence of but minute quantities of water vapour, the additional absorption by carbon dioxide is nil. Variation in the amount of carbon dioxide will not alter the absorbing properties of our atmosphere, and will have no effect whatever on climate. If, nevertheless, the "greenhouse effect" of carbon dioxide is sometimes mentioned, especially in popular books, this is due to lack of information regarding this particular problem of experimental physics. Practically all other theories of the ice ages and palaeoclimatic changes, which are based on purely terrestrial causes, are of a similar value and, thus, unfounded.

Apparently, the most probable explanation is variability of solar radiation. This is not a new idea, having been proposed already in 1893 by Dubois. In 1921, H. Shapley suggested the passage of the sun through clouds of interstellar diffuse matter as a possible cause of variability. It was thought then that matter drawn into the sun might increase solar energy at the expense of its kinetic energy; or that absorption by interposed dark matter might decrease the apparent intensity of solar radiation. It can be shown that in the second case a warming effect would result, too, because of the "greenhouse effect" of the dark matter in diminishing the loss of radiation from the earth to space. In any case, with our present knowledge of the amount of dark matter in interstellar space, none of the above-mentioned effects is likely to be anything but negligible. The generation of heat from kinetic energy of dark matter is by far the larger of the two effects; but even this can be shown to have been always negligible, providing less than a few millionths of the heat radiation of the sun. For accretion of interstellar matter to play a significant role—say, of more than 0.1 per cent—in the heat radiation of the sun, the mass and the luminosity of the sun would have had to increase considerably in the course of time, so that in the Cambrian, 500 million years ago, the sun would have been so much fainter (and the distance of the earth from the sun greater) that a continuous ice age should have taken place at that time. This is known not to have been the case: the Cambrian was mostly warm, except at the beginning.

Nevertheless, Shapley's idea about a long-term variability of the sun, caused by the passage through cosmic clouds, may be partly retained; an indirect effect, requiring much smaller amounts of matter, consisting in a change in the chemical composition and opacity (or transparency) of the outer layers of the sun, may be important. According to a scheme developed by the present writer, and described later on, accretion of chiefly hydrogen and helium during 250 million years may render the outer layers of the sun ripe for intense, but short (a few thousand years), repeated perturbations, causing temporary deep minima of solar luminosity, corresponding perhaps to the observed repeated advance of glaciers on earth, which happened on the background of longer-enduring (hundreds of thousands, or millions of years), but less "deep," major ice ages (Quaternary, Carbo-Permian). Also, the possibility of an influence of cosmic matter on cloudiness on earth must not be overlooked.

However, the basic cause of the ice ages and of the past variations in the mean temperature of the earth must be sought in real changes of solar radiation, depending upon the nature of the sun itself, and not upon external causes. In a series of publications, beginning in 1938 and ending in 1952 with a monographic study of the entire problem of the ice ages (*Armagh Obs. Contr.* No. 9), the writer has worked out theoretically a model of solar variability explaining the ice ages as the result of repeated disturbances and "non-static" changes in the interior of the sun. The surprising result is that such variability appears to be a general property of dwarf stars, and is not connected with some exceptional characteristics of their structure.

The mechanism of the disturbance, worked out theoretically and numerically with the aid of a great number of "numerical integrations" of various stellar "models" (some of which represent consecutive stages of the evolution of a given stellar mass, with energy generated from the transmutation of hydrogen into helium), can be briefly described as follows.

A star possessing atomic energy sources consists normally of three main parts: (1) a central core, comprising 5–15 per cent of the whole mass, which is the main seat of energy generation, and in which matter is stirred up and continually mixed by convective currents; it is called also the "convective core," or simply the core; (2) outside the core till quite near the surface is the "radiative equilibrium zone," comprising most of the stellar mass; this is a quiescent zone, no currents of matter distrubing its balance and no mixing happening there; the heat energy from the core flows through this zone in the form of radiation, without any displacement of matter; (3) at and below the surface, another convective region necessarily exists; it occupies a considerable volume, but contains very little mass, less than 0.001 of the whole, owing to the low density of the material; we call it the "outer" or the "subphotospheric" convective region.

Atomic energy is developed chiefly in the core, the chemical composition of which changes in the course of time, hydrogen being gradually converted into helium. The store of atomic fuel—hydrogen—decreases in the core, whereas outside it the atomic reactions are very slow and the hydrogen remains preserved. Calculations indicate that, as one of the consequences of the change in chemical composition, the core will decrease in size simultaneously with the decrease of hydrogen content; outside the decreasing core, the hydrogen content (percentage of hydrogen) will steeply rise along the radius until it attains the original, "unspent" value somewhere in the radiative equilibrium zone, still quite near the core. If it were only for these changes, the stellar structure would remain stable, and no distrubances leading to an ice age would be possible.

Here gas diffusion comes into play; it is chiefly only the diffusion of hydrogen that matters; the other elements are too slow in this respect. For stellar dimensions generally, even diffusion of hydrogen is too slow to produce appreciable effects during the life-time of a star. . . . However, within the restricted region around the central core, with a steep change of hydrogen abundance along the radius, diffusion becomes important already over periods of a new hundred million years. Hydrogen is caused to flow inwards by diffusion, through the quiescent layers just outside the core into the core. This has a double effect: first, in making available more atomic fuel for energy generation, from the outside quiescent parts in which otherwise the hydrogen could not have been used up, and lengthening thus the time scale of evolution; second, in increasing the heavy-element or "metal" content outside the core, the metals being forced gradually out of the core by the inflowing hydrogen, which replaces them and is itself currently converted into helium. Increasing metal content means increasing *opacity*, or resistance to transport of radiation outside the core; the free flow of radiation is there impeded, radiation becomes unable to deal with the heat provided by the core, and a *convective instability* outside the core is produced. Convective currents start mixing the material of the former quiescent zone—a convective disturbance in a layer somewhere outside, but near the core comes into being. The disturbance has self-supporting and self-increasing properties; it spreads and joins the core, so that a new temporary core of larger dimensions is formed. Fresh amounts of atomic fuel—hydrogen—are drawn into the core; the intensity of atomic reactions and the energy output in the core increasing over the former "equilibrium" value.

This is exactly what is required to produce an ice age. At the first glance it looks contradictory—how can an increased energy output lead to the decrease in solar radiation needed for an ice age? However, in this point the theory of stellar structure gives an unambiguous answer. Although the core has increased in size, most of the stellar mass still remains in quiescent, radiative equilibrium. In such a case, whatever the disturbance, the *average* outward flow of radiative energy through the quiescent layers depends only on the mass, radius and chemical composition of the star (sun), and must therefore remain more or less *constant.* The average is the mean of (1) the internal flow, at the boundary of the core, equal to the atomic energy output, and (2) of the external flow, which is nothing but the external radiation or luminosity of the star. If now the atomic energy output has *increased,* say, by 10 per cent on account of the disturbance, the luminosity of the sun must *decrease* by the same 10 per cent, to keep the average of the two constant. An increase of the internal energy output over the "equilibrium value" automatically leads to a decrease of the outward radiation by an equal amount. Actually things are more complicated than this, but a full mathematical treatment leads to essentially the same conclusion. The disturbance in the sun will lead to a dimming of solar luminosity and may thus cause an ice age on earth.

We note that, during the disturbance, the outward radiation is less than the atomic energy generation; not all the energy generated inside the sun can be radiated out to space, the "redundant" fraction remaining inside the sun, causing its *expansion* and being thus converted into potential energy of gravitation. The expansion, however, does not go on indefinitely. Expansion leads to a decrease in the temperature of the core, or to a decrease in atomic energy generation (which depends strongly upon temperature); the internal "redundant" amount of energy decreases, and, consequently, the luminosity gradually increases until its normal "equilibrium" value is again attained. The process of automatic recovery goes on *asymptotically,* or gradually. The time intervals involved are of the order of 500,000 years for the sun, for a single disturbance, and of a few million years for repeated or enduring disturbances—just enough to meet the requirements of the time scale of the Quaternary and the preceding Pliocene which already was a bit cooler than the Tertiary. The importance of this mechanism, consisting in the interplay of atomic reactions and gas diffusion, is that it necessarily acts and *necessarily* leads to disturbances, and that these *necessarily* will be *repeated,* after a few hundred million years: the material of the core, mixed by a disturbance, will settle down to a new course of evolution, along lines similar to those of the previous course, which eventually leads to a new disturbance. The period of recurrence cannot be exactly calculated at present, but from the repetition of the major ice ages we infer that it should be something like 250 million years [?]. After each disturbance, the hydrogen content and size of the core will be slightly smaller than on the preceding occasion; thus, this process cannot go on indefinitely but ends when the hydrogen in the core gets completely exhausted and the convective core itself disappears. This stage of the evolution of the sun may be still some 1,000 million years ahead; it means, among other things, a catastrophic "heat wave" on earth. Until then, the succession of long warm periods, interrupted by cooler ice ages of shorter duration, may continue as in the past.

TABLE 74.3
Limits of glaciation, and solar luminosity for present elements of the earth's orbit. Unit of luminosity = present luminosity.

Average latitude of ice limit, north	Average latitude of ice limit, south	Solar luminosity
(no ice)	90°	1.101
90°	76°	1.046
80°	65°	0.996
70°	62°	0.964
60°	50°	0.900
50°	42°	0.885

The disturbances in the core may trigger-off secondary disturbances in the outer layers of the sun. To produce these, it is only required that the "metal" (heavier elements) content increases inwards, from the bottom of the outer convective region; which means a similar effect of opacity to that required for the internal, or "deep-seated" disturbance. Besides, it is only natural to expect the heavier elements to sink deeper below the surface. The rather complicated conditions have been investigated by the writer in his monograph (1952). When an internal disturbance starts, accompanied by expansion of the star, it leads directly to an increase of the outer convective region, too; material from deeper regions is being mixed with the outer convective zone. This deeper material, if more opaque because of the greater metal content, will cause an additional dimming of solar radiation by mere screening effect; a more intense ice age, but of a relatively short duration of 1,000–5,000 years only, will be caused; this is exactly what is required by the last (Mankato-Wisconsin) glaciation, which retreated in only a few thousand years. The deep-seated inner disturbances are unable to account for so fast a retreat (although they may lead to a fast *onset* of glaciation), which in their case, without the outer disturbance, should have lasted 100,000 years or more. However, the general dimming of solar luminosity, lasting for about a million years, or more, and required to explain the cooler climate of present-day and of the Quaternary interglacial epochs, as compared with the Tertiary, can be traced to the deep-seated, principal disturbance, which still lasts and which may continue for hundreds of thousands, even for millions of years to come, judging from previous experience of the Carbo-Permian ice age.

Thus, the secondary disturbances in the outer layers of the sun are to be made responsible for the "acute" glaciations, at least for those of short duration (of a few thousand years). Theory shows that the number of secondary disturbances during one major ice age is limited to a few, say 3–6. If there are more of them, the depth of their minima will be smaller and unable to account for the glaciation. The four principal glaciations of the Quaternary may be identified with such secondary perturbations, which suggests that there will not be many of them, if any, in the future. . . .

The actual range of the past variations in solar luminosity may be inferred from the corresponding global changes of climate. From our quantitative treatment of climate, on the basis of the laws of convective exchange of heat, radiation and absorption, the limits of glaciation on earth, in response to variations of solar luminosity, are calculated as given in Table 74.3. The calculations take into account a certain increase of cloudiness outside the ice caps, proportional to the area of the ice caps ("pluvial" zones).

When the solar luminosity drops below 88 per cent of the present value, and the northern ice limit below 50° *average* latitude, the ice caps become unstable and extend themselves automatically over the whole earth, including the equator, on account of the high reflecting power and cooling effect of snow; to produce a complete effect, the luminosity must remain below 88 per cent for at least 3,000 years. Never since the Cambrian did this happen, otherwise it would have meant the destruction of most of life and an interruption in the continuous trend of biological evolution. It is possible that in pre-Cambrian times this happened repeatedly, the sun having been less luminous at earlier epochs; maybe this was the reason why life did not develop fully in Pre-Cambrian times, although very old traces of life are now known . . .

From all the climatic evidence, viewed in the light of our analysis, the actual limits of variation of solar luminosity may be estimated as follows:

Epoch	Luminosity
Present	1.00
Quaternary Glacial Minimum of Short Duration	0.87
Quaternary Warm Interglacial	1.02
Tertiary "Normal"	1.09

LITERATURE

Öpik, E. J., 1950a, Royal Astron. Soc. Monthly Notices, v. 110, p. 48; Armagh Obs. Contr. 5.

———, 1950b, Royal Astron. Soc. Monthly Notices, v. 110, p. 559; Armagh Obs. Contr. 7.

———, 1951, Royal Irish Acad. Proc., v. 54A, p. 49; Armagh Obs. Contr. 3.

———, 1952, A climatological and astronomical interpretation of the ice ages and of the past variation of terrestrial climate: Armagh Obs. Contr. 9. (This monograph contains a summary of previous work and a further development, including a new quantitative method of climatic analysis, and an index of literature.)

Öpik, Ernst, 1938, Tartu Univ. Acta et Comm. (Dorpatensis), v. A33, no. 9.

———, 1938, Tartu Obs. Pub., v. 30, no. 4.

———, 1943, Tartu Obs. Pub., v. 31, no. 1.

Umbgrove, J. H. F., 1947, Ths Pulse of the earth (2d ed.): The Hague, M. Nijhoff.

75

Living Records of the Ice Age

EDWARD S. DEEVEY, Jr.

1949

Why are there no snakes in Ireland? Popular legend says that St. Patrick drove them out. Science has a less romantic answer, but the popular one is not devoid of scientific significance, for whoever thought of it first must have recognized a real problem. That is, he must have realized that snakes *ought* to occur in Ireland, and concluded that they once did. There are no land snakes in Hawaii either, but I doubt that Hawaiian folklore has found it necessary to invent a story to account for the fact. On an oceanic island, separated from the nearest land by thousands of miles of deep water, one does not expect to find certain kinds of continental animals. But Ireland stands in relatively shallow water and must once have been part of the Continent. . . .

Great Britain, which is just as much an island as Ireland, has at least three kinds of native snakes. Moreover, Ireland does not entirely lack reptiles and amphibians; its inhabitants include a species of salamander, two tailless amphibians and a lizard, all of which also live in Great Britain. Clearly, if someone did not chase the snakes from the Ould Sod, some other sort of special explanation is called for.

This kind of question has an endless fascination for biologists. Usually it can be answered, if it is answerable at all, only by appeal to the geologist, who may explain the distribution of animals in terms of the rise and fall of seas and land masses, the invasion of glaciers, changes of climate, and so on. The present range of a plant or animal species is the product of past as well as present geographic conditions; avenues of dispersal may once have existed where there are barriers now and vice versa, and the geologist will know about past conditions if anyone does. I shall be concerned to show, however, that circumstances are sometimes reversed, and the biogeographer, dealing with the existing distribution of animals and plants, is able to aid the geologist.

The absence of snakes, and of many other animals that might be expected to live in Ireland, is a direct outcome of the Pleistocene geography of the British Isles. The matter has

From *Scientific American*, vol. 180, no. 5, pp. 48–51 (*Scientific American* Offprint 834).

been summarized by Hallam Movius of Harvard University, who, interestingly enough, is not a geologist but a student of paleolithic archaeology. As a member of the Harvard Irish Survey . . . he had good reason to attempt a synthesis of the problems of Britain during the Pleistocene.

Of the four major glacial ages into which the Pleistocene epoch is divided, we are sure that the latest, during its earliest part, saw all of Ireland and nearly all of Britain blanketed by ice. This glacial advance was followed by retreat and a time of genial climate. How far back toward Scotland the ice withdrew is not certainly known, but lime and holly grew at Kirmington in Yorkshire during the interval, and Aurignacian man, famous for his paintings in the caves of southern France, was able to push north as far as Yorkshire. After this comparatively warm episode the ice sheets advanced again as far as the English Midlands, Wales, and in Ireland as far as Tipperary.

Whether any of the animals and plants now found in Britain have lived there continuously since the last interglacial age is uncertain. It seems doubtful that more than a few of the hardiest—those now living in the highest parts of Ireland and Scotland—could have survived through the last glaciation. At any rate, the great majority of the present flora and fauna must have immigrated more recently. At the climax of the last glacial age England and Ireland were joined to the European Continent. This came about because so large a fraction of the Earth's supply of water was frozen and piled on the land in the ice sheets of Europe and North America that the sea level was lowered, probably by about 300 feet. But at this glacial time the British Isles would scarcely have offered a desirable goal for the immigration of animals from Europe.

The postglacial arrival of the seas at their present level was the result of two independent and partly opposed processes: the restoration of water to the oceans, and the recovery of the Earth's crust from its crushing load of ice. The latter, of course, was confined to the glaciated regions, while the former was world-wide in its effects. To a considerable extent the clarification of this complex history in Britain has depended on a time scale devised by biologists. This is the chronology based on analysis of ancient deposits of pollen (Figure 75.1). It enables the British geographers to say that though the land is still rebounding, the sea itself had nearly finished its rise by the end of the Boreal phase of postglacial time. This was an episode of warm and comparatively dry climate in western Europe, when Middle Stone Age man was adapting his hunting culture to the first postglacial forests. In early Boreal time man and many animals and plants were able to cross dry-shod from France into England. By the end of the phase or shortly thereafter the sea had risen about 150 feet, and the English Channel had come into existence.

It is only by the grace of a remarkable geological accident that this sequence of events has been determined. From the Dogger Bank and other places in the North Sea, down to a depth of 162 feet, there have been dredged up deposits of peat. Now peat is a fresh-water deposit, a fact which is confirmed in this instance by finding fossils of beetles in it. The peat cannot have been picked up from the land and redeposited by the waves of the North Sea, for there is too much of it, and it is too coherent, being in all respects like peat from swamps. It must lie on an old land surface. By the depth of the salt water over it we can measure the drowning, and the pollen that it contains establishes its age as Boreal.

The luck of the Irish geologists has not been so great. The bottom of the Irish Sea has apparently been much modified by marine erosion since its formation, and it offers no means for a geological determination of how long Ireland remained joined to England. The most one can say is that, as the water is deeper there than in the English Channel, it looks as though Ireland was severed from England before England was separated from the mainland (Figure 75.2).

This is just what biogeographers have maintained. The land animals of Ireland are fairly typical of an island that formerly was in direct communication with a neighboring continent. The island possesses a rich fauna, containing many animals, such as the frog, the salamander, the hedgehog, the pygmy shrew and the stoat, that seem to have required a land connection for their immigration. If only a few of these were present, one might put their occurrence down as a rare and unexpected instance of dispersal over water. But the Irish list is too balanced and representative to have been the result of a series of such casual migrations.

Yet when comparison is made with England, we see that the species missing from Ireland are as suggestive as those that are present. Ireland lacks the common English meadow mouse, or any other member of the vole subfamily of rodents. St. Patrick's curious prejudice seems also to have extended to the brown hare, the common shrew, the mole and the weasel, not to mention the dormouse and the yellow-necked field mouse. Perhaps because of the absence of competition with these common European and English types, certain Irish species have undergone considerable evolution in their proud Hibernian isolation, and they are now distinct from their representatives and presumed ancestors in Europe. Examples are the Irish hare and the Irish stoat.

These facts can mean only one thing: that a few early postglacial immigrants from Europe managed to reach Ireland over the land bridge via Great Britain, only to be cut off by the postglacial rise of sea level. England and Scotland, which maintained direct connection with

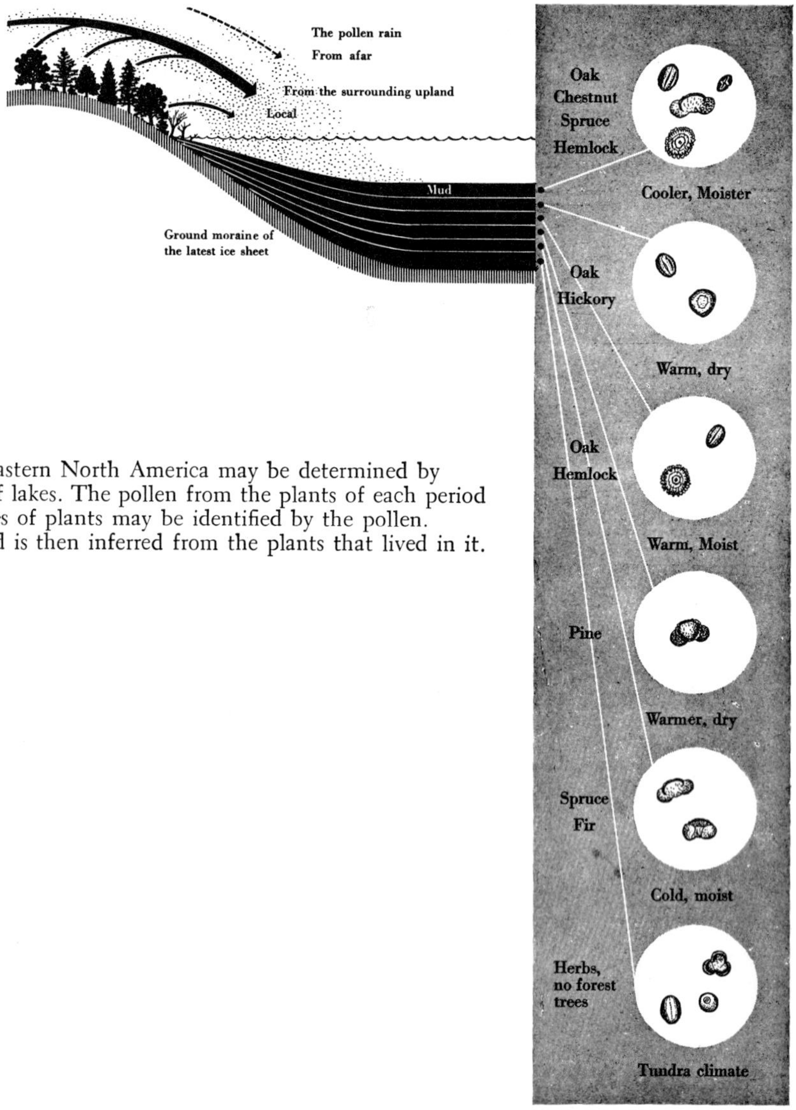

FIGURE 75.1
Climatic chronology of eastern North America may be determined by boring into the bottom of lakes. The pollen from the plants of each period lies in a layer. The species of plants may be identified by the pollen. The climate of the period is then inferred from the plants that lived in it.

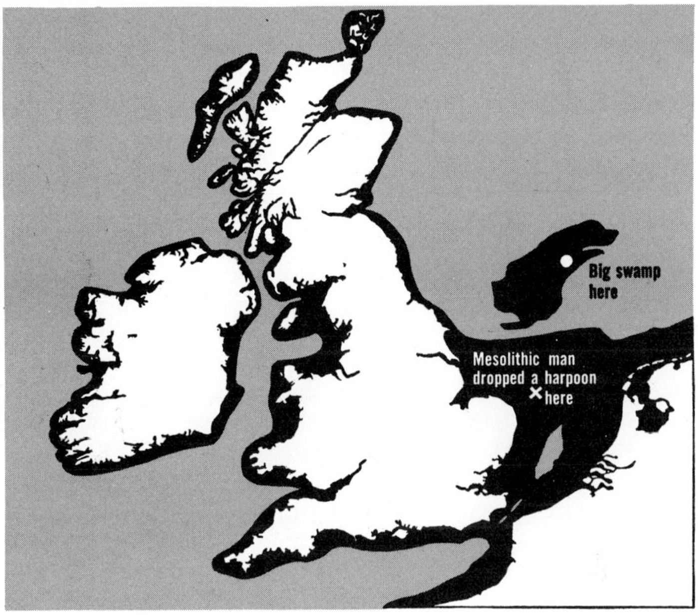

FIGURE 75.2
Pleistocene map shows that Ireland and England were separated from each other at a time when England was still joined to the Continent. *White*, present land masses; *black*, additional land exposed in the Pleistocene. The snakes that migrated from the Continent presumably could get no farther than England.

the Continent longer, received later waves of invasion by land animals.

The same type of problem as that of Britain and Ireland has been studied by biogeographic methods on the other side of the world, in the Philippines. The three islands of Negros, Panay, and Masbate, collectively called Visaya by Philippine biogeographers, stand together on a submerged shelf less than 160 feet deep. A lowering of sea level by that amount would make them all one island. They are separated from the nearby island of Cebu by a strait 320 feet deep. There are 32 kinds of nonmigratory birds restricted to Visaya, and 12 different kinds to Cebu. It does not surprise ornithologists to find birds so sedentary that they do not fly from one island to another. The significant fact is that the 32 endemic subspecies are common to the three islands joined together by the 160-foot depth contour, yet are lacking from nearby Cebu. Evidently the last glacial lowering of sea level was sufficient to permit free migration by land birds among the three islands of Visaya, but not great enough for interchange with the bird populations of Cebu. In other words, the lowering of the level was more than 160 feet but less than 320 feet. Most estimates of the world-wide fall of the sea level in the last glacial age range from 230 to 335 feet, so the agreement is encouragingly close.

Another dramatic study of Pleistocene geography has been based on the distribution of fresh-water fishes in the Great Basin of the western U.S. This subject has been investigated most recently by Carl L. Hubbs of the Scripps Institution of Oceanography and Robert R. Miller of the University of Michigan. Here the problem is not one of changes of land and sea but of cycles of rainy, or "pluvial," climate. The deserts of the world, including the middle-latitude deserts of North and South America, Asia, and North and South Africa, experienced pluvial climates during glacial ages of the Pleistocene. The deserts literally blossomed like the rose. Great lakes were formed, fed by many rivers. The Great Salt Lake, to name an example, is a pitiful remnant of its pluvial ancestor, Lake Bonneville.

To stand amid sagebrush and saltbush on the floor of a Pleistocene lake, with its ancient shore lines clearly visible on the surrounding mountains, is a stirring experience for a geologist. It is even more exciting for a biologist, in the same circumstances, to see at his feet a tiny water hole—a spring or perhaps a fragment of a stream that flows only during infrequent rainstorms—and to realize that fishes in the water are the last survivors of a Pleistocene fauna.

Geographic isolation is a powerful factor in

the formation of species. If the isolation is of long standing, evolutionary divergence proceeds so far that the distribution of existing species becomes a puzzle to the geographer. But where the isolation is the result of geographic changes since the last pluvial age, the finding of fishes of the same species in separate basins in a region demonstrates that the waters were once connected. In the western Nevada of Pleistocene times there was a large body of water, pluvial Lake Lahontan. Its only appreciable modern descendant is Pyramid Lake, but there are many dry or nearly dry basins in the area, such as Big Washoe Lake and Carson Sink, that were formerly either part of Lake Lahontan or held lakes tributary to it. Some of these basins still have fishes in streams and springs, and they invariably belong to the Lahontan fauna, as we can reconstruct it from the present species of Pyramid Lake and Lake Tahoe.

Sometimes the fish distribution points conclusively to the former connection of waters where the physiographic evidence is inadequate. More often, perhaps, the biologist is merely able to confirm the conclusions of the geologist. Physiographic data are more critical than biogeographic, and it would be idle to deny it. But when geologists showed that Pyramid Lake is too fresh to have existed in its present basin longer than about 4,000 years, and claimed that it must have dried up during an arid post-pluvial episode that ended about that long ago, biologists were quick to point out that this conclusion is incompatible with the existence of well-defined endemic fishes (a salmon and a sucker) in Pyramid Lake. These can only be Lahontan types, and therefore date back at least to the last pluvial age, 15,000 years or more ago. There must be some explanation other than youth for the continuing freshness of the lake. For instance, it might once have had an outlet that carried off the salts delivered by rivers, and most of the salts delivered in the past 15,000 years or so since the lake was isolated could have been deposited elsewhere by evaporation. And the geologists, reconsidering, admitted that such could have been the case, and that the Black Rock Desert, to the north, evidently received and then concentrated the overflow.

In Africa, biogeography suggests that the Sahara and other great deserts also had a rainy Pleistocene history. Some geologists deny that pluvial ages existed in equatorial Africa, but it is clear from the biologic data that a great deal of migration of animals and plants requiring a moist, temperate climate took place across regions that are deserts today, and this can only mean that the deserts had pluvial episodes. The evidence of the leakage of such species across the now arid regions is especially clear in the present distribution of aquatic animals and plants. The waterbug genus *Corixa*, which is an inhabitant of temperate Europe, has an outlying station in Lake Naivasha in the eastern Rift Valley of East Africa (Figure 75.3). In French Guinea on the West African coast lives a salamander that apparently migrated from Europe; it is the only salamander below the Tropic of Cancer in the Old World. The range of some species of birds, now divided between Abyssinia and the mountains of East Africa, shows that there was once a wider distribution of forests on the African plateau.

Though biogeography has its triumphs, it also has its failures. A method that places so high a premium on scientific imagination is peculiarly liable to error. In general, the farther back in geologic time a biogeographic theory is pushed, the more likely it is to be false. Some restorations of past geography, notably certain land bridges erected on insufficient evidence, have turned out to be monumentally wrong. Even in Pleistocene biogeography, where we deal with events that occurred only yesterday, geologically speaking, it is exceedingly easy to be mistaken.

One of the most famous theories erected on biologic evidence is the nunatak hypothesis, proposed in 1925 by Merritt L. Fernald of Harvard University. In the mountains of the Gaspé Peninsula, Newfoundland and Labrador, the higher peaks, in the opinion of some geologists, projected above the ice during the ice age, as some do in Greenland and Antarctica today. The Eskimo word *nunatak* is used for such bare peaks. Fernald argued that many plants now found in eastern North America are older than the last glacial age, and that they survived the glaciation by taking refuge on nunataks. There is no doubt that certain plants could have done so, for they have been collected on modern nunataks in Greenland.

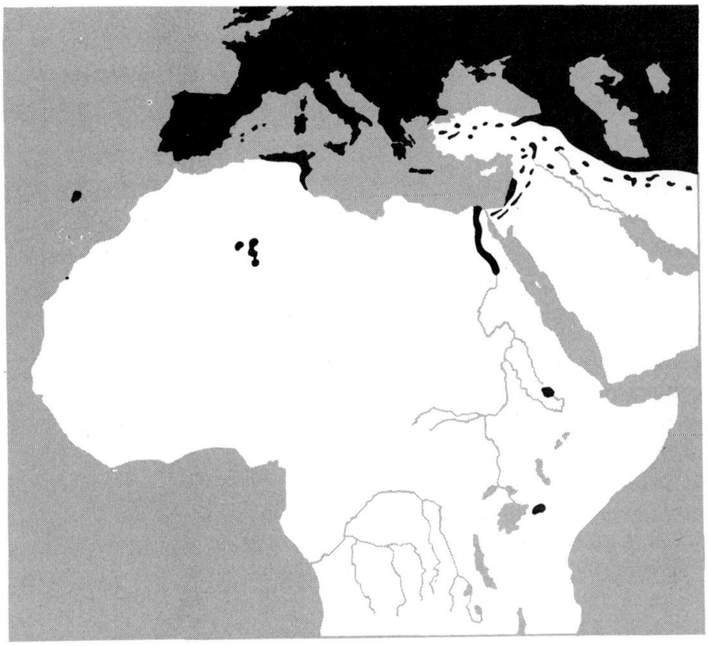

FIGURE 75.3
Present distribution of the waterbug *Corixa*. *Black*, areas inhabited by *Corixa* in Europe, Africa, and Asia Minor. Islands of *Corixa* in Africa have been interpreted by the Yale University zoologist G. Evelyn Hutchinson as remnants of pluvial period when the Sahara was easier for the species to cross.

But irises and lady's-slippers do not belong on such a list, and in applying his theory of glacial survival to warmth-loving types Fernald seems to have proved too much.

The basis of his argument was the occurrence, in the highlands around the Gulf of St. Lawrence, of many plants of peculiar distribution. Some of them, confined to patches a few acres in extent, have their only close relatives in the mountains of the West. In other cases even the same species is found in the Rocky Mountains and in Eastern colonies 2,000 miles away. Because the distance of these colonies from the main range in the Rockies is so great, and because so many of these plants have produced new varieties and species, their Eastern isolation implies an origin at least as old as the last glacial age. Since many of them are narrowly localized and evidently incapable of spreading, Fernald thought it impossible that they could have reached their present localities by migration from the Rockies in the relatively short space of postglacial time. But so many plants have this sort of distribution that Fernald's hypothesis cast doubt on the view that eastern North America was extensively glaciated.

Geologists who have re-examined the region with the nunatak hypothesis in mind have concluded that their predecessors relied too heavily on negative evidence in supposing that mountain peaks were left uncovered by the ice sheet. The frost action characteristic of mountain climates tends to destroy the indications of former glaciation that are customarily looked for. Striae are softened or obliterated, glacially modeled bedrock is blanketed by rubble, and it is difficult to distinguish glacial till from the bouldery material carried by mudflows. Occurrence of foreign stones in such a deposit is decisive evidence of an overriding ice sheet, but this is the sort of evidence that was usually missed by early geologic reconnaissance. Such boulders were found on the second try. Since we know now that active ice moved over the tops of some of the supposed nunataks, the plants must have had an uncomfortable time.

As one of the skeptical geologists has remarked, it seems easier for a plant to reach the top of a mountain in post-glacial time than for a foreign boulder to do so. The biogeographic evidence, in other words, cannot be conclusive. If there were nunataks projecting above the Pleistocene ice, a few of the hardiest species presumably lived on them, though not exclusively there. It is granted that some of the St. Lawrence plants may antedate the last glacial age, but so, obviously, do most other plants that were pushed south by an ice sheet and returned on its retreat. The present flora of the St. Lawrence region must have survived the latest glaciation in refuges south of the ice, and subsequently migrated north to its present position. The narrowly localized distribution of many species is not a proof of old age, for in some cases it is the result of a preference for a particular type of soil, while in others it is a sign of youth. The separation of the eastern and western populations is most simply explained by the hypothesis that the formerly continuous range of the plants was broken by glaciation of the continental interior.

Many biogeographers have made the mistake of underestimating the post-glacial and modern powers of dispersal of organisms. But the fair-minded geologist will not reject all biogeographic data on that account. For the solution of certain types of problems, especially the restoration of Pleistocene land connections and stream connections, the strictly geologic data are likely to be inadequate, and the present distribution of animals and plants can be extremely helpful. Of course, one would always prefer that the deductions from the existing distribution be documented by the distribution of fossils in a clear stratigraphic context. Yet such documentation is all too rare, and we have to work with the evidence we have.

The geologist can remind himself that geology itself is a field of historical inquiry, where recourse to experiment is impossible; therefore it must advance over a spidery network of hypotheses, few of which can be tested immediately. And in all such inquiry there is a human tendency to disparage someone else's legitimate hypothesis. To put it in the form of a Bertrand Russell conjugation, "*I* have scientific insight; *you* are carried away by your imagination; *he* indulges in irresponsible speculation."

BIBLIOGRAPHY

Cain, Stanley A., 1944, Foundations of plant geography: New York, Harper.

Flint, Richard Foster, 1947, Glacial geology and the Pleistocene Epoch: New York, John Wiley and Sons.

Quaternary Geology Reviewed

CHARLES B. HUNT
1965

From *Science*, vol. 150, pp. 47–50, 1965. Reprinted with permission of the author and the American Association for the Advancement of Science.

Quaternary geology in the United States and in northern Europe is summarized in two recently published books, and in a third that has been announced. One, *The Quaternary of the United States* (Princeton University Press, Princeton, N.J., 1965. 922 pp., $25), edited by H. E. Wright, Jr., and D. G. Frey, is a review volume for the VII Congress of the International Association for Quarternary Research. The second book, volume 1 of *The Quaternary* [Interscience (Wiley), New York, 1965. 322 pp., $15], edited by Kalervo Rankama, summarizes Quaternary geology in Denmark, Norway, Sweden, and Finland. The third book, announced as volume 2 of *The Quaternary* and also edited by Rankama, will summarize Quaternary geology in the British Isles, France, the Netherlands, and Germany.

The two published books are highly satisfactory reviews of present information and fashions in Quaternary geology, a chapter of geology that is becoming of increased interest because of growing awareness that the Quaternary offers more practical day-to-day challenges than the rest of the geologic column combined. This is the land and these are the surface deposits on which we live. Their economic aspects include water supply, mineral resources, vegetation, soils, and problems in erosion and sedimentation, engineering, and land use. Moreover, if the . . . present is the key to the past as geologists proclaim, the Quaternary needs intensive study for better understanding of processes that shaped the more ancient rocks and geologic past. . . .

The Quaternary of the United States is divided into four main parts. Part 1 treats the areal geology, with emphasis quite properly on the stratigraphy. The glaciated areas east of the Rocky Mountains are described in seven papers (128 pp.) covering Quaternary deposits in the northern Great Plains, Minnesota and Iowa, Indiana and Michigan, the Erie Lobe, New York, and New England. The unglaciated eastern and central United States are described in four papers (87 pp.) covering the

Quaternary of the Atlantic Coastal Plain and Appalachian Highlands, the western Gulf Coastal Plain and shelf, Nebraska and northern Kansas, and the southern Great Plains.

Quaternary deposits and related features in the western United States, including Alaska, are described in nine papers (157 pp.) covering the glacial geology of the Rocky Mountains, the history of the Columbia Plateau and the northern Rocky Mountains, the nonglacial Quaternary geology of the southern and middle Rocky Mountains, the Snake River Plain, the Great Basin, the southwestern states, the Pacific Mountains in California, western Washington and Oregon, and Alaska. Hawaii and Puerto Rico are not covered.

Part 2 deals with biogeography. A first section, of eight papers (131 pp.), discusses phytogeography (academicia for plant geography) and palynology in northeastern United States, unglaciated eastern North America, the Great Lakes region, the Southwest, southern Rocky Mountains, the Pacific Northwest, and Alaska; two rather specialized (for this volume) papers deal with bryophytes and polyploidy. A second section, of nine papers (133 pp.) deals with animal geography and evolution. Its first paper treats the Quaternary mammals. Others discuss avian speciation during the Quaternary, amphibian speciation, reptiles, freshwater fishes, insects, nonmarine mollusks, other invertebrates, and Recent adjustments in animal ranges.

A third section (one paper, 9 pp.) discusses Pleistocene nonmarine environments. This discussion, by E. S. Deevery, Jr., offers the provocative thought that our basic stratigraphy, the division of the Pleistocene into four glaciations and three interglaciations, may be incorrect. This thought points again to an old ailment in Quaternary stratigraphy, the numbers game. Given one glaciation, it must be Wisconsin; given two, they must be Wisconsin and Illinoian; given three they must be Wisconsin, Illinoian, and Kansan, and so on. To use a phrase borrowed from the *New Yorker*, this is reducing the infinite variety of glacial history to a classic norm. A little paleontology, as noted below, would help.

Part 3, which deals with archeology, consists of five papers (65 pp.) describing prehistory in the northeastern states, southeastern states, plains, desert west, and Pacific Coast. The archeology of Alaska is presented with the paper describing the areal geology.

Part 4, which is too varied to be summarized under a single topical heading, consists of 11 papers (170 pp.) categorized by the editors as "Miscellaneous studies." These papers cover such diverse Quaternary subjects as the continental shelves, isotope geochemistry, paleopedology, the geochemistry of some lake sediments, paleohydrology, glaciers and climate, volcanic-ash chronology, paleomagnetism, tectonics, dendrochronology, and theoretical paleoclimatology. . . .

One might quarrel here and there with overenthusiastic assertions; there is room for disagreement about the suitability of the emphasis in some papers, and even about the suitability of including some of the more narrowly specialized ones in so general a book. But these would be minor criticisms of a major work. The book provides an excellent basis for reviewing the status of this corner of geology, and I use it as basis for comment on a few problems of the science.

CURRENT PROBLEMS— STRATIGRAPHIC NOMENCLATURE

A first problem of Quaternary geology that struck me while reading the book concerns stratigraphic nomenclature. This has several facets.

One is the proliferation of *formal* (contrasted with *informal*) stratigraphic names. Cumbersome nomenclature hampers rather than aids communication, and Quaternary geologists need be wary of the bottomless pit of verbiage from which petrologists are extricating themselves and in which soil scientists still lie buried (and continue to burrow in the wrong direction!). Minor and isolated deposits that offer little promise of regional importance can be referred to informally without cluttering the nomenclature; simple descriptive English can assist communication where formal terms defeat it. As Arthur Holmes wrote: "There is undoubtedly an attraction in the creation of new names . . . [but, in many cases] three words are better than one. Brevity of expression is by no means an unmixed blessing and the one word may require a whole paragraph of explanation" [*The Nomenclature of Petrology* (Murby, London, 1920), p. 5].

In the glaciated Middle West, type section for our glacial chronology, a plethora of local subdivisions with new formal names has resulted in changes of names at state lines and confused correlations across them. The confusion simply illustrates that detailed and modern geologic reporting can successfully conceal mountains behind molehills.

The problem reappears in the glaciated West. There has been disagreement about correlations with specific Pre-Wisconsin or with specific Early or Late Wisconsin glaciations or interglaciations, but for more than half a century there has been general agreement about the separation and identification of deposits correlated as Pre-Wisconsin, Early Wisconsin, and Late Wisconsin. Why then not use those terms, which are widely known and meaningful, and end the nonsense of introducing new, formal stratigraphic names in every Rocky Mountain valley? It seems time to suggest that a committee of individuals, familiar with Rocky Mountain and Pacific Coast Quaternary, select for abandonment and burial as many as possible of the several dozen local names that have been applied there, and to substitute for them Late (Upper) Wisconsin . . . Early (Lower) Wisconsin, and Pre-Wisconsin. Minor subdivisions that can be recognized locally can be accommodated by this nomenclature, and the use of a query can indicate correlations that are doubtful. This change would reduce printing costs. It would no longer be necessary to print tables with every paper showing the correlations that explain what the author means; in this book alone at least a half dozen pages of tables, all showing about the same general correlations, could have been thus eliminated.

Still another facet of the nomenclature problem concerns the definition of "Recent." About a third of the 900 pages of this book deal with the Recent, yet hardly any two authors use the term in the same sense. The escapists' terms "Holocene," "post-glacial," and "post-Wisconsin" are no better. With so much emphasis on this youngest part of the geologic column, it would seem desirable to find a definition so we may all use the term in the same sense.

One difficulty seems to be a misconception that the Recent must begin simultaneously all over the world, although no other geological period did. This has led to the suggestion that a particular year or a change in sea level be designated as marking the end of the Pleistocene and the beginning of the Recent. But shoreline displacements are the net effect of eustatic change of sea level, isostatic change of the land, and tectonic displacement. I submit that the Pleistocene-Recent boundary should be defined on the same basis as the others in the geologic column, namely on the basis of paleontology, and that changes of sea level and absolute dates should be used to determine the direction and to measure the degree to which the boundary cuts across time lines. Charles Lyell, a hundred years ago, gave us such a definition when he wrote, "In the Recent we may comprehend those deposits in which not only all the shells but all the fossil mammals are of living species . . ." [*The Geological Evidence of the Antiquity of Man* (Childs, Philadelphia, 1863), p. 5]. This definition is perfectly usable, whether the geology is being done indoors or outdoors. Where formations are nonfossiliferous, other criteria must be used for making correlations, but this difficulty is not at all peculiar to Quaternary geology. If Lyell's definition is finally accepted, after a hundred years have been devoted to futile efforts to arrive at a better one, there still would be need to agree about whether the boundary should be taken at the last appearance of some species considered typically Pleistocene or at the maximum change in fauna.

Regardless of definitions, the problems of correlation would continue to be with us, but difficulties become compounded if our stratigraphic nomenclature is cumbersome or inconsistent.

BIOGEOGRAPHY AND QUATERNARY GEOLOGY

Refreshing recognition of the mutual interests of Quaternary geology and of biogeography, past and present, is provided by the fact that more than a quarter of the book is given to papers on this subject. Without saying so, the papers illustrate that, in order to study relationships and mutual dependencies between geology and, say, plant geography, maps are needed, at all scales, showing existing vegetation, not in terms of alleged climaxes or other genetic bases, but in the real terms of what is growing in particular areas.

Plant formations could be mapped and categorized with general names in the same way that geological formations are treated. It is true that no two plant stands have exactly the same composition, but neither do any two geological formations. Different names are not needed for every plant stand. Geologists may hide their mountains behind molehills, but botanists are equally successful in hiding their forests behind trees. Of course details are needed, but so are generalities. Satisfactory classification and nomenclature can bring out homogeneities and differences at all scales. C. H. Merriam generalized field distributions in what he termed life zones [*U.S. Dept. Agr. Biol. Survey* **10**, 79 pp. (1898)], but the tendency of modern botany is to discard this old and useful concept without substituting a usable alternative—another example of overly sophisticated education concealing the obvious.

Some of the problems of disjunct populations and of the extent of displacement of biotas during the glaciations, discussed in several of the papers, would be clarified if there were maps showing present plant geography. Such maps would have great scientific interest and would more than pay their costs in practical uses pertaining to problems like deterioration or destruction of stream and field habitats and, with growing population, increased problems of land use, development, and management. But there is no organization, no "U.S.B.S.," to provide such mapping.

PALYNOLOGY

That pollen studies, chiefly of late Pleistocene and Recent deposits, are very much in vogue is illustrated by the numerous papers on this subject. The laboratory methods for preparing and studying samples obviously are highly refined, but the stratigraphic usefulness of pollen profiles is severely limited because the techniques are poorly suited for facies studies. Little is known, for example, about irregularities or orderly changes in the distribution of even modern pollen. Profiles of older deposits are like other stratigraphic sections in which correlations must be based on similarity of fossil sequences. But we know well enough that such similarities can be introduced by lateral changes in facies as well as by changes with time. Willis T. Lee, 50 years ago, referred to them as "homogenetic equivalents" and recognized them as traps for the unwary stratigrapher. Any paleontological study must take account of the lateral as well as the vertical changes; pollen studies are no exception.

It would help if techniques were developed to enable the scanning of pollen samples *in the field*, sufficiently at least to identify and locate major lateral changes in pollen content, which then could be sampled and given proper laboratory analysis. The problem is like some in geochemistry where rocks selected in the field for analysis in a laboratory may first involve field microscopy. When pollen studies give adequate attention to facies changes in the older deposits and to the nature and kinds of irregularities in the distribution of modern pollen, a lot of stratigraphic surprises can be expected.

One of the papers in the miscellaneous section discusses the Quaternary history of the continental shelves and sea level changes, but marine biogeography and paleontology are given little other attention. This lack perhaps reflects the traditional bias towards, and emphasis on, continental Quaternary deposits and history. Yet the marine deposits offer greater promise for a complete Quaternary stratigraphic section and for correlations between the northern and southern hemispheres. In addition, those deposits possess very great resource potentials.

ARCHEOLOGY AND PREHISTORY

The archeological papers summarize what is known about our prehistory but give little hint of the usefulness of archeology for subdividing the Recent or for developing information about changes in environments—such as changes in water tables which lead to flooding or to drying up of springs, lakes, and streams; changes in position of some woodlands or of some meadows in mountain forests; deterioration of plant stands; rates of weathering; and changes of sea level. In regions that are tectonically active, archeology can be, and has been, used to develop information about late Pleistocene and Recent earth movements.

A satisfactory subdivision of United States prehistory, brought out in this book as well as elsewhere, begins with a Paleo-Indian period, which is late Pleistocene and ends with the extermination of the Pleistocene game animals (Lyell's definition). This is followed by an Archaic period, which is pre-pottery and pre-bow and arrow and ends roughly A.D. 1. In the western United States at least, this period probably can be divided into early and late Archaic, corresponding to the dry, early Recent (altithermal or hypsithermal) and the comparatively moist middle Recent millennia just prior to A.D. 1. The Archaic is followed by the pottery and bow-and-arrow period, but this change, like other paleontological changes, was not simultaneous everywhere; it occurred about 1000 B.C., or earlier, in the southeastern United States and about A.D. 500 on the Pacific Coast.

Several papers fashionably charge man with exterminating the Pleistocene animals in North America, although this ignores the fact of parallel exterminations in Eurasia where man lived during much or all the Pleistocene. Man no doubt contributed to the extermination, but, in my view, natural causes must have been paramount, for the change seems to have been worldwide.

Archeologists now accept man in North America at the time of the last glacial maximum. Thirty-five years ago such a view was heresy; now, whoever does not have a Paleo-Indian site just isn't in. Yet this volume again includes criticism of George Carter for his unorthodox views about the early arrival of man in this hemisphere.

It is doctrine in archeology that man came to North America by way of the Bering Land Bridge, although neither this book nor the rest of the archeological literature records any supporting evidence. The problem has overtones suggestive of those of the still undiscovered Tertiary land bridges that enabled North American vertebrate faunas to mix intermittently with European ones.

Constant reiteration does not make man's use of the land bridge a fact, and what little evidence there is suggests that he may have used some other route. In the first place, Late Tertiary mollusks along the arctic coast of Alaska have Atlantic rather than Pacific Ocean affinities, suggesting that the bridge existed during much or all of Pleistocene time and cut off contact between the Arctic and Pacific Oceans. There is no need then to labor the point about a bridge developing because of lowered sea level; the bridge was there, but it just was not used (according to doctrine) until the last glacial maximum. At that time, that area must have been bleak, permanently frozen ground and immigration across it would have been the original ice folly. To this observer it would seem that one of two archeological doctrines will have to go—either man reached North America by a route other than the Bering Land Bridge, or George Carter has been right in saying that man arrived on this continent before the last glacial maximum.

SOIL SCIENCE AND GEOLOGY

Soils of Pleistocene age, paleosols, are widely used for separating Pleistocene deposits of different ages, and are the subject of one of the miscellaneous papers. Recent soils, including the modern ones, are not considered in this book, which once again points up the unfortunate disciplinary split between Quaternary geology and soil science. Whether in universities or in government, soils are in one department, geology is in another. Yet the two subjects are obviously of great mutual interest. Quaternary geology, for example, might offer a solution to the classification and nomenclature dilemma that confronts soil science. The dilemma arises because no two spadefuls of soils are quite alike and there has been, and continues to be, a tendency to create a new name for every spadeful. Quaternary geology might offer a solution by providing a stratigraphic basis for

Recent as well as older soil features. But to develop a workable and mutually useful classification will require the joint efforts of the specialized departments now isolated from each other.

DATING METHODS

Varves, despite their importance to the development of thought about the Quaternary, here and abroad, do not receive enough mention in this book to be listed in the subject index. Dendrochronology and isotope dating receive up-to-date treatment. The discussion of dating by isotopes is encouraging. As some skeptics predicted, conflicting dates were to be expected when isotopic methods could be developed for checking one another (ten methods are described). This conflict has led to conservative interpretation of dates and less of a tendency to rewrite geologic history because of some new surprising laboratory tests. Some extravagant statements of the past might be reconsidered in the light of the cautious statement that ". . . much of what is said here will more than likely be out of date within a few years" (p. 737). Although many consumers continue to misuse the product, isotope dating of Quaternary events is achieving a disciplined basis.

Not discussed in the book, but still not to be overlooked, are such methods as fluorine, thermoluminescence, hydration of obsidian, development of iron and manganese stain (desert varnish), patination, depth or degree of leaching under various environments, and rates of speciation. All these methods, like rates of erosion and sedimentation, have major shortcomings, but they have their uses too. For example, the fluorine method, which has proved useful for determining the contemporaneity of associated bone, contributed greatly to settling the controversy about the Piltdown skull [W. L. Straus, Jr., *Science* **119,** 265 (1954)].

Finally, mention should be made of the usefulness of volcanic ash beds, which are discussed in one of the miscellaneous papers, not only for correlation but also for dating.

QUATERNARY IN EUROPE

Most of the foregoing observations about the Quaternary geology of the United States apply also to the Quaternary of Europe. . . .

Assuming that volume 2 of *The Quaternary* is as satisfactory as volume 1, both of these books and *The Quaternary of the United States* will be wanted by everyone interested in Quaternary geology, and they can be recommended for reading by those who are interested in the other geological systems; what is happening today happened during the Quaternary, and what happened then happened before.

Ancient Temperatures

CESARE EMILIANI
1958

From a piece of uranium-bearing rock we can estimate the age of the earth; from a sliver of bone we can date a prehistoric camp site. The clocks that make such dating possible are radioactive isotopes of the elements. Within the last few years isotopes have provided us with another tool for looking into the distant past—a thermometer which tells the temperatures of ancient seas. The measurements so far made with it have already deepened and revised our understanding of the history of the earth and of mankind. They have staked out the broad climatic trends of the last 100 million years and plotted significant details of the glaciation cycles of the Ice Epoch in which we are living even now. As a result, we can begin to get a better insight into the causes of this epoch and even attempt to project its future course. The new findings also seem to have considerably shortened the hitherto accepted chronology of human evolution.

As with so many fruitful advances in science, paleotemperature research originated in an almost casual remark. In December, 1946, the [then] University of Chicago chemist Harold C. Urey gave a lecture on his work with isotopes to a gathering of faculty and students of the famed Technische Hochschule of Zurich, Switzerland. Urey's theme in this lecture was that the isotopes of an element, although supposedly identical with one another chemically, did not actually behave exactly the same, even in chemical processes. For instance, he said, when a glass of water evaporates, the three isotopes of oxygen (oxygen 16, 17 and 18) do not go off at the same rate. The vapor will carry off a slightly higher proportion of the lightest isotope (common oxygen 16) than of the heavier ones. As a result, after a time the water in the glass will become slightly enriched in the rare heavy isotopes, 17 and 18. Urey concluded that the water in the oceans, long subjected to this process, should be a little richer in the heavier isotopes of oxygen than fresh water.

In the colloquy that followed, Paul Niggli, a distinguished Swiss crystallographer, drew a crystallographer's deduction from what Urey

From *Scientific American,* vol. 198, no. 2, pp. 54–63 (*Scientific American* Offprint 815).

had reported. He pointed out that if sea water and fresh water had different oxygen isotope ratios, oxygen-bearing substances precipitated from these waters also should show the difference. Niggli suggested that isotopic analysis of carbonate deposits—limestone, coral or the limey skeletons of aquatic animals—would show whether the deposits had originated in fresh or marine water.

THE THERMOMETER

Back in his Chicago laboratory Urey pondered this spur-of-the-moment remark and proceeded to calculate what the difference in isotope ratios between fresh water and marine carbonate would be. He found that the relative abundance of the oxygen isotopes in the carbonate would depend partly on the temperature of the water at the time the carbonate was deposited. As Urey later told the story: "I suddenly found myself with a geologic thermometer in my hands."

Actually in 1947 the thermometer was not yet in Urey's hands; it was still largely in his head. It took four more years to make isotopic temperature-measurement a practicable technique. One difficulty was that the temperature effect was too small to be measured by instruments then available. According to Urey's calculations, a difference of one degree centigrade in water temperature would produce a difference of only two hundredths of 1 per cent in the ratio of oxygen 18 to oxygen 16 in the carbonate. The smallest such difference measurable by the best mass spectrometer at the time was one fifth of 1 per cent. This meant that Urey's thermometer could not detect temperature differences smaller than 10 degrees C. —and a 10-degree difference in ocean temperatures can represent the difference between a temperate and an arctic climate! Urey's first task, therefore, was to improve the sensitivity of the mass spectrometer tenfold, and with the aid of a team of workers he was able to do this.

Second, it was necessary to establish an empirical temperature scale, in order to check and supplement the theoretical calculations. For this purpose the Scripps Institution of Oceanography supplied marine mollusks grown in the laboratory at known temperatures. The preparation of their shells for analysis, however, presented what Urey later described as "the toughest chemical problem I ever faced." Live mollusk shells contain not only carbonate but also small amounts of protein. The oxygen in the protein confused the first efforts to get a reading on the oxygen in the carbonate. But Urey and his collaborator Samuel Epstein

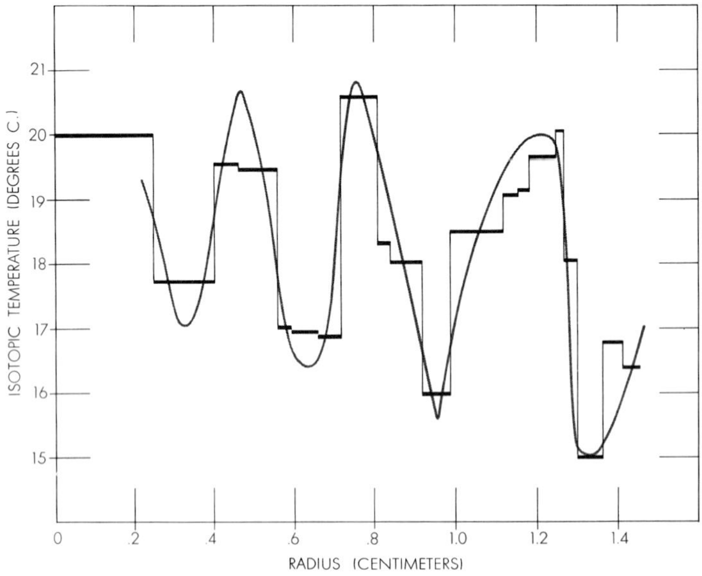

FIGURE 77.1
First measurement of ancient temperatures was made from a belemnite 150 million years old. A cross section of the cigar-shaped skeleton shows growth rings. When these concentric layers were analyzed, they yielded the temperatures plotted on the graph, showing seasonal changes and indicating that the animal was born in the summer and died in the spring four years later.

found a way to remove this contaminating oxygen, and were able, by analyzing pure carbonates deposited at different temperatures, to show that Urey's calculations were essentially correct.

In the fall of 1950 Urey's laboratory at Chicago was ready to attempt the measurement of a fossil temperature. Urey selected the cigar-shaped skeleton of a belemnite, an ancestor of the modern squid which lived some 150 million years ago in the warm, shallow sea covering what is now Scotland. In cross section this fossil shows growth rings resembling those in a tree trunk. But no one had yet determined how many seasons or years each ring represented. The concentric layers of the fossil were shaved off and analyzed one by one. The resulting measurements showed clearly the seasonal changes in temperature during the growth of the animal's skeleton (Figure 77.1). From these variations one could tell that the belemnite was born in the summer, lived almost four years and died in the spring. Clearly the geologic thermometer was usable.

Before it could be put to work, however, an inherent limitation of the thermometer had to be faced. Its readings depend not only on the isotope ratio in a carbonate but also on the difference between this ratio and that in the water in which the carbonate was formed. The ups and downs in the ratio found in the belemnite fossil could be taken as accurate indications of relative temperature; to place these variations on an absolute scale, however, required an assumption as to the isotope ratio in the ocean in which the creature lived.

Up to this point Urey and his associates had assumed that all oceans would show the same ratio of oxygen 18 to 16. A check of various waters, made by Epstein and Toshiko Mayeda, now disclosed that the ratio varied. Tropical surface water proved to be about .2 per cent richer in oxygen 18 than arctic; mid-ocean waters may differ considerably from those near shore, for excessive local evaporation or an influx of river water makes the sea water either richer or leaner in oxygen 18 than the average. Such variations must introduce error and uncertainty into the measurement of paleotemperatures. For the present, error is minimized by analyzing only fossils of animals that lived in the open ocean. Uncertainty remains, however, because the conversion of isotope ratios to temperatures must be based on estimates of the isotope ratio of the ancient ocean.

Eventually we hope to obtain absolute measurements with the help of another thermometer based upon the isotope ratios in the silicas or the phosphates sometimes associated with carbonates. These ratios also vary with temperature but on a different scale. With a little algebra, two such readings will yield an absolute temperature. We are reasonably confident, however, that our present measurements are close enough so that any future corrections we apply to them will not significantly alter the results.

CLIMATIC TRENDS

The first systematic paleotemperature study was addressed to a question that has attracted much investigation by other means: Why did the great dinosaurs die? It had long been thought that the 150-million-year reign of these reptiles on the earth was brought to an end by cooling of the earth's climate about 65 million years ago. This idea was supported by geology, but the evidence was incomplete. At Urey's suggestion, Epstein and Heinz Lowenstam set out to survey the climate of the latter portion of the Age of Reptiles, formally designated as the Upper Cretaceous. They analyzed a large number of fossils from Europe and North America, and their results showed that temperatures rose during the first half of the period and declined during the second half (Figure 77.2). Unfortunately they could not measure temperatures at the very end of the period, because they could not obtain suitable fossils. The study nonetheless supports the conclusion that a decline in temperature might well have played an important part in the extinction of the dinosaurs.

With the method now fully demonstrated, I undertook a study, in collaboration with Mrs. Mayeda and Harmon Craig, of temperatures during the last 65 million years. This long period of time—the Cenozoic Era, or Age of Mammals—has seen the emergence of many land areas, the building of many mountain ranges, the inception of the Ice Epoch and the evolution of man. Clearly a picture of its climatic trends would illuminate and clarify the record.

As our fossil subjects we chose the tiny one-celled marine animals called foraminifera. Our interest was sparked by a visit to Chicago in 1951 of Hans Pettersson, leader of the Swedish Deep-Sea Expedition of 1947–48. Most species of foraminifera live on the deep ocean bottom, but some of them float in the upper sunlit strata of the ocean, where they feed on microscopic plants. When they die, their skeletons—minute snail-like shells or clusters of crystalline bubbles of calcium carbonate—rain down upon the ocean bottom. There, mixed with fine silt and clay, they form the foraminiferal oozes that carpet much of the deep-sea floor. These oozes accumulate very slowly, at rates averaging an inch in 1,000 years. Yet in some places they have built up to thicknesses of hundreds and even thousands of feet.

Thanks to the Swedish expedition and the many expeditions of the Lamont Geological Observatory of Columbia University, we had excellent samples of these sediments. The Swedish expedition had used a "piston-corer" developed by B. Kullenberg. This instrument can bring up cylindrical samples (cores) of the bottom more than 60 feet long; the expedition had collected more than 300 such cores in both the Atlantic and the Pacific, some of them reaching from the present down into sediments a million years old and more. The Lamont Observatory, using similar equipment, had assembled a collection of more than 1,000 deep-sea cores.

THE ANCIENT ANTARCTIC

To develop the general outline of the climatic history of the Cenozoic Era we decided first to survey the bottom temperatures. These, we thought, would not be influenced by short-term fluctuations, and would therefore give us a better idea of long-term trends. The bottom water originates from the oceans' coldest surfaces; the cold water of the Antarctic Ocean, for example, sinks and flows into the deepest regions of the other oceans, because of its comparatively high density. Measurement of bottom temperatures would thus give us a pic-

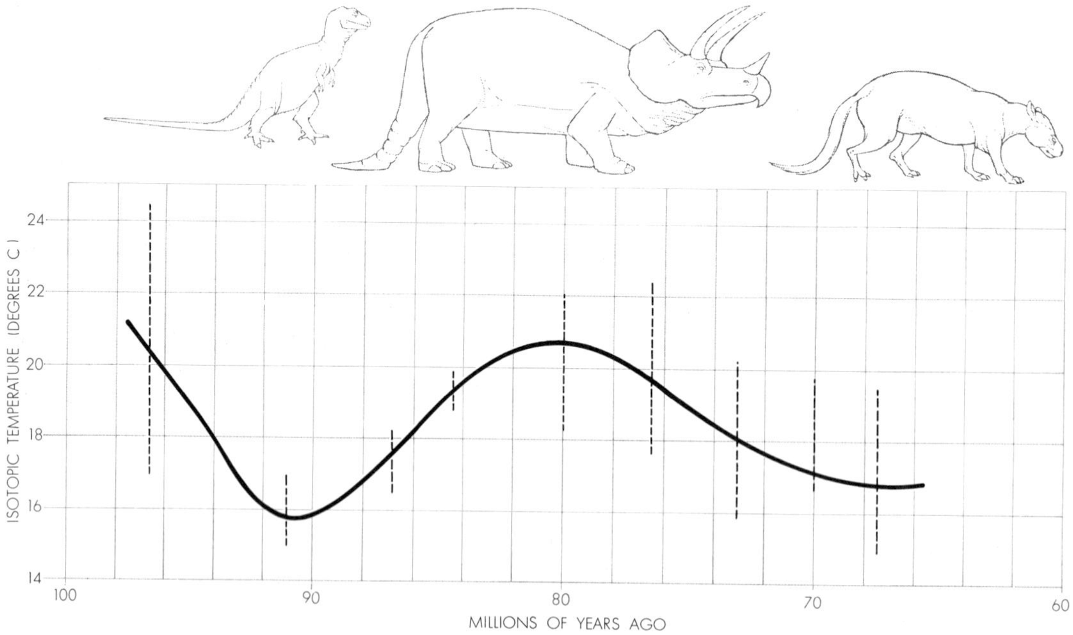

FIGURE 77.2
Temperatures fluctuated toward the end of the Age of Reptiles. A maximum was reached about 80 million years ago; the subsequent decline may have brought about the extinction of the dinosaurs. Above the graph are two dinosaurs and a primitive mammal.

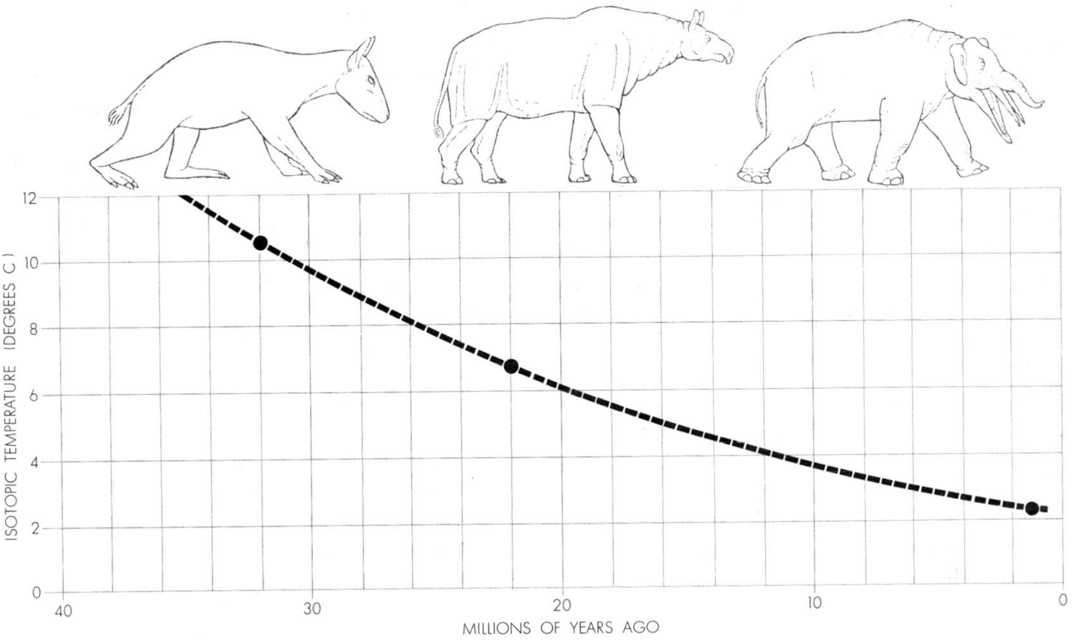

FIGURE 77.3
Temperatures declined during the Age of Mammals. Oxygen isotope temperatures (*dots*) show that Pacific bottom water originating around Antarctica dropped from 10° C to 2° C between 32 and 1 million years ago. At top are three extinct mammals.

ture of the climatic trend of the polar regions.

For this investigation we used three cores brought up from depths of more than 10,000 feet in the equatorial Pacific. Two of these cores were extraordinary because they contained sediments much older than expected. Evidently the piston-corer had hit an area of ocean bottom from which the more recent sediments had been removed (possibly by bottom currents). In order to measure the ancient bottom temperatures we had to sort out the fossils of bottom-dwelling foraminifera, which constituted only 1 per cent of the total. Several hundred shells were required to make up each five-milligram sample. Our analysis showed that 32 million years ago the bottom temperature of that part of the Pacific was about 51 degrees Fahrenheit; by 22 million years ago it had fallen to about 44 degrees; a million years ago the temperature was close to its present level—three degrees above freezing (Figure 77.3). During the last half million years the temperature has oscillated around an average somewhat colder than that of today.

Our measurements show, then, that 32 million years ago the water of the Antarctic Ocean was as warm as that off Rhode Island today. The waters of the Arctic must have been equally warm. Indeed, we know from fossils that parts of Greenland, now treeless, were then covered by pine and spruce forests. The low temperatures a million years ago indicate that by that time Antarctica had become ice-covered, and the stage was set for the beginning of the Ice Epoch. The oscillations during the last half-million years reflect the relatively rapid climatic shifts accompanying the advance and retreat of the glaciers.

We next turned our attention to these glacial climates. From geological evidence we know that at least four times during the last half-million years or so great ice sheets, thousands of feet thick, pushed down from the north, reaching points south of present-day Chicago and Berlin. As they ground southward, they planed off the tops of hills. When they retreated north, they left behind moraines of boulders, sand and gravel and thousands of lakes, of which our Great Lakes are the largest. South of their shifting margins cold, dry winds laid down thick layers of silty soil called loess. From these and other geological features we can map the course of the ice sheets and estimate their duration, as well as that of the temperate interglacial periods. But unfortunately nowhere on land is there a complete sequence of deposits representing the entire glacial epoch. Geologists have had to reconstruct the Ice Epoch piecemeal, often resorting to dubious correlations between landscapes of widely separated regions.

A NEW CALENDAR

The deep-sea cores, we believed, could help considerably to straighten out the confusion and discontinuity of the land evidence. The record contained in the oozes is continuous and their most accessible upper layers embrace much or all of the Ice Epoch. By tracing out the variations in ocean temperatures over this period, we could reconstruct the changes in the earth's climate during the ice ages.

The reconstruction of climatic history in such detail called for study of the variations in the surface temperatures of the ocean, rather than the long-term variations at the bottom. We therefore had to restrict this study to foraminifera of the floating species living within the top few hundred feet from the surface. Our first task was to establish the relative temperature level (*i.e.*, depth) at which each of these species lived; this we did by a preliminary analysis of present-day samples of the various species. We then examined a number of cores taken from the Atlantic, the Caribbean and the Mediterranean. We made an isotopic analysis of the foraminifera of each species at various levels down the core—each level representing a progressively older time. When we finally plotted the temperature curve for the successive times, it showed a series of climatic fluctuations. The peaks and valleys of these temperature cycles were quite consistent over the oceans, even in cores from sites several thousand miles apart (Figure 77.4).

With the temperature cycles thus established, the next step was to date them by radiocarbon analysis. This was done by Hans Suess and Meyer Rubin at the Radiocarbon Laboratory of the U.S. Geological Survey. The most recent low point in ocean surface temperature, it turned out, came about 18,000 years ago, which coincides with the peak of the last ice age glaciers in North America. The low points in the earlier cycles cannot be dated by the radiocarbon method, because they occurred too long ago, but by extrapolation and by comparing our cores with others dated by different methods we have worked out a tentative time scale for the full depth of our cores (Figure 77.5). We then correlated the temperature oscillations shown by the cores with the advances and retreats of the ice sheets on the continents. This correlation is certain for the last 100,000 years, but is less certain for older times. The analysis of still longer cores, which are not yet available, may require some revision of this correlation. If this dating scheme is correct, the first great ice sheet began its advance only 300,000 years ago, rather than 500,000 or more years ago, as geologists have hitherto estimated. [For a different conclusion, see Reading Selection 78.]

CAUSES OF THE ICE AGES

These results may be applied to the much-debated question of what caused the ice ages. Many theories have been proposed, ascribing the glaciations variously to changes in the earth's motions, to blanketing of the atmosphere by dust from volcanic eruptions, to mountain building, and so on. Our findings seem to give support to the theory worked out in the 1920s by the Serbian physicist Milutin Milankovitch. According to the Milankovitch hypothesis, fluctuations in the earth's orbit and in its axis of rotation periodically change the pattern of reception of heat from the sun, so that there are long periods when the summers are cool and the winters mild, alternating with periods of hot summers and cold winters. In a period of cool summers which fails to melt much of the winter snow, ice will cover a much larger part of the earth than it does now. Milankovitch calculated that the coolest summers would come at intervals about 40,000 years apart. Our analysis of the fossils in the cores indicates that the low points in ocean temperatures did indeed occur at 40,000-year intervals.

The main difficulty with the Milankovitch theory is that it fails to explain why the Ice Epoch developed only recently—within the last million years—after 200 million years dur-

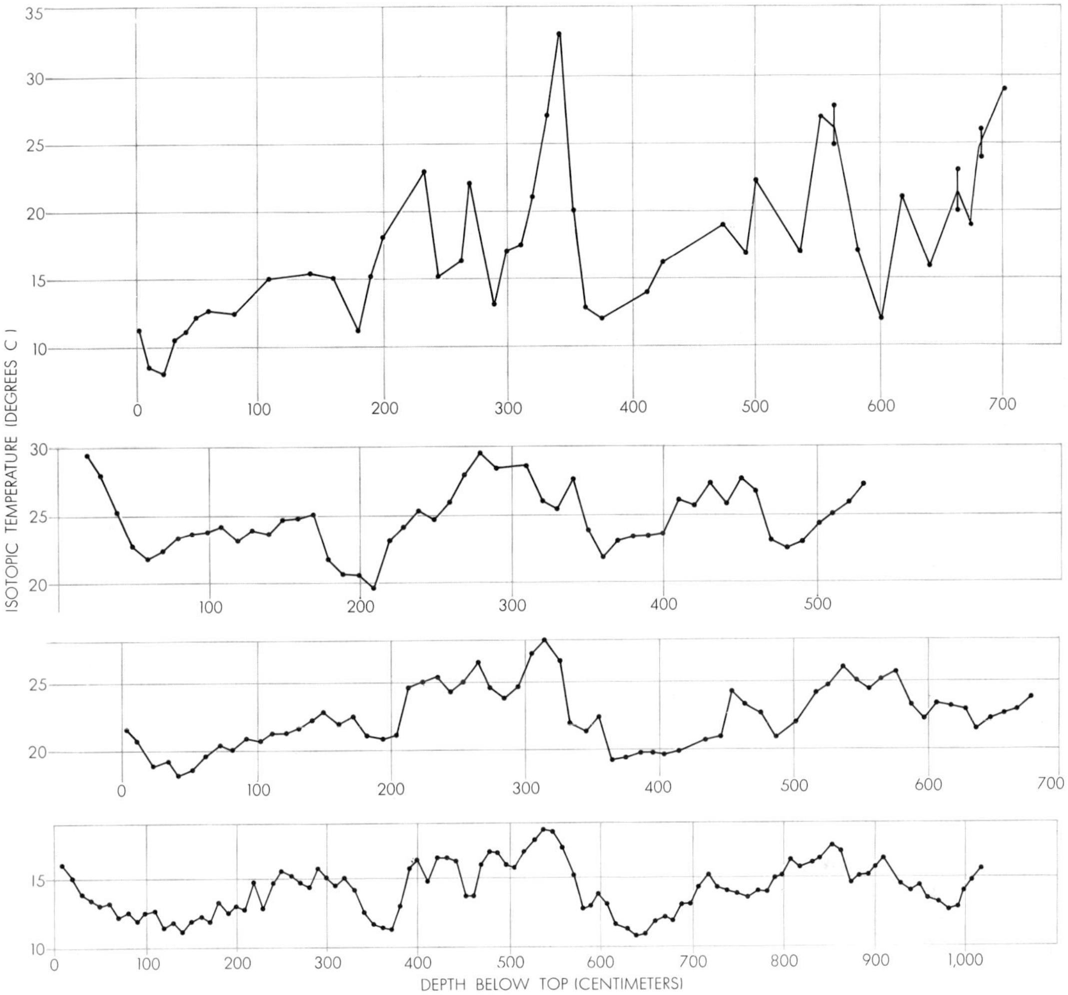

FIGURE 77.4
Temperature curves from cores originating in widely separated spots show strong similarites. The curves, covering some 200,000 years, are (*top to bottom*) from Mediterranean, Caribbean, equatorial Atlantic, and North Atlantic cores. The land-locked Mediterranean shows the greatest range of temperature variations: from 8 to 33 degrees C. (46 to 92 degrees F.) Differences in core length, shown by the varying horizontal scales, indicate that marine sediments accumulated at different rates in these four areas.

ing which the earth had no ice ages. Looking back over the climatic changes of the last 100 million years, we can now see a possible explanation of how the current Ice Epoch originated.

The Lowenstam-Epstein analysis of Cretaceous fossils shows that temperatures reached a high point about 85 million years ago. At that time shallow seas occupied vast areas which are now land, and there were only a few low chains of mountains on the continents (Figure 77.6). Toward the end of the Cretaceous Period a large part of the Pacific bottom southwest of the Hawaiian Islands began to sink, and similar founderings may have occurred elsewhere in the Pacific. Simultaneously there opened a great epoch of mountain building which ultimately produced the Rockies, Andes, Alps and Himalayas. These processes put millions of square miles of previously immersed land above water. Since dry land absorbs less solar radiation than water does, the world climate became steadily colder. Perhaps two million years ago permanent caps of snow and ice began to form in Antarctica and Greenland. This highly reflecting ground cover absorbed still less of the sun's rays. Some 300,000 years ago the climate had become so cold that one of Milankovitch's cool-summer cycles could have extended the northern ice south to northeastern North America and Scandinavia—both regions of heavy snowfall. Back-radiation of solar energy was still further increased, and the first great wave of ice was under way. The enormous mass of ice that overran the Northern Hemisphere must have influenced the climate of the entire earth. We know that glaciers formed over most of the great mountain chains of both hemispheres.

During this period, as our studies show, the oceans' surface temperature dropped sharply. This started a reverse process, for cooler oceans mean less evaporation, drier air and less snowfall. Eventually winter snowfall decreased to a

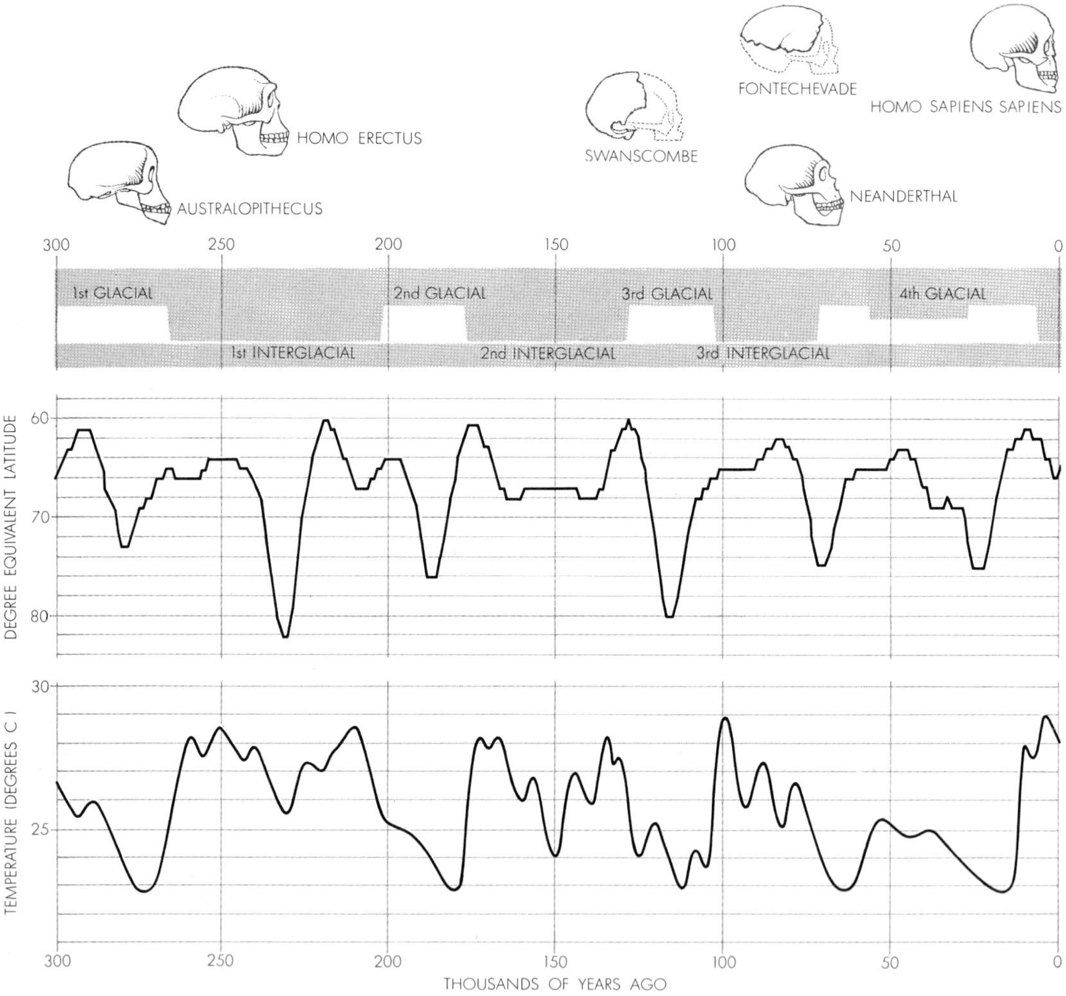

FIGURE 77.5
Climatic fluctuations and hominid evolution during the Pleistocene. Composite curve from six deep-sea cores (*bottom*) shows the climatic fluctuations during the Glacial Epoch. The similar curve above it shows variations in summer solar radiation 65 degrees North, where the great ice sheets were centered. These are expressed as apparent shifts in latitude; thus 25,000 years ago latitude 65 received no more solar heat in summer than latitude 75 does today. The human and prehuman skulls (*top*) are associated with the glacial events suggested by the gray area below them.

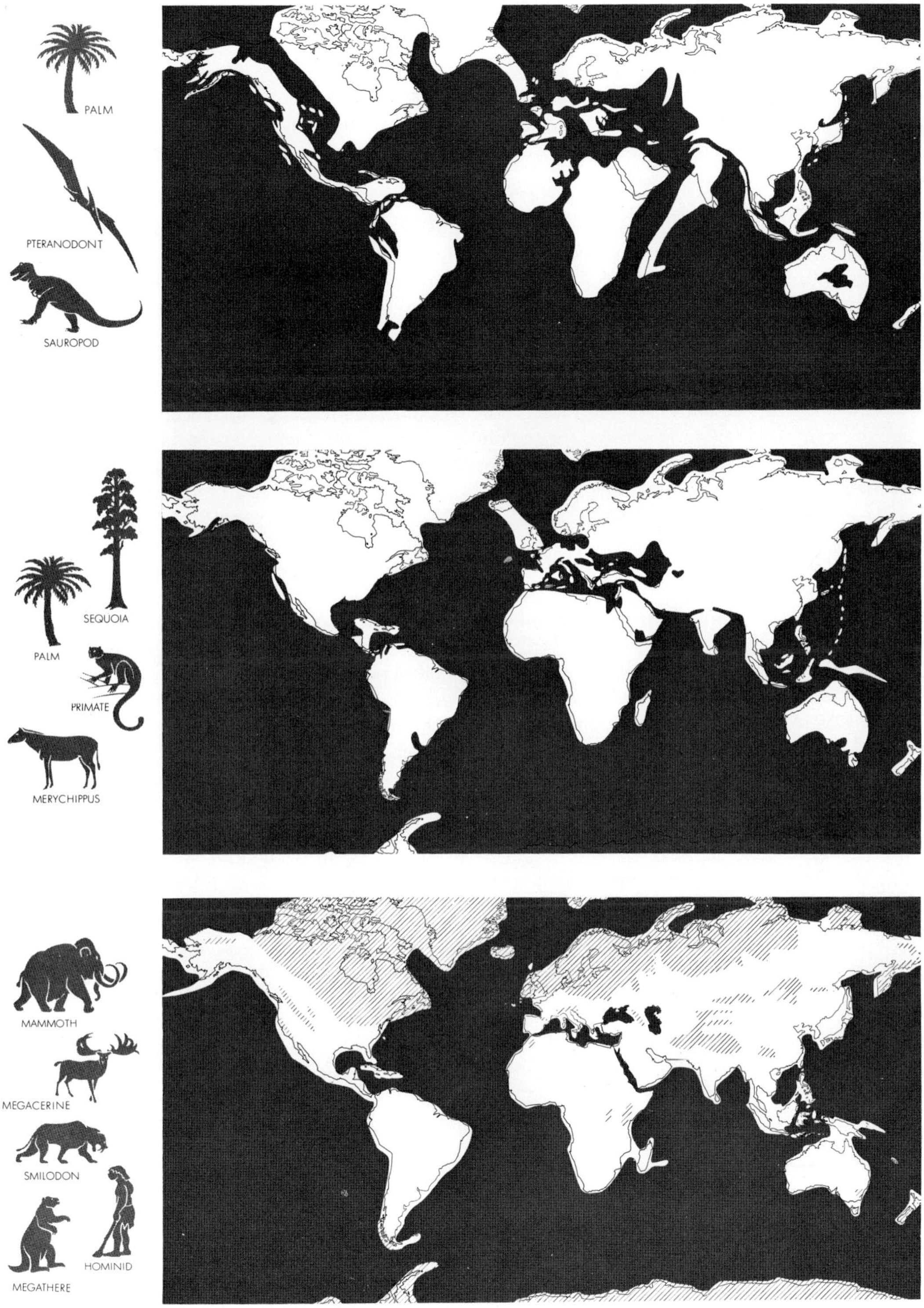

FIGURE 77.6
Land emergence helped bring on the Ice Epoch. Eighty million years ago shallow seas covered vast areas (*bottom*); climate was tropical almost to the poles. Ten million years ago less land was submerged (*center*); climate was cooler, though warmer than now. Maximum emergence was less than 500,000 years ago (*top*); hatching shows ice sheets. Present coast lines are in black; animals and plants of each period are at side.

point where the summer shrinking of the glaciers was greater than their winter growth. A period of hot summers accelerated this process and pushed back the ice sheets until only those of Antarctica and Greenland remained.

When the cool-summer part of the Milankovitch cycle returned, the glaciers began to grow again, and the whole process was repeated: advance of the ice sheets, cooling of the seas and eventually a new shrinking of the glaciers. If the theory is correct, about 10,000 years from now there will be another advance of the glaciers, burying Chicago, Berlin and Moscow under thousands of feet of ice. Indeed, we can expect periodic glaciations to continue until the earth's great mountain chains have been weathered down to hills.

DATES OF MAN

One of the most important products of the isotope thermometer is that it has given us a definite time scale, not only for the ice ages but also for the evolution of life. We can now date fossils of man and his ancestors and estimate the rates of human evolution with some confidence. In the past most of the human and manlike fossils have been dated, after a fashion, by the deposits in which they were found but the age of the deposits was often uncertain. With the fairly accurate new calendar of glaciation cycles obtained through Urey's thermometer, we can put the chronology of human evolution in order, for the migrations of early man and the rise of new types are often connected with glacial periods. We know, for example, that the man-apes of South Africa originated some time before the first glaciation and died out during the first interglacial period. According to the paleotemperature chronology, this means that they lived between about 400,000 and 200,000 years ago. Similarly we know that Pithecanthropus, Sinanthropus and Atlanthropus—men of a very primitive type which I prefer to assign to the single species *Homo erectus*—originated during the first interglacial, which we date at 200,000 to 250,000 years ago.

The Swanscombe skull bones, probably belonging to an ancestral sub-species of modern man, date from the second interglacial, about 125,000 years ago. The Fontéchevade remains, the oldest known fossils certainly belonging to modern man, are from the third interglacial, and are thus only about 100,000 years old. Since Neanderthal man also originated during the same interglacial period, he must be considered a separate offshoot parallel to modern man. Neanderthal, an unsuccessful experiment in humanity, became extinct during the last glaciation, about 50,000 years ago. Thus he lasted only about 2,000 generations. Evolution from *Homo erectus* to Swanscombe man took about 3,000 generations, and from Swanscombe to modern man, only about 1,000. This is evolution at a rapid rate. Equally rapid rates of evolution would obtain for other advanced animals.

So the reconstruction of the temperatures of ancient seas is only the beginning of the grand-scale prospects opened by our new thermometer. It enlightens us about the long-range climatic cycles of our planet. It will tell us much about how sediments are deposited in the oceans, about many animals of the sea (at what depths they live and how fast they grow), about the wandering of the geographic poles, about the history of man and about many other things. A number of scientists in the U.S., in Italy and in the U.S.S.R. are busy exploiting this wonderful tool.

BIBLIOGRAPHY

Emiliani, Cesare, 1954, Depth habitats of some species of pelagic Foraminifera as indicated by oxygen isotope ratios: Am. Jour. Sci., v. 252, no. 3, p. 149–158.

———, 1954, Temperatures of Pacific bottom waters and polar superficial waters during the Teritary: Science, v. 119, no. 3103, p. 853–855.

———, 1955, Pleistocene temperatures: Jour. Geology, v. 63, no. 6, p. 538–578.

———, 1956, Oligocene and Miocene temperatures of the equatorial and subtropical Atlantic Ocean: Jour. Geology, v. 64, no. 3, p. 281–288.

Flint, Richard Foster, 1957, Glacial and Pleistocene geology: New York, John Wiley and Sons.

78

Absolute Dating and the History of Man

WILLIAM T. PECORA

MEYER RUBIN

1967

From *Time and Stratigraphy in the Evolution of Man* (NAS-NRC Publication 1469), pp. 43–56. National Academy of Sciences, 1967. Reprinted with permission of the authors and the publisher.

The purpose of this review is to evaluate the numbers and methods applicable to geologic events of the past few million years, particularly with reference to man or to hominid remains. Because geologic techniques of correlation are so insensitive to stratigraphic sections formed under continental conditions, absolute [radiometric] dating will very likely be the most rewarding technique if we can but apply some rigid validity controls.

Validity . . . must be fulfilled in each of three areas: (1) experimental method employed, (2) geochemical "fitness" of the sample, and (3) geologic intelligence. Ideally, then, we can get "right" answers that can stand the test of most critical scrutiny. Experience has shown that if a group of knowledgeable geologists unanimously accepts an age assignment of a rock or mineral the chances are very good that the date is essentially correct. By the same token, if serious doubts are raised, all three "validities" need re-examination. The experimental and geologic validities are more amenable to successful re-examination, however, than geochemical validity of the samples. The experimentalists have been using the mass approach in their attempts toward greater geochemical validity. All applicable dating methods and all possible materials are being used. This shotgun approach is not thoroughly satisfactory but is recognized as part of the evolution of the science. The possibility that all methods used today are wrong must be acknowledged.

EXPERIMENTAL VALIDITY

Experimental work dealing with dating has been in the mainstream of research for two decades and has been characterized by an environment of invention. Validity is a function of the limitations imposed by the equipment used or devised; of the uncertainty of the physical constants, chemical analyses, and spectrographic apparatus; and of the firmness of the very assumptions of the method itself.

TABLE 78.1
Summary of Pleistocene age-dating methods

					Likelihood of applicability to*				
Isotope	Half-life (10^3 yr)	Method	Range (10^3 yr)	Materials	Ocean temperature	Sea level	Glacier extent	Arid lakes	Pollen sequence
^{14}C	5.7	Decay	0–35 35–70	Organics – calcium carbonate Organics	+	+	+	+	+
^{231}Pa	32.0	Decay Integration ^{230}Th normal	5–120 5–120 5–120	Red clay or Globigerina ooze	+	0	0	0	0
^{230}Th	75.0	Decay Integration ^{230}Th normal	5–400 5–400 5–400	Red clay or Globigerina ooze	+	0	0	0	0
		Growth	0–200	Organics – calcium carbonate	0	+	0	+	+
^{234}U	250.0	Decay	50–1,000	Coral	0	+	0	0	0
^{4}He	—	Growth	no limit	Mollusks or coral	0	+	0	+	0
^{40}Ar	—	Growth	no limit	Volcanics	+	+	+	+	+
^{36}Cl	300.0	Growth	50–500	Igneous or metamorphic rock	0	0	+	0	0
^{10}Be	2,500.0	Decay	100–8,000	Red clay	+	0	0	0	0

Source: after Broecker, 1965.
* Plus sign (+) signifies applicable; zero (0) signifies not applicable.

The dating methods we are concerned with as applicable to the last few million years of the geologic time scale include carbon-14 dating, potassium-argon (K-Ar) dating, and a whole group that can be called the uranium-series methods. Broecker (1965) has reviewed the several methods pertinent to the Pleistocene (see Table 78.1). In addition, there are the fission-track and obsidian dating methods, which are of a different genre. Isotopic ratios as a guide to temperature of carbonate formation are pertinent to our review.

All radiogenic dating methods . . . depend on . . . a measurable amount of parent material decaying at a fixed rate to a measurable amount of daughter products in a supposedly closed system. This means that there can be no addition or loss of parent or daughter product by means other than the ticking of this clock during the time range under review. Geologists would never grant that such a closed system exists in the crust of the earth, although there is much less opportunity for these additions or losses to take place in the relatively short time of Pleistocene and Recent.

An interesting problem has developed in ^{14}C dating, casting doubt on the basic assumption that activity of ^{14}C has been in the same equilibrium state in the atmosphere throughout its applicable dating range (but pre–atomic bomb). By measuring ^{14}C activity of sequoia tree rings, daters found that atmospheric concentration has oscillated, with an average amplitude of 3 per cent, from the present concentration during the past few thousand years (Figure 78.1). Measurements on the older bristlecone pine, however, indicate a rising concentration curve, so that for a date of 5,000 years a correction of 600 years is necessary. What is the extrapolation of this trend? We may yet find that the radiocarbon time scale is a rubber-band scale that can be stretched or contracted with each glaciation and interglaciation.

Currently, the half-life constant used for ^{14}C is 5,568 years. Although general agreement exists that 5,730 (recently established) is a better figure, the older one continues to be used. All published data, however, state what constants are employed.

Experimental precision in mass spectrometry has improved so notably that even with a half-life of 1.3 billion years in K-Ar decay, reproducibility of the measurement of ^{40}Ar is commonplace. This is evidence of the great progress achieved over two decades in instrumentation and precision of laboratory procedures. But because the initial assumptions of the methods themselves are less firm, reproducible results demonstrate merely the precision of the technique and not full validity of the numbers.

GEOCHEMICAL VALIDITY

Geochemical integrity permits determination of which minerals or rocks are indeed best for which methods. Leakage, alteration, inclusions, contamination, or recrystallization may cause rocks and minerals to tell false stories. Too frequently, different minerals in the same sample yield different ages by the same or other methods.

Some years ago, bone material, shells, and vegetative matter were all believed to be acceptable for ^{14}C dating. Today, bone material is used with considerable reservation, and shell dates are not considered reliable beyond 30,000 years, and even within that range they may have a possible error of 2,000 years.

In samples for K-Ar dating, we suspect that inherited argon exists in fluid inclusions in many minerals. Rama et al. (1965), for example, demonstrated this to be true for inclusions in quartz. Currently, one investigator is measuring several modern flows to see if they are dated as zero age, as they should be. The recognition of inherited argon recently caused correction of the age estimate for the Bishop Tuff by Dalrymple et al. (1965) from 1.0 to 0.7 million years. Minerals and rocks undergoing hydrothermal or surficial alteration do not provide a closed system for retention of all the potassium and argon or for withstanding invasions from other sources.

The assumptions regarding initial conditions are in even more serious difficulties in the uranium-series methods. Those depending on known thorium and uranium concentrations are plagued by detrital phases of sediments, whereas authigenic growth is usually assumed. With the ^{10}Be method, the concentration of this isotope is so small that it is difficult to determine just how much the ocean sediment should have contained initially. Experimenters using most of these methods have suffered the embarrassment of trying to explain nonzero ages at the very top of the sediment core.

Contamination by atmospheric ingredients is particularly acute in young volcanic glass that has undergone surficial alteration. Leaching outer layers of rock or mineral samples with hydrofluoric acid helps in removing possible atmospheric argon contamination. Earlier, ^{14}C daters removed the humic acid fraction from wood samples by boiling them in alkali and from surface layers of carbonate samples by treatment with HCl. Unrecognized natural contamination can prove to be serious in young age samples. For example, a rock or mineral granular sample from East Africa containing one Precambrian grain per thousand (0.1 per cent) can recast a zero age as 2 million years.

Geochemical validity of a sample is almost impossible to predict. Careful petrologic and mineralogic evaluation is necessary before beginning experimental procedure. The present search is directed toward minerals that do not normally exchange or absorb and that contain large quantities of the isotope in question. Whole rock samples, once in disrepute, are now often considered choice samples for dating. Hornblende, once ignored, is now being used. For the K-Ar method, certainly samples rich in potassium are necessary. The tide has turned, in some circles, against the use of glauconites. But the fitness of samples frequently is determined after much fumbling.

GEOLOGIC VALIDITY

If experimental precision is the least suspect and geochemical validity the least determinable, then certainly geologic validity is the most controversial. To develop a universal Pleistocene time scale we must correlate marine sediments of the Mediterranean with those of the ocean deeps and continental shelves, with ash falls in Africa, lava flows in Iceland, river terraces and cave deposits in Europe, continental glacial deposits and mountain glaciers in North America, and coral in the Atlantic. The task is herculean. These are the materials being dated today, and their interpretation is critical to the construction of a Pleistocene time scale.

But when did the Pleistocene begin? The Pliocene-Pleistocene boundary as now accepted is based on faunal changes in the Calabrian type section of Italy. Historically, the Pleisto-

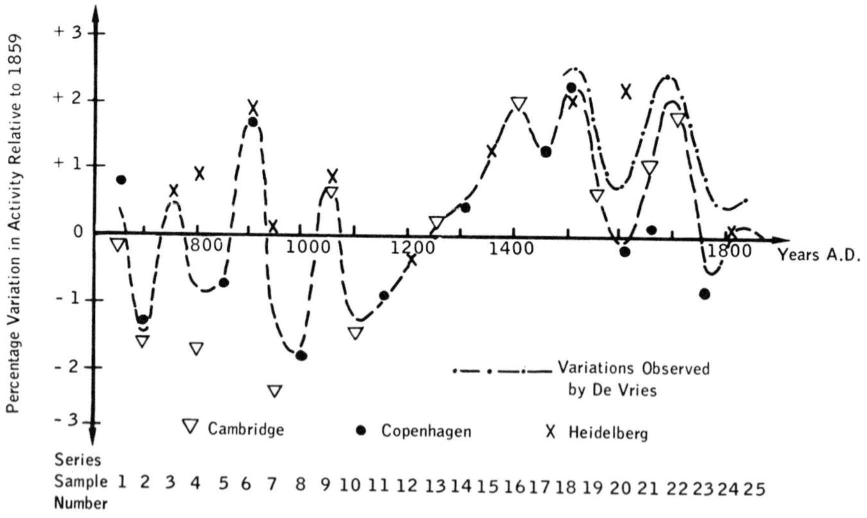

FIGURE 78.1
Sequoia tree ring series. Initial activities of 25 samples taken at 50-year intervals from a giant sequoia, represented as a percentage variation from the activity of the wood from the 1859 tree ring. (After Willis et al., 1960.)

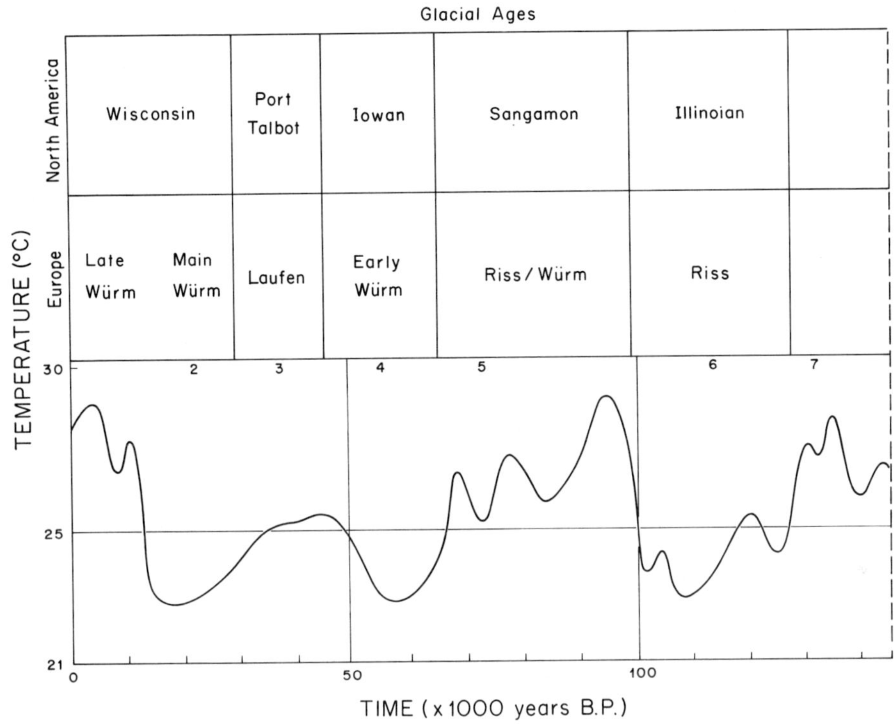

FIGURE 78.2
Generalized temperature curve and absolute time scale (by extrapolation for dates beyond 150,000 years B.P.). (Modified from Rosholt et al., 1961.)

cene time scale was determined by the depth of leaching on glacial soils, using the time since the last glaciation as the yardstick. This unit of time was estimated by extrapolating from the rate of waterfall retreat in a few critical places. When the estimated time span was reduced by ^{14}C dating from 25,000 to 11,000 years, the estimate of the duration of the entire Pleistocene was correspondingly reduced from 1 million years to 500,000 years. The oxygen isotope work of Emiliani (1955) appeared to substantiate the short scale.

The most important impact of K-Ar dating in recent years is reestablishment of the longer chronometry. Evidence to support this reversal is mounting. Some dates on continental deposits have stretched the Pleistocene to a duration of 2 or even 3.5 million years, if the deposits in question are truly Pleistocene as claimed. The ^{14}C dating of the fluctuations of the surface ocean temperature as reflected in the $^{18}O/^{16}O$ ratio of the carbonates in foraminifera in deep-sea cores has proved to be an important breakthrough. Emiliani (1955) plotted oscillations of his isotopic data as valid variations in ocean temperature and therefore implied valid correlation with planetary glacial episodes (Figure 78.2). The ^{14}C ages of the sediments assigned dated from the present to just short of the last interglacial, however, and the extrapolation beyond was based on interpretation of the peaks in temperature variation. Protactinium-ionium dates (Rosholt et al., 1961) substantiated part of this extrapolation. According to Emiliani's phases, the beginning of the four continental glaciations occurred some 300,000 years ago, and the Pleistocene began 600,000 years ago. His interpretation places strong reliance on complete geologic validity in the continuous record of the cores, the correlation of continental glaciation and oceanic temperatures, the rate of sedimentary accumulation, and the absence of significant temperature fluctuations within each of the glacial stages.

Emiliani . . . is correct in reserving correlations until the marine stage of the Calabrian has been dated. His current temperature curve carries no continental correlations (Emiliani, 1966).

A different time scale, also using the evidence from deep-sea cores, was arrived at by Ericson et al. (1964). Morphological changes in foraminiferal assemblages permitted a different interpretation of the importance of fluctuations (Figure 78.3). Ericson placed the beginning of the Pleistocene at 1.5 million years. Unfortunately K-Ar dating is not applicable to deep-sea cores. Emiliani questions the validity of the Ericson correlations on several grounds (Emiliani, 1964), pointing to internal contradictions in the method. If continental glaciation can be correlated with deep-sea cores, certainly the Emiliani and Ericson positions, each based initially on valid techniques, need re-examination and resolution.

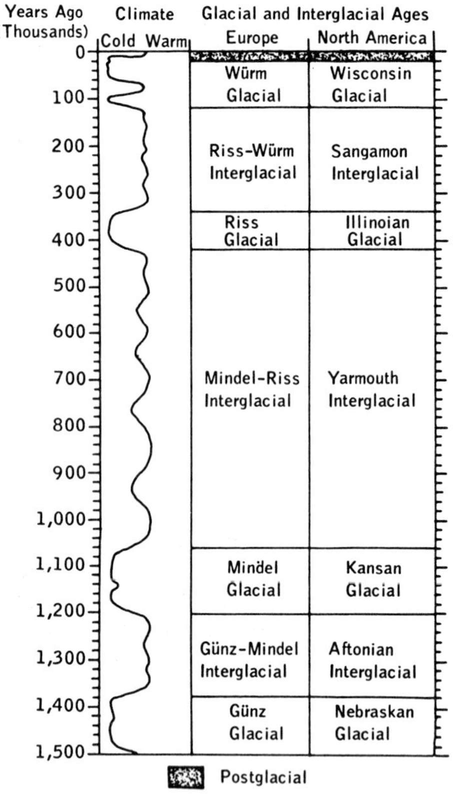

FIGURE 78.3
Pleistocene time scale and generalized climate curve based on the study of deep-sea sediment cores. The beginning of the Pleistocene is considered to be the onset of the first glaciation, the Nebraskan or Günz. (After Ericson et al., 1964.)

If not by sea, then perhaps by land, correlation can be accomplished. In California, the Bishop Tuff, overlying a till of Kansan(?) age (Blackwelder, 1931), was dated by Dalrymple et al. (1965) as 0.7 million years. In Iceland, a till contained in a section of basalt flows is dated as about 3.1 million years. The Villafranchian fauna of France, considered by some to be Pleistocene in age, has been dated by an associated tuff deposit at more than 3 million years. In contrast to these dates, however, the Upper Main Terrace of the Rhine, correlated with the Günz or first, glaciation, has been dated at 400,000 years. This underscores the principle that, where the geologic evidence is fallible, the results of dating are not valid even if the dating methods are.

The paleomagnetic-polarity technique developed by Cox et al. (1965) is emerging as an aid to correlation. It depends on observations that the earth's magnetic field changes with time and that certain rocks are permanently magnetized in the earth's field at the time of their formation. Lava flows measured for their polarity and their K-Ar dates lend themselves to a kind of magnetic time scale. Once there is agreement on the placement of the Pliocene-Pleistocene boundary in the polarity epoch time scale, the normal or reversed polarity of the rocks can be used as a correlation technique (Figure 78.4).

CASE HISTORY OF OLDUVAI

The combination of methods used in the investigations at Olduvai Gorge—absolute dating, sampling, and stratigraphic correlation—provides a good example of the kind of investigative approach needed for most localities before any confidence can be placed in the chronometry of geologic events. Straus and Hunt (1962) most properly called attention to the conflicts implied in the first dates published by Leakey et al. (1961) and cautioned against acceptance of any of the dates until much further work is done in the field and in the laboratory. Subsequent geologic study by

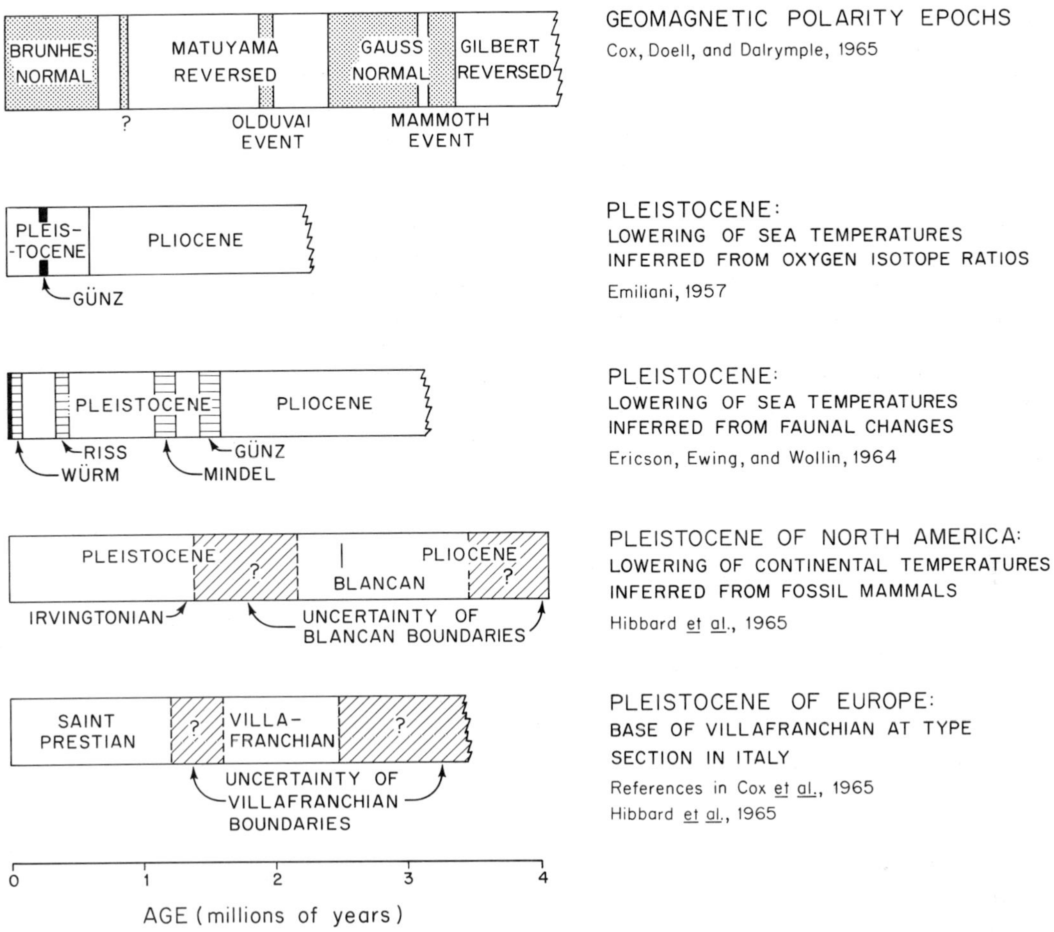

FIGURE 78.4
Geomagnetic polarity time scale, and various time scales for the Pleistocene. (Courtesy of Allan Cox and Richard Doell.)

Hay (1963) clarified some of the complex problems of correlation, provided a better basis for selection of samples, and afforded Evernden and Curtis more opportunity to test their experimental procedures to obtain higher confidence in their results. A second field visit by Hay, coupled with a detailed laboratory examination of mineral samples, increased the geologic intelligence of the site. A date of 1.8 million years for the part of Bed I containing *Zinjanthropus* is the most acceptable and apparently was the best of the three dates that formed the target of the Straus-Hunt review. Fleischer et al. (1965) obtained a fission-track age of 2.03± 0.28 million years on a pumice from Bed I. Despite the apparent agreement, the question of who collected the pumice, and with what geologic controls and validity, should be emphasized. The incorrect use of "bed" in Bed I and Bed II will unfortunately remain in the literature concerning the site.

CONCLUSIONS

It has become increasingly evident that under ideal conditions ^{14}C dating can exceed 30,000 years and K-Ar dating can extend its lower range to meet it, thus covering the entire Pleistocene time scale. The two scales may not be interchangeable, however, although many people would like them to be. The probability of ideality and truly "absolute" chronometry is too remote to be expected, except perhaps for an odd sample. For the most part, we may expect groups of samples to be acceptable or valid only after serious review, re-examination, and evaluation in a relative sense of proportion. Geochronometry in this light can then be derived through geochronology. Intercontinental correlation and chronometry during the hominid span remain an open question, still subject to a great deal of speculative interpretation. Absolute [radiometric] dating methods, however, still offer the most promising means of achieving this aim if the concept of full validity is not lightly put aside.

REFERENCES CITED

Blackwelder, E., 1931, Pleistocene glaciation in the Sierra Nevada and Basin Ranges: Geol. Soc. America Bull., v. 42, p. 865–992.

Broecker, W. S., 1965, Isotope geochemistry and the Pleistocene climatic record, *in* H. E. Wright, Jr., and D. G. Frey, eds., The Quaternary of the United States: Princeton, N.J., Princeton University Press.

Cox, A., and R. R. Doell, 1965, Paleomagnetism and Quaternary correlation: Boulder, Colo., INQUA Symposium VII.

Cox, A., R. R. Doell, and G. B. Dalrymple, 1965, Quaternary paleomagnetic stratigraphy, *in* H. E. Wright, Jr., and D. G. Frey, eds., The Quaternary of the United States: Princeton, N.J., Princeton University Press, p. 817–830.

Dalrymple, G. B., A. Cox, and R. R. Doell, 1965, Potassium-argon age and paleomagnetism of the Bishop Tuff, California: Geol. Soc. America Bull., v. 76, p. 665–674.

Emiliani, C., 1955, Pleistocene Temperatures: Jour. Geology, v. 63, p. 538–578.

———, 1964, Paleotemperature analysis of the Carribean cores A254-BR-C and CP-28: Geol. Soc. America Bull., v. 75, p. 129–144.

———, 1966, Paleotemperature analysis of Carribean cores P6304-8 and P6304-9, and a generalized temperature curve for the past 425,000 years: Jour. Geology, v. 74, p. 109–126.

Ericson, D. B., M. Ewing, and G. Wollin, 1964, The Pleistocene Epoch in deep-sea sediments: Science, v. 146, p. 723–732.

Fleischer, R. L., P. B. Price, R. M. Walker, and L. S. B. Leakey, 1965, Fission track dating of Bed I, Olduvai Gorge: Science, v. 148, p. 72–74.

Hay, R. L., 1963, Stratigraphy of Beds I through IV, Olduvai Gorge, Tanganyika: Science, v. 139, p. 829–833.

Hibbard, C. W., 1965, Quaternary mammals of North America, *in* H. E. Wright, Jr., and D. G. Frey, eds., The Quarternary of the United States: Princeton, N.J., Princeton University Press, p. 509–525.

Rama, S. N. I., S. R. Hart, and E. Roedder, 1965, Excess radiogenic argon in fluid inclusions: Jour. Geophys. Res., v. 70, p. 509–511.

Rosholt, J. N., C. Emiliani, J. Geiss, F. F. Koczy, and P. J. Wangersky, 1961, Absolute dating of deep-sea cores by the Pa-231/Th-230 method: Jour. Geology, v. 69, p. 162–185.

Straus, W. L., and C. B. Hunt, 1962, Age of *Zinjanthropus*: Science, v. 136, p. 293–295.

Willis, E. H., H. Tauber, and K. O. Munnich, 1960, Variations in the atmospheric radiocarbon concentration over the past 1,300 years: Am. Jour. Sci. Radiocarbon Supp., v. 2, p. 1–4.

New Fossil Primates

A Review

ELWYN L. SIMONS
1968

Revised from "New Fossil Primates: A Review of the Past Decade," *American Scientist,* vol. 48, no. 2, pp. 179–192, 1960. Reprinted with permission of the author and the Society of the Sigma Xi. Permission has been received from Holt, Rinehart and Winston, Inc., for the use of the revised and updated version of this paper, as it appears under the title, "New Fossil Primates: A Review" by Elwyn L. Simons, in their volume *Perspectives on Human Evolution 1,* edited by S. L. Washburn and Phyllis C. Jay.

The distinct rarity of fossil primates maintains the development of studies regarding the evolutionary appearance of man and allied forms in an intriguing but often frustrating state. Nevertheless, some of the mists obscuring the past of the order to which man belongs have recently been clearing. The years since 1950 stand as the most productive of new finds and new reports of any equal time period since the first fossil primate *Adapis* was described by Cuvier in 1822. Moreover, the steady climb in rate of recovery of new types and more complete individuals suggests that paleontologists and paleoanthropologists will augment the series of ancient primates which came to light in the first two-thirds of this century by at least an equal number during the remainder. Discoveries of particular value include several of nearly complete skulls together with postcranial remains. Such discoveries, belonging to a number of species previously known only from jaws and teeth, recently established another dimension for osteological comparison between fossil and living types. For reasons of brevity, not all the significant new types of primates described from dentitions alone can be considered in this report.

In spite of the additions to knowledge of primate history discussed here, many basic problems of the evolutionary differentiation of the order as a whole need clarification. A few such problems are: When and where did the common ancestor of the Old World monkeys, apes, and man arise? What are the nearest relatives, among known early Tertiary families, of surviving primates? At what time did the ceboids, or New World monkeys, branch off from the line of the higher primates of Europe, Asia, and Africa? Which of the many groups of North American Eocene primates make the most likely candidates for the ancestry of the Ceboidea? When did the ape and human stocks diverge? What is the relationship of the ape-like creatures *Aegyptopithecus* from the Oligocene of Egypt and *Dryopithecus* species (subgenus *Proconsul*) from the early Miocene of Kenya to this differentiation?

How should the earliest primates be distinguished from allied insectivores? What characteristics typified pre-Pleistocene hominids? How many of the genera and species currently assigned to Pleistocene man have taxonomic validity?

With such a variety of unsolved problems regarding the origin and radiation of the primates, much further geological exploration and collecting is needed. Some long-known localities for Old World fossil primates remain most likely to yield specimens which could answer a number of these problems and deserve further attention. Such areas include the Miocene and Pliocene beds of the Siwalik Hills in northwestern India and eastern West Pakistan, the Miocene deposits of Kenya and Uganda, and the Oligocene terrestrial deposits of the Fayum, southwest of Cairo, Egypt. In all these sediments primates which might pertain to the line of hominid differentiation occur. Recent collections show that fossil primates can be found abundantly in these three areas among many other potential sites in the Old World.

Apart from the distinct need for additional collecting lies the matter of interpretation and careful analysis of species now known. A remark attributed to the great paleoanthropologist Franz Weidenreich, even if apocryphal, serves to emphasize this aspect of the subject. When asked where the fossil ancestors of living man are, Weidenreich is said to have replied: "On our desks." The same possibility obtains for a number of fossil nonhominid primates, already available in museum collections. Restudy, and more critical comparison, pending recovery of new connecting links, stand as desirable objectives for correct assessment of currently known fossil specimens. . . . One improvement would be a freer exchange of specimens for description and study among competent researchers. A good example of such cooperation is the efficient and prompt reporting of new fossil mammals (including many primates) collected in Kenya and Tanzania in recent years and described by Butler, Leakey, LeGros Clark, Napier, Tobias, Simpson, Witworth, and a number of other colleagues.

Terminology in classification of primates varies greatly. Here catarrhine and platyrrhine are used as equivalents for Old and New

TABLE 79.1
Major subdivisions of primates

Suborder	Infraorder	Superfamily	Family
Prosimii (lower primates, or prosimians)	Lemuriformes (lemurs)		
	Lorisiformes (lorises)		
	Tarsiiformes (tarsiers)		
Anthropoidea (higher primates, or simians)	Catarrhini (Old World higher primates)	Cercopithecoidea (Old World monkeys, or cercopithecoids)	
		Hominoidea (hominoids)	Pongidae (apes, pongines, dryopithecines)
			Hominidae (hominids, or humanoids, men and allied forms)
	Platyrrhini (New World higher primates)	Ceboidea (New Wold monkeys, or ceboids)	

World higher primates, respectively. This procedure, by placing Cercopithecoidea and Hominoidea in one infraorder, avoids the cumbersomeness of having always to use both terms when contrasting (as a group) the monkeys, apes, and men of the Old World with other primates. In order to avoid additional confusion the classification followed here, except for insertion of Catarrhini and Platyrrhini as infraorders, is that of Simpson (1945), which is as indicated in Table 79.1.

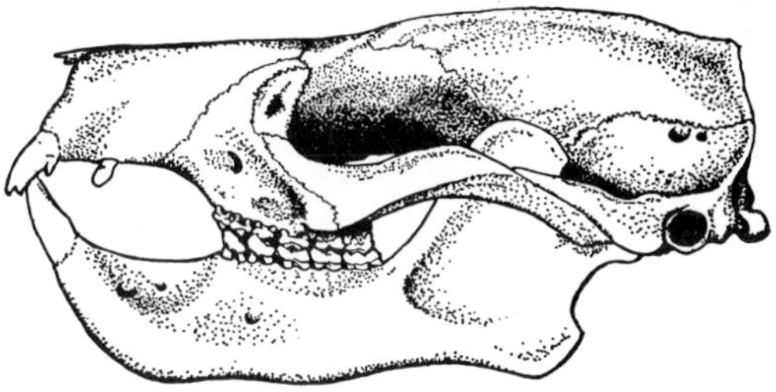

FIGURE 79.1
Skull of a Paleocene primate *Plesiadapis*, × 1. Age about 6.5 × 10^7 years. (Cranium with some correction for distortion.)

Discussion of the more significant new fossil primate finds is here divided into the chronological sequence of Tertiary epochs. Table 79.2 lists known partial or complete skulls of Tertiary primates. From this series four species are figured, together with one Pleistocene type, as illustrative of a temporal, not phyletic, sequence among Cenozoic primates.

PALEOCENE

During the last few years two almost complete skulls of Paleocene primates have been identified. These supply the first foundation for cranial comparisons between Paleocene and subsequent species. One of the two, currently under study by R. W. Wilson, South Dakota School of Mines, comes from mid-Paleocene deposits in New Mexico. This cranium has been provisionally assigned to one of the oldest known primates, *Palaechthon*, having an age of about 7 times 10^7 years. A second skull from sediments of Paleocene age was described by D. E. Russell (1960). Belonging to a species of *Plesiadapis* (a specialized lemur-like prosimian, known from both Europe and North America), this specimen was collected from late Paleocene beds near Cernay-les-Rheims in France (Figure 79.1). Neither the European nor the American Paleocene primate skull belongs to a species with much possibility of being ancestral to any surviving members of the order, but even so, comparisons of these with Eocene and later primates should help clarify opinions regarding early cranial morphology in the order.

An interesting lesson to be learned from examination of these two skulls is that, although ancient, they are not generalized. Truly primitive features, like absence of a postorbital bar, are combined with specializations such as premolar reduction. In fact, the structural alterations and partial loss of antemolar teeth in *Plesiadapis* are greater than in most of the more recent primates. A relatively complete series of limb and foot bones of this animal, also found at Cernay, is now being studied at Yale. A preliminary reconstruction of this skeleton is indicated in Figure 79.2. The significance of a primate skeleton of such antiquity is evident, and preliminary observations show that some features of the postcranial anatomy of the Cernay species would not have been postulated for a primate.

EOCENE

Significant additions to knowledge of anatomy of Eocene forms came recently through recovery of a magnificent series of skulls and other materials from the North American middle Eocene belonging to two primitive lemur-like primates, *Notharctus* and *Smilodectes*, reported recently by Gazin (1958, 1965). Together with remains of previously known lemuroids of the late Eocene of France and Switzerland these crania provide a broader basis for study of anatomical and zoogeographical relationships among Lemuriformes. Of about the same age as the lemuroid skulls discovered by Dr. Gazin are two partial crania, recently reported on by McKenna (1966) of the American Museum of Natural History. These two specimens, belonging to a family of ancient mammals, the microsyopids, show that this little-known group of insectivore-like primates or primate-like insectivores can be related with some certainty to archaic primates like *Plesiadapis*. They represent yet another branch of early separation—one of the many stocks which grade, almost insensibly, away from undoubted primates toward insectivores, and which clearly indicate the derivation, among placental mammals, of primates. Restudies of a number of primate species of Eocene age have also attempted to trace the origins of certain surviving prosimians, particularly in the case of the French tarsioid *Necrolemur* (Figure 79.3) (see Simons and Russell 1960, and Simons 1961a). Other lemur-like Eocene primates were reviewed by Simons (1962a). Species of two genera, *Anchomomys* and *Pronycticebus*, although presently classified in the Eocene family Adapidae, show interesting resemblances to the modern lorises, and this may indicate that the differentiation of the lorisiform primates goes back at least this far.

Simpson (1955) reviewed the aberrant prosimian *Phenacolemur*, and related forms, in a beautifully illustrated monograph. This curious, slightly rodent-like genus occurs in the late Paleocene and early Eocene of North America, and has also been identified in early Eocene collections from France. To date, only *Plesiadapis*, *Phenacolemur*, *Homo*, and perhaps *Pelycodus* occur, or are known to have occurred, in both the Old and the New Worlds. Distribution of all these genera demonstrates that in the late Paleocene, or slightly before, climate and land bridges made possible a Holarctic distribution for some primates. In the virtual absence of Asian specimens, the probability that some other early Tertiary prosimians of North America were also existing in Eurasia increases the importance of New World types as possible indicators of the nature of early Old World stocks.

OLIGOCENE

The Oligocene epoch was almost certainly a critical age for diversification of higher primates. Before the Yale expeditions of the 1960's and discovery of an Oligocene primate skull in west Texas in 1964, the known world primate fauna of that time consisted of only seven or eight individual specimens, all from the Fayum early Oligocene of Egypt, and of a further three types, *Macrotarsius*, "*Kansupithecus*," and *Anagale* (found elsewhere), which were thought to belong in this order. A

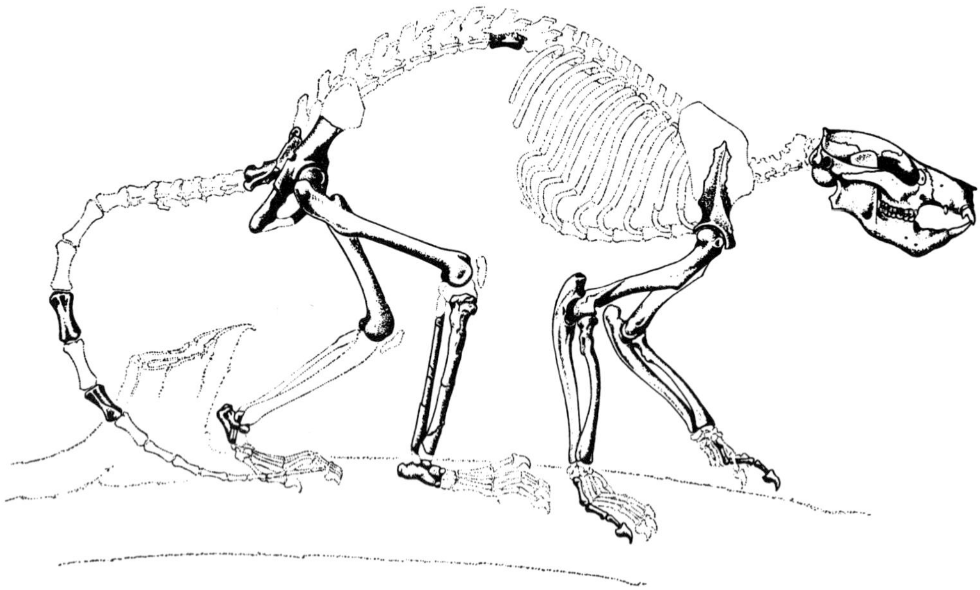

FIGURE 79.2
Preliminary reconstruction of the skeleton of *Plesiadapis*

small, but nearly complete, frontal bone from the Fayum desert (collected in 1908) was reported by Simons (1959). This skull fragment, the oldest of any known catarrhine primate, shows that postorbital closure, a distinctive feature of subsequent Anthropoidea, had been attained by the early Oligocene (Figure 79.3). Also, a mandibular fragment from the Fayum beds (at the American Museum of Natural History and from which tooth crowns have been lost) was described morphologically by Simons (1961b). This indicated another genus, somewhat larger than *Propliopithecus,* but differing from it through possession of an elongated third lower premolar as in later catarrhine monkeys and apes. Subsequent to this, finds in the Fayum made by members of the Yale expeditions under the author's direction made it possible to describe the genus and species represented by this jaw as *Aegyptopithecus zeuxis* (Simons, 1965). In addition,

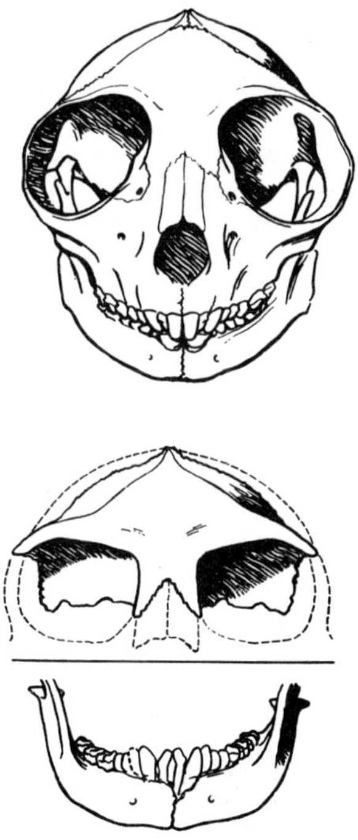

FIGURE 79.3
Eocene and Oligocene primates. *Left,* skull of the Eocene *Necrolemur,* × 1.2 approx. *Right,* parts of two Oligocene primates, × 1.2 approx.: *above,* an anthropoid frontal fragment from the Egyptian Fayum deposits; *below,* the mandibles of *Parapithecus,* a small Fayum species of uncertain taxonomic position.

three other new primates from the Fayum, *Oligopithecus savagei, Apidium moustafai,* and *Aeolopithecus chirobates,* have been described and reported on extensively elsewhere by Simons (1962b, 1963a, 1963b, 1965). Together with previously described Fayum primates these new species strengthen the impression that Anthropoidea may have been reasonably diversified by the early Oligocene. Absence of any antecedents for catarrhines in the late Eocene of Europe (although prosimians are numerous there) suggests a non-European and Asian or African origin for the group.* One problematical and very fragmentary primate "*Kansupithecus*" reported from the province of Kansu, China, by Bohlin in 1946 had been thought to represent an Oligocene Asiatic hominoid, but a more recent faunal correlation suggested by Thenius (1958) would place the Kansu fauna in the Miocene.

Anagale, long thought to represent an Oligocene occurrence of the tree-shrews, has been shown by McKenna (1963) not to belong to the order Primates. This leaves only two species of the order of Oligocene occurrence outside the Fayum. These are both North American monotypic genera, *Macrotarsius* and *Rooneyia.* New and unpublished finds of *Macrotarsius* should soon add to knowledge of its relationships. Simons (1961c) has pointed out that the lower jaw of this primate shows a morphologically intermediate stage between more primitive omomyid prosimians and later South American monkeys. Quite the most exciting recent addition to North American paleoprimatology was the finding of an Oligocene omomyid skull in 1964 by J. A. Wilson of the University of Texas. Wilson (1966) shows this cranium to be a mosaic of "primitive" and "advanced" features. Absence of postorbital closure, possession of simple molar cusp patterns, a somewhat backward directed foramen magnum, and placement of the lacrymal foramen outside the orbit are all primitive features of this skull. In contrast with these, the skull shows some features otherwise typical only of higher primates. . . .

* *Alsaticopithecus,* from the Eocene of Alsace, for which hominoid relationships have been suggested, has been shown by McKenna (1960) to be more probably a microsyopid.

MIOCENE

Additions to knowledge of Miocene hominoids during the last fifteen years have been substantial. Studies by LeGros Clark and Leakey (1951) on a skull and other remains of the early Miocene form of *Dryopithecus* (subgenus *Proconsul*)* were most recently enlarged by description of a forelimb of this primate by Napier and Davis (1959). Simons (1961d) demonstrated that the supposed dryopithecine *Ramapithecus* is on dental grounds perhaps better placed with hominids. In 1962 Leakey distributed a paper describing a new probable early Pliocene or late Miocene site, Fort Ternan, Kenya, and named a supposed new genus and species of primate *Kenyapithecus wickeri* from this locality. Simons (1963c, 1964a) pointed out that known species of *Ramapithecus* and *Kenyapithecus* are not dryopithecines and are all referable to the species *Ramapithecus punjabicus*. If species distinctions exist between the finds made in Africa and North India they cannot be demonstrated from known material. Simons and Pilbeam (1965) reviewed the twenty-eight genera with fifty contained species which had been considered members of the fossil ape sub-family Dryopithecinae. Of these, many were synonyms of *Ramapithecus punjabicus*, the earliest probable hominid species. The remainder were either *nomena vana, nomina nuda*, or were assignable to one of eight species of *Dryopithecus* or to the one species of *Gigantopithecus*. Several studies of limb bones and parts of crania of two other gibbon-like Miocene apes both belonging to subgenera of *Pliopithecus* (*Limnopithecus* and *Epipliopithecus*) were also published during this period (Figure 79.4). As a result of these reports one can now consider postcranial anatomy of mid-Tertiary hominoids in some detail. Perhaps the most striking findings to be drawn from study of the skeleton of Miocene apes is that, unlike surviving pongids, some at least of these ancient apes lacked a fully ossified auditory meatus, may have had a tail, and had forelimbs shorter than hind limbs. Miocene apes had apparently not yet acquired the elongated forelimbs which characterize brachiating anthropoids of the present day. Intermembral indices (combined length of radius and humerus relative to total length of femur and tibia) in both *Epipliopithecus* and *Limnopithecus* lie near 95. This figure is higher than in man and cercopithecoid monkeys (range 70–90), lower than that of living pongids (range 112–145). LeGros Clark and Thomas (1951) estimated the brachial index (length of radius in relation to humerus) in *Limnopithecus* as about 103, and limb bones of *Epipliopithecus* figured by Zapfe (1958), collected near Neudorf an der March in Czechoslovakia, have virtually the same index. The latter species is of mid-Miocene age. Of some interest is the fact that the brachial index of both these Miocene apes falls in an intermediate position between its mean in gibbons and those of the remainder of known hominoids, which reinforces the suggestion of gibbon affinities for species of these two genera, a relationship formerly based largely on dental comparisons. Recently an important study by Ankel (1965) has shown that because of the large diameter of the sacral canal in *Epipliopithecus*, this animal presumably had a long tail. From a monographic review of this primate by Zapfe (1960) it also emerges that in this Czechoslovakian ape there was only partial ossification of the ectotympanic tube, which is more extensively ossified in all living catarrhines. These primitive features led Remane (1965) to remove *Pliopithecus* to a separate, supposedly aberrant, family, Pliopithecidae. Nevertheless, one must realize that recovery of early forms of extant mammal families can and usually does necessitate expansion of the familial definition. By allocating these early apes to a distinct family without living descendants Remane has shifted attention away from the highly probable conclusion that these animals show us much about the condition of our own ancestors and in fact, of all hominoids at that time. There is little reason to doubt that these Miocene apes are in or near the ancestry of modern gibbons.

Considering, on the other hand, pongids of the genus *Dryopithecus*, the brachial index of *Dryopithecus* (*Proconsul*) *africanus*, lies considerably lower (86). Such a figure falls be-

* Classification of fossil apes followed is that of Simons and Pilbeam (1965).

tween the mean brachial index of the gorilla and that of the chimpanzee. However, this estimate derives from a juvenile *Dryopithecus africanus* and, as the brachial index typically increases with age in Anthropoidea, it was probably nearer 90 in the adult—a considerable remove from its mean in man, at about 76. Although presentation of a few indices of this sort cannot, of itself, serve to outline possible interrelationships of these pongids, it does represent one useful type of analysis made available by newly found limb bones. The relation of subgenus *Proconsul* to hominid differentiation continues to be obscure. In view of their generalized anatomy it seems unlikely that species of *Dryopithecus* would have looked very different from any hominids contemporary with them to an untrained eye, assuming that a dichotomy of the two families had occurred by then.

Another interesting observation derived from the new foot and hand skeletons of *Limnopithecus*, *Epipliopithecus*, and *Dryopithecus* (*Proconsul*) (noted by many who have studied them) is that the extremities of these early pongids retain many monkey-like features. In fact, it has been suggested that some of these bones would have been assigned to monkeys had they not been recovered in association with dentitions of essentially pongid type. In an analogous manner, the postcranial skeleton of *Homo sapiens* shows less differentiation from that of *Australopithecus* or *Homo erectus* than does the skull and dentition. Most discussions of australopithecine postcranial anatomy have been concerned with showing its manlike and non-ape-like construction. Relative to the broad stream of primate history this practice looks through the wrong end of the telescope. Living man retains, evidently with some additional refinements, the structural modifications for bipedality of *Australopithecus*. Thus, as bipeds, men could be said to be *Australopithecus*-like, and not the other way round. The broad pelvis and femoral conformation of *Oreopithecus* (see below), to the extent that these indicate bipedality, implies that bipedal trends in some lines of hominoids are of pre-Pliocene origin.

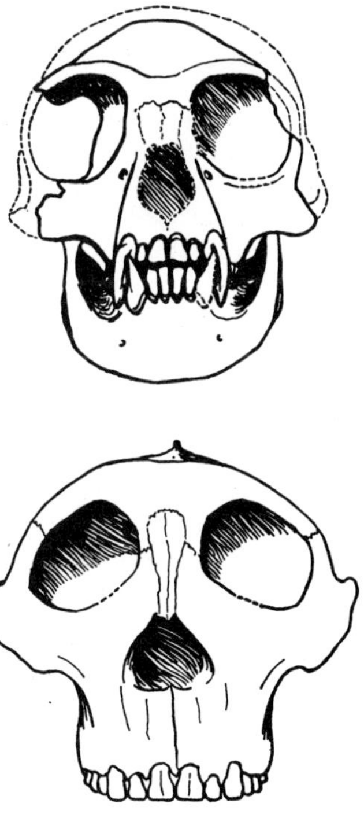

FIGURE 79.4
Miocene and Pleistocene primates. *Left*, skull of Miocene *Pliopithecus*, an early relative of the gibbons (after Zapfe, 1958), × 0.6 approx.; *right*, skull of a Pleistocene hominid *Zinjanthropus* (after Leakey, 1959), × 0.3 approx.

That Old World Anthropoidea were already considerably diversified and of wide distribution in this epoch is indicated by discovery of forms apparently assignable to the Indian subgenus of *Dryopithecus*, *Sivapithecus*, and to the Indian genus *Ramapithecus* in the Miocene Kenya deposits (LeGros Clark and Leakey 1951) and Leakey (1962). Moreover, in April 1965, Louis Leakey announced that teeth of something resembling *Oreopithecus* have been found at Fort Ternan, Kenya, along with at least two kinds of monkeys. Monkeys resembling *Mesopithecus* have also been reported from the Kenya Miocene beds by MacInnes (1943), but these may represent a new genus. *Mesopithecus* has been found at a number of localities in Europe and in the Near East. Recent reports on Miocene hominoids include that of Thenius (1954), a restudy of *Austriacopithecus* from Central Europe, and that of Burtschak and Gabachvili (1950) on a Dryopithecine(?) *Udabnopithecus* from Georgia, USSR. As mentioned above, Zapfe (1960) has fully illustrated the *Pliopithecus* skeletal material from Czechoslovakia, and knowledge of this ape has been further amplified by Ankel's study (1965) of the sacral canal and its implication that this was a tailed ape. Woo (1957, 1958) has discussed new materials of this genus from Keiyuan, Yunnan, China. Chow (1958) has demonstrated that this Hsolungtan coal field fauna probably correlates with the fossil ape-yielding deposits of the Chinji-Nagri zone of the Siwalik Hills, North India. These Chinese finds are not new species or are not demonstrably so. One specimen is evidently *Dryopithecus indicus*, the smaller, probably *Ramapithecus punjabicus*.

Relationships between early and late Cenozoic prosimian primates are hard to determine because of the rarity of Oligocene and Miocene species. Several new finds have been made. Jaw fragments and parts of two skulls of a Miocene prosimian were described by LeGros Clark and Thomas (1952) and by LeGros Clark (1956). These belong to an early Miocene genus *Progalago*, from Kenya, which can definitely be assigned to the lorisiform division of lower primates. Recovery of a primate of loris type of such antiquity indicates that the divergence of Madagascan lemurs and lorisiform prosimians cannot have occurred later than sometime in the Oligocene. Simons (1963*b*) noted the discovery in the Yale Siwalik collections of a mandible of the genus *Indraloris*. Recently Simpson (1967) has reviewed the African Miocene and Pleistocene lorisoids including *Progalago, Mioeuoticus* (Leakey, in Bishop, 1962). In this paper he also describes two new genera of African lorisids, *Komba*, from the Kiswahili name for species of *Galago*, and *Propotto*, from its evident similarity to the living Pottos. He concludes that these many new Miocene lorisids do not help much in closing the morphological gap between recent Lorisiformes and Eocene prosimians because in parts preserved they are only slightly more primitive than living relatives.

Stirton and Savage (1951) have contributed to knowledge of early platyrrhine monkeys in a study of a partial cranium of a Miocene Columbian primate *Cebupithecia*. Little definite information is available regarding earlier New World monkeys. Present evidences are that, by Miocene times, platyrrhines were of essentially modern type.

PLIOCENE

One of the most fascinating single finds in recent years was the skeleton of *Oreopithecus* recovered (1958) from the Grosseto lignites of Tuscany, Italy, by the Swiss paleontologist Hürzeler. This skeleton, as well as many more fragmentary specimens previously collected, comes from rocks deposited just after most scientists draw the Mio-Pliocene boundary and is, therefore, about 1.2×10^7 years old. Unlike all the remainder of pre-Pleistocene catarrhines, *Oreopithecus* possesses a number of dental and osteological characters that occur elsewhere only in undoubted hominids, such as relatively small canines, very short face, and broad pelvis. Careful analyses of some of these, and other features, have been made by Hürzeler (1954, 1958; and earlier) and by Butler (1959). Several studies now published help to clarify the problematic taxonomic position of this hominoid. Straus (1963) shows that hip and foot structure in this animal indicates that bipedal walking may have been possible. The form of the anterior inferior iliac spine and the large heel with reduced basal tubercle of calcaneus are more like the conformation seen in man in these regions than like any other hominoid. More recently, Kummer (1965) has emphasized that both femora of the 1958 *Oreopithecus* skeleton show laterally flexed distal condyles and a comparatively acute angle between the femoral shaft and the main axis of the femoral head and neck, both resemblances to bipedal man. Although aware of the possibility that these features could in part have been caused by crushing, he feels this unlikely to have occurred in the same manner on both sides. A consensus of current opinion is that this animal, if a hominid, is not on, or even very near, the ancestral line of living man. Such a conclusion is justified by a number of morphological features seen in this primate which would not be expected so late in man's ancestry, including marked increase in molar length posteriorly, highly cuspidate teeth, and long forelimbs. An alternative taxonomic placement which has wide support is to consider *Oreopithecus* as representing a separate hominoid family. Whatever its relationship to modern man may be, this find clearly raises the question: Do we really know what sort of anatomy to expect to find in a ten-million-year-old human ancestor? It should be mentioned in passing that, when contrasting this Tuscan primate with *Epipliopithecus* and the Miocene anthropoids of Kenya, it is well to remember that almost certainly *Oreopithecus* stands closer in time to the present day than it does to some at least of these earlier hominoids. Pronounced morphological alterations in various hominoid lines could have come about between early Miocene and the end of this epoch. *Oreopithecus* had comparatively long forearms and curved phalanges. Since the most distinctive skeletal alterations for brachiation among Anthropoidea are seen in the gibbon and siamang, one might expect to find more evidence of this in their Miocene forerunners. Instead, the earliest real elongation of the forelimb occurs later and in a possible hominid, *Oreopithecus*. However this may be, Hürzeler is to be commended for strikingly demonstrating the value of application to the task of collecting better osteological materials. If his example is followed elsewhere, students can look forward to the early accession of more extensive knowledge of the radiation and deployment of this order.

PLEISTOCENE

So many new reports on Pleistocene humans, and subhuman primates as well, have appeared in recent years that it is impossible to consider more than a few of the most significant early Pleistocene finds here. As they pertain to fossil man, the major middle to late Pleistocene discoveries have been discussed by LeGros Clark (1959). In general, it can be said that the extensive series of Pleistocene hominids now known gives evidence of a progressive morphological and temporal succession leading up to present-day man. No doubt many details of this sequence, so fascinating in an anthropocentric world, will be further refined, but the broad outlines of man's evolutionary development throughout most of the Pleistocene Epoch can now be drawn.

The beginning of the Pleistocene is today conventionally demarcated by the widespread appearance in the Old World of a characteristic fauna called the Villafranchian, at a time perhaps 2.0 to 2.5×10^6 years ago. It was apparently in this earliest part of the Pleistocene, in a world inhabited by an exotic series of giant mammals, as well as by the generally smaller ancestors of surviving forms, that the first modest evidences of human ingenuity appear. These take the form of crudely worked stone tools of a type called Oldowan pebble tools or pre-Chelles Acheul culture. Opinions vary as to the geographic distribution of this industry, but it may have occurred in Eurasia as well as at Olduvai Gorge and elsewhere in Africa. For decades, students of Paleolithic Man searched without clear success for an association of human remains with these earliest artifacts, and although a few tools of Oldowan type had been recovered from the South African brecchias containing *Australopithecus* (see Robinson and Mason 1957), it remained possible to question the assumption that *Australopithecus* was the tool-maker concerned.

All this was changed on July 17, 1959, when, at Olduvai Gorge in Tanzania, East Africa, a human skull which was almost complete, was found in association with a few tools, flint flakes, and parts of splintered bones of the animals upon which this "Oldowan Man" fed. The cranium, found by Mrs. Leakey, has been assigned (1959) by Dr. Leakey to a new genus *Zinjanthropus* ("Zinj" being an Arabic word for East Africa). Dr. Leakey has pointed out that *Zinjanthropus* shows distinct similarities to *Australopithecus*, and is an australopithecine, but these resemblances were not adequate in his opinion to indicate that the two types are congeneric. Later, most students came to realize that this was not a new genus but like the old familiar *Australopithecus* (or *Paranthropus*) *robustus* of South Africa. At first it seemed that this find, associated as it was with definite artifacts, demonstrated that the australopithecines could not be as far off the line of human ancestry as has somtimes been maintained. One of the most unique aspects of the original "*Zinjanthropus*" discovery is that the skull, a tibia, and perhaps other parts of the skeleton were in place on the living-floor inhabited by what were definably primitive men.

After further work at Olduvai, however, the Leakeys found evidence of another hominid species in Olduvai Bed I. These are by far the most ancient finds of hominid remains at camping sites in the open. Present evidence suggests that, in the early Pleistocene, man's ancestors did not know the use of fire, and therefore they probably did not consistently inhabit caves. Life in the open was apparently not conducive to the preservation of human remains at living sites, so that the majority of previous early finds, for instance those of Heidelburg, Swanscombe, Steinheim, and Java, consist of skeletal parts scattered by stream action. With luck, perhaps further very ancient associations of archaeological and osteological remains will be recovered from open sites; at least the finds at Olduvai Gorge show that this can be done.

More recently Leakey and his associates (1964) proposed the name *Homo habilis* for the second type of hominid found in Beds I and II Olduvai. To date, this taxon has not met with general acceptance, as has been discussed in some detail in Pilbeam and Simons (1965). Briefly, the situation is that the hominids from Olduvai Bed II included as paratypes of *H. habilis* are not the same morphologically and are perhaps almost a million years younger than the type jaw and other referred material from Bed I. Actually the Bed II hominids seem to be *Homo erectus* as is indicated by the detailed comparisons of Tobias and von Koenigswald (1964). As Robinson has repeatedly pointed out, most recently in 1965, the type mandible of *H. habilis* possesses all the morphological features of *Australopithecus*, not *Homo*. Robinson and a number of other scientists, including myself, have stressed the point of view that the minor differences from various *Australopithecus* specimens seen mainly in the premolars of the type specimen of *H. habilis* do not establish convincingly that this jaw is something other than a jaw of that genus. Moreover, compared to premolar size the lower canines in this type jaw are relatively huge for a hominid. This must be considered a primitive feature and is certainly not a resemblance to members of genus *Homo*. In any case, it is not a jaw that can be referred to the genus *Homo* unless the definition of this genus be enlarged to include all *Australopithecus* as well. Such a broad mandibular-dental definition of the genus is unworkable for it would cause one also to have to include *Ramapithecus* species (some of which date from the late Miocene) in the genus *Homo*. Nevertheless, in spite of these problems of terminology, the discovery of very ancient hominid material at Olduvai is particularly timely, coming as it does soon after the period in which two possible candidates as early Pleistocene ancestors of man, *Eoanthropus* and *Gigantopithecus*, were for different reasons eliminated from such a position.

The exposure as a forgery of the problematic Piltdown Man or "*Eoanthropus*" announced (1953) by Weiner, LeGros Clark, and Oakley requires little additional comment here, except to stress that elimination of this creature from the family tree removed a form with a morphology increasingly out of step with new finds of the last quarter century. Far from this detection being a scientific embarrassment, it demonstrated that, under the exacting scrutiny made possible by modern techniques, there is little need to suppose that deceptions of this sort will ever again pass unnoticed.

In connection with recent studies of mandibles of *Gigantopithecus* found *in situ* in caves in Kwangsi, South China (Pei 1957; Pei and Li 1959), it is advisable to consider the hypothesis of Weidenreich that the forms *Gigantopithecus, Meganthropus, Pithecanthropus* represent a successive evolutionary series of decreasing size. Pei suggests on the basis of faunal correlation that *Gigantopithecus* is of Villafrachian age and, insofar as such far-flung correlations have value, would therefore be an approximate contemporary of the australopithecines of Olduvai Bed I. Weidenreich's opinion that *Gigantopithecus* might stand in the line of human ancestry was derived from a few isolated teeth that were rather different from apes like *Dryopithecus*, but which also differ from *Australopithecus* and *Homo*. At that time (1946), when much less was known of the South African man-apes, such a conjecture was possible, but it has not been confirmed by the new South China mandibles. Following Weidenreich's idea that *Gigantopithecus* was a near-human type, Weinert suggested in 1950 that it should be called *Gigantanthropus*. Since this point has been brought up again more recently (Heberer 1959) perhaps it should be mentioned that, according to the international rules of nomenclature, changes of generic names as the taxonomic position of a given form is changed are not allowed, (see Linneus "Critica Botanica" 1737, aphorism 243). The report that *Gigantopithecus* and the large-jawed australopithecines were huge animals has been widely circulated, but has little basis. In the case of the latter group, such a conclusion has been seriously weakened by the absolute size of australopithecine pelves (now five in number) and other skeletal parts recovered in the past few years from the South African brecchias. These postcranial remains show that some australopithecines possessed, together with massive jaws, a body the size of a modern pigmy. Whether or not this was the case in *Gigantopithecus* remains purely speculative. Pei's opinion (1957) that *Gigantopithecus* does not belong among hominids gains support from the construction of a third jaw, described by Pei

TABLE 79.2
Partial or complete skulls of Tertiary fossil primates

Epoch and approx. years since beginning	Genus	Group	Continent
Pliocene 1.2×10^7	*Dolichopithecus*	cercopithecoid	Europe
	Libypithecus	cercopithecoid	Africa
	Mesopithecus	cercopithecoid	Europe, Africa
	*Oreopithecus**	hominoid	Europe
Miocene 2.6×10^7	*Cebupithecia**	ceboid	S. Amer.
	*Pliopithecus** [*Epipliopithecus*]	hominoid	Europe
	*Dryopithecus** [Proconsul]	hominoid	Africa
	*Progalago**	lorisiform prosimian	Africa
	*Komba**	lorisiform prosimian	Africa
	*Mioeuoticus**	lorisiform prosimian	Africa
Oligocene 4.0×10^7	Fayum frontal* [? *Apidium*]	catarrhine	Africa
	*Rooneyia**	prosimian	N. Amer.
	*Aegyptopithecus**	hominoid	Africa
Eocene 6.0×10^7	*Adapis*	prosimian	Europe
	Anchomomys	prosimian	Europe
	*Cynodontomys**	prosimian	N. Amer.
	*Hemiacodon**	prosimian	N. Amer.
	Microchoerus	prosimian	Europe
	*Microsyops**	prosimian	N. Amer.
	*Nannopithex** [Pseudoloris]		Europe
	Necrolemur	advanced prosimian	Europe
	Notharctus	prosimian	N. Amer.
	*Phenacolemur**	prosimian	N. Amer.
	Pronycticebus	prosimian	Europe
	*Protoadapis** [*Megatarsius*]	prosimian	Europe
	Pseudoloris	advanced prosimian	Europe
	*Smilodectes** [*Aphanolemur*]	prosimian	N. Amer.
	Tetonius	advanced prosimian	N. Amer.
Paleocene 7.5×10^7	*Plesiadapis**	prosimian	Europe
	*Palaechthon** (undescribed)	prosimian	N. Amer.

* Specimens identified, described or reassigned since 1950.

and Li (1958), which shows a short diastema behind the large lower canines, coupled with a slightly sectorial lower premolar following it. The creature possessed a simian shelf and elongate lower molars having distinct central constriction. On the other hand, the comparatively small and vertically placed incisors and curious wear on the lower canines suggest that the anterior upper dentition of *Gigantopithecus* may not have been particularly typical of apes at any stage, indicating a fairly long separate lineage for this Chinese primate. The possibility of a relationship with *Oreopithecus* should be examined.

A final issue that may be worth considering here is the question of the place of origin of mankind. Of course, this depends on how one defines humanity, but a second source of confusion derives from a rather widespread misunderstanding of species population distribution. Large mammals seldom occur in one place, being found throughout a large area. The prehistoric distribution of wolf, aurochs, horse, and lion are examples that come to mind. Taking the association of patterned tools with the hominids of Olduvai Bed I as evidence of the attainment of human status among australopithecines, it is then possible to consider the zoogeographic distribution of this group (rather than the disputed problem of occurrences of Oldowan artifacts), as evidence of the range of the earliest known humans. When this is done, the points made by Robinson (1953) in favor of *Meganthropus* from Java being congeneric with *Paranthropus* gain in importance. Since the latter is usually considered only a subgenus of *Australopithecus*, it becomes possible to maintain that distribution of this group stretched from South Africa to Southeast Asia. There has, however, been a general hesitancy to do this because of the fragmentary nature of the specimens of *Meganthropus*. Due to their proximity, one practice has been to rank *Meganthropus* as a subgenus of *Pithecanthropus*. *Pithecanthropus erectus* itself, however, is now commonly ranked only as a species of *Homo*, *H. erectus*. Description of a new hominid genus *Hemanthropus* by von Koenigswald (1957), based on a number of isolated upper and lower teeth from China drugstores, raises this issue anew. *Hemanthropus* is a *Paranthropus*-like form which evidently occurred in South China. Unless both of these assignments eventually prove to be incorrect, it would appear that australopithecine distribution covered a large area of the Old World. Clearly, more evidence will have to be recovered before theories as to which continent was the cradle of mankind gain a sound foundation.

REFERENCES

Ankel, F., 1965, Der Canalis Sacralis als Indikator für die Länge der Caudalregion der Primates: Folia Primatologica, v. 3, p. 263–276.

Arambourg, C., 1954, L'hominien fossile de Ternifine (Algerie): Acad. sci. [Paris] Comptes rendus, v. 239, p. 72–74.

Bishop, W. W., 1962, The mammalian fauna and geomorphological relations of the Napak volcanics, Karamoja: Geol. Survey Rec. [Uganda, Entebbe], 1957–58, p. 1–18.

Bohlin, B., 1946, The fossil mammals from the Tertiary of Tabun-buluk: Sino-Swedish Sci. Exped. N. W. Prov. [China] Rept., v. 6, p. 4.

Broom, R., and J. T. Robinson, 1949, A new type of fossil man: Nature, v. 164, p. 322.

———, 1950, Man contemporaneous with Swartkrans apeman: Am. Jour. Phys. Anthropology, v. 8, p. 151–155.

Burtschak-Abramovitsch, N. O., and E. G. Gabachvili, 1950, Discovery of a fossil anthropoid in Georgia: Priroda, v. 9, p. 70–72.

Butler, P. M., and J. R. E. Mills, 1959, A contribution to the odontology of *Oreopithecus*: British Mus. [Nat. Hist.] Geol. Bull., v. 4, no. 1, p. 1–26.

Cope, E. D., 1896, The primary factors of organic evolution: La Salle, Ill., Open Court Publishing Co.

Gazin, C. L., 1958, A review of the Middle and Upper Eocene Primates of North America: Smithsonian Misc. Colln., v. 136, no. 1, p. 1–112.

———, 1965, An endocranial cast of the Bridger Middle Eocene primate, *Smilodectes gracilis*: Smithsonian Misc. Colln., v. 149, no. 4, p. 1–14.

Herberer, G., 1959, The descent of Man and the present fossil record: Cold Spring Harbor Symposia on Quantitative Biology, v. 24, p. 235–244.

Huzeler, J., 1954, Zur systematischen Stellung von *Oreopithecus*: Naturf. Gesell. Basel Verh., v. 65, p. 88–95.

———, 1958, *Oreopithecus bambolii* Gervais, a preliminary report: Naturf. Gesell. Basel Verh., v. 69, p. 1–48.

Koenigswald, G. H. R. von, 1957, Remarks on *Gigantopithecus* and other hominoid remains from Southern China: Koninkl. Nederlandse

Akad. Wetensch. Proc., ser. B, v. 60, no. 3, p. 153–159.
Leakey, L. S. B., 1959, A new fossil skull from Olduvai: Nature, v. 184, p. 491–493.
———, 1962a, A new lower Pliocene fossil primate from Kenya: Ann. Mag. Nat. Hist., ser. 13, v. 4, p. 689–696.
———, 1962b (See Bishop, W. W.).
Leakey, L. S. B., P. V. Tobias, and J. R. Napier, 1964, A new species of the genus *Homo* from Olduvai Gorge, Tanganyika: Nature, v. 202, no. 4927, p. 7–9.
Le Gros Clark, W. E., 1956, A Miocene lemuroid skull from East Africa: British Mus. [Nat. Hist.] Fossil Mammals of Africa, v. 9, p. 1–6.
———, 1959, The crucial evidence for human evolution, Am. Sci., v. 47, no. 3, p. 229–313.
Le Gros Clark, W. E., and L. S. Leakey, 1951, The Miocene Hominoidea of East Africa: British Mus. [Nat. Hist.] Fossil Mammals of Africa, v. 1, p. 1–117.
Le Gros Clark, W. E. and D. P. Thomas, 1951, Associated jaws and limb bones of *Limnopithecus macinnesi:* British Mus. [Nat. Hist.] Fossil Mammals of Africa, v. 3, p. 1–27.
———, 1952, The Miocene lemuroids of East Africa: British Mus. [Nat. Hist.] Fossil Mammals of Africa, v. 5, p. 1–20.
MacInnes, D. G., 1943, Notes on the East African Miocene primates: East Africa Uganda Nat. Hist. Soc. Jour., v. 17, p. 141–181.
McKenna, M. C., 1960, Fossil Mammalia from the early Wasatchian Four Mile fauna, Eocene of Northwest Colorado: Univ. California Pub. Geol. Sci., v. 37, p. 1.
———, 1963, New evidence against tupaioid affinities of the mammalian family Anagalidae: Am. Mus. Novitates, no. 2158, p. 1–16.
———, 1966, Paleontology and the origin of the Primates: Folia Primatologica, v. 4, no. 1, p. 1–25.
Napier, J. R., and P. R. Davis, 1959, The fore-limb skeleton and associated remains of *Proconsul africanus:* British Mus. [Nat. Hist.] Fossil Mammals of Africa, v. 16, p. 1–69.
Pei, W. C., 1957, Discovery of *Gigantopithecus* mandibles and other material in Liu-Cheng district of central Kwangsi in south China: Vert. Palasiatica, v. 1, no. 2, p. 65–72.
Pei, W. C., and Y.-H. Li, 1959, Discovery of a third mandible of *Gigantopithecus* in Liu-Cheng, Kwangsi, south China: Vert. Palasiatica, v. 2, no. 4, p. 198–200.
Pilbeam, D. R., and E. L. Simons, 1965, Some problems of hominid classification: Am. Scientist, v. 53, no. 2, p. 237–259.
Remane, A., 1965, Die Geschichte der Menschenaffen, *in* Menschliche Abstammungslehae: Jena, Fischer, p. 249–309.
Robinson, J. T., 1953, *Meganthropus,* australopithecines, and hominids: Am. Jour. Phys. Anthropology, v. 11, p. 1–38.
———, 1965, *Homo 'habilis'* and the asutralopithecines: Nature, v. 205, no. 4967, p. 121–124.
Robinson, J. T., and R. J. Mason, 1957, Occurrence of stone artifacts with *Australopithecus* at Sterkfontein: Nature, v. 180, p. 521–524.
Russell, D. E., 1960, Le crane de *Plesiadapis;* note preliminaire: Soc. géol. France Bull., ser. 7, v. 1, no. 3, p. 312–314.
Simons, E. L., 1959, An anthropoid frontal bone from the Fayum Oligocene of Egypt—the oldest skull fragment of a higher primate: Am. Mus. Novitates, no. 1976, p. 1–16.
———, 1961a, Notes on a Eocene tarsioids and a revision of some Necrolemurinae: British Mus. [Nat. Hist.] Geol. Bull., v. 5, no. 3, p. 45–69.
———, 1961b, An anthropoid mandible from the Oligocene Fayum beds of Egypt: Am. Mus. Novitates, no. 2051, p. 1–5.
———, 1961c, The dentition of *Ourayia*—its bearing on relationships of omomyid prosimians: Postilla, no. 54, p. 1–20.
———, 1961d, The phyletic position of *Ramapithecus:* Postilla, no. 57, p. 1–9.
———, 1962a, A new Eocene primate *Cantius,* and a revision of early Cenozoic lemuroids of Europe: British Mus. [Nat. Hist.] Geol. Bull., v. 7, p. 1–36.
———, 1962b, Two new primate species from the African Oligocene: Postilla, no. 64, p. 1–12.
———, 1963a, A critical reappraisal of Tertiary Primates *in* J. Buettner-Janusch, ed., Genetic and evolutionary biology of the primates: New York, Academic Press, p. 65–129.
———, 1963b, Current research on fossil vertebrates in India: Soc. Vertebrate Paleontology Bull., June 1963, p. 5–7.
———, 1963c, Some fallacies in the study of hominid phylogeny: Science, v. 141, no. 3548, p. 879–889.
———, 1964a, On the mandible of *Ramapithecus:* [U.S.] Natl. Acad. Sci. Proc., v. 51, no. 3, p. 528–535.
———, 1965, New fossil apes from Egypt and the initial differentiation of Hominoidea: Nature, v. 205, no. 4967, p. 135–139.
Simons, E. L., and D. R. Pilbeam, 1965, Preliminary revision of Dryopithecinae (Pongidae, Anthropoidea): Folia Primatologica, v. 3, nos. 2–3, p. 1–70.
Simons, E. L., and D. E. Russell, 1960, The cranial anatomy of *Necrolemur breviora:* Mus. Comp. Zoology Harvard Coll. Bull., v. 127, p. 1–14.
Simpson, G. G., 1945, The principles of classification and a classification of mammals: Am. Mus. Nat. Hist. Bull., v. 85, p. 1–350.
———, 1955, The Phenacolemuridae, new family of early primates: Am. Mus. Nat. Hist. Bull., v. 105, p. 415–441.
———, 1967, The Tertiary lorisiform primates of Africa: Mus. Comp. Zoology Harvard Coll. Bull., v. 136, no. 3, p. 39–61.
Stirton, R. A., and D. E. Savage, 1951, A new monkey from the La Venta late Miocene of

Columbia: Ministerio Minas Petroleos Servicio Geol. Nac. Compilacion Estudios Geol. Oficales Columbia, v. 7, p. 347–356.

Straus, W. L., Jr., 1963, The classification of *Oreopithecus, in* Classification and human evolution: Viking Fund Pub. Anthropology, v. 37, p. 146–177.

Thenius, E., 1954, Die Bedeutung von *Austriacopithecus* Ehrenberg für die Stammesgeschichte der Hominoidea: Österreichischen Akad. Wiss. Mat.-Naturw. Kl. Anz., v. 13, p. 191–196.

———, 1958, Tertiärstratigraphie und tertiäre Hominoidenfunde: Anthropol. Anz., v. 22, no. 1, p. 66–77.

Tobias, P. V. and G. H. R. Von Koenigswald, 1964, A comparison between the Olduvai hominines and those of Java and some implications for hominid phylogeny: Nature, v. 204, no. 4958, p. 515–518.

Weidenreich, F., 1946, Apes, giants, and men: Chicago, University of Chicago Press.

Wilson, J. A., 1966, A new primate from the earliest Oligocene, west Texas—preliminary report: Folia Primatologica, v. 4, p. 227–248.

Woo, J.-K., 1957, *Dryopithecus* teeth from Keiyuan, Yunnan province: Vert. Palasiatica, v. 1, p. 25–32.

———, 1958, New materials of *Dryopithecus* from Keiyuan, Yunnan: Vert. Palasiatica, v. 2, no. 1, p. 38–42.

Zapfe, H., 1958, The skeleton of *Pliopithecus* (*Epipliopithecus*) *vindobonensis:* Am. Jour. Phys. Anthropology, v. 16, p. 441–458.

———, 1960, Die Primatenfunde aus der miozänaen Spaltenfüllung von Neudorf an. der March: Schweizerische Palaeontol. Abh., v. 78, p. 1–293.

The Distribution of Man

WILLIAM W. HOWELLS

1960

Men with chins, relatively small brow ridges and small facial skeletons, and with high, flat-sided skulls, probably appeared on earth in the period between the last two great continental glaciers, say from 150,000 to 50,000 years ago. If the time of their origin is blurred, the place is no less so. The new species doubtless emerged from a number of related populations distributed over a considerable part of the Old World. Thus *Homo sapiens* evolved as a species and began to differentiate into races at the same time.

In any case, our direct ancestor, like his older relatives, was at once product and master of the crude pebble tools that primitive human forms had learned to use hundreds of thousands of years earlier. His inheritance also included a social organization and some level of verbal communication.

Between these hazy beginnings and the agricultural revolution of about 10,000 years ago *Homo sapiens* radiated over most of the earth, and differentiated into clearly distinguishable races. The processes were intimately related. Like the forces that had created man, they reflected both the workings of man's environment and of his own invention. So much can be said with reasonable confidence. The details are another matter. The when, where and how of the origin of races puzzle us not much less than they puzzled Charles Darwin.

A little over a century ago a pleasingly simple explanation of races enjoyed some popularity. The races were separate species, created by God as they are today. The Biblical account of Adam and Eve was meant to apply only to Caucasians. Heretical as the idea might be, it was argued that the Negroes appearing in Egyptian monuments, and the skulls of the ancient Indian mound-builders of Ohio, differed in no way from their living descendants, and so there could have been no important change in the only slightly longer time since the Creation itself, set by Archbishop Ussher at 4004 B.C.

With his *Origin of Species*, Darwin undid all this careful "science" at a stroke. Natural

From *Scientific American,* vol. 203, no. 3, pp. 112–127 (*Scientific American* Offprint 604).

selection and the immense stretch of time provided by the geological time-scale made gradual evolution seem the obvious explanation of racial or species differences. But in his later book, *The Descent of Man,* Darwin turned his back on his own central notion of natural selection as the cause of races. He there preferred sexual selection, or the accentuation of racial features through long-established ideals of beauty in different segments of mankind. This proposition failed to impress anthropologists, and so Darwin's demolishing of the old views left something of a void that has never been satisfactorily filled.

Not for want of trying. Some students continued, until recent years, to insist that races are indeed separate species, or even separate genera, with Whites descended from chimpanzees, Negroes from gorillas and Mongoloids from orangutans. Darwin himself had already argued against such a possibility when a contemporary proposed that these same apes had in turn descended from three different monkey species. Darwin pointed out that so great a degree of convergence in evolution, producing thoroughgoing identities in detail (as opposed to, say, the superficial resemblance of whales and fishes) simply could not be expected. The same objection applies to a milder hypothesis, formulated by the late Franz Weidenreich during the 1940's (Figure 80.1). Races, he held, descended separately, not from such extremely divergent parents as the several great apes, but from the less-separated lines of fossil men. For example, Peking man led to the Mongoloids, and Rhodesian man to the "Africans." But again there are more marked distinctions between those fossil men than between living races.

Actually the most reasonable—I should say the only reasonable—pattern suggested by animal evolution in general is that of racial divergence within a stock already possessing distinctive features of *Homo sapiens* (Figure 80.2). As I have indicated, such a stock had appeared at the latest by the beginning of the last glacial advance and almost certainly much earlier, perhaps by the end of the preceding glaciation, which is dated at some 150,000 years ago.

Even if fossil remains were more plentiful than they are, they might not in themselves decide the questions of time and place much more accurately. By the time *Homo sapiens* was common enough to provide a chance of our finding some of his fossil remains, he was probably already sufficiently widespread as to give only a general idea of his "place of origin." Moreover, bones and artifacts may concentrate in misleading places. (Consider the parallel case of the australopithecine "manapes" known so well from the Lower Pleistocene of South Africa. This area is thought of as their home. In fact the region actually was a geographical *cul-de-sac,* and merely a good fossil trap at that time. It is now clear that such prehumans were widespread not only in Africa but also in Asia. We have no real idea of their first center of dispersion, and we should assume that our earliest knowledge of them is not from the actual dawn of their existence.)

In attempting to fix the emergence of modern races of man somewhat more precisely we can apply something like the chronological reasoning of the pre-Darwinians. The Upper Paleolithic invaders of Europe (e.g., the Cro-Magnons) mark the definite entrance of *Homo sapiens,* and these men were already stamped with a "White" racial nature at about 35,000 B.C. But a recently discovered skull from Liukiang in China, probably of the same order of age, is definitely not Caucasian, whatever else it may be. And the earliest American fossil men, perhaps 20,000 years old, are recognizable as Indians. No other remains are certainly so old; we cannot now say anything about the first Negroes. Thus racial differences are definitely older than 35,000 years. And yet —this is sheer guess—the more successful *Homo sapiens* would probably have overcome the other human types, such as Neanderthal and Rhodesian men, much earlier if he had reached his full development long before. But these types survived well into the last 50,000 years. So we might assume that *Homo sapiens,* and his earliest racial distinctions, is a product of the period between the last two glaciations, coming into his own early during the last glaciation.

When we try to envisage the causes of racial development, we think today of four factors: natural selection, genetic drift, mutation and mixture (interbreeding). With regard to basic divergence at the level of races, the first two are undoubtedly the chief determinants. If

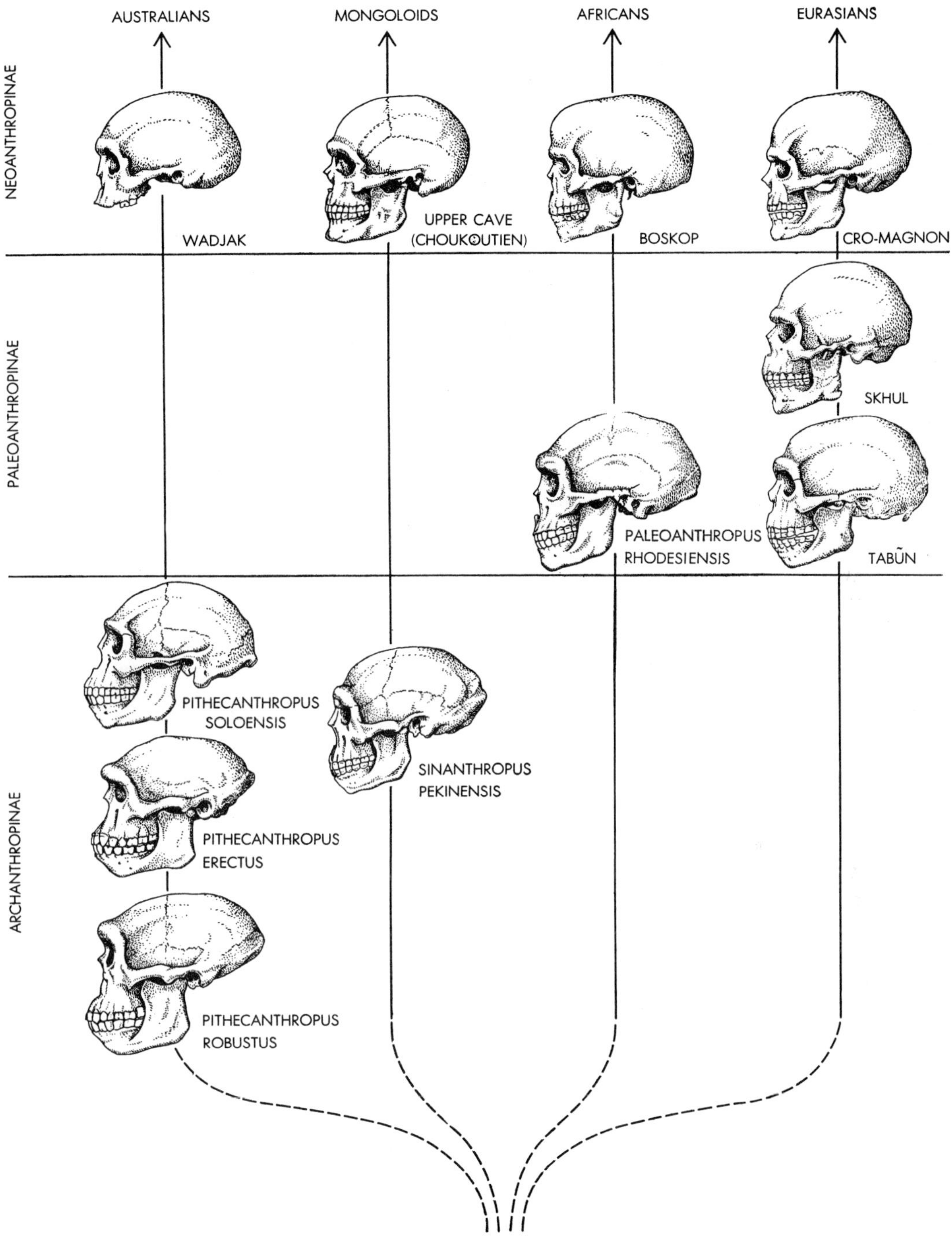

FIGURE 80.1
Polyphyletic school of anthropology. Chiefly identified with Franz Weidenreich; conceives modern races of man descending from four ancestral lines. According to this school, ancestors of Australians (*left*) include *Pithecanthropus soloensis* (Solo man) and *Pithecanthropus erectus* (Java man). Original ancestor of Mongoloids is *Sinanthropus pekinensis* (Peking man); of Africans, *Paleoanthropus rhodesiensis* (Rhodesian man). Four skulls at top are early *Homo sapiens*. [*Pithecanthropus robustus* is now usually referred to *Australopithecus*, and *P. erectus, P. soloensis, Sinanthropus pekinensis*, and *Paleoanthropus rhodesiensis* to the genus *Homo*, commonly to the single species *H. erectus*.—P.C.]

forces of any kind favor individuals of one genetic complexion over others, in the sense that they . . . reproduce more successfully, the favored individuals will necessarily increase their bequest of genes to the next generation relative to the rest of the population. That is selection; a force with direction.

Genetic drift is a force without direction, an accidental change in the gene proportions of a population. Other things being equal, some parents just have more offspring than others. If such variations can build up, an originally homogeneous population may split into two different ones by chance. . . .

Both drift and selection should have stronger effects the smaller and more isolated the population. It is easy to imagine them in action among bands of ancient men, living close to nature. (It would be a great mistake, however, to imagine that selection is not also effective in modern populations.) Hence we can look upon racial beginnings as part accident, part design, design meaning any pattern of minor change obedient to natural selection.

Darwin was probably right the first time, then, and natural selection is more important in racial adaptation than he himself later came to think. Curiously, however, it is extremely difficult to find demonstrable, or even logically appealing, adaptive advantages in racial features. The two leading examples of adaptation in human physique are not usually considered racial at all. One is the tendency among warm-blooded animals of the same species to be larger in colder parts of their territory. As an animal of a given shape gets larger, its inner bulk increases faster than its outer surface, so the ratio of heat produced to heat dissipated is higher in larger individuals. It has, indeed, been shown that the average body weight of man goes up as annual mean temperature goes down, speaking very broadly, and considering those populations that have remained where they are a long time. The second example concerns the size of extremities (limbs, ears, muzzles). They are smaller in colder parts of the range and larger in warmer, for the same basic reason—heat conservation and dissipation. Man obeys this rule also, producing lanky, long-limbed populations in hot deserts and dumpy, short-limbed peoples in the Arctic.

This does not carry us far with the major, historic races as we know them. Perhaps the most striking of all racial features is the dark skin of Negroes. The color of Negro skin is due to a concentration of melanin, the universal human pigment that diffuses sunlight and screens out its damaging ultraviolet component. Does it not seem obvious that in the long course of time the Negroes, living astride the Equator in Africa and in the western Pacific, developed their dark skins as a direct response to a strong sun? It makes sense. It would be folly to deny that such an adaptation is present. But a great deal of the present Negro habitat is shade forest and not bright sun, which is in fact strongest in the deserts some distance north of the Equator. The Pygmies are decidedly forest dwellers, not only in Africa but in their several habitats in southeastern Asia as well.

At any rate there is enough doubt to have called forth other suggestions. One is that forest hunters needed protective coloration, both for stalking and for their protection from predators; dark skin would have lowest visibility in the patchy light and shade beneath the trees. Another is that densely pigmented skins may have other qualities—e.g., resistance to infection—of which we are unaware.

A more straightforward way out of the dilemma is to suppose that the Negroes are actually new to the Congo forest, and that they served their racial apprenticeship hunting and fishing in the sunny grasslands of the southern Sahara. If so, their Pygmy relatives might represent the first accommodation of the race to the forest, before agriculture but after dark skin had been acquired. Smaller size certainly makes a chase after game through the undergrowth less exhausting and faster. As for woolly hair, it is easy to see it (still without proof) as an excellent, nonmatting insulation against solar heat. Thick Negro lips? Every suggestion yet made has a zany sound. They may only be a side effect of some properties of heavily pigmented skin (ability to produce thick scar tissue, for example), even as blond hair is doubtless a side effect of the general depigmentation of men that has occurred in northern Europe.

At some remove racially from Negroes and Pygmies are the Bushmen and Hottentots of

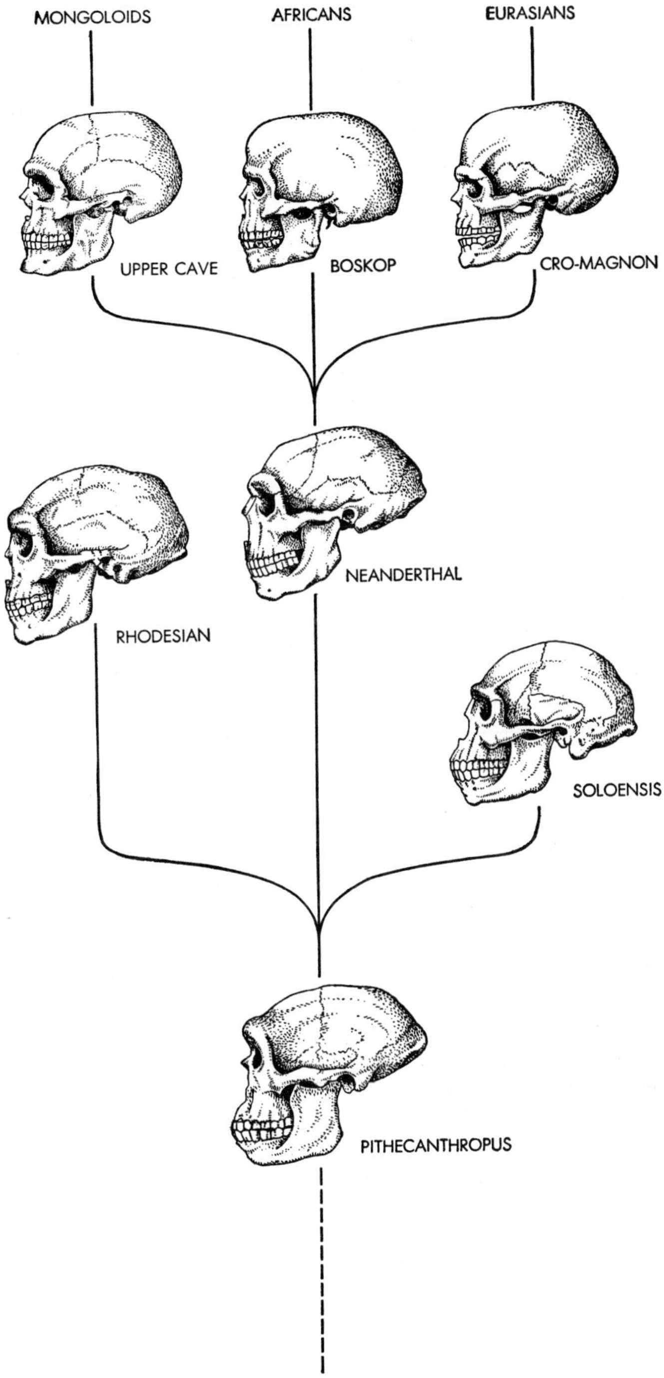

FIGURE 80.2
Unilinear or "hat-rack" school of anthropology. Predicates three races descending from single ancestral line, as opposed to polyphyletic theory of Figure 80.1. Rhodesian, Neanderthal, and Solo man all descend from *Pithecanthropus*. Neanderthal is ancestor of early *Homo sapiens* (Upper Cave, Boskop and Cro-Magnon) from which modern races descended. [See Figure 80.1. for nomenclatural note.]

southern Africa. They are small, or at least lightly built, with distinctive wide, small, flat faces; they . . . have a five-cornered skull outline that seems to be an ancient inheritance. Their skin is yellowish-brown, not dark. None of this has been clearly interpreted, although the small size is thought to be an accommodation to water and food economy in the arid environment. The light skin, in an open sunny country, contradicts the sun-pigment theory, and has in fact been used in favor of the protective-coloration hypothesis. Bushmen and background blend beautifully for color, at least as human beings see color.

Bushmen, and especially Hottentots, have another dramatic characteristic: steatopygia. If they are well nourished, the adult women accumulate a surprising quantity of fat on their buttocks. This seems to be a simple storehouse mechanism reminiscent of the camel's hump; a storehouse that is not distributed like a blanket over the torso generally, where it would be disadvantageous in a hot climate. The characteristic nicely demonstrates adaptive selection working in a human racial population.

The Caucasians make the best argument for skin color as an ultraviolet screen. They extend from cloudy northern Europe, where the ultraviolet in the little available sunlight is not only acceptable but desirable, down to the fiercely sun-baked Sahara and peninsular India. All the way, the correspondence with skin color is good: blond around the Baltic, swarthy on the Mediterranean, brunet in Africa and Arabia, dark brown in India. Thus, given a long enough time of occupation, and doubtless some mixture to provide dark-skinned genes in the south, natural selection could well be held responsible.

On the other hand, the Caucasians' straight faces and often prominent noses lack any evident adaptive significance. It is the reverse with the Mongoloids, whose countenances form a coherent pattern that seems consistent with their racial history. From the standpoint of evolution it is Western man, not the Oriental, who is inscrutable. The "almond" eyes of the Mongoloid are deeply set in protective fat-lined lids, the nose and forehead are flattish and the cheeks are broad and fat-padded. In every way, it has been pointed out, this is an ideal mask to protect eyes, nose and sinuses against bitterly cold weather. Such a face is the pole toward which the peoples of eastern Asia point, and it reaches its most marked and uniform expression in the cold northeastern part of the continent, from Korea north.

Theoretically the Mongoloid face developed under intense natural selection some time during the last glacial advance among peoples trapped north of a ring of mountain glaciers and subjected to fierce cold, which would have weeded out the less adapted, in the most classic Darwinian fashion, through pneumonia and sinus infections. If the picture is accurate, this face type is the latest major human adaptation. It could not be very old. For one thing, the population would have had to reach a stage of advanced skill in hunting and living to survive at all in such cold, a stage probably not attained before the Upper Paleolithic (beginning about 35,000 B.C.). For another, the adaptation must have occurred after the American Indians, who are Mongoloid but without the transformed face, migrated across the Bering Strait. (Only the Eskimos reflect the extension of full-fledged, recent Mongoloids into America.) All this suggests a process taking a relatively small number of generations (about 600) between 25,000 and 10,000 B.C.

The discussion so far has treated human beings as though they were any mammal under the influence of natural selection and the other forces of evolution. It says very little about

FIGURE 80.3
Distribution of man and his races in three epochs. Dark gray areas in *A* represent glaciers. According to available evidence, it is believed that by 8000 B.C. (*A*) early Mongoloids had already spread from the Old World to the New World, while late Mongoloids inhabited a large part of northern Asia. Distribution in A.D. 1000 (*B*) has late Mongoloids dominating Asia, northern Canada, and southern Greenland, and early Mongoloids dominating the Americas. The Pygmies and Bushmen of Africa began a decline that has continued up to the present. The present distribution of races of man (*C*) reflects dominance of White, late Mongoloid, and Negro races. Diffusion of Whites has been attended by decline of early Mongoloids in America, Bushmen in Africa, and indigenous population in Australia. Narrow band of Whites in Asia represents Russian colonization of southern Siberia.

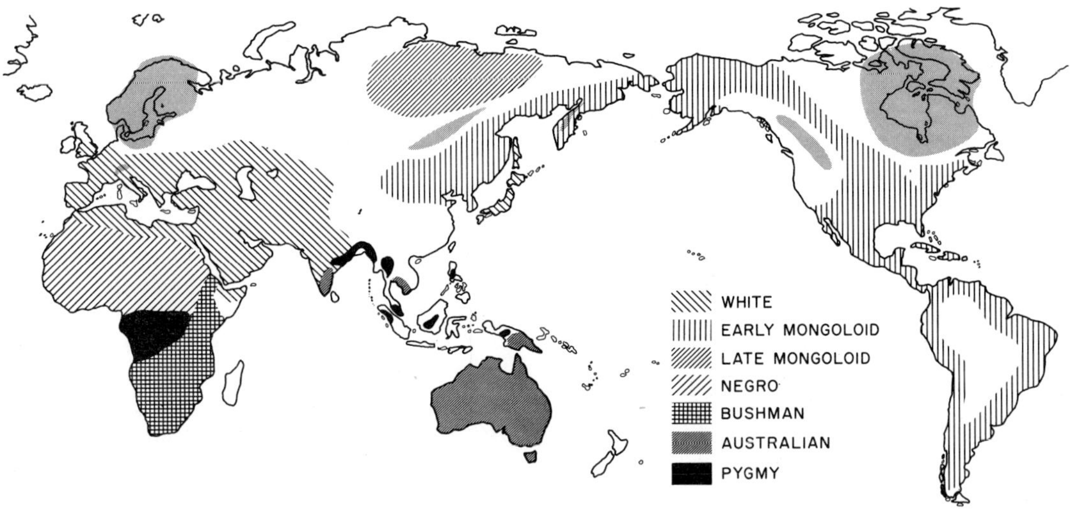
WHITE
EARLY MONGOLOID
LATE MONGOLOID
NEGRO
BUSHMAN
AUSTRALIAN
PYGMY

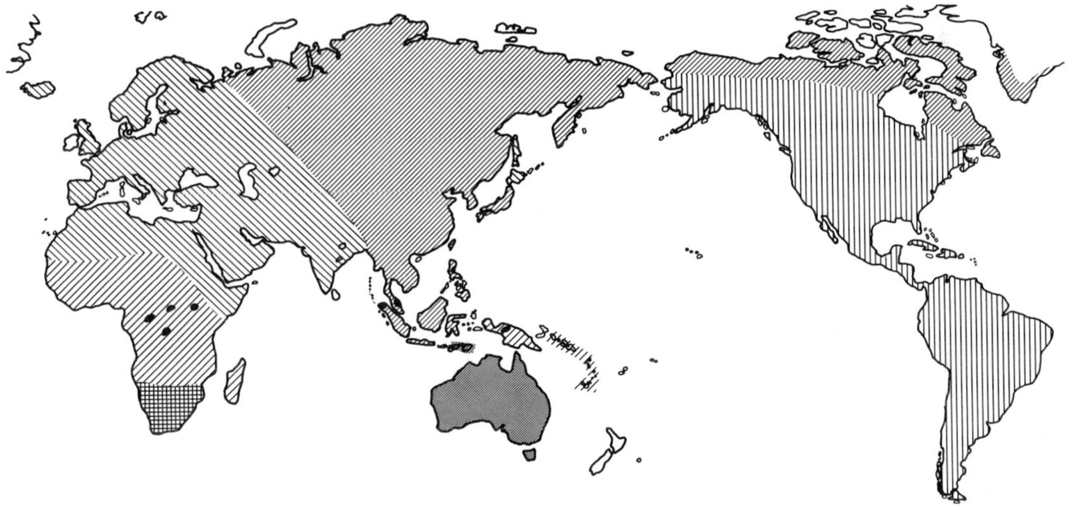

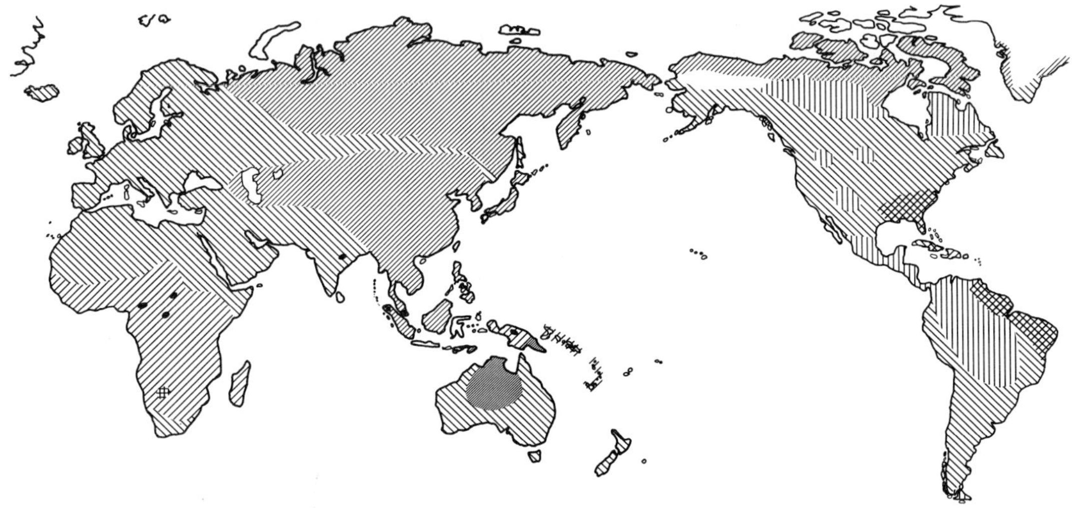

why man invaded the various environments that have shaped him and how he got himself distributed in the way we find him now. For an understanding of these processes we must take into account man's own peculiar abilities. He has created culture, a milieu for action and development that must be added to the simplicities of sun, snow, forest or plain.

Let us go back to the beginning. Man started as an apelike creature, certainly vegetarian, certainly connected with wooded zones, limited like all other primates to tropical or near-tropical regions. In becoming a walker he had begun to extend his range. Tools, social rules and intelligence all progressed together; he learned to form efficient groups, armed with weapons not provided by nature. He started to eat meat, and later to cook it; the more concentrated diet widened his possibilities for using his time; the hunting of animals beckoned him still farther in various directions.

All this was probably accomplished during the small-brained australopithecine stage. It put man on a new plane, with the potential to reach all parts of the earth, and not only those in which he could find food ready to his hand, or be comfortable in his bare skin. He did not actually reach his limits until the end of the last glaciation, and in fact left large tracts empty for most of the period. By then he had become *Homo sapiens*, with a large brain. He had tools keen enough to give him clothes of animal skin. He had invented projectiles to widen the perimeter of his striking power: bolas, javelins with spear throwers, arrows with bows. He was using dogs to widen the perimeter of his senses in tracking. He had found what could be eaten from the sea and its shores. He could move only slowly, and was probably by no means adventurous. But hunting territory was precious, and the surplus of an expanding population had to stake out new preserves wherever there was freedom ahead. So this pressure, and man's command of nature, primitive though it still was, sent the hunters of the end of the Ice Age throughout the Old World, out into Australia, up into the far north, over the Bering Strait and down the whole length of the Americas to Tierra del Fuego. At the beginning of this dispersion we have brutes barely able to shape a stone tool; at the end, the wily, self-reliant Eskimo, with his complicated traps, weapons and sledges and his clever hunting tricks.

The great racial radiation carried out by migratory hunters culminated in the world as it was about 10,000 years ago (Figure 80.3 A). The Whites occupied Europe, northern and eastern Africa and the Near East, and extended far to the east in Central Asia toward the Pacific shore. Negroes occupied the Sahara, better watered then, and Pygmies the African equatorial forest; south, in the open country, were Bushmen only. Other Pygmies, the Negritos, lived in the forests of much of India and southeastern Asia; while in the open country of these areas and in Australia were men like the present Australian aborigines: brown, beetle-browed and wavy-haired. Most of the Pacific was empty. People such as the American Indians stretched from China and Mongolia over Alaska to the Straits of Magellan; the more strongly Mongoloid peoples had not yet attained their domination of the Far East.

During the whole period the human population had depended on the supply of wild game for food, and the accent had been on relative isolation of peoples and groups. Still close to nature (as we think of nature), man was in a good position for rapid small-scale evolution, both through natural selection and through the operation of chance in causing differences among widely separated tribes even if selection was not strong.

Then opened the Neolithic period, the beginning of a great change. Agriculture was invented, at first inefficient and feeble, but in our day able to feed phenomenally large populations while freeing them from looking for food. The limit on local numbers of people was gradually removed, and with it the necessity for the isolation and spacing of groups and the careful observation of boundaries. Now, as there began to be surpluses available for trading, connections between communities became more useful. Later came a spreading of bonds from higher centers of trade and of authority (Figure 80.3 B). Isolation gave way to contact, even when contact meant war.

The change was not speedy by our standards, though in comparison with the pace of the Stone Age it seems like a headlong rush. The new economy planted people much more solidly, of course. Farmers have been uprooting and displacing hunters from the time of the first planters to our own day (Figure 80.3 C), when Bushman survivors are still losing reservation land to agriculturalists in southwestern Africa. These Bushmen, a scattering of Australian aborigines, the Eskimos and a few other groups are the only representatives of their age still in place. On the other hand, primitive representatives of the Neolithic level of farming still live in many places after the thousands of years since they first became established there.

Nevertheless mobility increased and has increased ever since. Early woodland farmers were partly nomadic, moving every generation following exhaustion of the soil, however solidly fixed they may have been during each sojourn. The Danubians of 6,000 years ago can be traced archeologically as they made the same kind of periodic removes as central Africans, Iroquois Indians and pioneer Yankee farmers. Another side of farming—animal husbandry—gave rise to pastoral nomadism. Herders were much lighter of foot, and historically have tended to be warlike and domineering. With irrigation, villages could settle forever and evolve into the urban centers of high civilizations. Far from immobilizing man, however, these centers served as fixed bases from which contact (and conflict) worked outward.

The rest of the story is written more clearly. New crops or new agricultural methods opened new territories, such as equatorial Africa, and the great plains of the U.S., never successfully farmed by the Indians. New materials such as copper and tin made places once hopeless for habitation desirable as sources of raw material or as way stations for trade. Thus an island like Crete rose from nothing to dominate the eastern Mediterranean for centuries. Well before the earliest historians had made records, big population shifts were taking place. Our mental picture of the aboriginal world is actually a recent one. The Bantu Negroes moved into central and southern Africa, peoples of Mongoloid type went south through China and into Japan, and ancient folk of Negrito and Australoid racial nature were submerged by Caucasians in India. Various interesting but inconsequential trickles also ran hither and yon; for example, the migration of the Polynesians into the far Pacific.

The greatest movement came with the advent of ocean sailing in Europe. (The Polynesians had sailed the high seas earlier, of course, but they had no high culture, nor did Providence interpose a continent across their route at a feasible distance, as it did for Columbus.) The Europeans poured out on the world. From the 15th to the 19th centuries they compelled other civilized peoples to accept contact, and subjected or erased the uncivilized. So today, once again, we have a quite different distribution of mankind from that of 1492.

It seems obvious that we stand at the beginning of still another phase. Contact is immediate, borders are slamming shut and competition is fierce. Biological fitness in races is now hard to trace, and even reproduction is heavily controlled by medicine and by social values. The racial picture of the future will be determined less by natural selection and disease resistances than by success in government and in the adjustment of numbers. The end of direct European dominance in Africa and Asia seems to mean the end of any possibility of the infiltration and expansion of the European variety of man there, on the New World model. History as we know it has been largely the expansion of the European horizon and of European peoples. But the end in China of mere absorption of Occidental invention, and the passionate self-assertion of the African tribes, make it likely that racial lines and territories will again be more sharply drawn than they have been for centuries. What man will make of himself next is a question that lies in the province of prophets, not anthropologists.

BIBLIOGRAPHY

Coon, Carleton S., 1954, The story of man: New York, Alfred A. Knopf.

Coon, Carleton S., Stanley M. Garn, and Joseph B. Birdsell, 1950, Races—a study of the problems of race formation in man: Springfield, Ill., Charles C. Thomas.

Gates, Reginald Ruggles, 1948, Human ancestry from a genetical point of view: Cambridge, Mass., Harvard University Press.

Howells, William White, 1959, Mankind in the making: New York, Doubleday.

81

The Biological Nature of Man

GEORGE GAYLORD SIMPSON

1966

It has often and confidently been asserted, that man's origin can never be known: but ignorance more frequently begets confidence than does knowledge: it is those who know little, and not those who know much, who so positively assert that this or that problem will never be solved by science. [1]

Those words were written by Charles Darwin nearly 100 years ago and were published in 1871 in the introduction to his book on *The Descent of Man.* In his even better known work on *The Origin of Species* [2], which had appeared 12 years earlier, he had been content to say (somewhat coyly) that by that work "light would be thrown on the origin of man and his history." Others soon indicated the nature of that light. Thomas Henry Huxley's classic *Man's Place in Nature* [3] was published in 1863, and by 1871 numerous other naturalists of the first rank had already accepted the evolutionary origin of the human species. Darwin's own contribution to the problem of man's origin firmly established two points: first, *Homo sapiens,* like all other organisms, has evolved from prior, extremely different species by natural means and under the directive influence of natural selection; and second, man is the descendant of apes or monkeys of the Old World.

Darwin's first point, that man is the product of evolution involving natural selection, has been attacked on emotional grounds, but it was not and is not now honestly questionable on strictly scientific grounds and by anyone really familiar with the facts. The second point, of man's descent from an Old World ape or monkey, was for some time more open to scientific dispute. However, here, too, the debate was often more emotional than objective. In some pedagogic circles it became usual to maintain that man is not descended from an ape but from a common ancestor neither man nor ape nor, if one cared to go still further afield, monkey. Some went so far as to attempt to enlist Darwin posthumously in their own pussyfooting ranks by saying that he never maintained that man arose from an ape

 Originally published in *Science,* vol. 152, pp. 472–478, 1966.

but only from a common ancestor . . . and so forth. In fact, although Darwin was slow to enter the dispute, when he did so he was more honest than those supposed defenders. He flatly said, "We must conclude, however much the conclusion may revolt our pride, that our early progenitors would have been properly . . . designated [as apes or monkeys]." The unscientific and really uncalled-for remark on pride does little to modify the forthrightness of the conclusion.

Darwin's conclusions in 1871 already covered what is most vital for consideration of man's biological status. Subsequent discovery and study have fully corroborated Darwin and have added an enormous amount of detail. That is interesting and important, and most of what I have to say here concerns it. At this point, however, the essential thing is that Darwin put the whole subject of the nature of man on a new and sound footing. To be sure, in the introduction of *The Descent of Man*, from which I have already quoted, Darwin went on to say that, "The conclusion that man is the codescendant with other species of some ancient, lower, and extinct form, is not in any degree new." He then cited Lamarck, Wallace, Huxley, Lyell, Vogt, Lubbock, Büchner, Rolle, Haeckel, Canestrini, and Barrago as "having taken the same side of the question." In fact, as regards this particular point, Darwin was doing too much honor to those worthies, some still famous and some now forgotten. It is true that they had all discussed the descent of man before Darwin himself did so in an explicit way, but with the sole exception of Lamarck they had done so after publication of *The Origin of Species* and on the basis of that work by Darwin. As for the few who really had postulated an evolutionary origin for man before *The Origin of Species*, their views were largely philosophical speculations inadequately or not at all supported by objective evidence and sometimes, as in the case of Lamarck, reaching a conclusion only approximately correct on grounds that were flatly wrong [4].

WHAT IS MAN?

The question "What is man?" is probably the most profound that can be asked by man. It has always been central to any system of philosophy or of theology. We know that it was being asked by the most learned humans 2000 years ago, and it is just possible that it was being asked by the most brilliant australopithecines 2 million years ago. The point I want to make now is that all attempts to answer that question before 1859 are worthless and that we will be better off if we ignore them completely. The reason is that no answer had a solid, objective base until it was recognized that man is the product of evolution from primeval apes and before that through billions of years of gradual but protean change from some spontaneously, that is, naturally, generated primordial monad.

It is the biological nature of man, both in his evolutionary history and in his present condition, that presents us with our only fixed point of departure. These are the facts we can find out for ourselves, in great, ever-increasing detail and soundness, open to all of us in irrefutable observations. Their interpretation is in some respects ambiguous and disputable, but interpretation at a given point becomes increasingly clear and undisputed as time goes on. Doubtfulness moves outward with the expanding frontier of knowledge.

I do not mean to say that the biological study of man or even that the scientific study of man in terms broader than biological can here and now—if ever—provide a satisfactorily complete answer to the question "What is man?" The other, older approaches through metaphysics, theology, art, and other nonbiological, nonscientific fields can still contribute, or can now contribute anew. But unless they accept, by specification or by implication, the nature of man as a biological organism, they are merely fictional fancies or falsities, however interesting they may be in those nonfactual categories. I am here concerned with man's biological nature in a rather broad sense, on the grounds that this is a necessary, even though it is not a completely sufficient, approach to comprehension of man's nature.

Already in Darwin's day it was clearly established that among living animals the great apes are anatomically most similar to man. Some anatomists, reluctant to acknowledge their poor relatives, stressed differences between man and any apes: the larger human brain, obviously; the longer and less divergent first toe of man; the absence or, more commonly, the only-sporadic presence in us of certain apish muscles and other structures. Such discussions completely missed the point. Of course men and apes differ. In itself, that means only that we belong to different species. The point at issue is not whether we differ, but in what way and how closely the different species are related.

All later study has corroborated the special relationship between men and apes and has made knowledge of it more precise. The evidence has lately been greatly increased in extent, in detail, and in its basic character. It now includes such fundamental points as the numbers and shapes of chromosomes, the exact molecular structure of hemoglobins, the resemblances and differences of serum proteins, and many others [5]. All the evidence agrees and the conclusion is unequivocal. Man is not identical with apes in these or other respects. However, he is clearly related to the apes, and among the apes he is most particularly related to chimpanzees and gorillas, which are closely related between themselves. A necessary inference from this evidence is that the common ancestor of apes and men was itself a member of the ape family. Not only that; we had a common ancestor with gorilla and chimpanzee after their ancestry had become distinct from that of the other living apes (orangutan and gibbons). Our relationships to gorilla and to chimpanzee are about equal, although gorillas may have become somewhat more specialized with respect to the common ancestry.

EVIDENCE FROM FOSSILS

More precise evidence as to relationships and as to the course of anatomical change in the human ancestry must come from fossils. There are special reasons why pertinent fossils are comparatively uncommon: Crucial stages apparently occurred in the tropics, where preservation and discovery of fossils are difficult and where exploration has generally lagged; populations of apes and of pre-humans were always small, not at all comparable with the great herds of grazing animals, for example, common as fossils; and the habits and abilities of apes and pre-humans were such as to reduce chances of natural burial and preservation as fossils.

Nevertheless, a great many fossils have been recovered and discovery is active at present. We are far from having the whole story, but parts of it are increasingly clear.

In Darwin's time only one really distinctive kind of fossil ape (*Dryopithecus*) and only one really distinctive kind of fossil man (Neandertal) were known. From the former, Darwin correctly inferred that by late Miocene, at least, the lineages of apes and monkeys had separated. He was not clear as to the possible implications for separation of the strictly human lineage, which he thought might have occurred much earlier. As regards Neandertal man Darwin could only express surprise that in spite of their antiquity the Neandertals had brain capacities probably greater than the average for modern man.

Now it is known that apes more or less similar to *Dryopithecus* were widespread and, as apes go, numerous through the Miocene and Pliocene of Europe, Asia, and Africa [6]. Present estimates place the beginning of the Miocene at approximately 25 million years ago [7]. The divergence of apes and Old World monkeys is thus at least that old. There is, in fact, some evidence that this divergence occurred in the Oligocene, which preceded the Miocene and began some 10 million years earlier. Divergence of apes and monkeys was identical with divergence of the human ancestry and monkeys, because the earliest apes were also ancestral to man. The time of the final split of the specifically prehuman lineage from that leading to gorilla and chimpanzee has not yet been closely determined. On present evidence it seems most likely to have occurred during the Miocene, that is, quite roughly between 10 and 25 million years ago. The earliest known forms that may be definitely on a prehuman line as distinct from a pre-gorilla-chimpanzee line are *Ramapithecus* from India and the closely similar, indeed probably identical supposed genus *Kenyapithecus* from Africa [8]. Unfortunately those animals are known only from teeth and fragments of jaws, so that their affinities are somewhat uncertain and the anatomy of their skulls and skeletons is entirely unknown. The known specimens are approximately 10 million years old, give or take a few million.

The next significant group of fossils is that of the australopithecines, literally "southern monkeys" although they almost certainly were not exclusively southern and with complete certainty were not monkeys. They are surely and comparatively well known from East and South Africa, doubtfully and, at best, poorly known from elsewhere in Africa and from Eurasia. In Africa they are clearly divisible into two distinct groups. There is dispute as to whether those groups should not be subdivided still further and whether they should be called species or genera. Although the specialists can become enraged over those questions, they have no real importance for others, the important fact being simply that the two separate groups did exist, a point on which even the specialists now agree. Both groups resemble apes much more than we do now, but both are more nearly related to us than to the apes—another point on which the specialists have finally agreed after years of wrangling. They definitely belong to the human family, Hominidae.

One group, typified by *Australopithecus robustus* or, as it is also often called, *Paranthropus robustus*, retained some particularly primitive (more or less apelike) features and yet became somewhat aberrantly specialized. It cannot have been directly ancestral to modern man. The other group, typified by *Australopithecus africanus*, although also primitive within the human family, more closely resembles our own genus, *Homo*. Both groups are now believed to have appeared at least 2 million years ago. For a long time, perhaps 1½ million years, there were at least two distinct lineages of the human family living in Africa and probably throughout the warmer parts of the Old World. One, more primitive and aberrant, showed little progress and finally became extinct. The other, more progressive, evolved into *Homo*. A matter still under sharp dispute is whether the latter lineage included *Australopithecus africanus* as our direct ancestor, or whether for a time there were not actually three distinct lines: the two kinds of australopithecines and still another more directly related to *Homo*. The latter suggestion arises from Leakey's discovery of what he calls *Homo habilis* [9]. However, some authorities believe that supposed species not to be on a distinct lineage but to belong to the line leading from *Australopithecus africanus* eventually to *Homo sapiens*.

That dispute is interesting and we hope it may soon be settled, but it is far less important than the fact that our ancestry passed through a stage closely similar to *Australopithecus africanus* if it was not that group itself. Our ancestors were then fully bipedal, ground-living animals, using their hands for manipulation as we do but perhaps not quite so skillfully. Their teeth were so like ours as to be hard to distinguish, but their brains were little larger than those of apes, and if we could see them alive their physiognomy, while distinctive, would probably strike us as more apelike than manlike.

By a time probably not later than 500,000 years ago and perhaps earlier, gradual evolution from australopithecines had reached a stage that was human in a more restricted sense, belonging not only to the human family, Hominidae, but also to the same genus as ourselves, *Homo*. Doting and ambitious discoverers have given many different names to such early fossil men, including *Pithecanthropus* and *Sinanthropus*, but most of them are now usually placed in a single species, *Homo erectus*. Bodily anatomy and even physiognomy were now almost fully human, but to our eyes there was still a coarse or brutish cast of countenance because of heavy brow ridges over the eyes and a low, small brain case. The brain size was neatly intermediate between australopithecines (or modern apes) and modern man.

Finally, and still gradually, our own species, *Homo sapiens*, emerged. Although not entirely certain, it is now the usual opinion that the quite varied fossils known collectively as Neandertal men belonged to *Homo sapiens* and only represent ancient races that were at first primitive (not so far removed from *Homo erectus*) and later somewhat aberrant. The more aberrant late Neandertals became extinct as such, although it is probable that some of their genes survive.

So much for more or less direct knowledge of man's physical, anatomical origin. The main points are these:

1) Man evolved from apes also ancestral to chimpanzees and gorillas, but less specialized than the latter.

2) The divergence of man's ancestry from the apes was early marked by bipedalism and upright posture, with extensive correlations and implications in anatomy, habits, and capabilities.

3) Also early was divergent dental evolution, again with other implications, for example as to diet and means of defense. It is not known whether posture and dentition diverged from the apes simultaneously or in which order.

4) Only after evolution of human posture and dentition was essentially complete did man's brain begin to enlarge beyond that of the apes. (Intelligence depends not only on size of the brain but also on its internal anatomy, and we do not know the internal anatomy of our fossil ancestors' brains. However, it is fairly certain that a species with average brain size as in apes could not be as intelligent as *Homo sapiens.*)

SYSTEMATICS OF MODERN MAN

Now let us briefly consider the taxonomic, biological systematic nature of mankind as it exists today. First and most important is the fact that mankind *is* a kind, a definite and single species. A biological species is an evolutionary unit composed of continuing populations that regularly interchange genes by interbreeding and that do not or cannot have such regular interchange with other species [10]. The definition clearly applies to mankind: all human populations can and, as opportunity occurs, do interbreed, producing fertile offspring and thus continuing the species and keeping it bound together as a unit. It is unlikely that, for example, a Greenland Eskimo has ever interbred with a South African Bushman, but since all intervening populations can and do interbreed they are nevertheless members of the same species. That species, *Homo sapiens,* is not connected with any other species by interbreeding.

Comparison of Eskimo and Bushman brings up the obvious (although occasionally denied) fact that the human species includes quite diverse races. A race is simply a population (or group of populations) that is genetically distinguished from others. The distinction is not absolute. It is unlikely that Negroes, for example, have any genes that do not occur in some white populations, or that whites have any genes absent in all Negro populations. The usual situation is that a race has certain genes and gene combinations that are more frequent in it than elsewhere, and therefore typical in that sense, but not confined to the race. Races always grade into each other without definite boundaries. There is not now and never has been such a thing as a pure race, biologically speaking. Any two human populations, no matter how small or how large, differ in some respects, so that there is no fixed number of races. One could count thousands or two, and no matter how many are counted, there will be some populations and many individuals that do not clearly fit into one or another. Moreover, races are evanescent in the course of evolution. A given race may change, disappear by fusion with others, or die out altogether while the species as a whole simply continues its evolutionary course [11].

Races of man have, or perhaps one should say "had," exactly the same biological significance as the subspecies of other species of mammals. Widespread animals have local populations that live under diverse conditions and that may become temporarily and in part isolated from each other. They may then more or less accidentally have different proportions of genes (in stricter technical language, of alleles) from other such populations, and if the situation continues long enough, they will almost inevitably evolve somewhat different adaptations to local conditions. Primitive men were relatively few in number and relatively immobile, but they spread over enormous areas —the whole land area of the earth except for Antarctica and a few small islands. They evolved into races or, in better biological terms, into subspecies exactly as any other animal would have under those circumstances.

Racial differentiation in man was originally geographic and, for the most part, adaptive.

That was the original biological significance of race. One must say that Negroes were biologically superior to whites, if reference is to prehistoric times, when the races were originating, and to African conditions, to which Negroes were biologically adapted and whites were not. At the present time race has virtually no strictly biological significance because of two crucial changes. First, human adaptation to different environments is now mostly cultural and is directly biological only in lesser part, so that the prehistoric biological adaptations have lost much of their importance. Second, tremendous increases in population size, in mobility, and in environmental changes brought about by man himself have the result that extremely few men are now living under the conditions to which their ancestors were racially adapted.

Evolution does not necessarily proceed at the same rate in different populations, so that among many groups of animals it is possible to find some species that have evolved more slowly, hence are now more primitive, as regards some particular trait or even overall. It is natural to ask—as many have asked—whether among human races there may not similarly be some that are more primitive in one way or another or in general. It is indeed possible to find single characteristics that are probably more advanced or more primitive in one race than in another. For example, the full lips and kinky hair of some Negroes are almost certainly progressive traits in comparison with the more primitive, decidedly apelike thin lips and straight hair of most whites. However, that does not mean that whites in general are more primitive than Negroes or otherwise inferior to them. Overall primitiveness and progressiveness in comparison of different groups of animals is practically confined to cases in which the groups are of different species, so that genes of the more rapidly evolving species cannot be transferred to the lagging species. Human races all belong to the same species and have generally had enough interbreeding so that genetic progress, as distinct from local adaptation, could and evidently did spread through the entire species. Only if some race entirely ceased to interbreed with any other would it be likely for it to fall behind and become definitely inferior. Let us hope that will not happen.

RESEMBLANCES ANATOMICAL AND PSYCHOLOGICAL

Regardless of the diversity of races, it is obvious that all men resemble one another much more than any of them differ from each other. They all share the basic qualities, anatomical, physiological and psychological, that make us human, *Homo sapiens*, and no other species that is or ever was. Something has already been said of anatomical peculiarities of *Homo sapiens* with respect to living apes and human ancestors. Here are some of the most striking human anatomical traits:

- Normal posture is upright.
- Legs are longer than arms.
- Toes are short, the first toe frequently longest and not divergent.
- The vertebral column has an *S* curve.
- The hands are prehensile, with a large and strongly opposable thumb.
- Most of the body is bare or has only short, sparse, inconspicuous hair.
- The joint for the neck is in the middle of the base of the skull.
- The brain is uniquely large in proportion to the body and has a particularly large and complex cerebrum.
- The face is short, almost vertical under the front of the brain.
- The jaws are short, with a rounded dental arch.
- The canine teeth are usually no larger than the premolars, and there are normally no gaps in front of or behind the canines.
- The first lower premolar is like the second, and the structure of the teeth in general is somewhat distinctive.

Given those characteristics, a museum curator could readily identify any specimen of *Homo sapiens* that was added to the collections, or that happened to walk into his office. However, we who are pondering the question "What is man?" must feel that these anatomical features, fully diagnostic as they are, yet do not amount to an answer adequate for our purposes. Even if we were defining, say, a species of mouse, the anatomical definition would not take us far toward understanding "What is mouse?" or, better, "What is mouseness?" unless we related the bodily mouse to the behaving mouse and the thinking mouse. Even thus, human anatomy reflects truly essential man-ness or human nature only to the extent that it is related to human activities and psychology. Already in *The Descent of Man* [1] Darwin discussed such traits in which man appears to be most distinctive. His points, here greatly abbreviated and paraphrased, were as follows:

In proportion with his higher intelligence, man's behavior is more flexible, less reflex or instinctive.

Man shares such complex factors as curiosity, imitation, attention, memory, and imagination with other relatively advanced animals, but has them in higher degree and applies them in more intricate ways.

More, at least, than other animals, man reasons and improves the adaptive nature of his behavior in rational ways.

Man regularly both uses and makes tools in great variety.

Man is self-conscious; he reflects on his past, future, life, death, and so forth.

Man makes mental abstractions and develops a related symbolism; the most essential and complexly developed outcome of these capacities is language.

Some men have a sense of beauty.

Most men have a religious sense, taking that term broadly to include awe, superstition, belief in the animistic, supernatural, or spiritual.

Normal men have a moral sense; in later terms, man ethicizes.

Man is a cultural and social animal and has developed cultures and societies unique in kind and in complexity.

The last point, which some students now consider the most important of all, was least emphasized by Darwin, who was here mainly concerned with the relationship of social evolution to the origin of the moral sense. Darwin's general purpose was not to characterize *Homo sapiens* as the unique species that he is. The purpose was to show that the characteristics that make him unique are nevertheless foreshadowed in other animals, and that the evolution of man from other, earlier, quite distinct species is therefore plausible. We are no longer concerned with *whether* man evolved, because we know that he did. We are still very much concerned with *how* he evolved, with what is most characteristically human about him and how those characteristics arose. The list of traits discussed by Darwin is still valid from this somewhat different point of view.

That list should not be taken as involving so many separate and distinct things. These are aspects of the behavior, capacities, and accomplishments of a species that is characterized by all of them together and not by each or any one separately. They interact and interlock not only with each other but also with the previously mentioned physical or anatomical characteristics of man. For example, complex human societies, especially the modern industrial civilization rapidly spreading to the whole world, require specialization of activities by different members of society further involving manipulation of complex machines. Such specialization, which is nongenetic, requires individual flexibility and could not occur in a mainly instinctive animal. The machines are tools and could only have been devised by a reasoning, tool-making animal. Invention also required manual deftness, which was provided by (and which also gave selective value to) the structure of the human hand, which required upright posture and could not have been acquired by a quadruped. Further evolution of the early cultural adaptations that led eventually to modern industry also had increased intelligence as a necessary concomitant, and that eventually required larger brains, which in turn involved change in skull structure and in stance—and so on. Even the changing pattern of the teeth can be related to this unitary complex.

THE MAJOR EVOLUTIONARY CHANGES

Because all the specifically human traits are integrated within the whole that is human, and because each of the traits as well as their integration must have arisen gradually, it is somewhat questionable to speak of definite milestones or even of particular critical phases in the evolution of man. Yet there are three among these slow and coordinated changes that seem particularly basic for the concept of human-ness. The most crucial single anatomical point is acquisition of upright posture and strictly bipedal locomotion. Most of the other main peculiarities of human anatomy either follow from that or are coadapted with it. The other two major factors are cultural, but are no less biological since both represent attainment and maintenance of biological adaptation by cultural means. They are tool making and language.

Extremely crude but unmistakable stone tools are found in the oldest rock strata containing indisputable members of the human family, nearly, if not quite, 2 million years old. It will be difficult to authenticate still older and more primitive stone tools, because they must have consisted of natural pebbles or rock fragments picked up and used with little or no modification. It has long been maintained that deliberate manufacture of a tool is the distinctive human trait, since many other animals, even including some insects, use natural objects as tools but do not make tools. Now it has been found that chimpanzees may trim and shorten twigs or straws for use as tools [12], and although that simple behavior is almost too primitive to be called tool making, it sufficiently demonstrates that the capacity for tool making is biologically ancient and prehuman. If one wants a more diagnostic statement, it probably is true that man is the only living animal that uses tools to make tools. However, that trait would follow soon and inevitably once tool making really got under way. A stone used to knock flakes off an incipient stone ax is already a machine tool.

Ancient tools more perishable than stone are rarely preserved. Nevertheless, the course of increasing diversity and complication of tools can be followed well enough to demonstrate the gradual and inconstant but generally continual progress through prehistory. The tremendously accelerated progress in historic times is very well documented and is familiar to all of us in general outline, at least. The whole sweep from stone axes to electronic computers is a natural and comprehensible extension of the biological capacities of an unusual species. It is uniquely wonderful, and yet, lest we stand too much in awe of our own products, let us remember that a digital computer is merely a rapid and automated tool for what amounts to counting on fingers.

As posture is focal for consideration of man's anatomical nature and tools are for consideration of his material culture, so is language focal for his mental nature and his nonmaterial culture [13]. Language is also the most diagnostic single trait of man: all normal men have language; no other now-living organisms do. That real, incomparably important, and absolute distinction has been blurred by imprecise use of the word "language" not only in popular speech but also by some scientists who should know better, speaking, for example, of the "language of the bees" [14].

In any animal societies, and indeed in still simpler forms of aggregation among animals, there must be some kind of communication in the very broadest sense. One animal must receive some kind of information about another animal. That information may be conveyed by specific signals, which may be of extremely diverse kinds both as to form and as to modality, that is, the sensory mode by which it is received. The odor of an ant, the movements of a bee, the color pattern of a bird, the howl of a wolf, and many thousands of others are all signals that convey information to other animals and that, in these and many other examples, are essential adaptations for behavioral integration in the species involved.

Human language is also a system of interpersonal communication and a behavioral adaptation essential for the human form of socialization. Yet human language is absolutely distinct from any system of communication in other animals. That is made most clear by comparison with other animal utterances, which most nearly resemble human speech and are most often called "speech." Nonhuman vocables are, in effect, interjections. They reflect the individual's physical or, more frequently, emotional state. They do not, as true language does, name, discuss, abstract, or symbolize. They are what the psychologists call affective; such purely affective so-called languages are systems of emotional signals and not discourse. The difference between animal interjection and human language is the difference between saying "Ouch!" and saying "Fire is hot."

That example shows that the non-language of animal interjection is still present in man. In us it is in effect not a part of language, but the negative of language, something we use in place of speech. In part we even use the same signals as do the apes, a fact already explored to some depth by Darwin in another of his basic works, *The Expression of the Emotions in Man and Animals* [15]. Much more is now known about such expressions in animals, and particularly in our closer relatives the apes and monkeys, and it is not surprising to find that the non-linguistic, affective system is particularly complicated in them and has not progressed but may even have retrogressed in man. Still we do retain that older system along with our wholly new and wholly distinct system of true language. It is amusing that the human affective interjectional reaction to a bad smell is practically the same as in all other primates, down even to the most primitive.

ATTEMPTS TO TRACE LANGUAGE

Darwin's study and many later studies sought to trace the evolutionary origin of language from a prehuman source. They have not been successful. As a recent expert in the field [16] has said, "The more that is known about it [that is, communication in monkeys and apes], the less these systems seem to help in the understanding of human language."

Many other attempts have been made to determine the evolutionary origin of language, and all have failed. Because language is so important for any concept of man and because this is an interesting example of methodology and limitations, it is worthwhile to consider some of these futile attempts. One, fairly obvious once the idea of linguistic evolution had arisen, was by comparison of living languages. One result was a supposed genetic sequence: (i) isolating languages, like Chinese, which string together invariable word roots; (ii) agglutinating languages, like Mongolian, which modify roots by tacking on prefixes and suffixes; and (iii) flexional languages, like Latin, which modify by (partly) internal changes in words. The trouble is that these categories are not really distinct and, especially, that they did not historically occur in this sequence. For example, Chinese was probably flexional at one time and is now becoming agglutinating with a possibility of becoming flexional again. English was flexional until quite recently and is now mostly isolating with a strong dash of agglutination. Moreover at the present time no languages are primitive in the sense of being significantly close to the origin of language. Even the peoples with least complex cultures have highly sophisticated languages, with complex grammar and large vocabularies, capable of naming and discussing anything that occurs in the sphere occupied by their speakers. Tales of tribal natives who cannot count beyond 4 and who have vocabularies of only two or three hundred words betray the shortcomings of gullible travelers, not of the natives [17].

Another approach is to follow back directly historical records, which cover several thousand years for some European, Asiatic, and north African languages. It is then possible to project still further and to reconstruct, for example, a proto-Indo-European anterior to Sanskrit. But this still leaves us tens or hundreds of thousands of years—perhaps even more—from the origin of language. The oldest language that can reasonably be reconstructed is already modern, sophisticated, complete from an evolutionary point of view.

Still another attempt, which now seems very naive, is through the ontogeny of language, that is, the acquisition of language by children. This relies on the famous but, as it happens, quite erroneous saying that ontogeny repeats phylogeny. In fact the child is not evolving or inventing primitive language but is learning a particular modern language, already complete and unrecognizably different from any possible primitive language. Moreover, the child is doing this with a modern brain already genetically constructed (through the long, long action of natural selection) for the use of complete, wholly nonprimitive language.

It is a tempting hypothesis that the time, at least, of the origin of language might be determined by structural characteristics in fossils. One rather elaborate attempt departed from the fact that all linguistic phonetic systems, varied as they are, depend in part on the shape of the lower jaw and the hard palate, anatomically quite different in typical members of the human and the ape families. It was postulated that speech began when these anatomical parts reached human form, which was in the australopithecines or somewhat earlier. But the postulate is clearly wrong. Audible signals capable of expressing language do not require any particular phonetic apparatus, but only the ability to produce sound, any sound at all. Almost all mammals and a great number of other animals can do that. Moreover, a number of animals, not only birds but also some mammals, can produce sounds recognizably similar to those of human language, and yet their jaws and palates are radically nonhuman. A parrot is capable of articulating a human word but is completely incapable of understanding what the word means.

Given any method of sound production, the capacity for language depends not on characteristics of the sound apparatus but on the central nervous system. Speech is particularly connected with the left temporal lobe of the human brain, as shown, for example, by the fact that ability to speak is generally lost if that lobe is severely damaged. The gross development of the lobe can be seen in plaster casts of the insides of fossil skulls, and that, too, has been proposed as a means of determining whether or not a given fossil individual could speak. But all mammals have left temporal lobes, some smaller and some larger. Those with smaller lobes do not speak just a little and those with larger lobes more. There is no graded sequence: normal men speak completely; other animals, whatever the relative size of their temporal lobes, do not speak at all.

The essential anatomical and physiological basis of speech is nevertheless in the structure and function of the brain [18]. That basis is not fully known, but it evidently involves not just a language center, such as might be localized in the temporal lobe, but an intricate and widespread system of associative connections throughout much of the brain. (The nature or presence of these connections cannot be determined in fossils.) Thus sensations of any kind derived from an external object or event can be generalized according to similarities with others. Each kind can then be associated with a distinctive symbol, which does not resemble the object or event at all but which arbitrarily stands for it. That symbol, a supreme element in the nature of man, is the word, and it is not surprising that words meaning "word," abstraction and symbolization on still another level, have acquired such mystical and philosophical overtones. (Λόγος!)

It is still possible but it is unlikely that we will ever know just when and how our ancestors began to speak. Yet it is certain that this ability depends on physical, structural, and chemical characteristics of the nervous system which evolved from our nonspeaking ancestors under the force of natural selection. The capacity for this unique kind of symbolization is quite general. It does not determine what symbol will be used for a given concept, but that any symbol can be associated with any concept. Thus we are all using exactly the same genetic capacity and symbolizing the same concept when various of us say "woman," "Weib," "femme," "mujer," "zhenshchina," or "imra," depending on whether we happen to have been raised in England, Germany, France, Spain, Russia, or Egypt. The words do not resemble each other and even less resemble the concept they stand for. Moreover, they can be written in different ways, as in Latin, Arabic, or Chinese characters, that do not resemble each other and that have no physical resemblance to the spoken words. They can even be associated with some symbol that is not verbal at all, as in this example with the simplified representation of Venus's mirror that biologists use to designate females: ♀.

CONCLUSION

Language has become far more than a means of communication in man. It is also one of the principal (although far from the only) means of thought, memory, introspection, problem-solving, and all other mental activities. The uniqueness and generality of human symbolization have given our mental activities not only a scope but also a quality far outside the range of other animals. It keeps us aware, to greater extent than can otherwise be, of past and future, of the continuity of existence and its extension beyond what is immediately sensed. Along with other peculiarly human capacities, it is involved in what I consider the most important human characteristic from an ethical point of view: foresight. It is the capacity to predict the outcome of our own actions that makes us responsible for them and that therefore makes ethical judgment of them both possible and necessary [19].

Above the individual level, language and related powers of symbolization make possible the acquisition, sharing, and preserving of knowledge far beyond what would be possible for any single individual. That is an indispensable element in all forms of human social organization and cultural accomplishment, even the most primitive.

It is obvious that I have by no means touched on all aspects of the biological nature of man. That would be impossible in one essay by one author. Those familiar with recent developments in biology may particularly miss reference to molecular biology and especially to the compound called DNA, now known to be largely involved in heredity and also in control of biochemical activities in cells. Those subjects are extremely fascinating at present and may be portentous for the future. However, in my opinion nothing that has so far been learned about DNA has helped significantly to understand the nature of man or of any other whole organism. It certainly is necessary for such understanding to examine what is inherited, how it is expressed in the developing individual, how it evolves in populations, and so on. Up to now the triumphs of DNA research have had virtually no effect on our understanding of those subjects. In due course molecular biology will undoubtedly become more firmly connected with the biology of whole organisms and with evolution, and then it will become of greater concern for those more interested in the nature of man than in the nature of molecules.

Finally, it should be pointed out that although man is a unique animal and although we properly consider his nature in the light of his peculiarities, he also has many non-peculiarities. Man is not *merely* an animal, that is, his essence is not simply in his shared animality. Nevertheless he *is* an animal and the nature of man includes and has arisen from the nature of all animals. Indeed if all the material characteristics of man could be enumerated, it would surely be found that the vast majority of them also occur in other animals. In fact at the level of molecular structure and interaction, information storage and transfer, energy transactions, and other defining characteristics of life, man is hardly significantly different from a bacterium—another illustration of the fact that that level of study is not particularly useful in considering the nature of man.

Like other animals, man develops, is born, grows, reproduces, and dies. Like other animals, he eats, digests, eliminates, respires, locomotes. He bends the qualities of nature to his own ends, but he is as fully subject to nature's laws as is any other animal and is no more capable of changing them. He lives in biological communities and has a niche and an ecology, just as do robins and earthworms. Let us not forget those aspects of man's nature. But let us also remember that man stands upright, builds and makes as never was built or wrought before, speaks and may speak truth or a lie, worships and may worship honestly or falsely, looks to the stars and into the mud, remembers his past and predicts his future, and writes (perhaps at too great length) about his own nature.

REFERENCES AND NOTES

1. C. Darwin, *The Descent of Man, and Selection in Relation to Sex* (London: Murray, 1871).
2. C. Darwin, *On the Origin of Species by Means of Natural Selection, or The Preservation of Favoured Races in the Struggle for Life* (London: Murray, 1859).
3. T. H. Huxley, *Evidence as to Man's Place in Nature* (London: Williams and Norgate, 1863).
4. Lamarck's view (unknown to most Neo-Lamarckians) was that *all* organisms are evolving toward and will eventually become human, after which they will degenerate through the inorganic world and eventually be spontaneously generated as lowly organisms and start again on the path to man. Today's amoeba is tomorrow's man, day after tomorrow's mineral, and still another day's amoeba once more. In the state of knowledge and philosophy of Lamarck's day it would perhaps be too strong to label his views as absurd, but they were certainly less sensible and less progressive than has often been claimed.

5. These new data are well exemplified in S. L. Washburn, ed., *Classification and Human Evolution* (Chicago: Aldine, 1963).
6. E. L. Simons and D. R. Pilbeam, *Folia Primatologica*, no. 46 (1965).
7. On this and other absolute (year) dates see D. E. Savage, J. F. Evernden, G. H. Curtis, and G. T. James, *Am. Jour. Sci.*, v. 262, p. 145 (1964).
8. E. L. Simons, *Postilla*, no. 57 (1961); [U.S.] *Natl. Acad. Sci. Proc.*, v. 51, p. 528 (1964).
9. L. S. B. Leakey, P. V. Tobais, M. D. Leakey, and J. R. Napier, *Nature*, v. 202, p. 3. (1964); P. V. Tobias, *Science*, v. 149, p. 22 (1965). For discussion and dissent see P. L. DeVore, ed., *The Origin of Man* (transcript of a symposium) (New York: Wenner-Gren Foundation, 1965).
10. Age-long argument on the definition of species is perhaps sufficiently summarized in G. G. Simpson, *Principles of Animal Taxonomy* (New York: Columbia University Press, 1961), and E. Mayr, *Animal Species and Evolution* (Cambridge, Mass.: Harvard University Press, 1962).
11. On animal races see especially Mayr (Ref. 10). On the perennial, knotty problem of human races, a sensible general statement with many references is in Th. Dobzhansky, *Mankind Evolving* (New Haven, Conn.: Yale University Press, 1962).
12. J. Goodall, in *Primate Behavior*, ed. I. DeVore (New York: Holt, Rinehart and Winston, 1965), p. 425.
13. The literature on human culture and linguistics is as voluminous as that of any field of science. Some recent studies especially pertinent to my text are: A. L. Bryan, *Current Anthropology*, v. 4, p. 297 (1965); M. Critchley, in *Evolution after Darwin*, ed. S. Tax (Chicago: University of Chicago Press, 1960), v. 2, p. 289; A. S. Diamond, *The History and Origin of Language* (New York: Philosophical Library, 1959); E. L. DuBrul, *Evolution of the Speech Apparatus* (Springfield, Ill.: Thomas, 1958); B. R. Fink, *Perspectives in Biology and Medicine*, v. 7, p. 85 (1963); C. F. Hockett, in *The Evolution of Man's Capacity for Culture*, ed. J. N. Spuhler (Detroit: Wayne State University Press, 1959), p. 32; C. F. Hockett and R. Ascher, *Current Anthropology*, v. 5, p. 135 (1964); A. Kortlandt, *Current Anthropology*, v. 6, p. 320 (1965). See also works cited in Ref. 16.
14. Misuses of the term "language" are too widely exemplified to need citation. The distinction is discussed by several of the authors cited in Ref. 13, also (among other places) in J. B. S. Haldane and H. Spurway, *Insectes Sociaux*, v. 1, p. 247 (1954), and J. B. S. Haldane, *Sci. Prog.*, no. 171, p. 385 (1955).
15. C. Darwin, *The Expression of the Emotions in Man and Animals* (London: Murray, 1872).
16. J. B. Lancaster, in *The Origin of Man*, ed. P. L. DeVore (New York: Wenner-Gren Foundation, 1965). See also discussions by A. R. Diebold, Jr., T. A. Sebeok, and D. Slobin in the same volume, and bibliography on p. 149–150.
17. I first began to appreciate the richness and complexity of "primitive" languages when I visited the Kamarakotos of Venezuela in 1939, and I commented on it in G. G. Simpson, *Los Indios Kamarakotos* (Caracas: Ministerio de Fomento, 1940).
18. N. Geschwind, *Brain*, v. 88, p. 237 (1965).
19. G. G. Simpson, *Am. Psychologist*, v. 21, p. 27 (1966).
20. During 1965 varying versions of this essay were presented as lectures at Randolph Macon College, the University of Paris, and the University of Washington. I have profited by discussions on those occasions.

Population Policy

Will Current Programs Succeed?

KINGSLEY DAVIS
1967

From *Science*, vol. 158, pp. 730–739, 1967. Reprinted with permission of the author and the American Association for the Advancement of Science.

Throughout history the growth of population has been identified with prosperity and strength. If today an increasing number of nations are seeking to curb rapid population growth by reducing their birth rates, they must be driven to do so by an urgent crisis. My purpose here is not to discuss the crisis itself but rather to assess the present and prospective measures used to meet it. Most observers are surprised by the swiftness with which concern over the population problem has turned from intellectual analysis and debate to policy and action. Such action is a welcome relief from the long opposition, or timidity, which seemed to block forever any governmental attempt to restrain population growth, but relief that "at last something is being done" is no guarantee that what is being done is adequate. On the face of it, one could hardly expect such a fundamental reorientation to be quickly and successfully implemented. I therefore propose to review the nature and (as I see them) limitations of the present policies and to suggest lines of possible improvement.

THE NATURE OF CURRENT POLICIES

With more than 30 nations now trying or planning to reduce population growth and with numerous private and international organizations helping, the degree of unanimity as to the kind of measures needed is impressive. The consensus can be summed up in the phrase "family planning." President Johnson declared in 1965 that the United States will "assist family planning programs in nations which request such help." The Prime Minister of India said a year later, "We must press forward with family planning. This is a programme of the highest importance." The Republic of Singapore created in 1966 the Singapore Family Planning and Population Board "to initiate and undertake population control programmes" [1].

As is well known, "family planning" is a

euphemism for contraception. The family-planning approach to population limitation, therefore, concentrates on providing new and efficient contraceptives on a national basis through mass programs under public health auspices. The nature of these programs is shown by the following enthusiastic report from the Population Council [2]:

> No single year has seen so many forward steps in population control as 1965. Effective national programs have at last emerged, international organizations have decided to become engaged, a new contraceptive has proved its value in mass application, . . . and surveys have confirmed a popular desire for family limitation . . .
>
> An accounting of notable events must begin with Korea and Taiwan . . . Taiwan's program is not yet two years old, and already it has inserted one IUD [intrauterine device] for every 4–6 target women (those who are not pregnant, lactating, already sterile, already using contraceptives effectively, or desirous of more children). Korea has done almost as well . . . has put 2,200 full-time workers into the field, . . . has reached operational levels for a network of IUD quotas, supply lines, local manufacture of contraceptives, training of hundreds of M.D.'s and nurses, and mass propaganda . . .

Here one can see the implication that "population control" is being achieved through the dissemination of new contraceptives, and the fact that the "target women" exclude those who want more children. One can also note the technological emphasis and the medical orientation.

What is wrong with such programs? The answer is, "Nothing at all, if they work." Whether or not they work depends on what they are expected to do as well as on how they try to do it. Let us discuss the goal first, then the means.

GOALS

Curiously, it is hard to find in the population-policy movement any explicit discussion of long-range goals. By implication the policies seem to promise a great deal. This is shown by the use of expressions like *population control* and *population planning* (as in the passages quoted above). It is also shown by the characteristic style of reasoning. Expositions of current policy usually start off by lamenting the speed and the consequences of runaway population growth. This growth, it is then stated, must be curbed—by pursuing a vigorous family-planning program. That family planning can solve the problem of population growth seems to be taken as self-evident.

For instance, the much-heralded statement by 12 heads of state, issued by Secretary-General U Thant on 10 December 1966 (a statement initiated by John D. Rockefeller III, Chairman of the Board of the Population Council), devotes half its space to discussing the harmfulness of population growth and the other half to recommending family planning [3]. A more succinct example of the typical reasoning is given in the Provisional Scheme for a Nationwide Family Planning Programme in Ceylon [4]:

> The population of Ceylon is fast increasing. . . . [The] figures reveal that a serious situation will be created within a few years. In order to cope with it a Family Planning programme on a nationwide scale should be launched by the Government.

The promised goal—to limit population growth so as to solve population problems—is a large order. One would expect it to be carefully analyzed, but it is left imprecise and taken for granted, as is the way in which family planning will achieve it.

When the terms *population control* and *population planning* are used, as they frequently are, as synonyms for current family-planning programs, they are misleading. Technically, they would mean deliberate influence over all attributes of a population, including its age-sex structure, geographical distribution, racial composition, genetic quality, and total size. No government attempts such full control. By tacit understanding, current population policies are concerned with only the *growth* and *size* of populations. These attributes, however, result from the death rate and migration as well as from the birth rate; their control would require deliberate influence over the factors giving rise to all three determinants. Actually, current policies labeled population control do not deal with mortality and migration, but deal only with the birth input. This is why another term, *fertility control*, is frequently used to describe current policies. But, as I show below, family planning (and hence current policy) does not undertake to influence most of the determinants of human reproduction. Thus the programs should not be referred to as population control or planning, because they do not attempt to influence the factors responsible for the attributes of human populations, taken generally; nor should they be called fertility control, because they do not try to affect most of the determinants of reproductive performance.

The ambiguity does not stop here, however. When one speaks of controlling population size, any inquiring person naturally asks, What is "control"? Who is to control whom? Precisely what population size, or what rate of population growth, is to be achieved? Do the policies aim to produce a growth rate that is nil, one that is very slight, or one that is like that of the industrial nations? Unless such questions are dealt with and clarified, it is impossible to evaluate current population policies.

The actual programs seem to be aiming simply to achieve a reduction in the birth rate. Success is therefore interpreted as the accomplishment of such a reduction, on the assumption that the reduction will lessen population growth. In those rare cases where a specific demographic aim is stated, the goal is said to be a short-run decline within a given period. The Pakistan plan adopted in 1966 [5, p. 889] aims to reduce the birth rate from 50 to 40 per thousand by 1970; the Indian plan [6] aims to reduce the rate from 40 to 25 "as soon as possible"; and the Korean aim [7] is to cut population growth from 2.9 to 1.2 per cent by 1980. A significant feature of such stated aims is the rapid population growth they would permit. Under conditions of modern mortality, a crude birth rate of 25 to 30 per thousand will represent such a multiplication of people as to make use of the term *population control* ironic. A rate of increase of 1.2 per cent per year would allow South Korea's already dense population to double in less than 60 years.

One can of course defend the programs by saying that the present goals and measures are merely interim ones. A start must be made somewhere. But we do not find this answer in the population-policy literature. Such a defense, if convincing, would require a presentation of the *next* steps, and these are not considered. One suspects that the entire question of goals is instinctively left vague because thorough limitation of population growth would run counter to national and group aspirations. A consideration of hypothetical goals throws further light on the matter.

INDUSTRIALIZED NATIONS AS THE MODEL

Since current policies are confined to family planning, their maximum demographic effect would be to give the underdeveloped countries the same level of reproductive performance that the industrial nations now have. The latter, long oriented toward family planning, provide a good yardstick for determining what the availability of contraceptives can do to population growth. Indeed, they provide more than a yardstick; they are actually the model which inspired the present population policies.

What does this goal mean in practice? Among the advanced nations there is considerable diversity in the level of fertility [8]. At one extreme are countries such as New Zealand, with an average gross reproduction rate (GRR) of 1.91 during the period 1960–64; at the other extreme are countries such as Hungary, with a rate of 0.91 during the same period. To a considerable extent, however, such divergencies are matters of timing. The birth rates of most industrial nations have shown, since about 1940, a wavelike movement, with no secular trend. The average level of reproduction during this long period has been high enough to give these countries, with their low mortality, an extremely rapid population growth. If this level is maintained, their population will double in just over 50 years—a rate higher than that of world population growth at any time prior to 1950, at which time the growth in numbers of human beings was already considered fantastic. The advanced nations are suffering acutely from the effects of rapid population growth in combination with the production of ever more goods per person [9]. A rising share of their supposedly high per capita income, which itself draws increasingly upon the resources of the underdeveloped countries (who fall farther behind in relative economic position), is spent simply to meet the costs, and alleviate the nuisances, of the unrelenting production of more and more goods by more people. Such facts indicate that the industrial nations provide neither a suitable demographic model for the nonindustrial peoples to follow nor the leadership to plan and organize effective population-control policies for them.

ZERO POPULATION GROWTH AS A GOAL

Most discussions of the population crisis lead logically to zero population growth as the ultimate goal, because *any* growth rate, if continued, will eventually use up the earth. Yet hardly ever do arguments for population policy consider such a goal, and current policies do not dream of it. Why not? The answer is evidently that zero population growth is unacceptable to most nations and to most religious and ethnic communities. To argue for this goal would be to alienate possible support for action programs.

GOAL PECULIARITIES INHERENT IN FAMILY PLANNING

Turning to the actual measures taken, we see that the very use of family planning as the means for implementing population policy poses serious but unacknowledged limits on the intended reduction in fertility. The family-planning movement, clearly devoted to the improvement and dissemination of contraceptive devices, states again and again that its purpose is that of enabling couples to have the number of children they want. "The opportunity to decide the number and spacing of children is a basic human right," say the 12 heads of state in the United Nations declaration. The 1965 Turkish Law Concerning Population Planning declares [10]:

> *Article 1.* Population Planning means that individuals can have as many children as they wish, whenever they want to. This can be ensured through preventive measures taken against pregnancy. . . .

Logically, it does not make sense to use *family* planning to provide *national* population control or planning. The "planning" in family planning is that of each separate couple. The only control they exercise is control over the size of *their* family. Obviously, couples do not plan the size of the nation's population, any more than they plan the growth of the national income or the form of the highway network. There is no reason to expect that the millions of decisions about family size made by couples in their own interest will automatically control population for the benefit of society. On the contrary, there are good reasons to think they will not do so. At most, family planning can reduce reproduction to the extent that unwanted births exceed wanted births. In industrial countries the balance is often negative—that is, people have fewer children as a rule than they would like to have. In underdeveloped countries the reverse is normally true, but the elimination of unwanted births would still leave an extremely high rate of multiplication.

Actually, the family-planning movement does not pursue even the limited goals it professes. It does not fully empower couples to have only the number of offspring they want because it either condemns or disregards certain tabooed but nevertheless effective means to this goal. One of its tenets is that "there shall be freedom of choice of method so that individuals can choose in accordance with the dictates of their consciences" [11], but in practice this amounts to limiting the individual's choice, because the "conscience" dictating the method is usually not his but that of religious and governmental officials. Moreover, not every individual may choose: even the so-called recommended methods are ordinarily not offered to single women, or not all offered to women professing a given religious faith.

Thus, despite its emphasis on technology, current policy does not utilize all available means of contraception, much less all birth-control measures. The Indian government wasted valuable years in the early stages of its population-control program by experimenting exclusively with the "rhythm" method, long after this technique had been demonstrated to be one of the least effective. A greater limitation on means is the exclusive emphasis on contraception itself. Induced abortion, for example, is one of the surest means of controlling reproduction, and one that has been proved capable of reducing birth rates rapidly. It seems peculiarly suited to the threshold stage of a population-control program—the stage when new conditions of life first make large families disadvantageous. It was the principal factor in the halving of the Japanese birth rate, a major factor in the declines in birth rate of East-European satellite countries after legalization of abortions in the early 1950's, and an important factor in the reduction of fertility in industrializing nations from 1870 to the 1930's [12]. Today, according to *Studies in Family Planning* [13], "abortion is probably the foremost method of birth control throughout Latin America." Yet this method is rejected in nearly all national and international population-control programs. American foreign aid is used to help *stop* abortion [14]. The United Nations excludes abortion from family planning, and in fact justifies the latter by presenting it as a means of combating abortion [15]. Studies of abortion are being made in Latin America under the presumed auspices of population-control groups, not with the intention of legalizing it and thus making it safe, cheap, available, and hence more effective for population control, but with the avowed purpose of reducing it [16].

Although few would prefer abortion to efficient contraception (other things being equal), the fact is that both permit a woman to control the size of her family. The main drawbacks to abortion arise from its illegality. When performed, as a legal procedure, by a skilled physician, it is safer than childbirth. It does not compete with contraception but serves as a backstop when the latter fails or when contraceptive devices or information are not available. As contraception becomes customary, the incidence of abortion recedes even without its being banned. If, therfore, abortions enable women to have only the number of children they want, and if family planners do not advocate—in fact decry—legalization of abortion, they are to that extent denying the central tenet of their own movement. The irony of anti-abortionism in family-planning circles is seen particularly in hair-splitting arguments over whether or not some contraceptive agent (for example, the IUD) is in reality an abortifacient. A Mexican leader in family planning writes [17]:

> One of the chief objectives of our program in Mexico is to prevent abortions. If we could be sure that the mode of action [of the IUD] was not interference with nidation, we could easily use the method in Mexico.

The questions of sterilization and unnatural forms of sexual intercourse usually meet with similar silent treatment or disapproval, although nobody doubts the effectiveness of these measures in avoiding conception. Sterilization has proved popular in Puerto Rico and has had some vogue in India (where the new health minister hopes to make it compulsory for those with a certain number of children), but in both these areas it has been for the most part ignored or condemned by the family-planning movement.

On the side of goals, then, we see that a family-planning orientation limits the aims of current population policy. Despite reference to "population control" and "fertility control," which presumably mean determination of demographic results by and for the nation as a whole, the movement gives control only to couples, and does this only if they use "respectable" contraceptives.

THE NEGLECT OF MOTIVATION

By sanctifying the doctrine that each woman should have the number of children she wants, and by assuming that if she has only that number this will automatically curb population growth to the necessary degree, the leaders of current policies escape the necessity of asking why women desire so many children and how this desire can be influenced [18, p. 41; 19]. Instead, they claim that satisfactory motivation is shown by the popular desire (shown by opinion surveys in all countries) to have the means of family limitation, and that therefore the problem is one of inventing and distributing the best possible contraceptive devices. Overlooked is the fact that a desire for availability of contraceptives is compatible with *high* fertility.

Given the best of means, there remain the questions of how many children couples want and of whether this is the requisite number from the standpoint of population size. That it is not is indicated by continued rapid population growth in industrial countries, and by the very surveys showing that people want contraception—for these show, too, that people also want numerous children.

The family planners do not ignore motivation. They are forever talking about "attitudes" and "needs." But they pose the issue in terms of the "acceptance" of birth control devices. At the most naive level, they assume that lack of acceptance is a function of the contraceptive device itself. This reduces the motive problem to a technological question. The task of population control then becomes simply the invention of a device that *will* be acceptable [20]. The plastic IUD is acclaimed because, once in place, it does not depend on repeated *acceptance* by the woman, and thus it "solves" the problem of motivation [21].

But suppose a woman does not want to use *any* contraceptive until after she has had four children. This is the type of question that is seldom raised in the family-planning literature. In that literature, wanting a specific number of children is taken as complete motivation, for it implies a wish to control the size of one's family. The problem woman, from the standpoint of family planners, is the one who wants "as many as come," or "as many as God sends." Her attitude is construed as due to ignorance and "cultural values," and the policy deemed necessary to change it is "education." No compulsion can be used, because the movement is committed to free choice, but movie strips, posters, comic books, public lectures, interviews, and discussions are in order. These supply information and supposedly change values by discounting superstitions and showing that unrestrained procreation is harmful to both mother and children. The effort is considered successful when the woman decides she wants only a certain number of children and uses an effective contraceptive.

In viewing negative attitudes toward birth control as due to ignorance, apathy, and outworn tradition, and "mass-communication" as the solution to the motivation problem [22], family planners tend to ignore the power and complexity of social life. If it were admitted that the creation and care of new human beings is socially motivated, like other forms of behavior, by being a part of the system of rewards and punishments that is built into human relationships, and thus is bound up with the individual's economic and personal interests, it would be apparent that the social structure and economy must be changed before a deliberate reduction in the birth rate can be achieved. As it is, reliance on family planning allows people to feel that "something is being done about the population problem" without the need for painful social changes.

Designation of population control as a medical or public health task leads to a similar evasion. This categorization assures popular support because it puts population policy in the hands of respected medical personnel, but, by the same token, it gives responsibility for leadership to people who think in terms of clinics and patients, of pills and IUD's, and who bring to the handling of economic and social phenomena a self-confident naiveté. The study of social organization is a technical field; an action program based on intuition is no more apt to succeed in the control of human beings than it is in the area of bacterial or viral control. Moreover, to alter a social system, by deliberate policy, so as to regulate births in accord with the demands of the collective welfare would require political power, and this is not likely to inhere in public health officials, nurses, midwives, and social workers. To entrust population policy to them is "to take action," but not dangerous "effective action."

Similarly, the Janus-faced position on birth-control technology represents an escape from the necessity, and onus, of grappling with the social and economic determinants of reproductive behavior. On the one side, the rejection or avoidance of religiously tabooed but otherwise effective means of birth prevention enables the family-planning movement to avoid official condemnation. On the other side, an intense preoccupation with contraceptive technology (apart from the tabooed means) also helps the family planners to avoid censure. By implying that the only need is the invention and distribution of effective contraceptive devices, they allay fears, on the part of religious and governmental officials, that fundamental changes in social organization are contemplated. Changes basic enough to affect motivation for having children would be changes in the structure of the family, in the position of women, and in the sexual mores. Far from proposing such radicalism, spokesmen for family planning frequently state their purpose as "protection" of the family—that is, closer observance of family norms. In addition, by concentrating on *new* and *scientific* contraceptives, the movement escapes taboos attached to old ones (the Pope will hardly authorize the condom, but may sanction the pill) and allows family planning to be regarded as a branch of medicine: overpopulation becomes a disease, to be treated by a pill or a coil.

We thus see that the inadequacy of current population policies with respect to motivation is inherent in their overwhelmingly family-planning character. Since family planning is by definition private planning, it eschews any societal control over motivation. It merely furnishes the means, and, among possible means, only the most respectable. Its leaders, in avoiding social complexities and seeking official favor, are obviously activated not solely by expediency but also by their own sentiments as members of society and by their background as persons attracted to the family-planning movement. Unacquainted for the most part with technical economics, sociology, and demography, they tend honestly and instinctively to believe that something they vaguely call population control can be achieved by making better contraceptives available.

THE EVIDENCE OF INEFFECTIVENESS

If this characterization is accurate, we can conclude that current programs will not enable a government to control population size. In countries where couples have numerous offspring that they do not want, such programs may possibly accelerate a birth-rate decline that would occur anyway, but the conditions that cause births to be wanted or unwanted are beyond the control of family planning, hence beyond the control of any nation which relies on family planning alone as its population policy.

This conclusion is confirmed by demographic facts. As I have noted above, the widespread use of family planning in industrial countries has not given their governments control over the birth rate. In backward countries today, taken as a whole, birth rates are rising, not falling; in those with population policies, there is no indication that the government is controlling the rate of reproduction. The main "successes" cited in the well-publicized policy literature are cases where a large number of contraceptives have been distributed or where the program has been accompanied by some decline in the birth rate. Popular enthusiasm for family planning is found mainly in the cities, or in advanced countries such as Japan and Taiwan, where the people would adopt contraception in any case, program or no program. It is difficult to prove that present population policies have even speeded up a lowering of the birth rate (the least that could have been expected), much less that they have provided national "fertility control."

Let us next briefly review the facts concerning the level and trend of population in underdeveloped nations generally, in order to understand the magnitude of the task of genuine control.

RISING BIRTH RATES IN UNDERDEVELOPED COUNTRIES

In ten Latin-American countries, between 1940 and 1959 [23], the average birth rates (age-standardized), as estimated by our research office at the University of California, rose as follows: 1940–44, 43.4 annual births per 1000 population; 1945–49, 44.6; 1950–54, 46.4; 1955–59, 47.7.

In another study made in our office, in which estimating methods derived from the theory of quasi-stable populations were used, the recent trend was found to be upward in 27 underdeveloped countries, downward in six, and unchanged in one [24]. Some of the rises have been substantial, and most have occurred where the birth rate was already extremely high. For instance, the gross reproduction rate rose in Jamaica from 1.8 per thousand in 1947 to 2.7 in 1960; among the natives of Fiji, from 2.0 in 1951 to 2.4 in 1964; and in Albania, from 3.0 in the period 1950–54 to 3.4 in 1960.

The general rise in fertility in backward regions is evidently not due to failure of population-control efforts, because most of the countries either have no such effort or have programs too new to show much effect. Instead, the rise is due, ironically, to the very circumstance that brought on the population crisis in the first place—to improved health and lowered mortality. Better health increases the probability that a woman will conceive and retain the fetus to term; lowered mortality raises the proportion of babies who survive to the age of reproduction and reduces the probability of widowhood during that age [25]. The significance of the general rise in fertility, in the context of this discussion, is that it is giving would-be population planners a harder task than many of them realize. Some of the upward pressure on birth rates is independent of what couples do about family planning, for it arises from the fact that, with lowered mortality, there are simply more couples.

UNDERDEVELOPED COUNTRIES WITH POPULATION POLICIES

In discussions of population policy there is often confusion as to which cases are relevant. Japan, for instance, has been widely praised for the effectiveness of its measures, but it is a very advanced industrial nation and, besides, its government policy had little or nothing to do with the decline in the birth rate, except unintentionally. It therefore offers no test of population policy under peasant-agrarian conditions. Another case of questionable relevance is that of Taiwan, because Taiwan is sufficiently developed to be placed in the urban-industrial class of nations. However, since Taiwan is offered as the main showpiece by the sponsors of current policies in underdeveloped areas, and since the data are excellent, it merits examination.

Taiwan is acclaimed as a showpiece because it has responded favorably to a highly organized program for distributing up-to-date contraceptives and has also had a rapidly dropping birth rate. Some observers have carelessly attributed the decline in the birth rate—from 50.0 in 1951 to 32.7 in 1965—to the family-planning campaign [26], but the campaign began only in 1963 and could have affected only the end of the trend. Rather, the decline represents a response to modernization similar to that made by all countries that have become industrialized [27]. By 1950 over half of Taiwan's population was urban, and by 1964 nearly two-thirds were urban, with 29 percent of the population living in cities of 100,000 or more. The pace of economic development has been extremely rapid. Between 1951 and 1963, per capita income increased by 4.05 per cent per year. Yet the island is closely packed, having 870 persons per square mile (a population density higher than that of Belgium). The combination of fast economic growth and rapid population increase in limited space has put parents of large families at a relative disadvantage and has created a brisk demand for abortions and contraceptives. Thus the favorable response to the current campaign to encourage use of the IUD is not a good example of what birth-control technology can do for a genuinely backward country. In fact, when the program was started, one reason for expecting receptivity was that the island was already on its way to modernization and family planning [28].

At most, the recent family-planning campaign—which reached significant proportions only in 1964, when some 46,000 IUD's were inserted (in 1965 the number was 99,253, and in 1966, 111,242) [29; 30, p. 45]—could have caused the increase observable after 1963 in the rate of decline. Between 1951 and 1963 the average drop in the birth rate per 1000 women (see Table 82.1) was 1.73 per cent per year; in the period 1964–66 it was 4.35 per cent. But one hesitates to assign all of the acceleration in decline since 1963 to the family-planning campaign. The rapid economic development has been precisely of a type likely to accelerate a drop in reproduction. The rise in manufacturing has been much greater than the rise in either agriculture or construction. The agricultural labor force has thus been squeezed, and migration to the cities has skyrocketed [31]. Since housing has not kept pace, urban families have had to restrict reproduction in order to take advantage of career opportunities and avoid domestic inconvenience. Such conditions have historically tended to accelerate a decline in birth rate. The most rapid decline came late in the United States (1921–33) and in Japan (1947–55). A plot of the Japanese and Taiwanese birth rates (Figure 82.1) shows marked similarity of the two curves, despite a difference in level. All told, one should not attribute all of the post-1963 acceleration in the decline of Taiwan's birth rate to the family-planning campaign.

TABLE 82.1
Decline in Taiwan's fertility rate, 1951 through 1966

Year	Registered births per 1000 women aged 15–49	Change in rate (percent) *
1951	211	
1952	198	−5.6
1953	194	−2.2
1954	193	−0.5
1955	197	+2.1
1956	196	−0.4
1957	182	−7.1
1958	185	+1.3
1959	184	−0.1
1960	180	−2.5
1961	177	−1.5
1962	174	−1.5
1963	170	−2.6
1964	162	−4.9
1965	152	−6.0
1966	149	−2.1

Source: data through 1965, *Taiwan Demographic Fact Book* (1964, 1965); data for 1966, *Monthly Bulletin of Population Registration Statistics of Taiwan* (1966, 1967).
* The percentages were calculated on unrounded figures.

The main evidence that *some* of this acceleration is due to the campaign comes from the fact that Taichung, the city in which the family-planning effort was first concentrated, showed subsequently a much faster drop in fertility than other cities [30, p. 69; 32]. But the campaign has not reached throughout the island. By the end of 1966, only 260,745 women had been fitted with an IUD under auspices of the campaign, whereas the women of reproductive age on the island numbered 2.86 million. Most of the reduction in fertility has therefore been a matter of individual initiative. To some extent the campaign may be simply substituting sponsored (and cheaper) services for those that would otherwise come through private and commercial channels. An island-wide survey in 1964 showed that over 150,000 women were already using the traditional Ota ring (a metallic intrauterine device popular in Japan); almost as many had been sterilized; about 40,000 were using foam tablets; some 50,000 admitted to having had at least one abortion; and many were using other methods of birth control [30, pp. 18, 31].

The important question, however, is not whether the present campaign is somewhat hastening the downward trend in the birth rate but whether, even if it is, it will provide population control for the nation. Actually, the campaign is not designed to provide such control and shows no sign of doing so. It takes for granted existing reproductive goals. Its aim is "to integrate, through education and information, the idea of family limitation *within the existing attitudes, values, and goals* of the people" [30, p. 8 (italics mine)]. Its target is *married* women who do not want any more children; it ignores girls not yet married, and women married and wanting more children.

With such an approach, what is the maximum impact possible? It is the difference between the number of children women have been having and the number they want to have. A study in 1957 found a median figure of 3.75 for the number of children wanted by women aged 15 to 29 in Taipei, Taiwan's largest city; the corresponding figure for women from a satellite town was 3.93; for women from a fishing village, 4.90; and for women from a farming village, 5.03. Over 60 per cent of the women in Taipei and over 90 per cent of those in the farming village wanted 4 or more children [33]. In a sample of wives aged 25 to 29 in Taichung, a city of over 300,000, Freedman and his co-workers found the average number of children wanted was 4; only 9 per cent wanted less than 3, 20 per cent wanted 5 or more [34]. If, therefore, Taiwanese women used contraceptives that were 100-per cent effective and had the number of children they desire, they would have about

4.5 each. The goal of the family-planning effort would be achieved. In the past the Taiwanese woman who married and lived through the reproductive period had, on the average, approximately 6.5 children; thus a figure of 4.5 would represent a substantial decline in fertility. Since mortality would continue to decline, the population growth rate would decline somewhat less than individual reproduction would. With 4.5 births per woman and a life expectancy of 70 years, the rate of natural increase would be close to 3 per cent per year [35].

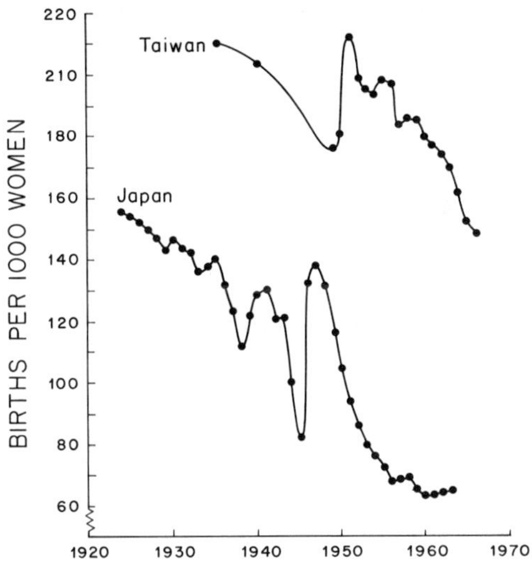

FIGURE 82.1
Births per 1000 women aged 15 through 49 in Japan and Taiwan

In the future, Taiwanese views concerning reproduction will doubtless change, in response to social change and economic modernization. But how far will they change? A good indication is the number of children desired by couples in an already modernized country long oriented toward family planning. In the United States in 1966, an average of 3.4 children was considered ideal by white women aged 21 or over [36]. This average number of births would give Taiwan, with only a slight decrease in mortality, a long-run rate of natural increase of 1.7 per cent per year and a doubling of population in 41 years.

Detailed data confirm the interpretation that Taiwanese women are in the process of shifting from a "peasant-agrarian" to an "industrial" level of reproduction. They are, in typical fashion, cutting off higher-order births at age 30 and beyond [37]. Among young wives, fertility has risen, not fallen. In sum, the widely acclaimed family-planning program in Taiwan may, at most, have somewhat speeded the later phase of fertility decline which would have occurred anyway because of modernization.

Moving down the scale of modernization, to countries most in need of population control, one finds the family-planning approach even more inadequate. In South Korea, second only to Taiwan in the frequency with which it is cited as a model of current policy, a recent birth-rate decline of unknown extent is assumed by leaders to be due overwhelmingly to the government's family-planning program. However, it is just as plausible to say that the net effect of government involvement in population control has been, so far, to delay rather than hasten a decline in reproduction made inevitable by social and economic changes. Although the government is advocating vasectomies and providing IUD's and pills, it refuses to legalize abortions, despite the rapid rise in the rate of illegal abortions and despite the fact that, in a recent survey, 72 per cent of the people who stated an opinion favored legalization. Also, the program is presented in the context of maternal and child health; it thus emphasizes motherhood and the family rather than alternative roles for women. Much is made of the fact that opinion surveys show an overwhelming majority of Koreans (89 per cent in 1965) favoring contraception [38, p. 27], but this means only that Koreans are like other people in wishing to have the means to get what they want. Unfortunately, they want sizable families: "The records indicate that the program appeals mainly to women in the 30–39 year age bracket who have four or more children, including at least two sons . . ." [38, p. 25].

In areas less developed than Korea the degree of acceptance of contraception tends to be disappointing, especially among the rural majority. Faced with this discouragement, the leaders of current policy, instead of reexamining their assumptions, tend to redouble their effort to find a contraceptive that will appeal to the most illiterate peasant, forgetting that he wants a good-sized family. In the rural Punjab, for example, "a disturbing feature . . . is that the females start to seek advice and adopt family planning techniques at the fag end of their reproductive period" [39]. Among 5196 women coming to rural Punjabi family-planning centers, 38 per cent were over 35 years old, 67 per cent over 30. These women had married early, nearly a third of them before the age of 15 [40]; some 14 per cent had eight or more *living* children when they reached the clinic, 51 per cent six or more.

A survey in Tunisia showed that 68 per cent of the married couples were willing to use birth-control measures, but the average number of children they considered ideal was 4.3 [41]. The corresponding averages for a village in eastern Java, a village near New Delhi, and a village in Mysore were 4.3, 4.0, and 4.2, respectively [42, 43]. In the cities of these regions women are more ready to accept birth control and they want fewer children than village women do, but the number they consider desirable is still wholly unsatisfactory from the standpoint of population control. In an urban family-planning center in Tunisia, more than 600 of 900 women accepting contraceptives had four living children already [44]. In Bangalore, a city of nearly a million at the time (1952), the number of off-spring desired by married women was 3.7 on the average; by married men, 4.1 [43]. In the metropolitan area of San Salvador (350,000 inhabitants) a 1964 survey [45] showed the number desired by women of reproductive age to be 3.9, and in seven other capital cities of Latin America the number ranged from 2.7 to 4.2. If women in the cities of underdeveloped countries used birth-control measures with 100-per cent efficiency, they still would have enough babies to expand city populations senselessly, quite apart from the added contribution of rural-urban migration. In many of the cities the difference between actual and ideal number of children is not great; for instance, in the seven Latin-American capitals mentioned above, the ideal was 3.4 whereas the actual births per women in the age range 35 to 39 was 3.7 [46]. Bombay City has had birth-control clinics for many years, yet its birth rate (standardized for age, sex, and marital distribution) is still 34 per 1000 inhabitants and is tending to rise rather than fall. Although this rate is about 13 per cent lower than that for India generally, it has been about that much lower since at least 1951 [47].

IS FAMILY PLANNING THE "FIRST STEP" IN POPULATION CONTROL?

To acknowledge that family planning does not achieve population control is not to impugn its value for other purposes. Freeing women from the need to have more children than they want is of great benefit to them and their children and to society at large. My argument is therefore directed not against family-planning programs as such but against the assumption that they are an effective means of controlling population growth.

But what difference does it make? Why not go along for awhile with family planning as an initial approach to the problem of population control? The answer is that any policy on which millions of dollars are being spent should be designed to achieve the goal it purports to achieve. If it is only a first step, it should be so labeled, and its connection with the next step (and the nature of that next step) should be carefully examined. In the present case, since no "next step" seems ever to be mentioned, the question arises, Is reliance on family planning in fact a basis for dangerous postponement of effective steps? To continue to offer a remedy as a cure long after it has been shown merely to ameliorate the disease is either quackery or wishful thinking, and it thrives most where the need is greatest. Today the desire to solve the population problem is so intense that we are all ready to embrace any "action program" that promises relief. But postponement of effective measures allows the situation to worsen.

Unfortunately, the issue is confused by a matter of semantics. "Family *planning*" and "fertility *control*" suggest that reproduction is being regulated according to some rational plan. And so it is, but only from the standpoint of the individual couple, not from that of the community. What is rational in the light of a couple's situation may be totally irrational from the standpoint of society's welfare.

The need for societal regulation of individual behavior is readily recognized in other spheres—those of explosives, dangerous drugs, public property, natural resources. But in the sphere of reproduction, complete individual initiative is generally favored even by those liberal intellectuals who, in other spheres, most favor economic and social planning. Social reformers who would not hesitate to force all owners of rental property to rent to anyone who can pay, or to force all workers in an industry to join a union, balk at any suggestion that couples be permitted to have only a certain number of offspring. Invariably they interpret societal control of reproduction as meaning direct police supervision of individual behavior. Put the word *compulsory* in front of any term describing a means of limiting births—*compulsory sterilization, compulsory abortion, compulsory contraception*—and you guarantee violent opposition. Fortunately, such direct controls need not be invoked, but conservatives and radicals alike overlook this in their blind opposition to the idea of collective determination of a society's birth rate.

That the exclusive emphasis on family planning in current population policies is not a "first step" but an escape from the real issues is suggested by two facts. (i) No country has taken the "next step." The industrialized countries have had family planning for half a century without acquiring control over either the birth rate or population increase. (ii) Support and encouragement of research on population policy other than family planning is negligible. It is precisely this blocking of alternative thinking and experimentation that makes the emphasis on family planning a major obstacle to population control. The need is not to abandon family-planning programs but to put equal or greater resources into other approaches.

NEW DIRECTIONS IN POPULATION POLICY

In thinking about other approaches, one can start with known facts. In the past, all surviving societies had institutional incentives for marriage, procreation, and child care which were powerful enough to keep the birth rate equal to or in excess of a high death rate. Despite the drop in death rates during the last century and a half, the incentives tended to remain intact because the social structure (especially in regard to the family) changed little. At most, particularly in industrial societies, children became less productive and more expensive [48]. In present-day agrarian societies, where the drop in death rate has been more recent, precipitate, and independent of social change [49], motivation for having children has changed little. Here, even more than in industrialized nations, the family has kept on producing abundant offspring, even though only a fraction of these children are now needed.

If excessive population growth is to be prevented, the obvious requirement is somehow to impose restraints on the family. However, because family roles are reinforced by society's system of rewards, punishments, sentiments, and norms, any proposal to demote the family is viewed as a threat by conservatives and liberals alike, and certainly by people with enough social responsibility to work for population control. One is charged with trying to "abolish" the family, but what is required is selective restructuring of the family in relation to the rest of society.

The lines of such restructuring are suggested by two existing limitations on fertility. (i) Nearly all societies succeed in drastically discouraging reproduction among unmarried women. (ii) Advanced societies unintentionally reduce reproduction among married women when conditions worsen in such a way as to penalize childbearing more severely than it was penalized before. In both cases the causes are motivational and economic rather than technological.

It follows that population-control policy can de-emphasize the family in two ways: (i) by keeping present controls over illegitimate childbirth yet making the most of factors that lead people to postpone or avoid marriage, and (ii) by instituting conditions that motivate those who do marry to keep their families small.

POSTPONEMENT OF MARRIAGE

Since the female reproductive span is short and generally more fecund in its first than in its second half, postponement of marriage to ages beyond 20 tends biologically to reduce births. Sociologically, it gives women time to get a better education, acquire interests unrelated to the family, and develop a cautious attitude toward pregnancy [50]. Individuals who have not married by the time they are in their late twenties often do not marry at all. For these reasons, for the world as a whole, the average age at marriage for women is negatively associated with the birth rate: a rising age at marriage is a frequent cause of declining fertility during the middle phase of the demographic transition; and, in the late phase, the "baby boom" is usually associated with a return to younger marriages.

Any suggestion that age at marriage be raised as a part of population policy is usually met with the argument that "even if a law were passed, it would not be obeyed." Interestingly, this objection implies that the only way to control the age at marriage is by direct legislation, but other factors govern the actual age. Roman Catholic countries generally follow canon law in stipulating 12 years as the minimum *legal* age at which girls may marry, but the actual average age at marriage in these countries (at least in Europe) is characteristically more like 25 to 28 years. The actual age is determined, not by law, but by social and economic conditions. In agrarian societies, postponement of marriage (when postponement occurs) is apparently caused by difficulties in meeting the economic prerequisites for matrimony, as stipulated by custom and opinion. In industrial societies it is caused by housing shortages, unemployment, the requirement for overseas military service, high costs of education, and inadequacy of consumer services. Since almost no research has been devoted to the subject, it is difficult to assess the relative weight of the factors that govern the age at marriage.

ENCOURAGING LIMITATION OF BIRTHS WITHIN MARRIAGE

As a means of encouraging the limitation of reproduction within marriage, as well as postponement of marriage, a greater rewarding of nonfamilial than of familial roles would probably help. A simple way of accomplishing this would be to allow economic advantages to accrue to the single as opposed to the married individual, and to the small as opposed to the large family. For instance, the government could pay people to permit themselves to be sterilized [51]; all costs of abortion could be paid by the government; a substantial fee could be charged for a marriage license; a "child-tax" [52] could be levied; and there could be a requirement that illegitimate pregnancies be aborted. Less sensationally, governments could simply reverse some existing policies that encourage childbearing. They could, for example, cease taxing single persons more than married ones; stop giving parents special tax exemptions; abandon income-tax policy that discriminates against couples when the wife works; reduce paid maternity leaves; reduce family allowances [53]; stop awarding public housing on the basis of family size; stop granting fellowships and other educational aids (including special allowances for wives and children) to married students; cease outlawing abortions and sterilizations; and relax rules that allow use of harmless contraceptives only with medical permission. Some of these policy reversals would be beneficial in other than demographic respects and some would be harmful unless special precautions were taken. The aim would be to reduce the number, not the quality, of the next generation.

A closely related method of de-emphasizing the family would be modification of the complementarity of the roles of men and women. Men are now able to participate in the wider world yet enjoy the satisfaction of having several children because the housework and childcare fall mainly on their wives. Women are impelled to seek this role by their idealized view of marriage and motherhood and by either the scarcity of alternative roles or the difficulty of combining them with family roles. To change this situation women could be required to work outside the home, or compelled by circumstances to do so. If, at the same time, women were paid as well as men and given equal educational and occupational opportunities, and if social life were organized around the place of work rather than around the home or neighborhood, many women would develop interests that would compete with family interests. Approximately this policy is now followed in several Communist countries, and even the less developed of these currently have extremely low birth rates [54].

That inclusion of women in the labor force has a negative effect on reproduction is indicated by regional comparisons [18, p. 1195; 55]. But in most countries the wife's employment is subordinate, economically and emotionally, to her family role, and is readily sacrificed for the latter. No society has restructured both the occupational system and the domestic establishment to the point of permanently modifying the old division of labor by sex.

In any deliberate effort to control the birth rate along these lines, a government has two powerful instruments—its command over economic planning and its authority (real or potential) over education. The first determines (as far as policy can) the economic conditions and circumstances affecting the lives of all citizens; the second provides the knowledge and attitudes necessary to implement the plans. The economic system largely determines who shall work, what can be bought, what rearing children will cost, how much individuals can spend. The schools define family roles and develop vocational and recreational interests; they could, if it were desired, redefine the sex roles, develop interests that transcend the home, and transmit realistic (as opposed to moralistic) knowledge concerning marriage, sexual behavior, and population problems. When the problem is viewed in this light, it is clear that the ministries of economics and education, not the ministry of health, should be the source of population policy.

THE DILEMMA OF POPULATION POLICY

It should now be apparent why, despite strong anxiety over runaway population growth, the actual programs purporting to control it are limited to family planning and are therefore ineffective. (i) The goal of zero, or even slight, population growth is one that nations and groups find difficult to accept. (ii) The measures that would be required to implement such a goal, though not so revolutionary as a Brave New World or a Communist Utopia, nevertheless tend to offend most people reared in existing societies. As a consequence, the goal of so-called population control is implicit and vague; the method is only family planning. This method, far from de-emphasizing the family, is familistic. One of its stated goals is that of helping sterile couples to *have* children. It stresses parental aspirations and responsibilities. It goes along with most aspects of conventional morality, such as condemnation of abortion, disapproval of premarital intercourse, respect for religious teachings and cultural taboos, and obeisance to medical and clerical authority. It deflects hostility by refusing to recommend any change other than the one it stands for: availability of contraceptives.

The things that make family planning acceptable are the very things that make it ineffective for population control. By stressing the right of parents to have the number of children they want, it evades the basic question of population policy, which is how to give societies the number of children they need. By offering only the means for *couples* to control fertility, it neglects the means for societies to do so.

Because of the predominantly profamily character of existing societies, individual interest ordinarily leads to the production of enough offspring to constitute rapid population growth under conditions of low mortality. Childless or single-child homes are considered indicative of personal failure, whereas having three to five living children gives a family a sense of continuity and substantiality [56].

Given the existing desire to have moderate-sized rather than small families, the only countries in which fertility has been reduced to match reduction in mortality are advanced ones temporarily experiencing worsened economic conditions. In Sweden, for instance, the net reproduction rate (NRR) has been below replacement for 34 years (1930–63), if the period is taken as a whole, but this is because of the economic depression. The average replacement rate was below unity (NRR = 0.81) for the period 1930–42, but from 1942 through 1963 it was above unity (NRR = 1.08). Hardships that seem particularly conducive to deliberate lowering of the birth rate are (in managed economies) scarcity of housing and other consumer goods despite full employment, and required high participation of women in the labor force, or (in freer economies) a great deal of unemployment and economic insecurity. When conditions are good, any nation tends to have a growing population.

It follows that, in countries where contraception is used, a realistic proposal for a government policy of lowering the birth rate reads like a catalogue of horrors: squeeze consumers through taxation and inflation; make housing very scarce by limiting construction; force wives and mothers to work outside the home to offset the inadequacy of male wages, yet provide few child-care facilities; encourage migration to the city by paying low wages in the country and providing few rural jobs; increase congestion in cities by starving the transit system; increase personal insecurity by encouraging conditions that produce unemployment and by haphazard political arrests. No government will institute such hardships simply for the purpose of controlling population growth. Clearly, therefore, the task of contemporary population policy is to develop attractive substitutes for family interests, so as to avoid having to turn to hardship as a corrective. The specific measures required for developing such substitutes are not easy to determine in the absence of research on the question.

In short, the world's population problem cannot be solved by pretense and wishful thinking. The unthinking identification of family planning with population control is an ostrich-like approach in that it permits people to hide from themselves the enormity and unconventionality of the task. There is no reason to abandon family-planning programs; contraception is a valuable technological instrument. But such programs must be supplemented with equal or greater investments in research and experimentation to determine the required socioeconomic measures.

REFERENCES AND NOTES

1. *Studies in Family Planning,* no. 16 (1967).
2. *Studies in Family Planning,* no. 9 (1966), p. 1.
3. The statement is given in Ref. 1, p. 1, and in *Population Bull.,* v. 23, p. 6 (1967).
4. The statement is quoted in Ref. 1, p. 2.
5. *Hearings on S. 1676, U.S. Senate, subcommittee on Foreign Aid Expenditures, 89th Congress, Second Session, April 7, 8, 11* (1966), pt. 4.
6. B. L. Raina, in *Family Planning and Population Programs,* ed. B. Berelson, R. K. Anderson, O. Harkavy, G. Maier, W. P. Mauldin, and S. G. Segal (Chicago: University of Chicago Press, 1966).
7. D. Kirk, *Am. Acad. Political Social Sci. Annals,* v. 369, p. 53 (1967).
8. As used by English-speaking demographers, the word *fertility* designates actual reproductive performance, not a theoretical capacity.
9. K. Davis, *Rotarian,* v. 94, p. 10 (1959); *Health Education Mon.,* v. 9, p. 2 (1960); L. Day and A. Day, *Too Many Americans* (Boston: Houghton Mifflin, 1964); R. A. Piddington, *Limits of Mankind* (Bristol, England: Wright, 1956).
10. *Official Gazette* (15 April 1965): quoted in Ref. 1, p. 7.
11. J. W. Gardner, Secretary of Health, Education, and Welfare, "Memorandum to Heads of Operating Agencies" (Jan. 1966), reproduced in Ref. 5, p. 783.
12. C. Tietze, *Demography,* v. 1, p. 119 (1964); Jour. Chronic Diseases, v. 18, p. 1161 (1964); M. Muramatsu, *Milbank Mem. Fund Quart.,* v. 38, p. 153 (1960); K. Davis, *Population Index,* v. 29, p. 345 (1963); R. Armijo and T. Monreal, *Jour. Sex Research,* v. 1964, p. 143 (1964); Proceedings World Population Conference, Belgrade, 1965; Proceedings International Planned Parenthood Federation.
13. *Studies in Family Planning,* no. 4 (1964), p. 3.
14. D. Bell (then administrator for Agency for International Development), in Ref. 5, p. 862.
15. *Asian Population Conference* (New York: United Nations, 1964), p. 30.
16. R. Armijo and T. Montreal, in *Components of Population Change in Latin America* (New York: Milbank Fund, 1965), p. 272; E. Rice-Wray, *Am. Jour. Public Health,* v. 54, p. 313 (1964).
17. E. Rice-Wray, in "Intra-Uterine Contraceptive Devices," *Excerpta Medica Internat. Cong. Ser.,* no. 54 (1962), p. 135.
18. J. Blake, in *Public Health and Population Change,* ed. M. C. Sheps and J. C. Ridley (Pittsburgh: University of Pittsburgh Press, 1965).
19. J. Blake and K. Davis, *Am. Behavioral Scientist,* v. 5, p. 24 (1963).
20. See "Panel discussion on comparative acceptability of different methods of contraception," in *Research in Family Planning,* ed. C. V. Kiser (Princeton, N.J.: Princeton University Press, 1962), p. 373–86.
21. "From the point of view of the woman concerned, the whole problem of continuing motivation disappears . . ." [D. Kirk, in *Popula-*

tion Dynamics, ed. M. Muramatsu and P. A. Harper (Baltimore, Md.: The Johns Hopkins Press, 1965)].
22. "For influencing family size norms, certainly the examples und statements of public figures are of great significance . . . also . . . use of mass-communication methods which help to legitimize the small-family style, to provoke conversation, and to establish a vocabulary for discussion of family planning." [M. W. Freymann, in *Population Dynamics*, ed. M. Muramatsu and P. A. Harper (Baltimore, Md.: The Johns Hopkins University Press, 1965)].
23. O. A. Collver, *Birth Rates in Latin America* (Berkeley, Calif.: International Population and Urban Research, 1965), p. 27–28; the ten countries were Colombia, Costa Rica, El Salvacor, Ecuador, Guatemala, Honduras, Mexico, Panama, Peru, and Venezuela.
24. J. R. Rele, *Fertility Analysis through Extension of Stable Population Concepts* (Berkeley, Calif.: International Population and Urban Research, 1967).
25. J. C. Ridley, M. C. Sheps, J. W. Lingner, and J. A. Menken, *Milbank Mem. Fund Quart.*, v. 45, p. 77 (1967); E. Arriaga, unpublished paper.
26. "South Korea and Taiwan appear successfully to have checked population growth by the use of intrauterine contraceptive devices." [U. Borell, in Ref. 5, p. 556].
27. K. Davis, *Population Index*, v. 29, p. 345 (1963).
28. R. Freedman, *Population Index*, v. 31, p. 421 (1965).
29. Before 1964 the Family Planning Association had given advice to fewer than 60,000 wives in 10 years and a Pre-Pregnancy Health Program had reached some 10,000, and, in the current campaign, 3650 IUD's were inserted in 1965, in a total population of 2½ million women of reproductive age. See *Studies in Family Planning*, no. 19 (1967), p. 4, and R. Freedman et al., *Population Studies*, v. 16, p. 231 (1963).
30. R. W. Gillespie, *Family Planning on Taiwan* (Taichung: Population Council, 1965).
31. During the period 1950–60 the ratio of growth of the city to growth of the noncity population was 5:3; during the period 1960–64 the ratio was 5:2; these ratios are based on data of Shaohsing Chen, *Jour. Sociology Taiwan*, v. 1, p. 74 (1963) and data in the United Nations' *Demographic Yearbooks*.
32. R. Freedman, *Population Index*, v. 31, p. 434 (1965). Taichung's rate of decline in 1963–64 was roughly double the average in four other cities, whereas just prior to the campaign its rate of decline had been much less than theirs.
33. S. H. Chen, *Jour. Sci. Taipei*, v. 13, p. 72 (1963).
34. R. Freedman et al., *Population Studies*, v. 16, p. 227, 232 (1963).
35. In 1964 the life expectancy at birth was already 66 years in Taiwan, as compared to 70 for the United States.
36. J. Blake, *Eugenics Quart.*, v. 14, p. 68 (1967).
37. Women accepting IUD's in the family-planning program are typically 30 to 34 years old and have already had four children. [*Studies in Family Planning*, no. 19 (1967), p. 5.
38. Y. K. Cha, in *Family Planning and Population Programs*, ed. B. Berelson et al. (Chicago: University of Chicago Press, 1966).
39. H. S. Ayalvi and S. S. Johl, *Jour. Family Welfare*, v. 12, p. 60 (1965).
40. Sixty percent of the women had borne their first childe before age 19. Early marriage is strongly supported by public opinion. Of couples polled in the Punjab, 48 percent said that girls *should* marry before age 16, and 94 percent said they should marry before age 20 (Ref. 39, p. 57). A study of 2380 couples in 60 villages of Uttar Pradesh found that the women had consummated their marriage at an average age of 14.6 years [J. R. Rele, *Population Studies*, v. 15, p. 268 (1962)].
41. J. Morsa, in *Family Planning and Population Programs*, ed. B. Berelson et al. (Chicago: University of Chicago Press, 1966).
42. H. Gille and R. J. Pardoko, in *Family Planning and Population Programs*, ed. B. Berelson et al. (Chicago: University of Chicago Press, 1966), p. 515; S. N. Agarwala, *Med. Digest Bombay*, v. 4, p. 653 (1961).
43. *Mysore Population Study* (New York: United Nations, 1961), p. 140.
44. A. Daly, in *Family Planning and Population Programs*, ed. B. Berelson et al. (Chicago: University of Chicago Press, 1966).
45. C. J. Goméz, paper presented at the World Population Conference, Belgrade, 1965.
46. C. Miro, in *Family Planning and Population Programs*, ed. B. Berelson et al. (Chicago: University of Chicago Press, 1966).
47. *Demographic Training and Research Centre* [India] *Newsletter*, v. 20, p. 4 (Aug. 1966).
48. K. Davis, *Population Index*, v. 29, p. 345 (1963). For economic and sociological theory of motivation for having children, see J. Blake, *Science*, v. 164, p. 522.
49. K. Davis, *Am. Econ. Rev.*, v. 46, p. 305 (1956); *Scientific American*, v. 209, p. 68 (1963).
50. J. Blake, *World Population Conference* [Belgrade, 1965] (New York: United Nations, 1967), v. 2, p. 132–136.
51. S. Enke, *Rev. Economics Statistics*, v. 42, p. 175 (1960); S. Enke, *Econ. Devel. Cultural Change*, v. 8, p. 339 (1960); S. Enke, *Econ. Devel. Cultural Change*, v. 10, p. 427 (1962); A. O. Krueger and L. A. Sjaastad, *Econ. Devel. Cultural Change*, v. 10, p. 423.
52. T. J. Samuel, *Jour. Family Welfare India*, v. 13, p. 12 (1966).
53. Sixty-two countries, including 27 in Europe,

give cash payments to people for having children [U.S. Social Security Administration, *Social Security Programs Throughout the World, 1967* (Washington, D.C.: U.S. Government Printing Office, 1967), p. xxvii-xxviii].

54. Average gross reproduction rates in the early 1960's were as follows: Hungary, 0.91; Bulgaria, 1.09; Romania, 1.15; Yugoslavia, 1.32.
55. O. A. Collver and E. Langlois, *Econ. Devel. Cultural Change*, v. 10, p. 367 (1962); J. Weeks [University of California (Berkeley)], unpublished paper.
56. Roman Catholic textbooks condemn the "small" family (one with fewer than four children) as being abnormal [J. Blake, *Population Studies*, v. 20, p. 27 (1966)].
57. Judith Blake's critical readings and discussions have greatly helped in the preparation of this article.

The Human Environment

MARTSON BATES
1962

THE IDEA OF ENVIRONMENT

Environment, at first glance, seems an easy concept: it covers the setting, the surroundings, everything outside of an organism. Here am I, and here is the world in which I live, the one sharply divided from the other by my skin. I may move among many environments—from Ann Arbor to Berkeley, from the woods to a lecture hall or a living room—but always there is I, and a world outside. Or is there? . . .

With environment, there are some simple problems of limits. I pick up an apple and start to eat it—at what point does the apple stop being part of the environment and begin being part of me? Perhaps as soon as it gets inside my mouth; perhaps not until digestion has been completed. A green apple resulting in a stomach-ache might still be considered an environmental effect. Certainly a tapeworm in my intestine would be considered part of my environment rather than part of me—though, as a friend suggested, anyone with intestinal worms is freely entitled to use the editorial "we."

But the limit problems are not very serious. I find the problems of interaction much more confusing. I interpret my environment through my sense organs—yet as the perception psychologists can so easily show, what I perceive is a consequence of my conditioning and my sensory system, as well as of the nature of the world out there. I am in a sense creating some aspects, at least, of the shapes, colors, sounds, smells that I perceive. I wouldn't want to go as far in this as Bishop Berkeley—as a scientist, I believe in external reality and in the possibility of making sense out of it. But perception clearly intervenes between me and the environment.

Organism and environment become blurred in another way: the physical environment is in part, at least, created by the organism. We now believe that the early atmosphere of the earth was very different from the atmosphere we know today: that, specifically, free oxygen and carbon dioxide, so necessary for living

The Human Environment (The Horace M. Albright Conservation Lectureship II) by Marston Bates, 22 pp. School of Forestry and Conservation, University of California, Berkeley, 1962. Reprinted with permission of the author, the publisher, and the executors of the Horace M. Albright Lectureship in Conservation.

process, are also the product of the living process. At another level, the type of forest growing in a given region is at least partly determined by the nature of the soil; but the nature of the soil, in turn, is partly governed by the kind of vegetation growing on it.

Organism and environment, then, are not contrasting or mutually exclusive terms; they are interacting systems. The distinction is valid only as long as we remember this. The long controversy over "nature versus nurture" in shaping human personality illustrates this. There is no "versus": every individual is the product of a certain genetic potentiality finding expression in a particular environment or series of environments. The environmentalists and the genetic determinists were both wrong—as is so often the case with controversy.

The distinction of organism and environment may be misleading, but nevertheless useful. We are trying, essentially, to separate factors arising internally within the system—genetic composition, for instance—from factors arising outside of the system. This is clearest and easiest when we are dealing with individual organisms, more difficult when we are concerned with populations or species, and most difficult in the case of biological communities.

In community study, we have the convenient word "ecosystem" which covers both the organisms and their setting. A pond, a forest, a coral reef, becomes much more understandable if we look at it, not as a collection of organisms occurring in a particular environment, but as populations interacting with each other and with the environment—as ecosystems. . . .

THE IDEA OF MAN

From the point of view of animal classification, the human species can be dealt with easily enough. It clearly belongs to the mammalian order of primates. Men, chimpanzees, gorillas and orangutans are quite similar and, along with the gibbons, are generally classed together in a suborder, the Anthropoidea. Man differs from the others by being relatively hairless, by having lobed, protruding ears, a prominent nose, everted lips, and flat feet—no longer much good for grasping. This, of course, is related to the upright, bipedal locomotion, which also involves other changes, including the balance of the skull on the spinal column. The legs are longer than the arms, and the brain is curiously enlarged—four times as big as that of a chimpanzee.

These anatomical characteristics are not very radical—a Martian zoologist, with nothing but pickled specimens to study, would probably put all of the anthropoids in a single family. But our classifications are made by men who have a high opinion of themselves as compared with their ape relatives, so *Homo sapiens* is put in a separate family, the Hominidae, and the apes in another, the Pongidae. The anatomical excuse is the big brain, but the real and important human peculiarities, of course, are not anatomical, but behavioral.

There is no use here in reviewing again the long search for the essence of humanness—for criteria clearly separating men from not-men. I think it was Carlyle . . . who first suggested that man should be distinguished as the tool-making animal. A common definition for man today is that he is an animal that makes tools according to a predetermined design—thus distinguishing him from the other scattered cases of animal tool-using.

But for most anthropologists, the essence of humanness lies not so much directly in the tool making and using, as indirectly in the symbol systems that make tool using significant. The essence of humanness lies in the whole vast complex of ideas, traditions, behavior, techniques that are transmitted by teaching and learning with symbols—the complex we call culture.

Culture is a cause of considerable misunderstanding between biological and social scientists. Many anthropologists insist that culture is uniquely human—that it differs qualitatively from anything found among other animals. On the other hand, many biologists consider that there is nothing really unique about human culture—that it is simply an enormous development of behavioral traits transmitted extra-somatically and found in many animals, especially vertebrates. This disagreement can be bitter, as I know, because I often get caught between the firing lines. As is so often the case, the difference is probably mostly a matter of definition. It seems to be easier and clearer to adopt the anthropological point of view and restrict the word culture to the human phenomenon. If we want a collective word for learned behavior among apes, monkeys, dolphins or bears, we could call it "protoculture" or a similar term.

I have been using "man" as equivalent to hominid, something different from the other primates. There is no problem with living animals, because all existing hominids are quite clearly a single biological species. But many fossil hominids have been found, differing in varying degrees from the species we know, and we have the problem of deciding at what point they should be called men. The earlier and more different types have been called ape-men or man-apes. I don't like these terms because they bring to mind something intermediate between a man and a gorilla or chimpanzee. . . .

The danger in the word ape-man lies in the assumption . . . that behavior would be intermediate between ape and man. But to generalize from the behavior of living apes to fossil hominids seems to me risky and possibly misleading in reaching an understanding of the origins of our behavior. Ape behavior has also been evolving since the Miocene. This is not to deny that we can learn a lot from the apes—but we should be cautious.

By human environment, then, I mean hominid environment—the environment of a toolmaking animal, an animal with culture. This would include the environment of those African Australopithecines about which we have been learning so much. . . .

CULTURE AND ENVIRONMENT

Is culture an aspect of man or of the environment? This is an academic question, but has its usefulness. If we make any study of human societies and their different ways of dealing with the world around them, we find ourselves at once involved with cultural factors. It is hard, in fact, to find any aspect of the human animal that can be studied without taking culture into account.

Anthropologists—or perhaps better, ethnologists—tend to treat culture as an integral part of the man. If we look at how Bantu, Polynesians, or Western Europeans cope with their environment, we are concerned essentially with cultural traits. We look at cultural adaptations, or maladaptations, study the development and diffusion of cultural traits, and the like. We can, and many anthropologists do, take human nature as a constant that can be ignored; culture becomes a thing-in-itself, the essence of human activity.

When we adopt the point of view of psychology, we tend to deal with cultural traits as part of the environment. We become interested in individuals and classes of individuals or personalities, and we inquire into the ways in which they are taught to accept their culture, or the ways in which they are frustrated by it and the forms that rebellion may take.

Biologists, I suspect, move back and forth, sometimes without knowing it. If we want to study heat stress, we tend to deal with a naked man on a treadmill under controlled climatic conditions—we try to eliminate culture, though probably cultural conditioning as well as plain habituation affects the results. On the other hand, when we investigate comfort zones, we assume that people are wearing clothes—our kind of clothes. The clothing problem dramatizes the whole culture-environment situation. Are my clothes a part of my environment in this room, or are they part of me? I tend, I am sure, to be a different person, depending on the clothes I am wearing. Golding, in his perceptive novel, *The Lord of the Flies*, about a group of young boys wrecked on a tropical island, shows how the pig-hunters could become desperately fierce after they had got themselves all painted up—and war paint is an aspect of clothing.

Ecologists have a number of ways of trying to analyze environments so that various factors can be studied and compared. No system is very satisfactory, which I think is one of the reasons why the progress of ecological knowledge is not spectacular. Most commonly, we try to sort out categories, talking about the biological environment, the chemical environment, the climatic environment and so forth. From the point of view of animal behavior, I like to look at the problem in a different way.

We have first the matter of total environment, of the complete setting in which an organism occurs, including elements that presumably have no effect whatsoever. Ordinarily, for instance, in describing an environment, we ignore the whole electromagnetic spectrum except for the wave lengths we call light. Yet, if we take a radio or a Geiger counter into a forest, we find that there are all sorts of phenomena there that should be included in any description of the total reality. I don't know whether we can ever hope to have a complete description of this physical world—but it is all there, to make up the total environment, and unsuspected parts of it may be having effects.

Our chief interest as ecologists, of course, is in the effective environment, in the factors that do affect whatever organisms we are studying. Part of this effective environment operates because it is intercepted by sense organs, forming the perceptual environment.

We tend, I think, to confuse our own perceptual environment with total reality. Yet it is obvious enough, when we stop to think about it, that each kind of animal lives in a particular sort of a perceptual world, all its own. A dog, ecstatically sniffing the breezes in the car by my side, is living in a world that I can only vaguely appreciate. I have spent many years of my life trying to understand the perceptual environment of mosquitoes, without much success. Yet behavior turns on perception, and we cannot hope to understand behavior without knowing the stimuli to which the organism is reacting.

When we turn to the human environment, this sort of an analysis proves inadequate. I lived for a while on a Micronesian atoll where it seemed to me that the people had learned to cope with their environment as effectively as any society I know. They were efficient fishermen and gardeners and, I suspect, had been living in equilibrium with their resources for something like two thousand years. But the environment of the atoll included not only sea and land, animals and plants, but a host of spirits that lurked everywhere—mostly innocuous or even kindly, but always likely to become malevolent if not properly treated. These spirits were a very real part of the Ifalukian environment—as much of a threat as sharks or moray eels. More so, because the spirits could make a typhoon, something far more destructive than any shark activity.

The anthropologist Peter Murdock calls this the supernatural environment. But when I think about it, this sounds a little condescending. I can see that these spirits of Ifaluk are something the people themselves have created —they are merely ideas. Merely? How overwhelmingly important ideas are in the environment of every man. I may not be worried about spirits in the bushes, but my behavior at every point is governed by ideas of some sort. Supernatural is too restrictive, too limited. Let's call it the conceptual environment. . . .

Somehow the interactions between man and his setting seem clearer to me when I think in terms of the conceptual environment. I see better how all of our relations with each other and the world around us are shaped by ideas; by ideas that we ourselves have made. The ideas often seem maladaptive. Our very survival is threatened by the consequences of some of our ideas. But if we made them, can't we change them? All we need are some good ideas, and if we are half as clever as we like to think we are, this should be possible.

It is through his ideas that man has shifted from being just one more species in a biological community into becoming a sort of geological force, altering the whole surface of the planet and affecting in one way or another the lives of all other organisms.

THE MAN-ALTERED LANDSCAPE

Ecologists divide the biosphere into a series of major subdivisions which they call biomes—desert, tundra, rain forest, grassland, and the like. I have never particularly liked the word biome, and it seems to me more reasonable to talk about different types of landscapes. If we do this, we need to add another landscape—the man-altered landscape—which is increasingly coming to dominate the land surface of the globe.

This man-altered landscape is of course varied, including orchards, fields, cities, cut-over forests and industrial wastes. The classification of these subdivisions can become a fascinating game, especially for the phrasemaker. I particularly like two words I picked up from workers at the Connecticut Agricultural Experiment Station—"derelict woodland" for the growth that now covers the abandoned New England farms; and "suburban forest" for the residential strip that covers so much of the eastern seaboard from Boston to Washington.

There is great variety in this man-altered landscape—rice paddies, apple orchards, highway rights-of-way, coffee plantations, pastures and abandoned fields. But deserts and forests also show great variety in different parts of the world. The different sorts of communities are classed together as a single biome or landscape type because of common adaptive problems of the animal and plant inhabitants. The adaptive problem in desert is to dryness, in tundra to cold; and in the man-altered landscape the common adaptive problem of organisms is that of developing some way of getting along with man.

The man-altered landscape is now the environment in which most members of the human species live. We have again the interaction problem—the environment is both a consequence of human activity and a determinant of that activity. And always between man and the landscape there is the mediating haze of the conceptual world. How did we get into this position?

ENVIRONMENTAL HISTORY

I suspect that the protohominids—our pre-human ancestors—were social carnivores. The carnivorous habit is rare among living primates. Most apes and monkeys are vegetarians or general scroungers—eating whatever they can get by way of insects, birds' eggs and the like. None could really be called predatory—which is one of the reasons I am suspicious of behavioral comparisons between men and apes. Man can digest a variety of raw meat, from oysters to beefsteak; but without cooking, his vegetable diet is limited, which is indirect evidence of a long meat-eating evolution. And then we have the direct evidence of predation from the animal bones found associated with even the earliest of the hominid fossils.

The protohominids must have long been social, because as individuals they hardly had the physical equipment for catching and killing any except the smallest and weakest of other animals. Social man can be a menace to anything from a grasshopper to an elephant or mammoth: but solitary man is liable to become the helpless victim of any passing lion or crocodile. It seems to me likely, then, that these protohominids played a role in the biological community more similar to that of a wolf pack than to anything else we know today. This theory was developed long ago by the British psychologist, Carveth Read, to explain the curious sympathy and understanding between men and dogs—they have evolved from similar backgrounds.

The protohominids must have started diverging long ago from the wolf pattern with the development of tools and weapons. Robert Ardrey in a recent book has proposed that man should be called the "weapon-making animal" because his tool-making has long emphasized instruments for killing food—or colleagues. But these hominids were hardly greatly different from any of the other animals that the ecologists call "higher-order consumers" until they hit upon the control of fire.

I suppose we shall never know with any certainty how man learned to use fire. We are coming to realize that grass fires and forest fires have been around for a long time, in the geological sense. But a wild fire is a terrifying thing—how did man stay around long enough to catch and tame it? I have come to wonder whether it may not have all started in the supernatural sector of that conceptual environment. Man often does practical things for impractical reasons—and fire and spirit are inextricably intertwined ideas. Think of the power and glory of the man who first kept a little fire and fed it and watched over it. He wouldn't need to use it for anything—just having it would be fascination enough. The comfort and usefulness would come later, with increasing skill in manipulation. But the spirit would always be there—we can still see it in the dancing flames of the hearth.

But with fire man started to become an agent of ecological change. He could—and undoubtedly did—set fires in forests and grasslands, so that the sporadic burning of the geological past became commonplace. Man had started altering the landscape.

I think the next great change in man's relations with nature is best covered by the label Neolithic Revolution. This revolution is ordinarily defined by a shift in the technique of tool-making; but along with this came the beginnings of agriculture, of pottery, of village life. With the domestication of plants and animals, man started to become an agent of evolutionary change as well as of ecological change. The changes that have occurred in both plant and animal cultigens over a period of at most some ten thousand years are startling. Corn or maize shows dramatically the changes that have occurred in many such organisms. Maize has become an obligate cultigen—it could not last for a generation without man to husk the ears, plant the seeds, and keep away competing weeds. . . .

With the clearing and planting of the Neolithic era, man started making open habitats, something otherwise confined to sandbars, landslides, or occasional forest openings created by falling trees. A considerable variety of animals and plants found new opportunities in this open habitat—thistles, robins, rats. Such opportunists were able to get along with man nicely, whether he wanted them or not. Other organisms—those I call the irreconcilables—started the retreat toward extinction. They cannot survive in the man-altered landscape.

Neolithic village man was still greatly influenced by the local landscape. The nature of his crops and herds depended on climate and soil. The next step, if we keep using the Gordon Childe vocabulary, was the Urban Revolution, affecting the transport and storage of materials, especially food such as the grains. Thus the city could develop, with classes of men independent of the chores of food producing—free to start the elaboration of that conceptual environment which so increasingly governs our behavior. Irrigation changed deserts, and drainage changed swamps into fields. Urban man got farther and farther from prehuman nature.

If we continue to mark this development by revolutionary stages, we have the Industrial Revolution of the 18th century, giving man new and vast command over energy and new materials. And I think C. P. Snow is right in recognizing also a Scientific Revolution, starting in Germany and becoming general in Western culture around 1900, through which science and technology became firmly wedded —with our nuclear age only one of the numerous consequences.

THE PRESENT WORLD

And so we find that we are a pretty clever sort of animal. We can make very loud and destructive bangs—we have caught a bit of the power of the sun. We can shoot artificial satellites off into space and dash around at supersonic speeds. We have come to look at our planet as a resource for our species, which is funny when you think that the planet has been around for about five billion years, and *Homo sapiens* for perhaps one hundred thousand. We have acquired an arrogance about ourselves that I find frightening. We have come to feel that we are so far apart from the rest of nature that we have but to command.

Yet, that old aphorism of Francis Bacon still applies—you cannot command nature except by obeying her. The laws of gravitation still operate within the material world of discrete objects. If you want to jump from an airplane and keep on living, you must use a parachute so that air resistance can counter gravitation. Our engineers haven't rescinded any physical laws: they have learned more and more about them, and learned to work with them. But the engineers, I am afraid, are careless about the ecological laws. If we want to survive, I suspect we had better learn more about them, and learn to work with them. The folly of ignoring them is shown by the salted deserts that were once the fields of Babylon. Or most recently by the fabulous British groundnut scheme in Africa.

I sometimes sound as though I advocated going back to the Neolithic era and to a peaceful village life with man and nature in harmony. Certainly Neolithic life can be very pleasant, at least as it has survived on some Pacific islands. But if I went back to the Neolithic age, I would want to carry my physician with me, and a small library—maybe even a phonograph, and I would be sorry not to get any mail. I can't go back because I can't shed my conceptual environment. The answer to the problem is not to go back to the past, but to find better adjustments to the present.

Actually, there isn't any past worth going back to. Periclean Athens or Elizabethan England sometimes sound exciting—but you would need to belong to the right class. The lot of a slave in Athens does not sound enviable. There is plenty of mental and physical misery in the world today; but relatively less, I suspect, than at any past time. And despite all of the fuss about organization men and conformity, there is a greater diversity, a wider choice of role for the individual—at least in the Western world—than ever before. Diversity, it seems to me, is in itself a good. The conformity of modern suburbia, depressing as it is, is nothing compared with the conformity of the Neolithic villager or the medieval serf or knight. But we are still a long way from Utopia, and our diversity needs to be carefully nurtured and prized if it is to survive and grow.

It is interesting in this respect that our appreciation of nature seems to be closely related to our increasing urbanization and industrialization. I wonder whether our increasing separation from the rest of the natural world isn't leaving us with a subconscious unease, a dimly felt need to get out into the woods, fields, mountains and deserts. The statistics on visitors to national parks would seem to support this, despite the behavior of the same people with beer cans along the highways. I wonder, even, whether the tropical aquarium and the philodendrons in a New York apartment don't reflect a need to have something alive around besides people, cats and pigeons. But maybe, of course, the aquarium is simply the equivalent of another picture on the wall. I have had a student from the slums of Chicago argue that he didn't see why people wanted to have a lot of messy trees around—he looked forward to that brave, new future world of cement and glass with perfect equanimity.

And so we have our man-altered landscape. Even when we have a bit of wilderness, it is left deliberately—man controlled. A Russian, Vernadsky, noted some years ago that the biosphere was giving way to the noösphere, to a world dominated by the human mind. This seems to me too simple, and I would prefer to think of the man-altered landscape not as a noösphere, but as a noösystem: an interacting complex like the ecosystem, but with a multiplying series of additional transactions involving that curious conceptual environment of the human species.

Whether we can guide or influence the developing noösystem in ways to promote what we can agree to be the good of mankind or of the rest of nature remains an open question. I think we can act reasonably and rationally as individuals, but I sometimes wonder whether this faculty carries over to groups and organizations, especially when one looks at the actions of the organizations that we call national states. Maybe we are trapped by some kind of inexorable laws of cultural development that can lead only to limbo.

The late Alan Gregg pointed out that human population growth within the ecosystem was closely analogous to the growth of malignant tumor cells within an organism: that man was acting like a cancer on the biosphere. The multiplication of human numbers certainly seems wild and uncontrolled. The present annual increase in human numbers on the planet is about 48 million individuals. Four million a month—the equivalent of the population of Chicago. And whatever one thinks of Chicago, a new one every month seems a little excessive. We seem to be doing all right at the moment; but if you could ask cancer cells, I suspect they would think they were doing fine. But when the organism dies, so do they; and for our own, selfish, practical, utilitarian reasons, I think we should be careful about how we influence the rest of the ecosystem.

There are practical reasons why we should be careful with our environment. There are ethical reasons—through what mandate did we get exclusive title to this planet? There are esthetic reasons—I can't agree with my friend from Chicago and look forward to a world of cement and glass and tanks of algal soup. People can be interesting—I find them fascinating—but so are squirrels, and foxes and mosquitoes. And however fascinating people may be, many of their activities and products are just plain ugly, by whatever standards. As John Pairman Brown has noted in a recent book, *The Displaced Person's Almanac*, "We've converted our rivers into sewers and our forests into funnybooks; this is our boon from the Gods, everything we touch turns to garbage."

Need it be? I find some grounds for hope—

and they go back to that conceptual environment that governs so many of our activities. We made it. Surely, then, we can alter it and patch it—somehow develop a noösystem that is more just, more practical, and more beautiful than the one we have. At least it is our duty to try—without trying we are surely doomed.

REFERENCES

Ardrey, Robert, 1961, African genesis: New York, Atheneum.

Bartholomew, G. A., and J. B. Birdsell, 1953, Ecology and the Protohominids: Am. Anthropologist, v. 55, p. 481–498.

Bates, Marston, 1960, The forest and the sea: New York, Random House. (Also available as a Mentor paperback.)

———, 1961, Man in nature: Englewood Cliffs, N.J., Prentice-Hall.

Bates, Marston, and Donald Abbott, 1958, Coral Island: New York, Scribners.

Brown, John Pairman, 1962, The displaced person's almanac: Boston, Beacon Press.

Bruller, Jean ("Vercors"), 1953, You shall know them: Boston, Little, Brown.

Calder, Ritchie, 1961, After the seventh day: New York, Simon and Schuster.

Chardin, Pierre Teilhard de, 1956, The antiquity and world expansion of human culture, *in* Wm. Thomas, ed., Man's role in changing the face of the earth: Chicago, University of Chicago Press.

Childe, Gordon, 1936, Man makes himself: London, Watts. (Also available as a Mentor paperback.)

Clarke, G. L., 1954, Elements of ecology: New York, John Wiley and Sons.

Dart, Raymond, with Dennis Craig, 1959, Adventures with the missing link: New York, Harper. (Also available as a paperback in the Viking Explorer series.)

Golding, William, 1954, Lord of the flies: New York, Coward-McCann. (Also available as a Capricorn Books paperback.)

Kluckhohn, Clyde, and A. L. Kroeber, 1952, Culture—a critical review of concepts and definitions: Peabody Mus. Archaeology and Ethnology Papers, v. 47, no. 1.

Leakey, L. S. B., 1960, The origin of the genus *Homo*, *in* Sol Tax, ed., Evolution after Darwin, v. 2. The evolution of man: Chicago, University of Chicago Press.

Oakley, Kenneth P., 1949, Man the tool-maker: London, British Museum (Natural History).

Odum, E. P., 1959, Fundamentals of ecology: Philadelphia, W. B. Saunders.

Read, Carveth, 1920, The origin of man and his superstitions: New York, Cambridge University Press.

Sauer, Carl O., 1952, Agricultural origins and dispersals: New York, American Geographical Society.

Snow, C. P., 1959, The two cultures and the scientific revolution: New York, Cambridge University Press.

White, Leslie, 1949, The science of culture: New York, Farrar, Strauss. (Also available as an Evergreen paperback.)

FORTY QUESTIONS

The questions below illustrate the kinds of issues around which study of the Reading Selections in this book might profitably be organized.

1. What are the central ordering principles of historical geology, and how do they work?
2. What are the major components that interact to produce the signals whose interpretation gives us earth history; and by what specific operations may we arrange events in sequence, and establish their equivalence or nonequivalence to events at other places?
3. How do we set limits of confidence, and how do we define "uncertainty" in geological interpretation?
4. What are the implications of "uniformitarianism"? (Consider the original controversy, the discussion between Kelvin and the geologists, the variety of definitions given, the terms used, and the present status of the concept.)
5. What criteria have suggested the concept of an expanding universe, and how might those criteria be interpreted as consistent with a static universe?
6. What theory of origin of the solar system would best account for the peculiarities of the sun and its planets, including the earth?
7. What are the principal theories of lunar origin, and what is the evidence for and against each?
8. What evidence from nuclear decay systems is useful in geochronology? (Consider the principal decay series, what happens in each, and their limitations.)
9. Where does carbon-14 come from; what happens to it, and how; upon what assumption does the radiocarbon method of geochronology depend, and what are its uses and limitations?
10. How does the record of the incremental growth of fossil shells bear upon geochronology and selenology?
11. What is the Coriolis effect, and how does it influence the general circulation of the atmosphere and the oceans?
12. What other factors affect the general circulation of the atmosphere and oceans, and in what way?
13. What models do we have for the composition of the primitive atmosphere; what is the evidence for and against each; and what are their testable corollaries?

14. What hypotheses have been proposed to account for the present volume and composition of the hydrosphere, and what is the evidence for and against each?
15. What do we know about the internal structure of the earth, and how do we know it?
16. What is the evidence for and against convection in the earth's mantle?
17. What is meant by "plate tectonics," from what data does the concept emerge, and what is its bearing on crustal structure and sedimentation?
18. How is plate tectonics related to continental drift, and what is the evidence for and against the latter?
19. What evidence bears on the timing and manner of the origin of the Atlantic Ocean; and of other oceans?
20. What is the current experimental and observational evidence bearing on the origin of life on the earth and elsewhere in the universe?
21. What might we learn from geochemistry about biologic evolution?
22. What are the likely relations between biospheric, atmospheric, and lithospheric evolution on the primitive earth?
23. How and when might the earth have undergone its first convective turnover, with differentiation of core, mantle, and protocontinents?
24. What is the evidence for upper mantle motions and subcrustal transfer of material, especially as elaborated by Gilluly for the western U.S.?
25. What relations can be observed between tectonism, volcanism, and plutonism, especially in the Phanerozoic of the western U.S.?
26. Under what circumstances do we find great lithologic continuity and cyclicity of sedimentation, and how do these contrast with those that characteristically result in striking, lateral changes in facies?
27. What is the facies concept, and in what ways does it apply to historical geology?
28. What is the significance of sharp tops and gradational bases in sandstone beds, or of gradational tops and sharp bases?
29. How is tectonic history reflected in the sedimentary record?
30. What principles might be called upon to explain the annual layering, the contained records of mass mortalities, and the geochemical peculiarities of sequences like the Green River Shale?
31. What problems are posed by discontinuities (such as gaps, extinctions, and so forth) in the records of biologic evolution, and how may they be resolved?
32. How does (or how might) a paleocologist obtain the kinds of information that an ecologist starts with (depth, salinity, *p*H, Eh, and so forth); how has the need to have such information affected the progress of paleoecology; and where should paleoecology go from here?
33. What are the relations between environment and evolution, and what are some likely illustrations from the paleontologic record?
34. What processes or events might have led to the appearance in the geologic record of major biologic innovations, such as life itself, the eucaryotic cell, the Metazoa, land plants, land animals, the classes of vertebrates, and the flowering plants?

35. What are the central problems of paleoclimatology, and what kinds of information do we need to solve them?
36. What is the synthetic theory of evolution, and what part do environmental influences play in it?
37. When, where, and why do we have ice ages?
38. What do we know about the origin, diversification, and dispersal of early man; why do we not know more; and how might we enhance our knowledge?
39. What has man's effect been as an evolutionary and ecologic factor, and how can we evaluate this effect for good or ill?
40. What is the outlook for *Homo sapiens?*

GLOSSARY

Å: Ångstrom unit, a unit of length equal to one ten-thousandth (10^{-4}) of a micron or one hundred-millionth (10^{-8}) of a centimeter.

abiogenesis: Originally referred to the development of living organisms from non-living matter through chemical evolution; now usually refers to the chemical evolution of pre-vital organic molecules; compare *biogenesis*.

ablation moraine: A kind of broad terminal moraine deposited from composite valley glaciers having several medial moraines, where ablation of unshielded ice causes spreading and loss of identity of the individual medial moraines. See also *moraine*.

acanthodian: Pertaining to the Acanthodi, an order of small, jawed fish of the class Placodermi from the upper Paleozoic, characterized by stout spines at the front end of each fin.

acetate: Salt or ester of acetic acid; for example, cellulose acetate (or acetate rayon).

acetyl: Referring to or containing the acetate derivative CH_3CO, a component of acetic acid.

acetyl coenzyme A: Coenzyme A bonded to an acetyl radical.

acritarch: A collective name for minute microfossils (nannofossils) of generally chitinous composition and uncertain affinities.

acyl: Any acid derivative; an acyl halite, for instance, would be a halogen ester of some acid.

adductor muscle: A muscle of bivalved invertebrates (pelecypods and brachiopods) that pulls the valves together after they have been sprung open by the ligament or by diductor muscles. Occurs in pairs (usually) or singly.

adenine: A purine; one of the nucleotide bases that link with sugar-phosphate chains to form DNA and RNA.

adenosine diphosphate: See *ADP*.

adenosine monophosphate: See *AMP*.

adenosine triphosphate: See *ATP*.

ADP: Adenosine diphosphate, an ester of adenosine and pyrophosphoric acid that transfers energy during carbon assimilation.

aeon: Years × 10^9. The term is used to avoid the confusion inherent in "billion years," which would be milliards of years in much of the world. *Aeon* is not to be confused with *eon* (the Phanerozoic Eon, for example), which refers to a systematic subdivision of geologic time larger than an *era*.

agglutinated: Consisting of particles stuck together, as the tests (or "shells") of certain foraminifers, and the dwelling tubes of some annelids and insect larvae.

alanine: An amino acid.

alaskite: A variety of granite containing few or no dark minerals.

Albian: A stage of the Lower Cretaceous.

alcohol: Hydroxyl derivative of hydrocarbons having the general structure of ethyl alcohol (C_2H_5OH).

alginic acid: A gelatinous organic acid found in certain algae.

aliphatic: Pertaining to the paraffin, olefin, and acetylene hydrocarbons and their derivatives.

alkane: A "saturated" hydrocarbon or "paraffin"; that is, a hydrocarbon that contains no double or triple bonds and is therefore relatively inactive, tending not to form addition products. Alkanes contrast with alkenes, in which some of the carbon–carbon bonds are double, and alkynes, which form triple bonds between carbons.

allochthonous: Of distant origin; compare *autochthonous*.

amidinium form: An organic molecule to which the amidine ion ($H_2N—C{=}N^+$) is attached.

amino acids: Compounds having the structure $NH_2—CHR—COOH$ (R representing an appropriate side chain), groups and yielding free H^+ ions in solution. They are the principal building blocks of peptides and protein. Although more than 170 amino acids are known, only 20 of them are common in protein construction.

ammonite: A cephalopod with a coiled shell consisting of a succession of chambers, the end-walls of which are complexly folded. When the outer shell material is removed, the edges of the folded walls appear as regular but complex zigzag lines of "lobes" and "saddles" that are referred to as sutures.

AMP: Adenosine monophosphate, an ester of adenosine and phosphoric acid, which with the addition of high-energy phosphates becomes ADP and ATP, and which functions in tandem with them in biological energy transfer.

amphibolite: A crystalline metamorphic rock composed of amphibole and plagioclase feldspar with little or no quartz.

anaerobic: Characterized by, or operating in, the absence of free oxygen.

anatexis: A metamorphic process involving the melting of deep crustal rocks to form a magma, which then recrystallizes. Contrasts with *rheomorphism,* which denotes only sufficient melting to produce some movement and a degree of recrystallization.

andalusite: An orthorhombic aluminum silicate mineral (Al_2SiO_5) common in metamorphic rocks, such as gneisses and schists, and denoting a particular grade of metamorphism (or level of temperature and pressure).

angiosperm: A flowering plant: a member of the class Angiospermae of the phylum Tracheophyta (vascular plants).

angular momentum: That property of a rotating or revolving object (or of an object or particle moving across a rotating gravitational field) that is equivalent to mass (m) times linear velocity (v) times the turning radius (r). Where angular momentum is expressed by the Greek letter omega, $\Omega = mvr$. It is an observationally unvarying law of physics, and a kind of summation of Newton's laws of motion, that, within any system that functions as a unit, angular momentum is conserved unless and until disturbed by an external force or torque. This is fundamental to an understanding of, among other things, the origin of the solar system, relations between Earth and its moon, and the Coriolis effect.

angular unconformity: See *unconformity.*

anion: A negatively charged ion, which moves to the anode (or positively charged electrode) in electrolysis. Compare *cation.*

anomodont: A member of the Anomodontia, a Permian and Triassic suborder of the order Therapsida (advanced mammallike reptiles), characterized by long canine teeth, irregular molars, and a horny beak.

anorogenic: Originating at a time of little or no mountain building.

antimetabolite: Something that inhibits or destroys the products of metabolism (metabolites).

aplite: A rock, ordinarily occuring in dikes, that consists mainly of light-colored minerals and has a very fine-grained granitic texture.

aqueoglacial: Pertaining to water bodies adjacent to glaciers.

archaeocyathid: A member of the phylum Archaeocyatha, an extinct group of spongelike animals essentially restricted to rocks of Lower Cambrian age and unknown above the Cambrian.

arenaceous: Pertaining to sand, as a deposit containing sand grains, or a foraminifer whose test consists of agglutinated sand grains.

arginine: An amino acid.

aromatic: In chemistry, refers to various cyclic (ring-structured) organic compounds characterized by the presence of the benzene ring (C_6H_6) and a resistance to oxidation. Named from the spicy fragrance associated with earliest recognized species.

Articulata: A class of the phylum Brachiopoda (a group of dorsoventrally bivalved marine animals). The members of the class have opposing calcareous valves ("half-shells") that swing open and shut along a toothed or articulated hinge-line. Compare *Inarticulata.*

Artinsk and Sosio fauna: Middle Permian marine invertebrates found in the Artinsk region of European Russia and the Sosio area of Sicily.

artiodactyl: A member of the order Artiodactyla, the even-toed hoofed mammals.

aspartic acid: One of the amino acids.

atmophile element: An element, such as hydrogen, oxygen, nitrogen, or carbon, that tends to be incorporated in the atmospheric gases.

atoll: A biogenic reef, usually with reef-islands, that surrounds a lagoon in which there is no pre-existing land.

atomic oxygen: O, consisting of single atoms of oxygen; a highly reactive form, resulting from absorption of light by O_2 in the far UV region (1,600–1,800 Å).

ATP: Adenosine triphosphate, an ester of adenosine and triphosphoric acid formed by the reaction of ADP and an orthophosphate, or by the interaction of ADP and phosphocreatine or certain other substrates. It is the universal energy source for biochemical reactions.

AU: Astronomical unit; distance from earth to sun; approximately 150 million kilometers or 93 million miles.

autochthonous: Of local origin. In geology, applies either to sediments or to structural features that originated within a given area, in contrast to *allochthonous* sediments or structures, which originated at some distance and were later transported to the places where found.

autotroph: An organism capable of creating its cell components from carbon dioxide, nitrogen, water, and an external source of energy. According to whether they derive their energy from light or chemicals, autotrophs are classed as photoautotrophs or chemoautotrophs. Green-plant photosynthesis is the most familiar and important type of autotrophy.

basalt: An extrusive igneous rock consisting mainly of calcic plagioclase and pyroxene, with or without olivene.

Basin Range (or Basin and Range) **province:** Large area of the western U.S. characterized by ranges of fault mountains elongated in a north–south direction and interspersed with prominent, internally draining desert basins.

batholith (or bathylith): A large body of intrusive igneous rock. Broadly speaking, such a body is called a *batholith* if its surface diameter is greater than about 70 km, and a *stock* if its diameter is smaller.

belemnite: The cigar-shaped internal skeleton of a member of the family Belemnitidae, an extinct group of squidlike organisms characteristic of the Mesozoic, but with ancestral forms in the upper Paleozoic.

Belt Supergroup (or Belt Series): A thick succession of mainly little-metamorphosed sedimentary rocks of upper Proterozoic age found in the northern Rocky Mountains of the U.S. and in the Canadian Rockies. Radiometric ages obtained from these rocks range from 1.1 to 1.4 aeons.

bienothere: Belonging to, or akin to, the genus *Bienotherium* of the Tritylodontidae, a family of the order Ictidosauria (which see).

biogenesis: Originally referred to the generation of life from pre-existing life, but is now usually taken as synonymous with *biopoesis*.

bioherm: Generally, a moundlike or lenslike mass of rock of biological origin (or with a framework of biological origin), the thickness of which is great in comparison to its lateral extent. A biogenic reef.

biophile element: An element, such as phosphorus, sulfur, iron, or magnesium, that tends to be incorporated in living matter.

biopoesis: Denotes the origin of life without regard for the mode of origin.

biosphere: The totality of life on earth.

biostrome: A laterally extensive tabular bed or lens of rock of biological origin, as certain algal limestones, or shell beds (some oyster reefs, for example).

biosynthesis: The biological synthesis of any product. The term has also been used as a synonym for *biopoesis*.

biota: The animals (fauna) and plants (flora) characteristic of, or found within, a given area or region.

biotite: A dark brown to black mica [$K(Mg, Fe)_3 AlSi_3O_{10}(OH)_2$] common in igneous and metamorphic rocks. Compare *muscovite*.

blastoid: A stalked echinoderm, in which cirrate food-gathering grooves extend along a pentameral globose body.

boreal: Northern, usually arctic and subarctic.

brucite: Natural magnesium hydroxide, $Mg(OH)_2$.

b.y. (or B.Y.): Billion years (years $\times 10^9$, or aeons). Also written b.yr.

Caledonides: Fold mountains resulting from the Caledonian orogeny during late Silurian and early Devonian time, espceially in Scotland and Scandinavia.

Campanian: The stage next below the top of the Upper Cretaceous series.

captorhinid: Belonging to the Captorhinidae, a family of captorhinomorphs (which see).

captorhinomorph: One of the Captorhinomorpha, a primitive suborder of Late Carboniferous and Early Permian cotylosaurian reptiles.

carbodiimide: An isomer of the compound H_2CN_2 having the form NH=C=NH; a tautomer of cyanamide.

carbonate: A mineral, rock, or compound in which a metal cation combines with the carbonate anion, $CO_3^{=}$. For instance, the rock called limestone consists primarily of the mineral calcite, $CaCO_3$; the rock magnesite consists of the mineral magnesite, $MgCO_3$; and the rock dolomite(or dolostone) consists of the mineral dolomite, $CaMg(CO_3)_2$.

carbonium: Refers to the carbonium or methyl ion, CH_3^-.

carboxylic: Containing or referring to the carboxyl group, COOH.

Carnic (Carnian): The basal stage of the marine Upper Triassic.

catalase: Any of several complex enzymes with molecular weights of 100,000 or more, which bring about the decomposition of peroxides in organisms.

cation: A positively charged ion, which moves to the

cathode (or negatively charged electrode) in electrolysis. Compare *anion.*

Cenomanian. Basal stage of the Upper Cretaceous.

cephalopod: A member of the molluscan class Cephalopoda, a group characterized by highly developed vision, by distinctive body structure, and, commonly, by a coiled or straight-chambered shell, the chambers being penetrated and connected by a tube, or siphuncle.

chitin: A complex polysaccharide, the principal component of the exoskeletons of certain arthropods. It also occurs in other organisms, including certain fungi.

cholestane: A 27-carbon sterane (which see).

chromatin: Cell material rich in nucleic acids, concentrated in the nucleus (if there is one) and in chromatin granules within the cytoplasm; so called because of its staining properties.

chromatogram: A tracing or spot-pattern produced by a chromatograph or by a chromatographic process (as a gas chromatograph or by paper chromatography) in which the reactions of different organic molecules cause them to occupy different distinctive positions.

circadian: Refers to rhythms in nature approximating the mean solar day; from *circa,* about, and *diem,* day. The word is incorrectly formed, but useful.

cirripede: A barnacle: a sedentary crustacean of the order Cirripedia, having a calcareous exoskeleton of many similar and overlapping parts, usually in the form of a truncated cone, a peaked oval, or a purselike structure.

cis-: On this side: in organic chemistry, a prefix that denotes isomeric hydrocarbons in which the substituting radicals are on the same side of a ring. Compare *trans-.*

class: Denotes a group of organisms next in rank below a phylum (or subphylum, or superclass) and above an order (or subclass, or superorder).

clast: A fragment of a detrital (or clastic) rock. Often used as a synonym for *megaclast,* a larger clastic particle within a rock of prevailingly finer grain.

clydonitic sutures: Sutures (which see) resembling those of the ammonite (which see) *Clydonites.*

Coastal Plain province: In the U.S. usually refers to the gently sloping eastern margin, veneered by Cenozoic and Cretaceous sediments, and extending from the Rio Grande to the Hudson River. It is divided into Gulf and Atlantic parts.

coelacanth: Any member of the Coelacanthidae, a family of primitive, lobe-finned, bony fishes of the superorder Crossopterygii.

coenzyme A: A protein molecule (much smaller than an enzyme) containing the vitamin pantothenic acid.

Condensation: In chemistry, refers to bonding between atoms or groups in the same or in different molecules to form a new compound of greater complexity and, commonly, of greater molecular weight, often with the elimination of water or some other by-product. Where no by-product is released, the reaction may be referred to as *polymerization.* In organic chemistry, the term *condensation* is usually reserved for a reaction involving the linkage of carbon atoms.

Coniacian: An intermediate stage of the Upper Cretaceous Series.

conodont: A small, phosphatic, toothlike hard-part found in Paleozoic and Mesozoic marine sediments. The conodont-bearing organism is as yet unknown.

coprostane: A 27-carbon sterane (which see).

cosmogony: Study of the origin of the universe and its parts.

cosmology: Study of the structure and evolution of the universe.

costations: Riblike linear ridges on the surface of a shell.

creodont: A member of the suborder Creodonta of the mammalian order Carnivora, showing relationships to the hoofed mammals and characteristic of lower Tertiary or Eogene strata.

crinoid: An echinoderm, generally stalked, in which cirrate food-gathering grooves are extended by means of arms that reach above a pentameral subglobose body.

cultigen: A plant race known only in the cultivated state.

cuspidate: Having a cusp or cusps; terminating in a point.

cyanamide: An isomer of the compound H_2CN_2 having the form CN—NH_2; a tautomer of carbodiimide.

cyanide: A compound containing the cyanide ion, CN^-; for example, hydrogen cyanide (HCN).

cyclic: In chemistry, the term refers to compounds having a ring or closed-chain structure, as in cyclic hydrocarbons. Where the ring consists of atoms of a single kind, the compound is homocyclic or isocyclic; where it is made of atoms of different kinds, it is heterocyclic.

cynodont: A member of the Cynodontia, a South African suborder of the mammallike therapsid reptiles.

cytochrome: Any of various iron porphyrin proteins, found in all cells capable of aerobic metabolism, which aid in transduction of absorbed energy to ATP, and which, on catalysis, absorb free O_2.

cytoplasm: The contents of a cell, excluding the nucleus.

cytosine: A pyrimidine, and one of the nucleotide bases that link with sugar-phosphate chains to form DNA and RNA.

dacite: An extrusive igneous rock having a high silica content and showing phenocrysts of plagioclase and quartz in a glassy matrix.

D-amino acid: A dextro, or right-handedly asymmetrical, amino acid.

Danian: The basal stage of the marine Cenozoic.

decarboxylation: The removal of a carboxyl group (COOH) from a chemical compound.

décollement: See *detachment thrust.*

ΔF (delta F): Free energy of formation: the energy, in calories, lost or gained in a chemical reaction where the same grouping of elements is transformed from one molecular arrangement to another.

dendrochronology: The determination of chronologies of past events by the comparative study of the growth rings of trees.

deoxyribonucleic acid: See *DNA.*

detachment thrust: A thrust fault produced by gravitational movement along a gliding surface.

diagenetic: Referring to the changes that take place in the conversion of a sediment to a rock (diagenesis), and to the processes that bring these changes about. The diagenetic realm grades into the metamorphic realm, comprising the changes and processes that convert an already formed rock into a different kind of rock.

diapir: A piercement fold; that is, an anticline or a dome produced or affected by a mobile core, such as salt, that has been injected from beneath, cutting across and deforming the overlying strata.

diastem: Any gap in a sequence. Usually refers to an interruption in sedimentation not conspicuous enough to be an unconformity or a disconformity. Bedding surfaces (planes) can be considered diastems, especially if they are sharp or slightly irregular, implying discontinuity.

diatom: Any of various microscopic golden-brown algae of the class Bacillariophyceae, having siliceous bivalved tests and distinctive surface ornamentation; an important group of Cretaceous and Cenozoic marine and nonmarine organisms.

dicarboxylic: Containing, or referring to, a pair of carboxyl ions.

dicyanamide: A dimer of cyanamide.

dike: A tabular cross-cutting body of rock. Dikes ordinarily consist of igneous rocks, but sedimentary rocks that have been injected across rocks of different kinds are also called dikes.

dimer: A pair of monomers, chemically bonded.

dimethallyl pyrophosphate: An isomer comparable to isopentenyl pyrophosphate.

dimict: Consisting of two classes or modes, as dimictite (or diamictite) sediment consists of relatively large clasts in a finer-grained matrix.

dinoflagellate: One of the Dinoflagellata, a class of the order Dinophyceae, a group of minute, mostly marine, phytoplanktonic protists, having a girdle and two flagella at the middle of the body, and a chitinous internal cyst.

disconformity: See *unconformity.*

DNA: Deoxyribonucleic acid, a large, two-stranded, helicoid nucleic acid that contains deoxyribose. It is the genetic coding and replicating molecule, and also serves as a template for the manufacture of RNA—a much smaller single-stranded molecule having a different base composition.

docodont: One of the Docodontidae, a family of the mammalian order Pantotheria from the Upper Jurassic, distinguished by their specialized molar teeth.

drift: Glacial deposits.

dropstones: Rock fragments, pebbles, or cobbles that have dropped from above into finer-grained sediments, as from melting ice into lacustrine or marine sediments.

e^-/β' branching ratio: Ratio of electron capture to beta decay. Referring to radiometric changes in K^{40}, for instance, this is the ratio between nuclear capture of an orbital electron to form Ar^{40} and emission of a nuclear electron (β decay) to form Ca^{40}.

eclogite: A granular rock of high density composed essentially of garnet and pyroxene.

edaphosaurid: A member of the Edaphosauria, a suborder of pelycosaurs (early mammallike reptiles) characterized by blunt teeth.

Eh: A measure of oxidation (or oxidation-reduction) potential, given in volts or millivolts, as determined from the flow of electrons between a reference (calomel) electrode and an inert platinum) electrode. In a relative sense, positive Eh indicates an oxidizing potential and negative Eh a reducing one.

endemic: Confined to, indigenous in, or native to a certain place or region. The term is usually used in reference to organisms.

enzyme: A protein that catalyzes biological reactions.

Eocambrian: A term used by some writers alternatively to indicate the uppermost pre-Paleozoic or the basal Paleozoic (but below the Cambrian).

eolian: Pertaining to wind.

epeirogeny: See *tectonic.*

epicontinental: On the continent.

epipsammonic: Living on the sand.

epizonal: Referring literally to the "upper zone" of metamorphism, or, in effect, to a metamorphic environment of low temperature and pressure characterized both by chemical and mechanical metamorphism and by the conspicuous development of hydrous silicates.

ergostane: A 28-carbon steroid.

erosional unconformity: See *unconformity.*

esker: A usually sinuous linear ridge of gravel resulting from deposition in streams of subglacial melt water.

ester: A compound formed by reaction between an alcohol and an acid (with the elimination of water), and only slightly ionized in solution.

ethmoid turbinals: Delicate grooved and folded bones along the side walls of the nasal cavity in the mammalian skull.

eucaryote. An organism consisting of eucaryotic cells. The eucaryotic cell differs from the procarotic cell in having a nucleus enclosed within a nuclear membrane and well-defined chromosomes, organelles, and in being capable of mitotic cell division, by which the genetic coding material is successively parceled out among different cells and descendant organisms.

eugeosyncline: An elongate subsiding depression parallel to, and offshore from, a continental shield or craton, and in which are deposited sediments that contain interbedded (usually mafic) volcanics and an abundance of graywackes. Eugeosynclines are often visualized as the trench deposits of former island-arc and trench systems. See also *geosyncline.*

Eurydesma fauna: A marine invertebrate fauna characterized by the distinctive pelecypod *Eurydesma,* widely distributed in marine strata interbedded with tillites in the Upper Carboniferous and Permian of the southern hemisphere.

eurypterid: A member of the extinct scorpionlike order Eurypterida of the class Arachnoidea of the phylum Arthropoda. Eurypterids are nearshore marine predators found especially in Silurian and Lower Devonian rocks.

eurytopic: Tolerating a wide variety of habitat conditions.

eustatic: At the same level. Referring to simultaneous world-wide changes in sea level, as from the formation and melting of ice sheets, or from a change in the volume of the ocean basins.

euxinic (euxine): From *Pontus Euxinus,* the Black Sea, an area of restricted circulation, density stratification, anoxygenous bottom waters, and reduced sediments—hence the adjective *euxinic,* to denote such an area.

excess volatiles: Refers to the H_2O, CO_2, Cl, N, S, and so forth, in the present atmosphere and hydrosphere that cannot be accounted for by release from the volume of rocks weathered during geologic time; and which must, therefore, have arrived at the earth's surface as a result of outgassing from below. For example, of the 14.6×10^{17} metric tons of H_2O at the earth's surface, a maximum of about 0.9 percent could have come from rock weathering; the other 99.1 percent is thus referred to as excess volatiles.

facies: Aspect, appearance. Denotes the characteristic expression, or variation in expression, of a unit or related set of rocks or fossils.

fall line: A line connecting the heads of navigation of a series of rivers draining the same topographic region where the navigable reaches are terminated by waterfalls or rapids related to a common change in slope. Usually refers to the Atlantic border of the U.S., and the succession of cities located at the navigable heads of its principal rivers.

fault: A break in the earth's crust along which perceptible movement has occurred.

feldspar: Any of various complex potassium-, sodium-, and calcium-rich aluminum silicates that are designated as plagioclase, when rich in sodium or calcium, or as orthoclase, microcline, or K-feldspar, when rich in potassium.

felsic: Refers to light-colored igneous rocks containing an abundance of feldspar and silica. Also designated as *acid.* Compare *mafic.*

fermentation: Anaerobic metabolism in which sugars are converted to alcohols with liberation of energy; for example:

$$C_6H_{12}O_6 \rightarrow \underset{\text{(ethyl alcohol)}}{2CH_3CH_2OH} + 2CO_2 + 50 \text{ Cal/mole}$$

See also *glycolysis, oxidative metabolism,* and *photosynthesis.*

fissiped: A member of the suborder Fissipedia of the mammalian order Carnivora, including dogs, cats, and bears.

ferredoxin: A simple iron-containing protein with only 55 amino acid residues but playing a key part in vital processes. Found in most (if not all) organisms, it is involved in oxidation, reduction, transfer of energy, fixation of nitrogen, formation of ATP, and synthesis of pyruvate.

fluviatile: Having to do with streams.

fluvioglacial: Pertaining to streams adjacent to glaciers; for instance, to gravels and sand deposited by periglacial streams.

flysch: A distinctive, thick assemblage of fine-grained, shaly, pelagic, sedimentary rocks episodically interbedded with extensive layers of impure sandstone and graywacke that commonly show graded bedding and sole markings of physical and biologic origin. Fossils, other than trace fossils and those of pelagic species, are uncommon in such sediments and have usually been carried there by submarine slides that moved from shallower to deeper water.

foliation: A laminated structure in a rock that results from segregation of minerals into parallel layers, often interpreted as the reflection of shearing stresses. Essentially synonymous with *flow cleavage* and *schistosity*.

Foraminifera (forams, foraminifers): An order of planktonic to benthonic, chambered, marine Protozoa having a hard, calcareous or agglutinated external covering or test, which, in many forms, is perforated by minute holes or foramina.

formaldehyde: The molecule CH_2O.

formate: A salt or ester of formic acid (HCOOH).

formation: A local rock unit of distinctive lithology suitable for representation as a fundamental stratigraphic subdivision on a geologic map or correlation chart. Formations may transgress time divisions, or may locally equate with them; and the boundaries between formations may be gradational, abrupt, or laterally transitional. A formation name denotes merely the persistence of a particular set of lithic characteristics over the space where that name is used. See Reading Selection 19.

freeboard to root ratio: The ratio between that part of an isostatically balanced, light (sialic) portion of the earth's crust that stands above the general surface, as a mountain or plateau, and that part that projects downward into heavier (simatic) material beneath.

frigophilic: Cold-loving. Synonymous with the more usual *psychrophilic*.

fructification: Any fruiting body, as a cone, fruit, or berry.

fusulinid (fusuline): Any member of the family Fusulinidae of the order Foraminifera (which see).

Gangamopteris: A genus of fossil fernlike plants of Permian and Triassic age, *Gangomopteris* is considered characteristic of the Gondwana flora.

garnet: A member of a group of complex silicate minerals whose general formula is $A_3B_2(SiO_4)_8$, where A is calcium, magnesium, iron, or manganese, and B is aluminum, iron, manganese, or chromium. The presence of garnet in metamorphic or igneous rocks implies sedimentary contamination.

geanticline: A broad upfold, or uplifted land area, from which the sediments in a geosyncline are derived.

genotype: The genetic composition of the individual, which, through interaction with environmental factors, determines the phenotype, or the morphological characteristics displayed by that individual. The term has been used in taxonomy to refer to the single species upon which a genus is based; but to avoid confusion, the term *type species* is now more commonly used in that sense.

geosyncline: A locus of relatively great subsidence and sedimentation from which fold mountains later arise as a result of thermal weakening and compression. Geosynclines may be of any shape, but they are usually visualized as relatively long and narrow. Concepts of plate tectonics are bringing about a reexamination of the characteristics and classification of geosynclines.

glaciolacustrine: Pertaining to glacial lakes.

glauconite: A complex hydrous potassium iron silicate having a micaceous structure and occurring characteristically as green or yellowish ovoidal grains in marine sediments.

g.l.c.: Gas liquid chromatograph, a device for chromatographic identification of organic chemicals.

Globigerina ooze: A marine deposit of intermediate (but generally bathyal) depth consisting largely of the tests (or "shells") of tiny foraminiferan Protozoa of the family Globigerinidae (including the genus *Globigerina*).

Glossopteris: A genus of fossil fernlike plants of Permian and Triassic age, *Glossopteris* is considered characteristic of the Gondwana flora.

glucose: A sugar having the composition $C_6H_{12}O_6$, which occurs naturally in the optical form known as dextrose.

glucosidic acid: An acid incorporating the glucose molecule.

glutamic aid: One of the amino acids.

glycine: An amino acid.

glycolysis: Anaerobic metabolism in which sugars are converted to lactic acid with liberation of energy. In simplified form, the reaction is as follows:

$$C_6H_{12}O_6 \rightarrow \underset{\text{(lactic acid)}}{2CH_3CH(OH)COOH} + 36 \text{ Cal/mole}$$

See also *fermentation, oxidative metabolism,* and *photosynthesis.*

Gondwana: A geological term denoting an inferred, continuously connected supercontinent in the southern hemisphere that included the present southern continents, plus India, and broke up in Mesozoic time. Literally, "forest of the Gonds" (from a district in India). It is sometimes called *Gondwanaland.*

granitization: Process of forming a granite by pervasive melting and assimilation of pre-existing rocks of suitable chemical composition, as contrasted to the formation of granite by consolidation from an initial melt.

granodiorite: A plutonic igneous rock that contains at least twice as much plagioclase as orthoclase, in addition to quartz and dark minerals.

graptolite: A member of the Graptolithina, a group of extinct, mainly planktonic organisms of uncertain systematic rank and position, but seemingly related to the invertebrate chordates of the subphylum Hemichordata. Graptolites are characterized by a chitinous exoskeleton or periderm, and a colonial habit of growth consisting of linear arrays of individuals grouped in a variety of distinctive patterns. They are restricted to the lower Paleozoic, and are considered good index fossils for the Ordovician and Silurian.

graywacke: A detrital rock that includes particles of pre-existing rock, as well as mineral grains, in a matrix of clay and silt-sized particles of silica. A characteristic eugeosynclinal sediment, graywacke commonly shows graded bedding and other characteristics of flysch-facies sedimentation.

greenstone: Any of various altered, mafic, igneous rocks having a green color due to the presence of the alteration minerals chlorite, hornblende, and epidote (as well as to the presence of any altered sediments associated with them).

ground moraine: See *moraine.*

Guanine: A purine, and one of the nucleotide bases that link with sugar-phosphate chains to form DNA and RNA.

guanylurea: A nitrogenous organic compound derived from guanine and urea.

guyot: A flat-topped seamount.

gymnosperm: A member of the class Gymnospermae of the phylum Tracheophyta (vascular plants) —a naked-seeded plant, its seeds being borne on special cones or conelike fructifications.

HCN: Hydrogen cyanide—one of the prime products of irradiation of model early atmospheres, which, under continuing high-energy irradiation in aqueous solution, may polymerize or combine with different substances to form a variety of amino acids and other biologically interesting molecules.

hemera: The period of time during which a species of organisms was at its evolutionary apex.

heterocyclic: A chemical ring composed of atoms of different kinds.

heterotroph: An organism that is unable to synthesize its own foodstuffs, and which is, therefore, dependent on available substances to grow and reproduce. Early heterotrophs, also anaerobes, presumably depended on a supply of abiogenically produced organic compounds; later, they became dependent on autotrophs as a source of food.

hexametaphosphate: A salt or ester of hexametaphosphoric acid.

hexametaphosphoric acid: A metaphosphoric acid having the composition $(HPO_3)_6$.

histogram: A kind of bar graph consisting of rectangles whose heights represent class frequencies and whose widths represent class intervals.

holarctic: Pertaining to the Arctic regions collectively.

homeostatic: Said of biologic systems that operate in accordance with Le Chatelier's principle—namely, that when one aspect of a dynamic equilibrium is disturbed, the system reacts in such a way as to restore the balance.

homeothermy (or homoiothermy): Warm-bloodedness; referring to the maintenance of a constant body temperature, as by mammals.

homotaxial. Having the same arrangement; a term proposed by T. H. Huxley to denote successions of fossil assemblages observed to be similar from one place to another, but not necessarily contemporaneous. Indeed, Huxley argued that, because of time required for migration, similar homotaxial arrangements in widely separated regions were probably not contemporaneous.

hornblende: A calcium- and sodium-rich monoclinic member of the group of complex aluminum silicates known as amphiboles. Hornblende is the commonest amphibole.

hydrocarbon: A compound that contains only hydrogen and carbon. Hydrocarbons are divided into straight-chain hydrocarbons and branched hydrocarbons, according to the geometry of the hydrocarbon chains.

hydrogenate: To combine with hydrogen.

hydrogenolysis: The splitting of a molecule by the addition of two hydrogens.

hydrogen peroxide: H_2O_2, a compound highly reactive and destructive to organic matter.

hydroxy acid: An acid that has one or more accessory hydroxyl groups besides that in the acid molecule itself. Examples are tartaric, salicylic, and lactic acids.

hydroxyl: Refers to the OH radical.

hystrichospherid: One of the Hystrichosphaeridae, a group of minute, usually spiny, chitinous marine nannofossils interpreted as the internal cysts of dinoflagellates, but included with the acritarchs.

Ictidosauria: A late Triassic order of either very advanced mammallike reptiles or very primitive mammals.

illaenid: Any member of the Illaenidae, a family of Ordovician and Silurian trilobites with large smooth cephalons and pygidiums.

Inarticulata: A class of the phylum Brachiopoda (a group of dorsoventrally bivalved marine animals). The members of the class have opposing chitino-phosphatic valves ("half-shells") that gape and close, or slide apart and together, without benefit of an articulated hinge-line. Compare *Articulata.*

indigenous: Endemic, autochthonous, or occurring naturally within a particular place or region.

infaunal: Living within sediments below the depositional interface.

infraorder: In systematic nomenclature, a hierarchical rank subordinate to a suborder but higher than a superfamily.

ion: An atom, or group of atoms, that carries an electric charge, because of its having lost or gained one or more electrons.

ionium method: Ionium is an obsolete term for the isotope thorium-230, which is involved in several nuclear dating methods. The ionium method depends on the assumption that the excess radium in oceanic sediments comes almost exclusively from rapidly precipitated Th^{230} (while its parents U^{234} and U^{238} remain in solution). It is useful for determining ages of 200,000–300,000 years. A more reliable method for oceanic sediments younger than 100,000 years is the *protactinium-thorium method,* using the ratio of Pa^{231} to Th^{230}; these isotopes have different half-lives but similar chemical behavior.

isochron: A line connecting points that indicate the same time value. The term is most frequently used to denote the curve defined by an array of the ratios of end members of nuclear decay series whose slope is interpreted as the age of the array.

isogam: A line connecting equal magnetic values (from *gamma,* a unit of gravity measurement equal to 10^{-5} oersted).

intracratonic: Within a craton or shield area; that is, an area of ancient crystalline rocks around which continents have grown and over which platform-type sediments may have been deposited.

isomer: One of two or more substances consisting of the same numbers of atoms of the same elements but with differing structural arrangement and properties.

isomyarian: Pertaining to pelecypods that have two adductor muscles of nearly equal size, or to the muscles themselves, or to their attachment scars.

isopach: A line connecting points of equal thickness of a designated unit on an isopachous map to show the varying thicknesses of any rock body or of deposits overlying any given surface.

isopentenyl: A five-carbon hydrocarbon radical, with a methyl side-chain and a double bond, $(CH_3)_2CH(CH_2)_2$.

isopentenyl pyrophosphate: A pyrophosphate (which see) containing the five-carbon isopentenyl radical.

isoprene: A five-carbon unsaturated hydrocarbon and terpene precursor, having the same chemical composition as natural rubber but a slightly different molecular configuration:

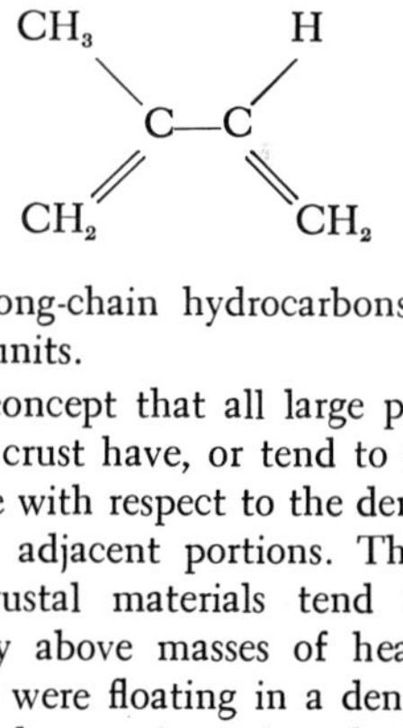

isoprenoids: Long-chain hydrocarbons made up of isoprene units.

isostasy: The concept that all large portions of the planetary crust have, or tend to attain, a state of balance with respect to the density of underlying and adjacent portions. Thus, masses of lighter crustal materials tend to rise topographically above masses of heavier material, as if they were floating in a denser underlying matrix; light continental rocks, for example, ride higher than the more dense rocks that floor the ocean basins.

isotope: A form (or atomic species) of an element having the same chemical properties as another isotope of the same element but having a different atomic weight. See also *nuclide.*

isotropy: The condition of having the same properties in all directions.

°K: Degrees Kelvin; referring to an absolute scale of temperature in which degree intervals equal those of the Celsius (centigrade) scale, but in which zero °K equals −273.16°C.

kame morane: Moraine consisting primarily of kame deposits, a kame being a mound or hill of stratified ice-contact drift. Kames are formed in a variety of locales—in crevasses or other depressions in or through the ice, between ice and valley wall, at the glacier front, etc. Often they are parts of other features, as of ablation moraines, or may comprise the bulk of a moraine.

kame terraces: Terraces found in glaciated valleys and representing the stratified deposits of glacial meltwaters flowing off or along the ice at the valley margin.

K-Ar: A radiometric dating method utilizing the ratio between potassium-40 and its daughter product argon-40. The validity of the results depends both on the accuracy of knowledge of the rate of decay of K^{40} to Ar^{40} (a process that takes place by electron capture) and on certain geologic factors, such as argon loss and the absorption of argon by pyroxenes.

K^{40}-Ca^{40}: A radiometric dating method utilizing the ratio between potassium-40 and its daughter product calcium-40. The validity of the results depends both on the accuracy of knowledge of the rate of decay of K^{40} to Ca^{40} (a process that takes place by emission of beta particles) and on certain geologic factors, such as the fact that Ca^{40} is the common isotope of calcium.

keratophyre: A mafic lava or dike rock that contains albite (or albite oligoclase), chlorite, epidote, and calcite. Keratophyric rocks are commonly associated with spilites and marine sediments in island-arc complexes.

K-feldspar (or K-spar): A potassium-rich variety of feldspar (which see).

Kimmeridgian: The middle stage of the Upper Jurassic Series.

Kittatinny surface: Accordant bench levels related to Pleistocene erosion of the Appalachian Mountains.

Labyrinthodontia: A superorder of the class Amphibia, comprising solid-skulled, mostly large, salamanderlike amphibians of the late Paleozoic and early Mesozoic that are characterized by complex infolding of the dentine of their teeth.

L-amino acid: A left-handedly asymmetrical amino acid.

lacustrine: Pertaining to lakes.

Laramide orogeny: The term is widely used to designate a long lasting episode of fold-mountain construction that began perhaps as early as Jurassic time, extended well into Cenozoic time, and is perhaps still going on. Strictly speaking, the term applies only to early Cenozoic movements—those of "Laramie time." It affected, primarily, the Rocky Mountain region; hence, the larger orogeny is also called the *Rocky Mountain orogeny*.

lee plucking: In glaciology, refers to the tendency of ice motion to pluck out and carry away relatively large, irregular blocks of rock from the lee ends of glacially modified rock forms, such as *roches moutonnées*.

left-lateral: In geology, refers to a strike-slip or transcurrent fault along which the movement on the side opposite the viewer has been to the left (when viewed from either side).

Liassic (or Lias): Lower division (or series) of European Jurassic beds in areas where stages are not defined.

lifetime: See *mean life*.

light-year: The distance light would travel in a vacuum in one year; that is, 9.46×10^{12} km, or 6×10^{12} miles [the speed of light being about 294,000 km (or 186,000 miles) per second].

lingulid: A kind of inarticulate brachiopod (see *Inarticulata*).

Lipalian: Pertaining to the Lipalian interval, a once supposedly world-wide break in the preserved geologic record between latest Precambrian and earliest Cambrian time. Also sometimes used to designate the younger Precambrian, or sediments from that part of geologic time.

lipid: Any of a group of substances characterized by a greasy feel, insolubility in water, solubility in chloroform and similar solvents, and comprising the fats and other esters having similar properties.

lithophile element: An element, such as silicon and iron, that tends to be incorporated in rocks.

litoptern: Any member of the Litopterna, an order of hoofed mammals of the Tertiary of South America that underwent an evolution parallel to, but separate from, the North American hoofed mammals, including horselike forms. They became extinct when the early Pleistocene Panamanian land bridge permitted the entry into South America of North American carnivores and competing hoofed mammals.

littoral: An oceanographic term broadly used to denote the nearshore environment. It also has two more formal definitions: the first, and now most generally used, denotes the sea bottom between the beach and the 200-meter line; the second denotes the sea bottom in the intertidal zone only.

"looking glass" sugars: Sugars that are structural mirror images of one another, being optically either dextro- or levo-rotatory.

lucinoid: Like *Lucina*, a distinctive marine pelecypod genus.

luminosity: Intensity of radiation of light-energy by a star or other heavenly body. The apparent luminosity is that recorded by the observer, uncorrected for distance. The intrinsic luminosity is the real "brightness," that is apparent luminosity multiplied by the square of the distance from observer to object.

"lumpers": Taxonomists who tend to use the minimum possible number of species and other systematic names. Compare *"splitters."*

Lyman line: One of a series of absorption or emission lines in the hydrogen spectrum resulting from transitions to and from the lowest energy states of the hydrogen atoms. The Lyman α-line is a standard astronomical calibration point that is normally found in the invisible ultra-violent, but which in very distant stellar sources may undergo "red shifts" into the visible blue spectrum.

M: Abbreviation of *molar* (which see).

$M_{\odot}$: Mass of the sun.

macro-: Prefix denoting large dimensions.

macroevolution: Evolutionary change from one species to another or from one higher systematic category to another, as compared to *microevolution*, which denotes changes within species.

Maestrichtian: The uppermost stage of the Upper Cretaceous Series.

mafic: Refers to dark-colored igneous rocks that consist mainly of magnesium- and iron-rich silicate minerals. Also called *basic*. Contrasts with *felsic* (which see).

magma: Molten material below ground (before it emerges at the surface to become a lava, or crystallizes below ground to form an intrusive igneous rock).

magnetohydrodynamic processes: Processes involving motions of hot ionized gases moving along magnetic fields in space.

Malthusian principle: That populations, especially human populations, must eventually be limited by the availability of resources, especially food.

mammallike reptiles: The subclass Synapsida, including the pelycosaurs and the therapsids, intermediate in evolutionary stage between the other reptiles and the most primitive true mammals.

Mankato: A substage of the Wisconsin, the uppermost glacial stage of the Pleistocene. Although the term is sometimes used to indicate the youngest glacial substage of the Wisconsin (now Valders), the Mankato is probably somewhat older—about equivalent to, or a little younger than, the Carey substage.

marl: A soft calcareous sediment that contains a lot of shell debris and is often clayey.

mass spectrometer: An instrument for separating, identifying, and measuring isotopes of the elements by deflection of their gaseous ions moving at high velocity in a strong magnetic field, the deflection being proportional to the atomic weight.

M discontinuity (Mohorovičić discontinuity, or Moho): A discontinuity in the velocity of transmission of seismic waves, usually taken as denoting the boundary between the crust and mantle of the earth.

mean life: In atomic physics and radiochemistry, refers to the statistically expectable duration of an atom of a given radioactive isotope taken at random from any large population of atoms of that isotope. Found by multiplying the number of atoms decaying at any time by the time elapsed, integrated from time zero to infinity. The mean life is equivalent to the half life of the decaying isotope divided by the natural logarithm of 2. Thus, for C^{14}, a half life of 5730 years divided by 0.693 gives a mean life of about 8270 years.

mega-: Prefix denoting large dimensions.

megafossils: Fossils easily visible to the naked eye and likely to be studied at low magnifications or without optical aids.

melamine: An amino compound consisting of three amines bonded to a ring of three nitrogens, $N_3(NH_2)_3$.

Mesozone: The intermediate level of temperature and pressure (hence, depth) at which certain categories of metamorphic and plutonic rocks were formed or emplaced.

meta-: A prefix meaning altered or transposed; hence, *metamorphic* (having a changed form); *metasedimentary* (a metamorphic rock of sedimentary origin); *metavolcanic*; and so forth.

metacryst: A relatively large and well-formed crystal within a generally finer-grained metamorphic rock; for example, garnet in mica schists. Also called *porphyroblast*.

metameric: In zoology, refers to serial segmentation of the body, or to the arrangement of similar body parts in longitudinal series, as in a centipede or trilobite.

metaphosphoric acid: A phosphoric acid consisting of chains of 3–6 phosphate tetrahedra bonded by oxygen atoms, and having the composition $(HPO_3)_x$, where x is 3, 4, 5, or 6.

metaphosphate: A salt or ester of metaphosphoric acid.

metazoan: Pertaining to the Metazoa; that is, to multicellular animal life in which more than one kind of cell is organized into tissues or organs.

mevalonic acid: A biosynthetic precursor of terpenes and steroids.

mica: Any of several varieties of silicate mineral that split into paper-thin sheets or flakes.

micro-: Prefix denoting small size.

μmole (micromole): One millionth of a mole, or one thousandth of a millimole.

μ (micron): One thousandth of a millimeter.

Migmatite: Also called *composite gneiss* or *injection gneiss*, migmatite (literally "mixed rocks") is produced by injection of granitic magma into schist in a bed-by-bed manner, or by local alteration to granite in a similar pattern.

milligal: One thousandth of a gal. The gal (for Galileo) is the standard unit of measurement of variation in the force of gravity, being equal to an acceleration of one centimeter per second.

miogeosyncline: An elongate area of subsidence and sedimentation at the edge of a craton or continental shield, ordinarily located between the craton and a eugeosyncline. Miogeosynclinal deposits are, characteristically, mature sediments of the shelf facies without a conspicuous volcanic component. See also *geosyncline*.

mmole (millimole): One thousandth of a mole.

molar: In chemistry, refers to a solution that contains one mole of solute per liter of solution. A *molal* solution, by comparison, contains one mole of solute per kilogram of solvent.

molasse: An array of sedimentary types contrasting to *flysch* (which see). Mainly near-shore marine and nonmarine sediments, with gravel, conglomerate, and coarse sandstone conspicuous, but including also fresh-water limestones and other fine-grained lake sediments. From an old Swiss vernacular term.

mole (or mol): A gram-molecule, or that quantity of a substance equivalent to its molecular weight expressed in grams.

molecular oxygen: O_2, made up of pairs of oxygen atoms; the usual and least reactive form of oxygen.

monocline: A flexure in the earth's crust along which rocks change from nearly horizontal to perceptibly inclined.

monomer: Basic building block that can be linked into a polymer by repetition of a single reaction. Thus, amino acids, which are monomers, can polymerize to yield peptides, polypeptides, and proteins.

Monoplacophora: A primitive class of molluscs, the members of which have single shells, paired muscle scars, and nontwisted nervous systems.

monsoonal: Pertaining to persistent winds that alternate directions annually as a result of seasonal temperature changes, such that the wind blows from land toward sea when the land is relatively cool (during the dry season) and from the sea toward land when the land is relatively warm (during the rainy season).

Montian: The basal stage of the Paleocene in Europe.

monzonite: A plutonic igneous rock that contains nearly equal amounts of orthoclase and plagioclase feldspars, as well as small amounts of quartz and dark minerals. When quartz exceeds 2 percent of its volume it is called *quartz monzonite*.

moraine: A chaotic deposit of usually angular rock fragments from diverse sources suspended in a matrix of rock flour. Moraines are deposited from melting glacial ice, either at the edge of a glacier (lateral moraine), at the end of a glacier (terminal moraine), where glaciers and their lateral moraines converge (medial moraine), or when a sheet of ice wastes away (ground moraine).

moulin kame: A stratified deposit formed in a nearly vertical shaft in a wasting glacier from the accumulation of sand and gravel washed in by surface meltwater.

multituberculate: Pertaining to the Multituberculata, an order of small Mesozoic and Eocene mammals of the subclass Allotheria, having a rodentlike habit and teeth with many small prominences.

muscovite: White mica. The commonest form of mica, it is a hydrous potassium aluminum silicate, essentially $KAl_2(AlSi_3O_{10})(OH)_2$. Compare *biotite*.

m.y.: Million years. Used in connection with a preceding number to refer to the age of a rock $\times 10^6$; often written m.yr.

nannofossil: A very small microfossil, diameter usually under 100 microns–by analogy from *nannoplankton*.

nannoplankton: Plankton so small that they pass through an ordinary plankton net.

Neocomian: The basal stage of the marine Cretaceous (sometimes replaced by three or four other stages).

neontologist: A person who studies living organisms; hence, a zoologist or a botanist.

Nevadan (or Nevadian) **orogeny:** Tectonism and batholithic emplacement extending from Jurassic into Cretaceous time in the western U.S.; exemplified by the Sierra Nevada.

new global tectonics: See *plate tectonics.*

niche: In ecology, denotes the sum of biological and physical factors necessary for the successful existence of a particular species of organism, or the habitat supplying those factors.

nonconformity: See *unconformity.*

Noric (Norian): The median stage of the marine Upper Triassic.

normal fault: A fault which, when viewed in vertical profile, shows downward movement along the side that makes an acute angle with the earth's surface (the "hanging wall" moves down).

nova: An exploding star whose sudden increase in radiant energy temporarily increases its luminosity by two to three orders of magnitude. Compare *supernova.*

nucleic acid: An organic acid characteristic of the cell nucleus; for example, deoxyribonucleic acid (DNA) and ribonucleic acid (RNA).

nucleotide: The basic unit building-blocks of the nucleic acids RNA and DNA; a nucleotide consists of the nucleotide base in combination with sugar and phosphoric acid.

nucleotide bases: The basic ring structures or "side chains" from which nucleotides are built. Nucleotide bases include the purines adenine and guanine, and the pyrimidines thymine, cytosine, and uracil. These, in combination with sugar and phosphoric acid, yield the nucleotides adenylic acid, guanylic acid, thyminic acid, cytidilic acid, and uridylic acid.

nucleus: That part of the cell in which the DNA or genetic coding material is concentrated.

nuclide: A species of atom characterized by the sum of protons and neutrons in its nucleus. See also *isotope.*

nuculoid: Resembling *Nucula*, a small genus of nutlike marine pelecypods with a distinctive denticulate hinge line.

obsidian: A volcanic glass, usually felsic (or silicic, or "acid") in composition and often grading into rhyolite.

olefin: Any of a class of open-chain hydrocarbons containing double or triple bonds; hence, unsaturated hydrocarbons.

olivine: A member of a mineral series comprising important rock-forming ferromagnesian silicates, olivine is a solid-solution series with the end members Mg_2SiO_4 (fayalite). It is characteristic of oceanic basalts and other mafic and ultramafic rocks.

ontogeny: The sequence of steps in the development of an individual organism from fertilized ovum or bud to adult.

ophiacodont: One of the Ophiacodontia, a Permian suborder of pelycosaurian reptiles (which see).

opisthodetic: Refers to a pelecypod (clam) in which the ligament that opens the shell is attached behind the beak or umbone, or to a ligament of that nature.

Orbitolina: A genus of relatively large foraminifers of Tertiary age.

order: Denotes a group of organisms next in rank below a class (or a subclass or superorder) and above a family (or superfamily or suborder).

orogenic: Refers to mountain building. An orogeny is a specific episode of mountain building. See also *tectonic.*

orthoclase: A potassium-rich feldspar (which see).

orthogenetic: Referring to persistent, strikingly directional, evolutionary trends, often interpreted as predestined and nonselective.

osteology: The study of the bones and bony structure of vertebrate animals.

outwash apron: A broad zone of fluviatile deposition washed out from the down-valley end of a glacier.

Oxfordian: The basal stage of the Upper Jurassic Series.

oxidative metabolism: Aerobic metabolism (respiration) in which sugars are converted to carbon dioxide with liberation of energy; in simplified manner, as follows:

$$C_6H_{12}O_6 + 6H_2O + 6O_2 \rightarrow$$
$$6CO_2 + 12H_2O + 686 \text{ Cal/mole (as ATP)}.$$

ozone: O_3, each molecule consisting of three atoms of oxygen; a highly reactive and unstable form of oxygen. The decomposition of 1 gram of ozone to oxygen is accompanied by the liberation of 675 calories of energy. Ozone is formed by the absorption of light in the far UV region (1,600–1,800 Å) by O_2, yielding 2 atoms of O, and a subsequent thermal reaction between O and O_2. The concentration of ozone in a layer about 15 miles above the earth's surface shields the earth from UV radiation in the range of 2,400–3,000 Å, owing to the absorption of these wavelengths by ozone.

pallasite: A kind of meteorite composed of nearly equal parts of metal and silicate. Also called *stony irons, siderolites,* and *syssiderites.*

pallial line: In a mollusc, the line along which the mantle is (or was) attached to the shell.

paraconformity: See *unconformity.*

parallax: The apparent angular displacement of an object when viewed from two different points.

parsec: The distance defined by a stellar parallax of one second of arc; taken as equivalent to a distance of 3.26 light years.

patination: The process of producing a patina or weathered surface film, as on a metal or a rock, by oxidation, hydration, or other processes.

pedal: Pertaining to the foot, as muscles that affect the movement of the foot of certain pelecypods are called pedal muscles.

pelycosaur: A member of the Pelycosauria, an order of mammallike reptiles (subclass Synapsida) comprising Permian carnivorous forms with long, slender, dorsal spines.

pentose: Any of a group of simple sugars containing five oxygen atoms and not fermentable by yeasts.

peptide: Relatively small polymers of amino acids; the subunits of proteins.

peridote: A common variety of olivene.

peridotite: An ultramafic plutonic rock consisting essentially of olivene, with or without other mafic minerals but definitely without feldspar.

periglacial: Marginal to glaciers or glacial deposits.

perissodactyl: A member of the order Perissodactyla, the odd-toed hoofed mammals.

pH: A measure of acidity or basicity, giving the hydrogen ion concentration expressed as the negative logarithm to the base 10 of the measured concentration in grams per liter of solution. A *p*H of 7 is neutral; a *p*H of less than 7 is acidic, and one between 7 and 14 is basic.

Phanerozoic: That part of geologic time during which a "visible" or metazoan fauna has existed.

phase transition: In mineralogy and petrology, a change involving physical transformations only, without change in bulk chemical composition.

phenoclast: A fragment within a detrital rock that is conspicuously larger than adjacent clasts or grains.

phenocryst: A relatively large and well-defined crystal within the finer-grained matrix of a porphyritic igneous rock. Corresponds to *metacryst* in a metamorphic rock, and to *phenoclast* (or, simply, *clast*) in a sedimentary rock.

phenol: An organic acidic compound, C_6H_5OH. It is caustic and poisonous.

phenotype: The physical appearance of an organism, resulting from interaction between its genetic constitution (or genotype) and the environment.

photophosphorylation: Light-induced production of adenosine triphosphate (ATP).

photosynthesis: The light-energized assimilation of CO_2; in green plants, this involves water as a source of electrons for energy, thus splitting the water molecule and releasing free oxygen. Green-plant photosynthesis can be described, in a simplified manner, as follows:

$$6CO_2 + 6H_2O + 686\ \text{Cal/mole} \rightarrow C_6H_{12}O_6 + 6O_2$$

phyletic: Pertaining to a phylogenetic line or an evolutionary lineage.

phylogenetic: Having to do with phylogeny.

phylogeny: The sequence of steps in the evolution of a species (or larger taxon) from the ancestral form to the fully evolved descendant group.

phylogerontic: Pertaining to the concept of phylogenetic old age.

phylum: A Latin term that formally denotes a major division of organisms next below a kingdom in rank. In an informal sense, it may denote any division or lineage of organisms. The plural is *phyla.*

phytane: A branched, cyclic, 20-carbon diterpenoid or isoprenoid hydrocarbon, related chemically to the phytol chain of chlorophyll, 2,6,10, 14-tetramethylhexadecane ($C_{20}H_{40}$).

phytoplankton: Planktonic (floating) photosynthetic organisms, including floating algae and chlorophyllaceous protists.

piedmont: Literally, "at the foot of the mountain." In geological usage, the term may refer to any feature that suits the term; or, specifically, to the Piedmont Plateau along the eastern margin of the Appalachian Mountains, or to the Piedmont Province of the Italian Alpine borderlands.

pillow lava: A volcanic rock, usually basalt, that displays a structure resembling bags of grain stacked in an overlapping manner. It results from the flowing of mafic lava over wet places or into the sea.

pisolite: A subspherical accretionary body having a concentric structure and a diameter of 2–10 mm. Similar smaller bodies are called *oöids* or *oöliths,* and larger ones, *concentric concretions, algal balls,* or *oncolites.* An origin in shallow turbulent waters—from, commonly, an algal source—is implied.

plagioclase: Any of a solid-solution series of feldspars that is rich in sodium or calcium or both.

planimetry: Refers to determination of horizontal distances, angles, or areas from measurements on a map; or to maps which show only horizontal components without devices such as contour lines to indicate topography.

planktonic: Floating—referring to organisms that drift in the surface waters of the sea or lakes.

plate tectonics: Refers to a model of the crust and uppermost mantle of the earth in which six major and several minor "plates" interact at their boundaries, accounting for the major orogenic and seismic belts of the earth.

pleochroic halo: A set of discrete, concentric rings encircling bits of uraniferous matter in biotite micas and showing pleochroism (varying color with different directions of transmitted polarized light). The rings are produced by the emission of alpha particles from the various isotopes of uranium and thorium. As they are discharged with different energies, each energetic level has its own ring. Because the rings of even very old pleochroic halos show no blurring, this is taken as evidence that there has been no change in decay rates (the rates of release of nuclear energy).

pluton: A sizable nontabular body of crystalline (and usually felsic) rock formed by condensation from a melt, or by pervasive metamorphism beneath a cover of younger rock. A degree of chemical and mineralogic homogeneity is implied, but specific limits of size are not. Several or many plutons may compose a single batholith (which see), or a batholith may be considered as an individual pluton.

plutonic: Refers to igneous rocks that crystallize deep within the crust—the deep-seated intrusive rocks.

pluvial: Pertaining to rain.

partial pressure of the gas phase referred to in

P_{O_2} (or P_{CO_2}, or P_H, and so forth): Indicates the partial pressure of the gas phase referred to in the subscript.

polyglutamic acid: A polymeric form of glutamic acid (an amino acid).

polyisoprenes: Several isoprenes (which see) bonded together.

polyisoprenoids: Several or many isoprenoids bonded together.

polymerize: To combine molecules of a specific kind into another compound having the same elements in the same proportions, but having a higher molecular weight and contrasting physical properties, without the release of by-products. See also *condensation.*

polymict: Consisting of more than two classes or modes, as a sediment that includes particles of several clearly separated grain size classes.

polymorphic phase transformation: A change of a substance (or several substances) into a number (or a sequence) of other substances having the same chemical characteristics but different physical properties.

polynucleotide: A chain of connected nucleotides. Where nucleotides are arranged in a prescribed manner, the polynucleotide is the nucleic acid DNA or RNA. Polynucleotides may also consist of a single nucleotide (such as uridylic acid) repeated over and over again. Polynucleotides have been synthesized in the laboratory from previously prepared starting materials.

polypeptide: A combination of amino acids smaller than a protein and larger than a peptide; a sequence of peptides linked together.

polyploidy: Having more than a diploid (or double) set of chromosomes (the diploid number being the number of chromosomes typical to the somatic cells of a given species).

polysaccharide: A glucose polymer of high molecular weight.

pontic: See euxinic.

porphyrin: A polycyclic organic structure consisting of four pyrrole rings bonded together, usually around a central metal ion. In the case of hematin, the porphyrin of both hemoglobin and chlorophyll, the central metal is either iron or magnesium. Such metal porphyrins degrade readily after death to metal-free porphyrins, which, in turn, provide sites for still later occupancy by different metals, such as vanadium and nickel.

porphyry: An igneous rock that contains conspicuously large and well-formed crystals (phenocrysts) in a finer-grained or glassy matrix.

Portlandian: A stage of uppermost Jurassic age.

Poynting-Robertson effect: Pressure-effect of solar radiation on small particles causing them to spiral slowly into the sun.

Precambrian: A formal major division of rocks and geologic time, generally considered synonymous with *pre-Paleozoic* (which see). Contrasts with the informal term *pre-Cambrian,* which simply denotes rocks and time older than Cambrian, usually (but not invariably) considered as basal Paleozoic.

pre-Paleozoic: Rocks and time older than Paleozoic. Avoids the ambiguity inherent in the term *Precambrian,* when, in discussing the question of the base of the Paleozoic, one must consider preCambrian rocks of possible post-Precambrian age.

pristane: A branched, cyclic, 19-carbon norisoprenoid hydrocarbon, related chemically to the phytol chain of chlorophyll, 2,6,10,14-tetramethylpentadecane ($C_{19}H_{40}$).

procaryote: An organism consisting of procaryotic cells—that is, cells that lack a nuclear wall, organelles, and well-defined chromosomes, and that are incapable of mitotic cell division.

productid: Any member of a group of spiny brachiopods having a concavo-convex shell and a long trail, especially a member of the distinctive genus *Productus*. The productids were characteristic of the upper Paleozoic.

protist: One of the Protista, the so-called unicellular or noncellular organisms.

protobranch: A member of the pelecypod order Protobranchia, in which the feeding gills comprise a double row of simple, discrete lamellae.

Protophyta: One-celled plants.

purine: The basic ring structure of adenine and guanine, two of the nucleotide bases.

pyrimidine: The basic ring structure of uracil, thymine, and cytosine, three of the nucleotide bases.

pyrophosphate: A salt or ester of pyrophosphoric acid.

pyrophosphoric acid: The compound $H_4P_2O_7$, which is derived by the removal of one molecule of water from two of phosphoric acid; that is:

$$2H_3PO_4 \rightleftharpoons H_4P_2O_7 + H_2O$$

pyroxene: Any of a group of complex aluminum silicate minerals of mainly monoclinic (but in part orthorhombic) crystal form. Includes some of the commonest rock-forming minerals among the mafic rocks.

pyruvate: A salt or ester of pyruvic acid (CH_3-COCOOH).

quanta: Plural of quantum, an elemental unit of energy in the quantum theory according to which the emission or absorption of energy by atoms or molecules occurs stepwise, the amount of energy involved in each step being defined as the quantum.

quantum evolution: Seemingly stepwise evolution, such as would result where populations evolving in response to new adaptive zones would become fully adapted to them while intermediate forms would not persist.

quasars (or quasi-stellar objects): Very distant visible radio sources, characterized by unusually strong emission of radio energy, exceptionally high intrinsic luminosity, and large red shifts. Although very dim to the light telescope, these stars must be pouring out unbelievable amounts of energy to be visible at all. They are believed by some astronomers to represent phenomena no longer existing—phenomena related, perhaps, to the very early history of the universe.

quaternary invariant point: Denotes, in chemical thermodynamics, the temperature and pressure at which six phases expressed by four components can coexist in equilibrium.

racemic: Refers to a mixture that contains equal parts of dextrorotatory (right-handed) and Rock forms that have been rounded off by glaciers, such that the ends that face in the levorotatory (left-handed) isomers of the same compound and, hence, is optically inactive.

radiogenic: Originating by the decay of radioactive isotopes.

Radiolaria: An order of minute planktonic marine Protozoa, any member of which has a spherical to bell-shaped, siliceous or horny covering or test, with a meshwork structure.

Rb-Sr: A radiometric dating method utilizing the ratio between rubidium-87 and its daughter product strontium-87. The validity of results obtained depends on the accuracy of knowledge of the half-life of Rb^{87}, on identification of nonradiogenic Sr^{87}, and on various geologic factors.

red beds: Sediments whose red color is due to the coating of their constituent particles (grains) with ferric oxides in an oxygenous weathering profile, such particles being subsequently moved to, and deposited in, depressions on continents or in marginal marine environments. Their preservation depends on their being protected from subsequent reduction, as by continued exposure to a richly oxygenous milieu, or by rapid burial beneath the reach of percolating reducing fluids.

red shift: A shift toward longer wave-lengths (the red end of the visible spectrum) on the part of the electromagnetic radiation from distant stellar sources. The red shift is conventionally interpreted as a Doppler effect, whereby any wave phenomena from a receding body are shifted toward longer wave lengths.

regression: In stratigraphy, refers to the seaward overlap of one type of deposit on another, occasioned by a subsidence of sea level, an elevation of the land, or change in sedimentary regime.

reverse fault: A fault which, when viewed in vertical profile, shows upward movement along the side that makes an acute angle with the earth's surface (the "hanging wall" moves up).

Rhaetic: The upper stage of the marine Upper Triassic.

rheotactic: Responding in orientation or movement to the influence of currents.

rhyolite: An extrusive igneous rock having a high silica content; it may be entirely glassy, or it may show phenocrysts of quartz and alkali feldspar.

RNA (ribonucleic acid): A small, single-stranded nucleic acid containing ribose and having a different base structure from DNA (usually uracil in place of thymine). RNA is replicated by using DNA as a template; it then serves, in turn, as the templates by which amino acids are assembled into proteins.

roches moutonnées: Literally, sheep-shaped rocks. direction from which the ice came (stoss ends) are smooth and gentle, and the lee ends are relatively steep and rough.

rudist: Any member of a group of thick-shelled, often massive, commonly reef-building pelecypods.

Santonian: An intermediate stage of the Upper Cretaceous Series.

saturated: In organic chemistry, refers to compounds that do not ordinarily unite directly with other compounds, or that contain no double or triple bonds.

scaloposaurid: One of the Scaloposauridae, a family of advanced mammallike reptiles of the infraorder Therocephalia.

schist: A metamorphic rock with a subparallel orientation of abundant micaceous minerals producing a marked foliation. It is usually a metasediment.

seamount: A conspicuous, isolated, submarine peak, usually volcanic, but often with a capping biogenic crust, that rises from deep into relatively shallow water, but does not break the surface.

secondary palate: The hard (bony) palate in the roof of the mouth, characteristic of mammals, but incipient in the mammallike reptiles.

Senonian: An intermediate stage of the marine Upper Cretaceous. The term is not in general use.

serial lobes: A succession of similar lobes in the suture of an ammonite (which see).

serine: One of the amino acids.

sial: Relatively light crustal rock, rich in silica and alumina.

siderolite: See *pallasite.*

sima: Relatively heavy crustal rock, rich in silica, magnesium, and iron.

sitostane: A 29-carbon steroid.

skarn: A metamorphic rock wherein silicate minerals, such as iron-rich garnets, pyroxenes, and amphiboles, replace ordinary carbonate rocks. From a Swedish word for rubbish, referring to the waste material from quarries worked for limestone.

solar wind: Pressure of radiation from the sun, deflected from the earth by its magnetic field.

sole markings: A variety of markings, of either biological or physical origin, found on the bottom surfaces of detrital or clastic strata, and representing molds of markings made in soft underlying clays.

sphenacodont: One of the Sphenacodontia, a Permian and Lower Triassic suborder of pelycosaurian reptiles. See *pelycosaur.*

spherical harmonics: A method of physical analysis that involves the determination of a function that will satisfy Laplace's equation for a particular region of space, often the surface of a sphere. Laplace's equation is a differential equation dealing with the rectangular Cartesian coordinates of a point in space. The mathematics are tedious, and not essential for appreciating the conclusions to which they lead about the earth's configuration and convection cells.

spilite: A basaltic rock with albitic feldspar that usually also includes low-grade metamorphic minerals such as chlorite, calcite, epidote, amorphous silica or quartz, actinolite, and so forth. It approaches greenstone, and it is characteristic of island-arc effusives.

"splitters": Taxonomists who tend to use the maximum possible number of species and other systematic names. Compare *"lumpers."*

stage: A stage, in the stratigraphic sense, is a time-stratigraphic subdivision that includes more than one zone, and which is characterized more by the general grade of evolution of the contained biota than by the particular composition of species and genera. In those parts of the geologic column where stages (named after geographic localities) have been defined, many can be recognized throughout the world by means of overlapping correlations, grade of evolution, or distinctive fossils. In a more general sense, *stage* denotes a particular level of development in either biological or physical evolution. See Reading Selection 19.

Stefan's law (Stefan-Boltzmann law): An equation that gives the total energy emitted per square centimeter per second by a nonreflecting body at a given temperature: $E(T) = \sigma T^4$, where E is the energy sought, T is the temperature, and σ (Stefan's constant) has the value 5.672×10^{-5}, if T is in degrees Kelvin and $E(T)$ is in ergs/cm²/sec.

sterane: A saturated hydrocarbon derived from a steriod but having a different geometry of the first two ring structures.

steroid: Any tetracyclic hydrocarbon composed of three six-membered rings and one five-membered ring fused together in sequence. A group of fatty organic compounds including cholesterol, vitamin D, and various hormones and carcinogens.

sterol: An alcohol derived from a steroid and containing 27 carbon atoms.

stoss: Refers to the end of a glacially modified rock

form (of a roche moutonnée, for example) that faces in the direction from which the ice came. Ice motion tends to smooth and reduce the stoss ends, whereas the lee ends are higher and rougher.

stromatolite: A thinly laminated, usually basally attached, morphologically distinctive, and biologically mediated buildup of sedimentary material, usually $CaCo_3$ but sometimes SiO_2. Stromatolites are formed under the metabolic and sediment-binding influences of various associations of microorganisms, most characteristically blue-green algae. Stromatolites that lack basal attachment are called *oncolites*.

sub-: Prefix denoting either beneath or somewhat less than; thus, *subcrustal* (beneath the crust); *subcircular* (almost circular); and so forth.

superfamily: Denotes a group of organisms next in rank below an order (or a suborder) and above a family.

supernova: An exploding star whose sudden increase in radiant energy temporarily increases its luminosity by five to eight orders of magnitude. Compare *nova*.

suture: A seam or juncture where something is stitched or joined together.

synorogenic: Originating during an episode of mountain building.

systematist: A person who practices systematics—that is, the study of the classification and nomenclature of natural phenomena, usually organisms.

tapinocephalid: One of the Tapinocephalia, a middle Permian infraorder of herbivorous therapsid reptiles (which see).

tautomer: One of two or more isomers which change easily into one another, and which therefore ordinarily exist together in a state of equilibrium.

taxon: A group of organisms constituting a systematic category such as subspecies, species, genus, family, order, class, or phylum. The plural is *taxa*.

taxonomist: A person who practices taxonomy—that is the description, naming, and classification of natural phenomena, usually organisms.

tectonic: Referring to the architecture or structure of the earth's crust. The main tectonic processes are the building of folded mountain chains by regional compression or gravitational sliding (orogeny) and the essentially vertical uplift or subsidence of large blocks of the crust (epeirogeny).

teleosts (or teleosteans): Bony fishes.

terminal moraine: See *moraine*.

terpane: A 30-carbon saturated pentacyclic hydrocarbon.

terpene: A class of organic compounds resulting from appropriate combinations of 5-carbon units similar to isoprenes and derived biologically from mevalonic acid.

terpenoid: Organic compounds based on five-carbon isoprene units with the following basic structure:

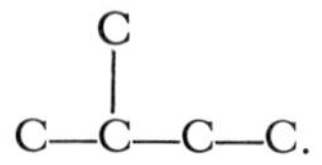

Tethys: A geological name denoting an essentially circumequatorial sea that, throughout late Paleozoic and Mesozoic time, separated the southern-hemisphere supercontinent (or continents) of Gondwana from the lands to the north. (Thetis, rendered *Tethys* in German, was the mother of Achilles. She lived in the depth of the sea with her sisters the Nereids and her father Nereus.)

tetramer: Consisting of four similar parts; in chemistry, refers to four similar molecules linked together.

therapsid: Pertaining to the Therapsida, an order of the mammallike reptiles (subclass Synapsida) comprising a variety of relatively advanced forms.

therocephalian: Belonging to the Therocephalia, an infraorder of the Therapsida (advanced mammallike reptiles).

tholeiitic basalt: A basalt that, in contrast to olivene basalt, contains little olivene but is rich in pyroxene (orthopyroxene or pigeonite). The matrix is commonly glassy but may consist of small crystals of quartz and potassium- or sodium-rich feldspars.

thrust fault: A reverse fault in which horizontal displacement exceeds vertical movement.

thymine: A pyrimidine, and one of the nucleotide bases that link with sugar-phosphate chains to form the DNA helix. The disruptive effect of UV on DNA is produced by the abnormal linkage of thymine on thymine to produce thymine dimers.

till: Moraine deposits. See *moraine* and *tillite*.

tillite: A lithified glacial till or morainal deposit.

time-stratigraphic: Refers to divisions of the rock succession or "geologic column" whose boundaries are based on geologic time; hence, rock units with synchronous boundaries.

titanosuchid: One of the Titanosuchia, a carnivorous middle Permian infraorder of therapsid reptiles (which see).

trans-: On the opposite side: in organic chemistry,

a prefix that denotes isomeric hydrocarbons in which the substituting radicals are on opposite sides of a ring. See also *cis-*.

transcurrent fault: A strike-slip fault.

transform fault: An offset of a mid-ocean ridge or comparable structure in which the real motion, as revealed by seismic data, is opposite to the apparent motion as deduced from observation of the offset.

transgression: In stratigraphy, refers to the landward overlap of one type of deposit over another, occasioned by a rise of sea level, depression of the land, or change in sedimentary regime.

trapdoor uplift: An expression used in structural geology to describe an uplift where beds from beneath have broken through those above as if they had been lifted up on a trap door.

triconodont: A member of the Triconodonta, an order of primitive (and divergent) Jurassic mammals having a carnivorous type of dentition.

trilobite: Any member of the extinct class Trilobita of the phylum Arthropoda. Trilobites had calcareophosphatic exoskeletons that consisted of head shield (cephalon), tail shield (pygidium), and thoracic plates, each in turn divided longitudinally into three lobes. They are characteristic of Paleozoic sedimentary rocks, especially Devonian and older.

triterpenoid: A 30-carbon polycyclic hydrocarbon.

tritylodont: Belonging to (or like) *Tritylodon*, a late Triassic and early Jurassic genus of mammallike reptiles of the order Therapsida, characterized by multituberculate teeth and once thought to be the oldest known mammal.

turbidite: A sedimentary bed deposited by a turbidity current, or a sequence of sediments in which turbidity current deposition has played an important part.

turbidity current: A gravity current of relatively high density and transporting power due to its high content of sediments maintained in suspension by eddies.

Turonian: A stage of the Upper Cretaceous.

turriliticonic: Having a shell morphology like *Turrilites*, a helically coiled ammonite that resembles a high-spired snail.

ultramafic: Refers to mafic igneous rocks in which magnesium- and iron-rich silicate minerals attain unusually high concentrations. See *mafic*.

ultra vires: Transcending authority, beyond resolution.

umbilicated: A coiled shell having a depression or pit at the center around which the whorls rotate.

unconformity: A significant discontinuity in a stratigraphic succession. It is a general term that includes *nonconformity*, where a sedimentary rock is deposited over an igneous or metamorphic rock; *angular unconformity*, where younger strata overlap the tilted and eroded surface of older rocks; *erosional unconformity*, where the underlying strata have been eroded to an irregular surface but are parallel to the overlapping beds; and *disconformity*, where the contact is not conspicuously erosional and the beds on both sides of it are essentially parallel to one another, but where a substantial gap in time is known or inferred. The term *diastem* (which see) may be used for still smaller discontinuities in time. The term *paraconformity* is also used by some to indicate a disconformity that shows no detectable irregularity.

underclay: A "fossil" soil beneath a coal deposit.

unsaturated: In organic chemistry, refers to the ability of a compound to form addition products without elimination of any side product.

UV: Ultraviolet; that is, beyond violet light in the electromagnetic radiation spectrum as far as x rays; corresponding to wave lengths from 100 to 4,000 Å.

valley train: A long outwash plain confined within a valley.

varve: A layer or pair of layers within a rhythmic sequence of sediments wherein each similar layer or pair of layers represents the deposits of a single year. Varved sediments are best known among periglacial lake deposits, but they also occur in other lakes, and quite probably among evaporite deposits of various ages.

vermes: An inclusive term to denote any and all members of the wormlike phyla of organisms.

vibrissae: Long, stout, tactile hairs ("whiskers") around the nose and mouth of certain mammals (cats, for example).

volatiles: See *excess volatiles*.

whorl: One complete turn or rotation of a coiled shell.

Widmanstätten figures: Graphic crystalline structure observed in smoothed and acid-etched surfaces of meteoritic iron and implying very slow solidification from molten parent material. (After A. B. Widmanstätten, who discovered them in 1808.)

xenolith: A rock fragment that is foreign to the surrounding matrix of the igneous rocks in which it occurs.

xerophytic: Pertaining to plants that are adapted to dry conditions.

x-ray diffractometer: An instrument that rotates a specimen under an x-ray beam and records the angles of diffraction distinctive of specific minerals or other substances.

zone: In a general sense, the term *zone* refers to any laterally extensive subordinate subdivision of rock, soil, biota, or whatever, usually, but not necessarily, restricted in a vertical sense. The term also has various specific and formal applications; for example, *biozone, faunizone, metamorphic zone*—referring to a division of rock characterized by distinctive fossils or minerals. In stratigraphy, the term is most commonly used in a time-stratigraphic sense to denote those sediments or sedimentary rocks deposited anywhere in the world during the time in which a particular name-giving fossil and distinctive associated fossils lived. In this sense, it has the strong implication of approximate contemporaneity throughout its range, although a zone is, by definition, a material thing characterized by particular fossils, and although no zones of global extent are known. See Reading Selection 19.

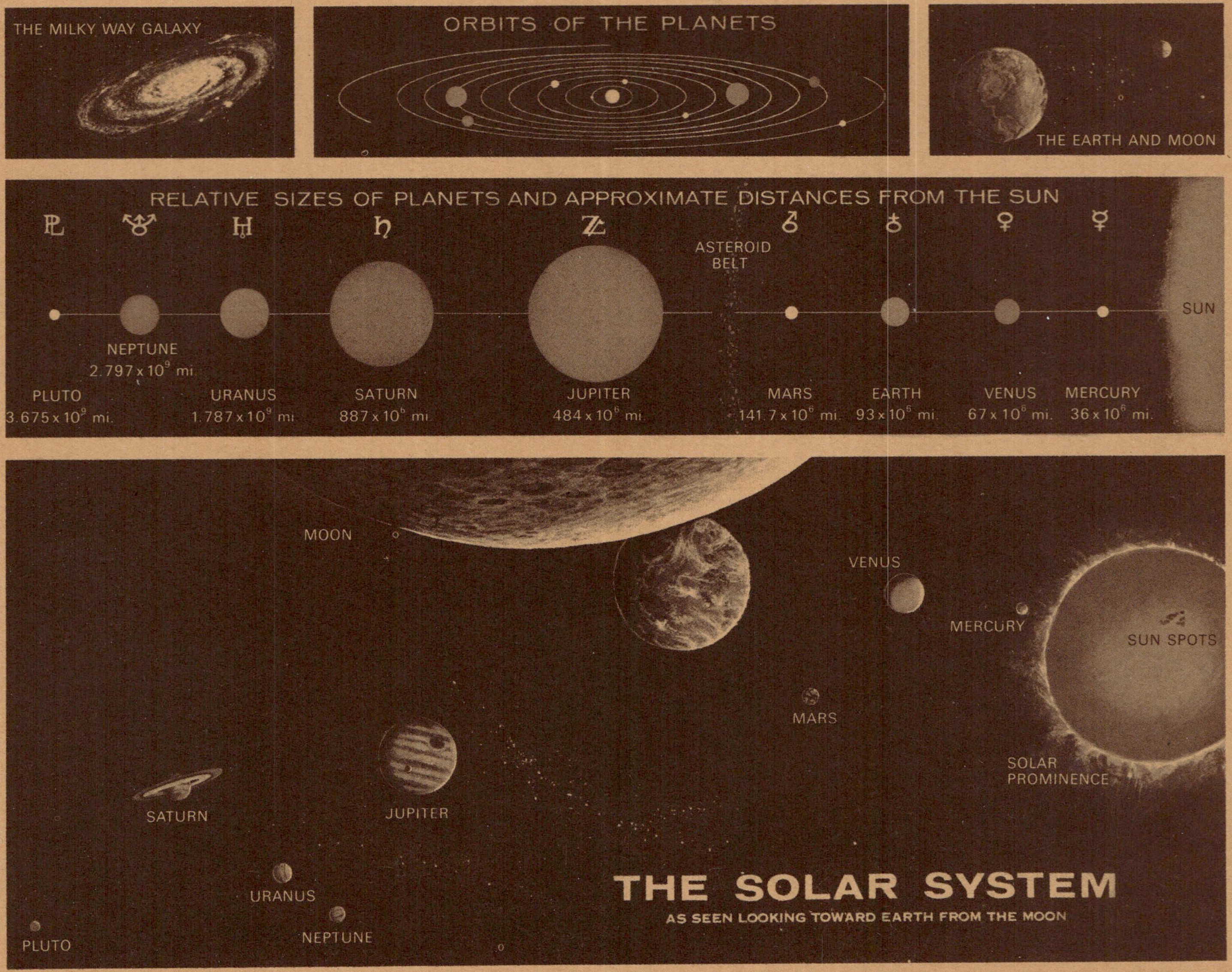

National Aeronautics and Space Administration Lithograph MSCL-7, reproduced by courtesy of the Public Affairs Office, Manned Spacecraft Center, NASA, Houston, Texas.